Rod Machado's Sport Pilot Handbook

Written and illustrated by
Rod Machado

Published by The Aviation Speakers Bureau

© Flight Design

D1210817

Copyright Information

**First Edition
October 2016**

Please visit (and *bookmark*) our web site for any additional book updates: *www.rodmachado.com*

Published by: The Aviation Speakers Bureau, P.O. Box 6030, San Clemente, CA 92674-6030

Cover layout by Rod Machado
Front cover picture provided by CubCrafters. Picture taken by Jon Bliss
All material created, written and produced by Rod Machado
All illustrations in this book designed and drawn by Rod Machado (QuarkXPress, Corel, Photoshop)
Photographs (unless marked otherwise or in the public domain) by Rod Machado

Table of Contents

The author wishes to acknowledge the help and or support of the following individuals, companies or groups:

Brian Weiss of WORD'SWORTH, Santa Monica, CA.

Diane Titterington of The Aviation Speakers Bureau, San Clemente, CA.

The New Piper Aircraft Corporation. Charts and graphs provided by Piper are to be used for information purposes only. The Pilot's Operating Handbook is the only true source of information.

The Cessna Aircraft Corporation. Cessna authorized the use of their materials with the understanding that they are to be used for training purposes only, not the actual operation of an aircraft.

Remos Aircraft Company

Air Time Aviation of Palomar airport, CA.

Robert Crystal of Simulator & Instrument Training Center in Van Nuys, CA.

Bill Johnson of Instrument Service Inc. of Van Nuys, CA.

John & Joanne Italiano of Windsock pilot supplies in Newport Beach, CA.

Jeannie and Fernando Molina at the Pilot Supply Shop at Long Beach Airport

Danny Mortensen, President of Airline Ground Schools

Skip Forster, President of Results Pilot Training, San Jose, CA.

Captain James P. Johnson of James Johnson Associates
Christopher W. Tompkins
John A. Ryan
Grahame K. Gates
Douglas L. Mather
Dave Gwinn
Al Chelini
Sarah Cochrane
Douglas Fairbairn
Ken Dravis
Captain Ralph Butcher
Tim Peterson
Captain John Dill
Cammie Thomas Patch
William Stevick
Sue Parker

Captain Al Englehardt
Captain Ed Shaffer
Gwen Ledbetter
Ed Helmick
Don Eick
Sherry Knight
Ron Marks
Chad Gregory Holcomb
C.J. Logue
Jackie Spanitz
Aviation Supplies and Academics (ASA)
Pat O'Brien of Mag Time, John Wayne Airport, CA
Iceman Aviation Supplies, Ontario, Canada
Simon Wheaton Smith
All the folks at ASRS, Moffett Field, CA
Paul & Linda Neumann
Phil Hewitt
Paul Stebelton
Dave Franson
Kim Wheeler
Barry Wallis
Gene Croxton
Rich and Ron Lovick
Fred L Gibbs
Joe Castrey of Southern Aviation Maintenance
Flight Training Magazine
Fotolia Photo source
Helen Woods
Bob Comperini
Jon Thornburgh
Prof. H. Paul Shuch
Donato Martino
Dr. Pat Ford
Jay Tevis
Kent Pramhus
Robert Borger
Ralph Alcock
Jon Bliss
Pat Brown
Randy Lervold
Steven Brooks
AvSport of Lock Haven
Kent Pramhus
Michael J. Bangert
Foothill Flying Club
General Aviation News
Meg Godlewski
(I apologize to anyone I left out. I'll add you next printing.)

Clipart from the following companies:
3G Graphics, Archive Arts, BBL Typographic, Cartesia Software, Image Club Graphics Inc., Management Graphics Ltd., One Mile Up Inc., Studio Piazza Xilo Inc., Techpool Studios Inc., Totem Graphics Inc., TNT Designs, SmartPics.

The instructor at American Flyers responsible for the "F111, C152, 1 Coke memory aid" (your name here when identified).

Rod Machado was born to write a sport pilot text book. His light hearted writing style, comical anecdotes, and most of all, his unending belief that learning is done best when learning is fun, truly embraces the spirit of sport pilot aviation.

When I was hired as the Chief Flight Instructor of a then fledgling sport pilot school I quickly gravitated towards Rod's books—his Private Pilot Handbook and Private Pilot Workbook—as the text books of choice for our students. I have never regretted this decision. Fast forward several years to the present and you will find dozens of happy sport pilot graduates from our school. All who used his books breezed through their knowledge and oral exams and display a wide grin when a discussion of his books inevitably arises.

Helen Woods

What did they like most? Sometimes it was the humor, but most often it was his anecdotes. Combining real world examples with wacky visualizations (seen any pit bulls climbing over VWs lately?) Rod's explanations prove not only easy to understand but impossible to forget. This style of teaching is ideal for the wide diversity of students attracted to the sport pilot certificate.

With this text book, Rod Machado's Sport Pilot Handbook, Rod advances the teaching of sport pilots to a whole new level. This book is the first and, at the time of this writing, the only text book published which is devoted specifically to teaching sport pilots. Whether it is the surprisingly complex regulatory structure for sport pilots or the mysteries of the Rotax engine, Rod explains it all in easy to follow and easy to remember terms.

I have thoroughly enjoyed working with Rod as he developed this book and know that it is truly a superb text for teaching sport pilots as well as transitioning general aviation pilots to flying light sport aircraft. I know that you too will enjoy this book as much as I have.

Helen Woods
Chief Flight Instructor
Chesapeake Sport Pilot, LLC
www.chesapeakesportpilot.com

DEDICATION

This book is dedicated to Princess Buttercup. She is the most wonderful woman in the world and I am the most fortunate man on that same sphere for having married her. She is patient, charming, quick witted, humorous and playful. The Princess gives wise counsel, is extremely smart, is very attractive and she is one heck of a good pilot, too. Without her support I'm not sure I would have completed even a small number of those projects that I began. She is my inspiration. I am a very fortunate man.

Rod Machado traded his motorcycle for flying lessons at the age of 16. His parents were delighted he gave up riding with the vegetarian motorcycle gang known as the *Sprouts*. Captured by the romance and adventure of flight in a Taylorcraft L-2 at Amelia Reid Aviation in San Jose, California, Rod has remained hooked ever since. In fact, he is one of the few airline-transport-rated pilots who still gets excited by a Cessna 150 fly-by.

Rod is a professional speaker who travels across the United States and Europe delighting his listeners with upbeat and lively presentations. Machado truly loves mixing it up with the audience. His unusual talent for simplifying the difficult and adding humor to make the lessons stick has made him a popular lecturer both in and out of aviation. Rod speaks on both aviation and non-aviation topics, including risk assessment, IFR charts, aviation weather, in-flight emergencies, and safety awareness. He is also known for his rapid fire, humorous banquet presentations.

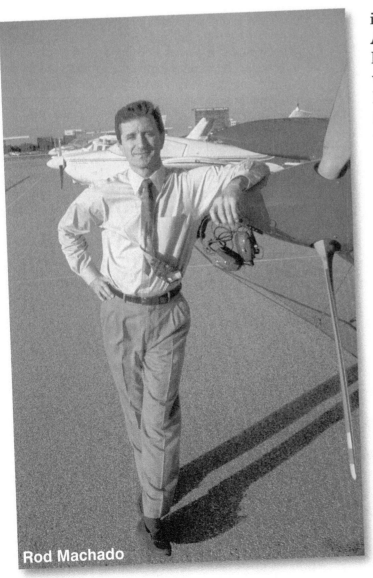

Rod Machado

A pilot since 1970 and an active flight instructor since 1973, Rod is also a National Aviation Safety Counselor. He has over 9,500 hours of flight experience earned the hard way—one CFI hour at a time. Since 1978, Rod has taught hundreds and hundreds of flight instructor revalidation clinics and safety seminars across the United States and Europe. He was named the 1991 Western Region Flight Instructor of the Year. You can read his monthly column, "License to Learn," in *AOPA Pilot* magazine as well as his monthly columns in *Flight Training Magazine*.

Rod's eclectic interests are reflected by his equally varied academic credentials. He holds degrees in aviation science and psychology.

Rod believes you must take time to exercise or you'll have to take time to be sick. Holding black belts in the Korean disciplines of Tae Kwon Do and Hapkido and ranking in Gracie Jujitsu, he gets his exercise from practicing and teaching martial arts. He also runs 20 miles a week and claims it's uphill both ways.

Visit Rod's web site at
www.rodmachado.com.

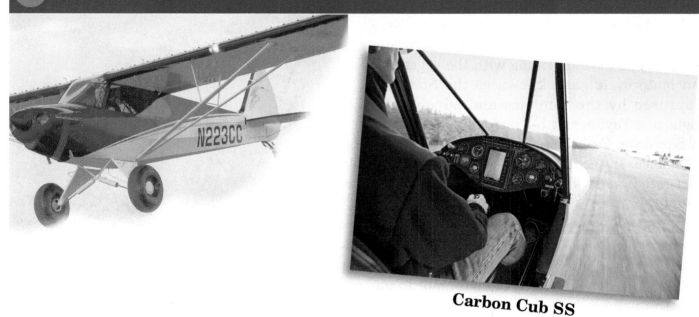

Carbon Cub SS

About CubCrafters

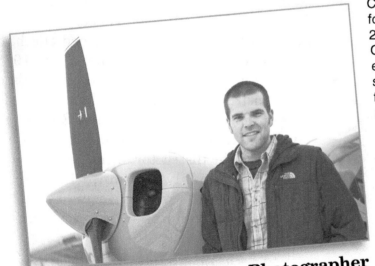

John Bliss - Front Cover Photographer

CubCrafters is located in Yakima, Washington and was founded in 1980 by current owner Jim Richmond. In 2007, CubCrafters was issued a FAA Production Certificate and is currently the only aircraft manufacturer in the nation to produce both standard and light sport category aircraft under and FAA-approved quality assurance program. CubCrafter's offers three all new, ready-to-fly aircraft: The *Sport Cub S2* is a thoroughly updated redesign of the classic airplane that inspired the light sport category. The *Carbon Cub SS* is a stronger and more powerful version of the S2 with 180 horsepower available for takeoff and climb, making it the mose powerful LSA aircraft in production. The *Top Cub* boasts a useful load of over 1,000 pounds, making it among the mose capable two-place personal and utility aircraft available.

Visit: http://www.cubcrafters.com/

"This book is an aviation bible. Obey these commandments and your rewards are endless."

Cliff Robertson

Basic aviation knowledge is to the sport pilot what the fish is to the angler—an indispensable part of the union. One cannot exist without the other. Yet, learning the basics of aviation is sometimes considered the least enjoyable part of the process. In some small way I hope this book changes that perception.

I wrote this book to make the process of basic aviation education a pleasant one. A little humor was an important ingredient, along with a reasonable amount of simplification. I've always believed that new ideas are easier to learn if you can compare them to things you already know. Throughout this book I try to make these connections. That's why I speak of aerodynamics in terms of how automobiles climb hills.

You do not need to be a physicist, aerodynamicist, scientist or engineer to become a sport pilot. In fact, the only math you'll need in this book is grocery-store math. That's basic *adds*, *takeaways*, *times* and *goes-intos*. If you need a cash chaperone at a grocery store, or think that doing addition in an airplane at 10,000 feet is higher math, then you might want to consider taking up sailing instead of flying. This is the extent of the technical knowledge required for the book. The rest of the information can be understood using your common, everyday experience. (Believe me when I say that you already know a lot more about the science of flying than you think you do. Honest!)

You've probably noticed this book contains quite a few pictures to supplement the text. These are not just for the learning impaired. In some cases the pictures and their accompanying text

Rod Machado

offer a slightly different subject explanation than that contained in the body text. This isn't unintentional redundancy—it's quite intentional. It's often nice to see something presented in more than one way. Pictures also allow you to review major concepts without having to reread entire sections of material. Most important, it's my book and I like pictures.

When asked, "How do you eat an elephant?" I hope you say, "Give me another menu" instead of, "one bite at a time." That's why I've included something known as *Postflight Briefings* at the end of some chapters. These are alternate menus. Some topics can be frustrating if consumed as a whole. It simply makes good sense to put them at the end of the chapter where they can be absorbed at your convenience once the necessary groundwork of knowledge has been laid.

If you're like me (and I know I am), you enjoy hearing about the experiences of others. Therefore, I've included excerpts from the Aviation Safety Reporting System (ASRS) files. These are reports sent to NASA by pilots describing their experiences, ideas and *faux pas*. They're the closest thing you get to real experience without being there.

Airplanes. Airplanes. Airplanes. Few words in the English language seem to embody as much adventure, reward and pleasure. That's what flying is all about, isn't it? I hope your experience learning to fly is filled with wonder and excitement. I hope this book makes the process of flight training more enjoyable for you.

Rod Machado

Updating Your Book

Because the world of aviation changes quickly, you should make it a regular practice to update your book by visiting my web site located at:

http://www.rodmachado.com

Visit the book/slide update page for any changes that may affect this text or changes in the FAA knowledge exam.

Author's Note

Any errors found in this book are solely the responsibility of the author, Rod Machado.

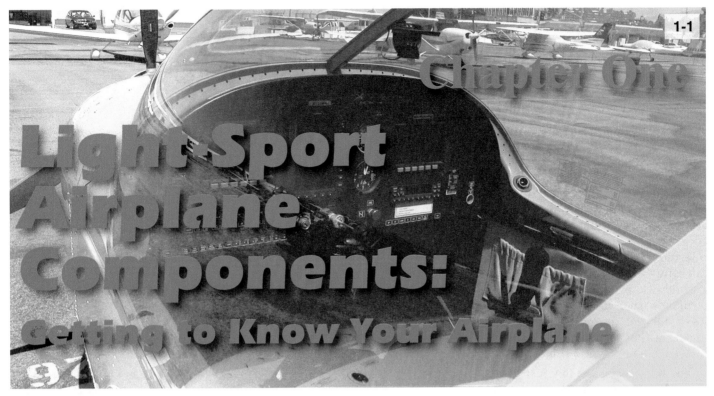

Light Sport Airplane Components:
Getting to Know Your Airplane

Let me take you on a short tour of a few typical general aviation light-sport airplanes. (*General aviation* is the term often used for "private" flying.) I want you to become familiar with the basic parts of these airplanes, and the common terminology you're likely to encounter at the airport and in the cockpit.

Before starting the tour, let me say that while almost everything I'll point out can be found on almost every airplane you're likely to fly, there are always exceptions. Be flexible (the wings are).

Airplanes are like people (sort of). They come in all sizes, shapes, and colors. But looks really can be deceiving. Airplanes are more similar than they are different (Figure 1). We'll examine several varieties in this chapter.

Think of an airplane as a cigar with two Hershey bars on the sides, a propeller beanie cap on the front, and a tail at the back and you'll have the general picture. The rest of this is just details.

In the Beginning

Let's begin at the beginning, with the *propeller*. Most light-sport airplanes have propellers of some shape or form (Figure 2). When spun by the engine, the propeller produces

thrust, which propels (as in propeller) the airplane forward. Atop the prop sits the spinner, a generally cone-shaped piece of metal which

deflects air slightly, encouraging it to enter the engine cowling where it helps cool the engine. Engines are by nature hotheads, and many airplane

AIRPLANES ARE MORE ALIKE THAN DIFFERENT

Fig. 1

AIRPLANE PROPELLERS

Courtesy: Foothill Flying Club

Fig. 2

Airplanes have propellers of some shape or form. One type pulls you while the other type pushes you through the air.

engines typically depend on air (rather than water, as in your car) to keep their cool. Most *light sport aircraft* (LSAs) have liquid cooled engines. The Flight Design CTLS is a good example (Figure 3).

Look down at the feet. Not yours, the airplane's. If it's like most modern light-sport airplanes such as the Flight Design CTLS, then your aircraft has three rubber feet attached to sort of spindly legs. This is referred to as a *tricycle gear,* and has nothing to do with your need for trainer wheels (Figure 4A). Other airplanes, such as the J3 Piper Cub have *conventional landing gear,* meaning that they have a tailwheel instead of a nose wheel (Figure 4B).

The nose gear assembly just above the rubber tire on a tricycle geared airplane often consists of either a *strut* (or oleo), a spring dampening mechanism, bungee or rubber puck style shock absorbers. If it's a strut assembly, then this most likely consists of a piston within a cylinder that acts to absorb the abrupt bounces you may encounter during landings as well as during taxiing on rough terrain.

The nose strut's major function is to help steer the airplane on the ground. Some LSAs have a mechanical linkage between the *rudder ped-*

ENGINE COOLING SYSTEMS

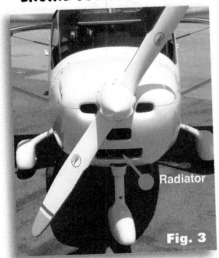

Fig. 3

Unlike traditional airplanes, the Flight Design CTLS has water cooled rather than an air cooled cylinder heads.

TRICYCLE AND TAILWHEEL LANDING GEAR

Fig. 4

Some airplanes, such as the Flight Design CT have tricycle landing gear while others, such as the J3 Piper Cub, have conventional landing gear (a tailwheel).

THE AIRPLANE'S NOSE STRUT ASSEMBLY

Fig. 5

The nose gear and the urethane polymer shock absorber in the Flight Design's nose strut assembly allows it to turn as well as provide dampening action to help smooth out hard landings. Pushing the right or left rudder pedal turns the nose wheel via a mechanical linkage.

als and the nosegear. By applying pressure on the rudder pedal as shown in Figure 5, the nosegear turns, resulting in the airplane turning during taxi (i.e., to maneuver on the ground). That's right, you steer an airplane that's on the ground with your feet. Other airplanes without these mechanical linkages can be steered on the ground by applying differential braking (applying either the right or left brake to turn right or left).

Of course, your basic instinct from inside the cockpit will be to try turing the airplane on the ground by moving the control wheel or joystick. This won't bring you much joy since airplanes aren't steered this way.

CASTERING NOSE GEAR

Fig. 6

A castering nose gear is one of the most common types of nose strut assemblies you'll find on light sport airplanes.

Who among us doesn't remember frantically whipping the control wheel back and forth in utter amazement as nothing happens? During my first taxi attempt I remember looking at my instructor like I looked at the DMV lady when she asked if I wanted to donate any of my organs (not realizing she meant *after the accident*). This demonstration, more than anything else, disabuses the pilot novitiate of the idea that learning to fly is just like learning to drive a car (it isn't).

Airplanes with a tailwheel are steered by applying differential braking to either right or left wheel. This is accomplished by either pushing on a separate set of brake pedals in the airplane or by a combination of rudder pedal and brake pedal.

Please note that you do not (intentionally, at least) ever land on the nose gear. When your instructor asks how many landing gear an airplane has, he or she doesn't mean to imply that you land on all three at the same time. You land on the two main gear, then (gently, we hope) lower the nose gear.

Many light sport airplanes don't have a rudder-controlled nose gear assembly (see, I told you there were exceptions). Instead, they have a castering (swiveling type) nose gear as shown in Figure 6. Applying either the right or left main gear brake (gently, please) sets the plane to pivoting about one of its main wheels, turning it the way Nureyev would turn a ballerina. Once airborne, aerodynamic pressure centers the castering nose gear.

The other two feet on an airplane are the *main gear*. These are fixed gear airplanes, which is another way of saying that the gear don't isn't retractable. Then again, some amphibious LSAs such as the Mermaid do have repositionable landing gear.

Wing a Ding

While you're crawling around down there, look up. The large things casting a big shadow are the *wings*. These are generally considered important because they make the airplane fly. We'll talk a lot more about wings in the next chapter; for now, it's enough to know that there should be two of them (one on each side of the plane, preferably).

At selected locations along the fuel system's plumbing are *fuel sump drains* (Figure 7). These are often found at locations where gasoline collects (think gas collectors) in special reservoirs, otherwise known as *gascolators* (Figure 7). Water and gunk of various sorts can invade the fuel system, and it should be sampled before each before flight. Using a fuel strainer (Figure 8), you drain a little fuel from each gascolator or drain site and examine what comes out for the presence of anything that shouldn't be there.

THE GASCOLATOR SUMP DRAIN

Fuel Drain

Gascolator

Fig. 7

Gascolators (gas collectors) can found at several locations along the fuel system's plumbing. The accompanying fuel drains allow you to sample the fuel for impurities before each flight and after every fueling.

FUEL CONTAMINATED WITH WATER

Water

Fuel

Fig. 8

Clear plastic fuel strainers are common equipment in a pilot's flight bag. These allow you to sample the fuel and look for contaminants.

Under the left wing of most light-sport airplanes, where it can poke a tall pilot in the nose, is the *pitot tube* (Figure 9). That's *pee-toe,* not *pilot.* Now you know one word of French, and speak it like a native. The pitot tube takes in moving air, which is mechanically converted into an air-speed reading and displayed on a the airspeed indicator located in the cockpit. I'll tell you how that happens later. As you will see, the opening on a pitot tube isn't very large; even a little bit of foreign matter, such as a kamikaze fly would plug up the operation, and without the pitot source, you wouldn't have an airspeed indication on your airspeed indicator. So check and make sure there's nothing blocking its opening. And whatever you do, don't blow inside the tube because it will ruin your airspeed indicator.

Not satisfied just to sample moving air, we also have a *static source* (Figure 10). This is not where you get static

THE PITOT TUBE

The pitot tube (usually located under the wing) collects moving air and ports it to the airspeed indicator where it's mechanically converted into an airspeed reading.

THE STATIC SOURCE

The airplane's static source is the mouth through which several of the flight instruments breathe. Non moving air pressure is sampled through this source (that's why this source is often flush with the flow of air).

THE COMBINED PITOT/STATIC MAST

Sometimes the pitot tube and static source are combined into a single unit (position A). The static source is a combination of small holes surrounding the pitot tube. The pitot tube and static source might consist of two tubes that separately sample ram and static air pressure (position B).

electricity when you want to make your instructor's hair stand on end (you'll learn lots of other ways to do that). The static source provides information about the outside air pressure. This information is used by several instruments, including the altimeter, vertical speed indicator and the airspeed indicator (which computes airspeed by mechanically subtracting static pressure from pitot pressure). Sometimes the static source is a dual port configuration that's located directly behind and below the opening on a different variety of pitot tube (Figure 11). No matter where they are, the openings for the pitot and static sources must be free of any foreign matter (bugs, dirt, bubble gum, etc.).

Stop Stalling

Most airplanes have a device to warn of an impending stall. (In aviation, the word stall means the wings have stopped flying, as opposed to an engine that won't start. I'll explain how and why this happens in the next chapter. Stay tuned.) The first type of *stall warning device* is the suction type (Figure 12A), and the second is the electric type (Figure 12B). Get the plane headed for a stall, and the warning horn will bawl.

The suction type works because a slight vacuum forms as air flows over it in an approaching stall. This sets off the horn. The electric version works because two metal contacts come into contact as the plane gets into an unhappy configuration. This closes a circuit, sounding a horn in the cockpit. Either way, you'll hear about it if a stall is imminent.

Figure 13 shows *fuel tank caps* in action—well, actually, in inaction. They don't jump around a lot, but they do keep the fuel in the tank, which is useful. Inside the tank you

A SUCTION-TYPE STALL WARNING DEVICE

Fig. 12A

A suction-type stall warning device located on the wing's leading edge provides an audible warning to the pilot when a stall is near.

AN ELECTRIC STALL WARNING DEVICE

Fig. 12B

An electric stall warning device provides the pilot with a similar stall warning by connecting two small metal tabs and activating a cockpit buzzer.

VENTED FUEL TANK CAPS & TANK TABS

A

B

Fig. 13

Vented fuel caps (position A) allow air to enter the tank (position B) and replace the fuel consumed by the engine. Without a venting of the fuel tank (if the vent became plugged) engine fuel starvation is likely.

FUEL TANK VENT LINE

FUEL TANK VENT
KEEP CLEAR

Fig. 14

Some airplanes have tank vent lines which also allows airflow into the fuel tanks. A tank filled to the brim may need to purge some of its fuel through this line as the air in the tank expands.

will sometimes see a marking tab, used to visually calibrate the tank's fuel quantity. Some caps are vented—they have an opening for air to enter and exit. If the tank were tightly sealed, as fuel was used in flight a vacuum would form in the tank, and eventually fuel flow would be restricted or might even stop. Not good. Instead of vented caps, some airplanes allow air into or out of the tank via tank vent lines (Figure 14).

"Instead of our drab slogging forth and back to the fishing boats, there's a reason to life! We can lift ourselves out of ignorance, we can find ourselves as creatures of excellence and intelligence and skill. We can be free! We can learn to fly!"

Richard Bach, Jonathan Livingston Seagull

A Homosapien Stall Warning Device

Bob! Lower the nose, you're stalling!!

THE POSITION AND ANTI-COLLISION LIGHTING SYSTEM

A green position light is found on the right wing.

Fig. 15A

A red position light is found on the left wing.

Fig. 15B

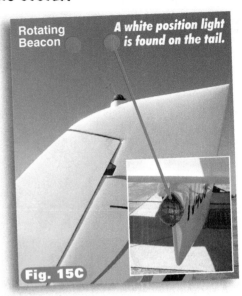

Rotating Beacon   A white position light is found on the tail.

Fig. 15C

An airplane's lighted position lights and an anti-collision light system help other airplanes better identify the airplane's position when it's in operation on the surface or in the air between the period from sunset to sunrise.

There are three *position lights* (also referred to as *navigation lights)* on the airplane, as shown in Figure 15 (A, B & C). Just as prairie dogs aren't really dogs, navigation lights don't actually help the pilot navigate. Each is a different color, and each has its assigned place. The one on the left wingtip is always red, the one on the right wingtip is always green, and the one atop the tail is always white. At night, this enables other pilots to know whether you're coming or going, since the plane itself is not visible. (There is, unfortunately, no device to tell the pilot whether he or she is coming or going. You have to figure it out for yourself.) An optical light sensor is sometimes placed on the wingtip, to let the pilot know if the navigation light is working. The rules require a plane's navigation lights to be illuminated any time the plane is moving between sunset and sunrise. While sport pilots are not allowed to fly at night, that doesn't mean that a private pilot or higher can't use a light-sport airplane for night flying. At least you now know why those wingtip lights are colored the way they are.

There are usually *strobe lights* on the wingtips (and sometimes the tail, as well). These powerful, flashing lights can be seen from a great distance, especially at night, and help alert others to your presence. This is necessary because screaming out the window does not work.

Moving Parts

The four basic fundamental maneuvers that airplanes can perform in flight are: *straight and level flight, turns, climbs* and *descents.* Airplanes can do these things because they have primary moving parts called ailerons, elevator and rudder control surfaces. The *ailerons* are the moveable, flap-like appendages found along the outer part of the wing's trailing edge

(Figure 16). Notice that as one aileron moves up, the other moves down. Yin and yang, cosmic balance, and the ability to turn the airplane all stem from this. Ailerons make slight changes in the lift developed by each wing, causing the airplane to bank and turn. A downward-moving aileron increases the wing's lift, and an upward-moving aileron decreases the wing's lift. Deflecting the control wheel or joystick (so that's what it does!) right or left deflects the ailerons in the appropriate direction for a turn. We'll be talking a lot more about the ups and downs of ailerons in the next chapter.

Flaps (Figure 17) allow the airplane to develop the lift needed for flight at slow speeds, such as when landing. When deflected, flaps change the wing's curvature, and in

THE AILERONS

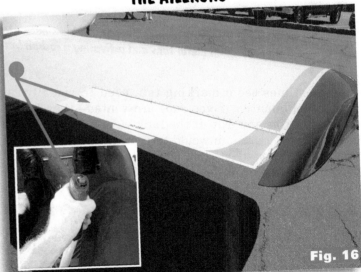

Fig. 16

Ailerons are the moveable appendages on the wing that allow the airplane to bank and turn. Turning the control wheel (or deflecting the control stick) deflects the aileron and banks the airplane.

THE FLAPS

Flaps

Fig. 17

Flaps increase the wing's curvature and its surface area. Pilots frequently use them during landing to produce the required lift at slower airspeeds.

THE FUSELAGE

Fuselage

Fig. 18

Courtesy: *Foothill Flying Club*

The fuselage is the long, cigar shaped portion of the airplane onto which everything else is bolted, riveted or glued.

some instances increase its surface area. An increase in curvature and surface area means the wing produces more lift, as well as more drag. The reason you care about all this will become evident in the next chapter.

The *fuselage* is the big piece in the middle (the cigar) to which everything else (wings, engine, etc.) is bolted (Figure 18). The *empennage* is the tail feathers, the aft part of the airplane (Figure 19).

Staying Stable

The empennage is home to the *vertical and horizontal stabilizers*. The horizontal version has a moveable surface *(the elevator)* connected to it (Figure 19). Forward or aft movement of the control wheel (or control stick) in the cockpit deflects the elevator. This changes the lift produced by the horizontal portion of the tail and points the

airplane's nose up or down. It's the elevator control that allows you to select the attitudes (the plane's attitude, not yours) needed for takeoff, climb, cruising flight, and descents.

Moving onward and upward, we see the *vertical stabilizer* (Figure 19). It, too, has a moveable appendage—the *rudder,* which you may recall is controlled by the rudder pedals beneath the pilot's feet. Application of right or left rudder changes the lift produced by the vertical portion of the tail and swings the nose to the right or left. This allows the pilot to point the nose of the airplane in the appropriate direction of turn (As you will soon learn, the airplane's nose doesn't always want to point in the direction the pilot wants to go.)

Instead of a horizontal stabilizer and elevator, some planes are designed so that the entire tail surface moves. Such structures are called *stabilators,* or flying tails (Figure 20).

THE HORIZONTAL AND VERTICAL STABILIZER

Rudder

Vertical Stabilizer

Horizontal Stabilizer

Elevator

Fig. 19

The horizontal and vertical stabilizers are the stationary portions of the tail surface. They contain moveable appendages called the elevator and rudder respectively.

THE STABILATOR

The Stabilator

Fig. 20

Some airplanes have a combination of horizontal stabilizer and elevator rolled into one. This is called a "stabilator" and the entire horizontal surface moves as a single unit.

THE TRIM TAB

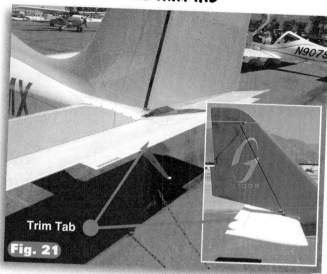

Trim Tab

Fig. 21

A trim tab on the tip of the stabilator or elevator is a small moveable surface that holds the elevator in the position desired by the pilot. This prevents the pilot's arms from becoming tired on long (or short) flights.

Most elevator surfaces have a small, moveable appendage called the *trim tab* (Figure 21). Turning the trim wheel (or pushing the electric trim button) in the cockpit moves the trim tab, which accomplishes aerodynamically what the pilot would otherwise have to do through brute force in order to maintain a desired pitch attitude.

THE COWLING

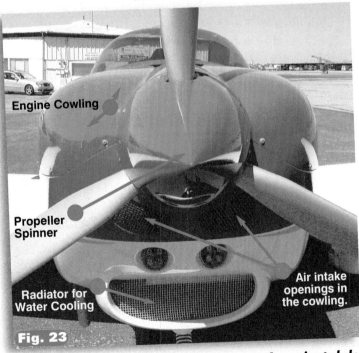

Engine Cowling

Propeller Spinner

Radiator for Water Cooling

Air intake openings in the cowling.

Fig. 23

The engine cowling modifies the flow of air into the engine to help keep it cool. The propeller spinner helps deflect air into the air intake sections of the cowling.

THE FUSELAGE

Communication Antenna

Transponder Antenna

Located under airplane belly

ELT Antenna

CTsw

Fig. 22

Airplanes are home to many antennas. It's not unusual to see five, six, seven or more antennas sprouting from some portion of an airplane.

OPENABLE ENGINE COWLING

Fig. 24

Some airplanes have cowlings that are easily opened for inspection.

AN ENGINE ACCESS DOOR

AUTOMOTIVE ENGINE OIL
API: SF, SG or higher
e.g. SAE 15 W - 40
(see ENGINE MANUAL)

Fig. 25

A small pop-open door is often your only immediate access to the engine.

ENGINE ACCESS

Fig. 26

We often check the engine's oil quantity just like we do in a car—with a dipstick located inside cap rim.

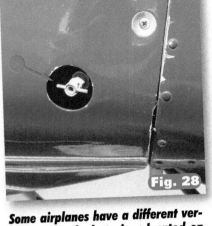

Fig. 27

On some airplanes, you pull on the quick drain lever for a fuel sample (watch your shoes!).

Fig. 28

Some airplanes have a different version of the fuel strainer located on the side of the cowling.

Antenna Farm Deluxe

Airplanes, like police cruisers, can sometimes sport several different antennas. Atop the airplane you may see one or two communication antennas as shown in Figure 22. Communication antennas permit you to communicate with air traffic controllers on the ground and even with other nearby aircraft in the air. Below the airplane you may see a transponder antenna (more on transponders later) and an ELT antenna (more on ELTs later, too).

Back Up Front

Let's get back to where we began—the front of the airplane, where you will find (I hope) the *engine cowling* (Figure 23). Some airplanes have engine cowlings that can be easily opened for inspection before every flight (Figure 24). Unfortunately, many light-sport airplanes have only a small pop-open door (Figure 25) through which you try to peer to see if everything under the hood is good. The experience is something like looking inside a Coke can through the pop top in the dark. It's through this door that you generally check for adequate engine oil (using a dipstick much like that of a car, as shown in Figure 26), and drain a sample of fuel from the lowest engine point to check for contamination before taking to the air (Figure 27).

Checking the fuel is a simple procedure. You pull on the lever in Figure 27 which activates a *quick drain valve*. Fuel drains onto the asphalt although you should try to capture it in a sampling container. This makes it easier to detect the presence of water. Some light-sport airplanes have a different version of a fuel strainer, as shown in Figure 28. These airplanes allow the sampling of the fuel strainer's contents by a valve located on the outside of the cowling. Most light-sport airplanes have one to three drain valves (one for each of the two fuel tanks, and one for the fuel strainer) while some airplanes have five or more drains.

Entering the cockpit (a.k.a. "the front office") you will see a wide (actually, bewildering) array of instrumentation as shown in Figure 29. These instruments are often known as *analog* flight instruments

THE TRADITIONAL INSTRUMENT PANEL

Attitude Indicator

Altimeter

GPS Equipment

Airspeed Indicator

Engine Instruments

Transponder

Comm Radio

Turn Coordinator

Heading Indicator

Vertical Speed Indicator

Brake

Throttle

Courtesy: *General Aviation News*

Fig. 29

No, it isn't the Space Shuttle, even though it seems to have as many dials, switches, knobs and lights. Soon they'll all become very familiar to you.

THE LATEST GLASS COCKPIT PANEL

PFD—Primary Flight Display containing all the flight instruments shown in 29.

MFD—Multi-function displays that can show: engine and navigation instruments, weather, traffic information, etc.

Fig. 30

The primary flight display uses solid state technology to generate its flight instruments. These instruments are similar to those found in the traditional analog-instrument equipped airplane. Nevertheless, the essential analog instruments (airspeed indicator, attitude indicator, magnetic compass and altimeter) are still found in many glass cockpit airplanes. The multi-function display provides computer generated engine instruments, checklists, weather information as well as GPS-generated information in the form of a moving map, terrain information, essential airspace information and much more.

because they are mechanical in nature. On the other hand, glass cockpit technology is often found in light-sport airplane cockpit as shown in Figure 30 and 31. (Read more about primary flight displays in Postflight Briefing #5-2 on page 5-36.) Each instrument or item has a specific name and serves an important purpose (this includes the plastic cup holders, if your airplane is so equipped). Before long you will become intimately familiar with each item. It may look overwhelming at first, but within a few hours of starting to fly you will be right at home with all these tools of the trade. Then you can bring your friends out and dazzle them with your knowledge. This is part of the thrill of aviation.

Now that we've become somewhat familiar with the airplane and its components, it's time to take a look at what makes an airplane fly. The science of aerodynamics is fundamental to the safe operation of any airplane. Since safe operation is really the only kind that makes a whole lot of sense when you're talking about airplanes, let's find out what's keeping you up in the air.

PRIMARY FLIGHT DISPLAY INSTRUMENTS

Turn rate indicator

Heading indicator

Altimeter

Airspeed indicator

Slip-Skid indicator

Vertical speed indicator

Attitude indicator

Fig. 31

The primary flight display (PFD) provides the same instrumentation as analog instruments. The main difference is in how these instruments are interpreted.

Chapter Two
Aerodynamics
The Wing Is the Thing

Courtesy Remos

We often use mechanical equipment without completely understanding how it works. Don't take my word for that. Go stand at a hardware store some Saturday morning, and listen to people talk about *thingamajigs, doohickies,* and *gizmos* while waving their hands, hyperventilating, and attempting to describe for the clerk what isn't working. Do you think Aunt Maude understands why her toaster toasts? Do you think your boss understands why his or her personal computer can do what it does?

As a young bachelor my parents gave me a vacuum cleaner for my birthday. Several months later mom called and asked, "Are you having trouble finding bags for your vacuum cleaner?" I said, "Bags? What bags?"

How was I to know the thing needed bags?

Technological ignorance has its advantages, but not when you're up in the air. You don't need a Ph.D. in aerodynamics to be a pilot, but moderate-to-decent understanding of why an airplane stays airborne will prove very helpful and life sustaining.

As one aviator elegantly put it, "The wing is the thing." It's the thing that performs the magic; the pilot simply manages the show.

May the Four Forces Be With You

Yoda, the transcendental handheld philosopher from the Star Wars movie trilogy, frequently dispatched Luke Skywalker with the benediction, "May The Force be with you." In aviation, there are Four Forces and they are *always* with us, whether Yoda or your flight instructor intervenes or not.

Under Yoda's tutelage, Luke extracted from Mother Nature the mightiest of her secret powers. Aeronautical engineers—taller, without green complexions, blanketed with pocket protectors—do the same, designing airplanes to create a compromise among The Four Forces. This results in the ability of your trusty airplane to fly. Compared to crafting this compromise, settling the Middle East conflict is novice-level work.

The Four Forces—*lift, weight, thrust* and *drag*—are present any and every time a plane is airborne. Look at Figure 1, which shows the action of The Four Forces. Of course, enormous arrows don't really protrude from the airplane. I know this will disappoint those of you who still

How am I going to land without grinding off the weight arrow?

LIFT

THRUST

DRAG

WEIGHT

FOUR FORCES ACTING ON AN AIRPLANE IN FLIGHT

When the airplane is in flight, there are always four forces acting on it: lift, thrust, weight and drag.

Fig. 1

Professor Bob:

**Professor Bob
Chief Paleoaerodynamicist**

WEIGHT · DRAG · THRUST · LIFT

While hiking on Mount Pinitubo during the last eruption, Professor Bob had an aerodynamic brainstorm when he fell into a lava pit. He reasoned that if your turned the airplane upside down and backwards, the drag vector would pull it forward as you reduced thrust. Reducing lift would allow the weight vector to pull the airplane skyward. Once again, we see the perils of skipping one's medication, even for a day.

expect the states to be colored blue and red and have lines drawn around their borders as you fly over them, but you'll get used to it. The arrows do serve to show that what we've got here is a highly competitive new game—four-way tug-of-war. Your job, as pilot, is to manage the resources available in order to balance The Four Forces. Learning to fly is really learning to manage The Four Forces. Almost everything you do in the cockpit will result in making a change to one or more of these forces. Let's see what they're all about.

Lift is the upward-acting force created when an airplane's wings move through the air. Forward movement produces a slight difference in pressure between the wings' upper and lower surfaces. This difference becomes lift. It's lift that keeps an airplane airborne.

I discovered how lift works at four years of age, during my very first visit to church. The collection plate passed in front of me and I picked out a few shiny items. My grandfather chased me around the pew and I thought, "Wow, church is fun!" Picking me up by my sweater, grandpa held me suspended four feet off the ground and toted me outside. It was the lift from grandpa's arm, precisely equaling my weight, which kept me airborne. Wings do for the airplane what grandpa's arm did for me—provide the lift to remain aloft.

Weight is the downward-acting force. It's the one force pilots control to some extent by choosing how they load the airplane. With the exception of fuel burn, the airplane's actual weight is difficult to change in flight. Once airborne, you should not be burning cargo or acquiring extra passengers (or losing them). Unexpected discharge of passengers while in flight is a violation of some FAA rule, so please don't do it.

In unaccelerated flight (when the airplane's speed and direction are constant), the opposing forces of lift and weight are in balance.

Thrust is a forward acting force produced by an engine-spun propeller. For the most part, the bigger the engine (meaning more horsepower) the greater the thrust produced

and the faster the airplane can fly—up to a point. Forward movement always generates an aerodynamic penalty, called *drag*. Drag pulls rearward on the airplane and is simply the atmosphere's molecular resistance to motion through it. In plain English (which pilots and engineers rarely use), it's wind resistance. Few things are free with Mother Nature. As Confucius might say, "Man who get something for nothing not using his own credit card."

Thrust causes the airplane to accelerate, but drag determines its final speed. As the airplane's velocity increases, its drag also increases. Due to the perversity of nature, doubling the airplane's speed actually quadruples the drag. Eventually, the rearward pull of drag equals the engine's thrust, and a constant speed is attained.

My high school VW Bug knew these limits well (it's called a Bug because that's the largest thing you can hit without totaling the car). The Bug's forward speed is limited by its engine size. With four little cylinders (three of which worked at any one time), this VW simply wouldn't go faster than 65 mph. Figure 2 shows the results of maximum thrust meeting the equal and rearward pull of drag at this speed. Maintaining a slower speed requires less power, since less drag exists. At any speed less than the maximum forward speed of the car, excess thrust (horse-

AN AUTOMOBILE'S THRUST AND DRAG

THRUST
Produced by engine power

I'm Rod's car. My horn doesn't blow but the tires do! The hood doesn't collapse but the steering wheel does.

DRAG
Caused by resistance of air molecules

THRUST ← → DRAG

Fig. 2

A constant velocity is attained when the automobile's engine thrust equals the drag produced by wind resistance. At full throttle, the car's top speed is limited by the maximum thrust the engine can produce (same for airplanes too).

AN AUTOMOBILE'S FOUR FORCES

I'm Rod's car. My Blue Book value varies with the amount of gas in my tank.

LIFT

Lift provided, by the road, acts 90° to car's motion

Thrust provided by engine

THRUST

Drag due to wind resistance

DRAG

WEIGHT

Weight of car pushing down on the road

The road supplies an upward force on the car at a 90 degree angle to the direction of travel. Lift (developed by the wings) supplies a similar force on the airplane at a 90 degree angle to the direction of travel .

Fig. 3

power) is available for other uses, such as accelerating around other cars or perhaps powering a portable calliope if you are so inclined.

The same is true of airplanes. At less than maximum speed in level flight, there's power (thrust) to spare. Excess thrust can be applied to perform one of aviation's most important maneuvers—the climb.

Climbs

One of aviation's biggest misconceptions is that airplanes climb because of excess lift. This is similar to believing that putting hand lotion in your airplane's fuel tank will make your landings smoother, softer and younger looking.

Airplanes climb because of excess thrust, not excess lift. Let's use my car as an example to see how thrust, not lift, is responsible for the climbing action of an airplane.

Figure 3 shows my car sprouting more arrows than the hat Custer wore at the Little Big Horn. Notice that the car's weight is offset by the upward push of the road on the tires. In effect, the road simulates the lift of an airplane's wings. In other words, if the road were quicksand, there would be little upward push (lift) and the car would slowly be absorbed by this evil liquid.

Figure 3 also shows the lifting force acting at a 90 degree angle to the car's motion (it's the only way this lift can possibly act since the road pushes directly against the car's tires). Weight, on the other hand, always acts downward toward the center of the earth (pointing toward a Kung-Fu school in China somewhere). Now let's allow the car to move up a hill (climb).

Figure 4 shows the forces on the climbing car. Notice that the lifting force is still perpendicular to the road, thus 90 degrees to the car's motion (arrow A). Lift appears tilted rearward slightly, because the road is inclined upward. The total weight of the car, however, still acts directly downward, toward that Kung Fu school (arrow B). No matter how steeply the road tilts, weight will always point toward the center of the

AN AUTOMOBILE'S FOUR FORCES IN A CLIMB

It is engine power (F) that pulls the car uphill, not the lift from the road (A). The steeper the hill the more the force of weight (B) acts aft (D), pulling in the direction of drag (E). Lift (A) still acts opposite weight (C), which is acting 90 degrees to the motion (the path) along the road.

Road lift 90° to motion

A

Scotty, I need more power!

F

THRUST

90°

E

DRAG

Steep Hill

Weight opposite lift

C

TOTAL WEIGHT

B

Weight

D

Fig. 4

earth (and the author's decision is final on that!).

We can think of weight as two separate forces. Part of the car's weight pushes on the road in a perpendicular direction (arrow C). A smaller part acts rearward (arrow D). Do you see what's happening here? In a climb, some of the car's weight starts acting rearward, in the direction of drag. Anything that pulls aft and impedes acceleration—even if it's the car's weight—acts like drag. The steeper the hill, the larger the rear-

A SINGLE FORCE CAN BE A COMBINATION OF SMALLER FORCES

We will think of arrows as showing the direction a force (a push) is applied. When Bud and Ed simultaneously push on the block in different directions, the block moves in a new direction that results from the combined forces. This new direction (Resultant Force #3) is simply a combination of the smaller forces (Force #1 and Force #2). The weight that pulls a car downward can be thought of as two individual forces when the car's on an incline.

HEAVY BLOCK

A

FORCE #2

Block moves in this direction as a result of Ed's push.

The block now moves in this direction as a result of the combined motions of both Bud and Ed.

RESULTANT FORCE #3

I'm Bud

HEAVY BLOCK

Block moves in this direction as a result of Bud's push.

FORCE #1

I'm Ed

B

Steep Hill

90°

FORCE #1

TOTAL WEIGHT

FORCE #2

On an incline the car's total weight can be thought of as being a combination of two individual weights: one that pushes directly on the road (Force #1) and one that pulls the car backward along the road (Force #2).

ward acting forces. (If you're having trouble with vectors, see the accompanying sidebar at the bottom of Page 2-3.)

Here's what you've been waiting for: The upward push of the road on the car (arrow A) is equal to the car's weight on the road (arrow C). In other words, lift still equals weight, even in a climb. Part of the weight, however, now acts like drag (arrow D), which really *is* a drag, because it gets added to the wind resistance. As we've already learned, thrust is the force that overcomes drag.

The forces acting on an airplane during a climb are similar to those of the car (Figure 5), the only major difference being that you (the pilot) choose the slope of the hill you climb. This is done using the elevator control in the cockpit (more on the elevator control later).

As you can see, it's excess thrust, not lift, that allows an airplane to climb. Given this very important bit of knowledge, you'll now understand why smaller airplanes with limited power can't climb at steep angles like the Blue Angels do at airshows.

Let's go back to the automobile and climb a steep hill (Figure 6). The maximum forward speed of our car

AN AIRPLANE'S FOUR FORCES IN A CLIMB

Similar to the automobile, it is engine thrust (F), not extra lift (A) from the wings, that pulls an airplane up its "pilot-made" hill. The steeper the angle of climb (the hill) the more the force of weight (B) acts aft (D). That portion of the weight (D), acting in the direction of drag (E), pulls the airplane aft and acts just like drag. Lift (A) still acts opposite the portion of weight (C) that acts 90 degrees to the flight path (which is also the relative wind).

Fig. 5

Capteen! Eyee kant gib yah nooo mur pawar sew stup askeen!

POWER AND CLIMB ANGLE

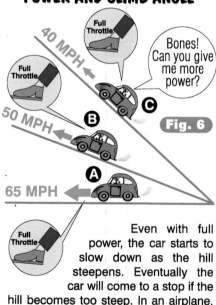

Even with full power, the car starts to slow down as the hill steepens. Eventually the car will come to a stop if the hill becomes too steep. In an airplane, you don't try to climb too steep a hill or you might slow down to the point where your wings can't develop the necessary lift to remain in flight.

on a level road with full power is 65 mph (Car A). As we move up a hill (Car B) our speed drops to 50 mph. An even steeper hill slows the car to 40 mph (Car C). The limited horsepower of the car's engine simply can't match the drag caused by wind resistance plus rearward-acting weight as the hill steepens, so the car slows. A bigger engine or redesign of the car to produce less wind resistance are the only options that will help.

The same analysis works, up to a point, for an airplane attempting to climb a hill in the air (Figure 7). Let's say your airplane has a maximum speed of 100 mph in straight and level flight with full throttle (Airplane A). (Airplane throttles are similar to automobile throttles except that they're hand operated. You push in for more power and pull out for less.) Applying slight back pressure on the elevator control points the airplane's nose upward (Airplane B). This causes the airplane to climb a shallow hill. The speed decreases to

80 mph just as it did in the car. Attempting to climb a steeper hill (Airplane C) slows our speed down to 65 mph. We can't climb the hill we just selected faster than 65 mph because we don't have the extra horsepower (thrust) to do so.

As we continue to steepen the angle of climb, our airspeed decreases further, just like the car's speed did. Here, however, is where the airplane goes its own way. Airplanes need to maintain a minimum forward speed for their wings to produce the lift required to stay airborne. Ever wonder why airplanes need runways? Same reason long jumpers do. Airplanes (and long jumpers) must attain a certain speed before they can take flight.

This minimum forward speed is called the *stall speed* of the airplane. It's a very important speed that changes with variations in weight, flap setting, power setting and angle of bank. It also varies among airplanes (no need to worry because later I'll show you how to recognize when you're near a stall). As long as the airplane stays above its stall speed, enough lift is produced to counter the airplane's weight and the airplane will fly.

If the stall speed of Airplane C (Figure 7) is 49 mph, then climbing at a slightly steeper angle will result in insufficient lift for flight. We call this condition a *stall*. Done unintentionally, it leads to such primitive linguistic sounds as "Uh-oh," "yipes," "ahhhhh," as well as "I think I need to have my chakras balanced." Needless to say, these sounds make passengers reluctant to ever fly with you again. This is why some of your time as a student pilot will be spent finding out about stalls, and doing them (intentionally, that is). Instructors have special biological filters installed that keep them from making these sounds on those rare occasions when you unintentionally stall the airplane. That's why they are sometimes referred to as *certified* flight instructors.

What you need to know is that airplanes with a lot of power (like jet fighters) can climb at steep angles; those with limited power, however, must climb at less steep angles.

Knowing it's extra thrust and not extra lift from the wings that is responsible for the climb allows you to draw some interesting conclusions. For instance, anything that causes the engine to produce less power prevents you from achieving your maximum rate of climb. Among the things resulting in less power production are high altitudes and high temperatures. More on these factors a bit later.

POWER, CLIMB ANGLE AND AIRSPEED

*Angles are exaggerated so you don't need to use too much imagination!

C Steep Climb Angle — Full Power

B Normal Climb Angle — Full Power

A Straight & Level — Full Power

Even with full throttle (maximum power), the airplane slows down as it attempts to ascend a steeper hill. Pilots adjust their climb angle (hill size) by selecting an attitude that gives them a specific climb airspeed.

Fig. 7

At this point you should be asking an important question. I certainly don't mean questions of the "Zen-Koan" type, such as "What is the sound of one cylinder firing?" or "If an airplane lands hard in the forest and nobody is there to hear it, does it really make a sound?" A good question for you to ask is, "How can I determine the proper size hill for my airplane to climb?" Let's find out.

Airplanes have a specific climb attitude (steepness of hill) that offers the best of all worlds—optimum climb performance while keeping the airplane safely above its stall speed. You can determine the proper climb attitude for your airplane by referring to its airspeed indicator.

With climb power applied (usually full throttle in smaller airplanes) the pitch attitude is adjusted until the airspeed indicates one of two commonly used climb speeds. These speeds are known as the *best angle of climb* and the *best rate of climb* airspeed. The best *angle* of climb provides the greatest vertical gain in height per unit of forward travel; the best *rate* of climb provides the greatest vertical travel per unit of time. You select best angle when you need to get up in the shortest possible distance, usually to clear an obstacle. You choose best rate of climb to gain the most altitude per minute. Let's put this in concrete terms. Say there's a concrete tower 750 feet high half a mile off the end of the runway. You definitely want to be above 750 feet at one-half mile out, and you

Wow! Those aftermarket add-ons are really something, aren't they?

What happens if the engine quits? The airplane becomes a glider, not a rock.

don't really care how long it takes you to get there. Your choice is best angle of climb.

Under normal circumstances you will climb at the best rate of climb speed, or a bit faster. Sometimes pilots climb at airspeeds slightly faster than the two reference airspeeds when better over-the-nose visibility is required. Raising the nose of the airplane results in a slower airspeed; lowering it picks up the pace. Where you place the nose—how steep you make the hill—determines what happens on the airspeed indicator. Unlike the ground-bound world, pilots decide how steep the hills in the air are going to be (within limits of course!). With just a little experience, you'll be able to determine the correct size hill (nose-up attitude) by simply looking out the front window instead of having to rely solely on the airspeed indicator.

When I was a student, any specific airspeed was the one place on the dial where the pointer never went. I was not gifted with much

---

During a climb with full power, where you place the nose—how steep you make the hill—determines what happens on the airspeed indicator.

---

coordination as a youngster. My reflexes were so slow I was almost run over by two guys pushing a car with a flat tire. I'm a living exhibit that one can be a competent pilot even without the coordination and reflexes of a 13-year-old Olympic gymnast.

Descents

While engine power moves a car uphill, gravity pulls it down. Without your foot on the throttle, the car's downward speed is

determined by the steepness of the hill it's descending (Figure 8). The steeper the hill, the faster it goes. If the hill shallows out, then the speed decreases. If the hill becomes too shallow, then some power is necessary to maintain sufficient forward speed.

Airplanes can also move downhill without power. Just lower the nose (Figure 9) and you'll get what appears to be a free ride (it isn't, but let's not get into *that*). You can adjust the nose-down angle with the elevator control and descend at any (reasonable) airspeed you desire.

You now have the answer to a question I guarantee every first-time passenger will either ask or want to ask you: "What happens if the engine quits?" The airplane becomes a glider, not a rock.

Unlike climbing, you may elect to descend within a wide range of airspeeds. There are, however, many factors to be considered such as forward visibility, engine cooling and the structural effects of turbulence on the airframe (all of these items will be discussed in this book).

However, during the last portion of the landing approach (known as *final approach*), you should maintain a specific airspeed. Usually this speed is at least 30% above the airplane's stall speed. When preparing to touch down, excess airspeed or erratic control forces often lead to difficulty in making a smooth landing (it's also the reason pilots make good humored fun of one another).

Now that The Four Forces are no longer a mystery, let's examine the most important force—lift. Without this force, airplanes are nothing more than very expensive ground bound vehicles that are impossible to parallel park.

AN AUTOMOBILE'S FOUR FORCES IN A DESCENT

The steeper the angle of descent, the more the car's total weight (B), acts forward (D), in the direction of thrust (E). Drag (F) primarily results from air resistance. Lift from the road (A) still acts perpendicular to the car's motion and is still equal and opposite to the car's weight on the road (C).

Fig. 8

AN AIRPLANE'S FOUR FORCES IN A DESCENT

The steeper the angle of descent, the more the airplane's total weight (B), acts forward (D), in the direction of thrust (E). Drag (F) is aerodynamic drag. Lift (A) still acts perpendicular to the flight path (the relative wind). Lift (A), is still equal and opposite to that part of the weight (C) which acts 90 degrees to the flight path.

*As you'll learn shortly, the thrust vector is not lined up with the axis of the airplane because the airplane must always fly at a slight positive angle to its direction of motion.

Fig. 9

The Wing and Its Things

Defining the Wing

In ground school many years ago, my instructor asked me about the origin and definition of the word *wing*. I replied, "Ma'am, I think it's Chinese and means 'the arm of a bird'." She mumbled something about why many animals eat their young at birth, then went to the dictionary to look up the definition. *Wing* was defined as "a moveable, paired appendage for flying." She looked at me and said, "Well, what does that sound like to you?" I said, "Well ma'am, that sounds like the arm of a bird to me." We agreed to disagree, even though I was right.

The wing has several distinct parts. These are the *upper cambered surface, lowered cambered surface, leading edge, trailing edge* and *chord line* (Figure 10).

Notice that the upper cambered (meaning *curved*) surface seems to have a greater curve to it than the lower cambered surface. This isn't accidental. In fact, this is so important that we'll talk about it in detail shortly.

Perhaps the only term whose definition isn't intuitively obvious is the *chord line*. The chord line is an imaginary line connecting the leading edge with the trailing edge. Believe me, there is no line inside the wing that looks like this. It's only imaginary, just like the arrows showing

Although wings vary in size and shape, they all have the same five basic components.

THE FIVE COMPONENTS OF A WING

Leading edge
Trailing edge
Upper cambered surface
Chord line
Lower cambered surface

The *chord line* is an imaginary line connecting the leading edge to the trailing edge of the wing.
Fig. 10

ANGLE OF ATTACK

The angle of attack in this example is 18 degrees.
(exaggerated)

Chord line

18°

WIND

The *angle of attack* is the angle between the chord line and the relative wind (this is the wind that's blowing on the airplane's wing).
Fig. 11

The red line shows the chord line of the wing.

The Four Forces. When the shoe salesman points to your foot and says, "Your toe is here," you want to respond by saying, "Thanks, I've been looking for that." In reality he or she is pointing out the position of something not visually obvious. The chord line does something similar. Given the wing's curved surfaces, it's difficult to tell which way the wing points. Since engineers don't like uncertainty, they agreed that the chord line will represent the general shape of a wing.

How the Wing Works

To understand lift, you must visualize how the wing attacks the air. Aeronautical engineers talk about the wing *contacting* or *attacking* the air at a specific angle. This occurs in much the same way a pitbull attacks a mailman—mouth first. What part of the wing does the attacking? Is it the leading edge? Is it the trailing edge? Or, is it the bottom of the wing? This is where the definition of chord line becomes useful.

Because wings come in variable sizes and shapes (just like airline pilots), it is sometimes difficult to determine exactly how and where the wind strikes the wing. Fortunately, the chord line substitutes as a general reference for the shape of the wing. If I say that the wind blows onto the wing at an 18 degree angle, I'm saying that the angle between the wind and the chord line is 18 degrees (Figure 11). This distinction, although seemingly trite, is as important to an engineer as tightly-stitched pant seams are to a matador. Only one more definition need be absorbed before the secrets of lift

Your author is especially proud of his Cessna "lifting body" airplane. He believes it has a glide ratio similar to a meteorite. Take special notice of the canvas cooling system!

Fig. 12

① Mother Nature's wind - 3 mph.

② Jogger running at 6 mph.

③ Relative wind on jogger's face at 3 mph.

The *relative wind* is wind resulting from an object's motion. Despite the actual wind blowing from behind him at 3 mph (position 1), the jogger (running at 6 mph, position 2) feels a 3 mph "relative wind" on his face (position 3) as a result of his running motion. Relative wind is *relative* (opposite and equal) to the movement of an object.

are revealed. That term is called the *relative wind* (which is not a reference to an uncle who's like a Kamikaze pilot—the type of person who does all his bragging ahead of time).

Relative Wind

Movement of an airplane generates wind over the wing. This wind is called the *relative wind* because it is relative to (or results from) motion. For instance, in Figure 12, no matter which way the jogger runs, he feels wind in his face that's relative (opposite and equal) to his motion.

Relative wind is movement-generated wind. To illustrate this point, stick your hand out the window of a moving automobile (keep all other body parts inside, please). You'll feel wind blowing opposite the motion of the car. Drive a car backwards on the freeway and you will feel wind, and hear a lot of horns, blowing from directly behind you (you'll also attract the police, so have those doughnuts ready). Relative wind is movement-generated wind

Relative wind is independent of which way the airplane's nose is pointed.

that's equal and opposite to the motion of the airplane.

Move the airplane forward as shown by Airplane A in Figure 13 and wind blows on its nose. Move the airplane up or down a hill and wind still blows on its nose (Airplanes B and C). Drop an airplane and the wind blows on its belly (Airplane D). As far as Airplane D is concerned, the wind is blowing on its belly despite the level attitude (as for the passengers, they're probably underneath

the front seat in the fetal position, making spiritual transmissions that don't require a radio—do not scare your passengers. It isn't nice, and they don't like it).

Relative wind blows from a direction that's opposite the direction of airplane motion, irrespective of what direction the airplane's pointed. The following point is so important I want you to put one finger in your ear. Go ahead, do it before reading any further! I want you to do this because I don't want this information to go in one ear and out the other. *The important principle to remember is that relative wind is independent of which way the airplane's nose is pointed.* Relative wind is opposite in direction and equal to the airplane's velocity. Let's see how the wing actually attacks the wind to develop lift.

Attacking the Air

Hunting is a sport to some people. It's also a sport where your opponent doesn't know it's a participant. Attacking a mammal means that the hunter must point his weapon precisely at the prey. The hunter looks though the gunsight and sees the path of the bullet. An airplane is unlike a gun (and a car) in that its vertical climb path is different from its

RELATIVE WIND DEPENDS ON YOUR MOTION

Ⓐ Note: Airplane shown at a positive angle of attack.

Relative Wind

Airplane's Motion

N2132B

The relative wind is opposite and equal to the motion of the airplane.

Ⓑ The relative wind is opposite and equal to the motion of the airplane.

Relative Wind

Airplane's Motion

N2132B

Ⓒ The relative wind is opposite and equal to the motion of the airplane.

N2132B

Relative Wind

Airplane's Motion

Ⓓ What's the number for 911?

N2132B

Airplane's Motion

Relative Wind

The relative wind is opposite & equal to the motion of the airplane.

Fig. 13

THE ANGLE OF ATTACK

Angle of Attack

Relative Wind

Airplane's Motion

Bob, when I say get your nose down, I mean the airplane's nose.

Fig. 14

A wise man (who is also a poet) says:
May the runway rise slowly to meet thee,
May your landings make nary a sound,
May your Hobbs meter fail completely,
May you never hear the words, "Go around."

incline (the direction it points upward). Remember that 750 foot tower off the end of the runway? On takeoff, if you point your airplane slightly above the top of that obstacle (like a rifle sight), it's unlikely that you're going to clear it. In fact, the only thing being cleared is the area—as the firemen try to talk you down from the side of that tower. Remember, airplanes with limited thrust have shallower climb paths—unlike some fighter jets.

The most important principle to understand here (put that finger back in the ear) is that the nose (therefore the wing) can be pointed on an incline that's different from the actual climb path. An angle exists

between the amount the wing is inclined and its climb path (you'll soon see why). Remembering that the relative wind is always equal and opposite to the flight path, it's more precise to say that an angle exists between the chord line and the relative wind. This angle is known as the *angle of attack* (Figure 14).

Figure 15 shows the wing (chord line) of Airplane A making a 5 degree angle to the relative wind. A more common way of saying this is that the wing's angle of attack is 5 degrees. Airplanes B, C and D show increasing angles of attack of 10 degrees, 30 degrees and 45 degrees, respectively. The greater the difference between the wing and the

relative wind, the greater the angle of attack. And, as you're about to see, the wing's lift is directly associated with its angle of attack.

How Lift Develops

The wing is the ultimate air slicer. As powerful as any Ginzu knife, Samurai sword or karate chop, it's a precision device for slicing air in a very specific way. Wings are expressly built to plow through air molecules separating them either above or below while offering little resistance in the horizontal direction. Any horizontal resistance slows the wing down. This horizontal resistance is drag, and it's definitely a case of less being better.

ANGLE OF ATTACK

Ⓐ **5 Degree Angle of Attack**

Relative Wind →

*Angles are exaggerated for comparison

Ⓑ **10 Degree Angle of Attack**

Relative Wind →

Ⓒ **30 Degree Angle of Attack**

Relative Wind →

Ⓓ **45 Degree Angle of Attack**

Now, that bright one over there is Jupiter.

Relative Wind →

Fig. 15

Figure 16 shows how the airfoil splits the wind when it's at a 10 degree angle of attack. Airflow strikes the leading edge of the wing forcing some air over and some under the *airfoil* (a fancy name for a wing). Both the air flowing over and the air flowing under the wing are responsible for generating lift. Let's first examine how the airflow striking the bottom of the wing produces some of the total lift that is developed.

Impact Versus Pressure Lift

Sticking your hand out the window of a moving automobile does two things: it demonstrates how a relatively flat surface develops lift and it signals a left turn. Figure 17 shows that wind is deflected downward when it strikes your hand.

According to Sir Isaac Newton, who knew about such things, for every action there is an equal and opposite reaction. Wind deflected downward by the airfoil creates an upward (opposite) movement of the wing. This upward movement is caused by the impact energy of billions of tiny air molecules striking the underside of the wing. Also, higher pressure on the bottom surface of the wing results from this molecular impact. The wing moves upward as if it were pushed from below.

This type of lift is known as *barn door* or *impact* lift. It generally contributes only a small portion of the total lift produced by the wings, which means that man and woman do not fly by barn door lift alone. If we could, it would mean people in the Midwest would report flying barn doors instead of UFOs.

A more subtle and powerful form of lift occurs from curved airflow over the top of the wing.

Wind deflected downward by the airfoil creates an upward (opposite) movement of the wing.

Bending the Wind With the Wing

The Japanese invented the art of paper bending and called it origami. They then experimented with people bending and called it judo. This art was not perfected, however, until the airlines adopted the practice, which is referred to as "flying coach."

Airliners (indeed all airplanes) bend something else—they use their wings to bend the wind. *Wind bending* did not sound sophisticated enough to explain why airplanes fly, so it was given a fancy Greek title. We call wind bending *aerodynamics*. Simply stated, the wing is a precision device for bending or curving the wind downward.

But how does bending the wind over the wing create lift? Let's find out.

Figure 18 shows a cross section of an airfoil. Examine its shape carefully. At small angles of attack, air flowing above the wing is bent or curved with great precision as it follows the upper cambered surface. A rather straight surface on the bottom of the wing leaves the air underneath relatively unbent. Bending or curving the wind above the wing forces air to travel a greater distance than the straighter airflow below. If the wind above the wing is to reach the trailing edge at nearly the same time as the wind below (science says that the air above the wing actually reaches the trailing edge sooner than the air below the wing), it must speed up to cover the greater distance.

For example, assume you are walking your pitbull (named *Bob*) on a leash. You are on the sidewalk and Bob is walking in the gutter (Figure 19). Bob encounters a parked VW and decides to walk over the car rather than around it (remember, it's a pitbull). Obviously, the distance over the car is greater than the distance you will travel on the sidewalk. In order for Bob to avoid being choked by the leash he will have to speed up slightly as he covers this greater distance.

AIRFLOW OVER AND UNDER A WING

Some Airflow Goes Over
Wing
Some Airflow Goes Under

Angle of Attack Approximately 10°

Lift from an airfoil is produced by air flowing over and under the wing.

Fig. 16

IMPACT LIFT

Airflow striking the hand is deflected downward. This imparts an equal and opposite upward force to the hand.

Total Lift

Airflow

High pressure is created on the bottom of the hand by impacting air molecules.

Fig. 17

AIRFLOW ABOVE AND BELOW THE WING (at a small angle of attack)

AIRFLOW
Air Above Wing Must Travel Greater Distance
Wing
Air Below Wing Travels Less Distance

At low angles of attack the air above the wing is curved while the air below the wing is relatively straight.

Fig. 18

I thought for sure that Frankie Vallee was one of the Four Forces.

DIFFERENT DISTANCES IN CURVATURE ABOVE THAN BELOW THE CAR (WING TOO)

Distance covered by pitbull

Direction of walk

Fig. 19

Distance covered by master

As Bob (the pit bull) walks over the car (shaped like a wing) he must cover a greater walking-distance than his master. Therefore, he must speed up to keep from being choked by his master's leash.

Hey! What Are You Doing Up There?

This pilot was caught checking for those mysterious little Bernoullis that are responsible for the creation of lift. He didn't find any.

Do you notice the resemblance of the VW's profile to a wing? It's curved on top and rather straight on the bottom. As air flows over the wing, it curves and speeds up.

Something remarkable happens when air, flowing over a surface, increases its speed. A physicist named Bernoulli (pronounced BRR-*NEW*-LEE) figured out that the faster air flows over a surface, the less pressure it exerts on that surface. High velocity airflow over the wing causes a slight decrease in pressure on the wing's upper surface. In other words, the pressure on top of the wing is now less than the pressure on the bottom of the wing (Don't ask why. It has to do with translational kinetic energy and explaining that will give you something that feels like a two scoop lobotomy). Known as *Bernoulli's principle*, this wonderful trick is what keeps airplanes from being large and expensive doorstops.

Try an experiment. Take a piece of writing paper and hold it in such a way that the top surface is curved downward (Figure 20). With a little imagination, you can see how the bent paper is similar in appearance to the wing's upper cambered surface. Blow over the top of the paper. What happens? The paper should rise upward (a hundred years ago the

Did You Know...

Did you know that the reduction in air pressure above the wing caused by higher velocity airflow is actually less than that of a young child sucking on a bottle?

When you take into account the total wing area, even a small amount of pressure reduction per square inch of wing adds up to a significant total pressure difference. Each square foot of wing area on a Tecnam P92 Echo Super provides 9.9 pounds of lift (at max gross). Since there are 144 square inches in a square foot, you can see that each square inch of wing provides less than .07 pounds of lift.

Idea Source:
Barry Schiff, *The Proficient Pilot*

BERNOULLI'S PRINCIPLE

Fig. 20

Same Pressure

Same Pressure

Lower Pressure

Higher Pressure

Blowing over the top of the paper creates higher velocity airflow which reduces pressure causing the paper to lift upward similar to a wing's lift.

Different Designs

CANARDS

Two lifting surfaces are apparent on airplanes having the canard design. Think of the forward surface as a miniature wing ahead of the main wing. Both wings produce lift, but the forward wing stalls at a lower angle of attack than the main wings. When this happens, the canard's angle of attack immediately decreases and the nose lowers. This prevents the main wings from stalling, thus making airplanes with the canard configuration stall resistant. Canards are also faster and more fuel efficient since there is no drag from a horizontal stabilizer and elevator. The canard design, however, is limited in its total lifting capability. Center of gravity travel is usually limited, as well.

Indians would have made you chief of the tribe for this magic demonstration!). Increasing the velocity of air over a surface reduces the atmospheric pressure on that surface. This means you have low pressure above the wing and high pressure underneath. Since high pressure always moves toward low pressure, the wing (which just happens to be in the way) is pushed upward in the process. Bernoulli's principle is responsible for the majority of lift developed by the wings of most small airplanes. Impact or barn door lift is an accessory, but Bernoulli does most of the work.

Most wings are designed with their upper surface curved and their lower surface relatively straight. Because of the wing's shape, even at a very small angle of attack, a cambered wing still adds a slight curve and acceleration to the wind. This produces the lift you learn to love, particularly if you think an airplane should fly.

There are more wing shapes than there are body shapes at a Weight Watchers convention. Each shape has its own lift and drag characteristics (bodies too!). Figure 21 shows a variety of these different airfoils. Big ones, thick ones, small ones, skinny ones. They all serve one purpose—generating lift. Sometimes, however, the engineered shape of the wing all by itself can't produce the necessary lift for flight. In these instances the angle of attack becomes the major player in lift production.

Angle of Attack And the Generation of Lift

During takeoff on a commercial airliner, have you ever noticed that the pilot always raises the nose slightly to begin the climb after attaining a minimum forward speed? This is called *rotation* and it isn't something done to the airplane's tires.

As the airplane accelerates for takeoff, it eventually reaches a sufficient speed to begin flying. At this relatively slow speed, however, the wing's engineered curve isn't capable of curving or deflecting enough air downward to produce the necessary lift for flight. This is why the airplane doesn't hop off the ground like a grasshopper that just landed on a hot barbecue. The pilot must do something extra to add an additional curve to the wind. Raising the nose slightly increases the angle of attack. This forces the air to undergo an additional curve greater than what the engineered shape of the airfoil can produce. Figure 22 depicts this process.

An intimate and sizzling relationship exists between angle of attack and lift.

With this additional curvature, air travels a greater distance, its speed increases, pressure lowers on top of the airfoil, and sufficient lift to begin flying is produced at a slower airspeed (thanks for the lift, Bernoulli!). Greater impact lift results from increased exposure of the wing's lower surface to the relative wind. The result is that an increasing angle of attack permits the airplane to produce the necessary lift for flight at a slower airspeed.

DIFFERENT AIRFOILS
Airfoils are a lot like people:

Some, are just average -

Others are sleek & thin -

Some are different -

And others are built to hold couches down

Fig. 21

Now you know how airfoils generate the required lift at slower airspeeds. You also know why airplanes, taking off or landing at slower speeds, seem to have a rather nose-high attitude. But what happens at higher airspeeds? Have you noticed that in cruise flight, at cruise airspeeds, airplanes fly at near-level flight attitudes?

Figure 23 shows an airplane at several different angles of attack. At higher speeds airplanes can fly at lower angles of attack because the wing's shape generates sufficient lift. Slow the airplane and the wing must artificially bend the wind by increasing its angle of attack.

An intimate and sizzling relationship exists between angle of attack and lift. If lift and angle of attack were Rhett and Scarlet, Atlanta wouldn't be the only thing on fire. At small angles of attack (such as during cruise flight), the engineered shape of the airfoil generates sufficient lift for flight as long the airspeed is high.

TWO FORMS OF LIFT

1 Lift From Low Pressure
At large angles of attack the airflow is forced to curve beyond the engineered shape of the wing.

It didn't seem to look quite this way in those da Vinci parchments.

N2132B

2 Impact Lift
Impact lift on the bottom of the wing increases at a high angle of attack. More air is deflected downward which results in an equal and opposite upward movement of the wing.

Fig. 22

The impact of air underneath the wing doesn't play as big a role in lift development at higher (cruise) speeds because less of the wing's underside is exposed to the wind.

In summary, the slower an airplane moves, the greater the angle of attack needed for flight. There is, however, such a thing as too much of a good thing. Bend the air too much and instead of flowing smoothly over the wing and creating lift, it bubbles and burbles and pretty much fails to be very uplifting. We call this condition a *stall*.

What kind of instructor would I be if I didn't say, "Let's find out how and why a wing stalls"?

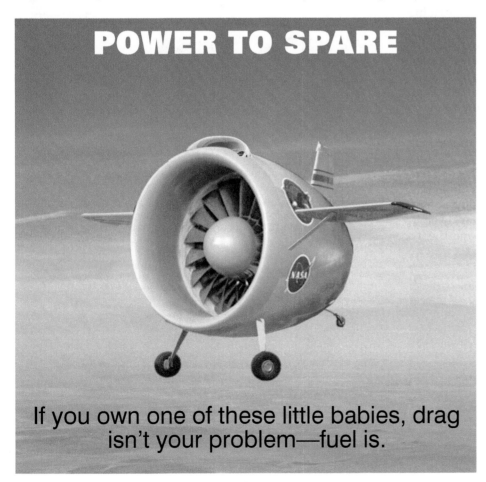

POWER TO SPARE

NASA

If you own one of these little babies, drag isn't your problem—fuel is.

RELATIONSHIP BETWEEN ANGLE OF ATTACK & SPEED

120 Knots   3° Angle of Attack

90 Knots   8° Angle of Attack

70 Knots   12° Angle of Attack

50 Knots   18° Angle of Attack

With speed variations in level flight, the relationship between the angle of attack and airspeed is clearly shown. With increasing airspeed, the airplane requires a smaller angle of attack to remain airborne. As the airplane's airspeed decreases, a larger angle of attack is necessary.

Fig. 23

STALLS

Stall, Angle of Attack, And How the Nose Knows

A pilot's job is to work The Four Forces, maintain lift, and avoid the burbling air condition that results in a stall.

Think of air molecules as little race cars moving over the wing (Figure 24). Each car and air molecule has one objective: follow the curve over the wing's upper cambered surface. Of course, if the wing is at a low angle of attack, the curve is not very sharp and it's a pretty easy trip (Figure 24A).

But look at the curve made by these cars and air molecules when the wing is attacking the wind at a very large angle. As the angle of attack exceeds *approximately* 18 degrees (known as the *critical angle of attack* for reasons you will soon see), these speed-racer air molecules don't negotiate the turn (Figure 24B). When this happens, they spin off or burble into the free air, no longer providing a uniform, high velocity, laminar airflow over the wing (Figure 25). The wing stalls.

(See "Seeing the Stall" in Postflight Briefing #2-6, page 2-46 for a view of how the wing stalls.)

Remember, according to Bernoulli, lower velocity airflow over the wing produces less lift. There is still impact lift provided by air molecules striking the underside of the wing, but we've already learned that this doesn't provide nearly enough lift to sustain the airplane. When there's less lift than weight, bad things happen to good airplanes. The wing goes on strike and stalls. Abandoned by Bernoulli, gravity summons the airplane to earth on its own terms.

All wings have a *critical angle of attack* (the angle varies slightly among airplanes). Beyond this angle the wing and the wind don't work and play well together. All the whispered theory in your heart won't overcome the laws of physics and aerodynamics. The wing police are always watching. Exceed the critical angle of attack and the air

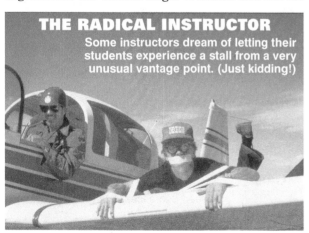

THE RADICAL INSTRUCTOR
Some instructors dream of letting their students experience a stall from a very unusual vantage point. (Just kidding!)

THE CRITICAL ANGLE OF ATTACK

Air molecules, like race cars, can easily curve around a wing at a small angle of attack.

Ⓐ WING

LOW ANGLE OF ATTACK

When forced to undergo too large a curve, air molecules, like race cars, may skid off the top of the wing resulting in a stall.

Ⓑ WING

Don't worry, it's a rental.

CRITICAL ANGLE OF ATTACK Fig. 24

STALLED VS. UNSTALLED WINGS

When the wings exceed their critical angle of attack, airflow over their upper surface, becomes chaotic and starts to burble. It is no longer smooth, high velocity airflow. Consequently, lift decreases.

WINGS STALLED

20° Angle of Attack

Wings operating below their critical angle of attack allow smooth, high velocity airflow to move over their upper surface. This keeps the pressure on the wing's upper surface low and maintains the required lift.

WINGS NOT STALLED

10° Angle of Attack

Fig. 25

STALLING AND EXCEEDING THE CRITICAL ANGLE OF ATTACK

A Pilot raises the nose too steep during a climb. The critical angle of attack is exceeded & the airplane stalls.

B The pilot lowers the nose (adds full power if not already so) and reduces the angle of attack (to less than the critical value). This action reestablishes smooth airflow over the top of the wing.

C Once the airplane is no longer stalled, the pilot raises the nose slowly. I think I've just reached my target heart rate for the day!

D Pilot now resumes climb without exceeding the critical angle of attack. Now my blood pressure is 3 over 1!

Fig. 26

molecules won't give you a lift. Sounds serious, and it can be. Fortunately, there's a readily available solution, and it is *not* screaming, "Here, you take it" to the instructor. Put your finger back in your ear; here comes the important

STALL RECOVERY

A This airplane is stalled with its nose pointed downward while doing 150 knots. A/C MOTION

Fig. 27

The only way to recover is for the pilot to move the elevator control forward. As contrary as this may seem, lowering the nose slightly by moving the elevator control forward (or releasing the back pressure on the elevator control) reduces the angle of attack to less than its critical value. The wing will once again start flying and the airplane will no longer be stalled. At this point the pilot should pull back slowly without (hopefully!) exceeding the critical angle of attack.

B This airplane is moving horizontally at 100 knots and stalls because the pilot pulled too hard on the elevator control. Bob, this is no time to be lighting candles! A/C MOTION

Recovery from the stall is accomplished by moving the elevator control forward (or releasing back pressure) and decreasing the angle of attack to less than its critical value.

These are illustrations for demonstration only. It's unlikely you'll ever find your airplane in these attitudes at these airspeeds.

stuff again. *You can unstall a wing by reducing the angle of attack.* You do this by *gently* lowering the nose of the airplane with the elevator control (Figure 26, sequence A, B, C and D). Easy does it here, Power Ranger. Once the angle of attack is less than its critical angle, the air molecules flow smoothly over the top of the wing and production of lift resumes. It's as simple as that. Please don't ever forget this.

Why am I making such a big deal out of this? Why did I make you put your finger back in your ear? Because in a moment of stress (having the wing stop flying creates stress for many pilots) you will be inclined to do exactly the opposite of what will help. It's a natural pilot response to pull or push on the elevator control to change the airplane's pitch attitude. During a stall, as the airplane pitches downward, your untrained instinct is to pull back on the elevator control. You may yank that critter back into your lap, and the result will not be good. The wing will remain stalled and you, my friend, will have the look of a just gelded bull.

If the wing stalls, you need to do one very important thing: reduce the angle of attack to less than its critical value. Only then does the wing begin flying again. Adding full power also helps in the recovery process by accelerating the airplane. The increase in forward speed provided by power also helps reduce the angle of attack.

Don't just sit there with stalled wings. There's a reason why you are called the pilot-in-*command*. Do something. But do the right thing.

Stall at Any Attitude Or Airspeed

You should realize that airplanes can be stalled at any attitude or at any airspeed. Put your finger back in your ear. *It makes no difference whether the nose is pointed up or down or whether you are traveling at 60 or 150 knots. Whether an airplane exceeds its critical angle of attack is independent of attitude or airspeed.*

Figure 27 depicts two instances showing how this might happen. Airplanes have inertia, meaning they want to keep on moving in the direction they are traveling. Airplane A is pointed nose down, diving at 150 knots (don't try this at home!). The pilot pulled back too aggressively, forcing the wings to exceed their critical angle of attack. The airplane stalls. Wow! Imagine that. It stalls nose down at 150 knots!

What must the pilot do to recover? The first step is to decrease the angle of attack by moving the elevator control forward or releasing back pressure on the control wheel/stick (remember, pulling back on the elevator control was probably responsible for the large angle of attack inducing the stall in the first place.) This re-establishes the smooth, high velocity flow or air over the wings. The airplane is once again flying.

The airplane will always stall when the wings exceed their critical angle of attack. It's the law!

The second step requires applying all available power (if necessary) to accelerate the airplane and help reduce the angle of attack

Once the airplane is no longer stalled, it should be put back in the desired attitude while making sure you don't stall again. Stalling after you've just recovered from a previous stall is known as a secondary stall. Unlike secondary school, it is not considered a step up, especially by the participating flight instructor. (You'll know your instructor is unhappy when you hear her make subtle statements like, "Hmm, come to think of it, childbirth wasn't all that painful.")

Stalling an airplane intentionally, at a safe altitude, is actually fun, or at least educational. Stalls are relatively gentle maneuvers in most airplanes. Stalling an airplane close to the ground, however, is serious business because it is usually not an intentional act. During flight training you'll have ample practice in stall recovery.

Managing a stalled airplane is one thing; managing your natural instincts, another. For example, a typical stall trap you could (literally) fall into involves a high sink rate during landing. While on approach, you might apply back pressure on the elevator, attempting to shallow the descent. If you exceed the critical angle of attack the airplane will stall. The runway now expands in your windshield like a low orbit view of a supernova.

If you follow your untrained instincts and continue to pull backward on the elevator, the stall deepens. Trained pilots know better. They are aware of the possibility of stalling and apply the appropriate combination of elevator back pressure and power during landing to change the airplane's glide path without exceeding the critical angle of

Managing a stalled airplane is one thing; managing your natural instincts, another.

Bad Thing

I recall a student who was a quick study and was a real pleasure to teach. During his first introduction to stalls he elected to pull all the way back on the elevator control and hold it there. He couldn't talk. He just looked at me, pointed to the elevator control with his right hand and said, "BAD THING." Because of this, the airplane remained in a stalled condition.

When stalled, the flight controls are relatively ineffective. As one wing dipped, he turned the wheel, attempting to raise the paralyzed half of the plane. Discovering that his controls were ineffective, he reached over and grabbed mine (I just love it when that happens!). He was thinking I might have played a dirty trick by somehow disabling his set of flight controls.

Upon discovering that my controls didn't work either, he grabbed my arm and made a sound somewhat similar to the stall horn but higher in pitch (probably causing bats to fly into walls). Once he let go of the controls, the airplane nosed forward on its own (as it's designed to do), decreased its angle of attack and recovered from the stall all by itself. Had he intentionally lowered the nose in the first place, I wouldn't have had an enormous bruise on my arm.

attack (your instructor will show you the appropriate use of elevator and power during landing). How do pilots know the proper amount of rearward movement to apply to the elevator? How do they know they won't stall the airplane?

If there was an angle of attack indicator in your airplane, stall recognition would be easy. You'd simply keep the angle of attack less than what's critical for that wing. Angle of attack indicators, although valuable, are very rare in small airplanes. Fortunately, there are several ways to recognize a stall's warning signs.

Five Stall Warning Signs

There are five good early warning clues to indicate the onset of a stall. Good pilots know and watch for all of them.

First, an unmistakable buffet or shaking is usually felt in the airplane and on the flight controls. You might think your instructor is shaking the other set of controls trying to get you to let go of them. Not true. As airflow begins to separate from the top of the wing, it buffets (burbles). For those with only food on their mind, this is *BUFF-ETTES, not BOO-FAYS.* One means getting lunch, the other can mean losing it. Inside the cockpit,

this buffet is felt as vibration and is one of the best early warning clues to an impending stall. If you feel this buffet, simply release some of the backward pressure on the elevator until the buffeting stops.

Second, flight control response usually diminishes when the airplane approaches a stall. If you feel the controls becoming mushy or less effective, this is your cue that things aren't going well. Think stall. Think lower angle of attack. Think quickly.

Third, when the airspeed indicator is nearing the beginning of the white or green arc, you're approaching stall territory. Airplanes must have airspeed to fly. Slow the airplane down too much and it will eventually stall.

Keep an eye on the airspeed indicator and make sure it's a healthy distance above the beginning of the green arc. This is the power-off stalling speed without flaps and gear extended (called the *clean configuration*). When approaching to land, the usual recommendation is to keep the airspeed at least 30% above stall speed. This gives you room to accommodate slight, unexpected variations in airspeed caused by poor technique or wind shear. A good visual clue indicating slow speed is when cars on the road below are moving faster than you are. . . at rush hour.

Having a bird fly up your exhaust stack is a good sign that you're flying too slow in the traffic pattern.

Fourth, a distinct difference in sound occurs when approaching a stall. When I was taking lessons this sound usually came from my instructor yelling, "Lower the nose, goofball, lower the nose!" When airflow strikes the airplane at higher angles of attack, it often makes a different, but recognizable sound.

Fifth, all modern airplanes have stall warning horns or lights. These tattletale devices activate a few knots above stall speed and provide an excellent pre-stall warning—when they're working and when the pilot's listening. On some airplanes it's difficult to test the stall warning horn during the preflight walkaround. That means you won't know it's not working until you need it. You will also be surprised what you can ignore while concentrating on the radio, your instructor, or the pretty colors on all the gauges. That's why you must use *all the clues*, not just one or two.

Aside from these five basic stall warning signs, the seat of your pants provides an additional clue. Let me explain.

Stalling Speed, Gee Whiz And G-Force

Ever watched somebody use a personal computer when something goes wrong? What's the first thing they do? They repeat what they just did, as if the electrons might go with a different flow the second or third time around.

Computers are highly predictable, and so are airplanes. For instance, when the weight of an airplane increases, the aircraft will stall at higher speeds. That's right, every time. Son of a gun.

Let's assume that a lightly loaded airplane begins flying at 42 knots when the angle of attack is slightly less than its critical value (Figure 28, Airplane A). At 42 knots, just enough lift is developed to equal the airplane's weight (although the airplane is on the verge of a stall). An increase in weight means the wings must develop more lift to remain airborne. Certainly the airplane won't fly at or beyond its critical angle of attack (18 degrees for *this* airplane) since this is the built-in design limit of the wing.

Under these conditions, the only way a heavier airplane can develop more lift is to move forward at a slightly faster speed. A heavier airplane in our example might need a minimum forward speed of 48 knots before the wings develop enough lift to equal the increase in weight as shown by Airplane B.

The critical angle of attack at which the wing stalls never changes, but the minimum speed at which the airplane begins flying does change. If the airplane is heavier, it stalls at a higher speed. The converse is also true; lighter weights mean slower stall speeds. (I don't want to give you the impression that we start climbing during the takeoff once we're at or slightly above the airplane stall speed. That's not true! We normally

HOW WEIGHT AFFECTS STALL SPEED

Airplane A, weighing only 1,000 pounds, starts flying at when it's slightly above 42 knots and the wing is just a little below its critical angle of attack. Another way of saying this is the airplane's stalling speed is 42 knots at this weight.

A heavier Airplane B needs to develop more lift than its lighter cousin before it can fly. At a little less than its critical angle of attack, Airplane B needs a little more than 48 knots of airflow over its wings before lift equals weight. In other words, the stalling speed of the heavier Airplane B is 48 knots. Despite weight differences between Airplanes A and B, both airplanes stall at the same critical angle of attack.

HOW CENTRIFUGAL FORCE CAUSES YOU AND THE AIRPLANE TO FEEL HEAVIER IN A TURN

A During a sharp turn on a level road, you feel a newly generated force known as "centrifugal force." This force pushes you out the door while gravity pulls you downward. If the door pops open, you'll move in the direction of the resultant force.

B Turning on a banked road causes the resultant force to pull you straight down in your seat. The sharper the turn in the car, the greater the resultant force or G-force you feel in your seat (i.e., the heavier you feel).

C Airplanes in a bank feel this same increase in G-force (load factor). Remember, if you feel heavier in a turn, then the airplane also feels heavier. Therefore the airplane must increase its lift to remain aloft in a turn.

I think some of our vectors fell out of the baggage compartment!

Fig. 29

accelerate to a safe margin above stall speed—30% or more depending on what your flight instructor recommends—then climb.)

Here's the question that wins a free pizza: Is it possible to make the airplane think it weighs more without adding any weight to it? May I have the envelope, please? The answer is *yes*. (Mushroom, no anchovies, thank you.) "Gee whiz," you're probably saying. No, not gee whiz, or Cheese Whiz, but simply G.

Think back to the last time you were on a rollercoaster. On the straightaway all you felt was speed. Turns, however, forced you down in the seat. You experienced an increase in your apparent weight when turning because of something known as centrifugal force. This is the same

force that makes you feel you might fall out of the car while turning if your seat belt isn't fastened (Figure 29).

Because airplanes bank (like cars on a banked road), centrifugal force and gravity pull you down in your seat. You and the airplane can expect to feel this apparent increase in weight during a turn. The wings don't know what's causing the airplane to feel heavier, and frankly, my dear, they don't give a darn. They only know that it's getting heavier.

The steeper the turn, the greater the centrifugal force and the more you and the airplane appear to become heavier. This force is often called *G-force*. Perhaps it was so named because students often say, "Geeeeeeeeeeee" whenever they feel

their apparent weight increase. The term the pocket protector set (or engineers) use for G-force is *load factor* (we'll use both terms synonymously).

Figure 30 shows a load factor vs. bank chart. Using this chart we can assess the exact amount of G-force you'll experience in any given bank while maintaining altitude. According to this chart, a 60 degree bank produces 2Gs. This means you and the airplane feel twice as heavy as you actually are. If the airplane weighed 1,300 pounds, its structure is required to support 2,600 pounds in a 60 degree bank at a constant altitude.

Here is the most important point about increasing the G-force (finger in the ear again!). *If the airplane feels twice as heavy as it actually is, then the lift must double if the airplane is to maintain altitude.* How can you increase lift? Creating a larger angle of attack by applying elevator back pressure, going faster by increasing the power, or a combination of both will increase the airplane's lift production.

During steep turns you typically apply back pressure on the elevator control while attempting to maintain your altitude. This increases your angle of attack and increases lift to compensate for the increasing G force (Figure 31). Prior to entering a slight bank at an airspeed of 100

LOAD FACTOR CHART

A 60° Bank Produces a Load Factor of "2" or "2Gs."

LOAD FACTOR G-Force

BANK ANGLE in DEGREES

Fig. 30

In a 60 degree bank at a constant altitude, the airplane experiences 2Gs. A 10 lb. weight produces a 20 lb. scale deflection.

knots, this airplane's angle of attack was 4 degrees. With a slight bank, back pressure is required and the angle of attack increases to 6 degrees as shown by Airplane A. The increased angle of attack provides an increase in lift but it also exposes more of the wing's underside to the airflow and increases drag. Now the airspeed drops to 93 knots.

As the angle of bank steepens the angle of attack must be increased to maintain altitude. The airspeed continues to decrease because of the increased drag. Airplanes B, C and D depict this sequence. If you were paying attention back in the stall department, you can see where this flight is going. When the bank is very steep, the airplane reaches its critical angle of attack as shown by Airplane D. Having slowed to 84 knots, Airplane D is now at its critical angle of attack. Any further attempt to increase the bank while holding altitude stalls the airplane.

There are five good early warning clues to indicate the onset of a stall. Good pilots know and watch for all of them.

While this particular airplane stalled at 60 knots in level flight, it now stalls at 84 knots in a very steep bank. The moral of this story is that an increase in weight (apparent or real) causes the speed at which the airplane stalls to increase. In other

ANGLE OF BANK AND ANGLE OF ATTACK RELATIONSHIP

SLIGHT BANK 6° Angle of Attack 93 Knots	LARGER BANK 10° Angle of Attack 90 Knots	STEEPER BANK 14° Angle of Attack 87 Knots	VERY STEEP BANK 18° Angle of Attack 84 Knots
A 1.1Gs	**B** 1.4Gs	**C** 1.8Gs	**D** 2Gs

As the angle of bank is increased in level flight, the angle of attack must increase to maintain the necessary lift. As the angle of attack increases so does the lift and the drag which causes the airspeed to decrease. Eventually the angle of attack required for level flight reaches its critical value (Airplane D). A further increase in angle of attack will cause the airplane to stall at a very high speed (also known as an *accelerated stall*). **Fig. 31**

words, when you feel an increase in G-force (load factor), the airplane's stalling speed is also increasing.

Normally you would increase your power in a steep turn to prevent the airspeed from getting too slow. Giving this particular airplane full throttle in a very steep turn might keep the airspeed at 90 knots. This gives you a 6 knot buffer above the steep turn stalling speed in this example. Of course, this assumes that your engine is capable of producing this extra power in the first place. This simply isn't an option in our smaller, horsepower anemic airplanes, is it?

The increase in stall speed with bank angle is as predictable as a politician's addiction to podiums. Figure 32 shows that a 60 degree bank increases stall speed by 40%. This is certainly nice information to know, but are you expected to carry a Cray supercomputer and punch in percentages prior to any turn? Of course not. What you need to have is a high index of suspicion. If the seat of your pants says you're weighing in at a level that qualifies you for the main event on a heavyweight boxing card, you should think (quickly) about how the stall speed increases in a turn. For those of you frightened by higher math (adds, take-

aways, times and goes-intos) there is an easier way to calculate this.

Figure 33 is typical of the stall charts found in most owners' manuals. It provides you with the stall speeds for specific angles-of-bank under variable flap conditions (we'll discuss flaps in a bit).

Avoiding stalls while in a steep bank with smaller, power-limited airplanes means you must be prepared to do two things. At the first sign of a stall, you must unload the wings by releasing back pressure on the elevator and simultaneously reducing the angle of bank. This decreases the load factor and reduces the stall speed.

For example, assume that you're in the traffic pattern and are making a turn onto final approach. Because of poor planning (it happens to everyone once in a while), you find yourself

STALL SPEED AND BANK ANGLE CHART

A 60° Bank Increases Stall Speed By 40%

Fig. 32

STALL SPEED CHART

Power Off **Stalling Speeds** Knots =IAS			
Gross Weight 2,550 lbs.	Angle Of Bank		
Condition	0°	30°	45°	60°
Flaps Up	50	54	59	71
Flaps 10°	42	45	50	59
Flaps 30°	40	43	48	57

Fig. 33

overshooting the runway centerline. Increasing the bank is a natural response to prevent overshooting—but it's also a risky one.

When the bank increases, the nose wants to lower or pitch down (I'll talk about why this happens later). Pilots typically pull back on the elevator control to maintain altitude in response to a dropping nose. Pulling back on the elevator increases the angle of attack and slows the airspeed. Now the airplane is closer to its critical angle of attack at a lower airspeed. If the airplane was flying slow to begin with, the airplane may stall. What's the solution?

Whenever you are making a turn, especially when close to the ground, be especially sensitive to the amount of bank you use. *Be sensitive to the G-force you experience.* If you feel your apparent weight increasing, you now know your stall speed is also increasing. Your derriere becomes the ultimate stall sensing device (and to think you've been packing that thing around all these years and didn't realize its usefulness). This is what is called, "flying by the seat of your pants." If anyone accuses you of sitting down on the job, you just tell them you're testing your stall detector.

By the way, there is a time when we want our wings to stall before they experience too many Gs. The speed at which this occurs is called

DEFLECTING AN ADVERSARY

The martial arts master gently deflects his opponent's energy in the vertical (up or down) direction. The master feels little horizontal resistance but his assailant feels an unusual amount of discomfort.

UPWARD

I know karate & 7 other Oriental words.

DOWNWARD

Fig. 34

the "design maneuvering speed." (See Postflight Briefing #2-5).

DRAG

What a Drag

You can't get something for nothing in aviation. Although Burt Rutan (a famed airplane designer) comes close, there is no free lunch when it comes time for an airfoil to pay for the lift it develops. Drag is that price.

Drag is the natural response to an object's movement through the air. Try an experiment. Stick your head out a moving automobile (amazing

THE WING & THE MASTER

Think of the wing doing the same thing as the martial arts master. The wing deflects the air molecules vertically (up or down), attempting to produce as little horizontal resistance as possible.

I am "Wing Man."

● = Air Molecule

Fig. 35

what you can learn about flying while sticking parts of you out a car window). At 60 MPH your mouth puffs open, your eyes bug out, your head is thrown back and your hair looks like it was blow dried with a Pratt & Whitney jet engine. You look like a rock star! This is all the result of the wind resistance known as drag.

Horizontal and Vertical Movement of Air

An Aikido martial arts master is trained to deflect his adversary vertically without offering any resistance in the horizontal direction. Upon encountering a head-on adversary, the Aikido master makes the Bruce Lee karate call sound and gently deflects the assailant either upward or downward (Figure 34).

Wings do something very similar. They are designed, as you will recall from our earlier discussion, to deflect air vertically while offering very little horizontal resistance (Figure 35).

Regardless of how efficient the wing is, some horizontal resistance to forward motion is always present. We discussed drag briefly at the beginning of this chapter, but let's take a somewhat closer look at the two kinds of speed retardant—*parasite drag* and *induced drag*.

As unusual as it may look, spins are perfectly safe maneuvers to practice (providing you have proper instruction and an airplane certified for spins). For an airplane to spin, it must first be stalled. When the stall occurs, rudder is applied in the direction you desire to spin. The elevator is held back and the airplane commences to autorotate. The outside wing is not as stalled as the inside wing, causing the airplane to rotate about the spin axis. After the first two turns the airplane's inertial forces balance and it settles into a predictable pattern of rotation. As unusual as it seems, the airspeed stabilizes at 65 to 75 knots for small airplanes while the descent rate can exceed 7,000 feet per minute. Recovery is accomplished by reducing power (if you haven't already done so), neutralizing the ailerons and applying opposite rudder. The elevator is then moved forward to decrease the angle of attack. See Postflight Briefing #2-1 for more info on spins.

THE SPIN

Bob, do you think this is a good way to enter the traffic pattern?

Outside wing: more lift & less drag (not as stalled)

Inside wing: more drag & less lift (fully stalled)

Lift

No.

DRAG

Yaw

Spin axis

Motion

Drag is a very complicated subject. I've seen both blood and entire pots of coffee spilled over the lurid details of a subject so arcane that even engineers with multiple degrees disagree. If you want some ammunition for the next session of hangar flying or want more indepth information, see Postflight Briefing #2-2 at the end of the chapter.

For the moment, what you need to know is that there are two kinds of drag. Parasite drag is the result of friction. Trying to move something through the air results in friction with air molecules. This resistance isn't useful and that's why it's called parasite drag. It's there because it's there. Hang on to the idea that as airspeed doubles, parasite drag quadruples, and there's very little you can do about it. Rats!

Induced drag is resistance to motion *induced* by the wing turning some of its lift into drag. (See Postflight Briefing #2-2 if you want a more detailed understanding of induced drag.) What you need to know here is that induced drag does the complete opposite of parasite drag—it increases as the airplane slows down.

Total Drag and Your *Go Far* Speed

What does all this talk about parasite and induced drag mean to you as a pilot? It could mean as little as knowing how to save a few bucks on fuel, or it could mean as much as knowing how to protect your remarkably fragile hide in the event of an emergency.

I gather I now have your full attention again?

As the airplane speeds up, induced drag decreases while parasite drag increases. Hmm. Is there a specific speed, a number better than all other numbers, where the total drag on the airplane is at a minimum? Yea verily, there is.

Figure 36 shows the airplane's *total drag curve,* affirming that—unlike Bigfoot, the Loch Ness Squid and Elvis—a minimum drag speed actually exists. When the induced and parasite drag curves are added together to produce a total drag curve, there is always a point where the sum of both curves is at a minimum. The lowest spot in the total drag curve is your magic number, a specific airspeed known as the *best L/D speed* (pronounced "best L over D speed," which stands for "lift over drag"). Put your finger back in your ear again, this is important! *Since minimum drag occurs at this speed, minimum thrust for forward flight must also occur at this speed.* So it is written. Verily, so it will be! Wow, this is good stuff!

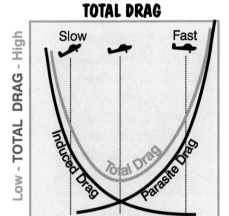

TOTAL DRAG

Parasite drag increases with increasing airspeed while induced drag decreases with increasing airspeed. The total drag curve is a summation of both types of drag. The lowest point on the total drag curve is the point where the airplane experiences the least amount of drag.

Fig. 36

Minimum thrust means we obtain maximum forward distance for a given amount of fuel consumption. The best L/D speed yields the maximum range for a tank (or a gallon or a thimbleful) of fuel in a no-wind condition. If L's and D's and minimum thrust don't stick well, try thinking of this magic number as your "maximum range" or "go far" speed. (See Postflight Briefing #2-3 for a more detailed discussion of the airplane's maximum endurance and maximum range capabilities.)

This speed also yields the airplane's maximum power-off glide range, which is where the saving your hide part comes in. "Power-off glide" is a nice way of saying the engine isn't working at the moment and you are now the pilot of a glider, looking for a landing spot. So immediately establish the proper gliding attitude and airspeed. This is a time when you will want the ability to go as far as is necessary to find that spot.

Figure 37 shows a typical *Best Glide Speed/Range Chart* found in many Pilot Operating Handbooks. This is the maximum distance power-off glide speed for a specified airplane. This speed should be as familiar to you as sandpaper is to a safecracker. Know the number for your airplane.

Best Glide Speed/Range Chart

* Propeller Windmilling
* Flaps Up
* Zero Wind

Height Above Terrain - Feet

Ground Distance - Nautical Miles

Best Glide Speed 65 Knots

Fig. 37

FLYING ABOVE OR BELOW BEST GLIDE SPEED

Fig. 38

If you try to glide at other than the best glide speed, (the speed for best L/D), the airplane won't cover the maximum distance it's capable of traveling.

This particular airplane's best glide speed is 65 knots.

14:1 Glide Ratio at Speed for Best L/D (65 Kts.)

Less Than 14:1 at Other Speeds

No Wind
Not to Scale

Good Speed

Too Fast

Too Slow

Stretching the Glide, Saving the Hide

A friend of mine was reading the newspaper *USA Today* (he's into primary colors). He said, "Hey Rod, it says here on page 13 that 52% of the American public is mathematically illiterate." I said, "That's not a good sign." He replied, "Yeah, imagine that, nearly one-third of the population can't do math!"

As a precaution, I have avoided, to the extent possible, using mathematics in this book. However, I want you to think of L/D as a ratio of lift to drag. Don't think about a ratio as a "goes-into" or division problem. Think of it as comparing one value

(lift) placed on top of another (drag), separated by a line.

A "power-off glide" happens under one of two conditions. One is instructor-induced. It comes accompanied by some ominous-sounding incantation such as "You've just had an engine failure," and the instructor pulling the throttle back to idle. This is a not-really-power-off glide. You may, at this awkward time, be asked what the plane's best L/D speed is, or what the glide ratio is.

The other occasion is a real power-off glide, caused by a real engine failure. This is the time when you wish you were wearing your Kevlar power suit and accompanying roll bar. At moments like that, you really do

want to know the best L/D speed and have some idea of what the plane's glide ratio is.

In a power-off glide, the best L/D speed allows the airplane to glide a maximum forward distance with a minimum amount of altitude loss. For example, the airplane in Figure 38 has a lift-over-drag ratio of approximately 14 to 1 (also written as 14:1) at its best L/D speed (65 kts.). At this speed the airplane experiences minimum drag (at the bottom of the total drag curve) and moves 14 feet forward for every foot it descends. No matter what you do to the airplane, this is the best glide ratio it's capable of attaining. You can rock back-and-forth in your seat and yell, "Come on big fellow, come on, yee-hawww!" and the airplane still isn't going to glide better than 14 feet forward for every foot it drops. If you attempt to glide at some speed other than this one, your airplane simply won't glide as far (Figure 38). It's possible that you're sitting there munching Doritos wondering, "Hey, what happens to the glide range if the airplane's weight changes?" If so, see Postflight Briefing #2-4 for more details on this interesting subject.

No, no no. I said I wanted you to put winglets on my airplane!

THIS BUD'S 4 YOU
BUD'S A/C MODS

SKYPARK B

Drooped wingtips help create a more efficient wing.

Fig. 39A

Winglets are another method used to increase wing efficiency.

USAF

Fig. 39B

WINGTIP VORTEX

Air sneaks from underneath the wing where the pressure is high, to the top of the wing, where the pressure is lower. As the wing moves forward, it creates a spiral of air trailing off the wingtips. This spiral moves outward, upward, and inward, trailing behind the wing.

Lower pressure (above wing)

Spiraling airflow

Higher pressure (underneath wing)

Fig. 40

Now you have a basic idea of how parasite and induced drag affect an airplane and you're ready to take a closer look at how induced drag can fool you into believing your airplane is ready to fly when it isn't.

Ground Effect

The object of golf is to hit the ball the least number of times. Do this and you win. Recently, I was asked to play at a professional tournament. I used a new strategy. I stayed home, never hit the ball, and claimed victory. If wings can bend air, why can't I bend the rules of golf?

Here's one of those nifty pilot nuggets (or nougats) with which you can win a hamburger some day. Is it possible to unbend the air which is bent by the wing at a large angle of attack? Yes, using the wizardry of something called *ground effect*.

Ground effect allows an airplane flying close to the runway to remain airborne at a slightly lower-than-normal speed. During landing, this means the airplane might have a ten-

dency to float (continue to glide just above the runway). During takeoff, the airplane can become airborne before it has sufficient speed to climb. Either event is like buying new glasses, taking them back because you can't read, then finding out you're illiterate. Both cause a lot of chagrin, but a takeoff like this can be dangerous. To understand how ground effect affects an airplane, you need to know something about how wind tries to escape around a wing.

Remember that a wing generates lift because of increased pressure on its lower surface and decreased pressure over its upper surface. At high angles of attack, this pressure differential is quite large. Large pressure differences cause air molecules to act like lots of little prison inmates, with each molecule waiting for the slightest chance to break out of jail. Given that chance, air molecules underneath the wing would

gladly sneak over the top, where lower pressure resides. This reduces the wing's lifting efficiency. Unfortunately, it's difficult to design wings that preclude this escape.

Figures 39A and 39B show several attachments added onto wingtips to thwart escaping air. Drooped wingtips are a common sight on many airplanes. They create a barrier to help contain escaping high pressure air from under the wing. Winglets are another common sight

Attempting to climb out of ground effect at too slow a speed can cause the airplane to sink back onto the runway (if there is any runway left to sink back to at this point!).

on larger airplanes. They also create a barrier that minimizes the escape of under-the-wing, high pressure air. Since they bend upward, they also give the impression that the airplane attempted to taxi between two closely parked gas trucks.

Air sneaking from under the wing spirals upward and over the wingtip (Figure 40). Couple this spiral with air moving backward over the wing and you get a vortex similar to a horizontal tornado. Called a *wingtip vortex,* this tornado spirals outward, then upward, then inward behind each wing. You can expect this vortex action to increase at large angles of attack, where the pressure differential between the top and bottom of the wing is greater.

!ERRRR (STALL HORN)

32

DEEP CANYON AIRPORT

The perils of ground effect become obvious when you're too fast on the approach!

If these vortices only affected the air at the wingtips, aerodynamicists would have many fewer design problems. Unfortunately, not only does this vortex spiral around the wingtips, it also adds a downwash or downward flow to the air behind and along the wing's span as shown by Airplane A in Figure 41. The wing itself also thrusts air downward. At higher angles of attack this results in the downward bending of the relative wind in the vicinity of the wing. This newly bent relative wind is often called the *local relative wind*. Recalling that lift is always perpendicular to the relative wind, the total lift now tilts rearward slightly. It does so to remain perpendicular to the newly bent relative wind. Part of the total lift is now acting in a rearward direction. This results in an increase in induced drag at high angles of attack.

When the wing moves close to the ground (usually within one wingspan's length or less), its vortices, thus its downwash, diminish. In other words, the downwash can't shove the air into the ground. Voila, the local relative wind in the vicinity of the wing unbends as shown by Airplane B.

This has the effect of allowing the wing's total lifting force to tilt upward slightly, despite the wing's large angle of attack. An upward tilting of the total lifting force means the airplane experiences less induced drag (less rearward pull of lift). This becomes quite evident when you compare Airplanes A and B in Figure 41. The net result is that it takes less power to produce the necessary lift for flight while in ground effect.

You win the hamburger.

Where to Use Caution

Attempting to emerge from ground effect before the plane is really ready to fly is like a newly hatched butterfly taking off before its wings are dry. It's not going to work. Trying to climb out of ground effect at this slower speed can cause the airplane to sink back onto the runway (if there's any runway left to sink back to at this point!).

WING PERFORMANCE OUT OF GROUND EFFECT

At large angles of attack, wingtip vortices result in a downwash behind the wing. This acts to bend the relative wind and tilt the total lifting force aft (the total lift force tilts so as to remain perpendicular to the bent relative wind). A component of the total lift force, called "effective lift," acts vertically, opposite weight. This is the component responsible for keeping the airplane in the air. Induced drag is part of the total lifting force which pulls the airplane aft. This makes the airplane slow down quicker and prevents faster acceleration.

Fig. 41

WING PERFORMANCE IN GROUND EFFECT

At the same large angle of attack within ground effect, the previously bent relative wind (in the vicinity of the wing) is straightened. Downwash can't blow into the ground. Therefore the total lifting force is tilted upward slightly to remain perpendicular to the relative wind. This acts to reduce the rearward pull of induced drag on the airplane, allowing the airplane to become airborne earlier and remain airborne longer (float) with less drag. Therefore, it's possible to float on landing or liftoff at too slow a speed for a safe climb.

GROUND EFFECT AND PITCH CHANGES

Fig. 42

You must reach the airplane's minimum climb speed before charging out of ground effect.

Because of the rather large reduction in induced drag, ground effect can also cause the airplane to float during landing. Higher approach speeds make this particularly noticeable. Certainly this isn't much of a problem if you're landing at the Bonneville Salt Flats (don't try it). If, however, you're landing on a 1,000 foot strip and approach at excessive speed, you might need a contractor's license (you'll need it to rebuild all the houses, fences and sheds at the runway's end).

Here's a big secret. If you're approaching at a speed above the normal approach speed, slow down before entering ground effect. Since ground effect becomes noticeable at a wing span's length and exists until touchdown, slow the airplane to the manufacturer's recommended approach speed before reaching this height. Continue your descent at this speed.

Different Designs

THE "T" TAIL

T-Tail Is Unaffected by Wing & Prop Downwash

Low Mounted Tail Lies in Wing & Prop Downwash

On airplanes having low mounted tails, downwash from the propeller and the wings provides a downward acting force on the tail. Power reduction reduces this downwash and is followed by a nose-down pitch. In this respect, the airplane has less longitudinal stability since its pitch is affected by power changes. T-tail airplanes are less affected by this since the tail is above this downwash. Additionally, the T-tail provides one of the best configurations for spin recovery. Disadvantages are usually heavier weight for T-tail construction as well as complicated elevator control and trim linkages.

HOW FLAPS CHANGE THE WING'S CURVATURE

Wing Slightly Curved

FLAPS UP

Chord Line

Wing Curved More

FLAPS DOWN

Chord Line

When flaps are lowered, the wing's curvature increases (surface area can increase too) and the chord line moves to increase the wing's angle of attack. This allows the wing to produce more lift for a given airspeed.

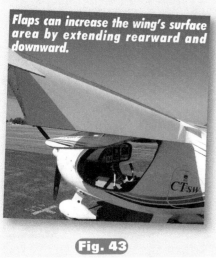

Flaps can increase the wing's surface area by extending rearward and downward.

Fig. 43

Pitch Changes In and Out of Ground Effect

As if floating on landing and an inability to climb after takeoff aren't enough of a problem, expect to experience subtle pitch changes when entering or leaving ground effect. As the airplane becomes airborne and flies out of ground effect, the wing's downwash increases. This blows air downward on the tail as shown by Airplane A in Figure 42. It's possible to become airborne without sufficient speed, then attempt to climb and have the nose pitch up slightly. This is the last thing you want to happen when the speed is low. If you're not prepared for this, it will be an unhappy surprise (and pilots don't like surprises!).

During landing, as the airplane enters ground effect and the downwash diminishes, the nose tends to pitch forward. If you are not prepared for this you might land suddenly or sooner than expected. The secret to managing ground effect is to anticipate it. Expect ground effect to increase when the airplane is within a wing span's height above the runway. Low wing airplanes experience more ground effect than their high wing cousins. Be prepared for a slight nose-up pitch during takeoff and a slight nose-down pitch when landing.

Flap Over Flaps

Ever wondered why the wings of large commercial airplanes sprout aluminum prior to takeoff and landing? Fast airplanes require small, thin wings to achieve the eye-popping velocity needed to satisfy today's speed-hungry air traveler. The problem with thin, small wings is that they stall at a very high speed. Most jet airliners would have to take off and land at close to 200 MPH to achieve a safe margin above stall if they couldn't enlarge their wing's surface area and change their camber to create a temporary low speed wing. Engineers, however, design wings to do just that by supplying them with flaps. Extending or retracting flaps changes the wing's lift and drag characteristics.

Lowering flaps lowers the trailing edge of the wing as shown in Figure 43. The wing's lift is increased in two ways. First, the lowered trailing edge increases the angle the chord line makes with the relative wind. Greater lift results from this increased angle of attack. Second, the lowered trailing edge increases the curvature on part of the wing resulting in increased air velocity over the wing's upper surface (many flaps even increase the wing's surface area by extending downward and outward).

Because of the larger angle of attack and greater curvature, flaps provide you with more lift for a given airspeed.

In case you haven't noticed, this is also why flight control surfaces (ailerons, rudders and elevators) work. They change the curvature of the surface to which they are connected. This changes the lift produced by that surface.

Flap Varieties

Flaps come in several varieties (Figure 44). They all serve two basic purposes: to increase lift and drag. Fowler flaps (A) extend downward and backward. This provides a nice addition to wing curvature as well as increasing the surface area of the wing. Fowler flaps are common on a few models of light sport airplanes, but are more common on traditional airplanes where weight isn't a limiting factor.

Other varieties of flaps, like the plain type (B), offer an increased wing curvature without an increase in the wing's surface area. Slotted flaps (C), increase curvature of the wing and add fast moving air to the trailing edge of the wing (fast moving air helps prevent burbling and airflow separation which results in a stall). This type of flap is more common on light sport airplanes mainly because of lowered construction costs (while still providing a strong aerodynamic benefit). Split flaps (D), found on airplanes like the Sting S3 or Gobosh, increase the impact energy under the wing, thereby adding to the wing's lift (this impact energy results from the barn door lift we previously discussed). These flaps also add a great deal of drag to the wing.

Why Use Flaps?

What's the reason for putting flaps on small airplanes? First and foremost, they create the lift necessary to maintain flight at slower airspeeds. When landing, your goal is to approach and touch down at a reasonably slow speed. You certain-

ly don't want to touch down at cruise speed. Such a high speed landing might just turn your tires into three little puffs of smoke. Flaps allow you to approach and land at a slower speed while maintaining a safe margin above the stall speed.

A slower speed on touchdown means less runway is used to stop. This is an important consideration if the runway is short. Alternatively, if the wind is gusty, you might consider approaching with little or no flap extension. At the slower speeds allowed by flaps, the airplane becomes more difficult to control (the controls are not as responsive). Let's see how effectively the flaps increase lift by referring to the airspeed indicator (Figure 45).

Since many flaps are painted white (we'll assume they are for this discussion), the airspeed indicator's white arc represents the flap operating range. The beginning of the white arc (B) is known as the power-off, full-flap stalling speed (in nonaccelerated flight at the airplane's maximum allowable weight). It's the speed at which the airplane stalls with flaps fully extended, power off and the gear extended. In Figure 45, the airplane will fly when 40 knots of wind blows over the wings if they are below their critical angle of attack.

The high speed end of the white arc is the maximum speed you may fly with flaps fully extended. Flying beyond this speed can damage the flaps. In this example, you wouldn't want the airspeed indicator to indicate more than 87 knots with flaps extended (some airplanes, however, allow you to fly at a higher speed with partial flaps extended). Bringing broken or bent airplanes back from a flight isn't a good idea, even if they are rentals (you'll find out how bad an idea it is when you get the bill for unbending the metal).

Notice that the white arc (B) begins at a speed seven knots slow-

TYPES OF FLAPS

A Fowler flaps move rearward and downward thereby increasing wing area and wing curvature. High velocity airflow from underneath the wing, flowing up and over the flap, helps delay the onset of a stall.

B Plain flaps lower the trailing edge of the wing, increasing its curvature. This acts to increase the wing's lift.

C Slotted flaps allow high velocity airflow from underneath the wing to flow up and over the flap. This helps prevent airflow separation and delays the onset of a stall.

D Split flaps generate some lift and a lot of drag since they disrupt airflow on the underside of the wing.

Fig. 44

FLAP SPEED RANGE

Flaps extended - 40 kts.
(beginning of white arc)

No flaps - 49 kts.
(beginning of green arc)

Fig. 45

er than the green arc (A). From an earlier discussion, we learned that the green arc is the power-off stalling speed with flaps retracted (gear retracted too). This airplane must have 49 knots or more of wind flowing over the wings to fly with flaps retracted. With flaps fully extended, you can touch down at a slower speed—seven knots slower, to be exact (the full flap stall speed on the airspeed indicator assumes the airplane is at its maximum allowable weight).

But, as Confucius might say, "Man who sow 'wild oats' . . . eventually have crop failure." In other words, you don't get something for nothing. Flaps provide you with lift but they also produce drag. Full flaps create a very low speed wing. Try to accelerate it and at some point, drag defeats your efforts. Fortunately, the first half of flap travel usually provides more lift than drag. The last half usually provides more drag than lift. This is why some aircraft manuals recommend only 10 to 25 degrees of flaps for takeoffs on short fields (usually one or two notches on a three to four notch, manual flap system).

If you're high while on approach to land, you can select full flaps to increase the airplane's drag. It's considered normal to use flaps only when descending within the traffic pattern and not when descending from cruise flight. After all, cruise flight descents are efficient and fast at higher speeds where the parasite

Nice to Know Ideas

FLAPS AND FORWARD VISIBILITY OVER THE NOSE

Application of flaps in the traffic pattern allows you to have better visibility over the airplane's nose, making it easier to observe traffic and see the runway.

drag is greater. If you wanted to descend with flaps from cruise flight, you'd have to slow the airplane down below maximum flap extension speed (the top of the white arc) before applying flaps. This would be cumbersome. The airplane can descend faster at cruise speed with reduced power while getting you to your destination sooner.

Since flaps provide more lift at slower speeds, think carefully about how and when they are retracted while airborne. If you're making a full flap approach and it's necessary to go around (i.e., give up this approach, climb, and return for another landing attempt), don't retract the flaps all at once! This would be like having someone remove a part of your wing at a slow speed. The sudden and often dramatic increase in stall speed could place

you near a stall before you can accelerate to a safer speed. Apply full power first, then retract the flaps in increments. In airplanes with 30 to 40 degrees of flap extension, retract the flaps to their least-drag/maximum-lift position. Usually, this position is found at one-half flap travel (depending on the airplane). In airplanes with three notches of manually applied flaps, retract one notch first, followed by the other two once the airplane begins to accelerate.

Do be careful in low wing airplanes when the flaps are up and someone is standing on the inboard section of the wing (be especially careful if you're airborne at the time—you're in a Twilight Zone movie). A friend was on the checkride for his pilot's license when he damaged the FAA checkpilot. Before takeoff, the check pilot boarded the airplane, realized he forgot something and decided to return to the flight school. He opened the door, stepped out on the wing over an "approved step" as labeled on the inboard flap section. My friend, realizing that he hadn't checked the flaps during the preflight, decided to lower the hand-lever-activated flaps. An "ahhhhhhh," then "thud," were heard. The checkpilot went aerobatic and fell straight down. My friend, trying to break the tension with a little humor, looked over and said, "Hey, while you're down there, how about checking those tires for me?" On his second checkride . . .

There are several officially recognized forms of drag: **THIS ISN'T ONE OF THEM!** You know you forgot to unhook the tail's tiedown chain and are towing the tiedown block when it takes full power just to taxi.

How Airplanes Turn

There are many misconceptions in aviation. For instance, there are pilots who think prop-wash is a highly specialized detergent. And a select few think that carburetor ice comes in three flavors. Sometimes pilots even have misconceptions about how airplanes turn. Let's examine what causes an airplane to turn, then look at how to perform this nifty little maneuver.

As a young student pilot, an FAA inspector asked me how an airplane turns. I looked at him and said, "With the wheel, sir." He clutched his chest and shook his head in disbelief. I admit that my answer was a little off and that he was a tad upset (the foam from around his mouth and his eyebrows merging with his hairline were good clues). Nevertheless, shouldn't I get partial credit? I guess Mother Nature doesn't grade on a curve.

Airplane A in Figure 46 shows a view of an airplane in straight, wings-level flight. From this vantage point, lift acts vertically. Lift pulls upward on the airplane, keeping it suspended in flight. Surely, if lift can pull upward, then it can pull a little to the left or right. When it does this, the airplane turns. (To be precise about it, lift actually pushes upward on the wing but I'll use the term *pull* instead. It makes the concept of forces a little easier to visualize.)

OK, so how do you make an airplane turn? If you said, "With the wheel," I am deeply indebted and promise not to have a heart attack. In fact, turning the wheel or deflecting the control stick (i.e., banking the airplane with ailerons), is exactly how we tilt the total lifting force and start a turn (I'll explain control usage shortly).

Airplane B shows the total lift force in a banked airplane. Part of the lift force pulls the airplane up (the vertical component of lift) and part pulls the airplane in the direction of the turn (the horizontal component of lift). You can use your imagination and visualize two separate and smaller forces making up the total lifting force. (There are those arrows again. You will not see these on a real airplane, so enjoy them while you can.) The arrows simply represent the forces of lift.

If you're asked why an airplane turns, respond by saying that it's the horizontal component of lift that's responsible. The horizontal component of lift pulls the airplane in an arc. The larger the angle of bank, the greater the horizontal component and the quicker the airplane can turn.

Remember, you never get something for nothing. Tilting the total lift force while in a turn means less lift is available to act vertically against the airplane's weight, as shown by Airplane B in Figure 46. The airplane responds by moving

The horizontal component of lift is responsible for turning the airplane.

HOW AN AIRPLANE TURNS

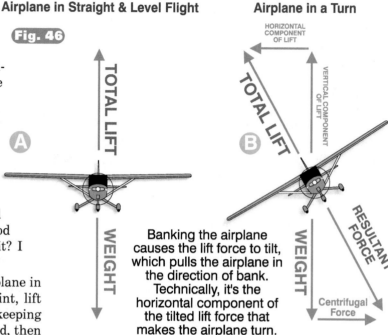

Airplane in Straight & Level Flight

Fig. 46

Ⓐ
TOTAL LIFT
WEIGHT

Airplane in a Turn

HORIZONTAL COMPONENT OF LIFT

VERTICAL COMPONENT OF LIFT

Ⓑ
TOTAL LIFT
WEIGHT
RESULTANT FORCE
Centrifugal Force

Banking the airplane causes the lift force to tilt, which pulls the airplane in the direction of bank. Technically, it's the horizontal component of the tilted lift force that makes the airplane turn.

in the direction of the momentarily larger force—downward, in the direction of weight. We compensate for this by increasing our lift slightly whenever we enter a turn. By now, diligent student that you are, you know that applying back pressure on the elevator will increase the angle of attack which increases the airplane's total lift. Unfortunately, the increase in angle of attack also increases the drag which slows the airplane down. In a shallow banked turn (somewhere around 30 degrees or less) this decrease in speed isn't a concern. Steeper turns (45 degrees or more) may require the addition of power to prevent the airspeed from decreasing too much.

Your job as a pilot is to keep The Four Forces acting on an airplane under control and in balance. To do so you need to know something about the airplane's flight control system.

THE THREE AXES OF AN AIRPLANE

Vertical Axis (Yaw)

Hey! What switch did you touch?

Longitudinal Axis (Roll)

Lateral Axis (Pitch)

Fig. 47

The aileron is the moveable appendage on the outer edge of each wing.

Fig. 48

HOW AILERONS BANK THE AIRPLANE

Ailerons are the moveable surfaces on the trailing edge of the wing.

Fig. 49

Ⓐ

N2132

Flight Controls

If you're ready-made pilot material you've been patiently licking your chops waiting for the discussion on flight controls. Gandhi would applaud your patience (but Gandhi isn't here, so I will). Figure 47 shows the three imaginary axes of the airplane. By use of the flight controls, the airplane can be made to rotate about one or more of these axes.

The longitudinal or long axis runs through the centerline of the airplane from nose to tail. Airplanes *roll* or *bank* about their longitudinal axis.

A sideways pass in football is called a lateral pass. Similarly, the lateral axis runs sideways through the airplane from wingtip to wingtip. Airplanes *pitch* about their lateral axis.

The vertical axis of the airplane runs up and down from the cockpit to the belly. Airplanes *yaw* about their vertical axis. Think of yawing motion as *yawning* motion. In the morning you yawn by standing and stretching vertically, rotating right and left, waiting for those vertebra to kick in. Let's examine each of the three main flight controls that cause an airplane to move about its axes.

Ailerons

Ailerons are the moveable surfaces on the outer trailing edges of the wings (Figure 48). Their purpose is to bank the airplane in the direction you want to turn (Figure 49). When the control wheel is turned to the right or the left, the ailerons simultaneously move in opposite

Banking to the Right

Wheel turned right

Ⓑ

Less lift with a raised aileron

More lift with a lowered aileron

N2132

Banking to the Left

More lift with a lowered aileron

Wheel turned left

Ⓒ

N2132

Less lift with a raised aileron

Ⓓ A lowered aileron increases the angle of attack and increases the wing's lift.

Chord Line

Angle of Attack

Ⓔ A raised aileron decreases the angle of attack and decreases the wing's lift.

Chord Line

Angle of Attack

directions. One raises and one lowers as shown by Airplanes B & C in Figure 49 (this doesn't mean they're broken either). Ailerons work this way on purpose, allowing one wing to develop more lift and the other to develop less. Differential lift banks the airplane, which tilts the total lifting force in the direction you want to turn.

A lowered aileron increases the curvature, angle of attack and lift on a portion of the wing as shown by Figure 49D. Conversely, an upward moving aileron reduces the angle of attack, decreases the curvature and decreases the lift on a portion of the wing as shown by Figure 49E. (Any reference to control wheel also applies to airplanes with a control stick.)

While ailerons change the wing's lift, they also change its drag, and the change in drag is different for each wing. This results in the airplane's nose yawing in a direction opposite the direction of turn. Right turn, left yaw. This is referred to as *adverse yaw,* since it tries to turn the airplane opposite the direction the pilot intended to turn.

Adverse Yaw

A few old sayings are still floating around that I'd like to revise. For instance, "The pen is mightier than the sword." This is true unless you're one-on-one with a modern incarnation of Zorro. A wonderful saying I wouldn't care to upend is, "You can't get something for nothing." It sure works that way in aviation. When an airfoil develops lift, it's always paid for by an increase in drag. The lift produced by the aileron is no different.

Downward moving ailerons create more lift and thus more drag (Figure 50). This results in *adverse yaw.* For instance, in a right turn, the downward moving aileron on the left wing creates more drag than the upward moving aileron on the right wing as

The Rudder

Fig. 51

Rudder Pedals

Fig. 52

shown in Figure 53A, and the airplane yaws (turns) to the left. A similar and opposite effect occurs with a left control wheel deflection (Figure 53B).

Adverse yaw presents a problem. You can't have the nose yawing or pointing in a different direction than you bank. Fortunately, airplanes have a control surface designed to correct for adverse yaw. It's called a rudder and is shown in Figure 51.

Rudders

The rudder's purpose is to keep the airplane's nose pointed in the direction of turn—not to turn the airplane! Remember, airplanes turn by

banking. Rudder simply corrects for adverse yaw and keeps the nose pointing in the direction of turn. Think of a rudder as a vertical aileron located on the tail of the airplane. A right or left deflection of the rudder foot pedals located on the cockpit floor (Figure 52) changes the vertical stabilizer's angle of attack and yaws the airplane about its vertical axis. This yawing motion keeps the airplane's nose pointed in the direction of turn.

Applying right rudder pedal, as shown by Airplane A in Figure 53, forces the tail assembly to swing in the direction of lower pressure. As the tail moves, the airplane rotates

ADVERSE YAW

Airplane banks to the right but nose yaws to the left.

Lowered aileron creates more lift but it also increases drag.

Airplane banks to the left but nose yaws to the right.

Fig. 50

A lowered aileron creates more lift but it also increases drag.

HOW RUDDER COMPENSATES FOR ADVERSE YAW

Applying right rudder yaws the nose of the airplane to the right.

Vertical axis

Applying left rudder yaws the nose of the airplane to the left.

Tail moves to the left

Nose yaws to the right

Nose yaws to the left

Tail moves to the right

Right rudder applied

Low pressure

WIND

High pressure

Tail movement

High pressure

WIND

Low pressure

Tail movement

Left rudder applied

Fig. 53

THE TURN COORDINATOR

DC
ELEC

NO PITCH INFORMATION

Turn needle

Inclinometer

TURN COORDINATOR

L   R

2 MIN

Fig. 54

The movement of the ball corresponds to the movement of the sunglasses on your car's dashboard. The same force that moves the glasses also moves the ball. The ball, however, slides more easily than the glasses. The ball's deflection from center identifies when the airplane's nose is pointed other than in the direction of turn. Rudder is used to move the ball back to the centered position.

about its vertical axis. Application of right rudder pedal yaws the nose to the right. Applying left rudder pedal (I'll just say *rudder* from now on), shown by Airplane B, yaws the nose to the left (surprising, huh?).

When should you use the rudder? Any time you turn the airplane. If you don't use rudder while trying to turn, part of the airplane is going one way, and another part points in the opposite direction. This is not a pretty sight, and your instructor's eyebrows will raise so high that they will scratch his or her back. Right turn, right rudder. Left turn, left rudder. Feet and hands move together.

Now the question foremost in your upper brain is "How much rudder is enough?" Good question. Figure 54 shows an inclinometer, also known as *the ball,* as a part of another instrument called the *turn coordinator* (located on the instrument panel).

The little white airplane in the turn coordinator shows the direction of turn, while the ball tells you if the proper amount of rudder is applied. The ball is free to roll right or left within the glass tube. Any inappropriate rudder use (or lack of use) applies an unnecessary side force to the airplane. This deflects the ball in much the same way sunglasses scoot across your car's dash when rounding a sharp corner. Your job is to keep the ball centered by using the rudder.

Figure 55 shows an airplane in a turn. Airplane A's nose is pointed outside the turn (probably because of insufficient right rudder or too much

SLIPS & SKIDS MADE EASY

An easy way to understand slips or skids is to think of the ball as the tail and the glass tube at the wings of the airplane. (Right turn shown.)

Wings   **Tail**

In a right turn, if the ball (tail) is to the left of center, this implies the tail is skidding to the outside of the turn.

In a right turn, if the ball (tail) is to the right of center, this implies the tail is slipping to the inside of the turn.

AN EASY WAY TO UNDERSTAND SLIPPING & SKIDDING IN AN AIRPLANE

Airplane Slipping: Nose is pointed outside the turn.

Glasses move to right

Ball in the inclinometer is forced to the right, just like sunglasses.

Right rudder necessary

Fig. 55

Airplane Flying Coordinated: Nose is pointed in direction of turn.

Glasses stay centered

Ball in the inclinometer stays centered just like sunglasses.

Correct rudder application

Airplane Skidding: Nose is pointed inside the turn.

Glasses move to left

Ball in the inclinometer is forced to the left, just like sunglasses.

Left rudder necessary

right aileron is applied). The ball and the airplane slip to the right, toward the inside of the turn. In other words, you need to point the nose slightly to the right for a precisely aligned turn. By adding enough right rudder to align the airplane in the direction it's turning, the ball returns to the center as shown by Airplane B.

Airplane C's nose points toward the inside of the turn (probably because too much right rudder is applied or insufficient right aileron is used.) The ball and the airplane skid to the left, toward the outside of the turn. Adding a little left rudder keeps the nose pointed in the direction the airplane's turning and centers the ball.

Simply stated, if the ball is deflected to the right or left of center, add enough right or left rudder to center the ball. Sometimes you'll hear your instructor say, "Step on the ball!" This is simply your instructor's way of telling you to add right rudder for a right-deflected ball and left rudder for a left-deflected ball. Don't even think about placing your foot on the turn coordinator, or your instructor will question you about your SAT scores. Don't put marbles in your shoes either.

When entering a turn, aileron and rudder are applied simultaneously, in the same direction. This is what pilots mean when they refer to flying coordinated. Aileron establishes the degree of bank and rudder keeps the nose pointed in the direction of turn. If the ball is centered during this process, we say that the controls are properly coordinated.

One last point about the rudder. It is the last control forfeited in a stall. Even when the airplane is stalled, it continues to move forward with airflow over its surface. This allows some degree of rudder authority even at very slow speeds. During a stall you'll find that the rudder is very effective for maintaining directional control. In a spin, the rudder is very important for spin recovery. More on spins in Postflight Briefing #2-1.

Elevator

The elevator is the moveable horizontal surface at the rear of the airplane. Its purpose is to pitch the airplane's nose up or down.

Coordination Lube

Devious Instructor Device

Hey! What about two boxing gloves suspended by string that act like the ball in the inclinometer?

It won't take long before you won't need to look at the ball in the inclinometer to know whether or not you're flying coordinated. With a little practice you'll be able to fly by the seat of your pants (assuming you wear pants while flying). Pressure on the right or left side of your derriere is caused by the same force that moves the ball to the right or the left. It doesn't matter how big the airplane is; a 747 or a Cessna Skycatcher Land-o-matic can be flown by the seat of the pants. Use the inclinometer as sort of a biofeedback device cuing you to sense pressure on your derriere when the ball is deflected. And don't feel bad if it takes a little practice to get used to coordinating rudder and ailerons. My first instructor told me that even if they put cold Vaseline in the inclinometer (instead of mineral oil), I would still get the ball to bang back and forth against the ends of the glass.

HOW THE ELEVATOR CONTROL CHANGES THE AIRPLANE'S PITCH

Pulling back on the control wheel deflects the elevator upward which forces the tail downward. This, in turn, causes the nose to pitch up.

Ⓐ

Tail moves down & nose moves up

Tail movement (down)

Fig. 56

Pushing forward on the control wheel deflects the elevator downward which forces the tail upward. This, in turn, causes the nose to pitch down.

Ⓑ

Tail moves up & nose moves down

Tail movement (up)

The elevator control works on the same aerodynamic principle as the rudder and aileron. Applying back pressure on the control wheel of Airplane A in Figure 56 deflects the elevator surface upward. Lower pressure is created on the underside of the tail which moves it downward, and the nose of the airplane pitches up.

Some elevator trim tabs are a single tab on one side of the elevator. **Fig. 57A**

Another version of the trim tab is a single tab spanning the stabilator. **Fig. 57B**

The Elevator Trim Wheel

Down Stabilator Trim Up

Fig. 57C

Airplane B shows what happens when the control wheel is moved forward. The elevator surface moves down creating lower pressure on the top side of the tail.

This causes the tail to rise. The nose rotates about the lateral axis in a downward direction. Simply stated, to pitch up, pull the control wheel back; to pitch down, move the control wheel forward.

Trim Tabs

If you had to apply continuous pressure on the control wheel to maintain pitch attitude, your arms would tire quickly (Schwarzenegger would be proud of you but I wouldn't). Fortunately, airplanes have something known as a *trim tab* to take the pressure off the control wheel (and off the pilot!).

A trim tab is a small, moveable surface attached to the main surface you want to control (in this case, it's the elevator. Ailerons and rudder can have trim tabs too). Figures 57A, 57B and 57C show two different types of trim tabs and the trim wheel used to change the trim tab's position (the wheel is usually located between the two front seats or the lower portion of the instrument panel).

Moving the trim tab creates a slight pressure difference on the very end of the control surface to which it's attached (Figure 58). Just enough pressure is created to keep

the primary control surface in the desired position without having to hold the control wheel in place. Notice that the trim tab moves in a direction opposite to the primary control surface it affects. If you want the elevator to deflect upward (as if you're pulling back on the wheel in a climb), the trim tab must move down as shown by Elevator A. To maintain a downward deflection of the elevator (as if you're in a descent), the trim tab must move upward as shown by Elevator B.

Using elevator trim is quite simple. Select the attitude desired with the elevator, then rotate the trim wheel (up or down) to take the pressure off the control wheel. How do you know which way to twist the trim wheel? Most trim wheels say *nose down* or *nose up* above or below the wheel. Simply twist the wheel in the direction you want the nose to stay. Aileron and rudder trim are equally simple to use.

When flying with other pilots, accept the fact that they won't like the way you trimmed the airplane. You might have flown the last 200 miles without touching the plane. Hand it over to the other person and the first thing he or she does is start fiddling with the trim. I can only conclude that this action is a form of primitive territorial claim. It's annoying, but it's better than how wild animals claim their territory isn't it?

HOW ELEVATOR TRIM WORKS

Applying nose-up trim moves the tab down, creating a small low pressure area on the end of the elevator. This causes the elevator to move upward.

A

Upward lift caused by trim tab

N2132B

Fig. 58

The trim wheel is usually located below the throttle in the center of the airplane.

Nose down

Nose up

N2132B

B

Lift acting downward caused by trim tab

Applying nose-down trim moves the tab up, creating a small low pressure area on the bottom tip of the elevator. This moves the elevator downward.

Left Turning Tendencies (not political)

Having mastered The Four Forces, you now need to know there *are* others. Not many others, and not as significant, yet they are forces to be reckoned with.

Torque—Newton (Isaac, not Wayne) once said that for every action there is an equal and opposite reaction. Crankshafts rotate to the right in most single engine airplanes (as seen from the cockpit). An equal and opposite reaction is for the airplane to rotate to the left. That's exactly what the airplane does when the engine is developing power. This is known as *engine torque* or just *torque,* as shown in Figure 59 (I've often wondered if Spanish instructors call this *Torquemada?*)

Expect the effect of torque to be greatest when power is at a maximum and the airspeed is slow. During the takeoff run, with maximum power, torque makes the airplane want to roll to the left, creating slightly greater pressure on the left tire. This creates a little more friction on the left tire and causes the airplane to turn to the left as it accelerates for takeoff (as you'll soon see, there are other forces that aid in this left-turning tendency). Once airborne, the airplane still wants to roll to the left because of torque.

Pilots can compensate for torque by the applying the appropriate rudder and aileron control inputs. This is one reason why you need a lot of right rudder on takeoff (there are other reasons as you'll see shortly). Use of rudder and aileron trim also helps when the airplane wants to go somewhere other than straight during a climb. Torque is only one reason most airplanes like to turn left as they accelerate for takeoff. There are other forces that yaw an airplane to the left during slow speed, high angle of attack

Before we proceed further, you should understand that the propeller is nothing more than a wing moving around a crankshaft.

ENGINE TORQUE REACTION

Propeller rotation

Airplane reaction

N2132

Airplane rolls to left as a result of engine power.

Fig. 59

flight. The effect of the propeller slipstream is one of these.

Slipstream Effect—A clockwise rotating propeller (as seen from the cockpit) imparts a curve or spiral motion to air flowing past the fuselage. This is known as the *propeller slipstream.* Figure 60 shows how this swirling air affects the airplane. Under high power conditions (such as during takeoff or climb), a curved spiral of air swirls around the airplane striking the vertical stabilizer and the rudder, yawing the airplane's nose to the left. Airplane design, power usage and airspeed all determine how the slipstream affects the airplane.

We now have two forces that separately roll and yaw our airplane to the left. This explains why flight instructors are always saying three things: "More right rudder," "Let go, I've got it," and "Do you want to pay me now?" Your instructor's admonition to use "more right rudder" to counteract the left-turning tendency is quite common during slow speeds and high power settings. Alas, there is still one more force that yaws an airplane to the left.

P-Factor—No, this is not something you experience on a long cross country flight. Often called *asymmetric disk loading,* P-factor (or "propeller factor") is one more thing that makes your airplane turn left. Think about the word "asymmetric." It means "not symmetrical," or "not spread out evenly." Asymmetric disk loading occurs when lift, produced by the propeller (which is a rotating disk), isn't evenly distributed.

Before we proceed further, you should understand that the propeller is nothing more than a wing moving around a crankshaft. While airplane wings develop lift when pulled through the air, propellers develop their lift when spun around a crankshaft. Each half of the propeller is

SLIPSTREAM EFFECT

The airplane yaws to the left as a result of the propeller slipstream.

Propeller rotation

Yaws left

Push on tail

N2132

Slipstream

Fig. 60

like a wing, and it follows all the laws that a wing must follow (i.e., the greater the angle of attack, the greater the lift and drag for a given speed, etc.).

If one side of the propeller develops more lift than the other, the airplane experiences a twisting or yawing motion. This causes one side to pull more than the other, inducing a yaw about the vertical axis.

P-factor is noticeable at *high angles of attack* for one very important reason: the downward moving half of the propeller develops more lift than the upward moving half. Figure 61 shows an example of this. At a low angle of attack (A), both the upward and the downward moving propeller blade strike the air at similar angles. At higher angles of attack (B), the downward moving blade has a larger angle of attack than the upward moving blade. This means the downward moving blade creates more lift than its upward moving companion (Figure 62). Therefore, the downward moving blade imparts a yaw to the left about the vertical axis.

Figure 63 is your last and final way of visualizing P-factor (honest!). Airplane A is at a *high angle of attack* and is moving toward you. Its downward

ASYMMETRICAL DISK LOADING (P-FACTOR)

At a low angle of attack, lift is evenly distributed on both the upward and downward rotating side of the propeller.

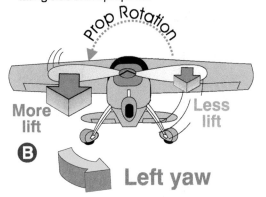

At higher angles of attack, lift increases on the downward rotating side of the propeller and decreases on the upward rotating side. This causes the airplane to yaw to the left.

ANOTHER LOOK AT P-FACTOR

When the airplane is at a low angle of attack, the rising and falling blades of the propeller have almost the same angle of attack. In other words, each half of the propeller produces an equal amount of lift and there is little or no P-factor.

B When the airplane is at a higher angle of attack, the falling blade has a larger angle of attack than the rising blade. This difference in angle of attack between blades results in the falling blade producing more lift than the rising blade. Thus, P-factor increases and the airplane yaws to the left.

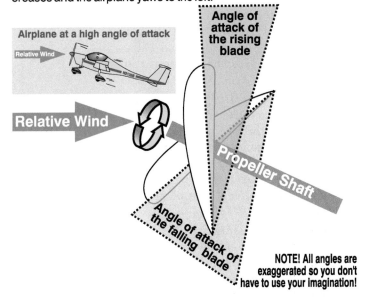

NOTE! All angles are exaggerated so you don't have to use your imagination!

moving blade swings forward into the wind. The upward retreating blade rotates with the wind. The downward moving blade feels more wind blowing on it than the upward moving blade. It is reasonable to conclude that the blade moving downward develops more lift than its rising counterpart. This is exactly what happens. Airplane B shows the net result of this lift differential as a left yawing tendency. Higher angles of attack increase this difference in lift, while lower angles of attack decrease it.

Expect to notice P-factor at higher angles of attack, such as during takeoff and climb. Couple this with the slipstream effect and torque, and it certainly seems like a left-wing conspiracy.

At slow speeds and high power settings, a healthy amount of right rudder is necessary to keep the airplane from yawing to the left in this condition. I fully expect that genetic engineers will, one day, create an entirely new breed of pilot known as Homo torquedown man. This hybrid species will have an enormous muscular right leg useful in correcting for torque, slipstream and P-factor when climbing airplanes without rudder trim.

Hopefully, this chapter has helped you understand how to make the wing of your airplane work better for you. Don't worry if you don't feel like you quite understand these concepts yet. Seeing is believing, and it almost always takes a few flight lessons before the practical realities of aerodynamics sink in.

Learning aerodynamics is like eating vegetables—they're good for you, even if you're not sure why. It's like my little nephew's first introduction to broccoli. My sister used guilt as a motivator to get him to eat the stuff. She'd always say, "Brad, eat your broccoli. Why? Because there are children in China who are starving." Little did he know that the parents of children in China were saying, "Chan, eat your rice. Why? Because there are children in America who have to eat broccoli." Hopefully this chapter was a little more pleasant than eating broccoli. The more you fly, the more you'll appreciate how important these concepts are.

ASYMMETRICAL DISK LOADING (P-FACTOR)

At a positive angle of attack, the downward moving blade develops more lift than the upward moving blade. This causes the airplane to yaw to its left.

Ⓐ

DOWNWARD MOVING BLADE
Downward moving propeller encounters wind blowing on it, thus providing more lift on this side.

Wind

Prop movement

Blade viewed from the tip

UPWARD MOVING BLADE
Upward moving propeller encounters wind blowing with it, thus providing less lift on this side.*

Wind

Prop movement

Airplane moving toward you at a large angle of attack

Prop movement

Prop movement

Fig. 63

Wind

*Note: The angle of attack of the upward moving blade is actually less than the downward moving blade (this is difficult to show, therefore, I simplified the concept). This difference in angle of attack is responsible for the differential lift produced by the propeller at high angles of attack.

Ⓑ

P-Factor causes the airplane to yaw to the left when it is flown at higher angles of

More lift

Less lift

Left yaw

Now that you know how an airplane flies, we'll turn our attention to the item that pulls an aircraft through the air in the first place—the engine.

Postflight Briefing #2-1

HOW A SPIN OCCURS

Stall, yaw & wing drop

Hey, wanna see something neat?

Incipient stage of spin

During the incipient stage of the spin the airplane stalls then commences to autorotate. At this point the nose may pitch straight down and the airplane may be slightly inverted. As the autorotation continues, the aerodynamic and inertial forces attempt to balance and settle the airplane into a predictable pattern of rotation. The incipient stage usually consists of the first two turns and takes five to six seconds to complete in most light airplanes.

Fully developed spin

In the fully developed spin, the rotation, airspeed and vertical speed stabilize. The descent path is nearly vertical as the airplane pivots about the spin axis. Despite the steep nose-down attitude, both wings are stalled. The higher wing is less stalled than the lower wing. Consequently, the higher wing produces slightly more lift and the lower wing produces slightly more drag. This helps establish the autorotating motion of the spin. Unless something is done to unstall both wings, the airplane will remain in the spin.

Spin recovery

Recovery occurs when autorotation is stopped by reducing power (if not already reduced), neutralizing ailerons and applying opposite rudder. The elevator is moved forward to decrease the angle of attack (as it is during a normal stall recovery).

Use caution. High airspeeds are possible during recovery. Avoid overstressing the airplane.

No!

THE FULLY DEVELOPED SPIN

Outside wing: more lift & less drag (not as stalled)

Inside wing: more drag & less lift (fully stalled)

Lift

DRAG

Yaw

Spin axis.

Motion

To enter a spin the airplane must first be stalled. As the stall occurs, rudder is applied and the elevator is pulled back to further increase the angle of attack. Applying rudder (to the left in the above example) causes the left wing to simultaneously move downward and rearward. This causes a left roll that increases the left wing's angle of attack and slows its speed relative to the right wing. The right wing, on the other hand, moves upward and forward. This decreases its angle of attack and increases its speed. Despite the fact that both wings are stalled in the fully developed spin, the outside (higher) wing is less stalled than the inside (lower) wing.

Pilots making skidding turns to final put themselves in a critical position that's conducive to spin entry. If the pilot sees he will overshoot the turn to final, he might apply rudder to align the nose with the runway while holding the bank constant with aileron. All the while, he's pulling back on the elevator control in an attempt to keep the nose up. This is the precise condition described above for entering a spin. Unfortunately, when a spin occurs in the traffic pattern, there is often insufficient altitude available for recovery.

In a fully developed spin, the airspeed remains constant (for smaller airplanes it's about 65 to 75 knots). The descent rate can exceed 7,000 feet per minute.

Postflight Briefing #2-2

Your Airplane-What a Drag

Drag is a passenger that doesn't chip in for lunch. It's also a constant companion on every flight.

Drag is not something a pilot has a great deal of control over, but understanding what the two types of drag are, and how they accumulate and affect flight, is important in certain situations.

Parasite Drag

A parasite is usually something you don't like that seems to attach itself to you or something you value. A large leech that bolts itself onto your forehead is a parasite. You don't like it, but it likes being connected to you (it is, however, good for sparking conversations at the airport). An airplane's struts, landing gear, wires and antennas (Figure 64) are all parasites as far as an aerodynamicist is concerned, and the drag they create is referred to as *parasitic drag*.

These protruding parts grab air molecules and slow airplanes down like flies doing touch-and-goes on No-Pest strips. These and other parts of the airplane are, however, necessary aerodynamic evils. Fortunately, clever engineers work remarkable magic in reducing the effect these parasitic items have on airplane performance.

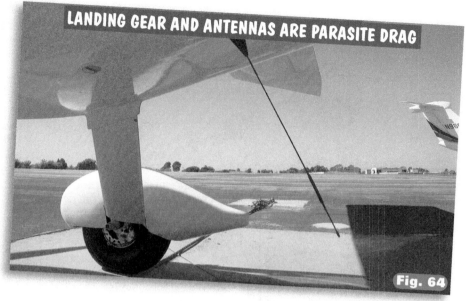

LANDING GEAR AND ANTENNAS ARE PARASITE DRAG

Fig. 64

You might wonder, "Why talk about drag if the pilot can't do anything about it?" Well, first off, it gives you something to debate with other pilots on a day when you can't go flying. Second, not many people understand this stuff, so it makes you sound cool. Third, pilots do have some control over an airplane's parasite drag. For instance, polishing the surface of the wings minimizes skin friction (one of several forms of parasite drag).

On certain high performance sailplanes, a good shine job can be good for several miles of increased glide performance. On training airplanes, the performance increase can be close to negligible. Nevertheless, it's a good excuse for a Saturday morning's escape to the airport. Curious spouses are simply told that important aerodynamic modifications are to be performed on the airframe (don't blink, look serious, control breathing and you'll pull this off).

Nothing can (or should!) be done about the struts on an airplane having them. They're holding the wings on, which is generally considered a good thing. Remember, no wings, no lift. No lift, no fly. No fly, no fun.

Unfortunately, struts clobber air molecules and increase parasite drag. Flying airplanes with struts and fixed gear has its advantages and disadvantages, and parasite drag is definitely one of the disadvantages.

Remember, parasite drag rises dramatically with increasing speed. In fact, doubling the speed of the airplane *quadruples* the parasite drag. Figure 65 shows how parasite drag increases with speed. You might get the impression that at slower speeds the airplane experiences very little total drag. While some parasite drag is always present at slower speeds, a different form of drag actually increases with a reduction in speed. This is called *induced drag*.

PARASITE DRAG

Slow · AIRSPEED · Fast

High · PARASITE DRAG · Low

Slow   Fast

Fig. 65

A Spoiler

Spoilers can be extended and retracted from inside the cockpit. They project upward into the airstream destroying some of the wing's lift. Higher performance airplanes, because of their low drag profile, often find these devices useful in aiding their descents.

INDUCED DRAG AND ANGLE OF ATTACK

NO LIFT

Ⓐ

Relative Wind

When your hand has a "zero" degree angle of attack with the relative wind, no lift and very little drag is produced.

Ⓑ

The total lift tilts aft so as to remain perpendicular to the locally bent relative wind.

Relative Wind

Total Lift

The local relative wind is bent down by the hand.

As the hand's angle of attack increases, the relative wind in the local vicinity of the hand (underneath it) is bent slightly. The total lift the hand produces is now tilted slightly rearward so as to remain perpendicular (90 degrees) to this newly-bent relative wind.

Ⓒ

Large amount of induced drag present.

Induced drag

Effective lift is acting 90 degrees to the undisturbed relative wind ahead of the hand.

Effective lift

Total Lift

Relative Wind

As the hand's angle of attack increases, the local relative wind is bent even more. This acts to further tilt the total lifting force aft. The component or portion of the total lift acting vertically is called "effective lift." The portion acting rearward is called "induced drag." It's very important to notice that the larger the angle of attack, the more rearward the total lift acts, thus the greater the induced drag becomes. Yet, the effective lift still acts 90 degrees to the undisturbed relative wind ahead of the wing.

Fig. 66

Induced Drag

People can sometimes be induced to act in an unfortunate way. This occurs when a TV commercial recommends that you purchase a do-it-yourself acupuncture kit. After a little experimentation, you discover

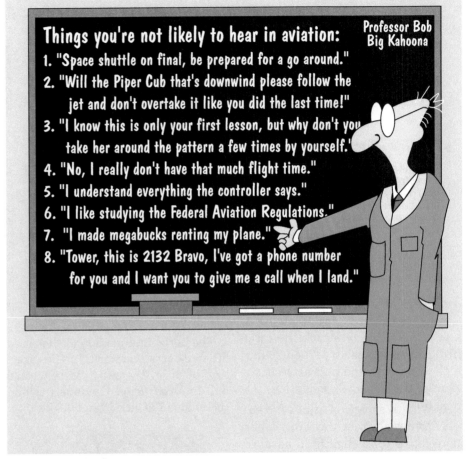

Things you're not likely to hear in aviation: Professor Bob Big Kahoona

1. "Space shuttle on final, be prepared for a go around."
2. "Will the Piper Cub that's downwind please follow the jet and don't overtake it like you did the last time!"
3. "I know this is only your first lesson, but why don't you take her around the pattern a few times by yourself."
4. "No, I really don't have that much flight time."
5. "I understand everything the controller says."
6. "I like studying the Federal Aviation Regulations."
7. "I made megabucks renting my plane."
8. "Tower, this is 2132 Bravo, I've got a phone number for you and I want you to give me a call when I land."

that you don't feel any better but your body is capable of picking up cable TV. Wings aren't people, but sometimes they induce the lift they produce to act in unfavorable ways. In particular, wings can induce their total lifting force to act rearward instead of in an upward direction. Remember, any force acting rearward on the airplane acts like drag. (At this point I'll offer you a choice. You can either believe me when I say that induced drag increases when the airplane slows down or you can plow through the following few paragraphs and I'll prove it to you. Most pilots can and do fly safely without knowing the nuances of drag formation.)

Time for another experiment (yes, back to the car again). Stick your hand (and *only* your hand) out the window as you're moving. Hold your hand parallel to the relative wind so that it has little or no angle of attack as shown by Figure 66A. You should feel little or no lift and relatively little rearward drag. Now, increase the hand's angle of attack as

shown by Figure 66B. Notice how your hand wants to rise (we call this *lift*) but it also wants to move rearward slightly (we call this *drag*). As the hand's angle of attack increases, the local relative wind in the vicinity of the hand is bent downward slightly. Earlier we learned that lift acts perpendicular to the relative wind. Therefore, the total lifting force is tilted rearward as the hand's angle of attack increases. A further increase in the hand's angle of attack, as shown by Figure 66C, increases the upward and rearward pull of the total lifting force.

Here's the point (finger in the ear again!). *The total lifting force acting on the hand pulls it upward and backward as the angle of attack increases.* The upward, or vertical portion of the total lift force works against the airplane's weight to keep it aloft. The rearward pull of the total lifting force acts in the direction of drag; we call it *induced drag*.

Although hands are much less sophisticated in generating lift than

TOTAL LIFT, EFFECTIVE LIFT AND INDUCED DRAG

Small angle of attack

A

Fig. 67

90°

Total Lift

Relative Wind

Weight

At small angles of attack the airfoil's total lifting force acts nearly 90 degrees to the relative wind. In other words, total lift acts upward without much of a backwards pull on the airplane. Similarly, this total lift force acts nearly opposite and parallel to the weight of the airplane.

Increasing angle of attack

B

Local relative wind bent downward by the wing's downwash.

Relative Wind

Local Relative Wind

As the angle of attack increases, the wing actually bends the relative wind (in its local vicinity) downward slightly. The downwash created by the wing at this high angle of attack is responsible for bending the local wind underneath and slightly ahead of the wing downward. The bent relative wind is called the *local relative wind*.

Large angle of attack

C

Induced drag

Effective lift

"Effective lift" acts perpendicular to the relative wind.

90°

Total Lift

Total lift acts 90° to the local relative wind

Relative Wind

Weight

At larger angles of attack, the total lifting force tilts backwards with the wing. The component of lift acting parallel and opposite to the weight is *effective* in keeping the airplane airborne. Thus, this vertical component of lift is called *effective lift*. The component of lift acting rearward is called *induced drag*.

---

are wings, there are similarities between them. In Figure 67, Wing A is at a low angle of attack. Its total lifting force is nearly perpendicular to the relative wind and acts nearly opposite the airplane's weight.

As Wing B's angle of attack increases, downwash from the wing bends the relative wind slightly in advance of the moving wing. The total lifting force tilts aft so as to remain perpendicular to the newly-bent, *local relative wind* as shown by Wing C. We can take the portion of the tilted lift force acting straight up, opposite the airplane's weight, and call that component the *effective lift*. It's the part that's effective in keeping us airborne since it acts opposite the airplane's weight. This effective lift also acts at a 90 degree angle to the

INDUCED DRAG

High - INDUCED DRAG - Low

Slow   Fast

Slow - AIRSPEED - Fast

Fig. 68

undisturbed relative wind ahead of the airplane.

The horizontal portion of the tilted lift force acts rearward, in the direction of drag. We call this rearward pull *induced drag*. Obviously, when the angle of attack is small, the total

Professor Bob Big Kahoona

Fuel Tank

Professor Bob carefully points out that max. endurance also applies to the human bladder since it's smaller than most fuel tanks.

lifting force acts in more of an upward or vertical direction with little rearward pull on the airplane. As the angle of attack increases the drag induced by the rearward component of total lift increases. Consequently, when the airplane slows, the angle of attack increases and induced drag increases. As the airplane's speed increases, the angle of attack decreases and the induced drag decreases. This relationship between induced drag and airspeed is shown in Figure 68.

Sort of wish you'd just taken my word for it, don't you?

Postflight Briefing #2-3

Maximum Endurance And Range

Maximum Range

If you are ever over water with limited fuel, trying to make the shoreline, you'll gain a fuller understanding of just *how* important it is to know the speed for attaining maximum range. Most new pilots believe that they can simply add more power and try to get to the shoreline quicker. You will soon discover that in aviation, the first thing that makes sense is often the last thing that's likely to work.

Faster speeds mean greater parasite drag. You end up going faster, at the tremendous cost of an increase in fuel consumption because drag has increased. The end result is that you land short of the maximum distance you would have traveled at the best L/D speed.

Some pilots think they can slow the airplane way down close to the stall speed to conserve fuel. This doesn't work either. Remember, when the airplane slows below the best L/D speed, induced drag increases. You'll simply run out of fuel without having traveled the maximum distance possible at the best L/D speed.

If you're ever trying to make a destination on limited fuel, use the airplane's maximum range speed. Unfortunately, this is often not published in your airplane's Pilot's Operating Handbook (POH). If you can't find the maximum range speed, use the airplane's best L/D speed (Figure 69). (Once again, aerodynamics has its catches and qualifications. In theory, best range should be precisely the speed for minimum total drag—the best L/D speed. However, based on propeller efficiency considerations, the maximum range speed can sometimes be a little higher than the posted best L/D speed for that airplane. Practically speaking, this doesn't amount to all that much of a difference.)

Maximum Endurance

Maximum endurance occurs at a speed where minimum power (thus minimum fuel consumption) is required to remain airborne. This is the speed that allows you to remain aloft for the longest possible time.

The maximum endurance speed becomes an important consideration when you're circling above the only airport within range while waiting for the weather to clear. The last thing you ever want to be is low on fuel (Oops! Excuse me. To be politically correct we now say "fuel challenged"). I hope you'll never find

RANGE AND ENDURANCE SPEED FOR A TYPICAL HIGH PERFORMANCE AIRPLANE

Fig. 69

POWER REQUIRED VS. AIRSPEED GRAPH

yourself in this situation. Not knowing anything about your airplane's maximum endurance (minimum fuel consumption) speed is like using a cast iron commode on the dark side of an iceberg—a very uncomfortable experience.

At first glance, it might appear that the speed for maximum endurance is the best L/D speed. After all, minimum drag at the best L/D speed should require minimum thrust, thus minimum power. This might be true if it weren't for the fact that parasite drag and induced drag affect the power requirements for level flight differently. Simply stated, the engine must work harder in overcoming parasite drag (as you speed up) than in overcoming induced drag (as you slow down). Therefore, flying a little below the best L/D speed, even at the expense of increasing induced drag, lowers the power required to sustain level flight (up to a point of course).

That's why you'll find the speed for maximum endurance (minimum power) below the minimum drag (best L/D) speed. The speed for maximum endurance (minimum power) is generally less than the best L/D speed (it's *approximately* 75% of the best L/D speed for most propeller driven airplanes, although this percentage can vary considerably from air-

plane to airplane). Think of this as you would the difference between gross and take home pay—one of them (maximum endurance speed) is smaller than the other (best L/D speed). Figure 69 shows these two speeds.

In some cases airplanes with long thin (high aspect ratio) wings have maximum endurance speeds that are very close to their stall speeds. This makes maximum endurance speed in these airplanes impractical to use.

The maximum endurance speed can be seen more clearly on the power vs. airspeed graph (Figure 70). This chart compares the power required to maintain altitude at different airspeeds. At the lowest portion of the power curve (A), the airplane maintains its altitude with minimum power, thus minimum fuel consumption. A speed of 74 knots establishes the minimum power point (maximum endurance speed) for this airplane. Airspeeds above or below this speed require that you increase power to maintain altitude.

Figure 71 shows maximum endurance speed occurring below the minimum drag speed as shown by the drag curve inserts in the top of the figure.

The power-required curve also provides a valuable clue as to how the airplane responds in a descent. Let's say you're descending at 74 knots

POWER REQUIRED VS. TOTAL DRAG

Fig. 71

Max. endurance (min. power) speed is less than the minimum total drag (best L/D) speed.*

Min. power

Increasing induced drag

Increasing parasite drag

*This occurs because the required engine power is more affected by increasing parasite drag than increasing induced drag. Therefore, the minimum power required speed is found to the left of the minimum drag speed, at a point where there is slightly less parasite drag.

Thrust Horsepower - High — Low

Power required to maintain altitude

Low - Airspeed in Knots - High

(the bottom of the power curve) at a slightly lower power setting than required to maintain altitude. Let's also say that this lower power setting produces a 500 foot per minute descent rate in this particular airplane. This is the minimum rate of descent you can expect in this airplane at this power setting. Any decrease in airspeed will increase the rate of descent. Why? The power required to maintain the descent rate *increases* as the airspeed *decreases*. This is a very important point!

If you haven't heard about it yet, you will eventually hear about an airplane operating "behind the power curve" or operating in the "region of reversed command." Either of these statements means the pilot is flying at a speed less than the minimum power-required speed. A decrease in airspeed requires more power to hold altitude or maintain a desired rate of descent (this is "reversed" from what you normally expect and explains why it's called the "region of reversed command"). Without this addition of power the airplane starts to descend or descend more quickly, as shown in Figure 72.

There comes a point where an airplane flying behind the power

curve is unable to hold altitude, even with full power applied. It's conceivable that a pilot flying a real slow approach might apply full power to go around and raise the nose too quickly before the airplane has a chance to accelerate to climb airspeed. The pilot notices that the airplane is still descending, even with

full power. He raised the nose further to arrest the descent and actually increases the descent rate. The pilot's only option in this instance is to lower the nose and allow the airplane to accelerate. Once the airplane is in a region requiring less power to maintain altitude, it can use its excess power to climb.

Suppose you're on an approach to landing and your airspeed is deep within the region of reversed command (close to stall speed). In this condition, you must not attempt to stretch a glide by raising the nose without adding power. Doing so will only increase your rate of descent. Many pilots have fallen victim to the region of reversed command. Think of it as licking honey off a thorn—you could get stuck if you're not careful. Operating in this region is perfectly safe as long as you're aware of these principles. But what happens if your engine quits and you have no power? What's the best way to obtain the airplane's maximum glide distance? To find out, we need to look a little closer at the best L/D speed (see Postflight Briefing #2-4).

THE REGION OF REVERSED COMMAND

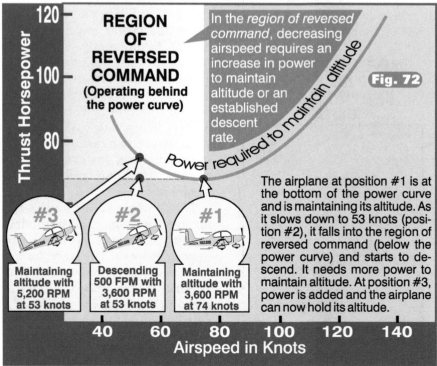

REGION OF REVERSED COMMAND (Operating behind the power curve)

In the *region of reversed command*, decreasing airspeed requires an increase in power to maintain altitude or an established descent rate.

Fig. 72

Power required to maintain altitude

Thrust Horsepower

#3 — Maintaining altitude with 5,200 RPM at 53 knots

#2 — Descending 500 FPM with 3,600 RPM at 53 knots

#1 — Maintaining altitude with 3,600 RPM at 74 knots

The airplane at position #1 is at the bottom of the power curve and is maintaining its altitude. As it slows down to 53 knots (position #2), it falls into the region of reversed command (below the power curve) and starts to descend. It needs more power to maintain altitude. At position #3, power is added and the airplane can now hold its altitude.

Airspeed in Knots

Weight, Glide & the Ride

The Best Glide Speed And Weight Changes

What happens to our glide distance as the weight of the aircraft changes? Strangely enough, a change in weight doesn't affect the glide ratio as long as you make a change in glide speed. To obtain the best L/D of which the airplane is capable, a decrease in weight requires a decrease in airspeed. Let's see why.

The best glide speed of the P92 Echo Super is 68 knots at its maximum gross weight of 1,320 pounds. This speed gives the airplane a maximum glide ratio of approximately 12:1. The L/D ratio can also be interpreted to mean that for every 12 pounds of lift developed by the wings, the entire airplane produces one pound of drag. At the airplane's maximum gross weight of 1,320 pounds (thus developing 1,320 pounds of lift), it produces 110 pounds of drag at its best glide speed of 68 knots.

Assume the P92 weighed 1,320 pounds before you took your flight bag out. Now it weighs 1,000 pounds (that's one heavy flight bag!). Only 1,000 pounds of lift are necessary to equal the airplane's weight in a descent. At 1,000 pounds of lift, an L/D ratio of 12:1 results in the airplane producing only 83 pounds of drag (remember, the L/D ratio is the best that specific airplane is capable

of doing). Therefore, if 68 knots of airspeed produces 110 pounds of drag, it stands to reason that a slower airspeed would produce less drag (up to a point, of course). As the airplane's weight decreases, its airspeed must also decrease to maintain the best L/D.

Engineers tell us that an airspeed of 59 knots produces 83 pounds of drag in the P92. At this slower speed, our L/D ratio is still 12:1 (1,000/83 = 12/1). At this lower weight, any speed other than 59 knots produces more than 83 pounds of drag which would decrease our 12:1 glide ratio (a shift of the total drag curve resulting from a change in weight). As the airplane's weight decreases, the speed to maintain the best L/D also decreases.

As long as the pilot keeps the airplane at the airspeed corresponding to the lowest part of the total drag curve, the L/D ratio remains constant. But how do you know what the best glide speed is if it varies with weight? Refer to the POH or to the owner's manual. Remember, in the event of a power failure, immediately establish the proper attitude to obtain the best glide speed.

Figure 73 provides information from a typical pilot handbook depicting several glide speeds for different weights. Remember, regardless of weight change, if the airplane is flown at the best glide speed for that weight, it will always glide the same maximum distance it's capable of. Keep in mind that most of the glide charts in your POH stipulate conditions like prop windmilling, no wind, flaps up.

LIFT/DRAG SPEEDS & VARIABLE WEIGHTS

Weight lbs.	Airspeed for Best L/D Knots - IAS
1,320	68 Knots
1,150	63 Knots
1,000	59 Knots

Best L/D 68 kts. — 1,320 lbs.

Best L/D 63 kts. — 1,150 lbs.

Best L/D 59 kts. — 1,000 lbs.

Distance of glide is the same

Fig. 73

Any deviation from these conditions changes your glide distance.

Most light sport airplanes have L/D's ranging anywhere from 8:1 to 17:1. In other words, at 17:1, you can glide approximately 17 times the distance of your height above terrain (assuming flat terrain). Now that's almost as good as some low performance gliders. Efficient gliders, on the other hand, have L/Ds upward of 40:1 or 50:1. (That's why they call them "gliders." Some aircraft, like the space shuttle, should be called "sinkers" for obvious reasons.)

HOW WE USE EXCUSES TO COMPENSATE FOR GLIDE PROBLEMS

Do birds fly?

OK Bob, can you put her on the numbers?

No, I meant the numbers you first flew over!

Oh.

Postflight Briefing #2-5

A Different Look at Maneuvering Speed

The first time you encounter turbulence I know what you're going to do. You'll peek out the right then the left window to make sure the wings are OK (as if you wouldn't know). Fair enough. Even though the wings are subject to lots of stress, you needn't worry about them breaking as long as you do one thing. Simply keep the airplane at or below its design maneuvering speed in turbulence. Here's how this works.

The design maneuvering speed (Va) is the speed at which the airplane will stall before exceeding its design limit-load factor in turbulent conditions or when the flight controls are suddenly and fully deflected in flight. Under these conditions the airframe experiences an increase in "G-force" or "load factor" (we'll use these terms synonymously).

The limit-load factor of special light-sport airplanes is based on the maximum amount of G-force the airframe can withstand before becoming damaged. Airplanes stressed up to but not beyond their limit-load factor should experience no structural damage. (This assumes the airplane is like new and not previously overstressed.)

Special light-sport airplanes have positive and negative limit load factors. While these may vary between manufacturers, the most common limits are: +4.0Gs and -1.5Gs. Let's examine how maneuvering speed prevents us from exceeding these limits.

Standing anywhere on planet Earth, you'll experience "one" time the force of gravity or 1G. It's gravity that pulls you toward Earth's center, providing the feeling of weight. On the surface, gravity exerts a constant 1G pull. In an airplane, however, you and the airplane can feel like you weigh more than your actual weight. This occurs when the airplane turns or the angle of attack suddenly increases (as it does in turbulence). This increase in apparent weight is called an increase in "G-force" or "load factor."

Let's suppose our airplane is cruising in straight and level flight at a constant airspeed. In this condition, lift is equal to weight and we experience a G-force of 1. We can represent G-force by the formula

Lift/Weight = G-force.

In straight and level unaccelerated flight the lift developed by the wings is equal to the airplane's weight. Thus, the G-force is 1G.

If the angle of attack suddenly increased (by pulling back on the elevator or encountering a vertical gust of wind for example), the wings would produce an instantaneous increase in lift. The airplane accelerates upward and you're forced downward in your seat. In other words, there is more upward pull by lift compared to the downward pull by weight. The G-force increases proportionally to the sudden increase in lift. Instantaneously doubling, tripling or quadrupling the lift doubles, triples or quadruples the G-force.

A direct (or nearly so), one-to-one relationship exists between lift and angle of attack. For instance, at a constant airspeed, in a 1G condition, a sudden doubling of the angle of attack doubles the wing's lift and doubles the G-force. Tripling or quadrupling the angle of attack triples or quadruples the G-force.

For instance, assume the airplane is flying at a fast cruise speed of 120 knots as shown in Figure 74. The airplane and its contents experience 1G at an angle of attack of 3 degrees for level flight. Suppose a *sudden* gust increases the angle of attack by an additional 3 degrees. The wing's original angle of attack has now doubled to 6 degrees (3+3=6). Consequently, lift *suddenly* doubles, producing 2Gs. A *sudden* increase in angle of attack to 9 degrees triples the lift and the G-force. An increase to 12, 15 and 18 degrees increases the lift and G-force to four, five and six times its original value.

At 120 knots indicated airspeed with an abrupt pull-back on the elevator or an encounter with a strong vertical wind gust. Fig. 74

1G	2Gs	3Gs	4Gs	5Gs	6Gs
3.0° Angle of Attack	6.0° Angle of Attack	9.0° Angle of Attack	12.0° Angle of Attack	15.0° Angle of Attack	18.0° Angle of Attack
3.0°	6.0°	9.0°	12.0°	15.0°	18.0° STALL
Original angle of attack in cruise flight at 140 knots	Sudden increase to twice the original angle of attack	Sudden increase to three times the original angle of attack	Sudden increase to four times the original angle of attack	Sudden increase to five times the original angle of attack	Sudden increase to six times the original angle of attack.

Since the wing stalls (and lift production decreases) at an angle of approximately 18 degrees, any further increase in angle of attack beyond six times the original value of 3 degrees won't increase the G-force. Therefore, at 120 knots this airplane is capable of experiencing 6Gs before the wings stall. If the airplane in this example had a limit load factor of 4Gs, the structure might experience some damage at this speed in strong turbulence.

At 100 knots indicated airspeed with an abrupt pull-back on the elevator or an encounter with a strong vertical wind gust. **Fig. 75**

1G	2Gs	3Gs	4Gs
4.5° Angle of Attack	9.0° Angle of Attack	13.5° Angle of Attack	18.0° Angle of Attack
4.5°	9.0°	13.5°	18.0° STALL
Original angle of attack in cruise flight at 110 knots	**Sudden increase to twice the original angle of attack**	**Sudden increase to three times the original angle of attack**	**Sudden increase to four times the original angle of attack**

If we slow our airplane down to 100 knots (Figure 75), then let's assume a 4.5 degree angle of attack is necessary for a 1G, level-flight condition. If, at 100 knots, we suddenly double the original angle of attack to 9 degrees, the lift doubles. We now feel 2Gs. A sudden tripling of the original angle of attack to 13.5 degrees, triples the lift and we experience 3Gs. And finally, quadrupling the original angle of attack to 18 degrees produces four times as much lift. Therefore, we experience 4Gs. It's not possible to pull more than 4Gs in this example since the airplane will stall at 18 degrees. Consequently, 100 knots is the maneuvering speed for our airplane having a limit-load factor of 4Gs. At 100 knots, the airplane will stall before it exceeds this limit load factor in turbulent air or with full deflection of the flight controls. (Personally, in turbulence, I prefer to fly 10 to 15 knots below Va to prevent a gust from temporarily raising my indicated airspeed above Va.)

Whether a specific gust doubles, triples or quadruples the angle of attack, depends on the angle of attack of the airplane in its 1G condition. As is clearly evident from these examples, it's easier for a gust to double, triple or quadruple the angle of attack over its starting value when the airplane is flying faster (because it's at a lower angle of attack to begin with). Consequently, it's easier to experience more Gs for a given amount of turbulence at higher airspeeds.

Weight Change and Va

The airplane's posted maneuvering speed (Va) is based on the airplane being at gross weight. What happens when the airplane's weight decreases? The answer is, the maneuvering speed decreases. Let me explain.

Airplanes flown at weights below their gross weight require less lift for straight and level flight. Less lift means the airplane can be flown at a smaller angle of attack. In other words, an airplane at 1,320 pounds may require a 4.5 degree angle of attack at 100 knots to remain in level flight. Decreasing the weight to 1,000 pounds may require only a 3 degree angle of attack to remain in level flight at this same speed. Does this angle of attack sound familiar to you?

With a speed of 100 knots, at this lower weight, a sudden and very strong gust could increase the angle of attack from 3 to 18 degrees. From our previous example, this produces six times the original lift for a force of 6Gs. This is way beyond the limit of a normal category airplane. At lighter weights, what can we do to keep from exceeding our example limit of 4Gs when in turbulence?

The answer is to slow the airplane down. At a slower speed (90 knots for example) a larger angle of attack (let's say 4.5 degrees) is necessary for level cruise flight at this lower weight.

At this speed, we can increase the angle of attack four times before the airplane stalls. Ninety-five knots becomes our new maneuvering speed if we want to limit ourselves to 4Gs. Thus, decreasing weight requires a decrease in the airplane's maneuvering speed.

Some pilot's operating handbooks publish two different maneuvering speeds for variable weight conditions (these are now called Vo's or *operating maneuvering speeds*, while the term Va refers to the maneuvering speed for max weight). If yours doesn't, try doing the following to compute a new one. For every 2% reduction in weight, reduce the max-weight maneuvering speed by 1%. In other words, if the gross weight decreases by 20%, reduce the max-gross weight maneuvering speed by 10%. This is simple math. (Besides, don't feel too bad if you are confused about math. Five out of four people are, you know.)

A few final words. If you encounter turbulence in flight, fly a level flight attitude. Attempting to hold altitude at the expense of maintaining the proper airspeed might overstress the airplane.

For those engineers reading this, the airspeed-angle of attack values are approximations only. I also assumed that the zero-lift angle of attack is zero degrees. A linear-lift curve is also assumed with a lift coefficient that increases 0.1 for each degree angle of attack increase (this is close enough to the real world for our purposes).

Postflight Briefing #2-6 Aerodynamic Ideas for Your Consumption

STALL PATTERN PROGRESSION

Wing design has an effect on how the airflow separates from the wing during a stall. The rectangular wing has the advantage of stalling at the root first. This keeps the ailerons effective at high angles of attack and provides you with a good stall warning buffet. A moderate taper on the wing allows more of the wing to reach a stall at the same time. This tends to reduce aileron effectiveness during a stall. All sections of the elliptical wing reach the stall at the same time. Ailerons may lack effectiveness during the stall on this wing. Pointed and swept wings stall at the tips first, then progress inward, rendering the ailerons ineffective during the stall.

STALL STRIPS

Some airplane manufacturers place "stall strips" on the wing's leading edge to ensure a specific part of the wing stalls first. Usually this is the inboard section of the wing. This keeps the ailerons effective during the stall. This means that the pilot still has roll control when experiencing the prestall (buffet) warning signs.

Stall Strip

FROST, ICE OR SNOW—THEY MUST GO

Courtesy *NASA*

Don't Even Think About It!

Frost on the airfoil disrupts the smooth flow of air over the wing. This causes earlier airflow separation resulting in decreased lift and increased drag. While the airplane may accelerate with frost on the wings, it may be impossible to achieve enough lift to become airborne. Frost also increases the stalling speed of the airplane. If a pilot does manage to become airborne, the airplane is now more likely to stall with any increase in load factor or decrease in airspeed.

Always remove all frost and ice from the airplane before takeoff. Usually it must be brushed off. Squirting down the airplane with a hose isn't a good idea either! Remember, frost forms when the temperature of the collecting surface is at or below the dewpoint of the adjacent air and the dewpoint is below freezing. Shooting water on the wings may simply increase the amount of frost and ice already present.

A

Photos courtesy of Captain Barry Schiff

B

Photos courtesy of Captain Barry Schiff

C

Photos courtesy of Captain Barry Schiff

Seeing the Stall

Stall progression is clearly seen with the placement of small strands of yarn taped along the wing. In picture A, air flows smoothly over the top of an unstalled wing. Picture B shows the progression of a stall from the wing root outward as the wing approaches its critical angle of attack. This is usually felt as a slight buffet which pilots know to be one of the early warning signs of the beginning of a stall. Picture C shows the wing in a complete stall. Notice how the yarn on the inboard section of the wing has actually reversed direction. This shows how the airflow over the wing becomes turbulent, no longer producing lift efficiently. Most general aviation airplanes have some variant of a rectangular-tapered wing. This allows the stall to progress from the wing root outward, allowing the ailerons to have some effectiveness for roll control as the stall is approached. This can be seen in C, above.

© Mark Rasmussen - Fotolia

Chapter Three

ENGINES

Knowledge of Engines Is Power

Introduction

"Ning, ning, ning, ning, ning," clanked the starter, but my 1963 high school Rambler refused to start. The light turned green. I turned red. A police officer walked up, gazed down over his lowered sunglasses and said, "What's the matter, don't we have a color that pleases you?"

I continued cranking. Suddenly, white smoke poured from beneath the engine. I thought this had to be the granddaddy of all fires, or perhaps a new Pope had just been elected. My car died.

Airplane engines have been far better to me than car engines. Good thing, given the difficulty of pulling over in the air to take a look under the hood.

The modern airplane engine is a thing of beauty. Not Meryl Streep or Margaux Hemingway beauty, you understand. More like Tom Hanks or Robert Redford beauty. Rugged, dependable. You, too, will learn to see the beauty in the bag of bolts up front as it churns away, hour after hour, turning the prop and helping to create lift so you can fly the friendly skies.

Due to the lack of backups for the engine after departing the ground, you will want to do everything possible to take care of the one you have on board (if you're lucky enough to have *two* engines on board, it still makes pretty good sense to take care of them). The reliability of modern aircraft engines is admirable, given the tremendous stresses and strains to which they're subjected. But don't get overconfident. The loudest sound in the world is an airplane engine that quits. At that precise instant, your body releases a jolt of adrenaline sufficient to keep all of New York City awake for a month and you suddenly remember all the words to *Ave Maria*—in Latin.

A little bit of care goes a long way toward making certain your engine goes a long way. Just as you didn't need a degree in aerodynamics to survive the last chapter, you won't need to demonstrate wrench-twirling skills in order to master this chapter and become a pilot. However, there are things you can and will do in the cockpit that have an effect on engine longevity and reliability. Besides, if you're going to order the correct maintenance for the workhorse under the cowling, you need to understand some of the basic principles of the internal combustion engine. That's what this chapter is about. So let's start with understanding the typical airplane engine you're likely to find in standard airworthy airplanes that fall into the light sport category (aircraft that you can fly as a sport pilot). Then, at the end of the chapter, we'll cover the Rotax engine that's common to many manufactured and amateur-built light sport aircraft.

The Airplane Engine

Those two brothers who made it possible for man to fly (and I don't mean Ernest and Julio Gallo) made history by wedding a relatively lightweight and powerful engine to the Wright Flyer. Modern airplane engines are even more impressive in their ability to generate a tremendous amount of power for a given engine weight, as well as for their outstanding reliability.

Most general aviation airplane engines are of the *horizontally opposed* variety (Figure 1). Please try and get the term correct. I had a student who spent six months laboring under the illusion it was *horizontally upholstered*. Things went along OK until he called the couch cleaners to do a routine inspection on the engine.

In a horizontally opposed engine, the cylinders are placed opposite each other (that's the *opposed* part), and they work lying down. What a deal. Horizontally opposed cylinder arrangements pack a lot of engine into a small amount of space. Less space used by the engine means less overall drag.

Within the engine there are a variety of metallic organs, each of which is vital to the engine's life (and thus your life). Every engine contains *pistons, cylinders, valves, connecting rods, camshafts,* and *crankshafts,* in varying proportions and arrangements (Figure 2). If you skipped Hot Rod 101 in school and don't know what any of these parts are, don't worry about it. Remember the people in the hardware store still understand terms such as—*thingamajigs, doohickies,* and *gizmos.*

Because of the reliability of airplane engines, you'll probably never witness any of these components, individually or collectively, departing your airplane (the last phrase a pilot wants to hear from a passenger is, "Hey look, there goes one of our pistons!"). Treated properly, it's unlikely that you'll ever have any serious trouble with your airplane's engine.

INSIDE THE ENGINE

Inside are such things as pistons, valves, a crankshaft, and much more.

Fig. 2

THE HORIZONTALLY OPPOSED ENGINE

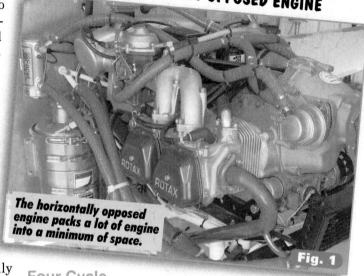

The horizontally opposed engine packs a lot of engine into a minimum of space.

Fig. 1

Four Cycle Engine

Airplane engines and humans are similar in how they process their fuel (food). Engines process fuel in a four-step or four-cycle process. Humans do likewise. Humans take in fuel by placing it in their mouths, compress it by chewing, digest it for power, and exhaust the remains (except that we don't have mufflers—now that would be a Kodak moment!).

Airplane engines also have four cycles: intake, compression, power, and exhaust.

The intake cycle occurs as the piston moves downward. Since the cylinder was filled with the piston as the cycle started, removing it creates a vacuum. Think of it as the presence of nothing, or the absence of everything (your choice). Nature abhors a vacuum. You've heard that fools rush in where angels fear to tread? While the piston is in its downward journey, the *intake valve* opens, and a mixture of fuel and air rushes in (Figure 3A). As you'll soon see, this sucking action is responsible for the term *manifold pressure,* which is used on higher performance airplanes.

The *compression cycle* occurs when the intake valve closes and the piston rises. The stuff that rushed in probably wouldn't have been in such a rush if it knew that the next thing to happen was The Big Squeeze (Figure 3B). With all the outlets closed, the fuel-air mixture gets compressed.

Now comes The Big Bang. A short chorus of "C'mon Baby, Light My Fire" would be appropriate here.

Just before the cylinder hits the top of its return journey, the *spark plugs* fire. (There are two plugs in each cylinder for increased safety and efficiency.) This sets off a wave of fire which spreads throughout the compressed mixture.

The burning mixture pushes the piston downward. This is the *power stroke* (Figure 3C). Once the expanding fuel's energy is absorbed by the piston, the piston

Liberty Aircraft With FADEC

Efficient New Ignition Systems

FADEC or *Full Authority Digital Engine Controls* is the wave of the future. This system eliminates the use of carburetors and magnetos and provides precise automatic control of the fuel-air mixture entering the airplane engine. Manual control of the fuel-air mixture is no longer required by the pilot, thus simplifying pilot workload.

FADEC consists of three major components. First, specially designed fuel injector nozzles precisely match fuel flow to the actual airflow entering the engine. Second, a FADEC computer captures the exact state of the engine and its operating environment. The third component of FADEC is a collection of small computers that manage each cylinder by reading engine and environmental conditions then computing the fuel and spark timing necessary to precisely control the combustion process in each cylinder.

FADEC provides for improved fuel consumption, reduced pilot workload, ease of engine starting, smoother engine operation, less vibration and high tech service and maintenance with downloadable data provided to mechanics by FADEC computers.

ascends, expelling exhaust gases from the cylinders through the exhaust valve (Figure 3D).

This hot act is playing simultaneously on all four (six, or eight, depending on the engine) cylinders, though each cylinder is in a different phase of the production at any instant. It all adds up to a horizontal tower of power.

THE FOUR STROKE ENGINE

A Intake Stroke

B Compression Stroke

C Power Stroke

D Exhaust Stroke

Fig. 3

The Ignition System

I casually mentioned *spark plugs* a moment ago. We're going to zero in for a closer look at what sparks your engine's fire, because managing that system is crucial to getting the most (or sometimes to getting anything) from the powerplant.

Once the fuel-air charge is in the cylinders, it must be lit to do any useful work. That's why all powered aircraft have some form of ignition system. Even the space shuttle has one (and I don't think it's some guy with a Bic lighter).

In an internal combustion engine, the ignition system is a one-trick pony. All it does, hour after hour, is send a jolt of electrical energy to the spark plugs so they can spark. Like many specialists, the ignition system is very good at what it does. That's fortunate, because getting the job done right depends on precise timing that makes trapeze artists look klutzy.

In order to create a sheet of fire that spreads smoothly across the cylinder, the spark has to light the fuel-air mixture at a precise instant. The cylinder will not sit around waiting. The precise time of this auspicious moment has been worked out by the pocket protector people, and is not your immediate concern. Let's just agree there is A Right Time. (It's not a secret; the correct timing is stated in the engine's service manual, and is often marked on the engine, as well). Too early a spark and the charge starts expanding down while the cylinder is still headed up. Bad. Too late and some of the energy never gets used. Also bad.

Dual Ignition Systems

A moment ago I said there are two spark plugs in each cylinder. This is not solely for the enrichment of the spark plug manufacturers. It's actually for your protection.

Modern airplanes have dual ignition systems (Figure 4). When dual anythings are put on an airplane, it's an engineer's way of saying "This is really, really important and I want you to have at least one of these that works at all times, no matter what." That's Reason 1 why you have two spark plugs in each barrel. The other reason is that lighting the fire from a couple of spots creates a smoother, more even-spreading flame sphere, which is the goal of the controlled burn we refer to as *combustion*.

A DUAL IGNITION SYSTEM

Left ignition system (magneto)	Right ignition system (magneto)

Dual ignition systems are installed in modern airplanes for increased safety. If the event one system fails, the other keeps the engine running. **Fig. 4**

Meet Mister Magneto

Having two spark plugs doesn't do an immense amount of good if you hook them up to *one* source of spark. It's the old thing about the chain and the weakest link. That's why I want you to meet Mr. Magneto (*mag* for short).

Magnetos contain spinnable magnets, housed in metal cases (Figure 5A). They are usually located on the rear of the engine as shown in Figure 5B. When their internal magnets are spun, they generate electricity for the spark plug. The magneto's electrical output forces electrons to rush to a tiny point on the spark plug. With millions more electrons pushing from behind like so many kids at a water fountain, each electron is forced to leap from the safety of that point to another spot located across a gap. In leaping the gap, a spark is created. That's why it's called a *spark plug*.

What's particularly interesting about magnetos is that they are self-contained spark generators. They require no outside source of electrical energy to work other than the turning motion of the airplane engine. That was a very important sentence, in case you were just scanning. It's important because it tells you the mags will work even if the alternator or battery is kaput.

From time to time I will let you in on some really fun instructor things—stuff we do that would be banned under the Geneva Conventions if it applied to flight instructors. One of those fun things to do is reach across in front of a student pilot, in flight, and turn off the big red switch that he or she has just learned is the electricity on/off gizmo. Whoa. That gets their full attention, because they are convinced the lights will go out (they will) and the engine will go off (it won't).

If you have an in-flight problem with your electrical system (alternator or battery failure for example), you won't need to worry about your engine being affected. In fact, your electrical system could be completely inoperative and the engine would continue to run. (A failed electrical system is an annoyance for a VFR pilot; on the other hand, a failed *engine* is like a dolphin hanging out with tuna—a more risky event).

Impulse Coupling

The next time a mechanic is hand-pulling a propeller through a couple of revolutions, listen for a clicking sound coming from the engine. The click results from something called an *impulse coupling* (Figure 5C). I know, you thought all couplings were impulse. Well, on some airplanes they are.

A. THE MAGNETO

B. The magnetos are usually located at the rear of the engine.

C. The Impulse coupling located on the magneto's shaft. **Fig. 5**

An impulse coupling does limited duty. It's there to help get the engine all fired up about starting. Then it steps back and waits quietly to be summoned on another flight.

When you turn the key in the cockpit, you put the engine's *starter* to work. The starter is a small, electrically-driven motor that sets the engine spinning. You could do the same thing by spinning the propeller (which is the way airplanes were started before starters were invented). However, *hand propping* an airplane is dangerous work, and almost impossible on a large engine.

The starter is the little motor that could. Except sometimes it can't. It often won't spin the engine quite fast enough to generate sufficient spark from the magnetos to set the fireworks show going. Enter the impulse coupling, stage left. The impulse coupling works somewhat like getting a boost over a fence. It's an extra shove that makes the climb easier. Impulse couplings are mechanical devices inside the magneto that save up a slight amount of spin energy on a spring. At a certain point, these springs release their energy causing the internal magnets to spin at a faster speed. This creates the electrical charge necessary to start the engine without having to equip airplanes with more powerful (and heavier) starters.

Once the engine starts, the impulse coupling stops, because the engine now generates sufficient speed and spark on its own.

Selecting Magnetos

From inside the cockpit, you have direct control over the magnetos using the switch shown in Figure 6A. Either the *left*, the *right* or *both* magnetos can be selected. Normally we operate with the magnetos in the *both* position, for maximum security and best spark distribution. You wouldn't want to select *off* in flight because it would kill the engine (and attract stares and gasps from your passengers) until you turned the mags back on.

Is there ever a time in flight when you might want to operate on only one magneto? Yes.

Fig. 6

Let's assume one magneto went bad in flight. It could randomly misfire, causing a very rough running engine despite the other magneto working properly. It could also stop working—the mechanical equivalent of a heart attack. You might try a single magneto and see what happens. Simply switch the mag switch from *both* to the *left* mag then to the *right* mag. How will you know which is the good or the bad mag? Don't worry, you'll know. You can tell by engine sound and vibration. If the engine sounds like it has lost power and/or runs rough, immediately switch to the other mag position.

Operating on one magneto is like operating on one lung. It can be done, but you're bound to experience a decrease in performance. In an airplane engine, this reveals itself as reduced engine RPM. Less spark within the cylinders means the combustion process takes longer. Therefore, the engine's speed typically drops around 100 to 150 RPMs (revolutions per minute). We refer to this as a *mag-drop* (no, this isn't where the mag falls off the airplane and rolls around on the runway).

In many cases we're concerned not only with the RPM drop on each magneto, but with the difference in RPM between each mag-drop (mag checks are done prior to takeoff in a special place called the *runup area*). This difference indicates the degree of timing error between each mag (since each mag is separately timed to the engine). For instance, the Pilot's Operating Handbook for a Cessna 172, Q-model, indicates that the drop for each mag shouldn't exceed 125 RPM, nor should the difference between the drops be greater than 50 RPM. A larger differential is symptomatic of an ignition system problem. Check your Pilot's Operating Handbook for acceptable drop limits.

Many pilots think that the lower the individual mag drop, the better. This isn't necessarily true. Little or no mag drop can mean improper engine timing or a broken P-lead.

The P-Lead

Selecting the right or left magneto deactivates the other mag by grounding it to the airframe (this neutralizes the magneto's ability to generate a spark). The absence of a mag drop can indicate that a mag that is supposed to be grounded (i.e., made inoperative) isn't.

Where that turns into trouble, appropriately enough, is on the ground. The mag is grounded to the airframe via a wire called the *P-lead* (Figure 6B). If the P-lead from a mag is broken or disconnected, it won't be grounded when it should be, including when the airplane is shut down. In that state, it is possible for the airplane to start (or the engine to at least turn over a bit) if the propeller is turned by hand or accidentally bumped.

You will soon learn that the way to properly shut down an engine is *not* by simply turning the ignition switch to off, but rather by pulling out the mixture control knob. The reason for that, which many pilots don't really know, is it leaves the cylinders without fuel in them and thus minimizes the risk of an inadvertent startup in the event of a bad P-lead.

Several years ago I saw one of our school's less illustrious rental pilots sitting in the flight lounge with a bright, new arm cast. I said, "Skiing accident Bob?" He yelled, "No, just got my hand caught on the prop." He was moving the propeller by hand attempting to hook up the airplane's towbar. The propeller kicked, whirled a half turn, struck and broke his arm (of course, he was one of those "brag-it-up" type of pilots who told everyone else that an old Vietnam War injury was acting up. I happen to know he met his wife during the Vietnam War—she's Canadian).

No matter how the plane is shut down, the prop should always be treated with the utmost respect. Just like the family pitbull, it's generally quite tame, but on occasion it *can*

CAPACITOR DISCHARGE IGNITION
Would you believe there's an ignition system that doesn't use magnetos, is completely free of maintenance and doesn't require any adjustment? It's true. It's a CDI or Capacitor Discharge Ignition system like the one found on the Katana DA-20. Unlike airplanes with magnetos, the CDI system uses solid state electronics to provide spark for the engine. This dual ignition system has two independent charging coils located on the generator stator that supply one ignition circuit each. CDI systems are very efficient in that there are no moving parts to wear and create errors in engine timing.

bite. Rod's Rule: Don't touch the thing if you don't have to.

Mechanics (and flight instructors) sometimes recommend doing a P-lead security check just before shutting down. With the engine idling, quickly turn the mag switch from *both* to *off,* then immediately back to *both* again. If the magnetos are grounding properly, the engine should hesitate as you flick through the *off* part of the sequence. Engines that keep running as though nothing had happened probably have a magneto that isn't grounding. Then it's time for *you* to run—to the mechanic. Don't touch the propeller. Just put the airplane away, walk over to the flight school and use the proper incantation to summon a mechanic from his dark, tool-infested chambers. Let the mechanic handle the problem . . . and the prop.

The Exhaust System

During the final cycle of a four-stroke engine, a rising piston forces hot gases out an opened exhaust valve and into the exhaust manifold (Figure 7). Most of the time these gases are released to the atmosphere, but in some instances they are put to productive use by the engine or the airplane.

When people say they're exhausted, it usually means that they are feeling useless, tired and worn out (perhaps from using exercise equipment like the StairMaster. That's why I prefer the ElevatorMaster). Exhaust gases, though, sometimes have an afterlife. They can be put to use spinning a *turbocharger* or indirectly heating the carburetor or cabin.

Air flowing over the outer shell of the exhaust manifold can be used to

HOW THE AIRPLANE HEATS AIR FOR CARBURETOR HEAT AND CABIN HEAT

Intake for cool air that flows over the hot exhaust manifold

Cool air is heated by passing it over a hot exhaust manifold. This becomes the source of hot air for carburetor heat and cabin heat.

Hot exhaust gases

Heated air for carburetor heat

Heated air for cabin heat

Exhaust stroke

Fig. 7

Air intake for carb heat.

Air intake for cabin heat and defrost.

The airplane's exhaust system.

ENGINE INDUCTION SYSTEM AS SEEN ON ONE SIDE OF THE AIRPLANE

To the cylinders

Fuel/Air

Induction manifold

Updraft type carburetor

Air filter

Fig. 9

raise the temperature of air entering the cabin or carburetor, as shown in Figure 7. Buildups of ice within the airplane's carburetor are prevented this way (we'll discuss carburetor ice later in this chapter). You simply pull the carburetor-heat lever to let heated air into the induction system which melts ice within the carburetor. Air used to heat the cabin results from the same process. Like carburetor heat, cabin heat is generated by bringing cooler air in contact with the hotter surface of the exhaust manifold.

Sometimes exhaust air is used to spin a small turbine, as shown in Figure 8. This, in turn, spins a compressor which sends compressed air to the cylinders. This device is a *turbocharger,* and it allows flight at higher altitudes by compressing air. Fed compressed air, the engine (which isn't all that smart) thinks it's at or near sea level, and puts out full power. This occurs because the presence of more air permits a larger fuel-air charge to be burned.

Think of it this way. If you go to the mountains, you will notice very quickly that you can't run, jump and play without huffing and puffing. The air is less dense. You simply don't have enough oxygen to perform at full capacity.

The same is true for a non-turbocharged engine. Less dense air at higher altitudes means decreased performance. Adding a turbocharger is like putting on an oxygen mask when you're in the mountains.

Airplanes with nonturbocharged engines typically fly at altitudes below 15,000 feet MSL (mean sea level, or above sea level). On the other hand, airplanes with turbochargers can fly at altitudes up to 25,000 feet MSL. Higher altitudes have other advantages—it's often possible to catch stronger winds, and if they're blowing your way, this cuts travel time and fuel consumption.

The Induction System

I had a student who'd apparently forgotten to register for the military draft. When I mentioned *the induction system,* he shot out the door leaving only a plume of smoking shoe tread.

To avoid problems, let me be specific. We're talking here about the airplane's induction system, which is the route by which fuel and air are absorbed for engine operations. The *air filter, carburetor* and *intake manifold* (pipes connected to each cylinder) make up the induction system on carburetor-equipped airplanes (Figure 9). Later on in this chapter we'll examine the induction system of airplanes with fuel injection. Let's start by examining an important part of the induction system known as the *carburetor.*

TURBOCHARGING SYSTEM **Fig. 8**

A "wastegate" valve controls the amount of air flowing over the turbine, thereby regulating how compressed the air is that enters the cylinders.

Air intake

Compressor   Turbine

On a turbocharging system, hot exhaust gases spin a turbine, which is connected to an air compressor (an impeller). The compressor compresses outside air before it enters the cylinders. This allows the engine to produce its "sea level" power as altitude increases.

Exhaust gases

The Turbocharger (compressor)

The Wastegate

A Different Version

The Carburetor

At a fancy party I once asked the bartender if he knew how to mix up a Grasshopper (the name of a drink). He said, "Well, you put a little blindfold on him and spin him around five or six times...." It seems that the bartender was as good at mixing-up answers as the carburetor is at mixing fuel and air. In fact, that's exactly what the carburetor is designed to do.

A carburetor is the ultimate mixmaster. Its job is to mix fuel and air in the right proportion for ideal combustion. Too much fuel, or too little air, and things won't go boom in the cylinder as they should. Since the fuel-air charge goes from carburetor to cylinder, you can think of this as the Shake 'n Bake system. The carburetor is one of the airplane's most important devices. You must understand its strengths and weaknesses, lest you become totally useless (kind of like a cabin attendant for a cargo airline) in the face of an engine problem.

Float-Type Carburetor – Have you ever looked in the tank of a toilet? It's the place where you're supposed to keep the brick if you want to conserve water (not in the bowl!). Perhaps you've noticed a float on a lever that was capable of upward and downward movement within the tank. A similar float arm (not as big of course) is found in the float chamber of the carburetor, as shown in Figure 10.

As the toilet's tank loses water, the float lowers and opens a valve, which lets water in to replenish the loss. As the tank fills, the float rises, shutting off the valve, which restricts incoming water. In this way the water level is maintained at some desired level. Carburetors have similar mechanisms. A rising or lowering float in the float chamber regulates fuel entering from the intake line.

Of course, float systems, like toilets, only work when they're right side up, not inverted. While I doubt you'll ever be piloting an inverted toilet, it's possible to pilot an inverted airplane. Fortunately, some aircraft have an inverted carburetor system, which allows them to operate in an aerobatic mode. These aircraft can sustain inverted flight without having the engine quit.

Workings of the Float Type Carburetor – Carburetors are often located in-line directly behind the air filter at the front of the airplane (Figure 11). Air flows through the air filter, into the carburetor, then upward into the individual cylinders via the induction manifold. Airplane carburetors located underneath the engine are called *updraft* type carburetors because air and fuel must

be drawn upward toward each cylinder. You'll find out in a moment why it's important to know what type of carburetion system you have on your airplane.

Air is drawn upward into the carburetor's throat and passes over a restriction—otherwise known as a *venturi* (see Figure 10). Notice that the cross section of the venturi is very similar in shape to the cross section of an airplane's wing. Air velocity increases over the venturi as it does when it flows over a wing.

Like an airplane's wing with high velocity air over the top, pressure decreases according to Bernoulli's principle. A reduction in pressure occurs near the outlet of the main discharge nozzle located in the middle of the venturi. Fuel in the float chamber is under normal atmospheric

CARBURETOR

AIR FILTER

Fig. 11

THROTTLE MOVEMENT & BUTTERFLY VALVE POSITION

Maximum air and fuel to engine

Minimum air and fuel to engine

Fig. 12

As power is added the butterfly valve opens.

As power is reduced the butterfly valve closes.

pressure, while the tip (outlet) of the main discharge nozzle is at lower pressure. Fuel flows from high pressure to low pressure as it's drawn upward into the carburetor's throat toward the cylinders.

As I mentioned earlier, air is drawn into the induction system by the sucking action of downward-moving pistons. This is similar to how air is drawn into our lungs. Our chest muscles expand, expanding the lungs, creating suction which pulls in air. If something is caught in our breathing passages, we're unable to inhale. We choke. Fortunately, we have the Heimlich maneuver to clear obstructions from blocked breathing passages (that's not the "Heineken" maneuver, so don't leave for a beer when someone's choking). Were it not for some restriction placed in the carburetor's throat, the engine would draw in maximum fuel and air and run at full power when started. Wouldn't that be interesting? You'd turn the key, crank the starter, pop a wheelie and take off! Air traffic controllers would love you.

THE CARBURETOR'S IDLING SYSTEM

Low pressure on engine side of carb sucks fuel out of idling jet at position (A).

Idle mixture adjustment

7 PSI

Butterfly valve

14.2 PSI

14.7 PSI

When the throttle is pulled all the way back, the butterfly valve closes and power is reduced. The engine continues to run at low power because the idle mixture screw (A) lets a small amount of fuel sneak by the throttle (butterfly) valve.

Fig. 13

Fortunately, there is a device that restricts airflow in the throat of the carburetor. It's called the *throttle valve* or *throttle butterfly valve* and it's shown in Figure 12. The throttle valve is connected directly to the throttle lever located in the cockpit. Moving the throttle forward or aft opens or closes the throttle valve, controlling the amount of air entering the carburetor.

When the throttle is fully opened, the throttle valve is parallel to the intake airflow. In other words, the valve offers no restriction to the engine's suction. The engine draws in enormous amounts of fuel and air and runs at full power. A closed throttle moves the throttle valve perpendicular to the carburetor's airflow. Downward-moving pistons are causing tremendous suction but only a small amount of air and fuel gets past the closed throttle valve (just enough to let the engine idle). That's why the engine doesn't quit when you pull the throttle all the way back. A fellow pilot had his mom in the airplane and pulled the throttle to its idle position. The engine sound decreased as expected, but the engine still idled. She looked over at him and said, "Hey, turn that thing back on right now mister." Moms! Don't you love them?

The Idling System

If the throttle valve completely restricted air from entering the carburetor, the engine would quit when the throttle was closed. Fortunately, a small amount of fuel and air flows past the closed throttle valve. It's the *idling jet* that allows this to happen (Figure 13, position A). An idling jet is *not* a 747 sitting around waiting for permission to take off. It's more like a deliberate leak. The reduction in pressure downstream of the throttle valve continues to draw a small amount of fuel into the cylinders through the idling jet.

Since there is a rather inefficient mixing of air and fuel when the engine is idling for long periods, it's not unusual for spark plugs to foul and the engine to run rough rather than purr. If you're going to be operating the engine at the idle position for long periods of time, you might want to occasionally clear the engine with short applications of power (How often? Often enough to keep the engine from *loading up*. Experience will tell you how often to do this with your airplane).

The Accelerator Pump

Surely you've had the experience of being so thirsty that you gulped down a soda pop and proceeded to choke yourself in the process. Engines aren't much different. They can choke themselves if they try to gulp air too quickly. When the throttle is opened quickly, the vacuum created by the pistons could gulp large amounts of air—too much air for a given amount of fuel. The initial rush of air over the venturi is so quick that fuel can't be sucked through the nozzle of the metering jet fast enough, and the result would be a sudden hesitation in the development of engine power with rapid throttle application. That's something that will test your triple bypass.

Fortunately, carburetor engineers solved this problem with something known as an *accelerator pump*. Figure 14 depicts a small plunger-type mechanism linked to the throttle within the carburetor. When the throttle is opened quickly, it pushes the plunger downward, forcing an extra shot of fuel from the metering jet into the carburetor's throat. This compensates for the sudden in-rush of air that accompanies quick throttle application and provides for a smooth, continuous increase in RPM. Opening the throttle slowly allows fuel to slip around the sides of the small plunger, preventing an extra injection of fuel into the carburetor. (For your information, most but not all carburetors have some type of accelerator pump.)

Assuming the airplane has an updraft carburetor with an accelerator pump, what happens when the engine isn't running and the throttle is pumped? Yes, the accelerator pump squirts fuel into the carburetor. Without the

THE CARBURETOR'S ACCELERATOR PUMP

Fig. 14

Extra shot of fuel to the cylinders to compensate for the sudden inrush of air.

PUSHES PLUNGER DOWN

When throttle is opened quickly, the accelerator pump squirts a small jet of fuel into the carburetor's throat to compensate for the sudden inrush of air into the engine. This pump prevents engine stammer and hesitation.

Initial rush of air into the carburetor when throttle rapidly opened.

AIR

engine running, there's no suction to inhale the fuel into the cylinders and fuel can fall to the bottom of the carburetor, soaking the air filter. Should the engine backfire during startup, your expensive airplane becomes a BBQ brazier. If you see people running toward you with hot dogs and buns, it may be a sign of the prime.

To avoid throwing an unscheduled BBQ event, it's best not to prime the engine by pumping the throttle on an engine with an updraft carburetor. If you insist on priming with the throttle, wait till the starter turns the engine, then pump the throttle. Any fuel squirted into the carburetor is more likely to be drawn upward into the cylinders. It's always safer, though, to use the engine primer. (See *Prime Time, page 3-23.*) That's what it's intended for. Besides, it gives you an extra thing to touch during engine start and this always impresses the passengers (especially if you mention phrases like, "Roger, Houston, we have T minus four and counting and are go for space dock....")

Atomization of Fuel

An atom is a very small particle of matter (about as small as the runway appeared during your first solo landing). Carburetors earn their keep by breaking up fuel into millions of tiny, atom-like droplets and mixing them with air. This process is called *atomization* and it makes the fuel-air mixture highly combustible—provided the fuel and air are mixed in the proper proportions.

The proportions or ratios of fuel to air must fall within certain limits for efficient combustion. The *fuel-air ratio*

NO MIXTURE ADJUSTMENT?

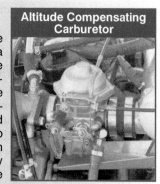

Altitude Compensating Carburetor

It's true. Some airplanes have carburetors that don't require a mixture adjustment. They're generically called *altitude compensating carburetors*. On the advantage side, these carburetors reduce the pilot's workload because there's no mixture to manually adjust with changes in altitude. Increased economy often results because pilots are prevented from flying on the *overly rich* side of the mixture. Additionally, the potential damage from overleaning isn't a problem since airplanes with these type carburetors don't have mixture controls. Because the mixture is preset, the pilot can't make mixture adjustments for best economy or best power. The engine runs on the mixture setting provided by the manufacturer.

is simply the ratio of the weight of fuel to the weight of the air entering the engine. Fuel-air ratios of approximately one part fuel to 13 parts of air are the most efficient for combustion. This particular ratio produces a highly powerful mixture within the cylinders. Combustion can occur with fuel-air ratios of 1 to 8, all the way up to 1 to 20.

Too little fuel (1 to 20 fuel-air ratio) means there isn't enough fuel to cause a useful burn in the cylinders. Too much fuel (1 to 8 fuel-air ratio) means there is not enough air within the cylinders to efficiently burn the fuel that's available. (Most flight instructor cars operated at a 1:8 ratio. This allows students to keep an eye on their instructor's whereabouts by tracking the car's dark exhaust clouds on a satellite map.)

If airplanes operated at one altitude (where air density never changes), you wouldn't need to worry about manually changing your fuel-air ratio. Not many pilots fly at only one altitude, which means you need to know how to use the mixture control to maintain a specific fuel-air ratio.

Your Carburetor, The Ice Maker

Carburetors are great at atomizing fuel and mixing it with air. An interesting side effect of that process is that temperatures drop downstream of the main discharge nozzle. Temperature drops of as much as 70°F within the carburetor's throat are not uncommon (similar temperature drops are experienced in airline cabins when brand new flight engineers are manipulating the air conditioning controls).

Do you remember the last time you spilled a little fuel on your finger? It evaporated quickly didn't it? It also got a little chilly out there, didn't it?

The process of evaporation requires heat. That's why you feel cooler when you sweat and the sweat evaporates, and why you feel miserable if you sweat and the humidity is high enough so there isn't much evaporation.

Your carburetor is a fine ice maker. Because of the considerable drop in temperature caused by the atomization and evaporation of fuel, any moisture present can and will freeze. Figure 15 is an actual shot of ice within the throat of a carburetor. With ice stuck in its throat, your carburetor (and thus your engine) can't breathe.

Carburetor Ice Can Occur At Any Temp – It's one of those gorgeous flying days. Bright, beautiful, maybe 80 degrees F outside. You're flying along without a care on your mind, and certainly no thought of ice.

Think again. A temperature drop of 70°F means that if the outside air temperature is 80°F, then the temperature in the throat of the carburetor can be 10°F! Wow, that's way below freezing. Be prepared for carburetor ice to form at almost any outside air temperature, though it's most likely to occur between outside temperatures of 20°F to 70°F. Soon you'll see how we can rid the carburetor of ice, should it form.

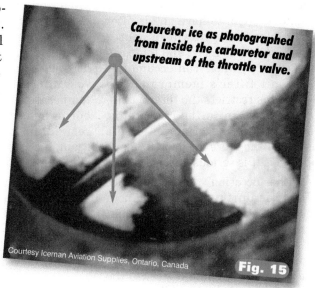

Carburetor ice as photographed from inside the carburetor and upstream of the throttle valve.

Courtesy Iceman Aviation Supplies, Ontario, Canada

Fig. 15

Impact ice seen on the airplane's nose area.

Courtesy NASA

Fig. 16

Ice: Just Your Type

Induction system ice comes in three varieties: impact ice, fuel ice, and throttle ice.

Impact Ice – *Impact ice* occurs when *visible moisture* is present (pilot term: *visible moisture* is water that can be seen, such as rain or a cloud) and the outside air temperature (OAT) is at or below freezing (Figure 16). Moisture can freeze over the induction system's air filter or inlet port and restrict incoming air. This deprives the engine of air and results in the engine taking a nap unless something is done to correct the problem.

Impact ice is usually the instrument pilot's dilemma because he or she is licensed to operate in the

How to get maximum life out of your engine:

1. Let it warm up   2. Let it cool down   3. Never run it too hot

clouds (i.e., in visible moisture). It is possible, though, to have an air filter freeze over while nowhere near a cloud. If the air is moist and temperatures are low, water can accumulate on the air filter's membrane and freeze. This restricts the filter's ability to pass air in to the carburetor, resulting in a loss of power. While not one of the more extreme forms of impact ice, it is serious nevertheless.

Another occasion where impact ice is likely is during freezing rain (a very serious type of impact ice that I'll discuss in Chapter 11). For now, just know that if your air filter ever becomes clogged by impact ice, you have a remedy at hand. It's called the *carburetor heat* control. When you pull this lever, air that is *not* passed through the air filter goes to the heating shroud around the exhaust manifold, and then on to the carb and engine. It's like having an emergency nose through which your airplane can breathe. Airplanes having fuel injection (we'll discuss this shortly) have something known as an *alternate air lever* or an *automatic alternate air door* which provides the same breathing redundancy for the engine.

Fuel Ice – *Fuel ice* and *throttle ice* (unlike impact ice) are both types of carburetor icing. Fuel ice is an internal problem, rather than an external one, as shown in Figure 17. Fuel ice forms downstream of the main discharge nozzle. The expanding fuel-air mixture cools the air stream in much the same way underarm spray deodorant cools you. It's not unusual to apply a spray of deodorant and find yourself physically airborne, shocked by the large glacier that just formed under your arm. If the carburetor's internal temperature drops below 32°F, airborne moisture freezes, causing a restriction to incoming air. Once again, the engine can't breathe, which results in reduced engine power.

Fuel ice can occur at outside air temperatures as high as 85°F and at humidities as low as 50%. It is, however, more likely to form at temperatures between 20°F and 70°F under high-humidity conditions. Carburetor ice is unpredictable. From practical experience I will tell you that fuel ice as well as throttle ice can form at almost any outside air temperature and humidity.

Throttle Ice – *Throttle ice* forms on the rear side of the throttle valve (Figure 17). It is more likely to occur when the throttle is in a partially closed position. When the throttle is partially closed, air curves and bends around this valve in much the same way it bends across a wing. Bernoulli's principle is once again invoked. Air accelerates around this valve and pressure lowers. A reduction in pressure causes a decrease in air temperature, resulting in airborne moisture freezing on the back side of the throttle valve. Given enough airborne moisture and the proper conditions, throttle ice can

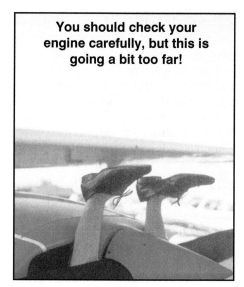

You should check your engine carefully, but this is going a bit too far!

also prevent an engine from breathing unless something is done to remove or prevent it.

It's been said that one day the cats and the birds will lie down together. I believe this is true if you have enough birds. Mixing cats and birds presents a significant hazard to the birds. Moisture and carburetors present a similar hazard to those not aware of icing problems. Smart pilots learn to anticipate carburetor ice during flight (we'll discuss the warning signs of carb ice in a moment). Regardless of your power setting or flight condition, you are not immune to carb ice. Remember (let's get that finger back in your ear), *visible moisture, in the form of clouds or rain, need not be present for fuel and throttle ice to occur.*

The Ice Eater: The Carburetor Heater

The antidote for carburetor ice is carburetor heat. Inside the airplane we have a carburetor heat lever (Figure 18). Pulling this lever allows heated air to enter the carburetor, raising the air temperature within its throat as much as 90°F. Provided you use it early enough, carburetor heat will quickly melt the ice and/or prevent further ice formation.

Heated air is obtained for the carburetor by passing air over the exhaust manifold, then piping it directly into the carburetor (Figure 19). This air is, as we've already mentioned, unfiltered. That's why you

TWO FORMS OF CARBURETOR ICE

Throttle ice forms on backside and downstream of throttle valve.

Fuel ice forms along throat of carb and upstream of throttle valve.

Fig. 17

Air Inlet

Carb Heat Lever

Fig. 18

Air from inside the engine cowling enters the carburetor (B) after it flows over the hot exhaust manifold (A).

Fig. 19

Let's suppose you're cruising along in your little Cessna 172 and notice a slow but consistent RPM drop of 200 RPM over a period of 15 seconds. Suspecting carburetor ice, you immediately apply full carburetor heat. Some Pilot's Operating Handbooks (POHs) recommend that full throttle be applied first, then carburetor heat. There's a very good reason for this. First, for carburetor heat to be effective, the engine must be producing a certain amount of power. After all, heat comes from the hot exhaust system. Full throttle ensures adequate heat production is available to melt the ice. Second, applying full throttle lets more air into the carburetor. This is certainly a good thing, since it's restricted airflow that's causing the problem.

reach for this lever if the air filter is iced over. However, it's the reason you do *not* want to use carburetor heat for long periods of time while on the ground. Damaging dust and dirt particles can be drawn into the engine.

Carb Ice Symptoms

Carburetor heat should be used whenever you suspect ice formation. The best clue to the presence of carburetor ice on fixed-pitch propeller airplanes is an uncommanded decrease in engine RPM. Engine roughness is another sign of carburetor ice. Whenever engine power unexpectedly decreases, suspect the presence of carburetor ice and apply full carburetor heat.

As you apply carb heat, the RPM decreases another 300 RPM (Figure 20 A and B), and you're looking around to see if the plane has parachutes available. Stay cool as a carb. You have not done the wrong thing, and in a few seconds things should get better. Honest! As we've previously seen, heated air is less dense than cooler air. Unleashing carb heat results in an RPM drop; in fact, that's how you test to make certain the carb heat is working before leaving the ground (more on this shortly).

If there is ice present, it will melt and RPM will rise, as shown in Figure 20C. In fact, the increase in RPM, after an initial drop, is a sure indication that you had carburetor ice. When the ice has melted, the rise in RPM ceases. As the carb heat is turned off, the RPM rises again to its previous (pre-ice) level as shown in Figure 20D.

DETECTING & RIDDING CARB-ICE WITH CARB-HEAT

Fig. 20

A — RPM decreasing (you suspect carb ice)

B — You apply full carburetor heat (RPM decreases further)

C — As ice melts the RPM increases (it rises then stops)

D — Carb heat is then turned off (RPM rises again)

Carburetor heat lever found on instrument panel

Instrument Panel

A — Carb Ice Formation — Carb ice forms & reduces air to cylinders — Cool moist air

B — Carb heat applied & ice begins to melt — Heated air enters carb

C — Melting Particles of Ice — Warm, less-dense air keeps RPM low — Heated air enters carb

D — Cool, denser air allows RPM to rise — Cool moist air

When you apply carb heat, the engine may cough a couple of times as it digests chunks of melting ice from along the throttle valve or throat. Try not to worry (easy for me to say). The engine isn't going to quit because it ingested a little water and ice under these conditions. Nevertheless, a rough running engine always makes me feel on edge—like a dog wearing contact lenses with small cats painted on them.

Carburetor heat is actually a deicing device. You apply full car-

Don't Be a Jerker

Be careful about pulling too hard on the carburetor heat lever. I had one student pull the lever and its associated cable completely out of the panel. The knob, followed by a very long wire, just kept flowing out of the socket. After three feet of naked cable protruded out of the panel, he turned and looked at me, his mouth as wide open as a blimp hangar. Not wanting to miss an opportunity to have a little fun I said, "Hey, I didn't say to use that much carburetor heat did I?" Of course the engine continued to run with the carburetor heat in its full *on* position, but it ran about 100 RPM slower. Let me explain why this is.

One of the ways we check the operating condition of the carburetor heat mechanism is to apply full heat at a moderate engine RPM (approximately 1,700 to 2,000 RPM). You'll know it's working properly if there is about a 100 to 200 RPM drop (this varies among airplanes). Heated air entering the engine is less dense than cooler air. Since hot air is thinner, this means there is less air entering the engine. What does thinner air to do to the engine's power output? It decreases it, resulting in a drop in RPM.

With the application of carburetor heat, you might notice a little engine roughness. Since hot air is less dense than cooler air, the mixture becomes richer when carburetor heat is applied. A richer mixture means less air is available for efficient combustion.

buretor heat when you suspect ice is present. Once the ice melts, you turn the heat off. Seems simple. Should the iceman cometh again, just reach for that trusty lever. Using carb heat does not hurt the engine in any way. Lycoming (a major engine manufacturer) says, ". . . at cruise power, even with full heat, we have never experienced detonation or damage to the engine." To be on the safe side, always check the Pilot's Operating Handbook (or the engine manufacturer's handbook) for your airplane to make sure they offer similar advice.

After a few dozen cycles of yank out, push in, yank out, push in, you will get either tired or bored. Thoughts will enter your mind. One

of them will be "Gee, I wonder what happens if I just leave the carb heat on?"

Be my guest. Keeping the heat on makes it too hot inside the carburetor for ice to form. Used this way, carburetor heat is an anti-icing device. Keep in mind that the mixture becomes richer when carburetor heat is applied. You'll need to re-lean the mixture with the application of continuous carburetor heat. Because of the reduced density of the air entering the engine, you should expect about a 10% to 15% reduction in power with application of full heat. That's the downside to using continuous carb heat.

Apply Carb Heat As A Precautionary Measure

Carburetor heat should be used as a precautionary measure when making descents at reduced power (reduced power means a closed throttle and a greater chance of throttle ice). I recommend that carb heat be applied fully when on final approach to land or when descending into the traffic pattern. Check your Pilot's Operating Handbook for specific recommendations on when to use carburetor heat.

If your airplane is equipped with a carburetor air temperature gauge (Figure 21), you'll have an even easier time anticipating the presence of carburetor ice. This gauge identifies

those critical carburetor temperatures (identified by a yellow-colored arc) conducive to the formation of carburetor ice. Applying enough carburetor heat to keep the needle out of the critical range should keep ice from forming.

CARBURETOR AIR TEMP PROBE AND GAUGE
Fig. 21

Carb-temp probe measures either air-temp before entering the carburetor or it measures the air-temp of the fuel-air mixture (depending on location of probe).

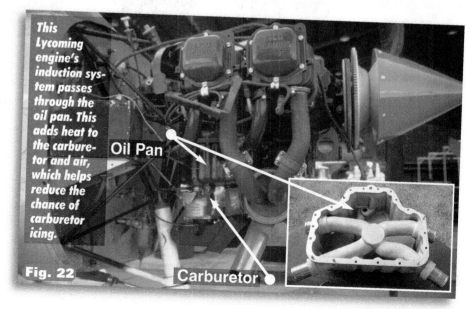
Fig. 22
This Lycoming engine's induction system passes through the oil pan. This adds heat to the carburetor and air, which helps reduce the chance of carburetor icing.
Oil Pan
Carburetor

Hot Stick

On a hot summer day many years ago a student pilot, belonging to another instructor, showed up at the flight school to do an hour of pattern work. He planned to fly his high performance, fuel injected airplane, which was on lease to the school. The airplane was late returning from a previous flight, so this fellow decided to fly one of the school's trainers instead. He didn't realize that, as a student, he was required to be checked out in each individual make and model of aircraft he was to fly, though he was about to find out why that rule existed.

He grabbed a Cessna 150, preflighted it, and headed for the runup area. Somewhere in the back of his mind, he remembered he was supposed to use carburetor heat—something he wasn't familiar with, since his fuel injected airplane didn't have carburetor heat (you'll find out why later).

He spent about 30 minutes in the pattern before returning, drenched in sweat. I happened to be standing in the lounge when he walked in. I said, "Hey Marty, were you attacked by a garden hose?" He responded, "No, but I've got to tell you, that carburetor heat in the Cessna 150 works pretty darn good." I said, "How do you know that?" He replied, "Because every time I turned it on, it not only heated up the carburetor, it heated up the whole darn airplane."

It didn't take but a few seconds to make the connection. He was so unfamiliar with using carburetor heat that he mistakenly applied cabin heat, which has a look alike lever.

Carburetor Icing Potential In Different Engines

All engines are not created equal, at least when it comes to carb ice. Some engine makes and models are more susceptible to carburetor ice than others. This doesn't make them unsafe, any more than singing Gregorian chants makes you a Gregorian. You simply need to be aware of the icing potential of different engine models.

For example, the induction system on some airplane engines make them a little more resistant to carburetor ice. Figure 22 shows the reason for

this. Lycoming engines with carburetors have their carburetor bolted to the bottom of the oil pan. An opening in the bottom of the oil pan is part of the induction system through which incoming air is warmed by the oil's radiant heat. The carburetor is also heated by conduction (touching) from the hot oil pan. This lessens the likelihood that the carburetor will develop ice as easily as carburetors on other makes of engines.

Frankly, it doesn't matter which engine your airplane has as long as you know what to do if carburetor ice appears. Don't be like those pilots who think they'll never get carburetor ice. You can tell who they are. They're the ones who drive through the hamburger stand and nod at the speakers—this doesn't bode well for humanity.

Fuel: Going With the Flow

The Mixture Control

The airplane's mixture control (the red knob with thorns along its side) allows you to keep the airplane operating at the proper fuel-air ratio as air density changes with altitude (Figure 23). Pulling out (toward you) on the mixture control decreases the amount of fuel for a given amount of air entering the engine. This process is called *leaning* (leaning is not where student pilots lean to the right or left during a turn). For now, just understand that leaning is accomplished by restricting the flow of fuel through the main metering jet (see Figure 10).

Pulling the mixture control out to its maximum rearward position of travel activates something known as *idle cutoff*. This kills the engine by restricting the fuel leaving the carburetor (Figure 24). Of course, we typically pull the mixture to the idle-cutoff position when stopping the engine on the ground at the end of the flight.

Be careful about mistaking the mixture control for the throttle.

MIXTURE CONTROL   Fig. 23

It happens. On some airplanes, especially older ones, the two knobs are not very distinct, and many a pilot has "throttled back" with the mixture control, producing the sounds of silence. At this point, your instructor starts making a lot of unusual noises. Any time the manufacturer paints something red and places symbolic thorns on its handle, I'd say they were trying to tell us something. Look or feel before you pull on a cockpit lever.

The Fuel/Air Mixture

With an increase in altitude the air becomes thinner and doesn't weigh as much for a given volume. The problem is that the amount of fuel flowing through the carburetor is regulated by the *volume*, not the *weight*, of

THE MIXTURE CONTROL

"Restriction" type of mixture control system

Fig. 24

Mixture knob rotates small valve

Main discharge nozzle

Idle cutoff shown

In the idle cutoff position the fuel flow is restricted through the main metering jet. Thus, no fuel flows.

Idle cutoff position

Carry On

Always Remember: Professor Bob
                        Big Kahoona

If the engine runs, you pay!

A young pilot taxied into his tiedown spot, pulled the mixture control to idle cutoff, and waited for his engine to quit. It didn't.

He tried turning off the magnetos but the engine continued to idle—albeit a rough idle. He was nonplused. Apparently there was just enough fuel getting by the carburetor's idle cutoff valve to fuel the engine. This, coupled with a hot spot in the cylinders acting like a spark plug, kept his engine running. I was walking by the flight line when I heard, "Help, help, help." I ran toward the voice and found this young fellow in the airplane yelling, "Help, it won't shut off, it won't shut off." He was afraid to leave the airplane so he remained inside.

I opened the door and pushed the throttle in all the way. This caused such a lean mixture (lots of air for little fuel) that the engine immediately quit. He had been sitting there for 15 minutes yelling, "Help, help."

His first question for me was, "Hey, does the Hobbs meter (flying cost meter) still run when the airplane does this?" Unfortunately it does.

VOLUME VS. WEIGHT OF THE AIR ENTERING THE CYLINDERS

Thicker air at sea level enters the cylinder

Thinner air at 10,000 feet enters the cylinder

The same volume of air enters the cylinders, but, at sea level, the air is more dense; thus, it weighs more. At 10,000' the air is less dense and weighs much less.

Fig. 25

the air passing over the venturi. Think about it this way: during the intake cycle, the pistons move downward, drawing air into the cylinders. The space within the cylinders is constant. The volume of air drawn into the cylinders is the same at sea level as it is at 10,000 feet MSL (Figure 25).

Since similar volumes flow through the venturi, the carburetor wants to send the cylinders the same amount of fuel at 10,000 feet MSL as it does at sea level. This presents a problem, since air has fewer molecules for a given volume at 10,000 feet MSL. In other words, the air at 10,000 feet MSL weighs less (fewer molecules) for a given volume than the air at sea level. To maintain the same fuel-air

ratio at higher altitudes (or in less dense air), we must manually adjust the amount of fuel leaving the carburetor.

When to Lean

Most engine manufacturers recommend leaning the mixture whenever you're operating at or below 75% of the engine's maximum power output (check your POH to be sure).

The reason for this magic dividing line is that above 75% power, engines need all the cooling help they can get, and as we'll see in our discussion on exhaust gas temperature (EGT) gauges, adding fuel helps cool the engine. At power levels above 75%, the mixture should be in the full rich position (EGT starts on page 3-18).

But how do you know when you're operating at power levels greater than 75%? A few assumptions are necessary here. First, as the airplane ascends, the nonturbocharged engine produces less power, since there is less air to aid in the combustion process. If the airplane is operating

with full throttle at less than 5,000 feet MSL, there's a good chance the engine is producing more than 75% of its maximum power output. Don't lean under these conditions. In other words, if you're climbing (with full throttle) at less than 5,000 feet MSL, the mixture should be full forward. Above 5,000 feet MSL, where the engine probably produces less than 75% of its maximum power (even with full throttle), you should lean the mixture for either best economy or best power. As a rule of thumb (aviation is all thumbs, and relies a lot on such rules), readjust the mixture every thousand feet of altitude change. (The 5,000 foot MSL recommendation is actually for a *density altitude* of 5,000 feet. We'll cover density altitude in Chapter 5. For now, 5,000 feet MSL is accurate enough).

Since most cruising is done at 55% to 65% power, you should always lean the engine regardless of your altitude at these power settings. Check the Pilot's Operating Handbook if you're not sure about the engine's power

OLE! TORO!

I was supposed to spray this field and I saw that two Black Angus bulls had strayed out of their pastures onto the field. On my second pass attempting to herd the bulls out of the field I reckon I got too low. This one bull made a lunge at me and my left gear hit him in the head. He knocked my left gear off but I killed him dayed (sic). I flew around to burn up some gas and then flew over to another airport and landed on the soft sod alongside the runway. Wiped off my left spray boom on the landing but otherwise no damage to me or the aircraft. I retrieved the gear, got some new parts, and was flying again in a couple of days. After talking with various people I am now in a heavy discussion with my insurance company.   **ASRS Report**

THE CARBURETOR'S ECONOMIZER SYSTEM

When throttle is opened to 60% or 70% of its travel, the economizer valve opens. Extra fuel flows into the carburetor's main metering jet, which helps cool the engine under high power conditions. It's called an economizer because the valve reduces the amount of extra engine-cooling fuel entering the cylinders at low power conditions (when it's not necessary).

Fig. 26

Needle moves up at the 60% to 70% throttle forward position

Economizer valve

Economizer valve is closed at these throttle positions.

Economizer valve opens at the "full" throttle position.

The Economizer Valve

Engineers were so concerned about the high heat production at power settings above 75% that they built a special device into the carburetor to aid in cylinder cooling. This device is known as the "economizer valve."

When the throttle is fully opened, the economizer valve is activated and an extra ration of fuel is fed to the engine (approximately 10% more). In other words, the mixture is purposely enriched at a full throttle setting. Dosing out extra fuel helps lower potentially higher cylinder temperatures at these power settings.

The economizer valve is activated by the throttle being in the full-forward position, as shown to the left. This is one reason you don't want to let the throttle creep backward during climb. In addition to a loss of power, you'll lose the additional cooling offered by the economizer.

output for a given altitude and power setting (I'll show you how to read and interpret that information in Chapter 14). Remember, failure to lean appropriately means you'll use up an extra portion of fuel unnecessarily. (It's important to note that some airplanes have *pressure type*

carburetors or *altitude compensating carburetors* that automatically make mixture adjustments with changes in air density. This is why you don't see a mixture control in some airplanes. The bottom of page 3-10 has a quick review of one of these carburetors.)

How to Lean

When someone asks you how you lean an airplane, don't say, "With the ailerons," or "Put it on a diet." You lean an airplane with the mixture control. There are a couple of ways to accomplish this, so let's take a look at them.

Airplanes with fixed pitch propellers (propellers having one pitch that can't be changed in flight) and float-type carburetors can be leaned using the tachometer. Simply ease the mixture control out slowly while watching the engine RPM change. As the mixture approaches the fuel–air ratio for best power, the RPM will increase (Figures 27A and B). An increase in RPM means the engine is using fuel more efficiently and is developing more power. When the RPM peaks, you are at the fuel-air ratio that produces maximum power for a given air density and throttle setting. This is known as leaning the

USING THE TACHOMETER TO ADJUST THE MIXTURE

Ⓐ RPM increasing

Ⓑ RPM increasing

Fig. 27

Ⓒ RPM at peak

Ⓓ RPM decreasing

Mixture is leaned

Mixture is further leaned

Mixture leaned to peak RPM

Mixture is excessively leaned

mixture for *best power* (Figure 27C). Further pulling of the mixture will cause engine roughness and reduce RPM from over-leaning (Figure 27D). If you feel the engine running rough during the leaning process, enrich the mixture slightly until the engine smooths out.

Sometimes airplanes are equipped with fuel flow gauges (Figure 28) and/or exhaust gas temperature (EGT) gauges (Figure 29). With a

FUEL FLOW GAUGE

Fig. 28

EXHAUST GAS TEMPERATURE GAUGE SYSTEM

Hot exhaust gas

Fig. 29

Temperature probe from exhaust to EGT gauge

MUFFLER ➡

EGT
25° F / DIV

fuel flow gauge you can set the manufacturer's recommended fuel flow rate for a given power condition. This is an approximate way of leaning the mixture for proper operation. Unfortunately, fuel flow gauges are often not accurate enough for precise leaning. Use of the EGT gauge offers a relatively precise means for leaning the engine (see Figure 30 for details).

Too Rich and Too Lean

Aside from inefficient fuel combustion, mixtures that are too rich or too lean cause difficulties with engine operation. A mixture that is too rich causes engine roughness. Spark plugs are carbon fouled when unburned fuel residue builds up between the plug gap, as shown in Figure 31. Lead, a component of high octane fuel, can also build up on spark plugs, exacerbating the fouling process. Fouled spark plugs can result in a rough and inefficient running engine.

It's interesting to note that a fouled spark plug in flight can be detected by an increase in EGT. Why? With only one flame source operating within the cylinder, it takes longer to reach the maximum combustion temperature of the cylinder's fuel-charge (it simply burns slower). As a result, the mixture is hotter as it exits the exhaust valve, resulting in a higher EGT.

Aside from a rough running engine, an excessively rich mixture contributes to high fuel consumption. This means you'll have less range, less endurance. and smaller fuel reserves. In fact, some estimates show operating at a full-rich mixture instead of a best economy setting can increase fuel consumption by as much as 70% (depending on the airplane, altitude and other variables). Even smaller percentages are significant. Do make it a point to lean properly.

A mixture that's too lean produces other problems. First, too lean a mixture means less power is produced. Small airplanes are anything but overpowered. We often need to use

every one of those horses under the cowling. This is especially true when flying at high altitudes, where nonturbocharged piston engine airplanes don't perform very well in the first place.

The biggest danger with an excessively lean mixture is that it burns hot. It does so because it burns slower. This exposes the cylinder, piston and valves to higher temperatures, and high temperature is the worst enemy of metal, causing reduced cylinder life and other problems that can blow a hole in your pocketbook.

High cylinder temperatures also lead to something known as *detonation*. Instead of a smooth, even expansion of the fuel-air charge within the cylinder, the mixture detonates (explodes), causing damage to the engine. For more information about detonation, see Detonation and Preignition on Page 3-27.

Leaning & High Altitude Takeoffs For Nonturbocharged Airplanes

Takeoffs are normally made with a full-rich mixture. Aviation, of course, is comprised of exceptions to most rules.

One of those exceptions is high altitudes, which you can generally take to mean any airport above 5,000 feet MSL. It often puzzles students, but the fact is the airplane doesn't know it's on the ground. Honest. To an airplane, 5,000 feet is 5,000 feet, at least from an engine performance point of view. Remembering that the rule is to lean above 5,000 feet, you now know there's something that needs to be done before takeoff.

How should you lean the mixture? During the *runup* (that's a preflight check of the airplane engine) hold the brakes, apply full throttle, lean the mixture, then return the throttle to its idle position (make sure no one behind you will be affected by the propeller blast). This procedure can also be done while holding in position on the runway prior to taking off (this is the best way to do it as long as there are no other airplanes on final approach to land).

USING THE EGT MONITOR TO ADJUST THE MIXTURE

Fig. 30

*Each bar in the engine analyzer represents a temp change of 25 F

A EGT increasing

B EGT increasing

C EGT at peak — The No.2 cylinder reaches peak EGT first.

D EGT for best economy — Temperature decreases two bars or 50°F

E EGT for *best power* — Temperature decreases five bars or 125°F

**Caution: Not all manufacturers allow leaning beyond peak EGT. Check your POH!

Mixture is leaned and EGT starts to increase.

Mixture is further leaned and EGT continues to increase.

Mixture further leaned until EGT reaches its *peak* indication.

Mixture is *leaned more* until EGT cools 50°F from peak for best economy.**

Mixture is *enriched* until EGT cools 125°F from peak for best power.

EGT Setting for Best Power or Best Economy

An EGT gauge is to a pilot what a drill is to a dentist—a fine, precision instrument with which to do good work. The EGT's precise measurement of exhaust gas temperatures allows you to select a mixture setting offering either best power or best economy of operation. Not every plane has a multi-probe EGT monitor, as shown above. Some have a simple gauge (Figure 29) that shows the EGT in only one of the engine's cylinders (typically the one that is known to operate the hottest). Here's how it works.

EGT monitors sense the temperature of the exhaust gas exiting one or more of the cylinders. This temperature is read on a calibrated vertical scale for each cylinder, as shown in Figure 30. Each vertical-bar increment on this six-cylinder engine analyzer represents a 25°F temperature change. As the mixture is adjusted, the EGT vertical bar responds rather quickly to changes in exhaust gas temperature.

The first step in leaning with an EGT analyzer is to find the peak exhaust gas temperature on the temperature scale. Pull the mixture back slowly until the one of the six vertical bar arrays peaks (as shown in Figure sequence 30 A through C). As you lean, not all cylinders will change their EGT at the same rate. Some become hotter than others. You want to reference the hottest cylinder.

The second step is to further lean or enrich the mixture (move the mixture control knob in slightly) to obtain either the *best economy* or the *best power* condition respectively.

For *best economy* (least fuel flow to develop a given amount of power), continue to **lean** the mixture until the temperature drops (cools) 50°F from peak EGT (Figure 30D). In real life, few engine manufacturers allow you to lean the mixture on the lean side of peak EGT (check your POH!). For *best power* (most usable power per unit of air), **enrich** the mixture until the temperature drops (cools) 125°F from peak EGT (Figure 30E). Cooling the exhaust gas from its peak value is also referred to as leaning X number of degrees *rich of peak.* It's a case of more is less; more fuel (a richer environment) produces less (cooler) temperature.

These numbers are general temperature values and vary between airplanes. You should refer to your airplane's Bible—the *Pilot's Operating Handbook*—for the specifics on the proper EGT values used for leaning your airplane.

Lead Fouled Spark Plugs

Carbon Fouled Spark Plugs

Fig. 31

Takeoff should be made at this mixture setting to ensure maximum climb performance. Leaning prior to departure is also a good idea when departing an airport (regardless of the elevation) where high temperature conditions decrease the air's density. Under certain conditions, if the outside air temperature is quite high, an airport at 2,000 feet MSL can have air with the same density as an airport at 6,000 feet MSL. Attempting to depart with a full rich mixture under these conditions produces the same decrease in performance as departing a high altitude airport.

TYPICAL GRAVITY FED (HIGH WING) FUEL SYSTEM

Fig. 32

Fuel tank built into wing

1. Fuel tank sump drain	5. Engine driven fuel pump	9. Throttle	13. Fuel rheostat
2. Fuel line strainer	6. Carburetor	10. Mixture control	14. Rheostat float
3. Fuel selector valve	7. Fuel primer lines	11. Fuel gauges	15. Fuel cap
4. Fuel strainer & valve	8. Primer	12. Tank interconnect	16. Fuel tank vent

The Fuel System

Unlike solids, liquids present problems in three areas: selection, availability and contamination. Knowing how to select the proper fuel, ensuring its availability for use by the engine, and preventing contamination is part of every pilot's job. Figure 32 shows a typical high-wing fuel system.

Components

As pointed out in Chapter 1, airplane fuel is stored in fuel tanks that are normally located in the wings. Two of the most common types of fuel tanks are the *wet wing* and the *bladder-type*. A wet-wing tank is simply an internal portion of the wing that is sealed to hold fuel. Bladder tanks are sealed rubber containers resting inside the wings as separate units.

Fuel tanks serve the important purpose of transporting food for the engine. Unfortunately, engine food as well as human food can be contaminated. Neither you nor the engine should consume anything that's contaminated (I just read where they now have non-toxic Crayola crayons. Which makes me wonder just what I was eating as a kid).

Water is the most frequent contaminant found in fuel. Water, weighing approximately 8 pounds per gallon, is heavier than fuel, which

TYPICAL LOW WING FUEL SYSTEM

Engine driven fuel pump

Electric fuel pump

Low wing fuel systems are slightly different from high wing systems in that most have an electric fuel pump in addition to an engine driven fuel pump.

weighs approximately 6 pounds per gallon. If it's present, water rests on the bottom of fuel tanks, where it's the first thing to go to the engine.

Fuel Tank's Sump Drain

Fig. 33

Fuel Sampling Device

Fig. 34

Fuel Sample With Water Contamination

Fig. 35

Since there are no engines that run on water (or walk on it, either), this presents a significant challenge.

One of the ways pilots try to avoid water contamination is by filling their fuel tanks after the last flight of the day. Air usually contains moisture—sometimes, a *lot* of moisture. When cooled, that moisture condenses, just as it does on the outside of a cold glass on a warm summer's day. Once it's been wrung out of the air, that water waddles down to the bottom of the fuel tank. By filling the tanks, you force most of the air (and its moisture) out.

Fuel tanks have sump drains at the lowest part of the tank (Figure 33). These drains allow you to remove the impurities that have found their way into the fuel system. Make sure to drain the sumps during each preflight. The sumps should also be drained after every refueling (you never know where that gas truck has been).

Sump draining isn't difficult at all. Simply take your draining device (usually a clear plastic container with a slim probe in the middle) and push it up inside the sump drain. This lets a small amount of fuel flow downward into the plastic drain (Figure 34), and sometimes onto your hand, down your arm, and onto your shirt, too.

Take a small sample, then remove the draining device. Make sure the drain is completely closed. Then inspect the sample. Check for water in the bottom of the container first. Then look for any impurities that may signal internal tank corrosion. Water is usually easy to identify since it visually contrasts with fuel, which comes in a variety of designer colors (I'll explain about those in a second). Figure 35 shows a sample of fuel with water contamination.

If you do strike water, don't throw your arms up and shout "I found it!" People won't have the slightest idea what you're talking about. And you don't want them guessing about a statement like that. Just keep on draining until you get only fuel. If there's a lot of water, prudence

Light My Fire

Be careful what you do with fuel samples after draining the sumps on the fuel tank. Most pilots simply throw the sample onto the ground. One of our flight school's chronologically challenged (old timer) flight instructors tossed a still-lit match on the flight line tarmac. A nearby student doing a preflight, casually tossed a rather large sample of 100 octane fuel near the burning match. Swooshhhhh, flames rose straight up like an earthly solar flare. The student, not aware a still-burning match had landed on that spot, looked over at his instructor and said, "Wow, that's some kind of powerful fuel eh?" I have no doubt this student's landings were a lot smoother that day.

dictates finding out why before setting forth into the sky.

On some airplanes, particularly high wing aircraft with bladder-type fuel cells, it's necessary to shake the wings and lower the tail in order to chase water from its hiding place among the folds of the rubber bladder.

What does it mean if you drain a sample from the fuel tank and it's perfectly clear? It probably means one of two things. You have either water or kerosene (jet fuel) in your tank. How would you know which one it is? The answer is to smell it. A little whiff of gas or kerosene isn't going to hurt you (unless you make it your job to whiff all the airplanes at the airport!). Kerosene has a distinctly oily smell to it. It's also oily to the touch, compared to aviation gasoline.

Fuel Colors

Your fuel is dyed. Not dead, dyed. And for a very good reason.

Different grades of aviation fuel (called AVGAS) are dyed for easy identification. Red colored fuel is of the 80 octane variety (very hard to find nowadays). Blue fuel is of the 100LL or low lead variety and is one of the most common aviation fuels in use today. Green fuel is 100 octane and is impossible to find (I haven't seen it in years, not even on St.

Patrick's day). Jet fuel or kerosene is clear colored and must not be used in piston powered airplanes.

It's important to use only the proper grade of fuel for your airplane. Using a lower grade can cause serious problems such as detonation. Higher grades can foul plugs. However, if faced with the choice of using a lower or a higher grade of fuel, choose the higher grade for temporary operations. Under no circumstances, however, should you use jet fuel in your piston powered airplane. Believe me when I say it won't make you go as fast as a jet. In fact, it won't make you go at all! Jet fuel doesn't work in these engines.

One last word on fuel. Don't use automobile gasoline in your airplane unless specific approval, in the form of a *Supplemental Type Certificate (STC)* has been issued to you for your aircraft (or it was originally certified for use with gasoline). An STC represents FAA permission for a modification to the original configuration or operating parameters of the airplane. It is granted after extensive testing and documentation, and frequently includes very specific instructions that must be followed. This is particularly true in the case of auto fuel. Unless your engine is specifically approved for automobile gasoline, it has *not* been tested and found safe for your specific engine. Using it would be both illegal and foolish, since you would be anointing yourself a test pilot.

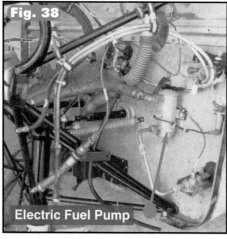
Fig. 38 — Electric Fuel Pump

Fuel Vents

If you've ever tried to suck milk out of one side of a carton without poking a hole in the other, you'll understand why fuel tanks are vented. As the fuel pump sucks fuel from the tank, air must replace the departing fuel or a vacuum forms. If that happens, fuel starvation isn't far behind, since at some point the pump can't overcome the vacuum. Some gas caps are vented, allowing small amounts of air to replace consumed fuel (Figure 36).

Fuel tanks can also be vented by small tubes, as shown in Figure 37. It's always a good practice to make sure these vent lines are unobstructed. Sometimes you can see fuel overflowing from them on hot days, when the tanks are filled. This occurs because air in the tanks expands slightly as the plane sits in the sun and warms. This is a good sign the tubes are free of obstructions.

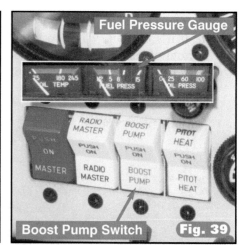
Fuel Pressure Gauge — Boost Pump Switch — Fig. 39

Auxiliary Fuel Pumps

High wing airplanes have gravity-fed fuel systems. Nevertheless, these aircraft (like all modern airplanes) still have mechanical fuel pumps to keep fuel within the system under pressure. Low wing airplanes, on the other hand, can't be gravity fed because the fuel tanks are located below engine level. These aircraft have auxiliary fuel pumps (sometimes called *boost pumps*) to maintain fuel pressure in the event of a mechanical fuel pump failure. Figure 38 shows a typical electric boost pump. While low wing airplanes are equipped with boost pumps as a matter of necessity, high wing airplanes can have them too. Airplanes like the Cessna 210, with fuel injection, have a boost pump to aid in starting as well as in emergencies.

Boost pumps are often used during engine start to pressurize the fuel system. This helps purge air trapped within the fuel lines. After the engine starts, the electric boost pump is turned off to see if the mechanical pump is operational and is pressurizing the system. Monitored by a fuel pressure gauge on the instrument panel (Figure 39), fuel pressure can be examined at any time by the pilot.

Most manufacturers of low wing airplanes recommend the boost pump be turned on for takeoff until the airplane is at least 1,000 feet above the ground. They similarly recommend it be turned on during descents when the airplane is within 1,000 feet of the surface (follow the specific recom-

Vented Fuel Cap — Fig. 36

Fuel Tank Vent Line — FUEL TANK VENT KEEP CLEAR — Fig. 37

Test pilot Bob gets his first whiff of a potential problem with the 2,000-horsepower engine retrofit unit he just installed.

mendations in your Pilot's Operating Handbook). A failure of the engine's mechanical fuel pump at lower altitudes is especially critical in low wing airplanes, since gravity won't feed the system. It's also a good idea to activate the boost pump when switching fuel tanks. This helps pressurize the fuel system and purge any air that may have slipped into the fuel lines.

Some airplanes have both *high* and *low* boost pump settings. Normally, low boost pump settings are used for engine start and takeoff. High boost pump settings can be used to stabilize fluctuating fuel flow indications during a high altitude, hot day takeoff, where vapor lock is a threat. This setting may also be used to help purge air that has entered the fuel lines (this may result from running a fuel tank dry—not a good idea!). Be careful. Under some conditions you can easily flood an engine in flight with the high boost pump setting. This could cause a temporary or complete loss of engine power. Study the recommendations in your Pilot's Operating Handbook regarding the proper procedures for your particular airplane.

Prime Time

Do you remember how we shut the engine off by pulling back the mixture control, thus burning off the last of the fuel in the cylinders? Great. Now it comes time to crank the cranky thing over. Where is the fuel supposed to come from to get started? It's time to prime.

Priming is sort of like tipping the maitre d' a few bucks on a crowded night when you don't have reservations. It just sort of helps get things going in your favor. Most airplane engines can be primed through the use of a small plunger-like device called the *primer* (PRY-MER, not PRIM-ER,) which is located in the cockpit (Figure 40). The primer usually squirts fuel in the upper portions of the induction system, bypassing the carburetor completely. This is especially useful for startups on cold days when fuel and air are disinclined to mix. Once you're done with prime time, make sure the primer is locked back in place (this generally takes a slight turn of the lever after it's pushed all the way in). An unlocked primer can allow fuel leakage into the induction system, making for an extra rich fuel-air mixture.

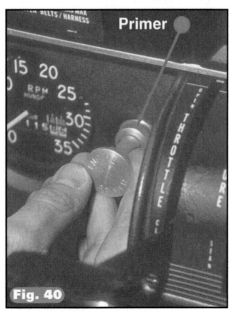

Primer

Fig. 40

Fuel Injected Priming

Fuel injected airplanes have lots of advantages. Starting, particularly in warm weather, isn't one of them. As a first resort, try doing what the Pilot's Operating Handbook recommends. The procedure generally goes something like this:

1. Activate the boost pump
2. Move the mixture to its full rich position
3. Open the throttle slightly until a fuel flow indication is noticed on the fuel flow gauge
4. Retard the throttle
5. Turn the boost pump off

The engine is started and the boost pump is usually turned on again prior to takeoff. As a general rule, if the engine has been run within the last 15 minutes, it probably doesn't need priming. More priming is necessary on cold rather than warm days. Be cautious not to over-prime, since this can lead to engine fires while on the ground. Engine fires during startup are more common on cold days.

If this fails, try asking others with the same kind of engine. If nothing else, you will hear many new incantations.

Fuel Gauges

I want you to trust your airplane, your spouse, and your accountant. I want you to never, ever trust your fuel gauge.

For a variety of reasons, airplane fuel gauges are notoriously unreliable. They couple outmoded technology to demanding conditions. Electric float type fuel measuring systems, shown in Figure 41, use 1930's technology to measure fuel quantity. The result is somewhat less believable than a Tarot card reading.

Unfortunately, lulled by their experience with car gauges (which are generally pretty accurate) many pilots think that what they see is what they can get. Every year, there are dozens of fuel exhaustion accidents in which people are needlessly endangered. (*Fuel exhaustion* is the term generally applied to what normal people think of as *screwing up and running out of gas*. I always thought *fuel exhaustion* was an interesting term. It makes it sound as though the gas just sort of got tired and fell asleep.) Try and keep in mind that the regulations require fuel gauges to be accurate in only two conditions: when the tank is full and when it's empty (no useable fuel on board). There are more accurate measuring systems available, but they are also more expensive and thus confined for the most part to larger airplanes.

So, what's the solution? Finger in ear, please. *Never, ever leave the ground without looking for yourself to verify what's in the tanks, and always know how much fuel you will burn per hour of operation.*

Fuel level determination is absolutely, positively a do-it-yourself task. Don't take anyone's word for how full the tanks are. Find out for yourself. I recommend using a calibrated dipstick measuring device to plumb the fuel level, as shown in Figure 42. Make sure the dipstick is calibrated for your airplane (you can purchase specific dipsticks for individual makes and models of airplane).

Be careful about making your own dipstick. One of my students made his own and calibrated it by progressively filling the tank and marking measurements on the stick. The only thing he didn't do was put a big enough lip on the end of it. While plumbing the fuel, it escaped his grasp and fell into the tank. He stared into the tank for 10 minutes in total disbelief. Imagine that, dipsticks don't swim! Our local mechanic had to remove it before we could fly.

RHEOSTAT-TYPE FUEL MEASURING SYSTEM

Tank rheostat connected to fuel gauge

Tank float

Wing's fuel tank

Fig. 41

FASTER THAN A SPEEDING BULLET

A flatlander flew her non-pilot husband across the beautiful but foreboding mountains of Alaska. Approaching a spectacularly high and jagged ridge, hubby climbed into the back seat to answer a calling. The pilot failed to inform her *nag-a-vator* of her decision to run the first tank dry before switching to the second tank. About midway through his task of a personal nature, the engine quit, leaving a tremendous auditory void. Quicker than Superman, her husband returned to the front seat, strapped in and sat wide-eyed alert. About that time, the aircraft responded to the pilot's flip of the fuel selector knob and the enormous silence was again interrupted with the sound of the purring engine. Today they <u>both</u> laugh about it.

Moral: Never run one tank dry before switching tanks. Foreign particles that settle harmlessly at the bottom of the tank could be forced into the engine causing damage. You could also damage your passenger's confidence in your piloting skills. D. T.

How Much Is Enough?

Everybody has their own idea on how much fuel is enough to carry. I'll share mine. Personally, I never operate an airplane with less than a quarter of its total fuel capacity. At the one-quarter mark, it's time to land and tanker up.

You will, until they invent midair refueling for small airplanes, have to land. This seems to be one of the reasons some pilots are reluctant to get fuel. Landing takes time and effort. It becomes easy to push on, because you know you've got enough fuel to make it to your destination, pretty much, sort of. Usually you will, too. Usually. But one time the weather gets bad, or the airport is closed because the person landing ahead of you neglected to unleash his retractable gear and the airplane has belly burns. That's how "accidents" happen. Fuel exhaustion accidents are one of general aviation's dark spots. They're needless, pointless, and dangerous.

One last word of caution. Be careful what you say to the gas person. Told to *top off* the tanks (which most pilots take to mean "fill 'er up,") the teenage boys who are usually gas wranglers have been known to take the tops off the tanks by removing the gas tank caps. With its cap off, a gas tank becomes a fuel dispersal

device via the large opening on the top of the wing, where all that nice low pressure says "Gas, come to me." I've had it happen before. Of course, this should never happen because you will always, always check the gas quantity visually after refueling— won't you? Remember Rod Machado's fuel axiom No. 13: If you smell fuel on takeoff, go back and land. You probably left the cap off your tank. This is easy to identify on a low wing airplane. You can generally look out the window and watch a very spectacular plume of $4+ per gallon fuel going up and out from the wing. On high wing airplanes, the smell of gas is a good clue.

A FUEL PLUMBING DEVICE

Fig. 42

Sudden Loss of Oil

A student and I had firsthand experience with sudden oil loss. We departed in a Cessna 150 and suddenly, *swoosh,* a black cloud started forming on the windscreen. My 16-year-old student must have been raised at the beach, because his verbal assessment of the situation went, "Oh wow, man, that's awesome dude!" (This confirms my theory that the closer you get to the beach, the shorter the sentences become.) I found it more worrisome than awesome. Must have been a generation gap.

It took only a few seconds for most of the engine oil to stream up from where the oil cap should have been. I called the tower, told them what happened, and received clearance to land immediately, in the reverse direction of the departure runway.

I wanted to minimize my time in the air to prevent damaging the engine. Landing was interesting, given that there was no forward visibility through the newly-painted windshield. I tilted the plane to one side so I could peruse the runway out my side window. It looked good to me. We landed successfully. After touchdown, I looked over at my student and said, "Where did that oil come from?" "From Texas?" he replied (they don't get any closer to the beach than that!).

Moral of the story: make sure the oil cap is on and make sure the cap is tight!

Fer sure.

The Oil System

If it weren't for engine oil, your engine would run for no more than a few minutes before seizing in a blob of useless metal molecules. Oil creates a thin film that clings to metal surfaces, allowing them to slide over each other with minimal contact. It also acts as a liquid shock absorber, preventing metal parts from banging directly into one another as well as providing a seal between pistons and cylinders. If that weren't enough, oil also helps clean the internal workings of the crankcase, like a chimney sweep. Metal, carbon and other impurities are carried on a river of liquid lubricant to the oil filter and removed from circulation.

This wonderful fluid also acts as the engine's thermal equalizer. Oil is to an engine as water is to a radiator. Water carries heat away from the engine; so does oil. This helps keep engine temperatures within acceptable limits.

Change of Life

Oil is the airplane's lifeline. Renewing it regularly is inexpensive insurance. If you own an airplane, don't be stingy with oil changes. Oil is made up of complex molecules and, like anything that takes a beating, these molecules break down over time. Heat, friction, oxidation, as well as contamination with water all contribute to making oil a less effective lubricant. Some pilots change their airplane's oil once every 50 hours of flight time (as a young flight instructor with a beat up automobile, I was always tempted to drain the oil and change the car).

Malfunctions In The Oil System

I make it a point never to fly one of those super discount airlines. The last time I did, the flight attendant announced it was a no smoking flight, and the captain had to shut down the right engine. Don't be caught by surprise (by disreputable airlines or your airplane). Know how to detect malfunctions in the oil system.

Low or Fluctuating Oil Pressure– After engine start, adjust for the proper engine speed (usually about 1,000 RPM), then immediately check the oil pressure gauge. The oil pressure needle should point into the green arc within approximately 30 seconds (for most airplanes). If it doesn't, shut the engine down. You may have had an oil pump failure, a leak in a line, insufficient oil quantity, oil that's too cold, or even a stuck oil pressure relief valve.

A decrease in oil pressure during flight is serious business. The engine's internal cooling capability decreases dramatically with less oil circulating through the engine. What little oil is left in the crankcase must now disperse more of the engine's heat. Because of this, oil temperature should increase with falling oil pressure. If you notice a decrease in oil pressure and the oil temperature doesn't increase, you may have an oil pressure gauge that has failed.

If you experience a decrease in oil pressure, I'd recommend heading for the nearest airport. On the way, however, I'd attempt to confirm that oil pressure is actually falling by looking for an increase in oil temperature. If I didn't see it, I'd still find an airport, land and have the gauge examined (but I'd feel something more akin to urgency than emergency).

A Tribute to the Forgotten Mechanic

Through the history of world aviation
Many names have come to the fore...
Great deeds of the past in our memory will last,
As they're joined more and more....

When man first started his labor in his quest to
Conquer the sky
He was designer, mechanic and pilot,
And he built a machine that would fly...
But somehow the order got twisted,
And then in the public's eye
The only man that could be seen
Was the man who knew how to fly...

The pilot was everyone's hero,
He was brave, he was bold, he was grand,
As he stood by his battered old airplane
With his goggles and helmet in hand...
To be sure, these pilots all earned it,
To fly you have to have guts...
And they blazed their names in the hall of fame
On wings with bailing wire struts...

But for each of these flying heroes
There were thousands of little renown,
and these were the men who worked on the planes
But kept their feet on the ground...
We all know the name of Lindbergh,
And we've read of his flight to fame...
But think, if you can, of his maintenance man,
can you remember his name?

And think of our wartime heroes, Gabreski,
Jabara, and Scott...
Can you tell me the names of their crew chiefs?
A thousand to one you cannot...

Now pilots are highly trained people
and wings are not easily won...
But without the work of the maintenance man
Our pilots would march with a gun...
So when you see mighty aircraft
As they mark their way through the air,
The grease stained man with the wrench in his
Hand is the man who put them there...

Author Unknown

Low Oil Temperature – If it's very cold, expect the oil pressure to take a large majority of those 30 seconds to rise. Starts under very cold conditions wreak a lot of havoc. During the time it takes the oil to loosen up and circulate properly, the engine's delicate metal parts are merrily grinding themselves into pixie dust. That's why engines are generally preheated in extreme cold. Lycoming, for example, recommends the engine be preheated at temperatures below 10°F to prevent engine damage during startup. (Continental says 20°F.)

High Oil Temperature – High oil temperature can result from several causes, one of which is not enough oil within the engine. Excessive engine temperature can cause excessive oil consumption, loss of power and detonation. It can also damage the engine internally by scoring cylinder walls, damaging the pistons and rings as well as burning and warping valves. Attempt to cool the engine before the needle moves into the yellow arc of the oil temperature scale. Simply climb at a higher airspeed by lowering the airplane's nose, open the cowl flaps if the plane is equipped with them, or level off for awhile or even descend at lower power settings if engine temperatures don't diminish.

High Oil Pressure – High oil pressure is not without its problems either. Inside most airplane engines is something known as an *oil pressure relief valve*. This valve provides an alternate path for the flow of oil if the pressure within the system becomes dangerously high. This prevents oil from damaging engine seals with its hydraulic pressures. Once the engine has had a chance to heat up, oil pressure normally decreases. Nevertheless, keep an eye on the pressure. If it's too high, have a mechanic examine the system.

The Engine Cooling System

The powerplant (the engine) is also a heat plant. All that local motion results in the production of calories galore, and every bit of the heat is looking for a home.

Getting it out of the engine and into the air is one of the jobs that keeps engine and airframe engineers working late at night. Most modern airplane engines are air cooled. Water cooling, however, is often more efficient, which is why the Rotax engine found in many small light sport aircraft has liquid cooled cylinder heads.

Fortunately, there are several routes out of town for engine heat. It can be dissipated by oil coolers, from heated exhaust gas, and from air flowing over the cylinders. Even propeller spinners help cool the engine. Air hitting the spinner is split and efficiently channeled into the engine's cowling, where it flows over the cooling fins (Figure 43). Cylinder fins help cool engines by providing more surface area for heat dissipation.

Keep in mind that engine cooling is least effective at high power settings and low airspeeds, where a limited amount of air enters the engine cowling. Maintain a good watch of your engine instruments, especially during climbs on hot days.

While overheating is damaging, excessive cooling can also shorten engine life. Long or rapid descents under low power conditions might cause *shock cooling* of the engine, a condition in which the various metals of the cylinders cool suddenly and at different rates. This can lead to something getting bent out of shape. That can lead to buying expensive new engine parts, so pilots generally have a strong imperative to avoid doing it.

Properly planning your descents means you maintain some power to prevent the engine from overcooling—the more power, the better. You want to try keeping the cylinder head temperatures and exhaust gas temperatures from decreasing too quickly.

Keeping the cowl flaps (Figure 44) closed helps maintain engine temperatures during the descent. By adjusting these flaps with a lever from inside the cockpit, you can regulate engine temperatures (it's like driving your car with the heater on and regulating temperatures by opening or closing the window). Normally, cowl flaps are kept open for climbs to allow for maximum engine cooling. They are usually closed for descents to aid in keeping engine temperatures from dropping too rapidly (not all airplanes have cowl flaps. They're usually found on airplanes with larger engines, typically those having 200 or more horsepower).

During a descent, your job is to maintain stable cylinder head temperatures (CHT) and oil temperatures (i.e.,

PROPELLER SPINNER
Fig. 43

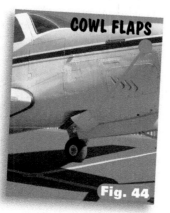
COWL FLAPS
Fig. 44

keep their temperature indications in the green). On some airplanes, gear extension or even partial flap extension at high speeds can be used in lieu of large power reductions to start a descent (check your POH). While momentary power reductions aren't as harmful if the power is immediately restored, large ones over long periods can be damaging. Try planning your descents so engine temperatures change slowly from their previous cruise values.

Detonation and Preignition

Detonation

Heat is something a pilot should pay close attention to. This was apparent to me even before I started flying. My grandparents smoked like crazy when I was a kid. I would feel their bedroom door. If it was hot, I knew they were still up, puffing away (on their cigarettes, you understand). If you want to avoid engine-damaging problems from excess heat, you'll need to learn something about detonation.

The cylinder's fuel-air charge expands as it's ignited by the spark plugs. Properly done, this isn't an explosion so much as it is a smooth, progressive burning of the combustible gases within the cylinder. As these gases expand, they increase pressure, pushing the piston downward during its power stroke (Figure 45A).

DETONATION

Ⓐ This is a normal power stroke with constant pressure on piston by expanding gases.

Ⓑ This is an abnormal power stroke where detonation causes sudden explosion of gases.

Fig. 45

Detonation occurs when the fuel-air charge explodes, burning in a short, fierce burst of energy rather than a controlled, even burn. Such an explosion (shown in Figure 45B) can be very damaging and sometimes fatal to the airplane engine.

Detonation occurs after the spark plug fires, when the unburned portion of the fuel-air charge, ahead of the burning charge, suddenly explodes. If you can imagine being kicked by a Kung-fu master from "Wong's Chinese Bulletproof Takeout" you might appreciate how damaging detonation can be to an engine. One kung-fu kick could damage the body as continued explosions damage the piston, cylinder and valves. Figure 46 shows detonation damage to an engine's components.

High engine and cylinder head temperatures increase the likelihood of detonation. They may aid in the abnormal exploding vs. the normal burning of the ignitable gases within the cylinder. As an interesting note, the EGT reading actually decreases during detonation, while the cylinder head temperatures increase. Why? With the exploding of the cylinder's fuel-air charge, combustion takes place earlier. This suddenly and dramatically releases the heat from the combustion process to the cylinder, piston and valves (too much heat at one time—that's the problem). The exhaust gases that are released have already expended their heat. They're cooler, which is reflected in a lower EGT reading. If the throttle and mixture aren't moved and you see the EGT decrease while cylinder head temperatures increase, suspect detonation. Do whatever you need to do to cool the engine.

If you suspect detonation, there are several ways you can cool the engine's cylinders. First, enrich the mixture. Second, lower the climb angle, improving airflow over the cylinders. Third, if the airplane has cowl flaps, open them. Finally, reducing power is always a good practice if detonation is suspected. Do what you need to do to reduce those cylinder head temperatures.

The following are several known causes of detonation:

1. Using a lower grade of fuel than what is recommended by the manufacturer. Higher octane fuels have additives that help prevent detonation.

Detonation-damaged piston and cylinder

Fig. 46

2. Using a time-expired fuel.

3. Over-leaning. Excessive leaning can raise cylinder head temperatures, increasing the likelihood of fuel exploding instead of burning within the cylinders.

4. Overheating an engine by climbing too steeply on hot days, as well as using excessive engine power (some engines have restrictions on the time maximum power can be used).

5. An abrupt opening of the throttle.

Preignition

Preignition isn't the ability to see sparks from the future. Preignition is ignition occurring before the spark plug ignites the cylinder's fuel-air charge. It's very different from detonation, which is an explosion within the cylinders. Preignition causes peak pressures within the cylinder to occur before the beginning of the power cycle. It is usually caused by a hot spot in the cylinders. This hot spot acts like a little spark plug, setting off the fuel-air charge prematurely. Glowing deposits of lead in the cylinders, overheated spark plugs, or using high power settings with lean mixtures can all lead to hot spot formation and preignition.

Preignition is by no means benign. It can cause a rough running engine, possible backfiring, a sudden rise in

engine temperatures, and possible engine damage (like piston or rod failure). Be alert for any of these signs and be prepared to reduce the temperature of the engine as recommended in the case of detonation.

Fuel Injection Systems

Fuel injection is a process in which fuel is directly metered and distributed to each cylinder without the use of a carburetor (Figure 47). A carburetor provides fuel for *all* the cylinders. A fuel injection system allows a precise amount of fuel to be delivered to *each* cylinder individually, via the fuel discharge nozzles. These discharge nozzles squirt fuel, under pressure, into the cylinder's intake ports near the intake valves. Better fuel distribution (more accurate fuel-air mixture to each cylinder) results from fuel injection compared to a typical carburetion system.

The fuel control unit (FCU) regulates both the volume of airflow entering the engine and the quantity of fuel delivered to the FMU (fuel manifold unit), shown in Figure 48. Movement of the throttle varies the position of the throttle valve, which regulates the amount of air flowing over the venturi (much like that found in a typical carburetor). A small tube from the FCU samples the amount of airflow over the venturi and, based on the volume of incoming air, regulates the amount of fuel flowing to the FMU. This allows the FMU to maintain a specific fuel-air ratio for each cylinder.

With fuel injection, no vaporization of fuel occurs within the induction system. This means that a fuel injection system isn't subject to the refrigerator-like problems associated with moist air and vaporizing fuel. You can't get carburetor ice in a fuel injection system for one very important reason: there's no carburetor.

However, fuel injection isn't completely invulnerable to the effects of Mother Nature. Impact ice, mentioned earlier, is the Achilles heel of fuel injection. Anything that plugs the air intake port will suffocate the engine. Fortunately, many fuel injected engines have something known as an alternate air lever located in the cockpit (Figure 49). Activating the alternate air lever allows the engine to draw air from an unobstructed source within the cowling. Some airplanes with fuel injection have a *suck-open alternate air door* in lieu of a manually activated lever. This is a spring- or magnet-held opening in the induction system. In the event the primary air source becomes plugged, the engine's sucking action automatically opens an alternate air door. Despite blockage of the primary air source, the engine still continues to run.

Most larger airplanes with bigger engines use fuel injection. The proper distribution of fuel becomes an important factor when larger, heat producing engines could be easily damaged from improper distribution of fuel within the cylinders.

Here are the advantages and disadvantages of fuel injection:

Advantages of fuel injection:

1. Improved control of fuel-air ratio.
2. More uniform delivery of the fuel-air mixture to each cylinder.
3. Increased engine efficiency.
4. Freedom from vaporization ice (fuel ice).
5. Instant acceleration of engine without tendency to hesitate.

Disadvantages of fuel injection:

1. Contamination by dirt and water can more easily affect fuel injected engines due to the small orifices of injector nozzles.
2. Difficulty starting engines on hot days due to vapor lock.
3. Any surplus fuel could be routed to one tank and cause a fuel imbalance if the pilot is not familiar with fuel system.

Up, Up and Away

You now know the basics of what makes an airplane engine tick, kick, heat, and freeze. As I said at the beginning of this chapter, you don't have to be a wrench jockey to be a good pilot. But now you do have some vital information under your seatbelt—information that can help you fly safely and economically.

Enjoy it.

Now let's take a look at the Rotax engine

THE ROTAX 912 ENGINE

If you hear the word "Rotax" and immediately think of someone from the Klingon empire, you're not alone. There is, however, nothing that's otherworldly about the Rotax engine's clean design and practical utility for today's modern airplanes (Figure 50).

Fig. 50

Rotax began building four stroke piston aircraft engines in 1982. Since then they've provided light weight and compact engines that have found a welcome home in the light sport airplane (LSA) market. These four stroke, four cylinder, horizontally opposed engines operate with an internal gearbox system that allows high engine RPM to be geared down for propellers that operate more efficiently at slower RPMs. Let's poke around a bit to better understand how these engines operate and how to better operate them.

There are two basic Rotax models that you're likely to encounter in the LSA market: the *912* and the *912S*. The 912 produces 81 HP and runs on 87 octane autogas as well as 100 LL (low lead) aviation gasoline (AVGAS). The 912S produces 100 HP and requires a minimum of 91 octane autogas or 100LL AVGAS. (There is also a 914 model that's turbocharged but these are not used in the LSA market so we won't discuss them here.)

The 912 and the 921S both come in two separate versions. The first is an FAA Part 33 certified engine found on airplanes with standard airworthiness certificates. These engines are identified as 912F or 912SF. The non-certified versions of these engines are ASTM (at one time this

meant *American Society for Testing Materials*) compliant and are found in your typical LSA. These engines are identified as 912UL or 912ULS.

The Internal Gearbox

Starting right up front behind the propeller of your typical Rotax 912 is the reduction gearbox (Figure 51). One of the great features of the Rotax engine is its ability to generate a great deal of horsepower despite its light weight. This is partially accomplished by having the engine run at RPMs that are typically much higher than the average airplane engine runs.

For example, one very popular airplane engine is the Continental O-200. This engine weighs in at approximately 170 pounds and produces 100 HP at approximately 2,500 RPM. The Rotax 912S, on the other hand, weighs in at 132 pounds, but produces 100 HP at 5,800 (engine) RPM. By reducing the weight by 23% and doubling the engine RPM, Rotax was able to generate the same amount of horsepower. Clearly, a reduction of engine weight allowed the development of reliable, safe light sport airplanes.

But how does higher RPM produce more horsepower? Think about it this way. If the crankshaft turns faster, then there's more rotational energy stored in this rotating assembly of moving parts. Rotate the crankshaft of the Rotax 912 to 5,800 RPM and the engine produces 80 HP. That's a lot of energy that the propeller can use to pull or push the airplane through the air. The only problem is that we can't run your typical airplane propeller at these high RPMs because of propeller inefficiency issues. Don't like the sound of that? That's understandable because the "sound" of that

THE ROTAX ENGINE GEARBOX

Fig. 51

THE LARGER PROPELLER SHAFT GEAR

Fig. 52

Photo courtesy of Robert Borger

THE SMALLER CRANKSHAFT GEAR

Fig. 53

Photo courtesy of Robert Borger

would be a propeller tip breaking the speed of sound because it's rotating at speeds close to 5,800 RPM. That would make all kinds of noise that irritates our neighbors around the airport. I'm speaking of those with hearing that so sensitive it would make a bat jealous. It turns out that most airplane propellers run efficiently at lower RPMs—generally below 2,700 RPM—where their blade tips stay below the speed of sound. Thus Rotax engine gearing (Figures 52 and 53) gives you the best of both worlds (no, not earth and the Klingon home world) with higher horsepower and good thrust production.

Both certified and non-certified Rotax engines on LSAs have something known as an overload clutch in the gearbox. Technically speaking, the Rotax gearbox is the spur type, with a dog axial shock absorber and an overload clutch that's optional. Now that sounds like something a guy would say if he were trying to impress girl, doesn't it?

What this means is that the gears in the gearbox have straight teeth (spur gears) that mesh with one another (dog gearing), with a small crankshaft gear (Figure 53) turning a larger propeller shaft gear (Figure 52), thus, reducing the prop speed. If, for some reason the propeller stopped suddenly (i.e., because of a ground/object strike), then the slipper clutch (Figure 54) would absorb some of that energy in the plane of propeller rotation. Figure 55A is the extracted slipper clutch. Figure 55B is the slipper clutch with the dog gear (Figure 55C) removed (the dog gear connects to backside of the large propeller shaft gear shown in Figure 52. Figure 55D shows the slipping plates extracted from inside the slipper clutch. These are the slipping plates that allow the engine to suffer less damage in the event of a sudden stoppage of the propeller. Whew! You made it. I almost ran out of fuel in that discussion. Speaking of fuel, let's speak about it.

THE SLIPPER CLUTCH

Fig. 54

Photo courtesy of Robert Borger

B

C

A

D

Fig. 55

Photos courtesy of Robert Borger

The Fuel System

To the right of the internal gearbox is the mechanical fuel pump (Figure 56). This pump is turned by the engine and draws fuel from the airplane's main fuel tank. Between this fuel tank and the pump, there is a fuel shut-off valve, a line drain and a fine particle filter (Figure 57). In other words, a drawbridge, a trap door and armed guards. The fuel shutoff valve is used during engine maintenance or if you have an in-flight fire to prevent any fuel flow from the tanks. The line drain allows you to eliminate any water in the fuel lines. The fine particle filter stands guard to catch any solid contamination that might have found its way into the fuel lines. As fuel exits the mechanical pump, it's directed to two Bing, *constant velocity* carburetors (Figure 58). These carburetors automatically adjust the fuel-air mixture entering the engine, thus limiting the need for adjusting the mixture on most light sport airplanes.

Constant velocity (or depression-type) carburetors are a little different than typical carburetors. First of all, they're called "constant velocity" carburetors because they keep the air that flows past the fuel jet (Figure 59, position A) at a constantly high velocity, which helps mixture fuel and air together more efficiently than other carburetor types. How does this happen? Let's see.

Inside the constant velocity carburetor is a vertical sleeve that slides up or down within its chamber, thereby varying the size of the carburetor's throat (Figure 59, position B and C). This sleeve is located ahead (upwind) of the throttle butterfly valve shown at Figure 59, position D. (no, there's not an actual butterfly in there as far as we know). The butterfly valve is controlled by throttle position and regulates the amount of air entering the engine. The top of the hollow vertical sleeve on each carburetor is connected to a sealed diaphragm via a flexible membrane (Figure 59, position E) that splits the chamber in two (Figure 59, position G). Because of a hole in the bottom of that sleeve (Figure 59, position F), the air pressure above the diaphragm (Figure 59, position G) is at the same pressure as that found at the bottom of the sleeve (Figure 59, position H). When the throttle is opened slightly, air flows past the sleeve and is drawn into the engine. As the air flows past the sleeve it experiences that sleeve as a restriction. This causes the air to accelerate down the carburetor's throat because of something known as the *venturi effect*. The pressure within the sleeve as well as above the diaphragm now reduces slightly. Since the area directly below the diaphragm is vented to the outside atmosphere (Figure XX, position I), it has higher pressure pushing constantly upward on the underside of the diaphragm. As the pressure inside the sleeve and above the diaphragm decrease, higher outside atmospheric pressure pushes up on the diaphragm causing the sleeve to rise a little into its sleeve chamber (Figure 59, position C). As a result, the needle connected to the bottom of the sleeve lifts out of the main fuel port slightly (Figure 59, position J), thereby allowing fuel to

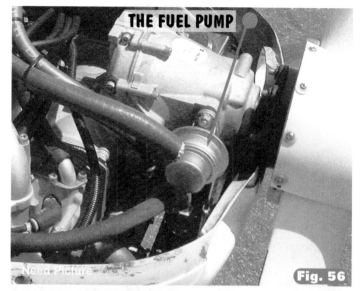

THE FUEL PUMP

Need Picture

Fig. 56

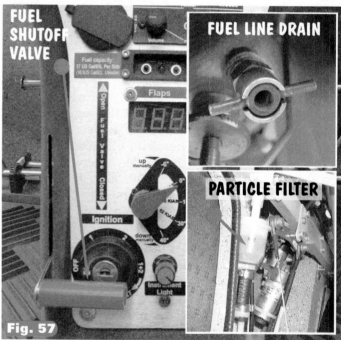

FUEL SHUTOFF VALVE

FUEL LINE DRAIN

PARTICLE FILTER

Fig. 57

TWO "BING" CONSTANT VELOCITY CARBURETORS

Fig. 58

INSIDE THE CONSTANT VELOCITY CARBURETOR

Fig. 59

flow past the throttle valve and into the engine. As the throttle is further opened (Figure 59, position K), the sleeve rises higher and more fuel ultimately enters the engine. The general idea is that there's a constant high velocity of air always flowing past the bottom of the sleeve to help mix the air and fuel together. Got that? If so, you'll definitely impress a girl (then again, you might impress her with the idea that she obtain a restraining order against you for talking like that).

Why use a CV type carburetor? One of the main reasons is that the venturi restriction made between the sleeve and the carburetor's throat provides for higher airstream velocities and much lower pressure in this location as a result. This allows for better engine acceleration since larger quantities of fuel are able to enter the engine as the throttle is opened. It also allows for better combustion since fuel and air are mixed more efficiently.

Since we've been talking about how the fuel moves through the system, you should know that your Rotax is somewhat like a vegetarian when it comes to the type of fuel it consumes. Vegetarians love diets of pigeon milk and wood chips, and your Rotax mostly loves low led fuel. Let's take a look a closer look the menu.

Fuel Considerations

The best fuel to use in your engine is automobile gas (Figure 60A) with a minimum octane rating of 87 or higher for the 912UL (81 HP), and 91 octane for the 921S (100 HP). Both engines can use 100LL AVGAS (Figure 60B) if autogas isn't available. Keep in mind, however, that low lead fuel contains about 18 times the lead found in automobile gas. This means that plug fouling and engine valve stress (caused by lead deposits on the valve seats in the combustion chamber) can be a concern (Figure 61). This is why some light sport airplane manufactures recommend the use of a mineral based engine oil or at least a semi-synthetic oil (not pure synthetic) when using 100LL. This type of oil helps scrub lead from the engine. Using higher power settings also helps reduce led deposits within the engine, too. There are also fuel and oil additives that can minimize lead deposits as per your airplane manufacture's recommendation.

On the other hand, 100LL AVGAS, as compared to autogas, is often an advantage when operating at higher altitudes because it's less likely to vaporize in the fuel lines (i.e., cause vapor lock) due to the lower pressures associated with higher altitudes. Once again, you must

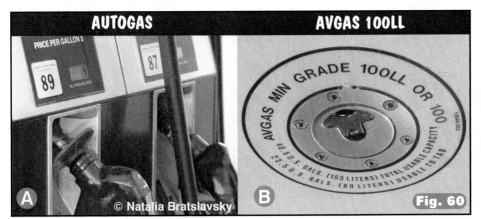

AUTOGAS AVGAS 100LL

© Natalia Bratslavsky

A B Fig. 60

LEAD PLUG FOULING

Courtesy Mike Busch Fig. 61

always follow the manufacturer's recommendation here. Please get used to me saying this because one size doesn't necessarily fit all when it comes to different airplanes, engines and manufacturers.

When lead additives were used in gasoline, they acted as an octane enhancing agent. Keep in mind that the octane rating of your gasoline is a measure of the gasoline's ability to resist pre-ignition and detonation. Eventually, lead and lead additives were restricted in automobile gasoline because of their environmental effects and their effects on an automobile's catalytic converters. Thus, lower leaded fuels typically have a lower octane rating. On the other hand, alcohol has become a rather common component of autogas in some parts of the country. While it's true that pure ethanol has an approximate 113 octane rating, this doesn't mean that gasoline containing alcohol automatically has a higher octane rating. The only way you know the octane rating of, let's say E10 (gasoline containing 10% alcohol) is by looking at the octane rating listed at the pump. So the octane rating is the essential item you must consider when selecting autogas for your airplane.

Rotax allows autogas with up to 10% alcohol to be used in their engines (if this is also approved by the aircraft manufacturer). Higher concentrations of alcohol are not recommended for your engine (and the pilot, too). The reason being that alcohol likes to absorb moisture. It suspends this moisture in the autogas and the moisture doesn't show up until it reaches a specific concentration, at which time it separates from the alcohol. This mixture might easily prevent combustion if not interfere with the proper fuel flow within the fuel lines. Additionally, the addition of moisture in your fuel can decrease the octane rating of that fuel by several points which can damage your engine (pre-ignition and detonation). So avoid higher than recommended alcohol concentrations in automobile gas. And yes, your airplane manufacturer's recommendation should always be followed in these instances.

Dual Cool—Air and Liquid Cooling

The Rotax engine uses a dual cooling system (Figure 62), with liquid cooling the cylinder heads and ram air cooling for the cylinders (animal lovers relax. No, no parts of an actual ram were used in creation of the cooling system). This is actually an efficient system since the cylinder heads are typically the hottest part of the head-cylinder arrangement. It's also where the intake and exhaust valves are located and these valves can deform or unseat when overheated. Liquid cooling of the heads helps prevent the temperature extremes that can cause engine damage.

Engine coolant is forced by a water pump (Figure 62A) located at the bottom rear of the engine and driven from the camshaft. Coolant is drawn into the pump from the radiator (Figure 62B) located in the front of the engine and forced over the cylinder heads. It flows over the tops of the cylinder heads and is drawn into an expansion tank at the top of the engine block (Figure 62C), where it eventually returns to the radiator for cooling. Since the radiator is often located below the engine level, the expansion tank is appropriately located above the engine's midline.

THE ROTAX DUAL (WATER AND AIR) COOLING SYSTEM

Fig. 62

Expansion Tank

C

D

E

Overflow Bottle

Water Pump Behind Engine

A

B

Fig. 63

What is this expansion tank that you speak of? Does the tank actually expand? Well, no, it doesn't. While water essentially doesn't expand when heated, solvents such as Anti-freeze can do expand a little when heated. In addition, when water, Anti-freeze or a combination of both are heated, there is an increase in vapor pressure within the cooling system's plumbing. If the engine temperatures increase sufficiently, there must be some way for that expansion to occur without damaging the cooling system. Clever engineers designed the pressure cap (Figure 62D) on your cooling system to prevent this type of damage. As pressure increases within the system, the pressure of the expanding fluid will exceed the expansion tank's pressure cap limit, allowing it to flow into the overflow bottle (Figure 62E). Since you've used the proper coolant and remained within the recommended engine temperature limits, there should not be any overflow of coolant beyond the overflow bottle's capacity. When the engine cools and the engine's internal coolant contracts, overflow coolant is drawn back into the expansion tank. Figure 63 displays the essential items of the cooling systems on the actual Rotax engine.

Now, what's all this stuff about coolant, engine temperature limits and the pressure cap? Well, if you have a *water-based* coolant system (a 50-50 mix of distilled water and some anti-freeze agent) with a pressure cap having a 1.2 bar (pressure) rating, then you must limit your coolant temperatures (coolant exit temperature) to 248F and cylinder head temperature to 275F. Why the limits? Exceeding these temperatures could cause the coolant to boil and flow out of the system, thereby depriving your cylinders of the liquid coolant they deserve. Therefore, if the airplane manufacturer allows you to operate the

Rotax with a water-based coolant, you absolutely must monitor engine coolant temperatures and CHTs to remain the limits of the pressure cap rating.

While I'll discuss *waterless* coolant shortly, here are a few other things to consider about water-based coolants. First, you never want to use only water as the coolant in your Rotax cooling system. Water is only allowed when mixed 50-50 with some recommended anti-freeze agent, which is typically based on ethylene glycol. This conventional coolant has the advantage of a higher thermal capability, meaning that engine temperatures are held more stable than a waterless coolant (coming up). Water-based systems can also run your system a little cooler, perhaps by 10F to 20F, compared to waterless coolant. As of this writing Rotax recommends that you use DEX-COOL coolant with water at a 50-50 ratio. Nevertheless, the airplane manufacturer's recommendation should always be followed in these instances (didn't see that coming, did you?).

If you system uses waterless coolant, such as Evans, then don't mix this with water. That's why it's called a waterless coolant. No water, please. Waterless coolants can typically absorb more heat than water-based coolants. Mixing water with waterless coolant means that as the mixture heats up, the vapor pressure from the water within the system will vaporize first, increase vapor pressure and eventually cause an overflow into the expansion tank. This results in a loss of some coolant, which can cause the engine to overheat. Rotax recommends the uses of Evans waterless coolant for its engines. Use this coolant if your airplane manufacturer hasn't offered a coolant recommendation.

THE ROTAX LUBRICATION SYSTEM

Fig. 64

The Oil Tank

The Oil Cooler

E: Oil pressure sensor, A: Pump
G: Filter, F: Oil temp sensor
D: Oil pressure regulator

The Oil Lubrication System

OK, don't get excited when I tell you that the Rotax uses something known as a *dry sump* lubricating system. Dry doesn't mean dry, as in there's no oil in the sump, otherwise known as *your engine will burn up*. In a wet sump oil system, oil is stored in the oil pan located at the bottom of the crankcase. The engine pumps the oil from the pan to various engine parts. In a dry sump oil system, the oil is stored in a tank outside the engine, rather than in the oil pan. The Rotax stores its oil in the oil tank to the left of the engine as seen from the front of the airplane. Sure, a little oil may remain in the engine, but most of it resides in the tank.

Why a dry sump? To keep the engine tidy and clean? Sorry Slick, not quite. It turns out that a dry sump means that your engine doesn't need an oil pan, and that means the engine takes up less overall space. Sure, the oil tank needs some space but the oil tank can be placed in any available location and its shape can be customizing to better fit that location. If you were an engineer, you could make it look like a coconut if it pleases you. You can also make the capacity of that oil tank any size you want. Which may explain why a mechanic might say, "Your engine runs fine, despite that big coconut you keep under the hood." It turns out that in a wet sump system, turning, banking, or generally frolicking with your airplane might cause the oil to pool to one side of the tank and possibly unport the oil's intake line. It's also possible that oil around the crankcase in a wet sump system can actually interfere with movement of the crankshaft and diminish the engine's operating efficiency to some small degree. These are the factors that cause "sump envy" among pilots having airplanes with wet sump systems.

Let's see how this dry sump system works in the Rotax. First, an engine driven oil pump (Figure 64A) draws oil from the oil tank (Figure 64B) and through the oil cooler (Figure 64C). Constant oil pressure is maintained by the pump via an integrated pressure regulator (Figure 64D) and an oil pressure sensor (Figure 64E). This ensures proper oil flow and delivery to essential engine areas. This constant pressure pump provides consistent oil pressure despite the tendency of oil pressure to change with variable engine RPM. An oil temperature sensor (Figure 64F) provides your oil temperature reading. As the oil leaves the pump, it flows through the oil filter (Figure 64G) and into the engine. After lubricating the essential elements of the engine, the oil accumulates at the bottom of the crankcase and is forced back into your coconut (the oil tank) by something known as "blow-by gasses." Huh? What is this blow-by gas you speak of, Lubeman?

It turns out that the inside of your crankcase is actually a tempest in a teapot. As the fuel-air mixture burns and expands inside each cylinder, some of those expanding gasses slip pass the piston's rings during each combustion cycle. Those gasses increase the pressure inside the crankcase thereby providing the pressure to move oil back to the oil tank (Figure 64B). Inside the oil tank, is a

screen that separates the incoming oil from the oil that's drawn back to the oil pump. Incoming oil circulates around the outside of the screen where any large particulate matter would be separated from oil sucked into the oil pump. The oil tank is vented via a bore in the tank (Figure 64H). So that's the basic setup for your oil system. Now for the details.

Before takeoff, you should always check the oil level in the oil tank. To do this, you have to draw any oil that's still in the engine back into the tank. That means you must burp the oil tank. Burp what? Is there a baby onboard? What gives?

Burping the tank means moving the propeller by hand until all the oil in the engine crankcase moves into the oil tank followed by air bubbles rising to the top of the oil that results in the "burp" sound you hear. Here's how you burp the tank (and no, you don't put it on your shoulder and pat its back...unless you want to).

First, you'll remove the cap on the oil tank so you can hear the burping sound of air entering the tank. Then you'll make sure the ignition keys are nowhere near the ignition switch, otherwise you might hear the "amputation" sound. Now you'll rotate the propeller in the direction it normally rotates, pulling it past its compression stroke. You'll know you're at the compression stroke of this four stroke engine because the propeller becomes more resistant to rotation. This causes some air to squeezes past the piston and pressurize the crankcase environment, ultimately causing residual crankcase oil to move into the oil tank. When no oil is left in the crankcase, air moves through the oil return line and flows into the oil tank. The air bubble that rises to the

Why You Want to Avoid Aerobatics in Aircraft With Rotax Engines

Oil pools at the bottom of the gearbox housing (position #1) where oil collects between the larger propeller shaft gear (position #2) and crankshaft gear (position #3) and is thrown against the curved oil baffle (position #4) to lubricate the gearing inside the gearbox. Because of this design, the oil system won't work properly in inverted flight or knife-edge flight. Thus, the Rotax 912 is not designed for aerobatic flight.

top of the oil tank is the burping sound you want to hear. Now, it's possible that you may have to turn the prop as many as 20 times to burp the tank. It may take this many revolutions to move to move all the residual crankcase oil into the tank.

Once burped, you know nearly all the engine oil is in the oil tank. This is why it's necessary to burp the oil tank before every flight to obtain an accurate oil level reading. If the oil level is low, then make sure you've accurately burped the tank. As an aside, you always want to rotate the propeller in the direction it normally rotates. Rotating the propeller in the opposite direction can draw oil out of the engine which prevents filling the oil reservoir and obtaining an accurate oil reading.

It Take Oil Types of Lubricants

Speaking about oil, what type should you use in the Rotax? Well, there are three different types of oil: a full synthetic, a semi-synthetic and petroleum based oil. Since the metals used in the Rotax are similar to the metals used in automobiles, you'll want to use automotive-type oil, instead of aviation oil. In fact, Rotax recommends that you use motorcycle oils of a registered brand name (i.e., don't buy, *Crude Sam Slicks Crude*) since they have an anti-wear additive that helps the engine gearbox. Oils with *friction modifier* additives should be avoided since they can cause slippage of the gearbox friction clutch during normal operations. In other words, you want you oil to work well, just not that well. These are additives such as Amsoil Slick Lock that further reduce friction between moving parts. Believe it or not, whale oil was once used as a friction modifier in automatic transmission fluid. This explains the seemingly strange request of some motorists who demand a quart of *Free Willie* or *Moby Dick*.

FULL SYNTHETIC OILS BEST FOR THE ROTAX

- These synthetics are high temperature oils.
- Don't use with 100LL AVGAS.
- These oils should be used with unleaded fuels only.
- Leaded fuels can lead to plug fouling.
- Synthetic oils don't hold lead and other particles in suspension where they do less damage to the engine.

Full synthetic oils provide mechanical and chemical properties that are superior to petroleum (mineral) based oils. In this category, Rotax recommends using Mobile 1 or Mobile 1 MX4T (among others, so check your manual). These are high temperature oils, for oil temperature operations higher than 248F or 250F, respectively. Full synthetic oils should be used with unleaded fuels only. Before we go any further, let's clear up one thing. AVGAS or 100LL is a "low" leaded fuel, not a "no" leaded fuel. For the purposes of the Rotax engine, 100LL AVGAS should be considered leaded. So, no using AVGAS with these oils. Why? Because lead in the fuel, along with combustion products can slip past the piston rings and enter the oil. Since synthetic oils don't hold lead in suspension as well as mineral based oils, these particles can cause build up on pistons, rings, valves and so on, causing a multitude of problems.

Semi synthetic oils are often blends of mineral oil (made from plump dinosaurs and very old plants) and no more than 30% synthetic oil. In this category, Rotax recommends using Shell Advance VSX4 or Mobile 1 Clean 750, but please check your manual for other recommendations, too. These semi-synthetics are recommended for use with leading or unleaded fuels, and both lower temperatures (less than 248F or 250F, respectively) and higher oil temperatures.

On the other hand, mineral based motor oil, such as Formula Shell (I don't know why they don't call this *Dinas-oil*), works well with 100 LL AVGAS. Mineral based oils tend to keep lead and combustion particles suspended, thus minimizing some of the build-up issues previous mentioned.

As far as the weight rating of engine oil, you should use the highest weight range for the climate in which you're operating. As a general rule, hotter climates use SAE 15W-50, which is a thicker oil. Normal or colder climates use thinner or lower viscosity oil in the SAE 10W-40 weight range. While you can get away with using a lighter oil weight in summer, you'll definitely want to make sure you're using the light weight during winter. Make sure you check the Rotax manual for specific oil recommendations.

Oil Temperatures/Pressures

Remaining within the recommended oil temperature range (Figure 65) is important for a number of reasons. First, oil helps transport heat energy to the oil cooler which helps dissipate it, and that helps keep the engine within its desired temperature range. Second, oil molecules tend can experience thermal breakdown at excessive temperatures, which causes them to lose their lubricating properties. These items, among others, makes it important to monitor your engine oil temperature range.

Before using takeoff power, you'll want to ensure that your engine oil temperature is at least 120F. This enables the oil to properly flow past the oil filter. Oil that's too cool might remain just thick enough to be unable to properly flow past the filter elements to the required points of lubrication. This means that an internal bypass valve inside the filter opens allowing the oil to enters the engine without filtration. This can accelerate engine wear, which is not a good thing. As an aside, this is why you want to make sure you use only those oil filters approved by Rotax (Figure 66). Additionally, if you have an S-LSA, you are legally required to use only those filters approved by the airplane manufacturer. Despite non-approved filters being cheaper, there's no guarantee that their internal bypass valves are set for proper operation at Rotax engine oil pressures.

Maximum engine oil temperature is 266F, with the preferred operational engine temperature anywhere between 180F and 230F. Rotax does recommend that you have an engine temperature of 190F sometime during the flight. The reason begin that the temperature of the engine oil is measured at the oil pump (at a point where

ONLY USE OIL FILTERS APPROVED BY ROTAX

Fig. 66

the oil is at its coolest temperature) after it has just come from the oil cooler. At temperatures lower than 190F there's no guaranteed that any moisture in the oil actually got hot enough inside the crankcase (where it's hotter than 212F) to boil away. Water, of course, changes the chemical composition of the oil as well as causes rust. You certainly wouldn't let a kid with a chemistry set play around with your engine oil, right? Water and oil shouldn't be in the same place at the same time. Perhaps that's why Mother Nature prevented them from mixing well together in the first place.

Immediately after engine start you'll want to check and see if you have an oil pressure reading somewhere between 29 and 73 PSI. On an airplane, that means you have to look at the oil pressure gauge. On a new car, you have a fancy lighted panel symbol that warns you of this. Unfortunately, most folks look at the oil bottle symbol and think there car needs more gravy. Go Figure. If you don't have a proper oil pressure reading within five seconds after engine start, then shut your engine down immediately.

You might be thinking that it's extremely unlikely that you'll be without oil pressure in most modern engines, but that assumes that there's always oil in the engine, right? There are more than a few stories where airplanes came from the maintenance facility where the mechanic forgot to put oil in the engine or pilots, doing their own maintenance have failed to do the same. Perhaps they didn't have enough "Free Willie" oil on hand. Either way, the pilots of these airplanes could have prevented major engine damage had they only looked at the oil pressure gauge immediately after engine start.

Kicking the Tire and Lighting the Fire

Get those steps things straight. You don't want to kick the fire and light the tire, unless you like landing hot. Lighting the fire, colloquially known as *engine start*, is simple enough if you can crank the engine to at least 220 RPM, which equates to a propeller speed of 90 RPM. Why? Because the Rotax has two AC coils at the rear of the engine that act like generators (Figure 67). One coil is used for the ignition system and the other is used to charge the battery. The ignition system consists of two, solid state breakerless, capacitor discharge units. That doesn't mean you can't break them, either. It does mean that they're less likely to break since they contain no moving parts.

It shouldn't, therefore, be difficult to reach 220 RPM when cranking the engine. The only issue you might have is if your battery charge is low. A well charged battery should crank the engine over 350 RPM. So if your battery is low, a few hours on the charger might be in order (umm, the battery, not you...unless this pleases you somehow).

Starting a cold engine is best done in the following manner. First, you want to keep the throttle at its idle setting. Next you'll engage the choke. The choke, however, won't engage unless the throttle is at its idle setting. Then you start the engine and, once started, immediately check for oil pressure. Now you'll want to advance the throttle to 2,000 RPM and gradually disengage the choke.

The recommended minimum idle once the engine starts is 1,400 RPM. It is, however, best to idle higher than this setting, especially if you have a relatively heavier propeller. The recommended idle with heavier propellers is between 1,600 and 1,800 RPM. The reason being that the gearbox contains a *torsional vibration dampener* that's designed to absorb vibrations caused by a heavier propeller that tends to act like a heavy flywheel. Idling too low or with your carburetors out of synch, causes too much torsional vibration and wears out the dampener sooner.

Torsional vibration? Well, that's simply the frequency at which the crankshaft vibrates when it's hammered by pistons and their rods during engine operation. Despite being made of hard metal, crankshafts (as well as other engine components) do flex a little. You can see of feel this because you're human. If you were from another planet, perhaps one called Vibraton, you'd be able to detect small wavy motions along the axis of the crankshaft, otherwise known as torsional vibration. Couple that vibration with a large flywheel-like mass (the propeller) at the end of the powerchain, and you can expose the crankshaft and gearbox to damaging stress. Built into the Rotax gearing system, however, is a torsional dampener, which aliens from Vibraton hate. This torsional dampener is best thought of as something like two meshed plates pressed together than can slip against one another when a large torque is applied to the rotating shaft. This is what helps reduce these vibrations effectively, but only if the engine is operating above its minimum recommended RPM when using a heavier propeller.

The Electrical System

The Ignition Coils – The Rotax has two charging coils that act like generators (Figure 67 and 68, position #1). Each charging coil generates electricity sufficient to charge one of the two independent electronic ignition circuits (Figure 67, position #2). These two circuits are solid state, breakerless, capacitor discharge modules and they rely exclusively on the two charging coils for electricity. Thus, the two charging coils and their respective ignition circuits provide the necessary electrical charge for spark-plug operation without the need for battery power. Simply stated, turn the propeller over fast enough and the engine generates its own electricity for ignition spark. In a sense, the engine is self-defibrillating, giving itself the spark of life every time the prop is turned by the starter. Don't you wish you had one of those installed on your body somewhere? Perhaps on your hand? Which would give an entirely new meaning to the term "hand propping." Given the solid state nature of this system (i.e., no points, rotors inside magnetos, etc.), the system is highly reliable and not prone to failure.

It's one thing to charge an ignition circuit, but it's an entirely different thing to get that electrical charge to the sparkplug at the right time. That why triggering of the ignition circuit (generating spark in the cylinders) begins with two *trigger* tabs (Figure 68, positions #6 and #7). One trigger tab is small (position #6) while the other is relatively larger (position #7). Both trigger tabs are located on the outer edge of the flywheel (Figure 68, position #8). Because the "A" set of ignition coils (Figure 68, position #3) are displaced outward slightly compared to the "B" set of ignition coils, each coil can only be activated one of the two triggering tabs. The larger trigger tab (Figure 68, position #7) activates the "A" set of ignition coils while the smaller trigger tab (Figure 68, position #6) activates the "B" set of ignition coils. At the moment of ignition, two of the four trigger coils cause the capacitors to release their charge via the dual ignition coils.

Since it's more efficient to start an engine when the ignition spark is retarded slightly, the Rotax ignition systems is set up to allow the ignition module to fire at the trailing edge of the trigger tab. Once the engine starts, however, the ignition modules trigger on the leading edge of the trigger tab. This is a pretty nifty way of retarding ignition timing for starting.

There is a fifth trigger coil (Figure 68, position #5) that is used as a revolution counter. This coil provides the electrical input necessary to measure engine RPM.

The Generator System – surrounding the generator rotor (Figure 68, position #9) are eight coils making up the generator's stator (Figure 68, position #10). This generates 14 volts of alternating current that's converted

THE ROTAX 912 ELECTRICAL SYSTEM

Ignition Circuit A

Two independent charging coils (1) located on the generator stator supply one ignition circuit each. The energy is stored in capacitors of the electronic modules (2).

At the moment of ignition two of the four external trigger coils (3) actuate the discharge of the capacitors via the primary circuit of the dual ignition coils (4).

Ignition Circuit B

Fig. 67

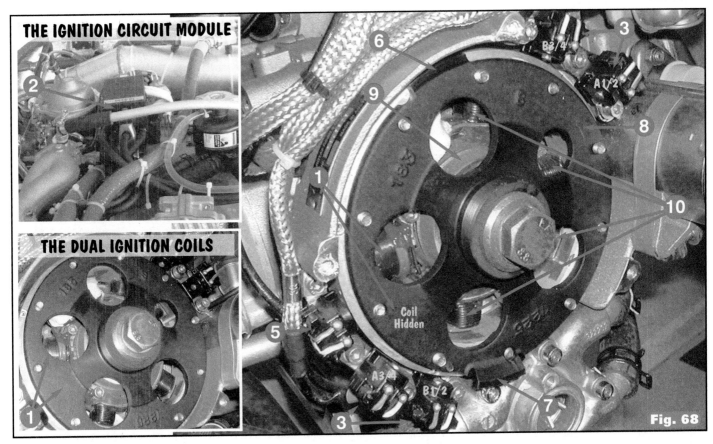

THE IGNITION CIRCUIT MODULE

THE DUAL IGNITION COILS

Coil Hidden

Fig. 68

THE BATTERY AND RECTIFIER

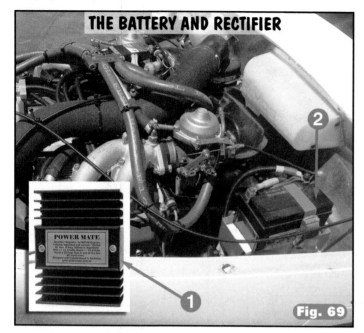

Fig. 69

AN EXTERNAL ALTERNATOR

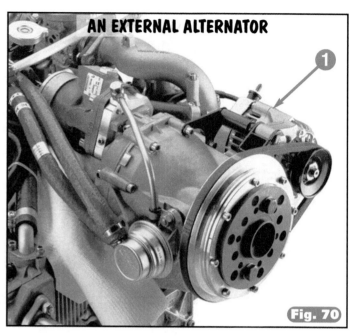

Fig. 70

into direct current via an external rectifier regulator located at the end of the engine (Figure 69, position #1). This direct current of 14 volts provides the necessary charge to sustain the 12 volt battery charge (Figure 69, position #2). (Note: the generator must produce a little more voltage than the normal battery charge to keep the battery charged to 12 volts.)

This generating unit produces about 250 watts of electrical energy at its peak capacity which is achieve at maximum continuous RPM (think "full power"). Given a pilot's natural desire for fancy electrical gadgets in the cockpit, it's entirely possible to add enough of an electrical drain to exceed the generator's 20 amp limit. Practically speaking, your electrical load shouldn't exceed 14 amps in this circuit. Exceeding 14 amps for a very short period of time is not necessarily a big deal here. Exceed this value for long periods of time, however, and you might drain the battery as well as overheat the generator's stator and melt its insulation. Sure, you may be used to the smell of burning insulation because you do a lot of your own home appliance repair, but this isn't something you want to experience in an airplane during flight.

Suppose that you're one of those pilots who just has to have his automatic coffeemaker, surround soft lighting for your makeup kit and a 30 watt leaf blower that subs as your hair dryer. Well, you're out of luck unless you install an accessory alternator on the Rotax as some pilots do (Figure 70, position #1). These units are specifically designed for the Rotax and produce an additional 40 amps that can easily power your extra electrical equipment, perhaps even your onboard disco strobe lighting system (but only if it pleases you).

As an aside, how do you know what your amp usage is in the airplane? You look at the ammeter, of course. Oh, you don't have one? Well, this is a wise thing to install for obvious reasons. Installing a volt meter is also a wise investment, too. Ammeters and voltmeters allow you to catch electrical issues long before they become electrical problems.

So there you have it. Your brief tour of planet Rotax has hopefully provided you with the essentials of properly operating that very important little machine stuck on the front of you airplane. The marines have a good motto that also applies to your Rotax engine: No better friend and no worse enemy. Be friendly to your engine.

Postflight Briefing #3-2

What does MOGAS (Automotive Fuel) RON 95/AKI 91 mean?

Donato Martino

The Antiknock Index (AKI) is the octane rating usually used in the US. It is the number displayed on gasoline pumps in the US and is the number used by automobile manufacturers in specifying the octane requirements of their engines. Rotax specifies a minimum AKI of 91 for the 912ULS. The AKI is determined by averaging the RON (Research Octane Number) and the MON (Manufacturer Octane Number) using the formula AKI = (RON + MON) / 2.

In Europe, RON is most commonly used to specify octane rating. This is the source of some confusion among owners of some European cars. Fuel with 91 RON in Europe is roughly equivalent to 87 AKI and fuel with 95 RON is roughly 91 AKI. So a Rotax 912 ULS powered aircraft sold in the US and requiring 91 AKI would be specified as requiring 95 RON if it were sold in Europe. The use of Premium Grade auto fuel is approved for the Rotax 912ULS aircraft engine. Refer to the Rotax Operator's Manual section 10.2.2 Fuel, Rotax Service Instruction SI-912-016 for the most current information.

Chapter Four

Electrical Systems
Knowing What's Watt

A Simplified Approach for Those With Little or No Understanding of Electricity

Welcome to Volts for Dolts, the Machado QuickCourse for those afraid of electricity.

Attention, class. This is going to be easy.

Watt? Easy? Yes, because we're going to learn what electricity does, rather than split atoms over what it is.

Let's be practical. You don't know, and don't much care, about the difference between jewels and joules. You do want and need to know how to detect and direct electrons in your airplane and put them to work for you. You also need to know when the electrical system is threatening to roll over and play dead, and what can be done about it.

Read on. Fear not. Think volt, not bolt.

Electricity and Water

Albert Einstein once said, "Make everything as simple as possible, but not simpler." For instance, Einstein's concept of time distortion is often discussed from a mathematical perspective. For most of us, this is like listening to a lecture delivered in Martian. Actually, Southern Martian. On the other hand, suppose someone said that the length of one minute depends on which side of the bathroom door you're on. Now we're communicating.

Unfortunately, the philosophy of simplicity has not been applied to understanding the airplane's electrical system—until now.

We're going to approach this like a plumber, by thinking about electricity as though it were water. This may be the only chance you will ever have to mix electricity and water safely, so pay attention.

A water model of electricity uses basic plumbing language to explain how electrons flow in a circuit. The only problem with the model is that you can't use it to build a computer.

The model's language isn't precise enough to describe the intricate electrical nuances necessary to accurately convey the point (besides, what would you do if water suddenly shot out of your hard drive?). You can, however, use the water model to describe—accurately enough to suit any normal sport pilot—how an airplane's electrical system works.

I caution you not to take this model literally, and if you actually are knowledgeable about things electrical, I also urge you not to take offense. The model is only used to help clarify certain cause and effect relationships.

IF YOU STUDY THE WATER THEORY OF ELECTRICITY...

Hey acorn head! Get off the cord.

... you need not worry that stepping on the electrical cord will cut off the flow of juice to your electrical equipment!

WATER ANALOGY OF ELECTRICITY

The water analogy of electricity uses water to represent the flow of electricity in a circuit and pipes to represent wires. Water pressure represents the amount of voltage in a system. More voltage means greater water pressure. A 24 volt system (the bigger balloon) can push more water through the pipes than a 12 volt system. The amount of water actually flowing within the pipes represents the electrical current within the system. Therefore, a 24 volt system can provide more electric current (more water flow) than a 12 volt system.

24 Volts "WATER UNDER PRESSURE"

12 Volts "WATER UNDER PRESSURE"

Fig. 1

5 Gal/Hr (Less Current)

10 Gal/Hr (More Current)

One more disclaimer. This model uses *conventional* current flow, where things go from positive to negative. In reality, electrons flow from the negative to the positive side of a battery. The reason for the difference lies in physics theory, but that's not what this book is about. I use conventional flow because it makes much more sense to mere mortals when things flow from high to low, plus to minus, big to little, etc.

Electricity involves many terms that can be directly related to water or plumbing (Figure 1). Voltage is comparable to, and can be thought of as, the pressure that pushes water through pipes. Current is the amount of water actually flowing through the pipes at any given time. The greater the water pressure (voltage) in a line, the greater the amount of water (electric current) that

flows (Figure 2). All the water analogy electrical definitions you'll need are listed in Figure 3.

For electrical equipment to work, something must provide voltage or electrical pressure. In most airplanes this device is called an *alternator,* as shown in Figure 4. Using the water analogy, the alternator can be thought of as the pump that provides water pressure to the *primary bus* and the *avionics bus* (Figure 5). (In the electrical world, a *bus* is a pathway for electricity, not a yellow conveyance for kids.)

A bus is essentially a drinking trough for hungry electrical equipment. Normally, it's a piece of conductive metal that thirsty electrical equipment taps into when drawing the electric current it needs to operate. (From now on I'll speak of electricity in terms of the water analogy as often as possible and, when possible, discuss how it relates to electrical theory.)

The Water Pump

Where might the water pump get the water it needs to pressurize the primary bus? Imagine a tray of water resting on the ground under the schematic of Figure 5. The water pump draws water up from the tray and pumps it into the primary bus. From here the water flows to the electrical equipment, where it does useful work. Then it flows back to the tray resting on the ground. This completes the circuit, allowing the water to return to its original source.

Electricity follows a similar circuit. A spinning alternator causes electric current to flow into the primary bus and through the electrical equipment, where it lights up lights, spins up motors, spins round gyros, and otherwise makes things go *bang, whang* and *clang* in the night (and day). After leaving the electrical equipment, electric current flows back to its original source in a manner similar to the tray in our water analogy. This tray is called the *electrical ground.*

WATER ANALOGY OF VOLTAGE AND CURRENT

At 24 volts of electrical pressure, only 20 amps of electrical current (water) can be pushed through this wire (tube).

20 — **24 Volt battery pressure**

At the same 24 volts of electrical pressure, electrical equipment draws only 10 amps of current (water).

10 — **24 Volt battery pressure**

Fig. 2

Even though 24 volts can provide 20 amps of current (water), the electrical equipment here draws only 5 amps of current (water).

5 — **24 Volt battery pressure**

Professor Bob
Big Kahoona

A 50,000 volt shock will make all your teeth even. However, numbers 1, 3, 5 and 7 will be missing!

WATER THEORY DEFINITIONS

Water ➡	Electricity
Pipes ➡	Wires
Pressure ➡	Voltage
Water flow ➡	Current
Balloon ➡	Battery
Water pump ➡	Alternator

Fig. 3

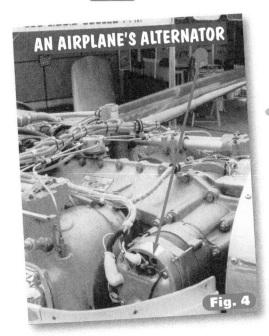

AN AIRPLANE'S ALTERNATOR

Fig. 4

WATER ANALOGY OF ELECTRICITY (SCHEMATIC)

Primary bus

CB — GYRO
CB — GYRO
CB — PANEL LIGHTS
CB — RADIO LIGHTS
CB — CIG
CB — LAND LIGHT
CB — NAV LIGHT

Engine driven water pump (alternator)

Fig. 5

Electrical ground

Battery

Avionics master switch

Avionics bus

CB — RADIO
CB — NAV
CB — RADIO
CB — NAV

CB = Circuit breaker

For electrical circuits to work, electric current must have a way of returning to its original source, as shown in Figure 6A. Electric current flows from one side of the battery, through the light bulb (doing useful work), then back into the other side of the battery. If the return wire is broken, there is no way for the current to return to its source and the light doesn't shine (Figure 6B).

Even though the wires are not connected, as shown in Figure 6C, the light shines because the bulb and one side of the battery are connected to an electrical conductor, which allows electricity to flow between them. This conductor is the electrical ground, which is represented by small slashed triangles.

The Electrical Ground

The electrical ground is not the ground upon which you stand. It's usually the airplane's metal frame—which is a great conductor of electricity. This frame acts as one large wire,

Flashlight Flukes

Prior to my departure on a nighttime currency flight I placed my mini-flashlight in my pants pocket. The flight proceeded without incident and, after landing, I took out the flashlight to complete some postflight paperwork. A penny had become lodged in the lens and the light was completely blocked. It took a pocket knife to dislodge the coin. This would have been difficult had the necessity arisen in flight.

ASRS Report

Next time: no coins in pocket.

Sorry, about that.

No worries mate!

Flashlight Rules

Rule Number 1:
Always carry one flashlight (preferably two) on every flight.

Rule Number 2:
Always have your flashlight within easy reach in the event of complete electrical failure at night.

Rule Number 3:
In addition to spare batteries, carry a spare bulb!

THE FLOW OF ELECTRICITY

Electricity flows from one side of the battery, through the bulb, then back to the other side of the battery.

Ⓐ

Electricity can't flow because of a broken wire.

Ⓑ

Fig. 6

Slashed triangles indicate that an electrical conductor, (usually the metal frame of airplane), allows electricity to flow.

Ⓒ

returning current to the alternator (or any other piece of electrical equipment that's connected to the electrical ground). It is similar to the water tray in our water analogy which allows water to return to the pump. Since the alternator is connected to this electrical ground, the circuit is completed as electric current returns to its original source—the alternator.

Load Meter

A load meter is located between the pump and the primary bus of our plumbing system (Figure 7). It shows the water load placed on the pump by the airplane's water (electrical) system. In other words, it shows how much water is demanded from the pump by the airplane's water (electrical) equipment.

If the load meter reads zero (a full left deflection), either the pump isn't providing any pressure to the primary bus or the electrical (water) equipment simply isn't demanding any water. Load meter readings above zero represent the pump's water output. This output should equal the total water draw by equipment connected to both buses. An actual load meter is shown in Figure 8.

The load meter provides similar information about alternator output in an electrical system. A zero reading means the alternator isn't providing electricity to the primary bus or there is no electrical current drawn

WATER ANALOGY OF ELECTRICITY

by the airplane's electrical equipment. This can happen because the alternator is disconnected from the bus, the alternator has failed, or all the airplane's electrical equipment is turned off.

Load meters are also known as *ammeters,* and their readings are calibrated in *amperes* (abbreviated as *amps*). Amps are a measure of current flow, equivalent to gallons per hour of water. If the airplane's electrical equipment demands 30 amps of current from the alternator, the load meter should indicate a 30 amp needle deflection.

The alternator circuit breaker (CB) is also located between the alternator and the primary bus, as shown in Figure 7. Circuit breakers protect electrical equipment (and wires) from receiving more current than they can safely handle. Figure 9 shows the airplane's alternator circuit breaker.

By now you should have a fair understanding of how the electrical system works when the alternator is turning. But since the alternator is driven by the engine, what source provides current for the airplane's equipment when the engine isn't running? The answer is simple. It's the thing missing from most children's Christmas presents—a battery. Figure 10A shows how the battery connects to the primary bus.

THE LOAD METER

Fig. 8

THE ALTERNATOR CIRCUIT BREAKER

Fig. 9

WATER PUMP (ALTERNATOR) & BATTERY PRESSURIZING THE PRIMARY BUS

Fig. 10

The Battery

Using the water analogy, the battery can be thought of as a box containing a thin, square piston with a powerful spring on one side. The battery's square piston is capable of sliding toward or away from the spring depending on whether water flows into or out of the battery. Water flowing into the battery is said to *charge* it; water flowing out of the battery, *drains* or *discharges* it.

Since the primary bus is already pressurized by the spinning pump, water should easily flow into the battery. As it does, it pushes the sliding square piston to the left against the spring (Figure 10A). The battery has now stored water pressure and can be thought of as being fully charged. In the event the water pump stops working, the battery provides water under pressure (electrical current) to the primary bus (Figure 10B).

Have you ever used a pressure-type thermos to store your coffee? It's the kind where you put in the coffee, pump the handle on top, open a spigot, and out squirts coffee. The thermos stores coffee under pressure, so that caffeine-hungry pilots can quickly slake their thirst (on late night flights, pilots often lock their lips onto the spigot, push the handle and absorb just enough caffeine to vibrate through solid matter).

In an electrical system, the battery chemically stores the electrical charge provided by the alternator. The process is different, but the principle is the same as that of the coffee thermos. Most airplanes have either a 12 or 24 volt battery (think of a larger battery as one with a bigger spring that puts water under greater pressure). It's the battery that allows you to operate the airplane's

electrical equipment when the engine isn't running or when the alternator fails in flight. Figure 11 shows an airplane battery.

Battery Potential

You should know how much electricity your battery stores for one good reason: in-flight alternator failure. How much power the battery stores is indicated by its *amp-hour rating*. A 35 amp-hour battery should (in theory) provide 35 amps of continuous current to the electrical system for one hour. In other words, if the electrical equipment draws a total of 35 amps, the battery should run that equipment for one hour before it's depleted.

I say *theoretically* because this rating assumes many things: a new battery, a new electrical system, ideal conditions and perfect harmony with the universe. In reality, many battery engineers (people with two terminals protruding from their necks) say that you should only count on half of that rating. In other words, 35 amps for 30 minutes or 17.5 amps for one hour. You know those federal ratings of how many miles per gallon some shiny new car will give you? Keep in mind that there's always that little disclaimer, the one that says "Your mileage may vary." Very right, and it's not likely to vary on the high side.

While airplane batteries are rated at 12 or 24 volts, airplane electrical systems (their alternators) are rated for 14 or 28 volts. Why does the alternator have a higher voltage rating than the battery it charges? It's a lot easier and quicker to charge a battery to its full potential when the alternator pressure is stronger than the battery pressure. If we want the pump in our water system to store water in the battery, the pump must provide a little more pressure than the spring to push the piston back. The alternator's extra 2 or 4 volts is all it takes to keep the battery charged (to push against its chemical potential).

THE AIRPLANE'S BATTERY

Fig. 11

The Charge-Discharge Ammeter

Between the positive terminal of the battery and the primary bus is another version of an ammeter found on some airplanes (Figure 12). Ammeters of this variety are often called *charge-discharge* ammeters. Figure 13 shows a charge-discharge ammeter. As the name implies, the charge-discharge ammeter tells you if electrical current is flowing into or out of the battery. This directly informs you about your electrical system's state of health. Whether you have a load meter or a charge-discharge ammeter depends on the specific make and model of your airplane. Most airplanes have one or the other but seldom both.

Current flow from the primary bus into the battery is indicated by a positive needle deflection (Figure 14). Think of water (electrical current) pushing the needle toward the (+) or (–) side of the ammeter as it enters or leaves the battery. A positive deflection usually implies that the battery is being charged (water is moving into the battery). A negative needle deflection indicates that the battery is supplying the primary bus with electrical current (water is moving out of the battery).

Normally, the needle should be resting near the zero or center mark. This implies that the battery is neither being charged nor discharged (a good sign). Continuous needle deflections too far from cen-

WATER ANALOGY OF ELECTRICITY

Water pump (alternator)

Load meter

ALT CB

ALT AMPERES 0 60

Charge/ discharge ammeter

60 – 0 AMPERES 60 +

Fig. 12

Electrical ground

Electrical ground

Battery

CB GYRO
CB GYRO
CB PANEL LIGHTS
CB RADIO LIGHTS
CB CIG
CB LAND LIGHT
CB NAV LIGHT

Primary bus

Avionics master switch

CB RADIO
CB NAV
CB RADIO
CB NAV

Avionics bus

ter, however, are cause for concern. There are circumstances where the needle will indicate a large deflection from the center position for short periods.

Starter motors demand large amounts of electrical current for their operation. After startup, the battery is sure to be slightly drained. Expect to see a positive (+) needle deflection of five, maybe six or seven needle widths on the ammeter right after engine start. This means that

the alternator is replenishing battery energy consumed by the current-hungry starter. Expect a similar ammeter indication if the radios were

THE CHARGE/DISCHARGE AMMETER

60 – 0 AMPERES 60 +

Fig. 13

A wise man says, "Man who use tongue to test airplane battery find experience re-volting."

POSITIVE (+) AMMETER INDICATION

Water (current) flow

Charge/ discharge ammeter

60 – 0 AMPERES 60 +

Fig. 14

Battery

Battery being charged

used extensively prior to engine start. But beware! Too much charge is not a good thing—for batteries or credit cards!

Most airplane operation manuals suggest that after approximately 30 minutes of cruising flight, the ammeter needle should return to within a two-needle-width deflection from center on the positive (+) or charging side. A larger (positive) needle deflection suggests problems with the battery or the alternator. A runaway (unregulated) alternator can provide too much current and overcharge the battery. This is usually indicated by a large positive needle deflection (more than one or two needle widths).The excess voltage can boil off battery fluid (electrolyte), damaging the battery and possibly causing a battery fire.

A needle deflection on the negative (–) side means current is flowing out of the battery onto the primary bus (Figure 15). It also means the alternator isn't providing the necessary voltage to keep the battery charged. This situation is similar to a flight instructor's bank account, where more is going out than is coming in. Chances are the alternator has failed, has been auto-

Airplanes With Volt and Ammeters

The voltmeter gives you more direct information about the alternator's output or, if the alternator isn't on line, about the energy available in the battery. Unlike the ammeter, the voltmeter can tell you the condition of your battery before the engine is started.

An excessive system-voltage reading probably indicates voltage regulator trouble that can lead to battery overcharge and electrical equipment damage. Insufficient voltage indicates that the battery isn't being charged properly. Remember, system voltage must be higher than battery voltage for the battery to charge.

matically disconnected from the system, or is being improperly regulated. Any way you look at it, you have a problem. The battery will eventually lose its charge.

This situation is best handled by conserving battery energy (turning off everything you don't need) and, if necessary, landing at the nearest airport. Remember, you may need battery power to lower landing gear or flaps, or power the landing lights if flying at night. This is why good pilots carry flashlights (and bad pilots use flashlights to carry their dead batteries). A nearly centered charge-discharge ammeter needle usually means an electrical system that knows what's watt and is taking care of business.

In the early 1980's I had the pleasure of checking out an airline captain in a small two-seat airplane. We had a wonderful time learning the systems and flying the aircraft. He did quite well except for one thing. On every final approach he would call the tower and say, "Ahhh, John Wayne Tower, this is United heavy, we're on a long final approach for 1-9-Left." The controller thought this was really funny. The pilots of the little planes on short final for runway 19 Left didn't. The thought of an enormous metallic Pac Man gaining on them was downright scary! Attempting to understand the electrical system is somewhat like being the guy on short final for 19L. It's scary at first, but when you get a good, clear look at the threat, it's not so bad after all. Hopefully, you haven't been scared by the electrical system so far. Let's return to our discussion on

load meters and discuss them in relation to the airplane's battery.

Load Meters

There are benefits and disadvantages to almost everything you do. For instance, whenever I travel to a location for a speech, I always get the most economical airfare for the client. However, economy is not without its disadvantages. On my last flight to Nome, Alaska I had four plane changes. Unfortunately, two were in flight. Load meters in lieu of charge-discharge ammeters have their benefits and disadvantages. Essentially, both kinds of meters provide pilots with the same type of information, but in a slightly different format.

Load meters provide important indications about the health of the airplane's electrical system. Unlike charge-discharge ammeters, they are calibrated to reflect the actual ampere load placed on the alternator. Both varieties of ammeter are shown in Figure 16. Remember, most airplanes will have either one variety of ammeter or the other.

NEGATIVE (-) AMMETER INDICATION

Water (current) flow

Charge/ discharge ammeter

Fig. 15

Battery

Water (current) flow

Battery being drained

TWO VARIETIES OF AMMETERS

Charge/discharge ammeter

Load meter type ammeter

Fig. 16

Load meters with a zero or full-left deflection indicate the alternator isn't providing current to the primary bus. Any electrical equipment that's in use must be receiving its electrical energy from the battery. A full left deflection of a load meter needle is similar to a charge-discharge ammeter reading pointing to the negative (–) side of its scale.

Load meter needle deflections to the right of the zero index represent the electrical current drain on the alternator. Another way of saying this is that a right needle deflection represents the alternator's output. If you add all the electrical current used by the active electrical equipment, this sum should be equal to the amount the needle's deflected. After all, the alternator should be producing what the system demands, otherwise battery energy is being drained.

A wise man says, "Pilot who thinks that 'primary bus' means good transportation, not travel far in world of aviation."

Electrical Drain

If you're piloting an airplane equipped with a load meter, you need to know how much electrical current each piece of electrical equipment consumes. Think of each piece of electrical equipment as having a minimum thirst level. Some equipment needs more water (current) to operate than others. *Amperes* are a measure of the amount of electrical current (gallons of water per hour) consumed by each of the airplane's electrical items. Understanding how thirsty each electrical item is, is the key to understanding if your alternator is working properly.

Radios typically consume one-half amp of current while receiving and about 5 amps while transmitting.

LOAD METER INDICATION & CURRENT FLOW

Water pump (alternator)

Load meter showing **16** amp deflection

The load meter needle shows the approximate amount of current output by the alternator.

Fig. 17

Electrical equipment on this bus uses a total of **16** amps

Nav radios and gyros require about 1 amp, transponders about 2 amps and autopilots about 10 amps.

With two receiving radios, two nav radios, one electric gyro, a transponder and an autopilot in use, a 16 amp deflection should be shown on the load meter (Figure 17). A needle deflection less than 16 amps implies that the alternator isn't providing enough current to run the equipment. Where is the extra electrical energy coming from? Need a hint? There's only one place: the battery. Needle deflections less than the summed amperage of active and properly working electrical equipment imply that the bat-

tery will eventually be drained. That's why it's absolutely necessary that you know how much current each piece of electrical equipment draws.

Suppose the load meter's needle deflection is greater than the needs of the electrical equipment, as shown in Figure 18. This is similar to a charge-discharge ammeter indicating a large, positive (+) needle deflection. In either case, such indications suggest that the alternator isn't working properly or that there is a leak in the electrical plumbing (otherwise known as a short). Soon, we'll discuss how the alternator is regulated and why it may develop problems.

ALTERNATOR REGULATION PROBLEM

Water pump (alternator)

Load meter showing **50** amp deflection

The load meter needle shows alternator output in excess of that used by electrical equipment.

Fig. 18

Electrical equipment on this bus uses a total of **16** amps

What is Electricity?

Skip Forster

Electricity is a form of energy that arises when electrons and positive ions become separated from each other. The atoms in the matter around us are made of a positively charged nucleus surrounded by negatively charged electrons. Sometimes an electron becomes separated from its atom. The part left behind (called a positive ion) has an electric charge equal to that of the electron but opposite in polarity.

How do electrons and ions become separated? One way is by a chemical reaction. In a battery, for example, a chemical reaction causes positive ions to collect at the positive terminal while electrons gather at the negative terminal. If a conductor is placed between the terminals, electrons will flow from the negative terminal to combine with the ions at the positive terminal. This flow of electrons is called electric current.

Another way to separate electrons and ions is by friction. In a thunderstorm, friction from turbulent air causes electrons and ions to separate, creating static electricity. Eventually, the electrons and ions dramatically recombine as lightning.

Electricity and magnetism are related. Movement of a conductor through a magnetic field will cause current to flow in the conductor. This principle is used in the magneto. Likewise, wherever current flows, a magnetic field is created. This is what makes the starter motor spin.

Skip Forster is president of Results Pilot Training, Inc. in San Jose, California and is a recovering electrical engineer.

Load meter indications in excess of the system's electrical demands are the system's cry for help. Ignored, this cry can lead to unhappy results such as evaporating battery fluid or battery and electrical fires. This is referred to as a battery losing its cool. You, in turn, will lose your juice. Remember, the alternator needs to replenish the battery energy drained by extended use of the starter or radio, so expect to see a slightly higher load meter reading immediately after engine start

I always make it a point to look at the ammeter right after engine start for two reasons. First, I get a sense of battery health by observing how fast the ammeter needle returns to its normal position after starter use. A failing battery will show up as an ammeter needle taking progressively longer to return to a normal position. Establishing a trend of needle response over a long period of time makes needle movement even more meaningful.

Second, starter motors have been known to stick and not disengage (actually it's the starter contactor that sticks but the results are the same). If this happens, the starter remains engaged, guzzling enormous amounts of battery current. You

might not be able to hear the engaged starter once the engine is running, but you will see a very, very large negative (−) needle deflection on the charge-discharge ammeter right after start. On airplanes with load meters, a stuck starter contactor might be identified by an abnormally large reading, indicating an enormous drain on the alternator. Shut the engine down immediately if you see this type of unusual needle deflection right after starting the engine.

Don't be too concerned with ammeter needles that wiggle slightly. Ammeters have needle dampening mechanisms in them to steady wiggling needles. Sometimes these mechanisms just wear out. As a student, I thought it was my careless application of rudder that caused needle wiggling. I mentioned this to my instructor. He said that this wasn't possible since I never seemed to use the rudder.

Does an unusual ammeter or load meter indication in the air mean an immediate need to land? It depends. There are several things we can do about airborne electrical problems, but solving system requires an understanding of how alternator voltage is regulated.

The Voltage Regulator

Airplanes with complete electrical systems have voltage regulators or alternator control units (they're essentially the same thing). As the name implies, these devices regulate the alternator's output. If the engine is turning the water pump (alternator), it's logical to assume that higher RPMs produce greater water pressure. In an electrical system this results in alternators producing variable voltage. This would wreak havoc with electrical components that demand consistent voltage for accurate operation. Fortunately, voltage regulators—the brains of the electrical system—help alternators maintain a constant voltage output under variable RPM conditions.

Voltage regulators consist of transistors, diodes, capacitors and possibly relays and contact points. Describing the workings of these intricate components by use of the water analogy would get us into deep water, where we don't want to go. Therefore, let's use a human brain with a big hand connected to its cortex to represent these detailed electrical components (artist's license is such a wonderful thing)!

Figure 19 represents a water model of how a voltage regulator might work. Most turbine pumps (similar to that used as the model for our alternator) need to be primed before they will start pumping water. In other words, they need to have a little water running through them before they can create enough suction to pump more water. Alternators operate in a similar manner. They need a little bit of electricity running through them before they'll start producing more electricity. This small amount of electrical prime is called the *alternator field current*. Take away this alternator field current (prime) at any time, and the alternator stops producing electricity.

Water prime flows directly into the pump through tube F. Like alternators, our water pump needs to be continuously primed if it is to keep on pumping. The greater the prime flowing through tube F, the greater the output of the pump. Alternator's operate similarly; varying the alternator field current varies the alternator's voltage output.

When the engine is not running, prime for the pump comes from the battery. In Figure 19, water flows from the battery to the primary bus. It then goes through line S and the alternator field circuit breaker T to the left hand side of a split-rocker master switch A. By turning on (pushing) the alternator side of the master switch (the left side), water flows into the voltage regulator V and through valve W which is inside the voltage regulator. Prime (alternator field current) must pass through valve W and through tube F, to get to the pump for priming.

Valve W is controlled by the hand attached to the voltage regulator's brain (those electronic components mentioned earlier). The brain tells the hand to open or close Valve W. This controls the amount of prime (alternator field current) reaching the pump.

WATER ANALOGY AND THE VOLTAGE REGULATOR

Fig. 19

How does the brain know whether to open or close the valve? It senses the pump's output water pressure, or in an alternator, its voltage. By comparing the pump's intake pressure at point G, with its output pressure at point B, the regulator's brain can compute the precise amount of prime needed to produce the required water pressure. In electrical terms, these sense lines allow the voltage regulator to restrict an alternator's output to 14 or 28 volts of electrical pressure.

When switch A is turned on during engine start, valve W starts in the full-open position, thus providing the initial prime. After engine start, the pump commences to produce water pressure (voltage) and brain V decides how much to close valve W to bring this output into regulation. It is in this initial startup period that the pump's output is momentarily unregulated and you DO NOT want your electrical equipment turned on. A sudden surge of pressure could damage this equipment—*despite* each piece of equipment having protective circuit breakers.

Sometimes brains in a voltage regulator, just like in humans, behave errantly. I recall a student pilot who was flying solo near the Southern California coast when he looked down and saw an aircraft carrier. A little devil on his left shoulder said, "Do it! Do it!!" A little angel on his right shoulder said, "Yeah, do it!" He did it—a carrier landing (actually, more like a touch-and-go). The captain of the ship was not amused. Neither was the FAA. It was a clearcut case of a brain gone astray, and it occasionally happens to voltage regulators as well. When the brain in a voltage regulator goes south, it usually presents definite symptoms. You can expect either an over or underproduction of voltage by the alternator.

Machado's Believe It or Not #1

Oh boy, I must have flown into an electrical storm.

Problems With Brains

Most airplanes have a warning light to alert pilots about electrical problems. This light is commonly known as either a high- or low-voltage warning light (Figure 20). When illuminated, it informs you that the alternator isn't supplying appropriate voltage to meet the system's electrical needs.

If your airplane has a low-voltage light, it can illuminate during low engine idle when there isn't enough RPM to develop even minimal voltage (pressure). Increasing the RPM raises the water pressure (voltage) and usually shuts off the light.

A low-voltage light can also illuminate if the alternator has been taken off line because of excessive voltage production. This usually follows a popped alternator *circuit breaker* or alternator field circuit breaker. As far as the electrical system is concerned, *no voltage* is interpreted as *low voltage*.

If your airplane has a high-voltage warning light, it can activate when an overvoltage condition occurs. The alternator field current (the prime) is automatically removed, which takes the alternator off line. This keeps the circuits from being damaged by excessive system voltage (pressure).

In either case, the activation of a high- or low-voltage warning light may follow a popped alternator or alternator field circuit breaker. When any circuit breaker pops, it is always worth paying attention. Personally, if I'm airborne and a circuit breaker pops, I don't reset it if the equipment it's protecting isn't essential. Resetting a circuit breaker is playing with fire—literally, and an in-flight fire is considerably less comforting than a campfire. If I need to use the equipment, I reset the circuit breaker once and only once, but only after letting it cool for several minutes. If it pops again, I leave it alone. In other words, it's not a good idea to reset a circuit breaker a second time.

If a popped circuit breaker (alternator CB or alternator field CB) takes the alternator off line, then if you manually pop either of these, it

THE LOW- OR HIGH-VOLTAGE WARNING LIGHT

Illumination of the high- or low-voltage warning light indicates the alternator isn't supplying adequate system voltage. Most airplane electrical systems have self-protection circuitry that takes the alternator off line in the event it produces excessive voltage. This results in the illumination of the high- or low-voltage warning light. Follow your POH's recommended procedure for bringing the alternator back on line.

THE VOLTAGE WARNING LIGHT

Fig. 20

produces the same result. Manually taking the alternator off line becomes an important consideration if an overvoltage condition occurs and the circuitry doesn't *automatically* isolate the alternator. Figure 21 shows three ways of *manually* taking the alternator off line.

Occasionally, a benign overvoltage condition exists and the voltage regulator's brain automatically takes the alternator off line. This is sometimes called a nuisance tripout. Even human brains experience nuisance tripouts. It happened to a student pilot in a small airplane. This fellow

taxied out to the runway and forgot his tail number (which is usually posted inside the airplane). Hoping to catch a glimpse of the number, he leaned out and slipped off his seat. He was hanging inverted, half outside, half inside the airplane, suspended by a loose shoulder harness. The funniest part was that he held onto the microphone and continued talking to the tower. I couldn't quite hear what he said, but I think it was, "Ahhh, tower... aghhh... I've fallen out and I can't get back in!" I ran over and helped this guy back into his airplane. I'm just glad he didn't forget

STOPPING A RUNAWAY ALTERNATOR (WATER PUMP)

Fig. 21

Turning the left side of the master "OFF," or pulling the alternator or alternator field circuit breaker will take an alternator off line.

his number while airborne! Mental nuisance tripouts are often amusing; in airplanes, they're simply annoying.

The brain in the airplane's voltage regulator is subject to similar perturbations. A nuisance tripout may be indicated by a low-voltage light or an overvoltage warning light, depending on how the airplane's electrical system is wired. We can attempt to reactivate the voltage regulator by turning the avionics master switch to the *off* position (to protect the avionics from a power surge), resetting the alternator or alternator-field circuit breaker (if popped), then turning both sides of the master switch *off* then *on* again (Figure 22). This signals the voltage regulator's brain to give the alternator another chance to produce normal voltage. Should the low-voltage or high-voltage light illuminate again, something is seriously wrong with the system. Conserve battery energy and land at the nearest airport.

Making Connections

Having gone downstream with our water analogy model this far, you now understand several important things about the limitations of alternators. First, if the battery is dead, the alternator isn't going to work. You can still start the engine by hand propping, but as explained earlier, this is a risky maneuver which is not recommended for those who enjoy being bilaterally symmetrical.

Since the magnetos are independent of the airplane's electrical system, they generate their own energy for ignition when spun. According to our water analogy, however, with a dead battery no prime is available through tube F in Figure 19 to coax the water pump into developing water pressure. The water pump will turn, but it will not pump. No priming, no pumping. It's as simple as that. In electrical terms, without enough battery energy for the alternator-field current, the alternator spins, but it doesn't produce any voltage. You will not have any electricity nor will the battery charge.

Second, if the brain in the voltage regulator goes bad and the alternator produces too much voltage, you can take the alternator off line. Pull the main alternator circuit breaker, located schematically between the alternator and the primary bus, as shown in Figure 23 (if the circuit breaker is the pullable type). Of course, this assumes that it hasn't already popped out on its own. You can turn off the alternator half of the master switch, which will shut off the alternator field current flow, thus deactivating the alternator. Pulling the alternator field cir-

cuit breaker eliminates the alternator-field current flow and shuts down the alternator.

Third, if you want to use the airplane's electrical equipment on the ground without starting the engine, you should activate only the battery half of the master switch. Leave the alternator half in the OFF position. This prevents alternator field current from flowing to the alternator, wasting precious battery power. It makes no sense to waste battery energy to prime the alternator if it won't be

HANDLING A HIGH OR LOW VOLTAGE WARNING LIGHT — Fig. 22

WARNING! Low/high voltage warning light illuminates

STEP 3
- (A) Master is "ON"
- (B) Turn both sides of master switch "OFF"
- (C) Turn both sides of master switch "ON" again

STEP 2 Reset these two circuit breakers (if popped) — ALT CB, ALT FIELD CB

STEP 1 Turn avionics master switch "OFF" — ON / OFF

WATER ANALOGY OF ELECTRICITY — Fig. 23

+ Pressure sense tube — B

Load meter — ALT CB, ALT FIELD CB

Pump priming flow (alternator field current) — W, V, F, G

Pressure sense tube

Water pressure regulator (voltage regulator) — A

Water pump (alternator)

Electrical ground

Charge/discharge ammeter

Primary bus — CB GYRO, CB GYRO, CB PANEL LIGHTS, CB RADIO LIGHTS, CB CIG, CB LAND LIGHT, CB NAV LIGHT — S, T

Avionics Master Switch

Avionics bus — CB RADIO, CB NAV, CB RADIO, CB NAV

Battery

4-12

in use. Airborne electrical emergencies caused by voltage regulator problems require conservation of battery energy. These situations should also be dealt with by turning the alternator half of the master switch to the *off* position.

If faced with an errant voltage regulator in flight, unload the system by turning off all nonessential equipment. This includes the waterbed heater and the disco strobe lights you installed in your Remos G3. See if this returns the needle to a normal deflection. If not, then deactivate the alternator by turning the alternator half of the master switch to the *off* position. Let the battery provide the energy needs temporarily. This will allow an overheated voltage regulator to cool down (assuming that's the problem). After 5 to 10 minutes, reactivate the alternator by turning the alternator half of the master switch back on. See if the voltage regulator functions normally. If not, then deactivate the alternator by turning the alternator half of the master switch off and land as soon as practical.

I've had great success using this "cooling off period" approach. Most voltage regulators have moving parts (relays and contacts) that can stick when subjected to high heat loads. Cooling lets the components contract and return to their normal position. If this doesn't work, then it's best to leave the alternator off line, conserve electricity and head towards an airport for repairs.

Drawing It All Together

Figure 24 is an electrical schematic excerpted from a general aviation airplane's owner's manual. I have taken the liberty of leaving out a few items, such as the clock, starter, battery and starter contactor, Hobbs meter, etc. Of course, we would all like to see electrical schematics without a Hobbs meter, but I did this for the sake of simplicity. This figure should look familiar to you. It's the electrical version of the water analogy drawing in Figure 23.

The first introduction to the electrical system in ground school is traumatic for most students. After the first view of a schematic, many students sit limp, eyes bugged as if they've been hit by a megawatt stun gun. I hope the water analogy makes consumption of this technical subject more palatable. Take time to compare Figures 23 and 24. I think you'll be surprised at how much less frightening electrical schematics are.

MODIFIED ELECTRICAL SCHEMATIC

Fig. 24

TAKING IT IN THE SHORTS

Battery

Think of a short as a leak in the plumbing. Water (electricity) can't get to its destination and electrical equipment won't work.

NAV

Have Rudder, Won't Travel

....This was the first flight after the annual inspection...I banked with the wind on takeoff and while moving the rudder to the right I noticed a restriction in rudder travel (I wasn't getting full rudder travel in both directions). So, I told the tower, "I have a problem...." The tower said I could have any runway.... I landed and taxied off the runway. After shutting down, I found my flashlight on the cabin floor near the rudder pedal on the passenger side. I usually keep it in the passenger seat before taxiing. It must have fallen to the floor on takeoff and gotten behind the rudder pedal....

ASRS Report

Proper stowage of cockpit equipment, including flashlights, will prevent hazardous incidents of this kind. Another preventive measure is to give special attention to the first preflight after annual inspection.

Tower, my controls stopped working at the same time my head did.

Postflight Briefing #4-1

Contact!
How the Battery Contactor Works

An aircraft battery (very much like a car's battery) stores a tremendous amount of electrical energy. Anyone who's ever banged cables together while jump starting a car has seen the sparks fly. This is raw electrical energy on tap. Controlling this amount of current from the cockpit would require a rather large, well-insulated switch. In the cockpit, however, big switches mean increased weight, cramped space and a greater chance of sparks flying during a malfunction. Airplane engineers prefer a more indirect means of battery control—the battery contactor.

The battery contactor allows a small switch (the battery half of the master switch) to control a great deal of electrical energy. It gives an itty-bitty switch, galactic-power-switching ability. Activating the battery half of the master switch closes a solenoid in the battery contactor (the big switch) allowing battery energy to flow directly onto the primary bus. Figure 25 provides a working water analogy model for the battery contactor.

Activating the battery half or the right side of master switch (A) allows water to flow from the positive terminal (C) of the battery up through line D and into the battery contactor (E). As line D enters the contactor, a smaller line (H), splits off and flows to a small turbine/pulley arrangement (J).

Water flows over the turbine (J), spinning it counterclockwise. Then it flows out and up line K toward the battery half of master switch A. From here it flows to the ground (remember, we learned to think of the electrical ground as a thin pool of water underlying our plumbing circuitry). This completes the flow of water through the master switch.

An interesting plumbing reaction occurs when turbine J spins counterclockwise. Pulley L is connected directly to turbine J and has a small rope wrapped around it that connects to the on/off lever of valve M. When pul-

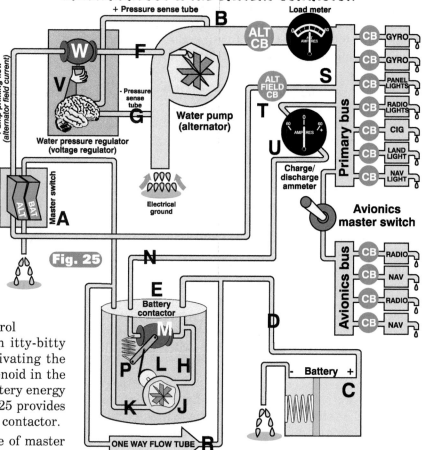

WATER ANALOGY & THE BATTERY CONTACTOR

BATTERY CONTACTOR SOLENOID & RELAY

Fig. 26

TO PRIMARY BUS

AMMETER

Z

Q

TO BATTERY HALF OF MASTER

TO (+) TERMINAL OF BATTERY

ley L spins counterclockwise, it pulls the lever down and opens valve M. This lets water from the battery flow through valve M and line N, pressurizing the primary bus.

In reality, a solenoid relay device in the battery contactor takes the place of turbine J, and valve M. Perhaps the most important item to be understood from this battery contactor model is that a small flow of water through line H and K allows a larger flow of water through line D and N. A small flow of electrical current, controlled from the cockpit via the master switch, allows the safe management of large amounts of battery energy.

Remember, the water model is for electrical cause and effect understanding only; don't take it literally. But do take the electrical results of our model's operation as fact. For instance, as water flows over turbine J it pulls the lever on valve M down opening the valve. For valve M's lever to remain open, water must continue to flow over turbine J. Turbine J will stop spinning once the pulley and rope have pulled the lever on valve M downward, into the on position. But a continuous flow of water over the turbine maintains the pressure needed to keep pulley L from unwinding. This keeps valve M open.

In the actual battery contactor, a solenoid opens valve M. Figure 26 shows this simplified schematic. Activating the battery half of the master switch sends a small amount

MODIFIED ELECTRICAL SCHEMATIC

Fig. 27

Having taken a reasonable amount of artist's license with this model, let's look at what it helps us understand. Unless a slight amount of battery energy exists, the battery contactor isn't going to work. Remember, it takes a slight amount of water pressure from the battery to pull valve M's lever open. Only the battery can provide the initial energy to activate the battery contactor. If the battery contactor doesn't work, water will not flow from the primary bus through line S to prime the water pump. In electrical terms, if the alternator field current isn't available, the alternator won't work. Inability to activate the battery contactor is another reason why an airplane with a dead or very low battery can't have its battery recharged by running the engine.

After engine start, assuming enough battery energy, the water pump will immediately provide water pressure to the primary bus. From the primary bus, water flows through the charge-discharge ammeter (U) (if your airplane has this type of ammeter) and down line N, through open valve M and into the battery. It does so until the battery is charged. Remember, the battery may have lost a little of its charge by operating a current-hungry starter or by operating the radios prior to engine start.

Because the pump is charging the battery, the ammeter has a deflection to the positive side. If your airplane has a load meter, it would indicate the water pump's output. If the battery's charge is low, expect an ammeter needle deflection to the positive side (+) until the battery regains its 12 or 24 volt charge. Similarly, expect the load meter needle to indicate an alternator output slightly greater than required by all the electrical equipment in use while the battery is being charged.

When the battery is charged, water no longer flows from the primary bus to the battery through line D. However, a slight amount of water continues to flow through valve M and down line H, over the turbine, thus keeping valve M open. This explains why the charge-discharge ammeter needle remains nearly centered in a healthy electrical system with a fully charged battery. Once the battery is charged, a load meter should show the approximate energy drain by the electrical equipment in operation. Readings higher than this should arouse a pilot's suspicion about the health of the electrical system.

Figure 27 shows a more complete electrical schematic with the battery contactor included.

of current flowing through coil Q. This creates a magnetic field that pulls a heavy duty relay (Z) down onto two circuit points. Electricity now flows from the battery to the primary bus between these contact points.

Turning the battery half of the master switch off prevents water from flowing over turbine J in Figure 25. This allows spring P to pull valve M's lever upward into the *off* position which shuts off battery power to the primary bus. In a similar manner, placing the battery half of the master switch in the *off* position releases the pull on the solenoid in Figure 26. Relay Z pops up preventing electricity from flowing to the primary bus.

Notice there is a one-way flow valve R connecting line K with line D in Figure 25. This is known as a *clipping diode* in electrical parlance. It's designed to avoid voltage spikes across the coil relay, caused by a collapsing magnetic field, when turning off the master switch.

What was that??? A clipping what??? Here's another way of looking at what a clipping diode does. Turning off the battery half of the master switch causes turbine J to momentarily spin in a clockwise direction. This occurs because spring P pulls valve M's lever shut and unwinds the pulley. This might create a spike or surge of water flow into line K (or any other delicate elements of the circuitry). To prevent damage to line K the one-way valve (diode) allows the pressure in line K and D to equalize.

Chapter Five
Flight Instruments: Clocks, Tops & Toys

Not everyone remembers their first date, but just about every pilot remembers his or her first look inside the trainer plane. Eyes riveted on the instrument panel, prospective pilots tend to respond with one- or two-word expletives, followed by a swelling tide of self doubt.

That was my experience. Opening the door of an early model two place airplane, I peeked inside the cozy, two-place trainer. I uttered the two-word initial response. My instructor, standing patiently nearby, was eager to offer encouragement on this demo flight. He said, "Well, what do you think?"

"Man, you sure can tell what time it is with all these clocks in here!," I said. "Clocks? Those aren't clocks, those are flight instruments," he barked, while rapidly recalculating the wisdom of trying to teach me to fly. "In a very short time, they'll become your best friend."

Uh huh. Those instruments and the IRS.

Well, it turned out to be true (about the instruments). If there is such a thing as pilot–instrument bonding, I experienced it. I learned to appreciate, respect and enjoy all those dials on the panel, except for one—the *Hobbs meter* (the meter that keeps track of how long the engine is running, and from which the flight school calculates how much you owe). Flight instruments provide you with valuable, essential information. Extracting and interpreting that information through our five sensory organs (OK, six, if you're into that theory) is the challenge we're about to address.

Figure 1 shows the basic instruments found on many traditional airplane panels. From the top left hand corner clockwise these instruments are: *airspeed indicator, attitude indicator, altimeter, vertical speed indicator, heading indicator* and *turn coordinator* Above the panel, near the top of the windscreen, you'll also find the *magnetic compass* (although not always part of the six basic instrument group, it's still as important as any other instrument). Figure 2 shows the basic fight instruments as they appear on a *primary flight display* (PFD). A PFD contains the same basic flight instruments but presents them using "glass panel" technology. You can learn more about PFDs in Postflight Briefing #5-2.

SIX FLIGHT INSTRUMENTS

Airspeed indicator
Attitude indicator
Magnetic compass
Altimeter
Vertical speed indicator
Turn coordinator
Heading Indicator

Murray, you can do it. There are four pedals, two wheels & you've got six legs! Do I have to do the math for you?

Fig. 1

ADVANCED GLASS COCKPIT INSTRUMENTATION

Turn rate indicator
Heading indicator
Altimeter
Airspeed indicator
Slip-Skid indicator
Attitude indicator
Vertical speed indicator

Fig. 2

INSIDE THE AIRSPEED INDICATOR

Metallic bellows

THE AIRSPEED INDICATOR

Static air line

Fig. 3

Pitot tube

Mechanical movement of expanding bellows converted into airspeed reading.

Expandable metallic capsule

Pitot tube measures ram air pressure.

You're probably thinking, "Do you need all these instruments to pilot a plane safely?" It's certainly possible for a more experienced pilot to fly visually and by feel while looking out the window. This, of course, is done in *visual meteorological conditions* (VMC), when weather permits visibility above certain minimums specified in the rules. These instruments, however, make it much easier for you to maneuver the airplane precisely.

Where the flight instruments really earn their keep, though, is in *instrument meteorological conditions* (IMC), otherwise known as clouds. While you shouldn't be in the clouds without a private pilot license and an instrument rating (an advanced license), these six instruments can help save your bacon should you accidentally fly into a cloud (many student pilots learn how to extricate themselves from this situation during their sport pilot flight training).

All six flight instruments, each in its own way, provides you with information on three things: airspeed, height and attitude.

Airspeed is a measurement of the airplane's velocity through the air. The altimeter and vertical speed indicator provide information about your height above sea level as well as how fast your height is changing. The heading indicator, turn coordinator and attitude indicator provide information on the airplane's attitude (i.e., the degree of nose-up or down pitch, as well as the amount the airplane is banked).

Flight instruments will talk to you, if you let them. They speak a distinctive language, and the ability to hear and interpret it quickly and correctly is an important pilot skill. To fly without understanding your flight instruments is very uncomfortable, and potentially dangerous. It's like the proverb that says, "One day the lion and the lamb shall lie down together." Maybe, but you can be sure the lamb won't get much sleep.

It's time to learn to speak the language of the panel. Let's start our examination with the non-gyroscopic instruments.

Non-Gyro Instruments

Airspeed Indicator

The airspeed indicator is a wind indicator. It tells you the amount of wind blowing over the wings of your airplane as a result of the airplane's movement. Such information is useful for several reasons. First, with sufficient airspeed, the airplane will fly. The airspeed indicator, then, lets you know when it's safe to point the nose upward during the takeoff. Second, the airspeed indicator lets you know when you're above or below any of the airplane's critical speeds (i.e., the stall speed, maximum flap speed, maximum gear speed, never exceed speed, etc.).

Airspeed indicators work by sensing the impact pressure of air. Part of the airspeed indicator shown in Figure 3 is connected to the pitot tube, which I pointed out as we circled the airplane in Chapter 1. High velocity air rushes into the pitot tube and applies pressure within the

---

Hey? What Did You Do That For?

I require all my students to be able to land an airplane without looking at the airspeed indicator. While downwind, I'll usually distract the student by saying something like, "Oh look, it's Elvis in a UFO," or something like that. While the student is looking outside I stick a circular rubber soap-dish holder (the one with 50 little suction cups on each side) over the airspeed indicator. After an unsuccessful search, the student returns to the panel, sees the instrument covered and says, "Hey, what did you do?" I reply, "I simulated airspeed indicator failure, so fly the airplane using your sense of feel." Most students handle this experience quite well.

I did this to a smart young lady student of mine. When she returned to the panel she said, "Hey, what's going on here?" I replied, "I simulated airspeed instrument failure, Ha!" As I turned away I heard the sound of 50 little suction cups releasing their grip as the holder was pulled off the glass over the airspeed indicator. I looked at my student who was holding the soap dish holder in her hands and asked, "Hey what did you do that for?" She replied, "I simulated fixing it, ha!"   **The Author**

ATMOSPHERIC PRESSURE CHANGES WITH HEIGHT

Ⓐ

The higher you go in the pile or in the atmosphere, the less pressure you experience.

Pressure is greater when there's more weight above you.

Ⓑ

Vertical Column of Air

Pressure at 18,000' MSL is approximately 15" Hg

Sea level pressure: 30" Hg

Fig. 4

metallic bellows located inside the body of the airspeed indicator. Expansion of the bellows is mechanically converted into movement of the airspeed needle via a gearing system (Figure 3 has been simplified slightly for ease of understanding and migraine prevention).

Notice that the container surrounding the bellows is connected to a static line which connects to a *static pressure* source. A static source allows non-moving (static) air to enter the airspeed container. This is simply the natural weight of the atmosphere, otherwise known as atmospheric pressure. A reading on

the airspeed indicator is nothing more than the difference between impact air pressure entering through the pitot tube and static air pressure surrounding the metallic bellows. Let's take a closer look at air pressure and how it's measured.

Static Pressure

Imagine you are sandwiched between a bunch of leotard-covered professional wrestlers as in Figure 4A. You are halfway from the top. Your friend, Bob, is on the bottom. Who feels the greater weight or pressure? Why of course, it's Bob. He has more people above him than you do.

Therefore, he experiences greater pressure. Atmospheric pressure behaves similarly.

Figure 4B shows a vertical slice of the atmosphere. Imagine air molecules piled on top of one another like professional wrestlers. At sea level, there is a great deal of static air pressure or weight because there are more air molecules at the top of the pile. As you ascend, there are fewer air molecules above you. *Atmospheric pressure or weight decreases with a gain in altitude.*

Since static pressure is the weight of non-moving air, how does an airplane measure something non-moving while it's in flight? The static port, shown in Figure 5, is the perfect device for such a task. Being flush against the side of the fuselage (out of the way of air striking it), the static port lets the natural weight of the air (atmospheric pressure) enter through its opening. Figure 6 shows an airplane's static port located on the side of the fuselage. Two additional instruments also require static air pressure to function: the vertical speed indicator and the altimeter. These instruments are also connected to the static port, as shown in Figure 5. We'll discuss these instruments later.

THE PITOT TUBE AND STATIC PORT

A static line connects to the altimeter, vertical speed indicator and airspeed indicator.

The static port is sometimes found flush against the side of the fuselage.

ASI   ALT   VSI

L   R

The airspeed indicator has a line connecting it to the pitot tube. This allows measurement of impact air pressure.

The pitot tube is normally found underneath the left wing.

Fig. 5

Fig. 6

CTsw

THE AIRPLANE'S STATIC PORT

Pitot Tubes

Pitot tubes and *static ports* were discussed earlier. They can be found located in a variety of places on an aircraft. A common location for the static port is on the front left side of the fuselage. Pitot tubes are most often found under the left wing. Figures 7A and B shows two common pitot tube and static port arrangements. Figure 7A shows the pitot tube typically found on small airplanes. Figure 7B shows another version of the pitot tube common to light sport airplanes. In Figure 7B, impact pressure is sensed through the pitot opening, while static pressure is sensed through the static tube located directly below the pitot tube. These two openings allow a balanced measure of static pressure.

Insects are a different matter. They don't drain as readily. On several occasions while giving flight instruction, I've had a small insect dive right into the pitot opening. Once, while approaching to land, a small bumblebee bumbled into the pitot tube opening. If the pitot opening is occluded by *anything*—animal, vegetable, or mineral—there is no impact air reading. This results, unfortunately, in an airspeed reading of zero. The student who was with me looked at the airspeed indicator and did what anyone

A. One version of a pitot tube.

B. Pitot and static port tubes.
Pitot tube
Static port

Fig. 7

would do to solve a similar problem—he hit it. In fact he was reaching for his airspeed indicator repair kit—his shoe—when I calmly reminded him that he should be able to land the airplane without having to look at the airspeed indicator. He did a fine job.

The Airspeed Indicator's Face

Modern airspeed indicators are color coded. This is not for your convenience in picking one that matches your airplane's carpet or curtains. Each of the colors is there to give you a piece of vital information about airspeed limitations (Figure 8). Four colors are used on single-engine airplanes: white, green, yellow and red.

The white arc of the airspeed indicator, as we learned earlier, repre-

sents the airplane's flap operating range. The beginning or low-speed end of the white arc is the power-off stall speed in the landing configuration (i.e., with flaps fully extended and gear down). This is called V_{so}. An easy way to remember this is to think of the velocity (V) of stall (s) with everything out (o) or V_{so}. Of course, by *out* I mean flaps fully extended and gear fully extended (assuming, of course, it's a retractable gear airplane).

Our figure says that at V_{so}, the airplane needs a minimum of 40 knots of wind flowing over the wings to become (or remain) airborne. The assumption here is that the airplane is always at its maximum allowable landing weight, since the airplane is configured for landing (i.e., flaps are

AIRSPEED INDICATOR MARKINGS

Primary Flight Display Markings

Traditional Analog Display Markings

The red line is the never to be exceeded speed—also known as Vne.

Stall region below Vso shown in solid red.

Beginning of the white arc is the power off stalling speed with gear and full flaps extended—also known as Vso.

Beginning of the green arc is the power off stalling speed with the gear and flaps retracted—also known as Vs1.

The high speed end of the white arc is the maximum flap operating speed—also known as Vfe.

The green arc is the normal operating range

The yellow arc is the caution range.

The high speed end of the green arc is the maximum structural cruising speed—also known as Vno.

Fig. 8

123 mph / 107 kts
Maximum airspeed in
high turbulence.

Maneuvering speed as a placard.

Oil Temp. Control
Pull = decrease
Push = increase

160 20

140 AIRSPEED

Fig. 9

dynamic divergence, or *aileron reversal.* Take my word for it, these are bad things. On the other side of the red line lies territory no pilot should ever deliberately explore without packing a parachute. Consider this your Surgeon General's warning to avoid flying above the airspeed indicator's redline.

V_{ne} is 90% of the speed at which flutter occurs. Yes, there is a slight, built-in safety factor. But don't ever count on built-in safety factors. Besides, you aren't being paid as a test pilot. If you want thrills, go bungee jumping or bullfighting or bungee-bull fighting (that's where they dangle the bull from a crane—which suggests an entirely new line of velvet matador pictures).

There is one other important speed that's not shown on the airspeed indicator. This is called *maneuvering speed* or V_a otherwise remembered as velocity (V) of acceleration (a). In turbulence, you should be at or below maneuvering speed, as we discussed in Chapter 2. I said the yellow arc is for smooth-air operations only. In strong turbulence, however, the only way to ensure that you won't exceed the airplane's structural limit is to fly at or below its maneuvering speed. Maneuvering speed is found well below V_{no}. Your Pilot's Operating Handbook or posted placards provide you with the airplane's maneuvering speed (Figure 9).

down). Lighter weights reduce the stall speed below the colored minimum. (For your information, all color coded stall speeds can also be the minimum steady speed at which the airplane is controllable. Either definition is correct).

Following the white arc clockwise, we come to its high-speed end. This represents the maximum airspeed at which you may extend the flaps or fly with them extended. Called V_{fe} or velocity (V) of flaps (f) extended (e), flaps may not be used above this speed for fear of structural damage (and the prime directive of any pilot is to avoid breaking the airplane).

Most things green are good (money, guacamole, traffic lights). A green arc represents the normal operating range of the airplane. The beginning of the green arc represents the power-off stalling speed or minimum steady flight speed in a specified configuration. For the small airplanes we fly, this configuration occurs when the airplane is at its maximum takeoff weight and the flaps and gear (if retractable) are up. This is called V_{s1} or velocity (V) of stall (s) with everything inside (1)—think of the *1* as the letter *i* representing gear and flaps up or *inside*. With flaps up, gear up and power off, the beginning of the green arc in Figure 8 suggests this airplane needs a minimum of 49 knots of wind flowing over its wings before it starts flying.

The top end of the green arc is called V_{no} or the maximum structural cruising speed. Since the green arc is

the airplane's normal operating range, think of the top of the green arc as the velocity (V) of normal (n) operation (o). At and below V_{no} airplanes have been certified to withstand substantial vertical gusts of air without experiencing structural damage (these may be vertical gusts of 30 to 50 feet per second—depending on the airplane manufacturer). Operations above V_{no} and within the yellow arc, are allowed only in smooth air.

Airplane wings are subject to a great deal of structural stress at higher airspeeds. Turbulence is a jolt of stress. If you add such a jolt to the stress of high speed, there are no promises about the wings remaining with you. Because the wings are very important, and because seeing them out there is such a comfort to most pilots, we'll talk more about handling turbulence in a bit.

There is one speed you should never exceed. Coincidentally, this speed is called V_{ne} or velocity (V) that you never (n) exceed (e). This is the red line on the airspeed indicator. It's also the maximum speed at which the airplane can be operated in smooth air. Things are painted red (by us or Mother Nature) when they are of critical importance (blood, chili peppers, traffic lights). Above redline, all bets are off (I hope you're getting test pilot pay if you fly beyond this speed). Exceeding V_{ne} can cause *flutter* (an uncontrollable and destructive vibration of certain airfoil surfaces),

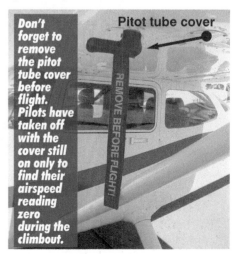

Don't forget to remove the pitot tube cover before flight. Pilots have taken off with the cover still on only to find their airspeed reading zero during the climbout.

Pitot tube cover

REMOVE BEFORE FLIGHT!

Indicated Airspeeds

You will soon find that many things in aviation come in several styles and flavors. Altitude is one of those, and so is speed. Unlike being on the ground, where speed is speed (though it can be expressed in different units such as miles per hour or kilometers per hour), there are a variety of airplane speeds, each with its own significance to you, the pilot.

The number showing on the airspeed indicator is (sound of drum roll) the *indicated airspeed (IAS)*. If the airspeed needle pointed to 80 knots, then 80 knots is the indicated airspeed (Sounds too simple doesn't it? It's somewhat like the question, "What time does the 11:00 a.m. flight leave?").

When a controller asks for your current airspeed, he or she expects to get back the indicated airspeed. (Controllers typically ask for this information by saying "Cessna 1234 Alpha, say airspeed." Those unable to resist the temptation to reply "airspeed" can expect to find a strange and inexplicable increase in their arrival and departure delays.)

Calibrated Airspeed

It's an imperfect world, and that's nowhere more evident than in aircraft instrumentation. The indicated airspeed is subject to (generally slight) errors due to a variety of factors including placement of the pitot and static sources, mechanical inaccuracies at various places in the range, etc. Like a trusty-though-cranky watch, if you know the amount of error, you can at any time correct the indicated time to get the actual time. The corrected, accurate reading is referred to as the *calibrated airspeed (CAS)*.

Here's an Official Aviation Secret. While very important on FAA knowledge exams and to flight instructors who enjoy dabbling in such things, the differences between IAS and CAS are generally much smaller than

Air Error

Pitot tubes are not always installed in such a way that they can accurately sample impact-air pressure. Flying at variable angles of attack, the airplane's pitot tube sometimes simply can't scoop up a sample of air that accurately reflects the airplane's speed (Figure 10). Sometimes the pitot tube scoops up less air than is actually striking it. Other times it scoops up air which has been artificially accelerated by a curved surface, giving a slightly higher than normal indicated airspeed reading. The net result is that the pitot pressure, and thus the indicated airspeed, aren't always an accurate reflection of the windspeed blowing on the airplane.

Once again, the engineers come through with an answer. In this case it's a chart that allows you to correct for such errors (Figure 11). This chart allows you to calibrate your indicated airspeed readings for accuracy. When this is done you have the more precise airspeed reading known as calibrated airspeed.

CALIBRATED & INDICATED AIRSPEEDS

107 knots calibrated

110 knots indicated

N2132B

Fig. 10

Airflow — Pitot tube

Sometimes the air striking the pitot tube is artificially accelerated which causes the indicated airspeed to read higher than the airplane's actual calibrated speed.

64 knots calibrated

60 knots indicated

Airflow — Pitot tube

Sometimes the pitot tube's position or angle prevents it from capturing the moving molecules of air flowing over it. This results in the indicated airspeed being less than the calibrated airspeed.

KIAS = Knots Indicated AirSpeed/KCAS = Knots Calibrated AirSpeed

AIRSPEED CALIBRATION CHART

FLAPS UP											
KIAS	50	60	70	80	90	100	110	120	130	140	150
KCAS	50	64	72	81	89	98	107	116	126	135	153
FLAPS 10°											
KIAS	40	50	60	70	80	90	100				
KCAS	55	58	64	72	81	90	107				
FLAPS 30°											
KIAS	40	50	60	70	80	85					
KCAS	54	57	62	71	80	85					

Fig. 11

Condition: Power required for level flight or maximum rated RPM dive

INDICATED & TRUE AIRSPEED DIFFERENCES

Fig. 12 All airplanes have the same indicated airspeed of 100 Knots, but their true airspeed varies with altitude.

the inaccuracies caused by the small size of the dials you're attempting to read, and the differences in angle at which you read them. There are very few pilots who can discern the difference between 56 and 58 knots on a small instrument with a fat pointer that they're looking at from an angle which makes *parallax* a serious vocabulary word. Differences between IAS and CAS are slightly larger at slower airspeeds and with flaps extended as well as at higher cruise speeds as shown in Figure 11, but overall these differences aren't worth worrying about. Besides, the errors at slower speeds usually work in your favor since your calibrated airspeed is usually higher than your indicated airspeed. In other words, you're going slightly faster than what you think you are. Don't worry, be happy. To facilitate this, we'll refer only to indicated airspeeds for the rest of this book.

While indicated airspeed represents the amount of wind blowing on the airplane, it doesn't reflect the airplane's true speed through the air. Welcome to aviation paradox #101.

True Airspeed

Indicated airspeed isn't the *true airspeed* (TAS).

While I promise to always tell you the truth, the airspeed indicator is incapable of such a promise. It's also incapable of such a performance, through no fault of its own.

It's the air's fault. Air at sea level is very dense. Drag is obviously quite high, since air molecules are packed closer together. As the airplane ascends, it experiences less-dense air. This means less drag since fewer air molecules are around to resist the airplane's forward motion. Airplanes flying at higher altitudes actually move faster through the air for a given power setting because of the decrease in density (Figure 12).

No problem, plane goes faster, airspeed indicator goes up. Yes, but it doesn't go up as fast as the real airspeed. While the airplane goes faster through the thinner air, there are fewer air molecules striking the pitot tube and expanding the bellows of the airspeed indicator. The result is that at higher altitudes you are moving faster than your airspeed indicator shows.

Space shuttle astronauts are cruising around at approximately 17,500 miles per hour while in low earth orbit. They have a very high true airspeed. Would this true speed be shown on the shuttle airspeed indicator (we'll assume it has one)? Hardly. There are too few air molecules to even flicker an airspeed needle at that altitude. If you ever achieved

low earth orbit in your little Gobosh G700 "orbit-o-matic," you would also have a zero indicated airspeed (but wouldn't notice since your blood would be boiling—and that always puts a damper on my flights).

True airspeed is one of those concepts that seems to give you something for nothing. One time my dad came home and told me we were getting a new swimming pool. I was excited until he told me to go out to the car and bring it in. There's always a catch! Not so with true airspeed. You actually go faster and use less fuel (up to a point) as your altitude increases.

Dense Doings

You must be thinking, "Hey, if I go faster by flying higher, why not fly real high?" Nice try, but it won't fly! This logic doesn't hold water (or air), due to the perversity of nature and aviation. A little while ago I said TAS increases with altitude for a given power setting. Notice the *for a given power setting* part. It's the equivalent of the fine print in a contract from an aluminum siding sales rep.

As you climb, the ability of the engine to produce power decreases due to the reduced air density. So, the very thing that allows you to fly faster for a given amount of power (thinner air), limits the power you can produce! *That's* what I mean about the perversity of aviation. Turbocharging, as we discussed earlier, helps but don't expect to find many light sport airplanes equipped with turbochargers. Your Pilot's Operating Handbook identifies altitudes where you'll obtain the greatest gain in true airspeed for a given decrease in engine power.

Two factors affect air density: pressure and temperature. Is there some way to precisely predict your true airspeed? Yes, and you don't have to be psychic to do so (the other day I called the Psychic Hotline and they told me they saw a big phone bill in my future). Fortunately, true airspeed prediction is a little more precise.

Air Density Lesson #1   Professor Bob
                      Chief Air Master

The air up there, at 10,000 feet,
Is thinner than my hair.
But if you want to go fast,
And spend less time in your seat,
Plan your <u>LONG</u> flights up there.

Touched by the New Age movement, professor Bob now believes the key to higher learning is based in making things rhyme. The professor's only problem is that he doesn't believe he's bald. He is convinced that he's simply taller than his hair.

Speed Math

Think of the airspeed indicator as a means of measuring molecule strikes per minute and you'll be on the road to understanding. It takes X number of molecules to push the dial to a given number. X pushes the dial to the right spot only (and only approximately) at sea level and a particular temperature. Everything else is an indicated airspeed that diverges from reality.

You'll find that for every thousand feet of altitude gain, true airspeed increases approximately 2% over indicated airspeed. Here's another way of saying the same thing: you go 2% faster than what is shown on your airspeed indicator for every thousand feet of altitude gain.

At 10,000 feet above sea level, with an indicated airspeed of 100 knots, your true speed through the air is approximately 120 knots. You simply take 2% and multiply it by 10 (which is your altitude in thousands of feet above sea level). This equals 20%. Take 20% of 100 knots which equals 20 knots and add this onto 100. This totals to a true airspeed of 120 knots.

Here's one more way of looking at the difference between true and indicated airspeed. At sea level, an indicated airspeed of 100 knots means that you have 100 knots of air moving over the wings. At 10,000 feet the airplane must move faster through the thinner air to grab the same number of molecule strikes per minute and indicate the same 100 knots of wind. Thus our true airspeed is greater (120 knots).

TAS and IAS While Approaching High Altitude Airports

The difference between true and indicated airspeed is very important for pilots making approaches to high altitude airports. Suppose you're on approach to an airport at 10,000 feet above sea level. Your indicated airspeed on approach is 80 knots. This means your true airspeed is 20% greater (or 96 knots). In other words, your wheels are going to touch down at 96 knots despite showing only 80 knots on the airspeed indicator (Figure 13). That runway is going to seem a lot shorter than it normally would. This is especially disconcerting if your mind was set for an 80 knot touchdown speed.

To lift off and accelerate for an 80 knot climb requires a longer-than-normal takeoff distance at high altitude airports. Your airplane must move along that runway a lot faster than 80 knots to generate an 80 knot indicated airspeed. In fact, at 10,000 feet, it must speed up to 96 knots to show only 80 knots on the airspeed indicator's face. What does that mean to you? It means high-altitude airports require longer takeoff runs and landing distances.

LANDING DISTANCE AND TRUE AIRSPEED

At sea level where the air is quite dense

Stop here   Touchdown here

True airspeed is 80 knots at sea level

Landing distances at sea level are shorter for a given indicated airspeed.

At 10,000' above sea level where the air is less dense

Fig. 13

Stop here   Touchdown here

True airspeed is 96 knots at 10,000' MSL

Landing distances at 10,000' MSL are longer for a given indicated airspeed.

Does this mean, while on approach to a high altitude airport, you should slow the airplane down? No! That wouldn't be good at all. Approach at the same airspeed you always use. Think about it for a second. The wings need a certain number of molecules per minute flowing over them to maintain lift. Your job is supplying those molecules. In thinner air, you will be moving faster (higher TAS) to achieve the same *indicated* airspeed, but indicated airspeed (total number of air molecules arriving at the leading edge) is all the wing (and the pilot) really cares about. *The airplane stalls at the same indicated airspeed whether you're at 1,000 feet or 10,000 feet.* If the airplane requires 60 knots of wind blowing over its wing to keep from stalling, you need to keep the indicated airspeed above 60 knots. (Remember, for most approaches, you want to be at least 30% above the stall speed.)

The moveable ring on some airspeed indicators allows you to quickly calibrate your TAS if you know the outside air temperature and pressure altitude.

Set outside air temp on this scale opposite...

...pressure altitude on this scale.

Read TAS on this scale.

Fig. 14

Primary flight displays often provide your TAS digitally.

OAT 25C
4500 FT
116 KTS

Fig. 15

Some airspeed indicators have a moveable ring on their outer scale to make determination of true airspeed easier (Figure 14 and 15). Just set the outside air temperature (OAT) on the outer ring directly over the pressure altitude (a value we'll discuss shortly) on the inner ring. The number to which your airspeed needle points on the outer ring is your true airspeed. Soon, I'll show you how to use a flight computer to determine your true airspeed based on the altitude and temperature conditions.

The Altimeter

Welcome to the third dimension. One of the things that makes aviation unique is your ability to operate in 3D. No, you won't need any of those funny-colored glasses, but you will need some assistance figuring out where you are in the third dimension. This is why I would now like to introduce you to your *altimeter*.

Airplanes move left or right with great precision, flying specific headings and airways. This is two-dimensional navigation. Altimeters allow airplanes to fly at specific altitudes—a third dimension—with equal precision.

There are lots of ways to get high in aviation (all perfectly legal and honest, honest!). In the next few minutes, you will discover that there's altitude and then there's *altitude*. Knowing one from the other is crucial to your success as a pilot, not to mention your longevity as a person.

An altimeter (Figure 16) provides you with your height above sea level—otherwise known as your *true altitude*. Sea level is a worldwide standard; therefore, it's a consistent reference for altimeter measurement.

Altimeters do not directly tell you your height above the ground. Why? The ground isn't a consistent reference. Ground height varies dramatically. If, however, you know how high you are above sea level, and you also know the ground's height above sea level (this is found on navigational charts as shown in Figure 17), then finding

FINDING YOUR HEIGHT ABOVE THE GROUND

3,000 feet above Sea Level

1,500' above ground level

1,500' Above Sea Level

Altimeters measure height above sea level, not height above ground level.

Finding your height above the ground requires that you subtract the ground's height (its MSL value is found on sectional charts — see Chapter 10) from your height above sea level (which is shown on your altimeter). **Fig. 16**

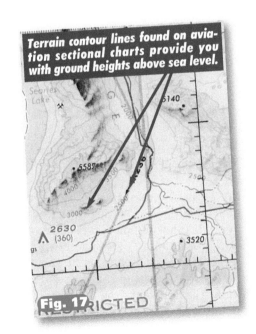

Terrain contour lines found on aviation sectional charts provide you with ground heights above sea level.

Searles Lake

5140

5587

2630
(360)

3520

Fig. 17 RESTRICTED

GPS SATELLITE CONSTELLATION

= Corrections sent to geo stat satellite

= Adjustments sent to WAAS GPS receiver

= Ground reference stations

= Master stations

= Geostationary satellite fixed above equator

= GPS satellite

SATELLITE STATUS — **EPE** 49ₜ — **Simulating Nav** — **DOP** 2.0 — **ALTITUDE** 250ₜ — **BAT PWR**

GPS Altitude Info

Aside from providing your location anywhere on earth, GPS can also provide you with a very accurate indication of your altitude. Using the 30+ GPS satellites now in orbit, your typical hand held GPS with WAAS capability is accurate to within three to seven meters vertically. Just like your altimeter, the GPS provides altitude above sea level and not above the ground.

your height above the ground is simply a "take-away" math problem. Height above ground is technically known as your *absolute altitude*.

An altimeter works by measuring the difference between sea level pressure and pressure at the airplane's present altitude. Figure 18 shows how this is accomplished. Inside the altimeter is a small, expandable capsule somewhat similar to a metal-skinned balloon (they're actually called *aneroid wafers*). The expansion or contraction of the capsule is mechanically converted into a movement of altimeter hands, resulting in an altitude readout.

Notice that the altimeter's case is connected to the static port. This allows static air pressure to surround the capsule. Any change in static air pressure is then reflected by an expansion or contraction of the capsule, providing the altitude reading. To understand precisely how this process works, we need a clearer understanding of how atmospheric pressure changes with height.

Atmospheric pressure used to be measured by a mercury barometer. A tube of the heavy liquid metal mercury is filled and placed upside down in a vat of mercury (Figure 19A). The weight of the mercury inside the inverted tube creates a small vacuum as the column attempts to sink out of the tube and into the vat. It's the vacuum that prevents the mercury from entirely sinking into the reservoir. The column finally stabilizes at a certain height (Figure 19B). Let's say the height is 30 inches

of mercury (sometimes abbreviated *Hg,* which is the chemists' symbol for the element mercury). Decreasing the atmosphere's pressure on the reservoir surrounding the tube allows the column to decrease in height. Increasing atmospheric pressure pushes on the reservoir, moving the column upward into the tube and increasing its height (Figure 19C).

INSIDE A BASIC ALTIMETER

Static air pressure (the air's weight) is sensed through the static line.

Static line connects to static port

Fig. 18

Low atmospheric pressure

More atmospheric pressure

The altimeter's capsules expand or contract based on the pressure of the atmosphere. This movement is mechanically converted into an altitude reading.

HOW A MERCURY BAROMETER WORKS

A Liquid mercury in vat

Test tube is full of liquid mercury.

B Column height (30" tall) is a measure of atmospheric pressure.

Atmospheric pressure

C An increase in atmospheric pressure causes the column to rise.

A decrease in atmospheric pressure causes the column to fall.

D Column height decreases 1" of mercury for every 1,000' altitude change.

28" Tall

29" Tall

30" Tall

2,000' MSL

1,000' MSL

Sea Level

Fig. 19

Let's say that at sea level, under typical pressure conditions, our mercury column stands 30 inches tall. We say the atmospheric pressure is *30 inches of mercury*. At 1,000 feet MSL (mean sea level), the pressure decreases and the mercury column falls approximately one inch. It now stands 29 inches tall. The atmospheric pressure at 1,000 feet MSL is properly stated as *29 inches of mercury*. Altitude measurement is based on the consistency of this known pressure change.

Aircraft altimeters don't use mercury barometers. If they did, there would be a big, three-foot long tube protruding from the instrument panel (Not a pretty sight. Besides, it would keep poking you in the eye). Instead, the small expandable capsule's expansion or contraction is calibrated in inches of mercury. In other words, taken from sea level to 1,000 feet MSL, the capsule expands a small but predictable amount. Altimeter designers calibrate this change as equaling one inch on the mercury barometer.

Now you are ready to understand how altimeters can determine your airplane's height above sea level.

Figure 20A shows an altimeter resting at sea level, where the pressure is 30" Hg. This is the pressure sensed through the airplane's static port; therefore, the pressure surrounding the expandable capsule is also 30" Hg. Let's say the pressure inside the capsule is also at 30" Hg. What's going to happen to the capsule? Will it expand? No. The pressure inside the capsule is the same as the pressure outside the capsule. Without any pressure difference, the capsule doesn't expand and the altimeter reads an altitude of zero feet.

The changing height of the mercury column represents atmospheric pressure in much the same way your tongue might represent the pressure of someone standing on your chest. A tongue sticking way out of your mouth would represent a lot of pressure on your chest. When the person stepped off your chest, your tongue would (we hope) recede into your mouth. One might be able to calculate the person's weight by measuring the exact amount of tongue protrusion. One might say that 200 pounds is worth 6 inches of tongue. Of course, I say this tongue in cheek since it's not all that accurate; after all, it's only a rule of tongue, and calibration would always be a challenge.

Even if we calculated tongue protrusion for a given amount of weight, this information is totally useless (but high in entertainment value, nevertheless). There is, however, great value in calculating the height, in inches, that a column of mercury will change if it's moved vertically. Since the weight of the atmosphere changes with height, this pressure change should be reflected by a lengthening or shortening of the mercury column. Indeed, this is exactly what happens. A column of mercury changes about one inch in height per thousand feet of altitude change, and this is the standard used to calibrate altimeters (Figure 19D).

HOW THE ALTIMETER CALCULATES YOUR ALTITUDE

3000' - 27"

B 27" 30"

The pressure inside the capsule is 3" greater than the outside static pressure. Therefore, the capsule expands an amount equivalent to three inches of mercury. This equates to an altitude reading of 3,000 feet above sea level.

2000' - 28"

The pressure inside the capsule is the same as the outside static pressure. Therefore, the capsule doesn't expand and the hands read "zero" altitude.

1000' - 29"

A 30" 30"

Fig. 20

Sea level 30"

Figure 20B shows an altimeter at 3,000 feet MSL. The static pressure at 3,000 MSL is 27" Hg. If the pressure inside the capsule is still 30" Hg, what will the capsule do? Yes, it will expand an amount equal to this difference in pressure. It will expand by an amount of pressure equal to three inches of mercury. This expansion equates to a 3,000 foot reading on the altimeter's face. (Remember, the capsule expands because its internal pressure is greater than the outside static pressure.)

Pressure Variations And The Altimeter

If the pressure at sea level always stayed at 30" Hg, this would be the end of our altimeter story. Unfortunately, the pressure at sea level varies daily, hourly, and sometimes even minute-by-minute. The atmosphere actually changes weight slightly, causing air to push down harder on some parts of the earth than others. In the weather section you will have a chance to study these pressure differences more thoroughly. For now, let's agree that the pressure at sea level changes often.

The altimeter's job is to measure the difference between sea level pressure and the outside static pressure of the altitude at which you are flying. As we've already learned, the difference between these two pressures allows the altimeter to calculate your height above sea level. Since we've already agreed that sea level pressure changes at a fixed location, think about how quickly it can change when moving across the country in your airplane. You obviously need some way to keep your altimeter informed about the changing pressure at sea level. A small knob at the front of the altimeter (Figure 21) allows you to do just that.

Did you feel something?

I did!

Twisting this knob rotates the little numbers in the *Kollsman window,* as shown on the face of the altimeter in Figure 22A. This is the pilot's way of telling the altimeter what the pressure is at sea level. Changing the numbers in the Kollsman window recalibrates the pressure inside the altimeter's expandable capsule. This is done mechanically by repositioning an internal linkage, which gives the capsule a new starting point from which to begin measuring. Whatever pressure value you set in the Kollsman window, the altimeter assumes this is the new sea level pressure. Now the altimeter measures the difference between the pressure value set in the Kollsman window and the outside static pressure to obtain your height above sea level.

For instance, when 30.10" Hg is set in the Kollsman window, the pressure inside the expandable capsule is recalibrated to 30.10" Hg as shown in Figure 22A. Now the altimeter thinks the pressure at sea level is 30.10" Hg. Setting 29.95" Hg in the Kollsman window tells the altimeter the pressure at sea level is 29.95" Hg (Figure 22B).

Figure 23 shows how this process works. Airplane A is over San Francisco (SFO) where the sea level pressure is 30.25" Hg. This value is set in the Kollsman window. The difference between 30.25" Hg and 27.25" Hg is three inches of pressure or 3000 feet. The altimeter reads three thousand feet—the airplane's true altitude.* Airplane B is over Santa Barbara (SBA) where the sea level pressure has lowered to 29.25" Hg. The static pressure at Airplane B's altitude of 3,000 feet is 26.25" Hg. The difference between these two is three inches. Therefore, the altimeter reads 3000 feet.

As you'll soon see, to obtain true altitude, you also need to correct the altimeter for non-standard temperature variations. For now, we'll just assume that true altitude is obtained by correcting the altimeter for pressure changes.

Turning the altimeter's knob allows you to tell the instrument what the pressure at sea level is.

Fig. 21

WHAT HAPPENS WHEN YOU CHANGE THE ALTIMETER SETTING

Rotating the altimeter's knob, changes the numbers in the Kollsman window. This mechanically repositions an internal linkage that changes the starting point from which the altimeter begins its measurement. It is, however, much easier to think of the pressure inside the sealed capsule changing to equal the barometric pressure value set in the Kollsman window (trust me! Think about it this way and you'll never have difficulty understanding how the altimeter works).

30.10"

29.95"

When the altimeter knob is rotated & 29.95" is set in the Kollsman window, the altimeter acts as if a pressure of 29.95" Hg has been set inside its sealed capsule.

Fig. 22

The point is that we should always set the sea level pressure in the Kollsman window so our altimeter can read true altitude. "OK," you wonder, "how do we get the sea level pressure to set in the Kollsman window in the first place?" This sea level pressure is called the *altimeter setting*. It's easily obtained from several sources, including air traffic control towers, flight service stations and automatic weather observation stations. A bit later in this chapter, I'll tell you about one more way you can get the right altimeter setting, even when nobody's home at the tower.

What happens if you don't continue to update the altimeter setting during every 100 miles or so of flight? There's a good chance your altimeter will not be providing the correct information—you're not going to be at the altitude you think you're at. This can be a problem.

Think of the problem as being similar to driving across the country while listening to your car radio. If you're listening to a lecture about Jung and yang on that philosophical radio station KYMI, after a short distance you'll need to re-tune to another station carrying the same program. You'll be out of range of the first station. If you fly more than 100 miles from the source of your last altimeter setting, you're technically out of range from this source. An error in the altimeter's reading is possible unless you reset the Kollsman window to a closer source.

Figure 24 depicts this process. Notice that at 1,000 feet MSL above SFO, the pressure is 29.25″ Hg (position A). This is the same as the sea level pressure at SBA (position B). Do you see how the 29.25″ pressure level gradually sloped from 1,000 feet MSL down to the surface, between SFO and SBA? It can be said that pressure levels drop when flying towards an area of lower pressure.

At 3,000 feet above SFO, the static pressure is 27.25″ Hg (position C). Approaching SBA, the 27.25″ pressure level slopes downward to 2,000 feet above the surface (position D). With the SFO sea level pressure of 30.25″ Hg set in the Kollsman window, the altimeter indicates 3,000 feet as long as you stay at the level where the outside pressure is 27.25″ Hg as shown by position C. Can you see what's happening? The level where the pressure is 27.25″ Hg

HOW THE ALTIMETER CALCULATES YOUR ALTITUDE

3000' MSL
27.25"

2000' MSL
28.25"

1000' MSL
29.25"

Sea level
at SFO
30.25" Hg

Kollsman window

3000' MSL
26.25"

2000' MSL
27.25"

1000' MSL
28.25"

Sea level
at SBA
29.25" Hg

Kollsman window

Each altimeter measures the difference between the pressure at sea level (as set in the Kollsman window) and the static pressure at its altitude. The difference between these two is mechanically converted into an altitude reading.

Fig. 23

actually slopes downward closer to the surface yet the altimeter is still reading 3,000 feet position D. If we don't continue to update the altimeter setting, the *indicated altitude* (what's shown on the altimeter's face) becomes different from our true altitude (our actual height above sea level).

HOW SLOPING PRESSURE LEVELS AFFECT YOUR ALTIMETER

Altimeter C reads the correct altitude of 3,000' MSL. Altimeter D reads 3,000' MSL even though it's only 2,000' MSL. This occurs because its altimeter setting hasn't been updated to the current sea level pressure at SBA of 29.25".

3000' MSL
27.25"

3000' MSL
26.25"

2000' MSL
28.25"

2000' MSL
27.25"

Pressure level slopes from SFO to SBA

1000' MSL
29.25"

1000' MSL
28.25"

Pressure level slopes from SFO to SBA

30.25"
Sea level
at SFO

29.25"
Sea level
at SBA

Fig. 24

Over SBA our indicated altitude is 3,000 feet but our true altitude is only 2,000 MSL as shown in Figure 24, position D. Is this a problem? Yes! What happens if there is a mountain at 2,500 feet MSL along your path? (Figure 25A). Looking at the face of the altimeter (its indicated altitude), it appears you'll clear the mountain by 500 feet. In reality, you're 500 feet below the top of the mountain. Under these conditions, there's a good chance that your airplane's landing gear might conk the head of some camper sitting around a campfire on top of that hill. What a shock it would be if it were night time and you thought you would clear that 2,500 foot mountain by 500 feet. You might end up with a Coleman stove, camping gear and raccoons stuck to your airplane.

Suppose you're over SBA and suddenly you realize your mistake of not updating the altimeter setting. You call the SBA tower and the controller tells you the altimeter setting is 29.25″ Hg (He or she will actually say "Altimeter setting is two-niner-two-five." The "inches of mercury" part is understood and never spoken.) You set this in the Kollsman window. What will your altimeter read? The difference between the recalibrated pressure in the expandable capsule and static pressure is now two inches. Therefore, the altimeter reads a true altitude of 2,000 feet (Figure 25B), at which point you immediately begin climbing back to your previously selected altitude of 3,000 feet. By updating the altimeter setting, the indicated altitude (what the altimeter shows) is now the same as the true altitude (your height above sea level). Good pilots make it a point to update their altimeter setting at least every 100 miles (if not more often).

In Figure 25B, did you notice that twisting the knob and moving the numbers down from 30.25″ Hg to 29.25″ Hg caused the hands to unwind 1,000 feet worth? This progression is shown in Figure 26. From a strictly mechanical point of view,

When There's No Sea Beneath Thee

Whenever an ATC facility gives you the altimeter setting, that's the pressure at sea level underneath them. You are, I hope, wondering how an airport near Denver, Colorado, located at over 5,000 feet MSL, measures the pressure at sea level when there is no sea under the airport.

Sea level is a relative constant across the globe (excluding tides). ATC personnel can easily calculate what the pressure at sea level underneath them would be, if they could dig down to that level and if there were a sea there. This is often calculated by a mechanical device at the ATC facility (later I'll show you the device they use to calculate sea level pressure—you're not going to believe it.)

FAILURE TO UPDATE YOUR ALTIMETER SETTING CAN CAUSE ALTIMETER ERRORS

A The pilot below starts off at 3,000' MSL over SFO with his altimeter set to the SFO station pressure of 30.25" Hg. He flies toward SBA and forgets to update his altimeter setting along the way.

With the wrong altimeter setting set in the Kollsman window, the pilot thinks he's higher than he actually is. He smacks into the mountain at the 2,000 foot level all the while thinking he's at 3,000' above sea level.

3000' MSL 27.25″   3000' MSL 26.25″
TOP 2,500' MSL
2000' MSL 28.25″   2000' MSL 27.25″
Pressure level slopes from SFO to SBA
I hate it when that happens!
1000' MSL 29.25″   1000' MSL 28.25″
30.25″ Sea level at **SFO**   **Fig. 25**   29.25″ Sea level at **SBA**

B When the pilot is over SBA and sets the altimeter setting of 29.25" in his Kollsman window, the altimeter hands move downward to show the airplane's true altitude above sea level which is 2,000'.

Since the pilot was lazy and didn't keep updating his altimeter setting, he now gets the shock of his life. He sees his altimeter indicating 2,000' and knows he's 1,000' below his desired altitude. He must immediately climb back to 3,000' to avoid the 2,500' mountain top.

3000' MSL 27.25″   3000' MSL 26.25″
TOP 2,500' MSL
2000' MSL 28.25″   2000' MSL 27.25″
Pressure level slopes from SFO to SBA
Head for the light Bob!
1000' MSL 29.25″   1000' MSL 28.25″
30.25″ Sea level at **SFO**   29.25″ Sea level at **SBA**

HOW A CHANGING ALTIMETER SETTING MOVES THE ALTIMETER'S HANDS

When you're over SBA and you rotate the numbers in the Kollsman window down from 30.25" to 29.25", (1" of Hg change) the indicated altitude moves down from 3,000 feet to 2,000 feet—which is now your true altitude over SBA. (Note: when the numbers go up or down, the hands also go up or down respectively. This is the way the mechanical linkage inside the altimeter works. Change the numbers 1" and the hands move 1,000', change them .5" and the hands move 500' or change them .1" and the hands move 100').

whenever the numbers in the Kollsman window move downward (get smaller), the hands also move downward (read less). Changing the numbers one inch in the Kollsman window is worth a one thousand foot altitude change on the altimeter's face. Figure 26 shows what the altimeter hands do when rotating the knob to the current altimeter setting over SBA.

There's a very important point to be made here (move that finger to the preferred ear position). *When the altimeter is set too high, it reads too high in terms of altitude, and you will be **lower** than you think you are.* If the altimeter is set too low, it reads too low. Flying from SFO to SBA, toward an area of lower sea level pressure, and not updating the altimeter setting, meant the barometric pressure setting in the Kollsman window was too high. Therefore, the altimeter reads too high. In other words, the indicated altitude (3,000 feet) was higher than our true altitude (2,000 feet) as shown in Figure 25A.

Figure 27 shows an airplane flying from a low pressure area toward a high pressure area (in the opposite direction of our flight from SFO to SBA). The airplane maintains a constant indicated altitude of 3,000 feet

without updating its altimeter setting. The airplane follows the 26.25" pressure level, which slopes upward as the high pressure area over SFO is approached. With the altimeter set too low, it will read too low and you will be **higher** than you intend to be. The indicated altitude will be 3,000 feet but you will actually be 4,000 feet above sea level when over SFO.

If you had to pick the most dangerous flight scenario, it would probably be flying from high pressure to low instead of low to high, and this is generally the example that shows up on FAA tests and instructor interrogations.

The point of all this is that you must keep the altimeter informed about the current altimeter setting. Regulations require you to adjust the altimeter to the current reported altimeter setting of a station along the route and within 100 nautical miles of your airplane. Keeping altimeters informed is similar to keeping your spouse informed. It produces a happy relationship.

FAILURE TO UPDATE YOUR ALTIMETER SETTING WHEN FLYING FROM A LOW TO HIGH PRESSURE AREA

A wise man says, "Pilot who refuse to get new altimeter setting feel let down—in more ways than one."

Temperature Variations and the Altimeter

Just when you think you've got all the exceptions down pat, another gem in need of consideration pops up. You just can't seem to win. It's like going to the one hour photo shop, only to find they have 30 minute parking. Don't fret. The altimeter's *temperature errors* are easy to understand.

Normal changes in temperature produce relatively small and negligible errors in altimeter readings. If, however, you're taking the family's Boeing 747 out for a little cross country flight, you could travel to exotic places having extreme temperatures (in particular, extreme cold). Under these conditions, it's possible to have altimeter errors of 500 feet or more. Practically speaking, most pilots never correct their altimeters for temperature variations. Nevertheless, it's important to know when these errors can affect you and how to correct for them.

Most of the time, pilots fly with plenty of terrain clearance and are not affected by small, temperature-induced altimeter errors. On the other hand, if you're planning a night flight over mountains and don't plan on crossing them by at least 2,000 feet or more, you should check and see if temperature errors will significantly affect your altimeter's reading. (You should also have a CAT scan to check for reduced blood flow to the judgment section of your cortex if you're crossing mountains at less than 2,000 feet above ground level at night.)

Figure 28 depicts the effect of temperature on columns of air. When air is at standard or normal temperature (59° F/15° C at sea level), the altimeter experiences no temperature error. Airplane B, sitting on top of a column of normal temperature air, has an indicated altitude (4,000 feet) which is equal to its true altitude (4,000 feet).

When temperatures are warmer, however, air expands. Airplane A rests atop an expanded layer of air. The air beneath Airplane A weighs the same as the air beneath Airplane B. The difference is that the warmer, expanded column of air is taller. This is similar to two guys both weighing 370 pounds, with one standing 6 feet tall and the other standing 4 feet tall. They both produce the same indication on a scale but their weight is distributed differently in the vertical direction. In a similar manner,

HOW TEMPERATURE AFFECTS THE ALTIMETER

Changes in temperature raise or lower the pressure levels of air. This causes slight differences between indicated altitude And true altitude.

A — Indicated altitude - 4,000'

B — Indicated altitude - 4,000'

C — Indicated altitude - 4,000'

4000' Pressure level

Fig. 28

True altitude 4,250 feet — Warmer air at 100°F expands sightly

True altitude 4,000 feet — Normal temp air at 59°F (standard conditions)

True altitude 3,750 feet — Cooler air at 32°F shrinks slightly

a mass of air having temperatures that are different from standard distributes its weight differently in the vertical direction.

Because the pressure levels are taller or expanded in warmer air, Airplane A's indicated altitude is 4,000 feet and its true altitude is 4,250 feet. Colder air produces shorter or more closely spaced pressure levels. Airplane C's indicated altitude is 4,000 feet and its true altitude is 3,750 feet.

Think about it in the following way. Without correcting the altimeter for temperature variations, if the temperature is going down, then the airplane is going down; if the temperature is going up, then the airplane is going up.

On a flight from a warmer area to a colder area, without correcting for temperature, the indicated altitude is greater than the true altitude. In other words, the altimeter will indicate 4,000 feet but the true altitude will be 3,750 feet. *The temperature went down, so the airplane went down.* It went down 250 feet and you still think you're at 4,000 feet above sea level.

On a flight from a colder area to a warmer area, without correcting for temperature, the indicated altitude is lower than the true altitude. Imagine the airplane in Figure 28 flying from right to left. In the warmer area, the indicated altitude is 4,000 feet but the true altitude is 4,250 feet. Therefore, *if the temperature is going up, the airplane is going up.* It went up 250 feet and you still think you're at 4,000 feet above sea level.

YOU KNOW YOU'VE BEEN FLYING TOO MUCH WHEN...
1. You use the emergency brake to drop the flaps.
2. You yell "clear" before starting your car.
3. You get out of your car and look for tiedown ropes.
4. You brake on left turns and speed-up on right turns.
5. You tell the police officer that you're allowed to go 250 below 10,000 feet MSL.
6. You drive into a fog bank and immediately go on instruments.
7. You are entering the highway and hit *rotate speed* for the Cessna Skycatcher. You pull back on the wheel and don't become airborne. In a panic, you abort the takeoff and hit the brakes. (This drives the guy behind you crazy.)

There's another excellent memory aid to help keep these altimeter errors straight: *When flying from high to low, look out below.* This rule assumes that you forgot to set in the nearest altimeter setting or correct your altimeter for temperature extremes. You must *look out below* because you are not as high as you think you are. The statement *look out below* should be an immediate cue of danger. Danger means that you are closer to sea level than your altimeter says you are.

Suppose you're arriving or departing an airport in extremely cold temperatures. You should think, "If the temperature is cold, then the thermometer has gone down. Therefore, the airplane is going down." In other words, your airplane's true altitude is lower than the indicated altitude.

You already know how to correct for pressure variations during flight. You simply adjust the altimeter setting to the nearest station within 100 nautical miles of the airplane. But how do you correct for variations in temperature? You can use your flight computer (mechanical or electronic) for these computations. Once again, we don't normally correct the altimeter for temperature variations unless the temperatures are extreme and we plan on crossing terrain at low altitudes.

Sensitive Altimeters

We call modern altimeters *sensitive altimeters.* This is not because they cry at movies. Sensitive altimeters are those with adjustable barometric scales and often have two or even three expandable capsules instead of one. This allows them greater precision or sensitivity in altitude measurement. It's possible to hold a sensitive altimeter in your hand, move it from the floor to the ceiling and record an altitude change (and poke a hole in your roof). Now that's sensitive!

Suppose you're departing an airport early in the morning before the tower opens and no altimeter setting is available. Remember, a couple of

sections back I promised you one more way to get a stealth altimeter setting. It's remarkably easy. Simply rotate the altimeter knob until the hands point to field elevation, as shown in Figure 29 (field elevation is a number that's listed on almost all aviation charts, and in many other published sources). This is what the hands would read if you had the current altimeter setting isn't it? Now, in a backwards sort of way, the numbers in the Kollsman window give you an approximate altimeter setting for that area. At least this allows you to start your flight with a correct reading on the altimeter. However, as you progress along your route, keep updating the altimeter setting at least every 100 nautical miles. Remember, pressure at sea level can change quickly. The altimeter must be kept informed so it will provide accurate altitude information.

Cross checking the altimeter setting with the field elevation is always a good idea. You can sometimes catch a mistake in the altimeter setting you've heard (or thought you heard) by noticing that the resulting altitude is way off from what it should be for the airport.

Do you remember our discussion on how ATC personnel determine the altimeter setting? I said you wouldn't believe it when I told you how they did it. Well, many of them do it with a small altimeter of their very own. They simply turn the knob until the altimeter reads the field elevation or elevation of the tower cab, then look at the numbers in the Kollsman window! That's the altimeter setting they issue (and you thought it was done with smoke, mirrors and controlled substances).

Pressure Altitude

Every family has a cousin Ed. He's the typical cousin who's just one taco short of a combo plate. Our Ed would always tell us that he lived in a gated community. We interpreted this to mean prison. Uncle Ed would tell the type of jokes no one laughed at. He would always say, "Well, you had to

If the altimeter setting is not available while on the ground at an airport, simply rotate the knob until the altimeter hands indicate field elevation. The numbers in the Kollsman window would be your altimeter setting if it were available from ATC.

Kollsman window

Fig. 29

be there!" I suppose if I was there I would understand his humor. The problem is, how do I get back there to understand?

A similar problem exists where airplane performance charts are concerned. When engineers create performance charts, they create them for specific altitude, temperature and pressure conditions. To use these charts, you must go back to the conditions the engineers used when the performance computations were made. We call the day on which these specific altitude, temperature and pressure conditions existed a *standard day.*

For an engineer, a standard day occurs when the temperature and pressure at sea level is 59°F (or 15°C) and 29.92" Hg, respectively. Most of the airplane's performance charts are based on these conditions. Here's the problem. What if the temperature and pressure at sea level isn't a standard 15°C and 29.92" Hg (and it rarely is)? Will these performance charts still provide you with reliable information? They will if you go back to standard day conditions. Let me show you how to do this with an actual performance chart.

Figure 30A is a climb performance chart. It requires two variables—pressure altitude and temperature—to

HOW TO FIND AND USE PRESSURE ALTITUDE

A Think of pressure altitude as the altitude the engineers were at when they created the airplane's performance charts. This is the altitude your altimeter reads when 29.92" of Hg is set in your Kollsman window.

WEIGHT LBS	PRESS ALT FT	CLIMB SPEED KIAS	RATE OF CLIMB - FPM			
			-20°C	0°C	20°C	40°C
1,320	S.L.	73	795	730	665	600
	2000	73	705	645	585	525
	4000	73	625	565	510	450
	6000	72	540	485	430	370
	8000	72	460	405	350	295
	10,000	72	380	325	275	
	12,000	72	300	250		

B   **How to obtain pressure altitude for the chart above**   **Fig. 30**

To find your pressure altitude, simply set 29.92" in your Kollsman window. The altitude the hands point to is your pressure altitude. Once you know this, reset the numbers in the Kollsman window to the previous altimeter setting. Note that rotating the numbers from 30.42" down to 29.92" (a change of .5") moves the hands down 500'. Therefore, the hands move from 2,500' down to 2,000'.

30.42 ◀   30.17 ◀   29.92 ◀

Ouch! I have tennis elbow.

I wish I had an elbow!

1   2   3

determine climb rate. This thing called *pressure altitude* is the pressure condition the engineers experienced when they determined the airplane's performance. Since the pressure at sea level was 29.92" Hg when they tested the airplane, all you need to do in determining pressure altitude is set the altimeter's Kollsman window to 29.92" Hg and read the

indicated altitude. This reading is your pressure altitude, as shown in Figure 30B. In this example, our pressure altitude is 2,000 feet. Using that value and the outside air temperature, we can determine our airplane's performance on the rate of climb chart provided.

Of course, once you've determined your pressure altitude you should

immediately reset the altimeter back to the altimeter setting provided by Air Traffic Control (ATC). This keeps the altimeter reading the correct height above sea level (true altitude).

Remember, pressure altitude is used for performance computations. It's the height above a *standard datum plane,* which is nothing more than a fancy phrase for *an imaginary reference point.* This reference point is what the engineer's altimeter would have read if temperature and pressure at sea level was 59°F and 29.92" Hg.

Reading the Altimeter

Reading the altimeter is very similar to reading a watch. I say this with caution, knowing that some readers have been raised on digital watches and no longer know what it means when Mickey's little hand is on the 3 and his big hand is on the 12. Some may not even know which way Mickey's hands used to turn. I know this is a problem because the tower pointed out traffic for one of my students by saying, "32 Bravo, you have traffic at 2 o'clock." My student replied, "Well, it's only 1:30, so we've got a half hour before it gets here!"

Figure 31A shows a typical altimeter found in most airplanes. It has three hands, which is how many you'll wish *you* had sometimes when

Know the Code

Many airplanes now have *automatic pressure altitude reporting equipment* (either an *encoding altimeter* or a *blind encoder* [most common]). Also referred to as *Mode C capability,* this equipment is similar to an altimeter. It sends encoded pressure information to ATC radar via the airplane's onboard transponder. The transponder is a device that makes the airplane appear as an electronic blip on radar. Airplanes with altitude encoding equipment have their altitude information shown as well as their horizontal position depicted next to the radar blip.

Altitude encoding devices have their Kollsman windows permanently set to 29.92" Hg. They send pressure altitude pulses to ATC radar, where the computer automatically corrects this reading for local barometric pressure. This correction allows controllers to read the pilot's true altitude on the radar screen.

Some misinformed pilots, finding themselves several hundred feet off an assigned altitude while being radar tracked, reach up and turn the Kollsman window knob on their airplane's altimeter so that the altimeter hands read the proper height. They're hoping that ATC is seeing what the altimeter on the instrument panel is showing. Nice try, but no banana. ATC is getting its info elsewhere. The airplane's altitude encoder, which is typically hidden behind the instrument panel and totally invisible to the pilot, is telling tales on him. The visible altimeter talks only to you; the encoding altimeter device talks only to ATC.

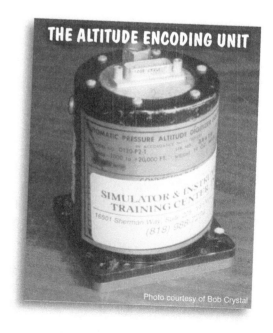

THE ALTITUDE ENCODING UNIT

Photo courtesy of Bob Crystal

READING THE ALTIMETER

A 10,000 Foot hand
ALT.
1,000 Foot hand
100 Foot hand
30.15

B A variation of the 10,000 foot hand
ALT.
30.15

Fig. 31

things get busy in the cockpit. The shortest hand points to numbers representing the airplane's height in tens of thousands of feet. The medium, thicker hand represents altitude in thousands of feet. And the long, thin hand represents the airplane's altitude in hundreds of feet. On some altimeters a very long, thin hand with a triangle on the end is substituted for the 10,000 foot indicator as shown in Figure 31B.

The easiest way to read an altimeter is to read it just like you would read a clock. For instance, if Altimeter A in Figure 32 were a clock, what time would it read? Yes, it would read 3:00 o'clock. Since Altimeter A isn't a clock, it shows an altitude of 3,000 feet. The long (hun-

dreds) hand points to zero hundred feet, and the medium (thousands) hand points to 3,000 feet. The altitude is 3,000 feet.

If Altimeter B were a clock, what time would it say? It would read 3:30, or half past 3:00 o'clock. As an altimeter it reads half past three thousand or 3,500 feet. The long (hundreds) hand points to 500 feet and the medium (thousands) hand points between 3,000 and 4,000 feet. The altitude is 500 feet past 3,000 feet or 3,500 feet.

What time would it be if Altimeter C were a clock? It looks like it would be somewhere around a quarter-to-seven. More precisely, the long (hundreds) hand shows 800 feet and the medium (thousands) hand points a

little shy of 7,000 feet. Therefore, the altimeter reads 800 feet past 6,000 feet or 6,800 feet. Not too tough, is it?

Try reading Altimeter D like a clock. What time is it? Yes, it looks like it's 3:00, but take a closer look at the very short (ten thousands) hand. This hand points a little past a value of *1*, meaning you need to add 10,000 feet onto the value shown by the altimeter's medium and long hand. Altimeter D indicates an altitude of 13,000 feet (sport pilots are restricted to altitudes 10,000 feet MSL and below or 2,000 feet AGL, whichever is higher). Keep an eye on the 10,000 foot hand, especially on FAA tests. It can be tricky if you aren't watching for it. A good general rule of aviation is to always check everything.

You're going to discover that the altimeter is a very handy little device (no pun intended). Not only is it useful for the obvious reason of maintaining a certain height above sea level, but it's also useful as a pitch instrument. Your first introduction to the altimeter will be during straight and level flight. I might warn you, these aren't two separate maneuvers; they're one. When my instructor first asked me for straight and level flight, I asked him, "Which one of those things do you want first, straight or level? I can't do them both at the same time."

DIFFERENT ALTIMETER READINGS

A 3,000 FEET

B 3,500 FEET

C 6,800 FEET

D 13,000 FEET

Analog Altimeter Indications

PFD Altimeter Indications

OAT 25C 3000 FT 112 KTS — 3000

OAT 26C 3500 FT 112 KTS — 3500

OAT 3C 6800 FT 117 KTS — 6800

OAT -10C 13000 FT 127 KTS — 13000

Fig. 32

The altimeter is relatively sensitive to pitch changes. Any deviation from level flight should be noticed as a slight movement of the altimeter's hundred-foot hand. You simply monitor the visual horizon to maintain a straight and level pitch while occasionally checking the altimeter for needle movement. When haze or other forms of obscuration make the horizon difficult to identify, the altimeter can be critical in confirming you're in a level-pitch attitude.

Referencing the altimeter also provides you with pitch-attitude feedback during steep turns. Since the horizon line changes quickly, glancing at the altimeter's hundred-foot hand is a good indication of any deviation from the desired altitude. Sharp pilots make it a point to constantly reference the altimeter during any maneuver requiring a constant altitude.

Learning to use your altimeter and other flight instruments properly should prevent the frustration I experienced as a student pilot many years ago. I was in the practice area with my flight instructor doing steep turns and having trouble maintaining altitude. During one turn my altitude dropped from 3,500 feet to 3,000 feet. In a humorous attempt to deal with the problem, I reached up, grabbed the altimeter knob and rotated it until the hands went back up to 3,500 feet. I looked over at my instructor and said, "Ahh, the altimeter setting has just changed." He looked back at me, smiled, and said, "So has the date you're going to solo!"

The Vertical Speed Indicator (VSI)

Also known as the vertical velocity indicator (VVI), the *vertical speed indicator* is located in the bottom right hand side of the instrument panel's six pack of instruments or often to the right of the primary flight display (Figure 33). Calibrated to read in feet per minute, the

THE VERTICAL SPEED INDICATOR
Traditional Panel VSI   One Type of PFD Panel VSI

Magenta bar grows up or down to show rate of climb/descent in feet per minute.

needle swings upward or downward, reflecting the airplane's rate of climb or descent.

Figure 34 shows the internal workings of the VSI. The case is vented to static pressure through an amazingly small opening called a *capillary tube* (also called an *airflow restrictor*). The expandable capsule connects to the static source via a normal size tube. At a constant altitude, the pressure in the case and the capsule are equal and no climb or descent rate is shown. During a climb, air pressure in the capsule decreases but air pressure in the case can't decrease as quickly because of the airflow restrictor. Therefore, pressure in the capsule is less than in the case, resulting in the capsule's *compression* which is mechanically converted into a *rate of climb* indication. Precisely the opposite happens during a descent, when the capsule is at a greater pressure than the case, resulting in the capsule's *expansion* which is mechanically converted into a *rate of descent* indication.

You'll find the vertical speed indicator very useful in helping you plan climbs and descents. Suppose you're 10 nautical miles from an airport and traveling at two nautical miles per minute (a 120 knot ground speed). It takes five minutes to cover those 10 miles. If the airplane's altitude is 3,000 feet above the airport elevation, a descent rate of 600 feet per minute is required to reach the airport. While this is only a rough estimate, it does aid you in planning your descents.

The VSI is also a useful instrument for detecting trends away from an established pitch attitude. We learned that the altimeter is very useful as a pitch instrument during straight and level flight, turns and steep turns. Frankly, I use the VSI more than I do the altimeter for determining changes in airplane pitch. During a steep turn I'll scan the VSI and watch for needle movement. Any deviation from a zero reading is quickly corrected by a change in elevator pressure. While the instrument does have a slight lag, it is hardly noticeable when small, non-abrupt pitch changes are made.

THE VERTICAL SPEED INDICATOR

Instrument case

Calibrated leak: a small opening that restricts (causes a lag in) the flow of static air pressure into the instrument's case.

The expandable capsule

Also called an *airflow restrictor*

Static source

The capsule expands or contracts at a rate predetermined by the calibrated leak. This expansion or contraction is mechanically converted into a rate of climb or descent.

Fig. 34

INSIDE THE ALTIMETER

Expandable capsules

INSIDE THE VERTICAL SPEED INDICATOR

My thumb (useful for preventing car doors from closing).

Tube connecting capsule to static source

Expandable capsule

To static source

Alternate Static Source

A pilot reported downwind at one of our local airports on a quiet, calm morning. ATC said, "2132 Bravo, which runway would you like to land on this morning?" The pilot replied, "Ah, that one." To which the controller responded, "Ah, could you point a little louder?" Sometimes a pilot's brain is like an airplane's static source—it becomes clogged. Fortunately for airplanes, there's often an alternate source of static pressure in the event the primary source becomes plugged.

Since the airspeed indicator, altimeter, and vertical speed indicator all rely on static pressure, any clogging of the static source will affect these instruments. In fact, a plugged static port will prevent any static air pressure change, causing the altimeter to freeze at its last indication and the VSI to read zero, regardless of altitude change. It will also cause the airspeed to be in error if a climb or descent is made. Fortunately, some airplanes have *alternate static sources* that tap into another source of static air pressure.

Figure 35 depicts the alternate static source for the airplane's three pressure instruments. If the primary static source becomes plugged, a little valve, normally located under the instrument panel above the pilot's knee, can be opened (Figure 36). Cabin static air pressure now becomes the pressure source for the airspeed indicator, altimeter and VSI. Cabin static air pressure is slightly less than outside pressure, so selecting it will cause a slight, temporary jump in the VSI's indication and a small gain in altitude (usually less than 50 feet). This will generally be the least of your problems.

THE ALTERNATE STATIC SYSTEM

Fig. 35

Static port

Static line connects to altimeter, vertical speed indicator and airspeed indicator.

Alternate static source line

Alternate static source

ASI ALT VSI

L R

N2

Fig. 36

INST PITOT HEAT NAV LIGHTS LD LIGH

The alternate static source is activated by this valve in the cockpit
(Note: Valve location and appearance will vary between airplanes.)

The Gyroscopic Instruments

The Attitude Indicator

The *attitude indicator* or *artificial horizon* is one of three gyroscopic instruments in the airplane. The other two are the heading indicator and the turn coordinator. The attitude indicator (Figure 37) is located in the top middle of the panel's six primary instruments (or in the background of the primary flight display). Consider this. If you acquired something important, like Leonardo da Vinci's "Mona Lisa" or its famed counterpart, the "Mona Larry," you'd put it on the wall for everyone would see. Well, that's why the attitude indicator is put smack in the middle of the instrument panel. You can safely assume it has considerable importance in order to merit such a position.

The attitude indicator provides you with attitude information in much the same way the outside, visible horizon does. Attitude indicators become especially valuable when the outside horizon is no longer visible. Accidentally flying into the clouds, flying in very hazy conditions toward the sun or night flight over the desert are all conditions where the attitude indicator helps you determine the airplane's pitch and bank condition (the only thing the attitude indicator can't help you with is when rear seat passengers put their hands over your eyes and say, "Guess where?" This is why you carry fire extinguishers in the airplane—one warning shot and they always let go).

Figure 38 shows how the attitude indicator presents its pitch and bank information. The basis of this presentation is a symbolic set of airplane wings resting over a moveable horizon card. Painted directly onto the horizon card is a white horizon line, a light colored area above the

THE ATTITUDE INDICATOR

Traditional Attitude Indicator   **PFD Type Attitude Indicator**

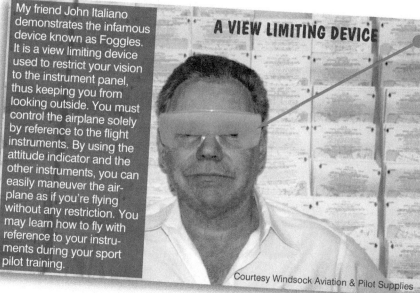

Fig. 37

line representing the sky and a darker colored area below representing the ground (Even in smoggy Los Angeles, these two colors shouldn't be reversed). Bank and pitch markings are also shown on the card.

The symbolic wings are attached to the instrument's case, while the horizon card is free to rotate underneath them. Because the horizon card is mechanically attached to a stabilized gyro, it essentially remains fixed in space while the airplane rotates about it during flight. This gives the impression the symbolic airplane wings are the things that move (they don't move since they're attached to the instrument's case which is bolted to the instrument panel).

Figure 39 shows a sequence of variable attitude conditions on the face of the attitude indicator. (Remember, in each case the airplane has pitched or rolled around the horizon card that's remaining stationary in space.) A straight and level pitch attitude is shown on attitude

THE ATTITUDE INDICATOR

Sky pointer — 10° Bank lines — 60° Bank line — Bank pointer — Degree pitch line — Sky — Ground — Airplane adjustment knob — Horizon line — Artificial airplane wing

Fig. 38

My friend John Italiano demonstrates the infamous device known as Foggles. It is a view limiting device used to restrict your vision to the instrument panel, thus keeping you from looking outside. You must control the airplane solely by reference to the flight instruments. By using the attitude indicator and the other instruments, you can easily maneuver the airplane as if you're flying without any restriction. You may learn how to fly with reference to your instruments during your sport pilot training.

A VIEW LIMITING DEVICE

Courtesy Windsock Aviation & Pilot Supplies

VARIOUS ATTITUDES AND BANKS

Fig. 39

the instrument points to the 30° bank increment (each of the first three indices represent 10° of bank). Therefore, the airplane is in a 30° right bank. If you wanted to return to straight and level flight, which way would you turn? You must turn the control wheel to the left to raise the right wing and return to straight flight.

Attitude indicator F depicts an airplane in a nose-up pitch attitude while in left 30° bank turn. Attitude indicator G shows an airplane in a nose-up pitch attitude while in a right turn at a very steep 60° of bank. Finally, attitude indicator H shows

indicator A. You know the airplane is flying straight because the symbolic airplane wings are not banked. The airplane's nose is level with the horizon, indicating it is probably holding its altitude (that's *probably* since we'd need to look at the altimeter to be sure). The picture made by the reference airplane is similar to the way reality looks out of your airplane's front windscreen during flight.

Attitude indicator B shows the airplane in straight flight with a nose-up pitch attitude. The little symbolic airplane's nose (the white ball—the head of a bald pilot) rests a little above the 10° pitch up index and the wings are level. Remember, the little airplane in the attitude indicator isn't moving, it's the horizon card behind the symbolic airplane that does all the moving (I'll explain how it does this in a moment).

Attitude indicator C depicts straight flight with a nose-down pitch attitude. The airplane's wings are level and the nose is pointed below the horizon.

Attitude indicator D depicts a left turn in a level pitch attitude. Sometimes it's a little difficult to determine which way the airplane is banked. Ask yourself, "Which wing is pointed toward the ground?" In this picture it's obvious that the left wing is pointed downward. The airplane must be in a left turn. I do hope this

is as obvious as a chin strap on a toupee. After all, if the left wing is pointed to the ground, you should be making a left turn. The only time this wouldn't be true is if you're inverted. And if you're making inverted turns at this point in your career, then you either need more dual instruction or you have been anointed by Chuck Yeager or Neil Armstrong (in other words, you probably don't need to read this book).

Another important question to ask is, "If you wanted to return to straight flight in attitude indicator D, which wing would you raise?" (you've got a 50-50 chance on this one). Yes, the left wing. It's the one dipping toward the ground. If you ever lost sight of the horizon, you could maintain straight flight by simply asking which wing needs raising. Then you'd simply keep the small white ball on the white horizon line to maintain a level pitch attitude. Keep in mind that we refer to straight flight as both wings being parallel with the horizon and level flight as the airplane's longitudinal axis being parallel with the horizon. Attitude indicator D shows the airplane in a level pitch attitude while in a bank.

What type of turn does attitude indicator E show? Ask yourself, "Which wing is pointed toward the ground?" The answer is, the right wing. The airplane is in a right turn. The vertical indicator at the top of

PITCH ATTITUDE AND FLIGHT CONDITIONS

All three airplanes have similar attitude indications on the attitude indicator.

Fig. 40

Movement in a climb

Movement in slow flight

Movement in a stall

Bob, that's not me, it's the stall horn.

GYROSCOPIC RIGIDITY IN SPACE

A child's toy top stays vertical or rigid in space when spun. When not spun, it easily falls to its side.

The same principle applies to modern day gyro instruments. A spinning gyro remains fixed in space allowing the airplane to rotate around it.

Fig. 41

Spinning

Not spinning

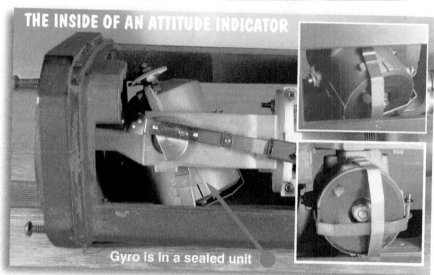

THE INSIDE OF AN ATTITUDE INDICATOR

Gyro is in a sealed unit

an airplane in a nose-down pitch attitude while in a right turn at 20° of bank.

Have you noticed that I have not mentioned climbing or descending in reference to pitch attitude? Even though a nose-up pitch attitude is normally associated with a climb, there are occasions where it's not. For instance, Figure 40 shows three different flight conditions associated with a nose-up pitch attitude. The airplane may either be climbing with full power, cruising with limited power, or stalling with no power. All these conditions are associated with a nose-up pitch attitude. When flying by reference to instruments, the only way you can tell what your airplane is doing is to consult some of the other flight instruments. You will learn about this a little later on.

How does the attitude indicator (as well as the other gyro-based instruments) accomplish the mysterious task of portraying attitude? It does this through a gyroscopic principle known as *rigidity in space*. Figure 41 shows a child's top in full spin. A spinning top, just like a spin-

THE ATTITUDE INDICATOR

When the attitude indicator's gyro is spun by air, it remains rigid or fixed in space. The airplane rotates around the gyro and mechanically converts this movement into pitch and bank information on the face of the horizon card.

Spinning gyro

Swivel points

Gyro gimbal system allowing two degrees of motion (pitch and bank)

Base of gyro's gimbal system

Movable horizon face card

Fig. 42

THE HORIZON LINE

The attitude indicator's horizon line remains parallel to the earth's surface at all times and the sky pointer always points upward toward the sky.

Fig. 43

ning wheel inside the attitude indicator (Figure 41), acquires the unusual property known as rigidity in space. A small wheel (a gyro) spun at high speed tends to remain in a fixed or rigid position. That's why the child's top remains upright until is stops spinning. It's this property that

allows the attitude indicator's horizon card to portray airplane attitude.

The internal workings of the attitude indicator are displayed in Figure 42 (see Postflight Briefing #5-4 for info on how the solid state gyros of the PFD work). While this is a highly simplified drawing, it does allow you to understand the principles upon which the attitude indicator works. Notice the circular disk in the center of the instrument. This is the gyroscope. It is mechanically connected to the sky/ground horizon card on the face of the indicator. When spun, this disk takes on gyroscopic properties and maintains its position, fixed in space, relative to the earth. Thus, the horizon's face card, which is mechanically connected to the gyro, also remains fixed in space. From inside the airplane, the horizon face card accurately represents the real horizon in either a right or left hand turn as shown in Figure 43. As you can clearly see, the airplane rotates about the attitude indicator's gyro-stabilized (fixed) horizon card.

Most light airplane attitude gyros are spun by air pressure. A vacuum pump (Figure 44) sucks air through the instrument and over the gyro, spinning it at high velocity (Figure 45).

THE SUCTION GAUGE

Fig. 46

Operation within the green arc tells you that all your gyro instruments are getting enough vacuum pressure for proper operation.

This system is known as the *vacuum system* (and this isn't something you use to keep your airplane clean!).

Notice that the vacuum pump is connected to two instruments—the attitude indicator and the heading indicator. Both these instruments use gyroscopes that are typically spun by vacuum air pressure. You may also come across an airplane with a heading indicator whose gyros are electrically spun. Either way, the spinning of a gyro allows these instruments to work their magic.

Malfunctions of the airplane's air-spun gyro instruments are usually caused by the vacuum pump providing insufficient vacuum pressure. An airplane's vacuum gauge (Figure 46) keeps you informed about the

THE AIRPLANE'S VACUUM PUMP

Fig. 44

THE VACUUM SYSTEM

Engine driven vacuum pump

Discharge air

Inlet air that spins gyro instruments

Vacuum system air filter

Suction gauge

The vacuum pump sucks air over the attitude indicator and the heading indicator. Air enters these instruments from the air filter located either on the engine side of the firewall or inside the cockpit.

Fig. 45

ATTITUDE INDICATOR ADJUSTMENT KNOB

Turning the adjustment knob allows you to re-set the small airplane's position. You may need to do this to show the straight and level position when flying at variable weights and speeds since this changes your angle of attack.

Fig. 47

THE ATTITUDE INDICATOR'S DIAGONAL BANK LINES

Fig. 48

(A)	(B)	(C)	(D)
These are the attitude indicator's 20° & 45° bank lines (sometimes it's a 15° bank line vs. a 20° bank line).	The airplane's wings are aligned with the first white line which produces a 20° bank.	The airplane's wings are aligned with the second white line which produces a 45° degree bank.	The wings are above and parallel with the 45° bank line. The airplane is in a nose-up attitude at a 45° bank.

amount of suction provided by the pump. Operations outside the normal range (green arc) on the gauge usually result in erroneous readings on your gyro instruments. On some airplanes, low power settings (such as a low engine idle before takeoff or long, low-power descents) produce insufficient vacuum for the instruments. Simply increasing power slightly usually takes care of the problem.

Here are a few more things about the attitude indicator you should know. First, observe the little knob on the bottom left of the instrument in Figure 47. Rotating this knob moves the reference airplane up or down in the attitude indicator's window. This allows you to set the symbolic wings precisely on the horizon line before takeoff and in flight. It's sometimes necessary to adjust the symbolic wings since there are several variables that can change the attitude required for level flight. These variables might be either the weight of the airplane or the speed at which it is flown.

The attitude indicator has bank markings calibrated at 10°, 20° and 30° increments with an additional calibration at 60° (there are no calibrations above 60° since no denture adhesive has been shown to work at these G-forces). But these bank

indices don't help much if you're trying to do a 45° bank turn do they? Fortunately, some attitude indicators have diagonal bank lines that help identify additional bank angles. Figure 48 shows the 20° and 45° white bank marks on the bottom portions of these particular types of attitude indicators.

Banking the airplane so the symbolic wings are aligned with the first diagonal line, as shown in position B, produces a bank of 20° (on some instruments it produces a 15° bank). Further banking so the wings are aligned with the second diagonal line produces a 45° bank as shown in position C. What's informative about these bank lines is that they also provide you with pitch information as shown in position D. In other words, these bank lines also provide you with a horizon reference.

The next time you try a 45° bank turn, place the symbolic airplane's wings on or slightly above the second diagonal bank line and keep them there. You'll find the bank line acts like the horizon line in level flight. You can use the bank line as an attitude reference instead of keeping the little white ball on the horizon line. The diagonal bank line is easier to use as a pitch reference than the little white ball.

The Heading Indicator

The airplane's *heading indicator* is shown in Figure 49. Sometimes called the *directional gyro* or *DG,* the heading indicator is a gyro instrument that provides the same information

THE HEADING INDICATOR

Traditional Heading Indicator

I'm telling you, it's safe back here. They never push on these things!

PFD Type Heading Indicator

THE HEADING INDICATOR

Fig. 49

THE HEADING INDICATOR

When the gyro in the heading indicator spins, it remains rigid (fixed) in space. The airplane rotates about the gyro as it turns and a gearing system converts this movement into a heading change on the face of the indicator.

Fig. 50

Gimbal system allowing two degrees of motion

Swivel points

Spinning gyro

I'm tellin' ya, the spinning wheel does something for me!

Face card that rotates with fixed position of gyro

found on the magnetic compass—heading information. Why have two instruments to do one job? Because the magnetic compass is an instrument best read by one of those bobbing dolls you see in the back window shelf of cars. Like some passengers, the magnetic compass makes a poor candidate for air transport. The heading indicator is an attempt to remedy some of the ills of the magnetic compass, though the latter remains a key component in your pilot's instrument kit—without it, you wouldn't be able to set the heading indicator in the first place.

On the face of the heading indicator is a small outline of a stationary airplane superimposed over a compass card that's free to rotate. The nose of the small outline airplane always points straight up to a number that is your airplane's present heading. As the actual airplane turns, the compass card remains stabilized or fixed in space by an internal spinning gyro, as shown in Figure 50. The small outline airplane points to your airplane's magnetic heading.

Before takeoff, after the gyros have had sufficient time to spin up, set the

heading indicator to the heading shown on the magnetic compass. Do this by pushing and rotating the heading indicator's adjustment knob, as shown in Figure 51. Once the heading indicator is set to the compass' magnetic heading, it should provide accurate directional information for a reasonable period of time. Like a cautious parent, you need to check up on this child occasionally, lest it wander. How much it wanders, and when, depends on how affected the heading indicator is by something known as *gyroscopic drift*.

Gyroscopic heading drift is caused by internal mechanical errors and/or the airplane's constantly changing position in space relative to the earth. The most important thing to remember is to keep checking or updating the reading on the heading indicator with the magnetic compass at least every 15 minutes. Do this more often if your airplane's heading indicator has a history of wandering, which is sometimes referred to as *precessing*. Despite gyroscopic drift, the heading indicator is much easier to use for navigation than the magnetic compass (as you'll soon see when we study the magnetic compass' errors).

Notice that the heading indicator in Figure 51 is calibrated in five degree increments. Every 30°, starting from north, is referenced by printed letters or numerals that are sometimes called *cardinal numbers* (which sounds much better than *archbishop numbers*). Between the letters and numerals are slashes, calibrated to five and ten degree increments. The slashes at 10° increments are slightly larger for easier identification (however, if the eye doctor tells you, based on your current eyeglass prescription, that you're only two lenses away from being a fly, you may need to move closer to the panel).

The heading indicator in Figure 51 shows that the airplane is currently heading north. This is called *360 degrees* or *zero* degrees, depending on who's talking. Either value is correct. The *E* represents east or 90°, *S* represents south or 180° and *W* represents west or 270°. If you want to sound like a pro, don't call them by the letters. I actually heard a pilot call a controller and say, "Ahhh, this is 2132 Bravo, ahhh, I'd like vectors to the airport." The controller said, "Roger 32 Bravo, what's your heading?" The pilot replied, "Ahhh,.. my heading is *Eeee!*" The controller came

HEADING INDICATOR

The outline airplane's nose in the heading indicator points to the actual airplane's magnetic heading. As the airplane turns, the numbered disk rotates under the outline airplane, allowing your new heading to appear on top.

Fig. 51

Outline airplane

Your current heading

Adjustment knob to correct for heading drift

DIFFERENT HEADINGS

Heading "zero-three-zero"
A

Heading "one-four-zero"
B

Heading "three-zero-zero"
C

Heading "three-zero-five"
D

Fig. 52

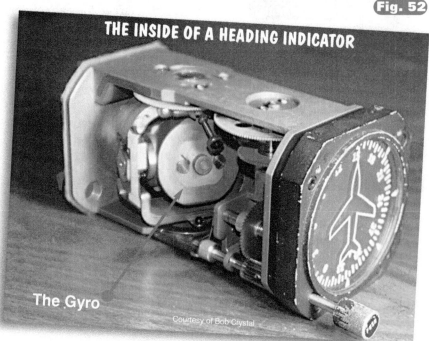

THE INSIDE OF A HEADING INDICATOR

The Gyro

Courtesy of Bob Crystal

back with, "Well, 32 Bravo, your heading is aiming you at another airplane, I suggest you do a W before you bump into it."

Heading indicator A in Figure 52 shows the airplane heading 30°. This is pronounced, "zero-three-zero degrees." Indicator B shows a heading of 140°. This is pronounced "one-four-zero degrees." Indicator C shows a heading of 300° or "three-zero-zero degrees." Indicator D depicts a heading of 305° or "three-zero-five degrees."

If you're instructed to turn to a particular heading, simply look for the number on the instrument and turn in the shortest direction toward it, unless instructed to "turn the long way" or "go the long way around." (This is similar to how we flight instructors find the exquisite dining facilities we're known to frequent. We simply turn in the direction of the nearest drive-through speaker).

Referring to Indicator B, which way would you turn to fly a heading of 60°? Yes, a left turn would be the shortest

direction to get to a heading of 60°. If you were instructed to fly a heading of 240° in the same figure, which way would you turn? Of course, a turn to the right would be the shortest direction to the new heading.

One last word on heading indicators. If you accidentally fly into a cloud, you can fly back out by making a 180° turn (something General Custer should have done shortly after leaving the fort). One of the biggest mistakes pilots make when starting a 180° turn is in forgetting to look at the heading representing 180 degrees of turn. Simply look at the tail (the bottom) of the outline-airplane and turn to the number it points to. This is similar to looking for the nearest exit in a hotel. You need to know exactly where to go (what heading to turn to for 180° of turn) if you need a quick exit (especially true if the hotel has a name like "La Casa de Flash Fire").

For instance, if you accidentally flew into the clouds while on a heading of 030° as shown by heading indicator A, what heading would you turn to? The tail points to a heading of 210°. Simply establish a 15 or 20° bank on the attitude indicator while keeping the airplane's attitude level with the horizon. When 210° appears at the top of the heading indicator, you've completed the turn. Roll the wings level and wait for blue sky to appear.

The Turn Coordinator

The turn coordinator sounds like the guy who calls those commands at a square dance (square dance is the

THE TURN COORDINATOR

Fig. 53

Traditional Turn Coordinator

PFD Type Turn Rate Indicator

THE TURN COORDINATOR

DC ELEC
NO PITCH INFORMATION

TURN COORDINATOR
L   R
2 MIN

I heard him say the radio has a few bugs in it; maybe some babes, eh?

The magenta horizontal rate bar grows right or left to show the what the airplane's heading will be in six seconds. The white ball at the bottom of the instrument is the inclinometer.

TURN COORDINATOR

DC
ELEC

NO PITCH INFORMATION

Fig. 54

TURN COORDINATOR

L   R

2 MIN

Inclinometer consisting of a black ball suspended in a liquid-filled glass Tube

Rate of turn needle that rotates right or left

Standard rate turn index

original source of rap music). The turn coordinator (Figure 53) is actually a gyro instrument that provides information on your airplane's direction of roll, rate of heading change and whether the airplane is slipping or skidding in the turns (i.e., movement about its yaw and roll axes).

Turn coordinators consist of two instruments: a needle and an inclinometer (Figure 54). We've already discussed the inclinometer in

Chapter 2, so let's concentrate on the turn needle. The turn needle consists of a small symbolic airplane in the center of the instrument capable of rotating right or left.

Unlike the spinning gyros in the attitude indicator and heading indicator, the turn coordinator's gyro is usually spun by electricity. This is what causes the whining sound you hear when the airplane's master switch is first turned on during preflight (if you hear the whining and you aren't in the airplane, it could be coming from a sorrowful student whose airplane is down for maintenance). The turn coordinator's gyro is electrically powered, to keep at least one gyro instrument operating during a rare failure of the airplane's vacuum pump. For instrument pilots, this is a blessing. In the event the vacuum pump fails, the airplane is controllable, while in the clouds, by reference to the turn coordinator alone.

Figure 55 shows the internal workings of the turn coordinator. The turn coordinator's gyro is free to move in only one dimension, instead of three like that of the attitude indicator. During any rolling, turning, or yawing movement, the instrument's gyro feels a force applied to its side.

This causes the gyro to precess in a predictable manner.

To present turn information, the turn coordinator relies on a principle known as *gyroscopic precession*. Precession causes a force applied to a spinning body (the gyro), to be felt 90° in the direction of rotation. To most people, gyroscopic precession is as much a mystery as is a cargo airline that hires flight attendants. If you're interested in how precession

THE TURN COORDINATOR

THE TURN COORDINATOR

Gyro in sealed unit

The gyro in the turn coordinator is free to rotate in one direction about the gimbaling system. When the airplane rolls or turns, gyroscopic precession rolls the gyro, causing a deflection of the turn needle.

Gimbal roll axis

Fig. 55

DC
ELEC

NO PITCH INFORMATION

TURN COORDINATOR

L

2 MIN

Spinning gyro

Gimbal system allows only one degree of motion about its axis (i.e., It can only rotate about its axis)

Turn needle (the reference airplane) that deflects with precession of the gyro

THE TURN COORDINATOR (Rolling Right/Left)

Force felt here (point 2) at 90° in the direction of rotation (above gimbal roll axis).

Gimbal roll axis

A tension spring attached below the gimbal roll axis keeps the gimbal in the default horizontal position.

Force (from a roll to the right) applied here at point 1 (below gimbal roll axis).

Fig. 56

When the airplane rolls (instead of yawing or turning), the turn needle deflects in the direction of roll.

THE TURN COORDINATOR (Yawing or Turning)

Fig. 57

When the airplane yaws or turns to the right, force is applied to the gyro at point 1 (above the gimbal's roll axis). Gyroscopic precession causes this force to be felt 90° in the direction of rotation, or at the top of the gyro at point 2. This rolls the gyro counterclockwise, resulting in a turn needle deflected to the right.

Airplane yaws or turns to the right

Gimbal roll axis

Force felt here, 90 in the direction of rotation (above roll axis)

Force from yaw to right applied here (above roll axis)

Gyro's gimbal system rotates counterclockwise

A right yaw or turn twists the gyro's spin axis & applies a force at point 1. The force is felt at point 2, 90 degrees in the direction of gyro rotation.

Yaw/Turn Direction

The turn coordinator's gyro in Figure 56 spins on its axis while held on a gimbal (the gimbal is connected to its base at a rearward up-sloping angle and is free to rotate only in one direction about its own axis). A small spring applies a slight tension on the gimbal which normally holds it in the horizontal position until the airplane *rolls, yaws* or *turns.* As the airplane rolls to the right, the gyro's spin axis is also forced to rotate. This applies a force to the bottom of the gyro at position 1 (Figure 56). To better understand how this force is applied, visualize yourself holding the axis of a spinning gyro (one hand on each side of the gyro) parallel to the floor. Twist the axis so that your right hand moves toward the ground and the left hand moves toward the ceiling. This simulates an airplane rolling to the right and results in a force applied to the gyro at position 1. Gyroscopic precession causes this force to be felt 90 degrees in the direction of gyro rotation at position 2. Since position 2 is above the gimbal's roll axis in Figure 56 (remember, the gimbal slopes at a rearward angle), the gimbal rotates counterclockwise. Mechanical gearing results in the *turn needle* (symbolic reference airplane) deflecting to the right, thus indicating a roll to the right.

In addition to the direction of roll, the turn coordinator also shows the direction of *yaw* and the *rate* at which the airplane changes *headings* (Figure 57). Yawing to the right applies a force to the gyro above the gimbal's roll axis at position 1. (See the small insert at the bottom right of Figure 57 to understand how the *yaw* or *turning* force is felt by the gyro.) Gyroscopic precession results in this force being felt 90 degrees in the direction of gyro rotation at position 2. This causes the gimbal system to rotate counterclockwise and, because of mechanical gearing, deflects the turn needle to the right. Once *established* in a right turn, this force is continually applied to position 1, resulting in a needle deflection which represents the airplane's rate of turn (how fast the nose moves across the horizon). The turn needle doesn't represent the angle of bank. It only shows direction of roll, yaw and the rate of turn. In fact, it's possible to bank the airplane to the right (or left) while adding opposite rudder to keep the nose from moving (heading is constant) and the turn needle shouldn't deflect. Try it with your instructor.

works, see Postflight Briefing #5-2, *Gyroscopic Precession Explained.* Other than personal curiosity, there is absolutely no need for you to understand how gyroscopic precession actually works. I provide the information for the intensely curious among you as well as for those who have taken up reading since your satellite dish was stolen.

Even though it may appear to, the turn coordinator doesn't show bank angle. Don't be fooled by this. Only *direction* of roll or yaw and *rate of turn* are derivable from the turn

coordinator. Refer to the attitude indicator for bank angle.

Figure 58 shows two turn coordinators, each with a different amount of wing deflection on the symbolic airplane. Airplane A's wing is deflected to the white index mark indicating the airplane's heading is changing at 3° per second. In aviation parlance this is called a *standard rate turn.* Since there are 360 degrees in a full circle, it takes 120 seconds or two minutes to make a complete turn (360°/3° per second). This is why the instrument is labeled *2 min turn.*

Some students think this means we're going to cook in the cockpit and use the turn coordinator as an elegant means of knowing when to flip the waffles. You'll soon find that the only waffling in the cockpit will be by the pilot-in-training.

Miniature airplane B's wings are deflected halfway between the zero and three degree per second turn marks. The rate of turn is 1.5° per second. At this slower rate, the airplane takes twice as long to make a complete 360° turn.

Fig. 58

RATE OF TURN ON THE TURN COORDINATOR

Standard rate turn of 3 degrees per second

Ⓐ

DC ELEC
NO PITCH INFORMATION
TURN COORDINATOR
L   R
2 MIN

3/sec index

Half standard rate turn of 1.5 degrees per second

Ⓑ

DC ELEC
NO PITCH INFORMATION
TURN COORDINATOR
L   R
2 MIN

1.5/sec point

Both airplanes were previously established in a turn passing through a heading of 300 degrees.

297°   300°

298.5°   300°

After one second, Airplane A will be on a heading of 297°

After one second, Airplane B will be on a heading of 298.5°

Why would you want to know the rate at which your airplane changes headings? Assume your heading indicator has failed and you accidentally fly into a cloud (it's obvious you're having an exceptionally bad day here). You could make a precise 180° exit from the cloud by making a standard rate turn for one minute (that's 3°/sec for 60 seconds=180°). This is one of several reasons why the

turn coordinator is a very useful instrument. Instrument rated pilots find it useful for helping them anticipate the time it takes to make heading changes. When you venture forth and obtain an instrument rating (a license that allows you to fly in clouds), you'll find the turn coordinator a worthy and welcome ally in the event of attitude gyro failure.

The Magnetic Compass

A friend of mine purchased a very nervous little puppy. Every time the phone rang, the puppy would wet the floor. My friend contemplated using radiator stop leak to solve the problem but decided on a better plan. He gave the puppy to his super mean mother-in-law. Every afternoon he would call her and ask, "Hey, ...how's your rug?" We call this *controlling an action at a distance*. The magnetic compass is similarly controlled (affected) by something a long distance away.

A *magnetic compass* (Figure 59) responds to the natural phenomena of the earth's magnetic pole, otherwise known as its *magnetic field*. This field is constantly pulling one end of the compass' nee-

dle, keeping it pointing north. Despite some peculiar errors in the compass, it is one of the oldest and most reliable navigational instruments known to man (next to moss, which supposedly grows on the north side of trees). In Chapter 13 we'll talk about navigational techniques. For now, let's discuss how the compass

THE MAGNETIC COMPASS
Fig. 59

THE MAGNETIC COMPASS NEEDLE

The north-seeking end of the compass needle always points toward the magnetic north pole.

Compass card

Fig. 60

The compass needle is a small magnetized element. It's connected to the compass card and rests on a pivot. This allows it to rotate within the compass housing.

THE NORTH SEEKING END OF THE COMPASS NEEDLE

Fig. 61

West **East**

Lubber line

A

B

C

As the airplane turns, the north seeking end of the magnetic compass needle continues to point to the magnetic north pole. Since the compass needle is attached to the marked compass card, the appropriate heading appears under the lubber line (reference line).

Compass B and compass C are rotated toward you for better viewing.

SKI SLOPES AND THE MAGNETIC COMPASS

Fig. 62

Skiers follow the profile of the terrain with their skis. As the terrain rises, their skis tilt up; as it dips, their skis tilt down. In other words, the slope exerts a force on the skis, making them tilt up or down. In much the same way, magnetic lines of force exert a vertical (downward) pull on the compass needle. This pull is known as *magnetic dip* and it's responsible for compass acceleration, deceleration and turning errors.

works and look at a few of its inherent errors (I don't trust moss as a navigational tool, since all four corners of my shower seem to point north).

Inside the magnetic compass is a small magnetic needle connected to a circular compass card (Figure 60). Both the card and the needle are free to rotate on a central pivot. One side of the needle is called the *north-seeking end* (dark-colored side in all my drawings) and it always points

towards the earth's magnetic north pole. Thus, like a gyro fixed in space, the needle attempts to remain stationary. As the airplane changes direction, it rotates around the needle and its attached card, resulting in new headings appearing in the compass' window, as shown in Figure 61 (and all this time you've been thinking that the compass card actually does the rotating. That's OK. A lot of people still think that the Magna Carta is what you use when you're over the limit on your Visa card. The airplane's actual heading is read under a reference line or *lubber line* running down the center of the window.

Notice that the numbers printed on the compass card appear to be in the wrong place. In Figure 61, Compass A is heading north, yet westerly headings are shown on the right side of its card (i.e., 330°, 300° and W or 270° which is not visible yet). Easterly headings are shown on the left side of its card (i.e., 030°, 060° and E or 090° which is also not yet visible). This makes sense when you consider that as the airplane turns left, toward the west, it pivots about the stationary compass card as shown by Compass B. Eventually, westerly headings appear under the lubber line. A right 90° turn causes the airplane to pivot about the compass card with easterly headings

MAGNETIC DIP

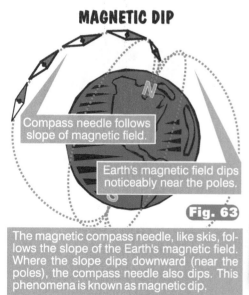

N

Compass needle follows slope of magnetic field.

Earth's magnetic field dips noticeably near the poles.

Fig. 63

The magnetic compass needle, like skis, follows the slope of the Earth's magnetic field. Where the slope dips downward (near the poles), the compass needle also dips. This phenomena is known as magnetic dip.

THE INSIDE OF A MAGNETIC COMPASS

Compass central pivot point

Compass needle

HANG THAT HEADSET ON YOUR HEAD

When making position reports I always used my headset, and upon completion I laid the headset on what seemed a very convenient place since the cockpit was crowded—the top of the instrument panel! During the few minutes it took to make the report I obviously never noticed that the compass read differently (I steered by the liquid compass because I had not found the operation of the slaved gyro satisfactory, and, of course I had swung the liquid compass)... Depending on how close to the compass I had laid the headset, the compass would show an erroneous reading of about 15 degrees to the left...

ASRS Report

The magnetic field from the mic can cause compass errors.

After | Before

The magnetic field from the headset can also cause compass errors.

After | Before

Fig. 64

MAGNETIC DIP CORRECTION

Instead of the simplified compass-needle drawing shown above, the compass actually has two needles, side-by-side with their north-seeking ends aligned. These needles are located on the bottom portion of the compass card and the entire card is suspended by a pivot. This gives the card a pendulous-type mounting (diagram below is also highly simplified for easy understanding).

The earth's magnetic field tries to pull or "dip" the compass needles and the card downward as shown below. This would render the compass useless if it remained this way.

If the compass card is tilted as shown above, the card naturally tends to return to a near level position because of the "pendulum" effect. With the mass of the needles and additional items, the card remains nearly level despite magnetic dip, as shown below.

appearing under the lubber line, as shown by Compass C.

To fly any heading visible on the compass card, you must turn in the opposite direction to center it under the lubber line. For instance, if the heading you want to fly is visible to the right of the lubber line, turn to the left to center its value (now you know why the heading indicator is easier to use!).

To better understand how the compass works, we can compare its magnetic needle with skis. Skis are similar to compass needles in how they respond to changing terrain. In Figure 62, notice that as the terrain dips, so do the skis. If the terrain slopes upward, the skis, likewise slope upward. If the terrain dips downward, the skis dip downward. The point is, the magnetic compass needle is like a ski and the earth's magnetic field is like the terrain. The compass needle will always try to dip in the direction of the magnetic field.

Figure 63 depicts the earth's magnetic field. Notice that the field dips downward at nearly a 90° angle at the poles while there is very little dip in the equatorial regions. For most of the United States, the downward dip

angle is around 70°. Just like skis following dipping terrain, the magnetic compass needle wants to tilt downward with the magnetic field. This is called *magnetic dip*, and is the only kind of dip pilots serve at parties.

It's also a serious problem for the magnetic compass. Unrestrained, this dip could render the compass unusable as a navigational device, since the card could get hung up on its pivot or in its container. Fortunately, the compass has been cleverly designed in such a way that the compass card's pendulous mounting counteracts this dip (Figure 64). As long as the compass card is allowed to hang parallel to the earth, it's not restricted by the dipping magnetic field. Therein lies the problem.

When the airplane accelerates or decelerates, the free-swinging compass card has inertia and tends to resist the speed change. This causes the compass card to tilt within its case. This results in what are known as *acceleration-deceleration errors* which are present on easterly and westerly headings only.

Whenever a turn is made, the compass card no longer hangs parallel to the earth's surface. Ordinarily, a turn won't affect the compass' reading unless the airplane is on a northerly or southerly heading at the time. Then the compass card temporarily leads or lags behind the airplane's actual heading. These are called the *northerly turning errors (even in a southerly direction)*. Let's examine the acceleration and deceleration errors first.

Acceleration And Deceleration Error

ACCELERATION AND DECELERATION ERRORS (on easterly & westerly headings)

Fig. 65

Magnetic North Pole

Dipping magnetic field

In level flight, on an easterly (or westerly heading), the compass reads the correct heading as long as the airplane doesn't accelerate or decelerate. Despite the dip in the earth's magnetic field, the compass card's pendulous mounting (and resultant center of gravity) keeps the compass needle from trying to bend downward with the dipping magnetic field.

As the airplane accelerates on an easterly (or westerly) heading, the rear of the compass card tilts upward as a result of the card's inertia. This allows the north-seeking end of the compass needle to dip downward as it tries to align itself with the earth's dipping magnetic field. This twists the compass card clockwise (as seen from above), resulting in the temporary appearance of a more northerly heading.

Deceleration on an easterly (or westerly) heading causes the rear of the compass card to swing downward. The north-seeking end of the compass needle dips downward, which causes the compass card to twist counterclockwise (as seen from above). This temporarily results in the compass indicating a more southerly heading.

Accelerating or decelerating on an easterly or westerly heading causes the compass to temporarily read in error. Accelerating causes the compass to give a more northerly heading than the one being flown. Decelerating causes the compass to read a more southerly heading than is actually being flown. An easy way to remember these errors is with the acronym: ANDS. This stands for Accelerate North, Decelerate South.

The acceleration-deceleration error occurs because a speed change forces the compass card to tilt within its case (Figure 65). As the card is forced to tilt, its pendulous properties are no longer as effective in correcting for the earth's dipping magnetic field. The compass needle's north-seeking end points downward in the direction of the dipped magnetic field. This results in a temporary heading error while the speed change is in progress.

Northerly Turning Errors

Turning errors are only experienced on northerly or southerly headings. These errors are also caused by

the compass card being forced to tilt when the airplane is in a bank. Now the pendulous properties of the card can't prevent the compass needle's north-seeking end from pointing downward in the direction of the dipped magnetic field. This results in

the appearance of a temporary heading error.

For instance, as the airplane turns from or through a northerly heading, the compass reading lags the airplane's heading (Figure 66). Airplane B is in a left turn and its heading is

The Whiskey Compass Made Easy to Remember

Here's an easy way to remember the northerly turning errors. A mechanic once told me that the magnetic compass used to be called the *whiskey compass* because it was filled with six ounces of clear whiskey. The liquid provides a dampening action for the compass card. (Don't rush to the plane. . .they don't use whiskey any more.)

Apparently, during World War II, Air Force mechanics would remove the top of the compass, insert a straw and suck out all the whiskey. Of course this didn't set well with compass manufacturers. A decision was made to put six ounces of kerosene into the compass. Then the Marine mechanics started drinking the liquid.

We flight instructors now inform our students that the compass is filled with molasses (not really, but read on). That's right! I said thick, gooey molasses. What happens when molasses gets cold? It thickens up. What happens when molasses gets hot? It thins out.

Therefore, if you're heading an airplane toward the cold north pole, think of the molasses thickening-up. As a result, the compass card lags within the thick fluid when turning.

Heading toward the hot, tropical south, the molasses heats up and thins out. The thin fluid causes the compass card to move more freely or lead the airplane's actual heading.

While the compass isn't actually filled with molasses, this little story does make it easier to understand which error is present on northerly or southerly headings.

approximately 360°. Yet its compass shows a heading of 030°—lagging behind its actual direction. Airplane C is in a right turn and its heading is also nearly 360°. Its compass shows a heading of 330°, which is lagging behind its actual direction. As the airplane turns away from a northerly heading, these turning errors disappear and the airplane's correct heading appears under the lubber line. Airplane A has no turning error because it's not in a turn. Its compass reads accurately.

Figure 67 depicts the turning error while on a southerly heading. Heading directly south with the wings level (the north pole is on the bottom of this figure) produces the correct reading in the compass window, as shown by Airplane A. As the airplane turns from or through a southerly heading, the compass reading leads the airplane's actual heading. As Airplane C turns from or through a southerly heading, its compass reading also leads the airplane's actual heading. As a heading of east or west is approached, the turning errors disappear.

Remember, all compass errors are caused by the dip of the earth's magnetic field. If it weren't for this, these troublesome errors wouldn't exist. With all these errors, why do we have a compass in the airplane in the first place? Because it works. The compass has only one moving part, making it one of the most reliable pieces of equipment in the airplane next to the ashtray. Unless someone has sucked the kerosene out of it, the magnetic compass will provide the most accurate heading information during straight and level unaccelerated flight. If that's not convincing, just remember, that the compass has only one moving part, requires no external power, air source or input, which can't be said for *any* other instrument on the panel! Learn to use the compass and you'll never worry about getting lost.

NORTHERLY TURNING ERROR

Fig. 66

As the airplane turns through or from a northerly heading, the compass needle (lying within the banked card) aligns itself with the earth's dipping magnetic field. This causes the card to twist, resulting in a heading that temporarily lags the airplane's actual heading.

SOUTHERLY TURNING ERROR

While on a southerly heading, the magnetic field rises upward from below the airplane. When the airplane turns from or through this southerly heading, the compass needle twists to align itself with the earth's dipping magnetic field. Thus, the compass card shows a heading that temporarily leads the airplane's actual heading.

Fig. 67

With a heading indicator you don't need to worry about turning errors or acceleration/deceleration errors. The heading indicator is gyro-stabilized and its accuracy isn't affected by turning or a change in speed. There is, however, one thing you need to be aware of. When initially setting the heading indicator to the value in the magnetic compass, make sure the airplane is in wings-level, unaccelerated flight (this is the only time you can be sure the compass value is most accurate). This prevents setting an incorrect heading into the heading indicator.

You'll learn a lot about the capabilities and idiosyncrasies of the airplane's instruments as you fly with them. Like me, I think you will learn to appreciate the hard-working instruments and the vital flight information they provide.

Now it's time to move on and find out about the rules you'll fly by.

Postflight Briefing #5-1

The following explanation on gyroscopic precession (Figure 68). It's a bit technical and not for the faint of heart, but it is certainly worth studying.

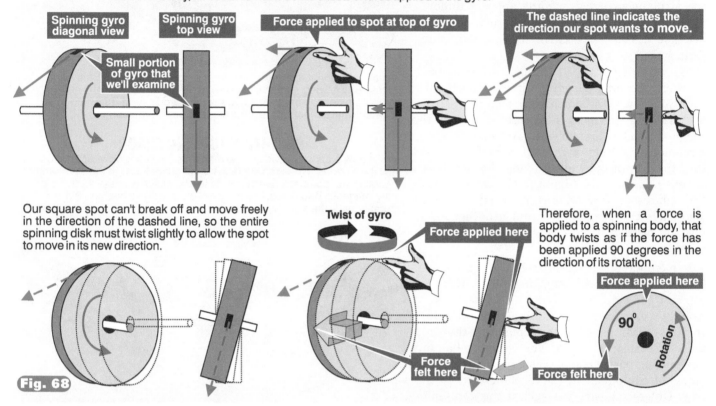

GYROSCOPIC PRECESSION

To understand gyroscopic precession we'll imagine a small square spot on top of a spinning gyro. This spot is made up of a small piece of the disk. Whatever happens to the spot also happens to the disk. In this way, it's easier to visualize the effects of force applied to the gyro.

Spinning gyro diagonal view · **Spinning gyro top view** · Small portion of gyro that we'll examine · **Force applied to spot at top of gyro** · **The dashed line indicates the direction our spot wants to move.**

Our square spot can't break off and move freely in the direction of the dashed line, so the entire spinning disk must twist slightly to allow the spot to move in its new direction.

Twist of gyro · **Force applied here** · **Force felt here**

Therefore, when a force is applied to a spinning body, that body twists as if the force has been applied 90 degrees in the direction of its rotation.

Force applied here · 90° · Rotation · **Force felt here**

Fig. 68

Postflight Briefing #5-2

Primary Flight Displays

If you've been observing the trends in aviation technology, you know that many of the newer airplanes on the market now have what is known as a primary flight display (PFD, also known as "glass cockpit" technology). Figure 69 shows a typical PFD.

Despite looking like something found on the Starship Enterprise, this large electronic crystal display provides the same information as the standard instrumentation found in other airplanes (and much additional information, too). The only difference is the way the information is presented. This is why you can transition from an airplane with mechanical-type gauges to one having a PFD with relative ease. However, mastery of all the bells and whistles on many PFDs will take hours of additional study time. Of course, you might be lucky enough to learn in an airplane having a PFD. Learning all the bells and whistles becomes part of your primary training, thus leading to mastery of all the instrument's gadgets *and* the ability to pilot the Starship Enterprise.

On the display to the left (Figure 70), you can see that the airspeed is read from a tape-type airspeed indicator. The background of the entire display is an attitude indi-

PRIMARY FLIGHT DISPLAY - PFD

Fig. 69

Avidyne's primary flight display and multi-function display are found in many technically advanced aircraft.

INDIVIDUAL INSTRUMENTS OF THE PFD

Airspeed and altimeter information are presented as a moveable digital-tape strips while the entire background of the PFD presents attitude information.

DIGITAL-TAPE AIRSPEED READOUT ON THE PFD

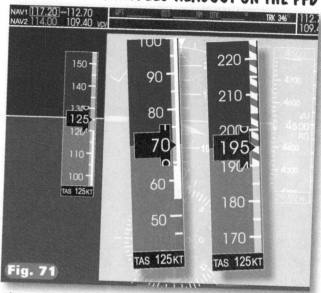

Airspeed information is presented in moveable tape format with the airplane's present airspeed shown digitally.

cator, with the white horizon line stretching from side-to-side on the instrument. At the top is the inclinometer-bank angle indicator. The altitude is also read from a tape-type indicator, and the vertical speed indicator is presented to the right of the altimeter tape. The heading indicator is similar in shape to an HSI.

Sure, it looks spooky, but it's only instrumentation. PFDs still use gyros as well as static and dynamic air pressure inputs to their air data computers to generate the information shown on their displays. We'll discuss this in detail, soon. First, let's examine each of the PFD's instruments in detail.

Digital Airspeed Readouts on PFDs

Primary flight displays provide digital airspeed readouts (Figure 71). The numerical airspeed tape moves vertically with airspeed change. The airplane's present airspeed is shown in the white-on-black box in the center of the tape. Notice that the yellow, green and white color codes correspond to the same color codes shown in Figure 8 of this chapter. On this primary flight display, the never-exceed speed region is indicated with a red striped line, and the stall speed region is marked with a solid red color. PFD manufacturers may vary the color coding used for these airspeed regions.

PRIMARY FLIGHT DISPLAY - PFD

The magenta trend line (position A) tells you what your airspeed will be in six seconds at the airplane's present pitch and power setting. Best rate, best angle and best glide speed are identified by the Y, X and G tabs, respectively.

Some PFDs provide you with an automatic calculation of true airspeed, as seen at the bottom of the airspeed tape in Figure 71. The airplane's air data computer calculates the TAS based on the calibrated airspeed, pressure altitude, and outside air temperature (OAT). Isn't that nice? Now, if you could just use an English accent and say, "Earl Grey tea, hot" into the PFD and get your drink. Someday, perhaps. But not quit yet.

Some PFDs provide you with trend lines (the magenta line, Figure 72, position A) that show where your airspeed will be in six seconds (more on this in a minute). Best rate, angle and best glide speeds may also be shown by thumbnail identifiers (position B).

THE PRIMARY FLIGHT DISPLAY'S TREND LINES

One of the very unique features of the primary flight display is the trend line. This is the magenta line in positions A, B, C and D that show where a particular airspeed and altitude value will be in the next six seconds based on the airplane's present pitch and power condition. For instance, the nose up attitude on the left PFD shows a decreasing airspeed and increasing altitude. The airspeed trend line in position A indicates that the airspeed and altitude will be at 107 knots and 4,630 feet in six seconds. The pitch down attitude shown on the PFD to the right has trend lines indicating that the airspeed and vertical speed will be 182 knots (position C) and 3,710 feet (position D) in six seconds. The wonderful thing about trend lines is that they help you anticipate airspeed and altitude targets. Anticipating trends with round-dial instruments was more a matter of feel and it took some time to develop this skill.

Trend Lines

Trend lines aren't proof that the PFD is reading your mind. The projection is based on the airplane's present pitch and power condition. For instance, the nose up attitude on the left PFD (Figure 73) shows a decreasing airspeed and increasing altitude. The airspeed trend line in position A shows that the airspeed and altitude will be at 107 knots and 4,630 feet in six seconds. The pitch-down attitude shown on the PFD to the right has trend lines showing that the airspeed and vertical speed will be 182 knots (Figure 74, position C) and 3,710 feet (position D) in six seconds. The wonderful thing about trend lines is that they help you anticipate airspeed and altitude targets. Anticipating trends with traditional analog flight instruments is more a matter of feel and it takes some time to develop this skill.

Digital Altitude Readouts

Primary flight displays use a tape display of altitudes (Figure 75). As altitude changes, the numerical display tape of altitude moves up and down in the display window, while the number values in the white-on-black window in the center of the display (Figure 75, position A) change to reflect the airplane's current altitude. Figure 75, position B represents the target altitude you may (or may not) have previously selected in the PFD. Figure 75, position C represents the latest barometer setting you've dialed into the altimeter.

PRIMARY FLIGHT DISPLAY - PFD

On the PFD, altitude is read on a similar moving tape. The airplane's present altitude is shown digitally (position A), the target altitude (selected previously by the pilot) is read at position B and the current altimeter setting is read at position C.

VERTICAL SPEED INDICATION ON THE PFD

Fig. 76

Vertical speed information is provided by a vertically moving pointer on the Garmin G1000 display (left) or a rotating needle on the Avidyne display (right).

Digital Vertical Speed Indicators

PFDs display vertical speed in similar but slightly different ways, as shown on the Garmin G1000 display (Figure 76, position A and the Avidyne display (Figure 76, position B). The G1000 PFD displays vertical speed with a vertically moving speed pointer. A numerical vertical speed value can also be read inside the moving needle

when the vertical speed value exceeds 100 feet per minute. The Avidyne display creates a traditional swinging vertical speed needle to provide the vertical speed reading, along with a digital readout at the bottom (or top) of the vertical speed scale.

These display differences reflect, in part, the fact that we are still working to understand how pilots can most easily comprehend various graphical presentations of information. Should PFDs just try and look like digital versions of traditional instruments, or unleashed from the mechanics of dials and pointers, are there better ways to show various things? Everyone has an opinion (some people have several, one for each of their personalities), but so far not a lot of scientific data exist.

Attitude Indication On a PFD

Primary flight displays (Figures 77A and B) present a larger sky-ground horizon picture than traditional attitude indicators, making it much easier to identify the airplane's attitude even if you're sitting in the back seat (which I hope you aren't doing when you're the pilot in command). The pilot's attitude, fortunately, is not displayed.

On many PFDs, if the pitch exceeds 50 degrees above the horizon or 30 degrees below the horizon, you'll see the appearance of large red chevrons on the display (Figure 77C). This doesn't mean you're over a service station, either. It is a not-too-subtle suggestion that it's probably time to apply your unusual-attitude recovery techniques. Other than size, there really isn't much difference between the attitude picture shown on a traditional instrument and the picture painted by a PFD.

PRIMARY FLIGHT DISPLAY - ATTITUDE INDICATIONS

Fig. 77

Attitude information on a PFD is a big deal, a really big deal, in that the background (so to speak) of the entire display fronts as the attitude indicator. The horizon line on two different PFDs in position A and B. When the attitude exceeds 50 degrees pitch above the horizon or 30 degrees below, large red chevrons appear (on Garmin's G1000 display, position C) pointing the direction toward a more normal flight attitude. Some PFDs use white chevrons to provide the same information.

Rod Machado's Sport Pilot Handbook

HEADING INDICATION ON A PFD

In lieu of the traditional slip-skid indicator to show rate of turn, the PFD shows a trend line whose end indicates the airplane's heading six seconds in the future.

Heading Indication on a PFD

The heading indicator as part of the primary flight display is often in the form of the traditional horizontal situation indicator (Figure 78, position X). The main difference here is that the airplane's present heading is shown digitally (white on black) in the heading box, at the top of the instrument (Figure 78, position Y).

Primary flight displays don't have the traditional turn coordinator commonly seen in non-technically advanced airplanes. Instead, the PFD often uses a trend line to identify turn rate, and a slip-skid trapezoid to indicate turn quality (Figure 78, position Y).

The right or left deflection of a magenta trend line shows what your heading will be in six seconds. The second hash mark (Figure 78, position Z) to the left of the airplane's present heading is 18 degrees off center. When the trend line touches this point, the airplane is turning at 3 degrees per second and is making a standard rate turn (18 degree offset/6 second trend= 3 degrees per second).

The inclinometer is represented by the bar under the trapezoid (Figure 78, position Y). Movement right or left

SLIPPING AND SKIDDING TRAPEZOID INDICATIONS ON THE PFD

The primary flight display inserts above show how the moveable slip-skid (trapezoid) bar indicates a slipping turn (position G), a coordinated turn (position H) and a skidding turn (position I). These three indications correspond with the indications in the inclinometers (D, E and F) above.

THE INSIDE OF AN AHRS (ATTITUDE AND HEADING REFERENCE SYSTEM)

Fig. 80

Courtesy Rotomotion.com

Avidyne's Air Data/Attitude and Heading Reference System (ADAHRS)

Fig. 81

Avidyne's PFD uses an integrated air data computer and attitude and heading reference system (AHRS) in their single unit, otherwise known as the ADAHRS.

of the triangle indicates the degree of slipping or skidding (see Figure 79). The PFD in Figure 79 shows how the moveable slip-skid (trapezoid) bar indicates a slipping turn (Figure 79G), a coordinated turn (Figure 79H) and a skidding turn (Figure 79I). These three indications correspond with the indications in the inclinometers (D, E and F).

Now that you have a basic understanding of how PFDs present their information, let's take a look behind the curtain, so to speak. Modern PFDs don't use spinning gyros. Instead, their attitude and heading data are often provided by a unit called the *attitude heading reference system (AHRS)*, which is solid state and contains no moving parts (Figure 80). This unit contains solid state gyros that provide the attitude information used by the airplane's pitch and bank gyro instruments. You can read about how these solid state gyros work in Postflight Briefing #5-4 on page 5-42.

The air data computer that's part of the Avidyne display (Figure 81) takes information from the airplane's pitot and static lines and from the airplane's thermometer and processes this to provide the airspeed, altitude and vertical speed readouts. The air data computer, along with heading information, can also provide wind direction and speed as well as altitude information for use in Mode C transponder operations.

Airplane heading information for the PFD can be supplied by an external magnetic flux detector (sometimes called a magnetometer-Figure 83), which also provides heading information to the slaved gyro in a traditional horizontal situation indicator.

On the other hand, some PFDs, such as Avidyne's display, have an integrated air data computer and attitude and heading reference system (AHRS) within the unit, in which case it's known as an Air Data Attitude Heading Reference System (ADAHRS, Figure 81).

While there's a lot more to know about primary flight displays, at least you now know what type of information they provide and how they provide it.

Postflight Briefing #5-3

The Remote Indicating Compass (RIC)

The remote indicating compass is essentially a heading indicator that automatically aligns itself to the proper magnetic direction without the pilot getting involved in the process. The RIC consists of two panel mounted components and two remotely located components (thus the genesis of the word remote in RIC). One of the common panel mounted components is the horizontal situation indicator or HSI as shown in Figure 82.

One of the two remotely located components is the magnetic flux detector (flux valve) which is located somewhere on the airframe (usually a wing tip) away from sources of magnetic interference (Figure 83). The other component is an electrically powered directional gyro unit remotely located on the airframe, too. Here's how the device works.

Fig. 82

Fig. 83

Magnetic Flux Detector

A flux valve senses magnetic direction by detecting the earth's lines of magnetic force in its spokes as shown in Figure 84. Changing headings results in a change in the concentration of these lines of force throughout the individual spokes, which provides the means of sensing direction. Electrical signals from the flux valve are then sent to a small electric motor in the remotely located directional gyro,

The RMI's Flux Valve

Airplane on a Northerly Heading

Airplane Turns to an Easterly Heading

1
3
2

Direction of earth's magnetic field.

2
3
1

Arm 1 - Largest voltage
Arm 2 - Voltage = to arm 3
Arm 3 - Voltage = to arm 2

Fig. 84

Arm 1 - Smallest voltage
Arm 2 - Voltage = to arm 3
Arm 3 - Voltage = to arm 2

which alters the position of (precesses) that gyro (no, there's no gyro in the HSIs found in most airplanes). As a result, the remotely located directional gyro is kept aligned to the airplane's current magnetic heading. The information from the remotely located directional gyro and flux valve is then sent to the HSI. Small motors in the HSI unit turn its vertical compass card to provide the airplane's correct magnetic heading. This process is called *slaving*, and it's what's being referred to when someone speaks of a *slaved gyro* (and no, you don't need to try and free all the world's slaved gyros, either).

The other component is a slaving meter-compensator unit (Figure 85). The slaving meter tells you when there's a difference between the airplane's actual magnetic heading and the heading displayed on the heading indicator. In the event an error between these two readings exist, the pilot could use the slaving meter to temporarily correct it before having the unit checked or repaired.

SLAVE IN

Fig. 85

Postflight Briefing #5-4

Three Ring Laser Gyro

To provide pitch and bank information, an attitude and heading reference system (AHRS) typically uses three laser gyros, one for each airplane axis (Figure 86). Computer assessment of all these three gyros (along with other components of the AHRS) provides the basic heading and attitude reference along with present position, groundspeed, drift angle and attitude rate information. The onboard computer begins assessing this information once it has been initialized by determining the initial vertical position and heading.

The ring laser gyro uses laser light to measure angular rotation. Each gyro (one for each airplane axis) is a triangular-shaped, helium-neon laser that produces two light beams, one traveling in the clockwise direction and one in the counterclock-

Courtesy of JAXA

Inside The 3-Ring Laser Gyro

Readout Detector

Corner Prism

Fringe Pattern

A small amount of light passes through this mirror.

Clockwise Light Beam

Counter Clockwise Light Beam

Anode

Anode

Gas Discharge Region

Fig. 87　**Cathode**

Mirror (1 of 3)

wise direction (Figure 87). Production of the light beams, or lasing, occurs in the gas discharge region by ionizing a low pressure mixture of helium-neon gas with high voltage to produce a glow discharge. Light produced from the lasing is reflected around the triangle by mirrors at each corner of the triangle to produce the clockwise and counterclockwise light beams.

When the laser gyro is at rest, the frequencies of the two opposite traveling laser beams are equal. When the laser gyro is rotated about an axis perpendicular to the gyro unit, a frequency difference between the two laser beams results. The frequency difference is created because the speed of light is constant. One laser beam will thus have a greater apparent distance to travel than the other laser beam in completing one pass around the cavity.

As a small amount of laser light from the two lasers passes through the mirror at the top of the diagram. Both light beams are now combined. If movement of the gyro has changed the frequency of the laser light, then the combined beams will produce a fringe or interference pattern. This is a pattern of alternate dark and light stripes. The onboard computer's analysis of this fringe pattern provides pitch and bank information to the airplane's instrument systems.

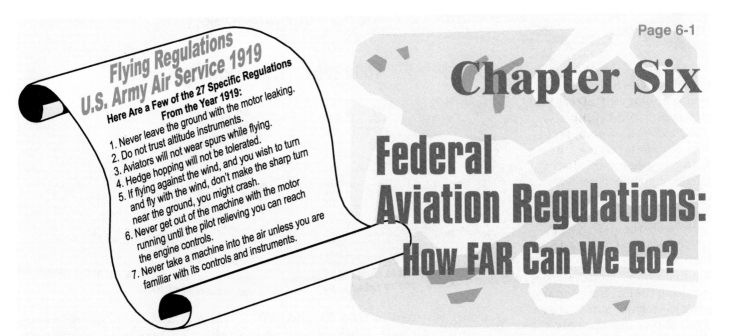

Flying Regulations
U.S. Army Air Service 1919

Here Are a Few of the 27 Specific Regulations From the Year 1919:

1. Never leave the ground with the motor leaking.
2. Do not trust altitude instruments.
3. Aviators will not wear spurs while flying.
4. Hedge hopping will not be tolerated.
5. If flying against the wind, and you wish to turn and fly with the wind, don't make the sharp turn near the ground, you might crash.
6. Never get out of the machine with the motor running until the pilot relieving you can reach the engine controls.
7. Never take a machine into the air unless you are familiar with its controls and instruments.

Chapter Six

Federal Aviation Regulations: How FAR Can We Go?

Aviation, like lots of other things in life, has rules. In this case, the rules are written down, which should make them easier to understand. Unfortunately, they were written down by lawyers, which means they don't always say what they mean in language you or I might understand.

The collective rulebook, presided over by the Federal Aviation Administration (FAA), is called the Federal Aviation Regulations, and referred to by most pilots as the FAR's (legally referred to as CFR's or Code of Federal Regulations but we'll call them FAR's, OK?).

Not all regulations are complex and confusing. In fact, some are pleasingly simple. One FAR actually states that the airplane's takeoff run must not be longer than the length of the runway. That's a good rule. Why aren't all regulations as simple?

Explained properly, many of them can be.

Lawyers write for reasons other than lay understanding. If you don't believe this, simply look at the back of any car rental agreement. By the time you're finished reading, you could have walked to your destination. What the agreement should say is, "If you crash the car then you buy the car or you mow our lawns for eternity."

Knowing what the rules say and mean is vital to your pilot health. Part of getting a sport pilot certificate is passing a test that shows you know the rules. Part of *keeping* your certificate, once you get it, is understanding the rules and how they're applied in the real world. (Sometimes people refer to a pilot *certificate* as a pilot *license*. Technically, it's called a certificate, not a license.)

Let's try to make sense of the regulations, despite their often complex and confusing nature. Because the by-the-book rules are long, complex, and boring many pilots never look at them and thus miss some vital information. What follows are the essentials, the information most often needed to safely and legally operate an aircraft.

Definitions

Understanding the regulations requires a working grasp of some basic definitions. For instance, some people in aviation are employed as fish spotters. At first glance, you might think this is someone who dabs a reluctant perch with oil based paint. Confusion is imminent when basic aviation definitions aren't understood. Here are some of the definitions you need to know in order to make some sense (as opposed to nonsense) of what goes on in aviation.

Aircraft – An aircraft is anything that flies. All airborne vehicles are divided into seven categories: *airplane, glider, rotorcraft (i.e, gyrocopter), lighter-than-air, powered-lift (not an LSA), powered-parachute and weight-shift-control*. Anything airborne (except UFOs or what's inside Hangar 18) falls into one of these categories (Figure 1).

AIRCRAFT CATEGORIES HAVE SIMILARITIES

Powered parachute vehicles have a semi-rigid wing connected to a fuselage.

Gliders have fixed wings and no powerplant.

Weight-shift-control aircraft have a pivoting wing that allows a pilot to control pitch and roll by shifting his weight.

A **powered-lift** vehicle is also a category of aircraft (there are no LSAs in this category).

Under the **rotorcraft** category are **gyrocopters** having powerplants and wings that rotate.

Lighter-than-air aircraft achieve lift by displacing air.

Airplanes have powerplants and fixed wings.

Fig. 1

Category – For the purpose of *pilot certification* the term *category* of aircraft represents something flyable having *similar* operating characteristics. For instance, gliders are distinguished by their fixed wings and lack of an engine (*fixed wing* doesn't mean the wings have been repaired or rendered sterile; it means they don't rotate as do the wings of a helicopter). Rotorcraft, on the other hand, have rotary wings—wings that move (gyrocopters are the only rotorcraft that can be LSAs). Powered-lift includes: tilt-rotor, VTOL (vertical takeoff & landing) and tilt-wing aircraft. The lighter-than-air category is unique in that lift for this type of aircraft is achieved by the displacement of air. Blimps, hot air balloons and gas balloons fit into this category. Finally, airplanes are distinguished by their fixed wings and powerplants.

As a sport pilot, you can be signed off to act as pilot in command of one or more of these different categories (and classes) of aircraft. You're not, however, automatically allowed to fly all categories of aircraft (I don't know how James Bond does it). Additional flight and ground training, a proficiency check from an authorized flight instructor, a logbook endorsement and an application form are required to fly any new category (and class) of aircraft. For instance, if you're certified to fly an airplane, you're not automati-

YOUR SPORT PILOT CERTIFICATE

Your sport pilot certificate shows the category and class of aircraft you're rated to fly.

Some pilots are rated to fly many categories and classes of aircraft.

cally certified to fly a weight-shift control aircraft, much less a powered parachute. Your sport pilot certificate identifies the particular category and class of aircraft you're licensed to fly as shown in Figure 2. Many pilots are certificated to fly in more than one category (and class) of light sport aircraft.

Light Sport Aircraft (LSA) - A light-sport aircraft (Figures 3 and 4) means an aircraft, other than a helicopter or powered-lift that, since its original certification, has continued to meet the following:

(1) A *maximum takeoff weight* of not more than either 1,320 pounds (600 kilograms) for aircraft not intended for operation on water, or 1,430 pounds (650 kilograms) for an aircraft intended for operation on water.

The FAA established this weight limit based on its reasoning that smaller aircraft are still capable of being piloted safely despite a sport pilot's reduced or limited flight training experience.

(2) A *maximum airspeed* in level flight with maximum continuous power (known as V_H) of not more than 120 knots CAS under standard atmospheric conditions at sea level.

The FAA assumes that this level-flight speed limit will be achieved either through reduced engine power, throttle restriction or prop pitch control. Less speed and inertia should make these aircraft simpler and safer to handle based on the reduced flight training experience a sport pilot is expected to have. This doesn't, however limit a pilot to going faster in a dive if this is permitted by the aircraft's POH.

(3) A maximum never-exceed speed (V_{ne}) of not more than 120 knots CAS for a glider.

The FAA set this speed limit to maintain consistency with the V_H for airplanes.

(4) A *maximum stalling speed* or minimum steady flight speed without the use of lift-enhancing devices

LIGHT-SPORT AIRPLANES

The Cessna SkyCatcher is Cessna's light-sport aircraft.

Fig. 3

Courtesy Cessna

A J-3 Cub having a standard airworthiness certificate can be flown by a sport pilot.

Fig. 4

© Gekon - Fotolia.com

Chapter 6 - Federal Aviation Regulations: How FAR Can We Go?

6-3

(VS1) of not more than 45 knots CAS at the aircraft's maximum certificated takeoff weight and most critical center of gravity.

A basic design principle for light-sport aircraft is that the stall speed for these machines is about one third of the aircraft's maximum speed. This makes 45 knots just a little more than a third of the 120 knots maximum speed restriction in level flight.

(5) A *maximum seating capacity* of no more than two persons, including the pilot.

The FAA chose a two-seat maximum (not four seats with two removed, either) based on their nearly 20 years of experience with the ultralight community (which successfully used two-place ultralights for training). Two seats and a single passenger is also reasonable given the 1,320 pound maximum takeoff weight restriction in light-sport aircraft. A single-seat aircraft could also qualify as a light-sport airplane, too.

(6) A *single, reciprocating engine*, if powered.

Thinking of sticking a jet engine on your light sport airplane? Think again. The FAA doesn't permit anything other than reciprocating engines on a light-sport aircraft. Their reasoning is that turbine engines possess inherent design characteristics that require stringent design, maintenance and operating criteria that are inconsistent with light-sport aircraft operating philosophy.

(7) A *fixed* or *ground-adjustable propeller* if a powered aircraft other than a powered glider.

The FAA doesn't permit automatic or manually adjustable variable-pitch propellers. They do, however, allow ground adjustable propellers on light-sport aircraft. This allows you to modify the pitch to give you better climb performance in lieu of cruise performance, something that might be helpful at higher altitude airports. And, in case you're wondering, gliders with small engines (thus the "propeller" reference) are still gliders (self launching gliders, that is).

(8) A *nonpressurized cabin*, if equipped with a cabin.

Knowing a bit about human nature, the FAA probably suspected that there had to be one guy out there that was thinking of building a light-sport airplane with a pressurized cabin. Doing so, of course, would reduce the allowable weight of pilot and passenger to about 25 pounds each. Jenny Craig, here were come.

(9) Fixed landing gear, except for an aircraft intended for operation on water or a glider.

Seaplane aircraft can make good use of retractable landing gear since it allows them to land on water or on land. Gliders also benefit from having a single retractable wheel to reduce drag. The FAA says that retractable landing gear on light-sport airplanes offers no safety benefit, but would increase the airplane's operational and mechanical complexity. Perhaps the FAA didn't want to see someone land gear up, then stick legs through the newly ground holes in the fuselage and walk the airplane off the runway (as if they're wearing an airplane costume).

(10) Fixed, retractable or repositionable landing gear, or a hull, for an aircraft intended for operation on water.

The FAA is making a provision here for "flying boat" type aircraft. These are aircraft where the bottom part of the fuselage is the float into which landing gear may retract.

Class – For the purposes of *pilot certification*, the term *class* represents a *subdivision* within a category. Powered parachutes and weight-shift control aircraft can be classified as either land or sea based. Lighter than air aircraft can be classified as either an airship or balloon. Either of these subdivisions are considered a class of aircraft within a specific category (Figure 5).

Because of the vastly different handling qualities of each vehicle, you also need to be qualified in each class of aircraft you fly. To operating a new class of aircraft you must meet the same requirements necessary to fly a new category of aircraft, as we previously discussed.

AIRPLANE CLASS VARIATIONS

Airplane single-engine land

Airplane multi-engine land

Airplane single-engine sea

Airplane multi-engine sea

Powered parachute vehicles are classified in the land and sea class.

Weight-shift-control aircraft are classified in the land and sea class.

Lighter-than-air aircraft are classified as either balloon or airship.

Fig. 5

Make and Model – Pilots are always asking each other what kind of airplane they fly. They aren't necessarily referring to the specific class aircraft as much as they are the particular *make and model* of light sport aircraft (from now on we'll always assume we're referring to an airplane since this is what this book is about). This can be a Remos G3 or a Cessna SkyCatcher (I once asked a lady taking her first demonstration flight if she wanted to fly a Piper Cherokee—that's a specific make of airplane. She immediately stated that she didn't care who came along nor what instrument he played.)

According to the FAA, once you have your sport pilot's certificate, you can legally fly any specific make and model of airplane within the same category and class of aircraft you're endorsed to operate (you also need something known as a "Vh endorsement" which will be discussed soon). If, for instance, you fly a Remos G3, you can legally fly a Cessna SkyCatcher without an additional endorsement. Both aircraft fall within the airplane category and within the airplane single-engine land class. You can't, however, operate a Remos G3 or Cessna SkyCatcher on floats. These airplanes are of the same category but fall in a different class than that for which you are endorsed (they fall within the single-engine sea class).

As a student pilot (all *student pilots* referenced in this chapter are considered "sport" students unless otherwise noted), however, things are a little different. You may only fly the specific make and model of aircraft endorsed by your instructor in your logbook as shown in Figure 6. If you are signed off to solo a Remos G3, you may not solo a Tecnam P92 Eaglet unless your

Presolo flight training: § 61.87(c)
I certify that Mr. Bjorn Tu Fli has received the required presolo training in a J3 Piper Cub. I have determined he has demonstrated the proficiency of § 61.87(d) and is proficient to make solo flights in a J3 Piper Cub. 3-16-2016
Rocket Rod 987654321 CFI Exp. 04-31-18

Fig. 6

instructor endorses your logbook for that specific make and model. Individual makes and models, even within the same class of aircraft, despite their similarity, might just be confusing enough to cause problems for a student pilot.

Visual Flight Rules (VFR) – The basic premise of *VFR flight* is to see and avoid other aircraft. To do so, visual flight rules stipulate a minimum in-flight visibility as well as a minimum distance from any cloud formation. This ensures that a pilot can control his or her airplane by visual reference to the horizon or the surface.

If you can't maintain this visual reference, you may be forced to fly by reference to your airplane's instruments. As you have probably guessed, this is a slightly more specialized skill, requiring an additional rating (an *instrument rating*) beyond the private pilot's certificate (sport pilots can't obtain an instrument rating). Sport pilots are only allowed to fly under visual flight rules. Later in this chapter and in Chapter 9 (the chapter on airspace), you will learn

the specific visibilities and distances from clouds that you're required to maintain for VFR flight.

Instrument Flight Rules (IFR) – If you eventually go on to obtain a private pilot's certificate, you can acquire the skills necessary to fly under *Instrument Flight Rules* (IFR). An instrument rating allows you to fly to your destination while in the clouds and land under low visibility conditions. *Air Traffic Control* (ATC), using sophisticated radar, provides separation between all airplanes operating under instrument flight rules. After all, if you're in the clouds, you can't see other airplanes; ATC acts as your eyes under these conditions.

As part of your sport pilot training your instructor may provide you with some experience at using your instruments to maintain control of your airplane. This doesn't mean you'll necessarily be in the clouds, but it does mean that your instructor will find some means of simulating instrument conditions by limiting your vision to the instrument panel. The most common way of doing this is with view limiting devices known as Foggles (Figure 7A) or a *hood* (Figure 7B). A hood is sort of like a visor on steroids. It permits you to see directly in front of you—the instrument panel—but not outside unless you have eyes on stalks.

Courtesy Cessna

Single-engine Land Class

Courtesy Flight Design

Single-engine Sea Class

Chapter 6 - Federal Aviation Regulations: How FAR Can We Go?

6-5

This is a view limiting device that restricts your vision to the instrument panel. It is used when your instructor wants to develop your instrument flying skills.

Fig. 7A

Courtesy of Windsock Pilot Supplies

This view limiting device is known as a hood. It is simply another form of view limiting device.

Fig. 7B

Courtesy of Windsock Pilot Supplies

Many years ago, during my first lesson on instruments, my instructor slipped the hood over my head. He told me it was used to simulate flying in the clouds. I put it on and reluctantly began to scan my instruments. After a few minutes I lifted the hood up, looked around and put it back down. I did this three more times before my instructor said, "Hey, what are you doing?" I replied, "I'm practicing flying in and out of the clouds." At that point he said, "You owe me $5." "Why?," I replied. "It's a stupid-tax, that's why. You just did something stupid, so pay up." I paid him the money. He immediately looked over and said, "Well, that proves it, now you owe me another $5." (I guess I shouldn't have paid him that first $5. Pretty stupid, eh?)

Night – As a sport pilot you are not allowed to fly at night. Why?

Well, it's dark for one, and there are a number of skills that you'd need to fly safely at night that aren't necessarily part of the required sport pilot training curriculum. So let's talk about the dark side a bit.

It would seem like the definition of *night* is pretty straightforward, right? Not quite. *Night* is officially defined as *the time between the end of evening civil twilight and the beginning of morning civil twilight*, as published in the American Air Almanac, converted to local time. I mention this because most regulations deal with the hours of darkness by referencing the time from sunset to sunrise. If the term *night* or *nighttime* is specifically used, you should refer to the definition listed above.

Pilot In Command (PIC) – The pilot in command is the captain of the ship and is responsible for the

safe operation of the aircraft during flight. He or she is also the person the FAA will look to in the event of a violation, accident, or other unhappy event. No matter what the category or class of aircraft, there is always one (and only one) legal pilot in command at any particular instant during a flight. (PIC duties can change back and forth during a flight.)

There may be a passenger who thinks he or she's pilot in command, but the PIC is the legal decision maker (that's why some pilots make their passenger or *nag-i-va-tors* wear an oxygen mask—it muffles his or her's constant complaints).

These are the definitions needed to get started. As we go along, we'll uncover more useful words and define them as necessary. You can also visit the Glossary for more definitions. Let's jump directly into the regulations. We're concerned about two main groups of rules: *Part 61* and *Part 91* (the FARs are part of the Code of Federal Regulations, which is divided into numbered parts; thus *Part 61* and *Part 91*.)

Part 61 deals with the certification of pilots. It's the paperwork regulations concerned mostly with the administrative or record keeping duties of flying. Part 91 is the "how to" regulations concerned with the operational rules of flight. Let's start with Part 61.

Evening Twilight

© Michael Mill

Morning Twilight

© Benoit Cornet

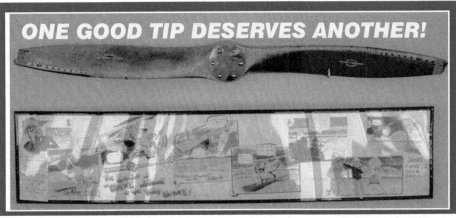

ONE GOOD TIP DESERVES ANOTHER!

The propeller tips on both sides of this prop are damaged. The pilot and his front seat friend were on a flight to their favorite hunting grounds in a J-3 (Piper) Cub. The airplane has tandem seating (one seat in front and one behind) and fold down doors. The front seater saw a coyote from a low altitude, got excited and took a shot at it through the open door and blew off one prop tip. The pilot had to land the airplane because of the prop imbalance. The front seater, realizing what he had done, shot off the other side of the propeller to balance it. Take it from your author, the way to balance your propeller isn't with a shotgun! This was quite dangerous.

PART 61

FAR 61.3 Requirement For Certificates, Ratings And Authorizations

To act as pilot in command of an airplane as a sport pilot, you must have your pilot certificate and photo identification (a valid drivers license for example, but hopefully not your prison ID and gun permit) in your personal possession or readily accessible in the aircraft. These can't be home in your dresser drawer or in your disco-dance van. You must also carry your pilot logbook (or other evidence of required authorized instructor endorsements such as photocopies of those endorsements) on all flights, too. A sport pilot certificate has no expiration date but, as you'll soon see, it can only be used if you meet a few other requirements. For instance, to act as PIC as a sport pilot you need a U.S. drivers license, which serves as a validation that you meet a minimum standard of medical health. You don't generally need an FAA medical certifi-

cate. However, if your state has a minimum drivers license age of 18 and you are 16 years of age—the minimum age at which you can solo an airplane—then you'll need a medical certificate to fly solo in this instance (medical to be discussed shortly). Your sport pilot certificate, logbook and U.S. driver's license (or medical certificate) are documents that need each other, and you need all of them to offer proof that you've acquired the skills needed to pilot the plane, are healthy enough to do so and that you are who you say you are.

You can be asked to present your pilot certificate, medical certificate and/or photo ID for inspection by the Federal Aviation Administrator, a National Transportation Safety Board or Transportation Security Administration representative or any federal, state or local law enforcement officer. The U.S. Customs service is also authorized to act on behalf of the FAA and request these documents. I can almost guarantee

that doing steep turns around the White House is sure to get your pilot certificate inspected by some official looking person (hopefully it won't be an ex-Green Beret pumped up on Maxwell House coffee).

Note that I said *present for inspection,* not *give the certificate up to this representative.* Don't let anyone take your pilot or medical certificate without due process. There are ways and means by which the FAA can suspend your flying privileges, but none of them involve physically turning over your license or medical certificate until an appropriate investigation is conducted.

Carrying these three items isn't much of a problem for most pilots. In fact, as a young aviator I was always trying to find a reason to show someone my pilot certificate. Cashing a check at a supermarket was usually the best place. When the teller asked for ID, I'd proudly whip my license out for display. The teller would look at it, raise an eyebrow and ask, "What the heck is that?" Of course, this required an explanation that I was more than willing to give.

61.15 Offenses Involving Alcohol or Drugs

If you get high, it better be in an airplane. Don't even think of mixing airplanes with alcohol or drugs. If you're convicted for almost any illegal drug activity, there's a very good chance you'll have your pilot certificate suspended or revoked.

Any suspension, albeit temporary, is a blot on your record. Revocation is

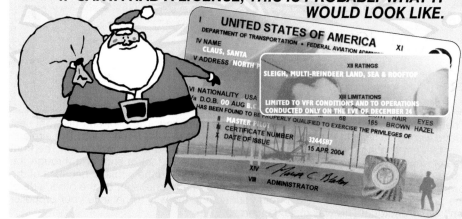

IF SANTA HAD A LICENSE, THIS IS PROBABLY WHAT IT WOULD LOOK LIKE.

Chapter 6 - Federal Aviation Regulations: How FAR Can We Go?

6-7

> ### Three Things Your Passenger Doesn't Want to Hear From You
> 1. Hey, wanna see something neat?
> 2. OK, let's see if this works.
> 3. I don't understand; it shouldn't make that noise.

even more extreme. Once a certificate is revoked, it no longer exists. In some cases it's possible to reapply for that certificate after a minimum waiting period. A one year wait is not uncommon. Reapplying means a pilot must retake all applicable knowledge exams as well as the flight tests. On the other hand, your previous flight time is still applicable toward any rating you might wish to pursue.

Convictions for alcohol-related offenses are no less benign in the eyes of the FAA. Action taken against your U. S. driver's license because of a drug or alcohol problem is known as a *motor vehicle action*. After November 29, 1990, two or more motor vehicle actions within three years of each other is grounds for suspension or revocation of a pilot certificate or rating. This is also grounds for denial of an application for a certificate or rating up to a year after the date of the last motor vehicle action.

Unfortunately, those individuals who marinate their brains in drugs and alcohol may contemplate not informing the FAA about their alcohol or drug related offense. Well, FAA rule creators weren't born last night. These regulations require all drug and alcohol motor vehicle actions to be reported to the FAA within 60 days. Failure to do so is itself grounds for suspension or revocation of a certificate or rating as well as denial of any application for a certificate or rating for up to one year after the date of the motor vehicle action.

The Bottle to Throttle Rule

Regulations require you to avoid acting as pilot in command or as a required crewmember (copilot or flight engineer for instance) for 8 hours after consuming alcohol. In other words, you should have 8 hours from bottle to throttle. If you're a balloon pilot, think of it as 8 hours from bottle to bag!

Personally, I'd recommend at least 24 hours from bottle to throttle. Why? Another part of this rule states that you may not act as PIC if you have blood alcohol content of .04% or more (by weight). It takes about three hours to metabolize one ounce of alcohol, though individuals vary widely in their capacity to process booze. Age, sex, and genetic factors all enter into an equation over which you have no control and about which you may have little information. It's safe to say there is significant alcohol in your bloodstream long after you have ceased to feel any physical effects.

Depending on the amount of alcohol consumed, its effects can last up to 36 hours. Unfortunately, some people think they can drink on a full stomach and not be affected by alcohol. These are often the same folks who

drink on an empty head. Besides, this regulation also states that you may not operate under the influence of alcohol or use any drug that can influence your faculties contrary to safety. Consider that some cold and cough medicines contain significant amounts of alcohol (I've often wondered why the cold medicine Nyquil doesn't have a worm at the bottom of the bottle). There are ample other reasons why you should not be flying when you have a cold. Be careful!

61.23 Duration of Medical Certificates

As mentioned in FAR 61.3, and unlike someone with a private pilot license or higher, sport pilots do not need to have a FAA issued medical certificate as shown in Figure 8. You do, however, need to have a valid U.S. driver's license (or medical and photo ID if unable to obtain a drivers license) if you're a student pilot who is seeking to exercise sport pilot privileges. That's you, right? The FAA's assumption here is that a person who is healthy enough to drive is probably healthy enough to be a sport pilot. Clearly, you're not getting a driver's license if you can't see. Even if you wrapped your car in mattresses, you need sight to drive. No license, no fly. Period. Despite this, there is actually a medical requirement that sport pilots must always meet. According to FAR 61.53, you shall not act as pilot in command if you know or have reason to know of any medical condition that would make you unable to operate an aircraft in a safe manner.

For example, if you're in a complete body cast, then it's hard to deny that you know about it (unless, of course, you feel that the reason you can't move is explained by the fact that you haven't moisturized lately). Realistically speaking, it's more likely that some debilitating flu or other malady might prevent you from safely operating an aircraft. You'll have to make the call here.

Fig. 8

Sport-pilots are required to have a valid U.S. driver's license to exercise the privileges of their sport pilot license. A medical certificate is not required.

On the other hand, some student pilots obtain an FAA medical certificate (Figure 9) because they don't have a drivers license (they're under 16) or were originally training for the private pilot certificate (which requires a medical certificate), then switched to the sport pilot certificate (which doesn't). They may also plan on obtaining the private pilot license soon after they earn their sport pilot license. Either way, you should know that there are three different types of medical certificates (first, second and third class medicals), as well as how long each medical is valid.

Before I tell you about the medical, I want you to know one very important thing. If you take an FAA medical exam and find that you can't pass it, then you may not operate a sport aircraft as pilot in command. Period. The FAA is very clear when they say that you only need a driver's license to act as PIC of a light sport airplane, but you may not have taken and then failed to pass your most recent FAA medical exam. The FAA's assumption here is that there must be some good reason why you couldn't pass this exam and it must be significant, despite the fact that you probably drove to the doctor's office for that exam. Go figure. So keep this one thought in mind. If you're healthy enough to have a driver's license but don't know if you can pass an FAA medical exam (and don't need to), don't take that exam. If you do and fail, you can't fly as a sport pilot until you can actually pass that FAA medical exam. This is a no brainer (which is one of the big reasons you may not be able to pass an FAA medical exam since you need a brain).

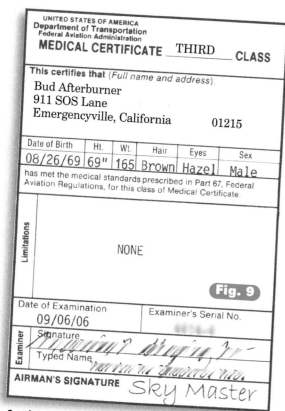

A private pilot is required to have at least a third-class medical certificate to act as pilot in command.

DURATION OF A THIRD-CLASS MEDICAL

For private pilots or higher, the medical certification process is there to weed out people who have physical or psychological problems which represent a compromise of safety. How well it does this is a matter of some controversy. The FAA tends to place great emphasis on some areas (such as cardiovascular problems) where the predictive value of a physical exam is not great, and where the ability of a physician to detect, during a brief exam, someone who should be wearing one of those neat jackets with arms that tie in the back is also limited. Whether it achieves its stated purpose or not, if a medical certificate is necessary, the you must pass the exam. Period.

To obtain a medical certificate, you'd visit an *Aviation Medical Examiner* (AME). These physicians are appointed by the FAA and are schooled in the requirements for administering an official aviation physical exam and doing the necessary paperwork. You can obtain the names of local AME's from any flight school, or from any FAA office.

Generally speaking, the greater the passenger carrying responsibility you have, the more stringent the medical exam, the shorter the duration of the medical certificate, and the more the exam will cost. For instance, if you are the captain of an airliner, you need a *first-class medical* (an exam having the most stringent health requirements). A first-class medical certificate is valid for 6 *cal-*

Chapter 6 - Federal Aviation Regulations: How FAR Can We Go?

6-9

endar months for operations requiring an airline transport pilot certificate (12 calendar months for those under the age of 40). For use with a private pilot certificate, it's good for 24 or 60 calendar months depending on whether you're 40 years of age or older or under 40 years of age, respectively.

The terms of all medical certificates are calculated in *calendar months*. In other words, the clock starts ticking on the first day of the month *after* the month in which you obtain your exam. If you obtain your medical in January, the monthly count starts the following month (February). Think of the month in which you get your medical as free time. For instance, if you're an airline pilot (that's not you...yet) over 40 and take your first class medical on January 13, 2006 (or January 29th, or January 3rd), it is valid through July 30, 2006. This should make sense since February, March, April, May, June and July equal six calendar months of time.

If you have a commercial pilot certificate and are flying commercially (banner towing, pipeline patrol, sightseeing flights, etc.), you need a *second-class medical*. This medical is valid for 12 calendar months for commercial operations. For operations as a private pilot, the second-class medical is good for 24 calendar months if you're 40 or older and 60 calendar months if you're under 40. For commercial operations, if the medical is issued on July 13, 2006, the certificate is valid through July 31, 2007 for someone 40 or older. The monthly count starts in August (the month after it was issued) and goes 12 calendar months later to the end of July 31, 2007.

As a private pilot (or student pilot soloing in other than a light sport aircraft), you are required to have a *third-class medical certificate* to act as pilot in command. A third-class medical is valid for 24 calendar months if you're 40 or over and 60 calendar months if you're under 40.

For instance, if you're under 40 and obtain a third-class medical on September 6th, 2006, it's valid through September 30, 2011 (Figure 7B). If you're 40 or over and obtain a third-class medical on September 6, 2006, it's valid through September 30, 2008 (Figure 7B).

Someone once said that if you can see lightning and hear thunder, you can obtain a third-class medical. Well, the requirements are a little more stringent than that. Suffice it to say a third-class medical exam is a lot less stringent than the exam for a first-class medical.

Medical exams aren't too tough. Frankly, the only tough thing I remember about the third-class exam was when the doctor had me jump up and down on one foot for 20 seconds. I always thought this was some sort of standard in-flight maneuver used to dislodge a stuck gear. It's not. It's a heart stress test. In fact, as of this writing, no EKG (machine heart test) is required for the third or second-class exam.

A few conditions are outright disqualifying. Many others, however, fall in a gray area where the FAA *might* grant a medical, based on evidence you submit. If you don't meet the normal criteria, you must apply for a *waiver*. In some cases this means submitting to additional medical testing; in others, it involves demonstrating through a flight test that the condition does not limit your capability in the cockpit. It is possible to get a medical certificate if you only have vision in one eye, or have limited hearing, although restrictions may be imposed on when and where you may fly.

Remember, the medical information here is only for those who plan to become a private pilot, not a sport pilot.

A Few Additional Things You Need to Consider About Medical Certification

1. While sport pilots can use a U.S. driver's license to meet FAA medical requirements to act as PIC, there are instances where a medical certificate might be required. In some states you're required to be 18 years of age to obtain a drivers license, yet it's possible to solo an airplane at 16 years of age. Here is where a sport pilot applicant would need at least a third-class FAA medical certificate to act as PIC.

2. When using a driver's license for medical certification, you must adhere to any limitations on the back of your driver's license. You might, for instance, be required to wear glasses when you fly. But please be prepared for unusual limitations that don't make much sense. One instructor has a sport pilot student with a license limitation requiring mirrors on both sides of the vehicle. She sent him to the checkride with two make-up mirrors and roll of duck tape.

3. If you elect to obtain an FAA medical certificate and fail to pass that exam, then you cannot act as a sport pilot until you do pass that medical exam. Keep in mind that if, during the medical exam, you have to discontinue that exam because the doctor wants you to submit additional information to him, then this counts as a failure of that exam (at least until you successfully pass it again). This is why it's often best to visit an FAA medical examiner and ask to take an evaluation medical exam to see if you could actually pass a real FAA exam if you have any doubts about your medical state. Just make sure that the FAA medical examiner knows that this is a practice exam, not a real one. You won't, shouldn't and will not fill out any FAA paper work here.

4. Most of the issues pilots face with passing their medical exams deal with the medication they're using. The FAA has a list of prohibited medications, including many mood altering drugs and blood pressure medications. Please visit AOPA.org to view a list of these medications (AOPA membership required).

61.56 Flight Reviews

Have you ever wondered just how long your *pilot* certificate is valid? Well, it's technically valid forever. That's right, a sport pilot certificate never expires. But having a certificate and being able to act as PIC of a light-sport aircraft are two different things. In addition to having a pilot certificate, you need to meet a few additional requirements to act as PIC of an airplane.

To act as PIC, you must have had a *flight review* within the preceding 24 calendar months. Just as with the medical, the clock starts on the month following the month in which the review takes place. If you take a flight review on April 19, 2006, this review is valid through April 30, 2008 as shown Figure 11 (May 1, 2006 to April 30, 2008 is 24 calendar months). Of course, you can take as many flight reviews as you like, whenever you like. Each one resets the clock and gives you another 24 months of pilot life. Since it takes place every two years, this is sometimes referred to as a *biennial flight review* or *BFR*.

The purpose of the flight review is to ensure that you are still in possession of the basic piloting skills needed to fly safely. Flight reviews consist of a refresher on Part 91 of the regulations and the necessary flight maneuvers to convince the instructor giving you the review that you know what you're doing. A minimum of one hour of flight training and one hour of ground training is required for this review.

Since the purpose of the flight review is to determine your level of flight skill and ground knowledge, taking any checkride for a new certificate (such as a private pilot certificate) or rating (an instrument rating, for example) automatically counts as a flight review. If you complete one or more phases of an FAA-sponsored pilot proficiency award program (sometimes called the *Wings Program*), this also counts as a flight review.

Keep one more thing in mind about the flight review. It's applicable for anything you're endorsed to fly as a sport pilot. Suppose you are endorsed to fly a weight-shift control aircraft, a powered parachute and an airplane. You decide to take your flight review in an airplane. Does this flight review apply to the other category and class of aircraft in which you're endorsed? Yes, it does. You don't have to take a flight review in each individual category and class of aircraft. This means you can pass a BFR in a powered parachute and be legal to fly an airplane, even if

DURATION OF THE FLIGHT REVIEW

Flight review taken on April 19, 2006

Flight review good till the end of April 30, 2008

Fig. 11

This is what a flight review endorsement looks like in your pilot logbook.

REMARKS, PROCEDURES, MANEUVERS	NO. INSTR APP.	NO. LDG.
I certify that Ms. Martha Spinproof, sport pilot, #212234521, has satisfactorily completed a flight review of § 61.56(a) on (10/13/20XX).		6

Rod Machado 10/13/XX, Rod Machado 123456 CFI, Exp. 4/30/XX

Fig. 12

you haven't touched one in years (Remember Rod's Rule of Rules. It doesn't have to make sense. Just follow it.)

What about sport pilots flying single-placed aircraft? Sorry, but you can't take a flight review in a *single-place* airplane. There was a time when a flight instructor could give a flight review by observing you from the ground as you flew a single-place airplane overhead. Flight instructors often considered this the safest flight review they could give (especially when standing under the protective umbrella of a steel shed). If you own a single place light-sport airplane then you must take your flight review in an aircraft for which you are rated and it must have a minimum of two seats. That means you'll have to rent a two-place airplane with an instructor who is qualified to fly it (meaning that he or she in an appropriately rated instructor). It is possible, however, to take your sport-pilot practical test in a single place airplane. I'll talk about this shortly.

Many years ago a crusty pilot showed up in a four-place airplane with three of the four seats yanked out. He

Chapter 6 - Federal Aviation Regulations: How FAR Can We Go?

6-11

tried to convince me to give him a flight review by observing him from the ground. No dice. When I asked why he took his seats out, he replied, "Flight instructors make me nervous." I wonder if he ever had one?

If you feel nervous about taking a flight review, find some comfort in this thought: You can't fail a flight review. You might not pass immediately, but you can't fail. There's no provision for marking a failure in your logbook. In other words, the instructor doesn't use an enormous red pen to indelibly write in a pilot's logbook "Bob has miserably failed his flight review, he's only half the man he should be." If at first you don't succeed, try, try again. The concept here is that the flight review is an educational experience, not a punitive one.

One time I gave a flight review to a fellow in a Citabria (a taildragger). He hadn't flown in quite a while, so his first landing was a thriller. We smacked the ground and started swerving down the runway. After swerving for a few hundred feet, the tower called and said, "32 Bravo, do you need some assistance, or perhaps you'd like a little music?" We continued practicing until he became proficient. Then, I signed him off for the flight review similar to the endorsement shown in Figure 12.

61.57 Recent Flight Experience: Pilot In Command

A flight review gets you PIC privileges, but the FAA thinks you ought to do a bit more to be entitled to carry a passenger. The FAA assumes your passenger is an innocent and trusting soul, unschooled in the ways of aviation, and thus dependent on the pilot. More often than not, this is true.

If you want to take a passenger flying, you must have recent experience in the particular category and class of aircraft you intend to fly. Welcome to the *recency* rule.

The FAA states that, to act as PIC while carrying passengers, you must have made, within the preceding 90 days, at least three takeoffs and three landings as the sole manipulator of the flight controls in the same category, class of aircraft you intend to fly. (Yes, it *is* possible to have more takeoffs than landings logged, or vice versa. Remember earlier that I said PIC designation can change at any time. If you go flying with a pilot friend, she could make a takeoff and you could make a landing. Each gets the appropriate credit.)

RECENCY OF EXPERIENCE

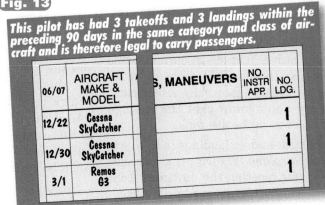

Fig. 13

This pilot has had 3 takeoffs and 3 landings within the preceding 90 days in the same category and class of aircraft and is therefore legal to carry passengers.

Figure 13 shows an example of a pilot's logbook. If today's date is March 15th, 90 days into the past would be December 16th. Does he meet the recency requirement? Yes, he has two landings in a Cessna SkyCatcher and one in a Remos G3—both single-engine land airplanes. He may act as PIC carrying passengers in a single-engine land airplane.

Suppose you only have two takeoffs and landings logged within the preceding 90 days? You aren't current to carry a passenger until you log one more takeoff and landing. Simply go out, do one more takeoff and landing, log it, then invite your passenger into the airplane.

This is where tact becomes an asset. I do *not* recommend saying "Hey, you wait here, I'm going to go out and get current, then I'll come back and pick you up." That's one of those declarations that makes people suddenly remem-

Fig. 14

Fig. 15

© Donald Neuberg

Strange Airport Events That Happened!

No, I'm Hispanic.

Airplane circling the tower, are you a Cessna?

ber they left the water running at their summer home 150 miles away, and they need to go deal with it immediately. Either get current before having a friend join you at the airport, or be creative. "Let me go burn off some fuel, so there will be more room for your luggage" is usually a bestseller. They don't know that the luggage doesn't go in the fuel tank.

Touch-and-go landings in a *tricycle gear airplane* (Figure 14) are acceptable for meeting the daytime recent experience requirements. If, however, you are planning on flying a *taildragger* (Figure 15), the landings must be made to a full stop. The reason is that the FAA doesn't consider a taildragger to have stopped flying until it has come to a complete rest. Of course, if you obtained your recent experience in a tailwheel airplane, this automatically applies to a tricycle gear airplane.

FAR 61.60 Change of Address

You've won the lottery and bought a big new house. You filed a change of address card to tell everyone from Aunt Mildred to the people who send you the mail order catalogs for rubber duckies. The one notification you're most likely to forget is the FAA. Unfortunately, your right to fly as PIC expires 30 days after the move unless you've told the FAA where you'll be headed.

Simply send a postcard (or anything else) with your new address to the: FAA, Airman Certification Branch ASF-760, P.O. Box 25082, Oklahoma City, OK, 73125-0082 (or notify them via email at www.faa.gov and follow the links). Whatever you do, don't send them your logbook, your pilot certificate, or a picture of you in a U-Haul moving van enroute to your new place.

FAR 61.87 Solo Requirements For Student Pilots

Nothing is more exciting than soloing (flying alone) an airplane. Your first command!

My flight instructor took me by complete surprise when I first soloed. I simply didn't expect it. He pulled out my logbook and endorsed me for solo. Glancing over at me he gave his typical pre-solo speech, "Remember, it will be lighter with me out of the plane and it will want to climb faster." I was so nervous I thought he said, "Revenge her, it grills my ladder, it will help extinguish the pain and you'll turn to crime faster." I figured this was some sort of cryptic pre-solo benediction, and waited for the secret handshake that never came.

My instructor shut the door, saluted, mentioned something about insurance deductibles, and motioned

Tower, this is captain Bob, we just hit a bird, over.

OK captain, where did you hit the bird?

This is captain Bob. I think we hit him in the head.

Chapter 6 - Federal Aviation Regulations: How FAR Can We Go?

6-13

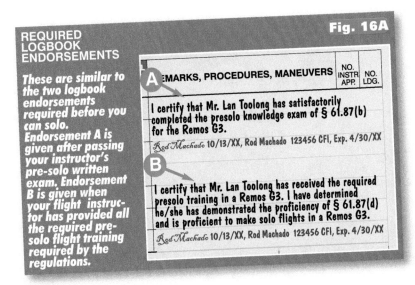

REQUIRED LOGBOOK ENDORSEMENTS

These are similar to the two logbook endorsements required before you can solo. Endorsement A is given after passing your instructor's pre-solo written exam. Endorsement B is given when your flight instructor has provided all the required pre-solo flight training required by the regulations.

Fig. 16A

REMARKS, PROCEDURES, MANEUVERS	NO. INSTR APP.	NO. LDG.

A I certify that Mr. Lan Toolong has satisfactorily completed the presolo knowledge exam of § 61.87(b) for the Remos G3.
Rod Machado 10/13/XX, Rod Machado 123456 CFI, Exp. 4/30/XX

B I certify that Mr. Lan Toolong has received the required presolo training in a Remos G3. I have determined he/she has demonstrated the proficiency of § 61.87(d) and is proficient to make solo flights in a Remos G3.
Rod Machado 10/13/XX, Rod Machado 123456 CFI, Exp. 4/30/XX

THE OLD STUDENT PILOT CERTIFICATE

As of April 1, 2016, traditional paper-type student pilot certificates (shown below) will no longer be issued by the FAA. Plastic student pilot certificates (see Fig. 18) will be issued and all solo endorsements will be entered in the student pilot's logbook.

Fig. 16B

me on. It would have been real quiet in there except for the loud pounding sound. I thought it was the flight guru trying to get back in. It was my heart, trying to get out. Smart heart.

Solo flight time was not created just to give your instructor a rest. It's primarily a confidence building exercise. This is why regulations presently require a minimum of 20 hours total flight time with a minimum of 15 hours of flight training (sometimes called *dual instruction* from an authorized flight instructor) and 5 hours of solo flight training (that's by yourself) in preparation for the sport pilot certificate. Flying alone, dependent only upon yourself, builds tremendous self reliance.

It is, however, necessary for your instructor to accomplish several paperwork items before you solo. First, your instructor must give you all the instruction required by the appropriate parts of FAR 61.87. This is the basic knowledge required to competently handle a light-sport airplane in solo flight. You must also take a pre-solo written test. Unlike the FAA knowledge exam, this is a rather informal exam consisting of about 20 questions designed by your instructor to test your understanding of the airplane, regulations and procedures.

Four administrative acts must be accomplished by your instructor before you take to the sky for solo flight. First, your logbook must be endorsed for the specific make and model of airplane you'll solo (Figure 16A). If you are endorsed to solo a Remos G3, you couldn't fly a differ-

ent model of the Remos unless your instructor endorsed your logbook for this specific light sport airplane. Second, your instructor must provide you with a "Vh" endorsement (Figure 16C) stating your proficiency at operating an aircraft with a specific maximum forward airspeed of greater than 87 knots or 87 knots or less (see FAR 61.137 on page 6-20).

Finally, before your first solo, your instructor must also endorse you logbook for with a 90 day solo endorsement (Figure 17A). Thereafter, your instructor is required to endorse your logbook every 90 days for you to continue exercising your solo privileges (Figure 17B). Clearly, you aren't escaping from the supervision of your instructor once you are kicked out of the nest for solo operations.

"VH" STUDENT ENDORSEMENT

Before solo, a students needs a "Vh" endorsement indicating proficiency at operating an aircraft of a specific speed (see FAR 61.317 on page 6-20).

REMARKS, PROCEDURES, MANEUVERS	NO. INSTR APP.	NO. LDG.

I certify that Ms. I certify that Mr. Sonic Boom has received the required training of § 61.327 in a (Remos G3). I have determined him/her proficient to act as PIC of a light-sport aircraft that has a Vh greater than 87 knots (or 87 kts. or less).
Rod Machado 10/13/XX, Rod Machado 123456 CFI, Exp. 4/30/XX

Fig. 16C

90 DAY STUDENT ENDORSEMENTS

Student pilots need an initial 90 day solo endorsement in their logbook prior to their first solo flight (Figure 17A), then they need one every 90 days thereafter to continue flying solo (Figure 17B)

REMARKS, PROCEDURES, MANEUVERS

I certify that Mr. James T. Kirk has received the required training to qualify for solo flying. I have determined he/she meets the applicable requirements of § 61.87(n) and is proficient to make solo flights in a Remos G3.
Rod Machado 10/13/XX, Rod Machado 123456 CFI, Exp. 4/30/XX

Fig. 17A

REMARKS, PROCEDURES, MANEUVERS

I certify that Mr. James T. Kirk has received the required training to qualify for solo flying. I have determined he/she meets the applicable requirements of § 61.87(p) and is proficient to make solo flights in a Remos G3.
Rod Machado 10/13/XX, Rod Machado 123456 CFI, Exp. 4/30/XX

Fig. 17B

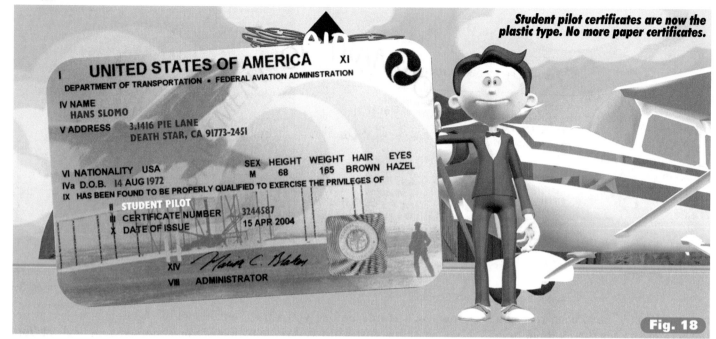

Student pilot certificates are now the plastic type. No more paper certificates.

Fig. 18

As a student pilot, you need a student pilot certificate (Figure 18). This is an authentic license—a student pilot's license, that is (we normally call it a *certificate*). It allows you to exercise all the privileges for which you've been endorsed as a student pilot. That's why you always need to carry it with you when acting as PIC.

Keep in mind that student pilot certificates are issued by the FAA's Civil Aviation Registry. You can apply for this certificate through your flight instructor, a designated pilot examiner or directly at your local FAA office (your instructor is your best bet here). Your instructor will accept either a paper application (an FAA 8710 form) or help you fill out the web-based IACRA (Integrated Airman Certification and/or Rating Application) form. It will take about three weeks for your student pilot certificate to arrive as the TSA does its typical background checks (I don't mean they check your backyard, either). When it arrives, you'll have a nice, new, shiny, solid plastic, student pilot certificate that has no expiration date.

Several years ago, I came across a student pilot with an extraordinary amount of time. He had over 10,000 hours of flight time spaced over a 20 year period. In 1968, he soloed in his own airplane, flew away from the airport, and never flew back. I can only imagine his instructor standing by the runway watching this guy fly off into the sunset and disappear like those six TBM avengers over the Bermuda Triangle. The way he told the story he didn't think he had to fly with another instructor once he soloed. Always make it a point to keep your instructor informed about your solo flight activities.

FAR 61.89 General Limitations

As a student pilot you must adhere to several limitations. First, you can't carry a passenger. No, your flight instructor isn't a passenger. He or she is your guru, teacher and your ticket down. Flying for hire isn't allowed, either. You can't use an airplane to make money as a student pilot, nor may you use an airplane in any business pursuit.

During the cross country flight phase of his training, one of my students decided to spend time at his destination soaking up the sights. I became suspicious when he spent an entire day at the desert airport of Needles, California. After all, how many cacti, sand dunes and lizards can you drink in during an eight hour period? I discovered he was plying his trade as an appliance repairman during these solo excursions. It was an illegal activity. As punishment I made him repair all my appliances.

These are a few of my conditions for student solo flight. I vary these conditions based on the skill of that particular student. No, there isn't a 10th limitation that says, "Student shall not have any fun." These limitations protect the student & the flight instructor.

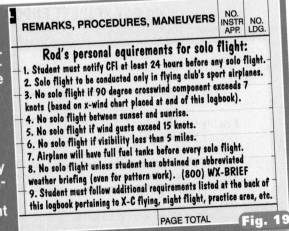

REMARKS, PROCEDURES, MANEUVERS	NO. INSTR APP.	NO. LDG.

Rod's personal equirements for solo flight:
1. Student must notify CFI at least 24 hours before any solo flight.
2. Solo flight to be conducted only in flying club's sport airplanes.
3. No solo flight if 90 degree crosswind component exceeds 7 knots (based on x-wind chart placed at end of this logbook).
4. No solo flight between sunset and sunrise.
5. No solo flight if wind gusts exceed 15 knots.
6. No solo flight if visibility less than 5 miles.
7. Airplane will have full fuel tanks before every solo flight.
8. No solo flight unless student has obtained an abbreviated weather briefing (even for pattern work). (800) WX-BRIEF
9. Student must follow additional requirements listed at the back of this logbook pertaining to X-C flying, night flight, practice area, etc.

PAGE TOTAL   Fig. 19

Chapter 6 - Federal Aviation Regulations: How FAR Can We Go?

6-15

Student pilots (remember, we're talking about *sport* students) are not allowed to fly when flight or surface visibilities are less than three miles during the day nor are they allowed to fly at night, either (see page 6-5 for the official definition of *night*). Students may not fly without visual reference to the surface. In other words, no flying above the clouds where you can't see the ground. Think about it this way. If you were on top of a cloud layer and had to make an emergency descent, cloud penetration would be inevitable. Since you don't have an instrument rating, you can't fly in the clouds.

Good instructors will stipulate conditions for solo in their student's logbook. For instance, I wrote the conditions shown in Figure 19 in one student's logbook. These are my personal (and very reasonable) limitations that I place on my students when they begin flying solo. One of my students added an additional item at the bottom of the list that said, "No solo if student expects to have any fun!"

Students are required by the regulations to adhere to any limitations their instructor places in their logbook. It's not unusual for instructors to list these and similar restrictions. Instructors are not attempting to prevent you from having fun. They're attempting to minimize your exposure to unnecessary risk.

FAR 61.93 Solo Cross Country Flight Requirements

As a beginning student pilot, you are on a 25 mile leash when flying solo. You can go up to but not beyond that distance without obtaining an endorsement for cross country flight in your logbook (Figure 20 and 21). You are also required to land at the airport where you took off (in other words, no stops at the edge of your 25 mile world for a Coke and burger).

Cross country endorsements require additional training. Navigation, weather, and traffic pattern entries are just some of the skills required for cross country flight. The main objective of cross country flight training is to keep

Fig. 20

Solo cross-country flight: § 61.93
I certify that Mr. Hue Gottalan Sumtime has received the required solo cross-country training. I find he has met the applicable requirements of § 61.93, and is proficient to make solo cross-country flights in a J3 Piper Cub, airplane.
Rocket Rod 987654321 CFI Exp. 04-31-18

An endorsement for cross country flight made by your flight instructor allows you to fly beyond the 25 nautical mile limit.

you from getting lost. The next most important objective is teaching you to find out where you are if you manage to get lost. If you do get lost once in a while, though, don't feel too bad. It happens to everybody. As a student pilot, I got lost so many times that I had to keep changing where it was I wanted to go. The flight school finally bought a St. Bernard and named it *Rod*. With proper training you'll have no problem finding your way around.

There is a provision in the regulations for student pilots to practice solo takeoffs and landings at another airport without having a cross country endorsement. This is allowed if the airport is within 25 nautical miles of the departure airport at which instruction is received, and the instructor gives training in both directions over the route and endorsed your logbook for that operation. The only requirement is that the instructor must determine that you are competent and proficient to make takeoffs and landings at that airport. To do this, the instructor must give you training in both directions over the route and endorsed your logbook for that operation (Figure 22). This is the only time you, as a solo student, can land at another airport (other than the point of departure) without a solo cross country endorsement.

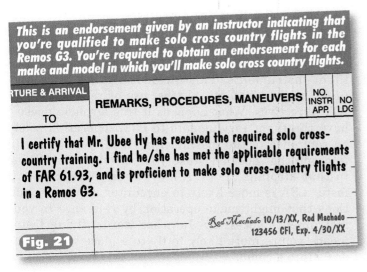

This is an endorsement given by an instructor indicating that you're qualified to make solo cross country flights in the Remos G3. You're required to obtain an endorsement for each make and model in which you'll make solo cross country flights.

RTURE & ARRIVAL	REMARKS, PROCEDURES, MANEUVERS	NO. INSTR APP.	NO LDG
TO			

I certify that Mr. Ubee Hy has received the required solo cross-country training. I find he/she has met the applicable requirements of FAR 61.93, and is proficient to make solo cross-country flights in a Remos G3.

Rod Machado 10/13/XX, Rod Machado
123456 CFI, Exp. 4/30/XX

Fig. 21

This is an endorsement for repeated flights to another airport within 25 nautical miles.

ARRIVAL	REMARKS, PROCEDURES, MANEUVERS	NO. INSTR APP.	NO. LDG

I certify that Mr. Ubee Hy has received the required training of § 61.93(b)(1). I have determined that he/she is proficient to practice solo takeoffs and landings at Oceanside airport. The takeoffs and landings at Oceanside airport are subject to the following conditions: (listed at end of logbook).

Rod Machado 10/13/XX, Rod Machado
123456 CFI, Exp. 4/30/XX

Fig. 22

A solo cross country endorsement in your logbook is not a *carte blanche* authorization to fly when and where you wish. Before any cross country flight you'll need to have your flight planning checked by an instructor. This can be any flight instructor, not just the one from whom you're taking flight instruction.

Simply present your flight planning for the proposed cross country flight to an instructor. He or she will examine it, make sure it contains proper headings, checkpoints, fuel consumption figures, and several other important items. Then the instructor will endorse your logbook for that specific flight. This endorsement, shown in Figure 23, usually states that you can make the flight safely as planned.

In the endorsement, instructors can also specify conditions that must be followed. One time I stipulated in a logbook that a student should return to his home base if convective clouds were present over a mountain range notorious for its cloud buildups. I knew that clouds, in this instance, meant a little more turbulence than he could comfortably handle. Remember, these individual endorsements are made in the student's logbook for every cross country flight.

A cross country endorsement in your logbook allows you the additional privilege of making repeated solo cross country flights. If your instructor approves, you can make repeated solo cross country flights to an airport within 50 nautical miles from the point of departure. See, your leash is getting longer. You must have been given instruction in both directions over the route, including takeoffs and landings at the away-from-home airport. You must also adhere to any conditions specified by the instructor in the logbook. This privilege is different from solo takeoffs and landings within 25 nautical miles because it requires a cross country endorsement in your logbook.

Make sure it's a flight instructor who signs off your flight planning. I was watching the desk at the flight school many years ago. A student pilot walked in, took a

After takeoff the blimp climbs out at the best angle of bag.

Due to some optical effect, the blimps looks big when far away and really small when viewed close up.

Blimps are sometimes used to move industrial equipment like small patio heaters.

look at a fellow in the corner, walked up to him, and began chatting. Some paperwork changed hands, then the student departed. I walked over to the corner and asked, "What did that student want?" "Oh, he just wanted me to review his flight planning for a cross country flight," he quipped. "It looked pretty good to me so I told him to go give it a try." I said, "Hey, I didn't know you were an instructor." He replied, "I'm not, I'm just a student myself." "Then how come you signed that other student off for his cross country flight?" I said. "Because he asked me to. Besides, I learned a few good tips for my next cross country flight." (I made $5 on that deal.)

Before you can be signed off for a cross country flight, you might need some additional instruction that you didn't anticipate. For instance, if your light sport airplane has navigation and communication radios, then you must learn how to use them. Sure, there are many sport airplanes that don't have any radios. No problem. You can't be trained on equipment that you don't have in the airplane you're flying. If, however, those radios are in the plane, you must learn how to use them before flying solo cross country.

Additionally, if you're doing cross country training in a light sport airplane with a V_H greater than 87 knots CAS, then you'll need training in maneuvering and controlling the airplane solely by reference to the flight instruments. This includes straight and level flight, turns, descents, climbs, use of radio aids, and ATC directives. What happens if this airplane doesn't have the flight instruments to allow operation solely by reference to the instruments? Well, you'll have to find one that does and take your instrument training in that airplane. The FAA's rational here is that a faster LSA is more likely to encounter weather conditions that might make operation by reference to your instruments necessary. In other words, flying faster means you're more likely to fly to a place with clouds or fly into a cloud.

This is an endorsement given by an instructor indicating your cross country flight planning has been checked and found satisfactory for that flight.

REMARKS, PROCEDURES, MANEUVERS	NO. INSTR APP.	NO. LDG.
I have reviewed the cross country planning of Mr. Paul Gofar. I find the planning and preparation to be correct to make the solo flight from Palomar airport to Chino airport via CRQ direct OCN VOR direct Chino with landings at Chino in a Cessna SkyCatcher on 10/13/XX. *Rod Machado* 10/13/XX, Rod Machado 123456 CFI, Exp. 4/30/XX		
PAGE TOTAL		

Fig. 23

Chapter 6 - Federal Aviation Regulations: How FAR Can We Go?

6-17

FAR 61.305 Sport Pilot Requirements

A minimum age of 16 is required to solo an airplane. For balloons and gliders, the minimum age is 14. Why the difference? Apparently the FAA perceives the privileges associated with flying gliders and balloons to be less susceptible to problems of immaturity (mainly because these activities involve small groups, which increases the chance of some adult supervision). The risk to others is probably less in a balloon, too; even if you were doing bag-and-goes on a busy street, most people could dive out of the way. I'm being facetious here, but I think you get the point.

Sport pilot certificates require a minimum age of 16 for glider and balloon pilots and 17 for airplanes (as well as the other light sport categories). You must be able to read, speak, write and understand the English language. Yes! You must be capable of writing English. Apparently those flight plans written in Tagalog or Swahili are real show stoppers on your sport pilot checkride.

You need to pass a 40 question knowledge examination before you can take a flight check for the sport pilot certificate. A grade of 70% is the minimum to pass. The knowledge exam is good for 24 calendar months from the date the test is taken. If you don't take your flight test before this deadline, you'll have to retake the knowledge exam.

When I first went to the FAA to take the knowledge exam for my Airline Transport Pilot certificate, I had a little fun with the pilot applicants in the room. I had been teaching ground school and had access to a large, six foot, wooden, E6-B type computer (basically a round slide rule, for those who haven't yet encountered this instrument of torture). I walked in for the examination. The lady behind the desk took one look at the thing and said, "No way!" I said, "Yes, way." She called Mr. Allen, the FAA chief, over. He said, "Good golly, I'd like to see the airplane that thing goes with." They eventually let me take it in the room. As I walked in I could immediately tell who all the private pilot applicants were. A few of them dropped their jaws and said, "Wow, I'm going to have to get one of those!"

FAR 61.313 Flight Experience

In preparation for the sport pilot's certificate, certain minimum flight requirements must be met. First, you must meet the basic aviation knowledge requirements found in FAR 61.309. These minimums specify the aeronautical knowledge required to make you an educated pilot.

Let's keep in mind that this book is preparing you to operate airplanes that fall under the light-sport aircraft category. Once you've obtained your sport pilot certificate and are endorsed to fly light-sport airplanes, you can obtain additional endorsements to fly any other category and class of light-sport aircraft. This involves additional ground and flight training as well as a proficiency flight check given by an authorized flight instructor (other than the one who provides the ground and flight training) who evaluates your ability to fly this aircraft safely.

The FAA requires a minimum of 20 hours total flight time to be eligible for the sport pilot certificate. At least 15 hours of this time must be with an instructor and five hours must be done solo. For various reasons, most people take more time than this to obtain their certificates. For instance, training time can vary depending on where the training occurs. If you learn to fly in Los Angeles, for instance, you will probably need a few extra hours of preparation. L.A. is a beautiful place (during a cease fire), but it's also one of the most complicated, crowded, and communication-intensive chunks of airspace in the country.

You must also have at least two hours of cross-country flight training. That means you and your instructor will make these trips together, which is how you'll learn the essentials of flying cross-country. You're also required to make one solo cross-country flight of at least 75 nautical miles total distance, with a full-stop landing at a minimum of two points. One segment of this trip must consist of a straight-line distance of at least 25 nautical miles between the takeoff and landing locations as shown in Figure 24. This figure shows that Examples A and B meet the sport pilot solo cross country flight requirements. Example C does not meet the cross-country flight requirement.

THE SPORT PILOT 75 NAUTICAL MILE CROSS COUNTRY FLIGHT REQUIREMENT

Example A

Total distance is 85 NMs with three stops (the departure airport is considered one of the stops). One segment (Z to X) is at least 25 nautical miles between the takeoff and landing location. This flight meets the sport pilot solo cross-country flight requirement.

Example B

Total distance is 80 nautical miles with 2 stops (the departure airport is considered one stop) and one segment (V to Z or Z to V) at least a 25 nautical mile, straight-line distance. This flight meets the sport pilot solo cross-country flight requirement.

Fig. 24

Example C

Total distance is 61 nautical miles but there is no straight-line segment of at least 25 nautical miles between the takeoff and landing points. Thiis flight doesn't meet the sport pilot solo cross country flight requirement.

Note: For any flight to count as a cross country for the sport pilot rating (other than for powered parachutes) the flight must include a landing with at least a straight-line distance of "more" than 25 nautical miles from the original point of departure (the original point of departure is always where the flight began or originated, which is at airport V). In Example C above, the distance from airport V to any other airport is not more than 25 NM, and this is another reason this flight can't be logged as a country flight to meet the sport pilot cross country requirements.

You must also have at least 10 takeoffs and landings to a full stop at an airport. And yes, landing in someone's field is considered an airport. These landings must also involve flight in that airport's traffic pattern. Ultimately, this means that you'll make at least 10 circuits in an airport's traffic pattern, coming to a full stop each time, to meet this requirement. You may do these landings with an instructor or by yourself (solo), assuming you feel comfortable operating in the pattern alone. The FAA's intent here is to make sure you know how to get along with the other pilots of other aircraft that use the airport.

There is no requirement, however, that these takeoffs and landings be done at a tower controlled airport. That's because to fly at a tower controlled airport as a sport pilot, you'll need to be trained and endorsed by an instructor to operate at tower-controlled airports (these are airports having Class D, Class C or Class B airspace. More on this later). When you're ready to operate at an airport with a control tower, then your instructor will teach you the necessary skills and appropriately endorse your logbook.

Finally, at least two of the 15 flight training hours must be used in preparing you for the sport pilot flight test within two calendar months prior to that test.

FAR 61.315 Sport Pilot Privileges and Limits

What's the difference between a student pilot seeking a sport pilot certificate and someone who actually has a sport pilot certificate? There's a big difference, and it's spelled *supervision*. As a student pilot, you're always your instructor's leash, even when flying solo. Once you obtain your sport pilot certificate, you're on your own, sort of.

The important part of this regulation says:

• You are limited to carrying no more than one passenger (obviously in a two-place light-sport airplane, which is limited to a maximum of two seats).

• You can't fly at night (between the beginning of evening civil twilight and the end of morning civil twilight).

• You must always have at least three miles visibility (flight visibility and reported ground visibility)

• You must always have some visual reference to the surface during flight.

• You can't operate at an altitude of more than 10,000 feet MSL or 2,000 feet AGL, whichever is higher. If a mountain is 12,000 feet tall, then you can operate over it at an altitude no higher than 14,000 feet MSL.

• You cannot operate an aircraft having a V_H that exceeds 87 knots CAS or one that has a V_H of 87 knots or less, unless you have met the requirement of FAR 61.327.

• You can't operate in Class A airspace. Nor can you operate in class B, C and D airspace unless you meet the requirements of FAR 61.325 (coming soon).

• You can't tow any object (in other words, no glider towing)

Yes, believe it or not, this is a four engine, two place ultralight. This is actual photographic proof that someone wasn't mowing his or her lawn on the day this picture was taken.

• You can't act contrary to an operating limitation placed on the airworthiness certificate of the aircraft being flown. Nor can you act contrary to any restriction on your U.S. driver's license or any restriction or limitation imposed by judicial or administrative order when using your driver's license to meet the requirements discussed here.

• You may not act as PIC in a passenger-carrying airlift sponsored by a charitable organization.

• You can't fly for compensation or hire as a sport pilot nor can you act in the furtherance of any business. This requires an explanation.

Compensation or Hire? What Does That Mean?

Drachmas, yen, shillings, moolah, bucks, dinero. What do all these have in common? All are forms of legal tender which can be exchanged for goods or services. If the service happens to be the piloting of a light-sport airplane, then it's the ultimate dream come true for most pilots. Unfortunately, if you're a light-sport pilot, then this is just a dream, nothing more.

Not unreasonably, the FAA rules are both specific and demanding about the training, experience, and capabilities of anyone who hopes to fly for hire.

Many pilots, unfamiliar with the rules governing flights for hire, have created damaging blotches on their otherwise spotless aviation records. It's a blotch that can keep you from having a career in aviation, or limit how far your career will go. Before ever exchanging a nickel for your services as pilot in command, know (and follow) the rules about flying for hire.

A sport pilot certificate allows you to do two things: fly without supervision and carry a passenger. Notice I didn't say anything about carrying *paying* passengers. You may not act as pilot in command of an aircraft carrying a passenger or property for compensation or hire nor may you, for compensation or hire, act as pilot in command. It all boils down to this: furthering your economic interest by transporting a passenger or property smacks of a commercial flight operation.

Chapter 6 - Federal Aviation Regulations: How FAR Can We Go?

6-19

Don't Even Think About It!

> I pray that you won't think about it.

...The subjective intent relates to the actor, whereas the objective result relates to the act itself. It is only natural that good will results between individuals and businesses when a party accommodates and assists another, and it is unlikely that a free ride would have been given to any stranger off the street who happened by. Here, the individual wanted to get to Honolulu to catch a flight to the mainland. However, because of the lateness of the hour, there were no scheduled flights nor any jets available for charter. Thus, not only would the flight be appreciated for the transportation it provided when there was no other desirable means, but in addition, the individual believed it would essentially be a complimentary flight. His natural appreciation no doubt produced good will which likely would lead to future business and referrals. Therefore, the flight did result in compensation, at least in the form of good will, even if the gratuity is discounted. As a result of the above reasons, the flight was found to be operated for compensation or hire.

Official NTSB Case Statement

Finally, if you're thinking about using your sport pilot certificate to conduct your business, you might want to think a second time. The FAA is very clear here that a sport pilot certificate is meant for sport and recreational flying, not business. For instance, if you own a pet store, you simply can't hop in your light-sport airplane and visit your customers all the while attempting to sell them one of your monkeys, no matter how seemingly appropriate this appears. Clearly, the FAA considers this the furtherance of a business (monkey business), and will have none of it. Sorry, no banana.

On the other hand, the regulations say that you may share the operating expenses of a flight with a passenger, provided the expenses involve only fuel, oil, airport expenses (think tie down or landing fees), or aircraft rental fees. You must, however, pay for at least half of the operating expenses of the flight.

In the mid 1970s, a Cessna 150 touched down at what was then Orange County airport in Southern California. This wasn't a normal touchdown. Smack once! Smack twice! Whoomp, whoomp, whoomp flapped the landing gear. The pilot had ground looped his airplane, nearly ripping the right wing off his bird. He had turned his Cessna 150 into a Cessna 75. What was so unusual was, when the doors popped open, two of his paying passengers could be seen running from the airplane. What's interesting about this

is that a Cessna 150 only holds a pilot and *one* passenger!

The PIC lost his pilot certificate, his plane and his wife (she divorced him). Had he been a country western singer he would have made millions, considering the amount of tragedy he

experienced. As it was, he never flew again. Take the extra step to ensure your flying activities are legal and above board. If in doubt, talk to your local FAA representative. There's so much to lose by doing it wrong; there's more than enough to be gained when it's done right.

Did You Know?

Jon Thornburgh

Did you know that there are seven different types of light-sport aircraft? The aircraft are: airplane, glider, gyroplane, weight-shift-control "trike," powered parachute, balloon, and airship.

An *airship* is the FAA's terminology for a blimp. Yes, it's true. A sport pilot can fly a blimp, as long as the maximum takeoff weight is not more than 1,320 pounds, has no more than two occupants, and it meets the other criteria of *light-sport aircraft* specified in FAR 1.1.

Here's one of the unique and amazing features of the sport pilot rule. If you have a pilot certificate to fly any one of the aircraft types listed above you may transition to any one of the other six types of light-sport aircraft with no minimum required flight time. That's right—no solo flight time, no cross-country flights, and no specified dual flight instruction. Then how much training do you need? You need whatever training is required until you can do the maneuvers specified in the sport pilot *Practical Test Standards* (PTS) guide.

But wait, there's more! After you finish your training in the new flying machine you don't even have to take a practical test. You take a *proficiency check* from a flight instructor, instead of getting your test from an FAA Examiner. The flight instructor who administers the proficiency check has to be an instructor other than the one who trained you.

The proficiency check is a new concept in flight training, because normally a student takes his flight test from an Examiner. But sport pilot examiners can often be difficult to find, especially for the new trike and powered parachute light-sport aircraft. There are many more sport pilot instructors than there are examiners, so it's easier for a student to find an instructor to administer a proficiency check than it is to find an examiner. The flight instructor, acting as an examiner, should administer the proficiency check to the same standards as an examiner would.

Another nice sport pilot feature is that any training you receive in a Cessna, Piper, or other general aviation airplane counts toward your sport pilot airplane certificate. So for anyone who started training for private pilot and didn't complete the training, you can switch over to sport pilot and get credit for all your private pilot flight time.

Jon Thornburgh, Sport Pilot Examiner, *sportpilotexaminer.com*

FAR 61.317 Is my sport pilot certificate issued with aircraft and category and class ratings?

Your sport pilot certificate won't show any category and class *ratings* because sport pilots have privileges, not ratings. Therefore, on the back of your sport pilot certificate under the *limitations* section, you'll see the category and class limitations placed on that certificate as shown in Figure 25.

YOUR SPORT PILOT CERTIFICATE

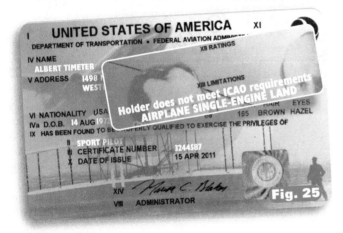

Fig. 25

After you pass the sport pilot practical test (the oral and flight test) and have your sport pilot certificate (this will be issued to you in the form of a temporary airman certificate until the plastic one arrives in the mail), an FAA inspector or an FAA designated examiner will provide you with a logbook endorsement that indicates the category and class of aircraft you're licensed to fly as shown in Figure 26.

REMARKS, PROCEDURES, MANEUVERS	NO. INSTR APP.	NO. LDG.
I certify that Ms. Martha U. Spinproof has met the training and endorsement requirements of FAR 61.309, 61.311 and 61.313. I have determined her proficient to act as PIC of (category and class) of light sport aircraft.		

Rod Machado 10/13/XX, Rod Machado 123456 CFI, Exp. 4/30/XX   Fig. 26

As a licensed sport pilot, your endorsement allows you to fly any light-sport, single-engine-land airplane with two exceptions. The FAA has established a performance dividing line at a V_H of 87 knots. If the light sport airplane you intend to fly has a V_H less than or equal to 87 knots (CAS), then you'll need ground and flight training as well as an endorsement to fly an airplane of this lower performance level (Figure 27). If, on the other hand, the light sport airplane you intend to fly has a V_H greater than 87 knots (CAS), then you'll also need ground and flight training as well as an endorsement to fly an airplane of this higher performance level (Figure 28). I'll discuss the reason for this on the next page in FAR 61.327.

REMARKS, PROCEDURES, MANEUVERS	NO. INSTR APP.	NO. LDG.
I certify that Ms. Sonic Boom has received the required training of § 61.327(a) in a Quicksilver Sprint. I have determined him/her proficient to act as PIC of a light-sport aircraft that has a Vh less than or equal to 87 knots CAS.		

Rod Machado 10/13/XX, Rod Machado 123456 CFI, Exp. 4/30/XX   Fig. 27

REMARKS, PROCEDURES, MANEUVERS	NO. INSTR APP.	NO. LDG.
I certify that Ms. I certify that Mr. Sonic Bume has received the required training of § 61.327 in a (Remos G3). I have determined her proficient to act as PIC of a light-sport aircraft that has a Vh greater than 87 knots CAS.		

Rod Machado 10/13/XX, Rod Machado 123456 CFI, Exp. 4/30/XX   Fig. 28

FAR 61.321 How do I obtain privileges to operate an additional category or class of light-sport aircraft?

Suppose you want to combine fishing with flying and you want to do it in a power parachute for sea operations. If you could fly a powered parachute on floats, you could land in the middle of a lake and do some sport fly fishing. This is known as "sport-flying-sport-fly-fishing." Since you are endorsed to fly a single-engine land airplane, what does it take to move into a new category and/or class of aircraft?

If you want to exercise your sport pilot privileges in an additional category and class of light-sport aircraft, you need to take the ground and flight training in this aircraft that's specified in FAR 61.309 and 61.311 (these areas are not listed in this book. See the FARs for a detailed description of this training). Once you've been trained to the satisfaction of your flight instructor, he or she will provide you with a logbook endorsement indicating that you've met the aeronautical knowledge and flight proficiency requirements for the light-sport aircraft privileges you seek as shown in Figure 29.

REMARKS, PROCEDURES, MANEUVERS	NO. INSTR APP.	N(LD
I certify that Ms. Maggie Kompass has received the required training of §§ 61.309 and 61.311. I have determined that he/she is prepared for the (powered parachute sea) proficiency check.		

Rod Machado 10/13/XX, Rod Machado 123456 CFI, Exp. 4/30/XX   Fig. 29

The next thing you're required to do is to take and pass a *proficiency check* to see if you're qualified to fly this new category and class of aircraft. This isn't another FAA

Chapter 6 - Federal Aviation Regulations: How FAR Can We Go?

6-21

practical test, either. This is a proficiency check that can be given by any appropriately rated flight instructor, but not the instructor that originally trained and endorsed you. The intent here is to offer a degree of objectivity in assessing your skills. So you'll train with your instructor, then fill out the application form for your new sport pilot privileges then give it to the instructor who conducts the proficiency check. He or she will complete the form once your proficiency is established. Then that instructor will provide you with the following endorsement (Figure 30) in your logbook. Now you're qualified to act as PIC in this new category and/or class of aircraft.

REMARKS, PROCEDURES, MANEUVERS	NO. INSTR APP.	NO LD
I certify that Ms. Maggie Kompass has met the training and endorsement requirements of §§ 61.309 and 61.311. I have determined her proficient to act as PIC of a (powered parachute sea) light-sport aircraft.		
Rod Machado 10/13/XX, Rod Machado 123456 CFI, Exp. 4/30/XX		**Fig. 30**

Now you can exercise all the privileges of your sport pilot certificate in a powered parachute on floats.

FAR 61.325 How do I obtain privileges to operate a light-sport aircraft at an airport within, or in airspace within, Class B, C and D airspace?

At this point we haven't talked about airports having operating control towers, much less different Classes of controlled airspace. These items will be covered later in this chapter as well as in Chapter 9. That said, you will eventually learn that some airports have operating air traffic control towers that govern aircraft taking off or landing at that facility. These locations have something called *controlled airspace* (either Class B, C or D) that surround their primary airports. When you're within that controlled airspace you must be in contact with the tower or ATC facility in charge of that airspace.

Fortunately, both student pilots seeking a sport pilot certificate and sport pilots themselves can operate into and out of these tower controlled airports as long as they have the proper training and endorsements in their logbooks.

For instance, a student pilot seeking to fly solo (but not land) in Class D, C and B airspace must have the following endorsement in his or her logbook (Figure 31).

A student pilot who seeks to fly solo to, from or at an airport (to land at this airport) located within Class B, C

REMARKS, PROCEDURES, MANEUVERS	NO. INSTR APP.	NO LDG
I certify that Ms. May Day has received the required training of § 61.94 (a). I have determined he/she is proficient to conduct solo flights in (name of Class B, C, or D) airspace. (List any applicable conditions or limitations.)		
Rod Machado 10/13/XX, Rod Machado 123456 CFI, Exp. 4/30/XX		**Fig. 31**

and D airspace, must have the following endorsement in his or her logbook (Figure 32). For student pilots, this endorsement is required for each additional 90 day period of operations in/at Class B, C or D airspace/airports.

REMARKS, PROCEDURES, MANEUVERS	NO. INSTR APP.	NO LDG
I certify that Ms. May Day has received the required training of § 61.94 (a) (1). I have determined that he/she is proficient to conduct solo flight operations at (name of airport) located in Class B, C, or D airspace or on an airport having an operational control tower. (List any applicable conditions or limitations.)		
Rod Machado 10/13/XX, Rod Machado 123456 CFI, Exp. 4/30/XX		**Fig. 32**

Finally, if you're already rated as a sport pilot and desire to operate in, or land at an airport within, Class B, C and D airspace, you'll need the following endorsement from your instructor in your logbook (Figure 33). And if you're planning on taking your FAA practical flight test at an airport located in Class B, C or D airspace and you pass that checkride (as I know you will), then you won't be able to fly out of that airspace unless your instructor has previously given you this endorsement.

REMARKS, PROCEDURES, MANEUVERS	NO. INSTR APP.	NO LDG
I certify that Ms. May Day has received the required training of § 61.325. I have determined he/she is proficient to conduct operations in Class (B, C, or D) airspace, at an airport located in Class (B, C, or D) airspace, or to, from, through, or on an airport having an operational control tower.		
Rod Machado 10/13/XX, Rod Machado 123456 CFI, Exp. 4/30/XX		**Fig. 33**

FAR 61.327 Are there specific requirements to operate a light sport aircraft based on VH?

As I discussed on the previous page, the FAA makes a distinction between light sport airplanes at a V_H of 87 knots. Why? Two reasons. First, a light sport airplane with a V_H less than or equal to 87 knots is light enough to more easily be affected by wind and turbulence. It's also a potentially a high drag airplane, thus requiring a different skill set to fly safely compared to faster airplanes. Then again, the FAA says that faster airplanes (those with a V_H greater than 87 knots) require their own set of skills and don't adequately prepare a pilot to fly slow speed airplanes. Therefore, the FAA requires two different types of flight and ground training as well as two separate endorsements to operate these airplanes as a sport pilot.

Tailwheel Endorsement

If you plan on soloing in a taildragger, then your instructor will also need to provide you with a tailwheel endorsement as per FAR 61.31(i).

I certify that I have given Mr. Sho Lo, holder of pilot certificate # 2345321 the flight instruction required by FARS 61.31(I) regarding the operation of a tailwheel airplane and find him competent to act as pilot in command.	
Fig. 34	*Rod Machado* 10/13/XX, Rod Machado 123456 CFI, Exp. 4/30/XX

PART 91 GENERAL OPERATING AND FLIGHT RULES

FAR 91.3 Responsibility And Authority of The Pilot In Command

Greetings, Captain, and welcome to FAR 91.3, one of the most powerful regulations in the book. Essentially, it gives you, the pilot of a small airplane, the same authority as the captain of a Boeing 747. The regulation states that you, the pilot in command, are directly responsible for, and are the final authority as to the operation of the aircraft. It doesn't get much simpler than that.

Declaring an emergency is one of the most important options of this rule. For instance, you might be experiencing engine problems and need tower assistance to clear the runway for landing. Stating, "I'm declaring an emergency" puts all available resources at your beck and call. When experiencing an emergency requiring immediate action, this regulation allows you to deviate from any rule to the extent required to meet that emergency.

Let's say the tower controller gave you a specific heading to fly while on your approach to an airport. Suddenly your engine starts running rough. You're calm, but the passengers are saying, "Hello Allah, come in Buddha, speak to me Krishna!" You decide to turn in a different direction, toward terrain more suitable for an off airport landing should the engine quit completely.

Flying a different heading than one given by Air Traffic Control is a deviation from a regulation. ATC says to you, "32 Bravo, why are you changing heading?" You respond by saying, "I'm having engine problems and I'm going to fly over a field on my way to the airport." ATC may ask, "32 Bravo, are you declaring an emergency?" In which case I would recommend you say, "Affirmative!"

Tower controllers now have more flexibility to help you with the problem. They can move other traffic, clear runways and summon ground emergency equipment if necessary. Don't ever be afraid to declare an emergency if you need help. Do this whether or not you think you may break a regulation.

Pilots are sometimes reluctant to declare an emergency. I remember one pilot at a Southern California airport who reported downwind with smoke coming from his engine. The tower called and said, "911 Charlie X-ray, would you like to declare an emergency?" The pilot immediately replied, "No, no way, I mean, no possible way. I'd just like to land as soon as possible!" I spoke with this fellow and asked why he didn't want to declare an emergency. He said, "I was afraid of having to do a lot of paperwork." I guess he wasn't afraid of a smoking airplane.

In refusing to declare an emergency, the pilot completely deprived himself of a very useful service. Even though it was only a leak in an oil cooler, his engine might have caught fire. Tower personnel could have launched fire trucks with fire suppressing foam that can save a burning airplane and its pilot.

The only time you must send in a written report is when requested to by the administrator. This request could come from tower personnel, FAA inspectors or anyone else operating in an official capacity for the FAA. At seminars across the country I constantly ask how many people in the audience have ever declared an emergency. Then I ask how many have had to send in paperwork. Of those declaring emergencies, only two to three percent have had to send in paperwork. They did so because of the administrator's request.

Such a request is often made when the events surrounding the emergency seem unusual enough to warrant inspection. Sometimes paperwork is necessary for ATC personnel to justify their actions in helping you with your problem. In one instance, a pilot declared an emergency, landed on a golf course, dropped off two passengers and took off. The FAA was very interested in his paperwork.

FAR 91.7 Aircraft Airworthiness

The next time you think about doing a less-than-thorough preflight, think again. This regulation states you may not operate an aircraft unless it's in an airworthy condition. It also makes you responsible for terminating a flight any time you believe the airplane is not airworthy due to the failure of a mechanical, electrical, or structural component. Personally, I think both of these are great rules!

You, the pilot in command, are personally responsible for determining whether the airplane is in a safe condition for flight. Disassembling the airplane prior to each flight isn't practical. The next best bet is to walk around the aircraft, preferably with a written checklist, prior to every flight (always be thorough and systematic, especially if this is the first flight of the day). This ensures that all necessary items are checked in a logical sequence. Checklists are provided by the aircraft manufacturer or they may be constructed and personalized with the help of your flight instructor.

A thorough preflight is especially important if the aircraft has been stored for an extended period of time. In this instance you should also make a special check for damage or obstructions caused by animals, birds

INSTRUCTOR COMMUNICATION FAUX PAS #1

No, no, no, when I say "back pressure" I don't mean push your back against the seat. I mean pull back on the control wheel!

Chapter 6 - Federal Aviation Regulations: How FAR Can We Go?

6-23

or insects. As strange as it may seem, pilots occasionally find birds' nests inside the intake ports of an airplane's engine cowling. Had they not done a thorough preflight, all those little birdies would have had to solo a lot earlier than expected.

Several years ago, at an airport in the Los Angeles area, an unsuspecting pilot had an interesting experience with airworthiness. The senior partner in their single-engine Cessna had taken the elevator off to have it painted. The junior partner wasn't notified about this. He showed up at the airport in a rush to make a business flight. With only a cursory preflight, he untied the airplane, taxied out and lined up for takeoff. Halfway down the runway he pulled back on the controls. Nothing happened. "Thump, thump, thump" went the airplane into the grass. It didn't take long for the FAA inspector to arrive and look the bent airplane over. "What happened?" asked the inspector. The pilot replied, "Ahhh, I think my elevator blew off while I was accelerating down the runway." Nice try! An improper preflight caused this gentleman a great deal of unnecessary grief. I believe the inspector said, "Well, this looks like the easiest $5 I've ever made."

If there is anything that looks like it might pose an airworthiness problem, get it checked out. Willingness to do this is one of the qualities separating mediocre pilots from aviators who think professionally.

Color codes are operating limitations. Placards list operating limitations. Approved documentation lists operating limitations.

Fig. 35

FAR 91.9 Civil Aircraft Flight Manual, Markings And Placard Requirements

The next time you walk onto an elevator, notice the placard next to the door. It usually says, "Weight not to exceed 3,000 pounds." The elevator can't safely hold more than ten 250 pound guys and a 500 pound gorilla. This is known as an operating limitation. Airplanes have similar limitations.

Airplane operating limitations come in the form of color codes, placards, limitations provided by the manufacturer and approved documentation (Figure 35). As PIC, you are required by this regulation to comply with all the operating limitations specified in any of these ways.

Operating limitations are seldom expressed in only one form. Most airplanes use several means to express these limitations. For instance, a typical general aviation airplane has color codes (which represent limitations) on

the airspeed indicator; placards to identify maneuvering speed for turbulence and other maneuvers; and information on these limits in the Pilot's Operating Handbook (POH). An approved Airplane Flight Manual (AFM) usually identifies the maximum gross weight for the airplane (the POH and AFM can often be the same book). No matter how these limitations are expressed, they must be followed. Exceeding specific operating limitations is a violation of the FARs. It's also an act of profound mental ineptitude.

FAR 91.15 Dropping Objects

I recall a discussion among several pilots where the topic was about the legality of throwing things out of airplanes. One pilot said his instructor threw a roll of adding machine paper out of an airplane and chased it earthward. Another pilot suggested that real macho pilots might throw out the entire machine and chase it earthward. Is such activity legal?

According to the regulations, the pilot in command may not drop any object in flight if it creates a hazard to persons or property. Since even a tiny object rapidly accelerates to bullet-like speed, and can cause as much damage as a bullet when striking a person, pet, or property, it's pretty hard to argue that tossing anything out of an airplane doesn't at least cause a hazard, whether or not it actually strikes something. Unless you're capable of seeing everything from spotted salamanders to Spot the dog from several thousand feet up, I'd suggest keeping everything that's in the airplane in the airplane.

That Runway Has a Short on It!

It was a warm summer morning at Fullerton airport when a Piper Arrow taxied into position for takeoff. My friend John, a tower controller, cleared the pilot for a right turnout after departure and the airplane started its takeoff roll. As soon as it was airborne John noticed something leaving the aircraft. It seems that the rear baggage door had popped open and clothing was slowly leaving the airplane. Apparently, the pilot's luggage had also popped open and his undergarments were being sucked out. John tried calling the pilot but he had apparently switched frequencies and wasn't monitoring the tower.

91.17 Alcohol or Drugs

We've already talked about alcohol and drugs, but let's do a brief review here. Regulations strictly prohibit you from acting as a crewmember of any aircraft within eight hours after consuming any alcoholic beverages. This regulation also prohibits you from acting while under the influence of alcohol. In other words, if you'd had several of those "World's Fair" cocktails—drink two and make an exhibition of yourself—you might still be tanked long after eight hours have passed. Having an alcohol concentration of .04 or greater in blood or breath specimen is prohibited according to this regulation.

If a law enforcement officer notices or suspects a pilot is affected by alcohol or drugs, he or she can request a blood test. The pilot must, by law, submit to this test. A law enforcement officer probably isn't going to become suspicious just because he sees your airplane weaving on final approach. If that were the case, I would have had so many blood tests that I would have surely died from anemia. On the other hand, if you smell like a microbrewery while telling the nice officer about why you landed on the taxiway instead of the runway, expect to make a blood donation.

If the FAA suspects that someone acting as pilot in command or as a required crewmember might be under the influence of alcohol, then that person must furnish to the FAA the results of an alcohol-blood concentration test (or authorize the release of such a test), taken within four hours of attempting to act as PIC or as a required crewmember.

Be very careful about carrying an intoxicated passenger aboard your airplane. The regulation states that, except in an emergency, you may not carry a person who appears to be intoxicated or under the influence of drugs or alcohol on your airplane. This obviously excludes a medical patient under proper care (and not under the care of Doctor Jack Daniels either).

Bob carefully considers the importance of the item seen underneath his airplane.

91.103 Preflight Action

Before you begin any flight you are required to become familiar with all the available information concerning that flight. This is one of the many catchall regulations with enough loops in it to snare almost anybody who messes up. "All available information" is a bit broad, but it's clear that several critical items are *de regieur*. For a flight not in the vicinity of the departure airport, you must check the weather reports and forecasts, fuel requirements, alternatives available if the flight cannot be completed, and any known traffic delays advised by ATC (*vicinity* is defined as more than 5 miles from the airport according to a 1982 copy of *FAA General Aviation News*.)

What does all that mean? Basically, before every flight you must obtain a weather briefing. This is normally accomplished by calling the Flight Service Station (this is a weather service, not where you go to get windows cleaned) or by using a computer briefing service like DUAT. Not only do you want the current weather, you want forecasts (weather to be expected). Alternate airports are technically not required for VFR pilots. The official language states that the pilot must have *alternatives* available if the planned flight cannot be completed. A 180 degree turn is a reasonable alternative. However, any pilot who doesn't figure out where he or she would go if they can't get where they're going is simply one fry short of a Happy Meal.

You are also required to check the runway lengths at the airport you'll use. Now, this is one of those "Duuuh" sort of things, but you'd be

THE HEAT IS ON: Talk to That Passenger

A new flight instructor decided to treat his wife to a flight on a clear cold winter's night. As with a car, in small planes the heater works best when you pour on the power. They both felt cold while taxiing, so the pilot had the heater adjusted to high. Pushing the throttle in for takeoff brought the heater to life with a hearty blast of hot air. Feeling uncomfortable with this rush of heat, the wife reached down and turned off the heater. When only a few hundred feet in the air, the engine sputtered and died. The pilot landed in the trees with no damage to the occupants; unfortunately the aircraft sustained a great deal of damage. Have you deduced what killed the engine, Dr. Watson? The knob that the nonpilot wife pushed was not the heater at all. It was the fuel control knob and she switched it off!

Moral: Before the engine is started, all nonpilot passengers should be given a thorough briefing that they shouldn't touch ANYTHING without the pilot's permission. This would be a good time to also explain the importance of a sterile (no-talking-to-the-pilot) cockpit below 1000 feet (airlines use 10,000 feet) during takeoff and landing.   **D.T.**

Chapter 6 - Federal Aviation Regulations: How FAR Can We Go?

6-25

surprised how many pilots every year manage to make a 900 foot landing on a 500 foot runway. You have to know how long the runway is, and you have to figure out whether your airplane, loaded as it will be loaded, can take off, land, and take off again from the runways you intend to use.

For airplanes with approved flight manuals containing takeoff and landing distance information, simply check the airplane performance for the runway lengths and conditions of the flight. If your airplane has no approved flight manual, you can use any reliable information concerning takeoff and landing performance data that considers elevation, runway slope, gross weight, wind and temperature to compute takeoff and landing distances. Checking runway performance is required when taking off or landing at *any* airport, whether it's within or beyond the vicinity of the departure field.

The intent of the takeoff and landing regulation is to prevent you from using gut feel to estimate airplane performance. Your gut has no brains. Neither does the seat of your pants. Keep that in mind. It will save you much aviation grief. If the performance chart says the takeoff requires 350 feet and the runway is 300 feet long, take a taxicab instead of a taxiway.

FAR 91.105 Flight Crewmembers at Stations

During takeoff, landing, and while enroute, you, the pilot in command, shall be in your seat (sometimes called a station). On big airliners, all the other command performers (copilot, flight engineer) have to be in their places, all with smiling faces, as well. You are required to keep your safety belt fastened while seated, and if your airplane is equipped with a shoulder harness and wearing it doesn't interfere with your duties, it must be kept fastened during takeoff and landing. The rules do not demand that a shoulder harness be worn while enroute, but doing so is good practice. Besides, anything that protects you from becoming tossed salad in turbulence is good. One bang of your head against the roof of the cockpit can be incapacitating. It can also leave an enormous lump on your melon which always prevents a headset from fitting correctly.

There are only two times when you are not required to be in your seat as a required flight crewmember. First, you may leave the seat when your absence is necessary to perform duties in connection with the operation of the airplane. This could happen if you're a flight crewmember on a Boeing 727. It's highly unlikely on anything you'll probably fly with a sport pilot certificate. Besides, where are you going to go in a Cessna SkyCatcher, outside to check the engine oil?

The other time you can get up and go is to get up and go. As the regulations delicately put it, you are permitted to leave your seat to attend to your *physiological needs*. The vast majority of light-sport aircraft have no bathroom, so I don't expect to bump into the PIC in the aisle while flying in a Remos G3.

Wearing seatbelts and shoulder harnesses is good for your pilot health. Please keep in mind that most of the time you are not only the pilot in command, you are the *only* pilot on board. A whack up the side of the head from unexpected turbulence can leave the airplane without a pilot and the passengers without a way to get home safely. They will bear a grudge.

Sometimes people feel trapped when strapped in their seats. I had one student who was emphatic about not wearing a shoulder harness. We argued about this for almost 15 minutes. Then, in a sing-song voice she quipped, "I want to be free, I've got to move around; I'm a butterfly, and you don't strap butterflies down!" Slapping my hand to my forehead, I looked at her and said, "If you're a butterfly, why are you taking flying lessons?" She buckled up.

FAR 91.107 Use of Safety Belts

What about the passenger and seatbelts? Prior to takeoff, the PIC is required to brief your passenger on how to fasten and unfasten his or her seatbelt and shoulder harness. Getting into and out of an aviation seatbelt and shoulder harness is not always the most obvious thing in the world, as you will see from Figure 36. Keep in mind that your passenger is counting on you to keep him safe. Do not assume he or she knows how to operate the seatbelts. You are also required to notify the passenger prior to moving (taxiing), takeoff, and landing to fasten his safety belts and shoulder harnesses (if installed).

Some seatbelts are the double shoulder strap type.

Fig. 36

Courtesy Remos

Actually Heard...

Pilot: "Golf Sierra Bravo, request instructions for takeoff."

Unknown Person: "Open the throttle smoothly, check temperatures and pressure rising, keep the aircraft straight using...."

(I say, *if installed*, because some aircraft falling into the light-sport category such as the Piper Cub and the Aeronca Champ, weren't originally equipped with shoulder harnesses and are not required to have them under the present regulations.)

One brand of safety belt requires pulling a lever to unlatch the belt. Several years ago a young lady went for a ride in an older, open cockpit biplane having this unusual belt lock. Her boyfriend strapped her in without showing her how to unlatch the belt. Parking at a refueling stop, he went for a quick snack while she remained strapped in the airplane. The gas person (liquid fuel liberator) was fueling the airplane from on top when the gas nozzle stuck. Gasoline rained down on her. Unable to release the belt, she was stuck until her friend returned. She had serious irritation to her mucous membranes. Be smart; inform all passengers about the use of their seat belts.

During takeoff and landing your passenger should be in his or her seat with safety belt and shoulder harness on (if the airplane has shoulder harnesses). Roaming around the airplane isn't allowed, and in most general aviation aircraft it also isn't possible (even if you're a Roman).

Our family had a close friend who insisted on never using safety belts when driving. I asked him why. He said, "If I crash, I want to be thrown clear." I replied, "Then you might want to ride on the hood. That way, if you crash you don't have to go through the windshield!" He still doesn't wear seatbelts, but I did make $5 off his answer.

FAR 91.111 Operating Near Other Aircraft

No person may operate an aircraft so close to another aircraft as to create a collision hazard. In other words, don't even think about buzzing another airplane in flight or on the ground. There is no such thing as a buzzing license. This is a very unsafe practice.

No person may operate an aircraft in formation flight except by prior arrangement with the pilot in command of each aircraft in the formation. You're not allowed to join up with another airplane in flight without letting the pilot know about it beforehand. Think how jolting it would be to look out your left window and view another pilot waving at you!

Have you ever wondered why you've never seen two passenger-carrying airliners in close formation? This regulation also states that no person may operate an aircraft carrying passengers for hire in formation flight. Nothing would scare me more than having the captain of my jetliner roaming the sky, looking for one of his or her buddies to play with.

FAR 91.113 Right of Way Rules: Except Water Operations

Now comes the mother of all rules. This is It, folks. The Big One, the Whopper of the FAA liturgy.

See and avoid. I want you to read and remember *see and avoid.*

To make a complicated bunch of words easy, the FAA says it is your responsibility above all else to see and avoid airplanes and obstacles. If you munch, crunch, or otherwise run into something in the air, the FAA says you're responsible under 91.113 for "failure to see and avoid."

Several right of way rules exist that determine who gets to go first in case of conflict. When a pilot must give the right of way to another aircraft, that pilot shall give way and may not pass over, under or ahead of the aircraft unless well clear. Just because you must legally maneuver

to avoid an aircraft, you shouldn't return to your original course so quickly that you scare the daylights out of the other pilot.

Distress – Remember our discussion a while back about declaring an emergency? Aircraft in distress have the right of way over all other air traffic. If you had an engine failure and needed to land, you'd appreciate this rule. It would be quite scary if you called the tower, told them your engine quit and they said, "Roger 32 Bravo, we can't let you land right now because we're busy!" Fortunately, they are not going to say that for two reasons. First, because they really want to help you, and second, because of 91.113.

Converging – When aircraft of the same category are converging at approximately the same altitude, except head on or nearly so, the aircraft to the other's right has the right of way. This scenario is shown in Figure 37. Airplane B is to the right of airplane A, giving B the right of way. Airplane C is to the right of airplane D, giving C the right of way. Avoiding collisions while converging is best handled by climbing, descending, maneuvering or any combination of these. Personally, I prefer to maneuver in such a way that I never lose sight of the converging airplane.

CONVERGING AT THE SAME ALTITUDE

Airplane B has the right-of-way since it's to the right of airplane A.

Fig. 37

Airplane C has the right-of-way since it's to the right of airplane D.

AIRCRAFT CONVERGING HEAD ON OR NEARLY SO

Since both aircraft are approaching each other head on, or nearly so, each shall alter their course to the right and pass well clear. **Fig. 38**

Aircraft approaching head on, or nearly so, shall alter their course to the right to avoid a collision (Figure 38).

Even though you may have the right of way, be careful about insisting on it. Pig headed pilots are a danger to themselves, their passenger, and others in the sky and on the ground (falling airplane pieces can cause serious damage). Be reasonable, be sensible, be safe.

Aircraft Categories – Aircraft of different categories on a converging course offer different right of way possibilities. The right of way usually belongs to the least maneuverable category of aircraft. For instance, a balloon has the right of way over any other category of aircraft. This makes sense, since you can't do steep turns in a balloon to avoid traffic. Balloons just sort of hang in midair, hoping no one will hit them. Since no evasive action is possible, balloons have the right of way over all other aircraft.

A glider has the right of way over an airship, airplane, rotorcraft,

AIRCRAFT OVERTAKING EACH OTHER

Each aircraft that is being overtaken (regardless of its category) has the right-of-way. The pilot of the overtaking aircraft shall alter his course to the right and pass well clear.

powered parachute and weight-shift-control aircraft. An airship (blimp) has the right of way over an airplane, rotorcraft, powered parachute and weight-shift-control aircraft. However, an aircraft towing or refueling other aircraft has the right of way over all other engine driven aircraft. Don't expect to see a glider towing an airplane. (If you do see such a thing, take a picture of it and immediately send it to me. It's worth millions!)

Overtaking – One aircraft overtaking another presents its own right of way solution. The aircraft being overtaken has the right of way. The pilot of the overtaking aircraft must alter her course to the right to pass well clear of the slower aircraft (Figure 39). Fortunately, this is one regulation the Goodyear blimp doesn't have to worry about. The only time the blimp worries about this is when it's following a slower, fatter blimp. In this case the overtaking process may take hours and hours!

Landing – Landing presents yet another right of way scenario. Aircraft, while on final approach to land or while landing, have the right of way over other aircraft in flight or operating on the surface (Figure 40). Assume that airplane B has just taxied onto the runway. Therefore, airplane A has the right of way. Airplane A also has the right of way over helicopter C that's performing crop dusting short of the runway. Pilots should not take advantage of this rule to force an aircraft, that has already landed, off the runway.

When two or more aircraft are approaching an airport for the purpose of landing, the aircraft at the lower altitude has the right of way

RIGHT-OF-WAY DURING LANDING

Fig. 40

Airplane A has the right-of-way over airplane B (which is taxiing onto the runway for takeoff) and helicopter C, which is crop dusting next to the runway.

(Figure 41). Airplane B has the right of way over airplane A because it's at a lower altitude. An alternate way of thinking about this is to consider the right of way as belonging to the airplane that's most committed to landing. Once again, pilots should not take advantage of this rule to cut in front of or overtake another aircraft that is on final approach to land.

Pilots are generally a very courteous group. Unfortunately, a few bad apples exist. Over the years I've come across a few pilots who were so ornery that they couldn't get along with dead people. These were the type of folks capable of rubbing entire cities the wrong way. I've actually witnessed two aviators coming to blows over who had the right of way in the pattern. Several flight instructors gathered around and no one knew what to do. One instructor actually suggested we jump in and help the bigger guy. Like cats twirling in heated frenzy, they eventually climbed into their airplanes and flew off to lick their wounds. It's a good policy never to insist on the right of way. Take it if it's yours, but demanding it is dangerous business.

RIGHT OF WAY DURING LANDING

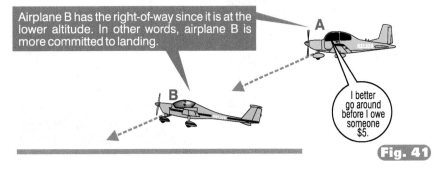

Airplane B has the right-of-way since it is at the lower altitude. In other words, airplane B is more committed to landing.

I better go around before I owe someone $5.

Fig. 41

FAR 91.115 Right of Way Rules: Water Operations

If you're landing a seaplane, you're required to keep clear of all vessels and avoid impeding their navigation. The notion here is that boats belong on the water, while airplanes are sort of odd ducks.

If you're on a crossing course with another aircraft or surface vessel, the aircraft or vessel on your right has the right of way. While approaching head on, or nearly so, each vessel should alter its course to the right to keep well clear. If you are overtaking another aircraft or vessel, you should alter your course to keep well clear (either a right or left turn is acceptable). This last regulation is different from overtaking in the air, where the overtaking aircraft should alter its course to the right. Operations on water may not allow you the option of passing on the right. There could be scuba divers or water skiers in that direction. There's nothing like going for a little scuba dive and getting conked on the head with the float of a big Cessna.

FAR 91.119 Minimum Safe Altitudes

The rules designate certain minimum altitudes that you must maintain under given circumstances. These altitudes are designed to protect people on the surface as well as the pilot and passengers in the aircraft. For some aircraft, the risk associated with flying too low is greater than for others. Airplanes must be operated higher than helicopters because they require more distance to land. As a student pilot, I always thought helicopter pilots liked to fly low because it was easier to stop and ask for directions. (OK, I was wrong).

None of the following minimum altitude rules pertain to takeoff or landing at an airport. Taking off or landing obviously requires climbs and descents at closer than nor-

Let's see, who has the right of way when fueling another airplane? Ahhh... I'm sure they do. After all, they have guns. Oh well, I think I'll just get in line and get some gas.

mal altitudes to the surface. Don't try stretching the rule by flying at treetop height 50 miles from the airport and then claiming you were just setting up your approach (you're going to owe someone $5 on that deal). Also, don't delay your normal climbout after takeoff just so a passenger can check her house for holes in the roof.

Here are some of the most important rules about how low you can go:

Rule No 1: No person may operate an aircraft below an altitude allowing an emergency landing to be made without undue hazard to persons or property on the surface in the event of an engine failure. This is another of the famous FAA catchall rules. On land, there's always a "basic speed law" that says that no matter what the posted speed, you can't drive faster than is prudent under the circumstances. In aviation, you can't fly any lower than it is safe, and if something bad happens, that proves you weren't high enough. You'll have a difficult time convincing an FAA inspector that flying 50 feet above a crowded beach on July 4th is a safe practice (besides, you never want to give someone a moving target to aim a bottle rocket at).

A Congested Area

© Jurgen Effner

MINIMUM ALTITUDES WHEN OPERATING OVER A CONGESTED AREA

When operating over a congested area, you should be at least 1,000' above the highest obstacle within a 2,000' radius of your airplane.

1,000'

1,750' MSL

2,000'

750' MSL

Fig. 42

A Congested Area

© OrdinaryLight

Chapter 6 - Federal Aviation Regulations: How FAR Can We Go?

6-29

A Legal Interpretation of the Terms: City, Town, Settlement, Open Air Assembly of Persons

The following is the FAA Legal Counsel's response requesting a clear-cut definition or meaning of a city, town, settlement, or open air assembly of persons, as used in Sec. 91.119 of the Federal Aviation Regulations:

© icholakov - Fotolia

The term "congested area" has been applied on a case by case basis since it first appeared in the Air Commerce Regulations of 1926. No precise mathematical or geographic definition has yet been developed. However, the following guidelines have been applied by the Civil Aeronautics Board (new National Transportation Safety Board) in attempting to give the term fair and equitable affect:

1. The term is administered so as to protect persons and property in small, sparsely settled communities, as well as persons and property in large metropolitan areas from the hazards and from the noise of low flying aircraft. Thus, size of the area is not controlling, and violations of the rule have been sustained for operation of aircraft (i) over a small congested area consisting of approximately 10 houses and a school, (ii) over the campus of a university, (iii) over a beach area along a highway, and (iv) over a boy's camp where there were numerous people on the decks and children at play on shore.

2. The presence of people is important to the determination of whether a particular area is "congested". Thus, no violation was found in the case of a flight over a large shop building and four one-family dwellings because, in the words of the CAB Examiner, "it is not known whether the dwellings were occupied." In that case, the area surrounding the buildings was open, flat, and semi-arid.

3. The term is administered to prohibit overflights that cut the corners of large, heavily congested, residential areas. As made clear in the rule, the congested area must be an area of a city, town, or settlement. However, no precise density of population, ground traffic, or congestion, or precise description of the proximity of buildings or number of residences, has yet been devised that will achieve both the intended protection of persons and property on the ground and fair application of the rule to operators of aircraft.

Common sense and good piloting practice dictate flying high enough so you can glide to an acceptable landing site. Professional pilots think this way and they never allow themselves to become trapped by circumstances and altitude.

Rule No. 2: When flying over any congested area of a city, town or settlement or over any open air assembly of persons, the aircraft must be operated at an altitude of 1,000 feet above the highest obstacle within a horizontal radius of 2,000 feet of the aircraft.

Figure 42 depicts a building in a congested area topping out at 750 feet MSL. An aircraft operating horizontally, within 2,000 feet of that building, needs to fly at a minimum altitude of 1,750 feet MSL for legal flight. The question pilots frequently ask is, "What is the definition of a congested area?" FAA officials have

yet to define this concept. Frankly, it's often the NTSB (National Transportation Safety Board) that defines these concepts by legal precedent when pilots are called into an

> *Prior decisions which the NTSB therein cited include those which concerned situations of (1) 10 houses and a school as a "small congested area," a university campus not shown to be part of a city or a town, and (3) a group of 60 to 70 cottages.*
>
> **Official NTSB Case Statement**

NTSB hearing to explain their actions. One thing is clear though: you'll have a lot of explaining to do if you violate this regulation.

While a precise definition of *congested area* is lacking, we can understand what the FAA considers a congested area by examining a few NTSB court decisions. On one occasion, a pilot was cited for operating

an airplane within a radius of 2,000 feet and less than 1,000 feet above a few isolated homes with smoke rising from their fireplaces. Smoke was a vital factor, since, by its presence, it implied the homes were occupied. On another occasion, a pilot wasn't cited for flying within a few hundred feet of an industrial warehouse. The reason? It was Sunday and no cars were in the parking lot. The implication here is that the presence of people is the major factor in determining the congestion quotient of an area. You'll need to use your good judgment on this one because of the vague definitions involved. Be conservative. Don't fly too low where there are lots of people.

One old timer summed it up very well when he said, "Never fly low enough so someone can get your aircraft tail number." Of course, that

conk!

Plucky Bird

A Navy pilot called the radar controller and said, "Center, we've just taken a bird strike and are declaring an emergency." The controller working the flight made radar identification of the aircraft and asked for additional details on the bird strike. "It was a northeast bound chicken hawk," the navy pilot said. "He was big, too. He hit our canopy head-on at 300 knots." Maintaining his composure, the controller replied, "Roger, and how fast were you going, sir?"   **ASRS Report.**

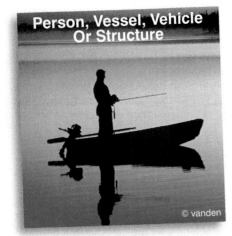

Person, Vessel, Vehicle Or Structure

© vanden

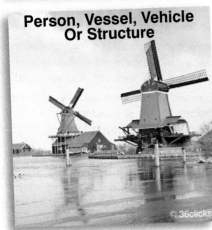

Person, Vessel, Vehicle Or Structure

© 36clicks

SPARSELY POPULATED AREAS

Over sparsely populated areas the air-craft may not be operated closer than 500 feet to any person, vessel, vehicle or structure.

500' above outhouse

I said land on the runway, not the fairway!

Well, it's not a birdie but it's close.

500'

500'   500'

Fig. 43

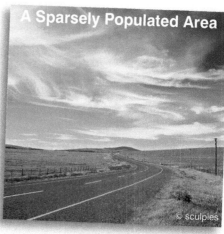

A Sparsely Populated Area

© sculpies

A Sparsely Populated Area

© arenysam

was the intelligent part of the statement. He went on to say, "Always fly an airplane with a two-tone paint job so that you can have conflicting eye witness reports."

Rule No. 3: When operating an aircraft over other than a congested area, no person may operate below an altitude of 500 feet above the surface, except over open water or sparsely populated areas. In those cases, the aircraft may not be operated closer than 500 feet to any person, vessel, vehicle or structure.

When over open water or a sparsely populated area you may take your plane right down on the deck if you wish. But do so only if you can land safely in an emergency (see Rule 1). The moment you spot a person, boat, car or structure, you need to move

away by a distance of at least 500 feet vertically or horizontally as shown in Figure 43.

In Honolulu, Hawaii, the pilot of a small aerobatic biplane had an unusual collision. He was flying just above the water when he collided with a surfboard. Smack! It was a

Where the landing conducted by a pilot involved a final flight path under the bridge which was both unnecessary and inappropriate, the operation within 500 feet of structures was not excused by the prefatory clause of FAR 91.119 ("Except when necessary for takeoff or landing...").

Official NTSB Case Statement

direct hit on the leading edge of his wing. After landing at the airport, the pilot called the local FAA office and reported the encounter. He must have thought that the surfer intentionally

tossed the surfboard toward his air-plane during the fly-by. Otherwise, why report it to the FAA? Unless this was a particularly strong surfer, I hardly think it's possible to throw a surfboard 500 feet into the air (the minimum distance the airplane should have been from the surfer).

Personally, I think the surfer saw the airplane and dove into the water to avoid being hurt. Imagine the conversation with the FAA inspector. "Is this the FAA?" "Yes, it is." "I was flying along minding my own business when some dude threw a surfboard at my airplane." "Oh, really, what's your name...?" Perhaps this pilot didn't think carefully before he made this call. One thing is sure, the FAA inspector was $5 richer at the end of the day.

Chapter 6 - Federal Aviation Regulations: How FAR Can We Go?

6-31

FAR 91.121 Altimeter Settings

In Chapter Five we discussed setting the local barometric station pressure into the altimeter's Kollsman window. We did this so the altimeter would correctly read our height above sea level. Of course, as we move away from the last altimeter setting source we need to update this setting.

Regulations require that you maintain a cruising altitude by reference to an altimeter that is set to the current reported altimeter setting of a station along the route and within 100 nautical miles of the aircraft. This regulation applies to aircraft operating below 18,000 feet MSL.

Aircraft operating at or above 18,000 feet MSL set their altimeters to 29.92" Hg. Fast moving jet-type aircraft are usually found operating at these high altitudes. Having to readjust altimeters every 100 miles or so would send most jet pilots to their carpel tunnel specialist.

Figure 44 depicts a typical cross country flight and the associated altimeter adjustment points. Assume your altimeter is set to the altimeter setting for Jabba International (the departure airport). You may fly for 100 nautical miles along the route before needing an altimeter update.

At position A, the Chewbacca international AWOS Station is within 90 nautical miles of your airplane. You set your altimeter to Chewbacca's altimeter setting and continue on to position B, where you are now 100 nautical miles from this source. A new altimeter source within 100 nautical miles of the aircraft is needed. Fortunately, the Obewan AWOS Station is along the route and within 100 nautical miles of the aircraft. Setting the altimeter to Obewan's altimeter setting, you continue to Skywalker Airport. On the last part of the flight, you should be within 100 nautical miles of Obewan. Therefore, you'll only need to keep the altimeter set to Obewan's station pressure.

ALTIMETER SETTING REQUIREMENTS

Skywalker airport

Chewbacca International AWOS Station

100 nm

100 nm

100 nm

Uh-oh, I think there's a disturbance in the force.

90 nm

B

Obewan AWOS Station

100 nm

A

Jabba airport

Fig. 44

Set your altimeter to the nearest reported altimeter setting of any station along the route. That station should be within 100 nautical miles of the aircraft. Stations beyond this distance may not accurately reflect the appropriate barometric pressure for your position.

What Did You Do That For?

After a particularly lousy landing by the copilot of an Australian airliner, that copilot heard the captain announce, "Ladies and gentlemen our airline wishes to apologize for the copilot's rough landing."

Some months later, the same crew was together and, you guessed it, the captain did an even worse landing. The first officer immediately jumped on the intercom and announced, "Ladies and gentlemen, our airline would like to apologize for the captain's rough landing."

The captain responded angrily, "What did you say that for?"

The copilot replied, "Remember a couple of months ago? I owed it to you."

The captain said, "But I never keyed the microphone!"

Source: The First General Aviation WWW Server

Realistically, try to update the altimeter every chance you get. This prevents altimeter errors and keeps pilots safely separated by using the same barometric pressure source.

FAR 91.123 Compliance with ATC Clearances and Instructions

This regulation states that when an ATC clearance has been obtained, no pilot in command may deviate from that clearance unless an amended clearance is obtained, an emergency exists or in response to a traffic alert and collision avoidance system resolution advisory.

Like many adolescents, some pilots have trouble with the concept of authority. They hate to admit someone else has the right to control their actions. In the case of Air Traffic Control, the authority is clear; your job is learning how to follow directions.

ATC clearances are authorizations to proceed under specific traffic conditions in controlled airspace. These clearances come in all sizes and shapes. Most commonly, they are headings to fly. When receiving VFR vectors from ATC, it's not unusual to be given a heading that puts you on a collision course with a cloud. Since ATC radar can't see clouds and VFR pilots are prohibited from flying into clouds, what do you do if you find yourself being vectored toward one?

You are required to follow the ATC clearance unless an amended clearance is obtained. Given the above situation, the only logical thing to do is to request another heading. ATC is almost always accommodating in these cases. Simply call the controller and say, "Sir (or Ma'am), this is N2132 Bravo, I'm unable that heading due to clouds." They may respond by saying, "32 Bravo, will a heading of such-and-such keep you away from the clouds?" You'll be surprised how helpful ATC is when they're not too busy. Remember, since you are a VFR pilot, under no circumstances should you fly into a cloud.

This regulation goes on to say that if a pilot is uncertain of the meaning of an ATC clearance, the pilot shall immediately request clarification from ATC. Simply stated, if you don't understand, ask.

A friend of mine took a fellow pilot on a demonstration sales flight in his cherried-out small airplane. When asked what she did for a living the pilot stated she was a controller. "Excellent," my friend thought, "I can relax while she flight tests the airplane. After all, she's probably a controller at some big airport and is very familiar with airplanes, airspace and procedures."

She started up the airplane, taxied out and requested a clearance out of the Class C airspace. Her departure proved interesting. She flew the wrong headings, the wrong altitudes, and was smitten with confusion over ATC's directions. My friend was perplexed but didn't intervene. After all, she was a controller. He thought she must have known something he didn't. Finally, he couldn't take it any longer. When she wouldn't ask for clarification of an ATC clearance, he grabbed the controls and immediately followed ATC's directive. Looking over at her he asked, "Why are you having such trouble? I thought you were a controller!" She replied, "I am a controller—at Woolworth's!" Being an accountant with limited piloting experience, she certainly had her hands full.

Sometimes it's necessary to deviate from the rules in an emergency situation. This regulation also states that, except in an emergency, no person may operate an aircraft contrary to an ATC instruction in an area in which air traffic control is exercised. All this statement does is clarify that an emergency situation allows deviation from an ATC clearance.

Each pilot in command who, in an emergency, deviates from an ATC clearance or instruction is obligated to notify ATC of that deviation as soon as possible. Let's assume you just departed from a tower controlled airport when you notice smoke billowing up from under your panel. An electrical fire is the likely cause so you immediately turn off your master switch and follow the electrical fire procedure. Not wanting to fly away from the airport, you turn back to the field. You're supposed to call ATC but you've got a burning problem that keeps you from doing that. Stay cool, you're not in trouble, and the FAA is not about to fan the flames. This is an emergency, and your obligation is simply to call ATC as soon as possible after things are under control.

Under certain conditions you might not need to deviate from a rule or declare an emergency. You might only need priority handling by ATC.

There's one last section to this block of regulations that I've always found fascinating. Unless otherwise authorized by ATC, no person operating an aircraft may operate that aircraft according to any clearance or instruction that has been issued to another aircraft for radar air control purposes.

Who'd fly someone else's headings? This rule dates back to a time when equipment was much more archaic. To identify which blip was which on the radar screen, a controller would have an aircraft fly a series of specific headings. If the blip turned right/left/left/right as directed, the controller felt pretty sure he knew what he was looking at. Who else would fly like that?

Emerging From an Emergency

I departed John Wayne airport many years ago and immediately had a partial power failure in a small airplane. My student looked over at me and said, "OK, knock it off; what did you do this time?" He thought I was playing one of my little educational tricks on him. I wasn't (you might think the large beads of sweat accumulating on all my skin surfaces would have tipped him off).

Barely able to maintain altitude, I turned back toward the airport. I called the controller and requested an immediate landing on the runway opposite that used for takeoff. I glanced over at my student and noticed his lips were moving but no sound was coming out. He looked like a fish freshly pulled from water that was still trying to breathe. We landed without incident, and my student regained his speech.

Although not deviating from any rule, I was given priority handling. Under priority conditions, where no deviation from a rule has occurred, the pilot in command must submit a detailed report of that emergency within 48 hours to the manager of that ATC facility *if requested to do so*. Sometimes they ask, sometimes they don't. It sort of depends on how much commotion is created and whether it demands a paper explanation. If they have to close down JFK for half an hour to accommodate your priority condition, expect to write a letter. If you had to awaken the controller at Prozac International for priority handling (his second operation of the month), it's unlikely a report will be requested.

The controller didn't request a report from me so I didn't send one in, and that was the end of the matter.

Rod Machado

That's Not What I Meant!

A Cessna 172 landed at a tower-controlled field and came to a complete stop on the runway. The pilot then made a 180 degree turn and commenced to taxi back on the runway while two airplanes were on final to land. The controller yelled, "Hey, 2132 Bravo, we don't allow one-eighties on the runway." The pilot replied, "Well what are you gettin' in a huff about? I'm a 172!"

Well, as it turns out, student pilots did. Instructors, for practice, would sometimes have their students respond to the controllers' commands. On several occasions aircraft were misidentified and vectored in the wrong direction, perilously close to other airplanes or higher terrain. That's how the rule came to be. The moral is, don't do what you're not told.

FAR 91.125 ATC Light Signals

When radios stop working, tower controllers fall back on a primitive but effective means of communication to control traffic in the landing pattern—light signals. These signals are shown in Figure 45. Holding a small but powerful light gun (Figure 46), controllers can direct a concentrated beam of light directly at your aircraft. Using one of three colors—red, green, white—controllers can communicate several important commands to pilots.

Light Signals in the Air – If your radio fails under VFR conditions, simply enter the traffic pattern at a tower controlled field after observing the flow of traffic (not going with the flow could result in a few unusual signals from the pilots in the other airplanes). Keep an eye on the tower cab for a light signal. If, while airborne, you receive a steady green light, this means you are cleared to land. Think of a steady green light as being similar to the three green landing gear lights on a retractable geared airplane. If they're all indicating green, then it's OK to land.

If you saw your three green landing gear lights flickering or flashing instead of painting a steady green, you'd probably go around and solve the problem. Likewise, a flashing green light from the tower means you should return for landing, to be followed by a steady green light at the proper time. This is essentially a go-around command.

The tower's light gun is used to deliver light signals.

Fig. 46

LIGHT GUN SIGNALS FROM THE TOWER

Color & Type Of Signal	Meaning With Respect To Aircraft on The Surface	Meaning With Respect To Aircraft in Flight
Steady green	Cleared for takeoff	Cleared to land
Flashing green	Cleared to taxi	Return for landing (to be followed by steady green at proper time)
Steady red	Stop	Give way to other aircraft and continue circling
Flashing red	Taxi clear of runway in use	Airport unsafe, do not land
Flashing white	Return to starting point on airport	Not applicable
Alternating red & green	Exercise extreme caution	Exercise extreme caution

Fig. 45

A steady red always means stop. At least that's what it should mean to you at a stoplight. Of course, the only way to stop in the air is to give way to other aircraft and continue circling. Controllers might use this signal if they see you (a non-radio airplane) approaching the traffic pattern and are unable to sequence you into the flow of traffic. They'll hold you in your present position until they can clear you to land. At that time you'll probably receive a steady green light.

Whenever you see a flashing red light in the air, it indicates danger. Think of all those red flashing beacons you see on tall TV towers. Tower controllers send out a flashing red light when the airport is unsafe for landing. The runway could be torn up, there could be a disabled plane on the runway, or perhaps there are deer and antelope at play. Whatever is wrong, the controller is telling you that bad things will happen to your good airplane if you land there. It's time to head for the next closest airport.

Alternating red and green lights, on the ground or in the air, mean exercise extreme caution. There might be another no-radio airplane in the pattern. Or, there might be wild animals running across the runway. Don't think that this can't happen. A

fellow pilot in Florida had an alligator crawl onto the runway during landing. I'm not sure what would happen if you hit one of these big guys. Perhaps you'd leave a trail of boots, assorted baggage and Gucci belts scattered along the runway.

Light signals also apply to surface movement at tower controlled fields. Radios do go on the fritz occasionally, though many general aviation airplanes have a double set of communications radios. If there is no avionics repair shop at your home field, you'll need to fly somewhere to get it fixed. If you have no communications capability, simply call the tower by phone and tell them you want to depart the airport. They'll probably tell you to taxi out and visually monitor the tower for light signals.

Light signals also serve as your taxi instructions after a no-radio landing.

Light Signals on the Ground – A steady green light on the ground means the same to an airplane as it does to a car—go. A steady green light means that you're cleared for takeoff (in your airplane, not your car). A flashing green light on the ground means that you're cleared to taxi. If you look in your rear view mirror and see a steady red light you'd better stop. It's the law and they want to talk to you. A steady red light from the tower means you should stop. The controller wants you to hold your position. When the time is right, they'll provide you with a flashing green signal to continue taxiing.

A flashing red light in your rear view mirror usually belongs to an emergency vehicle. Your natural response in a car is to get off the road. In an airplane a flashing red light from the tower is a signal to taxi clear of the runway in use. You might have just landed without a radio and are taxiing down the active runway. The controller may have another airplane waiting to land. A flashing red light is a signal to clear the runway on which you've landed. Simply find the nearest taxiway and get on it.

The last light signal is the flashing white light. It only pertains to operations on the surface. If the airport suddenly becomes very busy, your no-radio takeoff might be more appropriate at a later time. Controllers will signal their desire to have you return to your starting point on the airport with a flashing white light. Think of the newer automobiles that have flashing headlights to warn you that you must return to your starting point to turn them off (my original car had headlights that flashed, not because of new technology, but because of a bad circuit. It did have a heated rear window that kept my hands warm on those cold days when I had to push it in for repairs).

Cessna 2132 Bravo, use caution, a helicopter just landed on the taxiway and we're not talking to him.

Roger tower, then I won't talk to him either!

Actually Heard....

Source: Dave Gwinn

FAR 91.126 Operating on Or In the Vicinity of an Airport In Class G Airspace

As you have probably already guessed, we're using letters to describe certain types of airspace. In order to understand regulations 91.127, 91.129, 91.130, 91.131, 91.135, 91.155, 91.157 and 91.215, it might be better for you to jump ahead to the chapter on airspace (Chapter 9). You might also choose to skip these regulations and return to them after reading the airspace section. Even though it's not mentioned in the following material, landing at any airport requires a minimum flight visibility and distance from any clouds. These VFR requirements are also described in the airspace chapter.

With only a few exceptions, airports lying in Class G and Class E airspace don't have control towers (we won't discuss the exceptions). These airports have been called *uncontrolled airports*, but can also be described as *nontower airports*. Since there are no operating control towers at these airports, pilots must follow specific procedures to prevent bumping into each other.

When approaching to land at an airport without an operating control tower in Class G airspace, each pilot of an airplane must make all turns to the left. (The exception to this is when the airport displays visual marking (at/on the segmented circle) indicating turns should be made to the right or the sectional chart or A/FD indicates a right traffic pattern. In that case, the pilot must make right turns.) Why are left turns the norm? The answer is standardization. Someone decided a long time ago that if everyone made a left traffic pattern, there'd be less chance of confusion. Shown in Figure 47, these patterns make it easy to sequence yourself with the flow of traffic.

A segmented circle, shown in Figure 48, sometimes shows a non-standard, right hand traffic pattern is in effect (you'll find out why in Chapter 7). Pilots can see these large segmented circles from several thousand feet in the air. Mountains, towers or noise sensitive areas often dictate that a pattern be flown on the opposite side of the field.

IT'S THE LITTLE THINGS...

I lost radio contact with Tower. By accident my daughter disengaged my hand-mike jack from its receptacle enough to cut off communication, but I could not tell. She was in right front seat with a blanket over her legs that prevented my noticing anything wrong. After landing I discovered the problem and contacted Ground Control for taxi instructions. Tower said they gave me a red signal when our communications went out, but unfortunately I did not see it.

Moral: If you are NORDO (no radio) near a controlled airport, keep a sharp eye out for lightgun signals. Even in this high-technology era you sometimes have to fall back on the old reliable methods.

ASRS Report

AIRPORT TRAFFIC PATTERNS (FOR RUNWAY 18)

Fig. 47

Standard pattern
(left traffic)
All turns are to the left.

Nonstandard pattern
(right traffic)
All turns are to the right.

SEGMENTED CIRCLES SHOWING NONSTANDARD RIGHT-HAND TRAFFIC PATTERNS

Fig. 48

I've got a feeling that Stephen King has something to do with this airport!

Nonstandard pattern
(right traffic for RWY 36)

Nonstandard pattern
(right traffic for RWY 18)

*Note: Airplanes only land in one direction at a time (into the wind).

Segmented circle

HOW CAN THAT BE?

The controller sitting next to me (a fellow controller) is trying to change Mooney 45Q to my frequency, but gets no response. Thinking that the Mooney may have already switched to my frequency since he's a local pilot who knew it was coming, he asks me to check:

Me: "Mooney 45Q, are you on this frequency?"

45Q: "Negative, but I should be any time now."

Pilots not flying the correct traffic pattern often cause dramatic adrenaline rushes in those who do. At Corona airport in Southern California, a pilot entered the pattern the wrong way opposite seven other airplanes in the lefthand circuit. They scattered like frightened chickens with the Colonel close behind. This pilot was probably thinking, "Hey, look at all those guys going the wrong way! What's the matter with them?" Fortunately he finally got the idea, switched his pattern and landed. Several new EKG records were set that day!

Another part of this regulation requires that all helicopters and powered parachutes approaching to land should avoid the flow of fixed-wing aircraft. Perhaps this explains why a friend once said that the Bible specifically states that all pilots should fly helicopters. I asked him to quote me the specific passage. He said the Bible clearly states, "Lo, I am with you always." I replied, "Five dollars. Pay up now."

FAR 91.127 Operations on or In The Vicinity of an Airport In Class E Airspace

This regulation is essentially the same as FAR 91.126. The only difference is that the airports referenced here lie within Class E surface-based controlled airspace, thus requiring a stricter visibility and cloud clearance requirement for landing. These airports occasionally have control towers but don't have an established Class D surface area (these are rare instances, and usually involve military installations). These airports may also have more stringent noise abatement requirements under FAR Part 93.

Many people around airports are quite vocal about airport noise. They want to reduce the noise by getting rid of airplanes. Some of these folks have mentioned to me that they don't care if airplanes fly as long as they don't use their engines. To them, the only good aircraft is a glider. Be very careful about adhering to local noise abatement procedures at the airport. Good relations with airport neighbors keeps aviation alive in your community.

At the Los Alamitos (CA) airport several years ago a C5A galaxy transport airplane was practicing touch and goes. The tower controller heard the phone ring and picked it up to find a local resident saying "Hey, why don't you let that man land his airplane?" Don't think this doesn't happen. The same tower controller told me that he once received a noise complaint about one of the gliders operating out of the same field! (Truth is stranger than fiction because fiction must make sense.)

FAR 91.129 Operations in Class D Airspace

If you've read the airspace section, you know that Class D airspace generally extends upward from the surface to 2,500 feet above the airport elevation as shown in Figure 49. Its radius around the primary airport varies based on the instrument procedures for which the controlled airspace is established. I've seen the radius vary from a little less than 3 nautical miles to 7 nautical miles with the typical radius being a little less than 5 nautical miles. You'll be able to determine the specific size of an airport's Class D airspace by looking at the aeronautical sectional chart. The Class D airspace, shown in Figure 49, looks somewhat like a can of tuna since it has a short, cylindrical shape. Let's refer to Class D airspace as the *tuna can*.

Airports in Class D airspace have an operating control tower. The purpose of a control tower is to provide information and instructions to airplanes taking off or landing at the primary airport within that airspace. The primary airport (the one that's usually in the center of the tuna can) is the airport for which that airspace (Class D) is designated. It's possible to have one or more additional airports lying within Class D airspace. These airports are often called "satellite" airports (signifying that they "orbit" or lie close enough to the primary airport to be within its Class D airspace).

Equipment Required – The minimum equipment required to operate within Class D airspace is a two-way radio. You can, however, request permission from ATC to fly into or out of this airspace without a radio. You might, for example, need to take your airplane to another airport to have the radio repaired. By calling ATC (the tower controllers) on the phone, they'll provide you with instructions for departing and/or arriving at the airport without two-way radio communication.

Arrivals and Fly-Throughs – If you want to fly through this airspace or land at the primary airport, you must establish two-way radio communication with the ATC facility that is responsible for that Class D airspace. Normally, this ATC facility is the control tower located at the primary airport. Once established, you must maintain communication with the air traffic control tower while in this airspace. In other words, you must give the tower controller a call before entering the tuna can boundaries,

have them acknowledge you, and once inside the can you must maintain communication at all times.

Pilots sometimes become confused about the precise definition of *establish communication*. Technically, you've established communications anytime ATC acknowledges your aircraft call sign (the airplane's N number, such as N2132B). For instance, on your initial call, while outside or above the physical dimensions of the tuna can, you give the tower your position, altitude, destination and any requests you have. They'll normally call you back using your aircraft call sign and give you directions for entering the traffic flow around the airport.

If the controller says, " N2132B, stand by," you've technically established communications and may continue into the tuna can toward the airport. If the controller says, "Aircraft calling Onfire Tower, standby" (that is, if you aren't called by your N-number name) then you have not established communications and should remain outside or above the tuna can. Of course, if the controller says, "N2132B, remain clear of Class D airspace" (they don't say *tuna can*), then you must follow their instructions even though two-way communication has been established.

These communication requirements are in force even if you are landing at one of the satellite airports within Class D airspace. In other words, if another airport lies within the boundaries of the tuna can (typically an airport without an operating control tower) and you're interested in landing there, you must establish two-way radio communication with the air traffic control tower at the primary airport before entering this airspace. You must maintain these communications during your flight to this airport.

Departures – If you're departing from the primary airport, you must establish and maintain two-way radio communication with ATC within Class D airspace. In other words, don't take off without calling the tower and listening to them while in the tuna can.

Suppose you're taking off from a non-tower satellite airport within Class D airspace? Do you still need to call the ATC facility for the primary airport? Yes. You must establish and maintain two-way radio communication as

CLASS D AIRSPACE
(Found at airports with operating control towers) Fig. 49

< 25 >

It does look like a tuna can! Ahhhhhhh!

2,500 Feet AGL

Radius varies from airport to airport but averages 4 to 5 nm

Primary airport   Satellite airport

Class D airspace is shaped somewhat like a tuna can. Any pilot flying within its boundaries must establish two-way radio communication with the control tower (that's right, no telepathy!).

If you are departing a nontower satellite airport within Class D airspace, you must establish and maintain two-way radio communication with the tower at the primary airport as soon as practicable after departure.

Chapter 6 - Federal Aviation Regulations: How FAR Can We Go?

6-37

TAXI CLEARANCES

Taxi!

No, I brought my car.

Delta

Delta

Echo

Bravo

Charlie

Alpha

Fig. 50

If Airplane 1 is cleared to RWY 36, it needs a clearance to cross RWY 22. With this, the pilot may taxi to but not onto RWY 36. If Airplane 2 is cleared to RWY 18, it needs a clearance to cross RWY 22 and RWY 18 with each clearance being issued only after the first runway is crossed.

soon as practical after departing. In other words, take off and give the tower at the primary airport a call as soon as it's reasonable for you to do so. Let them know what you're doing, follow their directions and keep listening to them while you're anywhere within the tuna can.

Communications Failure – Your radios could give up the ghost enroute. Does this mean you can't fly back into the Class D airspace you departed from? Not necessarily. A provision in this regulation allows you to enter Class D airspace under VFR conditions (we'll explain VFR in more detail in Chapter 9). In other words, you can get back into the tuna can as long as you have weather conditions at or above basic VFR minimums. How do you do it? Simply fly to the airport, enter the traffic pattern, watch the tower for light signals and land when you receive a steady green light from the tower.

Minimum Altitudes – The important section here is the part

saying that you must stay at or above the glideslope (until a lower altitude is necessary) when approaching to land on a runway served by a visual approach slope indicator (VASI). We'll discuss VASIs in Chapter 7. For now, accept the fact that a VASI consists of light bars that tell you if you're on the proper glideslope for the runway you're approaching.

Takeoff, Landing, Taxi Clearance – No person may, at an airport with an operating control tower, operate an aircraft on a runway or taxiway, or take off or land an aircraft, unless an appropriate clearance is received from ATC.

If this ATC clearance is to a runway via a specific taxi route, and if a runway (closed, active or inactive) intersects your path along the way, then the controller must also issue (and you *must obtain*) a clearance to cross that runway before proceeding. In fact, you must receive a specific crossing clearance for *each runway* that your route crosses. This applies even if you're told to follow another aircraft to a specific runway.

For example, airplane #1 (Figure 42) will be cleared to departure Runway 36 as follows: *StingSport 714CT, Runway 36, taxi via Charlie and Alpha, cross Runway 22, hold short of Runway 36.* Airplane #2 will be cleared to departure Runway 18 as follows: *StingSport 714CT, Runway 18, taxi via Bravo, Echo and Delta, cross Runway 22, hold short of Runway 18 at Bravo.* To cross Runway 18 at the midfield point, 714CT must obtain another clearance which would eventually lead it to the Runway 18 departure threshold via taxiways Bravo, Echo and Delta.

Since ATC is required to obtain a readback of all *runway hold short instructions*, ATC will consider your readback of those instructions containing runway assignments as confirmation of those runway assignments. When ATC is ready for you to taxi onto the departure runway, the controller will instruct you to, *lineup and wait Runway 18.* At this point you are expected to taxi onto the departure runway and line up, then wait for your takeoff clearance.

FAR 91.130 Operations In Class C Airspace

An example of Class C airspace is shown in Figure 51. This type of airspace is larger than Class D airspace in that it has two cylindrical components instead of the single, tuna-can-shaped Class D airspace. Class C is a double-decker tuna can. The physical dimensions of Class C airspace consist of a lower tuna can having a radius of 5 nautical miles and extending vertically from the ground to 4,000 feet above the airport elevation. The upper and larger tuna can has a radius of 10 nautical miles. It starts at 1,200 feet and extends vertically to 4,000 feet above the airport elevation. For the sake of continuity, we'll refer to Class C airspace as the *double tuna can.* (I do feel it's necessary to mention that no dolphins have been hurt, injured or eaten in the writing of this material.)

Simply stated, Class C airspace goes with airports that handle larger, faster airplanes (generally this means significant quantities of commercial traffic). It's established to keep the small airplanes and bigger airplanes from bumping into one another. Since there are faster airplanes involved, it makes sense that the airspace must cover more area (refer to Chapter 9 for more information on Class C airspace).

As with Class D airspace, there is a primary airport in the center of the double tuna can. This is the airport for which the Class C airspace was established. The double tuna can usually sits directly over this airport. As with Class D airspace, there may

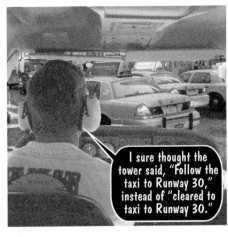

I sure thought the tower said, "Follow the taxi to Runway 30," instead of "cleared to taxi to Runway 30."

CLASS C AIRSPACE

Class C airspace exists at airports having operating control towers and a large amount of IFR traffic or passenger activities. Class C airports are normally serviced by a radar approach control facility.

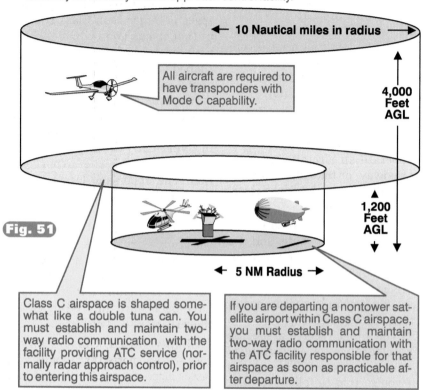

10 Nautical miles in radius

All aircraft are required to have transponders with Mode C capability.

4,000 Feet AGL

1,200 Feet AGL

Fig. 51

5 NM Radius

Class C airspace is shaped somewhat like a double tuna can. You must establish and maintain two-way radio communication with the facility providing ATC service (normally radar approach control), prior to entering this airspace.

If you are departing a nontower satellite airport within Class C airspace, you must establish and maintain two-way radio communication with the ATC facility responsible for that airspace as soon as practicable after departure.

be satellite airports within the boundaries of Class C airspace. In other words, there may be other airports, with and without control towers, within the surface area covered by the double tuna can.

You're going to find there is very little difference between the requirements for flight in Class C airspace compared to Class D airspace. Whether you're in the single or double tuna can airspace, the requirements are essentially the same. The main difference is that the airport tower typically has a *clearance delivery* (a controller dedicated to providing you a route to fly when departing the airport). There is also radar associated with the airport in the form of approach and departure control. Let's examine the Class C requirements.

General Requirements – All operations in Class C airspace must comply with the previous regulation—FAR 91.129. In other words, the operating rules are essentially the same as in Class D airspace. This

makes sense since both Class D and Class C airspace have primary airports with operating control towers. Therefore, they should have similar requirements for aircraft operations.

Traffic Patterns – If you're taking off or landing at a satellite airport within Class C airspace, you must comply with the FAA arrival and departure traffic pattern established for that airport. There's nothing new here. Just because the primary airport is a little bit busier, there's no reason why you should do anything different at one of the satellite airports than you would for Class D airspace.

Communications - Arrival or Through Flight – If you want to land at the primary airport in Class C airspace, or if you just want to fly through that airspace, you must establish and maintain two-way radio communication with the facility providing air traffic services prior to entering that airspace. In other words, the double tuna can of airspace may be controlled by either a

tower, an approach control facility, or a combination of both. Your aeronautical sectional chart (charts used for aerial navigation) will generally instruct you to contact Approach Control on a specific frequency within 20nm from the primary airport having Class C airspace (of course, you're *required* to establish and maintain two-way radio communication prior to *entering* Class C airspace).

Communications - Departing Flight – If you're departing the primary airport within Class C airspace, you must establish and maintain two-way radio communications with the tower prior to departure. If the controller hands you off to Departure Control, talk and listen to the departure controller until you're out of the double tuna can (Class C airspace). If you're departing a nontower satellite airport lying within the surface boundaries of Class C airspace, you must establish and maintain two-way radio communications with the Approach or Departure Control facility having jurisdiction over that airspace. Do this as soon as practicable after departure. (An approach or departure control facility is usually the ATC facility having jurisdiction over Class C airspace.) In the rare event the satellite airport has an operating control tower, do exactly as you would do if you were departing the primary airport having an operating control tower. In other words, establish communications with the tower at the satellite airport and follow their instructions.

Equipment Requirements – The minimum equipment required to operate within Class C airspace is a two-way radio and a transponder with altitude reporting capability (per FAR 91.215). You'll learn more about transponders shortly. These are electronic devices that allow your airplane to be identified on the approach or departure controller's radar scope. The altitude reporting capability allows the controller to see your altitude on his or her radar screen.

Chapter 6 - Federal Aviation Regulations: How FAR Can We Go?

6-39

FAR 91.131 Operations In Class B Airspace

Class D airspace was small (a single tuna can). Class C airspace was slightly larger because there were bigger and faster airplanes there (a double tuna can). Class B airspace is the biggest of these tuna can stacks of airspace. It usually extends up to 10,000 feet MSL and often has horizontal dimensions of many miles as shown in Figure 52. This airspace is larger than Class C or D airspace because its primary airport has many very large and fast airplanes like Boeing 747s and DC-10s and much IFR activity.

In some cases Class B airspace (Figure 52) looks like several stacked cans of tuna. Actually it looks more like an inverted wedding cake with individual tiers or floors contributing to its structure. Extra tiers allow faster jet airplanes to make long arrivals and departures into and out of the primary airport while remaining within the protected airspace. The following are the requirements to take off or land at the primary airport or operate within the wedding cake airspace.

Operating Rules – First, you must follow all the rules of FAR 91.129 (Class D airspace) while in Class B airspace. In addition, before you can enter Class B airspace you'll need a *clearance* from the ATC facility having jurisdiction over that airspace. A clearance is essentially verbal permission for entry into this airspace. This is different from the entry requirements for Class C or D airspace which only required that you establish and maintain two-way radio communication before entry.

Pilot Requirements – You need to be at least a sport pilot (who meets the requirements in FAR 61.325) to take off or land at any airport within Class B airspace. If, however, you are a student pilot seeking sport pilot certification and have met the requirements of FAR 61.94 and 61.95, then you may take off or land as well as fly in Class B airspace. (your instructor will give you the details if she/he intends to have you

CLASS B AIRSPACE

Exists at some of the nation's busiest airports. Its shape and size are customized to accommodate the arrival and departure paths of the many airplanes using this airport. Because the airport is so busy, Class B airspace almost always exists on a 24 hour basis.

CLASS B AIRSPACE
(Generally goes up to 10,000' MSL and has variable horizontal dimensions)

Relax, I'm tellin' ya they can't see us!

Fig. 52

An ATC clearance is required (usually from radar Approach Control) before entering this airspace. All aircraft must have a two-way radio with the appropriate frequencies, mode-C equipped transponder & a VOR or RNAV for IFR operations. To land at the primary airport, pilots must have at least a *sport pilot certificate (students can enter and land if they meet the requirements of FAR 61.94/95). *Airports listed in section 4, appendix D of FAR 91 require a private pilot certificate to land.

tooling around with 747s). No matter how confident you may be as a student pilot, there are some primary airports within Class B airspace that are just too darn busy for you to take off or land at unless you have a private pilot certificate or better. (See Appendix D of FAR 91, Section 4, for a list of these airports—not included in this book.)

Equipment Required – The minimum equipment required to operate within Class B airspace is a two-way radio with all the frequencies needed for ATC communication, a transponder with altitude encoding capability and, for IFR operations, a functioning VOR receiver or RNAV system (i.e., think GPS unit here).

FAR 91.133 Restricted And Prohibited Areas

Across the United States you will find areas known as *special use airspace*. Restricted and prohibited areas (Figures 53 & 54) are part of this special use airspace group. *Restricted areas*, while not wholly prohibited, subject flights to certain restrictions. These restrictions may be based on

A restricted area on an aeronautical sectional chart.

A prohibited area on an aeronautical sectional chart.

RESTRICTED AREAS

Here is one of the "fun things" you can find in a restricted area. Remember, the Apache helicopter adds a whole new meaning to the phrase "Do you wanna come out and play?"

Go ahead, make my DAY!

Fig. 54

time, altitude, or other requirements. Operations within a restricted area assume that pilots have the permission of the controlling agency responsible for that area. It also requires that pilots follow whatever restrictions are imposed by the agency.

A restricted area is often used for military activities. Fighter pilots might be performing their tactical maneuvers and wild aerial dances designed to frighten off an archenemy (Figure 54). These dances often frighten off little general aviation pilots too. You should avoid these areas unless you have permission to enter.

What can you do in a prohibited area? It's reasonable to say you can do a lot less than in a restricted area. There are certain areas of the country where flight is prohibited. For instance, the capital of the United States in Washington, D.C. is surrounded by a prohibited area. I doubt that you'll get permission from the U.S. government to fly into this prohibited area. This is usually the case with most prohibited areas. They're prohibited for a good reason.

A friend living on the east coast played a nice little practical joke on one of his first flight instructors. He obtained a few large color aerial photographs of the capitol building and had them converted into smaller 3 inch by 5 inch photographs. He flew a solo cross country near

the Washing-ton, D.C. area and took a few actual photographs of the trip.

When he met his instructor the following week he interspersed his Capitol dome shots in with the scenic shots. Giving them to his instructor he said, "Here are a few aerial photographs I took from the plane." When his instructor saw the capital shot his eyes bugged out and he said, "Oh man, you're going to owe me a few bucks for this one." What is aviation if you can't have a little fun with your instructor?

While restricted and prohibited airspace are found on a sectional chart, there's another type of restriction that's considered temporary, but equally important. It's called a *temporary flight restriction* (TFR) and usually involves one of three things: either disaster/hazard areas, presidential visits or airshows. Let's examine all three.

FAR 91.137 Temporary Flight Restrictions (TFRs) In Disaster/Hazard Areas

In the event of either a disaster or a hazard, the FAA might find it necessary to restrict aviation activities to protect persons or property on the ground, to provide safety for those involved in the disaster relief or to prevent sightseeing congestion from intense public interest. This regulation specifically deals with *disasters and hazards*. A NOTAM (such as the graphically displayed NOTAM shown in Figure 55 and found on AOPA's site at www.aopa.org) will define (using a red fade border in this instance) the TFR restrictions. You may not operate within the TFR without meeting one of the specific exceptions in this regulation.

The exception that's relevant to you as a sport pilot says you may not enter a TFR involving disasters or hazards *unless* the operation is conducted directly to or from an airport within the area, or is necessitated by the impracticability of VFR flight above or around the area due to weather or terrain, and the operation is *not* conducted for the purpose of observing the incident or event that generated the TFR. This is the type of TFR that won't necessarily restrict you from your home airport lying within the disaster/hazard area.

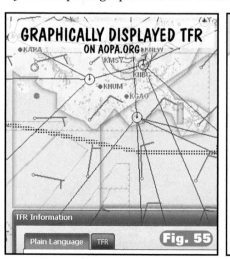

GRAPHICALLY DISPLAYED TFR ON AOPA.ORG

TFR Information

Plain Language | TFR | **Fig. 55**

Federal Aviation Administration

GRAPHICALLY DISPLAYED TFR NOTAM AT FAA.GOV | **Fig. 56**

TFR List | TFR Map | Map Airports | TFR Help | PilotWeb | SUA-TFR

NOTAM Number :
Number: FDC 0/70688 Download shapefiles
Issue Date : June 19, 2010 at 1828 UTC
Location : Chicago, Illinois
Beginning Date and Time : June 21, 2010 at 1530 UTC
Ending Date and Time : June 21, 2010 at 2145 UTC
Reason for NOTAM : Temporary flight restrictions for VIP (Very Important Person) Movement
Type : VIP
Replaced NOTAM(s) : N/A

Jump To: Affected Areas
Operating Restrictions and Requirements
Other Information

Affected Area(s) | Top

Chapter 6 - Federal Aviation Regulations: How FAR Can We Go?

6-41

BASIC VFR WEATHER MINIMUMS IN CONTROLLED AIRSPACE

Altitude or Airspace	Flight Visibility	Distance From Clouds
Class A	not applicable	not applicable
Class B	3 statute miles	clear of clouds
Class C	3 statute miles	500' below 1,000' above 2,000' horizontal
Class D	3 statute miles	500' below 1,000' above 2,000' horizontal
Class E .... Less than 10,000' MSL......	3 statute miles	500' below 1,000' above 2,000' horizontal

BASIC VFR WEATHER MINIMUMS IN UNCONTROLLED AIRSPACE

Altitude or Airspace	Flight Visibility	Distance From Clouds
Class G .... 1,200' or less above the surface Day, ... *(Note: sport pilots are always required to have at least 3 miles visibility for flight even though the visibility requmt. can be less in Class G.)*	3 statute miles	clear of clouds
More than 1,200' above the surface but less than 10,000 feet MSL: Day	3 statute miles	500' below 1,000' above 2,000' horizontal

FAR 91.141 Presidential TFRs

Unlike major disasters and hazards, some TFRs pertain to the *president of the United States* and his associates. This regulation says that you may not operate an aircraft in the vicinity of any area to be visited by the president, vice president, or other public figures contrary to the limitations in the TFR NOTAM. This essentially means "stay away" unless you want to engage in aquatic sports with the Secret Service, such as *water boarding.* OK, it's not that severe, but you get the point, right? As with all TFRs, you'll find this one described fully in the appropriate NOTAM (Figure 56).

FAR 91.145 TFRs Covering Aerial Demonstrations and Sporting Events

TFRs are also issued for *aerial demonstrations* (think airshows) or *major sporting events.* These TFRs protect persons or property on the surface, help maintain safety and prevent congestion in the vicinity of these events.

When TFR NOTAMs are issued for aerial demonstrations, the restricted airspace will usually be limited to a five nautical mile radius of the event and less than 17,000 feet MSL (or 13,000 feet AGL for parachute operations). And no, you can't just join up with the Blue Angles during an airshow with your Whifferdill Six, either.

For some sporting events, the TFR-restricted airspace will usually be limited to a three nautical mile radius from the center of the event and 2,500 feet above the surface. So avoid these TFRs. It's pretty hard to deny flying over a TFR'd sporting event when NBC shows the nation your instant "violation" replay on national TV. These NOTAMs are normally issued at least 30 days in advance of the aerial demonstration or sporting event.

Keep in mind that all TFRs can be found by calling the automated flight service station (1-800-WXBRIEF), or by visiting (http://tfr.faa.gov/tfr2/list.html) which is the FAA's web site, where TFR NOTAMs are graphically displayed. The TFR shown in Figure 56 is defined textually and shown by a red border.

FAR 91.151 Fuel Requirements For Flight in VFR Conditions

This regulation states that no person may begin a flight in an airplane under VFR conditions unless (considering wind and forecast weather conditions) there is enough fuel to fly to the first point of intended landing and, assuming normal cruising speed, during the day, to fly for at least an additional 30 minutes (the dark side of this regulation is that there is a night fuel requirement which we won't discuss, since you won't fly at night).

FAR 91.155 Basic VFR Weather Minimums

As you'll discover in Chapter 9, a VFR pilot must always maintain a minimum visibility and clearance from any clouds while flying. Known as *Basic VFR Weather Minimums,* these visibilities and cloud clearance requirements vary depending on the particular class of airspace in which you are flying. I've listed these VFR requirements in Figure 57 and I'll offer detailed explanations in Chapter 9.

FAR 91.159 VFR Cruising Altitude/Flight Level

The *lambada* is often the forbidden dance at high school proms because it involves close physical contact and wild gyrations of the hip that might easily dissolve the pelvis of anyone over 40. Likewise, there are forbidden altitudes that you want to avoid in preventing close physical contact with another airplane (otherwise known as "preventing a mid-air collision"). The altitudes you're allowed to fly will keep VFR aircraft separated vertically by 1,000 feet and they are based on the aircraft's direction of flight. In this way, altimeters become vertical traffic separators that prevent pilots from bumping into one another.

This regulation states that during VFR flight, when operating more than 3,000 feet above the surface, you are to fly at an altitude appropriate for your direction of flight. If you are on a magnetic course of 0° through 179°, you should fly any odd thousand foot MSL altitude plus 500 feet. Altitudes such as 3,500 feet, 5,500 feet, 7,500 feet, etc., are appropriate for that direction. While on a magnetic course of 180° through 359° you should fly at an even MSL altitude plus 500. Altitudes such as 4,500 feet, 6,500 feet, 8,500 feet, etc., are appropriate for this direction. This provides you with a minimum 1,000 foot clearance from other VFR airplanes heading in opposing directions (Figure 58).

Are you wondering who uses the even (4,000, 6,000, etc.) or odd thousand (5,000, 7,000, etc.) foot altitudes? IFR pilots do. If you're flying on an airway you can probably expect some IFR traffic 500 feet above or below your airplane. Since you'll be in VFR conditions, you should be able to see and avoid these airplanes, and in VFR conditions they have the same obligation toward you. Comforting, isn't it, to know that everyone is looking out for everyone else?

Remember, these cruising altitudes apply only if you're operating at more than 3,000 feet AGL (above ground level). Operations at and below 3,000 AGL can be flown at whatever altitude you choose. These rules don't apply if the airplane is turning. If you're maneuvering while practicing your stalls, steep turns and other activities, you're not required to maintain a specific altitude.

FAR 91.203 Civil Aircraft: Certifications Required

Several years ago I wanted to discover if a student of mine knew what documents were required to be carried on board the aircraft. I said to him, "Hey Bob, what things are required to be in the airplane for it to be legal for flight?" He looked at me, scratched his head and said, "Ahh, the pilot?" I gave him the same look that I gave the seafood waiter who was supposed to bring me a twin lobster dinner. Instead he brought me a lobster and a crab. I said, "Hey what gives? I ordered twin lobsters." He said, "Well, they're fraternal twins." In both cases I lifted a single eyebrow and radiated one of those "You're going to owe me $5" looks.

There are six items that must be on board an aircraft at all times when it's being operated. Two of these are certification documents: the *airworthiness certificate* and the *registration certificate*. The other two items are the airplane's *operating limitations* and its *weight and balance information*. If the aircraft is a special light-sport aircraft, then it will also have two additional items. These are the *flight manual* (ASTM now calls this the POH or *pilot operating handbook*) and the *flight training supplement*.

The first certification document is the airworthiness certificate (Figure 59). This is issued for a specific aircraft at the time of manufacture,

and it remains valid as long as the aircraft receives the required *annual inspection* (for an airplane with a standard airworthiness certificate) or annual *condition inspection* (for an aircraft certified in the light sport aircraft category) by a licensed mechanic or appropriate and certified repairman and meets other legal requirements.

The airworthiness certificate must be displayed at the cabin or cockpit entrance so that it is legible to the passenger or crew. Take a look the next time you get on board a commercial airliner. There, in the vicinity of the smiling cabin attendant and the cockpit, will be a plastic pouch bearing the airworthiness certificate. It's supposed to make you feel secure. Frankly, I'd feel better if they showed me the pilot's license. I *know* the airplane can fly.

The second certification document that must be on board is the registration certificate issued to the owner of the aircraft. The registration (Figure 60) need not be displayed; it just needs to be in the aircraft.

FAR 91.207 Emergency Locator Transmitters

Except for planes equipped to carry not more than one person, all U.S. registered civil airplanes must be equipped with an automatic-type emergency locator

HEMISPHERICAL CRUISING ALTITUDES
(For VFR Flight)

EASTERLY
Flying on a magnetic course between 0 and 179 degrees, these aircraft must fly odd thousand altitudes + 500'.
3,500'
5,500'
7,500'
up to
17,500'

WESTERLY
Flying on a magnetic course between 180 and 359 degrees, these aircraft must fly even thousand altitudes + 500'.
4,500'
6,500'
8,500'
up to
16,500'

These airplanes, at 3,000' or less AGL, are not required to fly at any particular altitude.

Fig. 58

3,000' AGL

3,000' AGL

3,000' AGL

Chapter 6 - Federal Aviation Regulations: How FAR Can We Go?

6-43

Fig. 59

Fig. 60

Note: Aircraft registration certificates must be renewed every three years.

transmitter or ELT (Figure 61). The ELT must be in operable condition. These transmitters are impact-activated devices that send out pulsed transmissions on the emergency frequency (121.5 MHz & 243 MHz). Should you land hard enough (usually a 5G or greater impact) or crash, an inertial arm on the transmitter is activated and the transmission begins. Satellites and search and rescue pilots can easily track ELT signals to find downed pilots.

As a flight instructor, I've heard of students landing hard enough during practice to activate the ELT. Although the airplane wasn't damaged (airplanes can take a lickin' and keep on tickin') the ELT went off. Like Pinnochio's nose, ELTs don't lie. Imagine a student returning from touch and go practice. Tires are smoking (not really) and the instructor is suspicious. He asks, "Did you have a hard landing?" The student straightens and replies, "No way, they were all greasers." The instructor says "Well let's see how greasy they were," as he tunes the airplane radio to 121.5 (the emergency frequency). Suddenly the speaker wails with, "Whewwww, whewwww, whewwww..." It seems like you can't get away with anything nowadays!

The most important thing to remember about your ELT is that the batteries must be replaced or recharged if the device has been in use for more than one cumulative hour, or when 50% of their useful life (or life of charge) has expired. If you want to manually test the airplane's ELT on the ground you may do so during the first five minutes past the hour (you're limited to three audible sweeps during the test).

Additionally, each ELT must be inspected within 12 calendar months after the last inspection for: proper installation, operation, battery corrosion and for the presence of a sufficient signal radiated from its antenna.

As a final note on ELTs, you might not have heard that there is a new kid on the block known as a 406 MHz ELT. This newer type of ELT is superior to its older (121.5 MHz) cousin in that it has a more precise signal and is compatible with our present search and rescue satellite system (current satellites no longer monitor 121.5 MHz). The newer ELT system makes search and rescue (SAR) operations easier and more efficient, leading to a greater chance of rescue in the event of an emergency. The 406 MHz ELT can also be coded with the airplane owner's serial number. There is, however, no requirement for airplane owners to replace their older ELT systems with the newer 406 MHz systems. This remains a voluntary operation on the part of airplane owners.

Fig. 61

FAR 91.209 Aircraft Lights

Several years ago a truck driver was driving beyond official sunset with his headlights off. A highway patrol officer gave chase. Feeling a little ornery, the truck driver didn't stop for several miles. When he did stop, the officer was fuming as he exited his vehicle. The truck driver knew he was in trouble. Approaching the truck the officer said, "Hey buddy, I've been chasing you for several miles to tell you your lights need to be on past sunset. Why didn't you stop?" The truck driver thought fast and said, "Well officer, several years ago my wife ran off with a fellow from the highway patrol and, quite frankly, I just thought you were trying to bring her back!" The moral to that story is—turn your lights on from sunset to sunrise.

Let's remember that night time for pilots is officially defined as *the time between the end of evening civil twilight and the beginning of morning civil twilight.* This is when you, as a sport pilot, must be on the ground and not in the air. On the other hand, official night time for airplanes is defined as the time from sunset to sunrise. During this period, you can't operate an aircraft unless it has lighted position lights (Figure 62).

Therefore, as a sport pilot, it's entirely possible for you to be airborne in a light-sport aircraft after sunset and before the beginning of evening civil twilight (or after morning civil twilight and before sunrise). Either way, if you're airborne during these times, your light-sport airplane must be equipped with lighted position lights. In addition, if the airplane has an anti-collision lighting system, those lights must also be activated.

Lighted position lights make it easier for pilots to see each other at night. An easy way to remember the color of these lights for airplanes is to ask the following questions. What color means it's all RIGHT to go? Yes, a green light and that's the color light on the RIGHT wing, as shown in Figure 62A. What do we call the radical LEFT-wingers in our political system? Yes, we used to call them Commies or Reds. Therefore, LEFT wings have a red position light. The tail carries a white light.

These lights are called position lights for a good reason. Since it's difficult for someone outside the airplane to tell which way an airplane is headed at night, specific colors are needed to help get the job done. For instance, suppose you see a white light and a red light as shown in

AIRPLANE LIGHTING

Position lights, in this arrangement, indicate the airplane is moving from right to left.

Position lights, in this arrangement, indicate the airplane is moving from left to right.

Figure 62B. Which direction is the airplane traveling? Of course, it's moving from right to left. A white light and a green light means the airplane is moving from left to right as seen in Figure 62C. A red light on the right and a green on the left means the airplane is coming toward you. This becomes especially obvious if the distance between these lights is increasing.

Airplanes with an anticollision light system must have these lights on at *all* times when the airplane is in operation. This typically consists of white strobe lights or a red rotating beacon. Pilots are allowed to turn off the anticollision lighting system if the pilot in command determines, because of the operating conditions, it is unsafe. In hazy conditions at night, strobe lights can be quite distracting. But don't turn them off

---

A PROTEIN A DAY KEEPS THE DOCTOR AWAY

ASRS Pilot and Flight Surgeon: *GA pilot became confused during approach after a 1.5 hour flight at 12,500 - 13,500 feet. He porpoised on landing, made a go around, and struck the prop before finally landing successfully. Pilot suspected oxygen deficiency following the time at altitude. The pilot's last meal before takeoff had consisted of clear broth and a candy bar. Story fits a diagnosis of either hypoxia or hypoglycemia (low blood sugar). I favor the latter because confusion persisted to a low altitude in an acclimatized person and because symptoms cleared rapidly after the pilot* became frightened during initial attempt to land. Surge of adrenaline in such a situation will produce a very rapid increase in blood sugar level. It must be noted that hypoxia could have made the problem worse. The reporting pilot was counseled about the avoidance of hypoglycemia by use of protein meals. Using supplemental oxygen on long flights at those altitudes would be wise too.   **ASRS Report**

Be sure to preflight the pilot before flight too. Make time for nutritious meals. In your flight case, have a plastic bag stocked with natural almonds (no salt) and cartons of juice. These are perfect for emergency in-flight refueling of the pilot.

Chapter 6 - Federal Aviation Regulations: How FAR Can We Go?

6-45

unless it presents a real serious problem. On one flight where we were in the clouds my right seat, nonpilot passenger became annoyed by the flashing white light on the right wing. He looked over at me and said, "Hey, turn your blinker off if you're not going to make a turn."

If you're piloting a seaplane, you may not anchor an aircraft unless it has lighted anchor lights or is in an area where anchor lights are not required on vessels. A friend had a student who was a crusty old mariner. He spent so much time on boats that he'd show up for the flight lesson with clams, mussels and lobsters still attached to his jeans. During one preflight, he untied the ropes and, out of habit, threw them away from the airplane while yelling, "Cast off, cast off!"

If you're in Alaska, where night time and day time take on different meanings, another method of determination is used. Read the next sentence only if you're an Alaskan (in an igloo wearing seal furs). In Alaska, during the period a prominent unlighted object cannot be seen from a distance of three statute miles or the sun is more than six degrees below the horizon, the aircraft must have lighted position lights and an anticollision lighting system in operation. In these northern territories the sun could shine for 20 hours at a stretch in the summer months. That sure adds some excitement to those Fourth of July fireworks shows, doesn't it? You can hear the explosions, but you don't know where they're coming from.

FAR 91.215 ATC Transponder and Altitude Reporting Equipment and Use

Transponders are electronic devices that allow an aircraft's position to be precisely identified on radar. Transponders absorb radar energy, modify it with a special numerical code, then send that numerical code back to the radar. Controllers, asking pilots to squawk (set in the transponder's window) a four digit code, can see those exact numbers on the radar screen (Figure 63). This makes for positive identification of each airplane.

These transponders are known as Mode 3/A 4096 code capable transponders. The 4096 represents the number of possible combinations of codes capable of being set in the transponder. (For the math maniacs, there are four window each with 8 possible numbers. $8^4 = 4096$.) Some transponders have *Mode C* or *Mode S* capability otherwise known as *altitude reporting capability*. This means they can display the airplane's altitude on the radar screen (Figure 63).

You'll learn more about using the transponder in Chapter Eight. For now, let's understand when and where we're required to use the transponder. We'll also assume you aren't flying either a balloon or glider and that your airplane was originally certified with an engine-driven electrical system (or hasn't been subsequently cer-

VFR CODES SHOWN ON RADAR SCOPE

The ATC radar computer is programmed to look for a pilot's assigned transponder code (4632 in this instance). When it sees the code, the computer converts the code to the aircraft's tail number. The controller then refers to the pilot of the aircraft by the tail number seen on the radar scope.

Radar Screen

Fig. 63

tified without such a system). After all, if there's no electrical source on board, a transponder isn't going to work. Transponders with Mode C capability are required if operating in any of the following:

1. In Class A, Class B and Class C airspace areas as well as in all airspace above the ceiling and within the lateral boundaries of a Class B or Class C airspace upward to 10,000 feet MSL

2. In all airspace within 30 nautical miles of certain airports listed in appendix D, section 1 of FAR Part 91, from the surface upward to 10,000 feet MSL. (I won't bother to list these airports since they can be identified from your aeronautical sectional charts by thin, magenta, circular rings.)

3. In all airspace of the 48 contiguous states and the District of Columbia at and above 10,000 feet MSL, excluding the airspace at and below 2,500 feet above the surface.

Aircraft Without Electrical Systems

Suppose your airplane wasn't originally certified with an engine-driven electrical system. Can you fly without a transponder in controlled airspace? Yes. You're allowed to operate without a transponder if you remain outside Class B or C airspace. If you're operating within the 30 NM veil established for some airports in Class B airspace, you may operated within that veil as long as you remain lower than 10,000 feet MSL or the top of any Class B or C airspace within that veil, whichever is lower. What constitutes an electrical system? The FAA says the aircraft must have a generator/alternator turned by the engine, a regulator to adjust the power generated and a battery. All three are necessary to be considered an official electrical system.

4. In the airspace from the surface to 10,000 feet MSL within a 10 nautical mile radius of any airport listed in appendix D, section 2 of FAR Part 91. This also excludes the airspace below 1,200 feet outside the lateral boundaries of the surface area of the airspace designated for that airport. (At the time of this writing, there are no longer any airports listed in this section of appendix D.)

One last thing about this regulation. It requires you to keep your transponder turned on while in the airspace listed above, or in any controlled airspace. In addition to keeping it turned on, you must also operate it in Mode C (the altitude mode) if you are so equipped. You are also required to turn your transponder to the "on" or normal altitude reporting position prior to moving on the airport surface to ensure the aircraft is visible to ATC surveillance systems.

You are probably wondering, "What do I do if my transponder, or Mode C, fails in flight or fails at some intermediate stop on a cross country flight?" Well, fear not. ATC can waive the transponder requirements, regardless of the airspace in which you're flying. ATC can honor this request at any time. Simply call the Center or approach controller with your request. If, however, you don't have a transponder, ATC wants at least a one hour notice before they approve a flight in an area requiring a transponder. In other words, if you want to depart the primary airport in Class C airspace, you should call the tower at least one hour before departure and request a waiver if your aircraft is not transponder equipped.

PERSONAL BACK PACK PARACHUTES

© get4art

FAR 91.307 Parachutes And Parachuting

Pilots often confuse the parachute rule with the aerobatic flight rule. The parachute rule states that unless each occupant of the aircraft is wearing an approved parachute (Figure 64), no pilot carrying any person, other than a crewmember, may execute any intentional maneuver that exceeds a bank of 60° relative to the horizon or a nose-up or nose-down attitude of 30° relative to the horizon.

The aerobatic flight rule (FAR 91.303) never mentions the aircraft's pitch or bank. It only talks about abrupt or abnormal maneuvers or accelerations. It's technically possible to perform an aerobatic maneuver and not be required to wear a parachute. Simply pointing the nose downward at a 29° angle and radically pulling up to 29° might be considered an aerobatic maneuver since it's abrupt and certainly abnormal. It doesn't, however, require a parachute. I use this example only for clarification; do not attempt to do this at home. Without a doubt, a snap roll, loop or Cuban Eight is an aerobatic maneuvers requiring parachutes.

If you are by yourself in an aircraft, parachutes are never required regardless of the aircraft's pitch and bank. The FAA figures that you have enough common sense to measure risk for yourself. When it comes to the passengers,

Fig. 64

Unless you're doing aerobatics, your instructor shouldn't come to the airport dressed like this!

though, they aren't betting on your risk assessment abilities.

Parachutes are not required when on flight tests for pilot certification. They are not required when practicing spins or other flight maneuvers required by regulations when given by a certified flight instructor.

If you're thinking about carrying any parachute in your airplane, it must be an approved type and have been packed within either 60 or 180 days depending on the type of material from which it's constructed. See the actual regulation for a detailed description of this requirement.

A fellow pilot (we'll keep him anonymous) had an unusual occupation: he threw people out of airplanes (parachute jumpers). Flying a Cessna 206 with the door removed, he would hold the brakes as jumpers exited the plane. These folks would grab onto the strut and stand on the locked wheel. Upon the jumpmaster's command, these jumpers would let go of the strut, and sink into an ocean of air.

Chapter 6 - Federal Aviation Regulations: How FAR Can We Go?

6-47

On one flight, the last jumper got cold feet, literally and figuratively. He stood on the wheel, holding the strut, but refused to let go. The jumpmaster yelled, "Jump! Jump!" The reluctant jumper said, "No, no, I'm not going!" Both the jump-master and the pilot looked at each other and the pilot knew exactly what to do. He let go of the brakes (what a rat). While this is not what pilots normally mean when they refer to *rotation,* it worked. The strut-clinger suddenly became a skydiver.

Two Types of Airworthiness Certificates

In the world of government paperwork, there's never a shortage of ways to create more paperwork. This is especially true when it comes to an aircraft's air-worthiness certificate. You'd think there would be a need for only one type of airworthiness certificate that says, "This thing can actually fly." Period. In a perfect world with limit-ed paper, this is all you'd need. But lo, this wasn't to be.

As it stands, when an aircraft comes off the production line it is issued one of two types of airworthiness certifi-cate, each having several sub-categories within it. It's given either a *standard airworthiness certificate* (Figure 65) or a *special airworthiness certificate* (Figure 66). So, let's examine each.

Standard airworthiness certificates cover aircraft certified by the FAA in the normal, utility, acrobatic, commuter, or transport category, and are also issued for manned free balloons, and for aircraft designated by the FAA as special classes of aircraft (Figure 67).

Special airworthiness certificates are primary, restricted, limited, light-sport, and provisional airwor-thiness certificates, special flight permits, and experi-mental certificates (Figure 67). Those aircraft falling with-in the *light sport* sub-category are not certified by the FAA. Instead, they are certified by their manufacturer to meet a set of standards developed in consensus with the light sport air-craft industry, also known as *consensus standards.* These standards specify certain design, manufactur-ing, testing and quality control requirements and don't involve FAA oversight or participation.

While it's not necessary to know about all the dif-ferent sub-categories within each airworthiness cer-tificate type, you should be familiar with two that fall within the special airworthiness certificate category.

Two Types Of Airworthiness Certificates

Standard Airworthiness Certificate (sub-categories): Free Balloon, Normal, Transport, Utility, Special Class, Aerobatic, Commuter

Special Airworthiness Certificate (sub-categories): Primary, Exhibition, Limited, Special Flight Permit, Restricted, Provisional, Light Sport, Experimental

Note: There are as many as nine different sub-categories of experimental certificates. We are only concerned about three of them.

Three Sub-Categories of Experimental Certificates
• Experimental Amateur-Built Aircraft
• Experimental-Light Sport Aircraft (ELSA)
• Experimental Exhibition Aircraft

Experimental-Light Sport Aircraft (ELSA) Include:
• SLSAs deregistered and converted to ELSAs
• Kits based on special light sport aircraft (SLSA)

Fig. 67

Fig. 65

Fig. 66

I'm speaking of the *experimental* and the *light-sport* aircraft sub-categories. In order to help you better understand what follows, let me do for you what Michelangelo did for the Pope— paint you the big picture, but using my words instead of paint.

The Big Picture

As a sport pilot you are restricted to flying those aircraft that meet the definition of *light sport aircraft* (LSA). This includes aircraft with any type of airworthiness certificate, such as special light sport aircraft (SLSA), experimental amateur built aircraft, experimental light sport aircraft (ELSA), or those aircraft with a *standard airworthiness certificate,* such as a Piper J-3 Cub (Figure 68) and Aeronca 7AC Champ. The important point here is that the aircraft must meet the definition of *light sport aircraft* shown on Page 6-2 of this chapter (i.e., a maximum takeoff weight of not more than 1,320 pounds, have two seats or less, and so on).

Within the *special airworthiness certificate* category, there are two different sub-categories of aircraft that are of interest to us here: special *light-sport* and *experimental.*

A special light sport aircraft (SLSA) is a manufactured aircraft, constructed according to industry consensus standards (Figure 69). These are aircraft that are originally certified as SLSAs. Anyone performing the required maintenance and inspections on SLSAs will need either a repairman certificate with a maintenance rating or an A&P license. More detail on maintenance coming up soon.

An experimental aircraft also falls under the special airworthiness category and has three common subdivisions (Figure 70). They are:

1. experimental amateur-built aircraft (Figure 71),
2. experimental light-sport aircraft (ELSA) (Figure 72),
3. experimental exhibition aircraft (Figure 73).

AN AIRCRAFT IN THE STANDARD AIRWORTHINESS CATEGORY MEETING THE DEFINITION OF A LIGHT SPORT AIRCRAFT

© Donald Neuberg

Fig. 68

Experimental aircraft are machines that you typically build all or some of the machine yourself (no, this doesn't mean that you can do experiments in them, either). These airplanes were constructed according to rules that are different than those under which standard production airplanes are built. Experimental means you can do the maintenance on these aircraft without having to have a repairman certificate. Anyone can work on an experimental aircraft. To do the required inspections, however, requires either an A&P license or some type of repairman certificate, which will be discussed later.

Don't forget this very important point: your sport pilot license allows you to exercise sport pilot privileges (with appropriate training and endorsements, of course) in *any* aircraft that meets the definition of a LSA, regardless of the original certification category of that airplane. This is a very important distinction for you to understand. Now for the details. Let's begin our discussion with experimental aircraft that meet the definition of a LSA.

FAR 91.319 Aircraft Having Experimental Certificates: Operating Limitations

The special airworthiness certificate has three different sub-categories listed as experimental. Let's examine each one individually.

Experimental amateur-built "homebuilt" aircraft are those where the major portion (at least 51%) of the fabrication, construction or assembly was done by amateur-builders solely for the purpose of recreation or education (Figure 74). As long as this airplane meets the definition of a light sport aircraft, then you can fly it as a sport pilot, hereby referred to as *experimental amateur-built aircraft (LSA-definition).* As you'll soon see, the amateur-built status means that you, the builder, can qualify to do the required inspections on this aircraft, too. How sweet is that? Keep in mind that these aircraft are to be used for sport and recreation only. You can certainly take flight instruction in them but you can't do instruction for hire, tow gliders/ultralight vehicles for hire, or use them as rental aircraft.

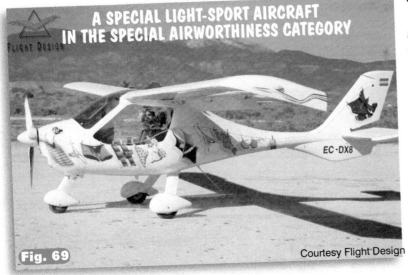

A SPECIAL LIGHT-SPORT AIRCRAFT IN THE SPECIAL AIRWORTHINESS CATEGORY

FLIGHT DESIGN

EC-DX8

Fig. 69

Courtesy Flight Design

Chapter 6 - Federal Aviation Regulations: How FAR Can We Go?

6-49

Fig. 70

Primary

Exhibition

Limited

Special Airworthiness Certificate (sub-categories)

Special Flight Permit

Restricted

Provisional

Light Sport

Experimental

Note: There are as many as nine different sub-categories of experimental certificates. We are only concerned about three of them.

Three Sub-Categories of Experimental Certificates
- Experimental Amateur-Built Aircraft
- Experimental-Light Sport Aircraft (ELSA)
- Experimental Exhibition Aircraft

Experimental-Light Sport Aircraft (ELSA) Include:
- SLSAs deregistered and converted to ELSAs
- Kits based on a special light sport aircraft (SLSA)

EXPERIMENTAL AMATEUR-BUILT

Fig. 71

EXPERIMENTAL LIGHT SPORT (ELSA)

Fig. 72

EXPERIMENTAL EXHIBITION

Fig. 73

© Theresa Martinez

Experimental light sport aircraft (ELSA) come in two important flavors. They are:

A. SLSAs that were re-registered so as to convert them to an ELSA. Why would someone convert an SLSA to an ELSA? As you'll see later in this chapter, this allows them to perform their own maintenance, which may save them money. (Note: you can only register such a kit as an ELSA "if" the manufacturer has produced an SLSA version of that same kit.)

B. kits that do not have to conform to the amateur-built certification requirements (ELSA kits don't require that you build at least 51% of the aircraft). These kits come out of the factory either fully built or in a box where very little, some or very much assembly is required (Figure 75). If assembly is required, then you must assemble them in accordance with the manufacturer's instructions. This might be a little more challenging than assembling your typical Weber BBQ, but you don't take your BBQ, flying, do you? (The "steaks" would be higher if you did.) ELSAs

are based on ASTM compliant design standards (ASTM stands for *American Society for Testing Materials*. This organization helps set the standards for the design, performance, quality and safety monitoring for light sport aircraft). As with amateur-built aircraft, these vehicles are

EXPERIMENTAL AMATEUR-BUILT

Fig. 74

THE RV-12 CAN BE LICENSED AS AN EXPERIMENTAL LIGHT SPORT AIRCRAFT (ELSA)

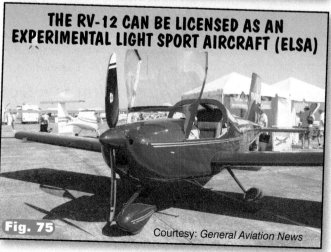

Fig. 75

Courtesy: *General Aviation News*

Experimental Aircraft Operating Limitations

What can't you do with an aircraft having an experimental airworthiness certificate? Here are some of the major limitations:

Flight operations may be conducted under day VFR conditions only, unless the FAA specifies otherwise. When operating out of airports with operating control towers, you must notify the tower of the experimental nature of the aircraft. An experimental aircraft can not be operated over a densely populated area or on a congested airway. Pilots of experimental aircraft may apply for a waiver to these last two limitations.

ANNUAL CONDITION INSPECTION

YEAR: DATE	RECORDING TACH TIME	TODAYS FLIGHT	TOTAL TIME IN SERVICE	Description of Inspections, Tests, Repairs and Alterations Entries must be endorsed with Name, Rating and Certificate Number of Technician or Repair Facility. (See back pages for other specific entries.)
2010 7-9-10	Hobbs: 1131.8			Completed 100HR/Conditional Inspection. This Aircraft found to be in Air worthy Condition. Lubercated all Flight Controls. Checked A/C Electrical system CW SB_LSA 31 0109, Rev. 1 Circuit Breakers Safety. Clew Fuel gascolator carburator Bowls. Installed New Brake Linings. P/N 010203209, Serviced w/5606 Hyd. Fluid. Serviced Air Filter. Tested ELT IAW 91.207D But March 2014. A/C Ground Run Satisfactory. A+P 2152282G

Fig. 76

AIRCRAFT LOGBOOKS

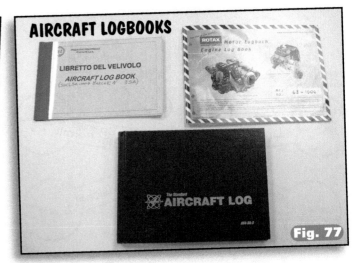

Fig. 77

to be used for sport and recreation, and not to be used as a for-hire flight training or rental aircraft. Just to be clear, you can take instruction in an ELSA, but you can't use it for hire to instruct others. (Note: ELSAs can, for compensation or hire, be used to tow gliders in the LSA category or unpowered ultralight vehicles).

Experimental exhibition aircraft are those aircraft often found at airshows, such as warbirds. I won't discuss these here since it's unlikely that you'll go to war after receiving your sport pilot certificate. (See Postflight Briefing #6-2.)

Experimental Aircraft Requirements - If your airplane has an experimental airworthiness certificate, you are required to advise your passengers of the experimental nature of the aircraft. I know you'll choose your words carefully, and not say something such as, "By the way, I just wanted to let you know that I built this thing and there's nothing wrong with it...any more." This statement is usually followed by, "Hey wait, come back, don't run away, I was only kidding, geesh." Kit-built and amateur-built aircraft constructed correctly, are as safe to fly as any other aircraft.

Flight operations in experimental aircraft should be conducted under day VFR conditions only, unless you are authorized by the FAA to do otherwise. These operations must also be conducted within the operating limits specified for that particular airplane. When operating out of airports with operating control towers, you must notify the tower of the experimental nature of the aircraft. Keep in mind that experimental aircraft may only be used for the purpose for which their certificate was issued, and

that means sport and recreation, and not flight for compensation or hire.

Perhaps you've seen one of those large (and experimentally certified) hot air balloons that drifts around the country and are used by individuals to tout their personal companies and products. There is one in particular that impresses me. It's a large Tyrannosaurus Rex dinosaur that stands many stories tall. The problem with this type of balloon is that it causes the occupants of Japanese restaurants to run out into the street shouting, "No, not again. Make him stop."

Now we're ready to examine the specific maintenance and inspection requirements for both amateur-built aircraft (LSA-definition) and experimental light sport aircraft (ELSA).

Maintenance and Inspections on Experimental Amateur-built Aircraft (LSA-definition)

We've seen that anyone (you, him, that guy over there, your uncle Fred, and so on) can perform any maintenance on any experimental airplane. You don't need any license, rating or certificate to do so. That's because the FAA believes that anyone who owns an experimental aircraft will use a little common sense and only let someone who knows what they're doing work on the machine. And if you happen to own the experimental airplane, hopefully you won't touch it unless you know the difference between a doohickey and a thingamajig. On the other hand, all aircraft are required to have an inspection every 12 calendar months. Let's see who can do this inspection as well as

There's Something I've Got to Tell You...

As a pilot of an experimental aircraft or a special light sport aircraft, you are required to notify your passenger that he or she is going flying in an aircraft that doesn't meet the airworthiness requirements for an aircraft that was issued a standard airworthiness certificate. Of course, you'll modify that statement so as not to scare anyone, right. Perhaps you'll say:

"I want to advise you that this aircraft has an experimental airworthiness certificate and is not required to meet the airworthiness requirements for aircraft issued a standard airworthiness certificate." If it's an SLSA, you might say, *"Because this aircraft complies with industry consensus design standards, it's allowed to fall into the light-sport aircraft category and isn't required to meet the airworthiness requirements for aircraft issued a standard airworthiness certificate.*

Chapter 6 - Federal Aviation Regulations: How FAR Can We Go?

6-51

Requirements for Doing Maintenance or Inspections on Light Sport Aircraft

Special Airworthiness Certificate

Experimental — Special Light Sport

Amateur Built (LSA-definition)

Maintenance	Inspections	
Anyone	**A&P**	**R**EXP must be primary builder of aircraft

Fig. 78A

Experimental Light Sport (ELSA)

Maintenance	Inspections		
Anyone	**R**LSA**+I** must own aircraft	**R**LSA**+M** must be trained in "category" of aircraft	**A&P**

Special Light Sport

Maintenance		Inspections	
RLSA**+M** must be trained in "category" of aircraft	**A&P**	**R**LSA**+M** must be trained in "category" of aircraft	**A&P**

who is responsible for ensuring this inspection is completed.

Required Inspections - As a sport pilot, if you own an experimental amateur-built aircraft (LSA-definition), then it must have had a *condition inspection* (Figure 76) within the preceding 12 calendar months to be considered airworthy. This is sometimes called the *annual condition inspection*. The person performing this inspection (we'll discuss who can do this inspection next) must approve the aircraft for return to service by providing the appropriate endorsement in the aircraft's logbooks (Figure 77). Experimental amateur-built aircraft (LSA-definition) typically have three logbooks, one for the airframe, the engine and the propeller. All required inspections and maintenance must be logged in the appropriate logbook(s).

Who is responsible for ensuring that any required maintenance and inspections are logged into the appropriate maintenance records? The pilot? The aircraft fueler? No. The FAA requires the *owner* (the person who has legal title to the aircraft) or the *operator* (this can be the person who *operates* the flight school, but this isn't relevant for amateur-built experimental aircraft since they can't be used as rental aircraft) to ensure that the aircraft is properly maintained and inspected, as well as ensure the maintenance records are endorsed properly.

Who Can Perform the Annual Condition Inspection on Experimental Amateur-Built Aircraft (LSA-definition)?

As you know, if you built or purchased an experimental amateur-built aircraft, then *anyone* can perform the maintenance on that airplane. The annual condition inspection, however, must be done by either:

● a certificated *repairman (experimental aircraft builder)* (Figure 78A and 78B), or

● an appropriately rated mechanic (i.e, an A&P or airframe and powerplant mechanic, Figure 78A and 78C), or

● an appropriately rated repair station.

REXP **= repairman (experimental aircraft builder)**

To obtain a repairman (experimental aircraft builder) certificate as the primary builder of your airplane, you would apply to the FAA via an application form. No training is required. The repairman (experimental aircraft builder) certificate allows you to perform the required inspections on the amateur-built aircraft that you personally constructed.

Fig. 78B

A&P = airframe and powerplant mechanic (or appropriately rated repair station)

This is an FAA issued certificate that requires both practical and knowledge tests as well as many hours of actual hands-on experience. Licensed A&P mechanics can work on almost anything that flies.

Fig. 78C

If you are the *primary builder* of the amateur-built aircraft, then you can obtain a repairman certificate with an *experimental aircraft builder* classification (no, this isn't a home repairman certificate, either. To obtain the certificate, you simply apply to the FAA for one. No training is necessary. This certificate allows you to perform the annual condition inspection on the amateur-built aircraft (LSA definition) listed on your repairman certificate because you were the primary builder of this aircraft.

Since FAR 65.104[a][2]) states that you have to be the "primary builder" of the aircraft for which you're seeing repairman privileges, any future owner of this aircraft cannot qualify for the repairman certificate (experimental aircraft builder) for this airplane. That means if you purchase an already constructed experimental amateur-built LSA, then an A&P (or the person who holds the repairman certificate for that airplane—if one exists) must do the inspections on this machine from now on. Please remember that we are talking about amateur-built aircraft that meet the definition of light sport aircraft here.

Fig. 79

Fig. 80

Maintenance and Inspections On ELSAs (Experimental Light Sport Aircraft)

Keep in mind that ELSAs are airplane kits (fully or partially built) or special light sport aircraft (SLSAs) that were re-registered so as to convert them to ELSAs. (SLSAs to be discussed next.)

Required Inspections - Despite being allowed to do the maintenance on your ELSA, the aircraft must have an annual condition inspection within the preceeding 12 calendar months for it to be considered airworthy (Figure 79). In addition, if the ELSA is used for hire (i.e., towing services), then the airplane must have had a 100-hour inspection within the preceeding 100 hours of time in service (known as the *100-hour inspection*). The person performing either of these inspections (we'll discuss who can do these inspection next) must approve the aircraft for return to service by providing the appropriate endorsement in the aircraft's logbooks (Figure 80).

ELSAs typically have three logbooks, one for the airframe, the engine and the propeller. All required inspections and maintenance must be logged in the appropriate logbook(s).

Who is responsible for ensuring that any required maintenance and inspections are logged into the appropriate maintenance records? Ricardo, the airport Elvis impersonator? The Pilot? No. The FAA requires the *owner* (the person who has legal title to the aircraft) or the *operator* (this can be the person who *operates* the flight school that provides towing services for compensation or hire to gliders in the LSA category or unpowered ultralight vehicles) to ensure that the aircraft is properly maintained and inspected, as well as ensure the maintenance records are endorsed properly.

Let's be clear on the point about flight instruction. ELSAs (or any experimental aircraft, for that matter) can't be used for hire to instruct others nor can they be used as rental aircraft for the purposes of flight training. Yes, you can take instruction in an ELSA (or any experimental aircraft) and you can pay the instructor for that training. An FBO isn't, however, allowed to rent you an ELSA for that purpose.

Who Can Perform the Annual Condition Inspection on an Experimental Light Sport Aircraft (ELSA)?

You must know by now that anyone can perform the maintenance on an experimental airplane. The annual condition inspection, however, must be done by either:

- a certificated *repairman (light sport aircraft)* with an *inspection* rating in the *category* of aircraft for which the holder has completed training (i.e., *airplane* category), or
- a certificated *repairman (light sport aircraft)* with a *maintenance* rating in the *category* of aircraft for which the holder has completed training (i.e., *airplane* category), or
- an appropriately rated mechanic (e.g., A&P mechanic), or
- an appropriately rated repair station.

Let's examine each of these in more detail.

Repairman Certificate (LSA) - Inspection Rating

If you hold a *repairman (light sport aircraft)* certificate with an *inspection rating,* in the *airplane* category, then you can perform the annual condition inspection on an aircraft that you *own* as shown in Figure 81A and 81B. The reason the FAA wants you to own the airplane is that the *inspection rating* doesn't require a great deal of training to obtain (more on obtaining this certificate shortly). Therefore, owning the airplane assumes that you will have greater familiarity with the machine and a willingness to accept more of the risks associated with performing the annual condition inspection yourself. When you obtain your repairman certificate, the specific aircraft you'll be allowed to inspect will be listed on that repairman certificate by make, model and serial number. If you sell your ELSA and buy another one, or acquire an additional one to add to your neighborhood air-defense fleet, then the annual condition inspection can't be done on that aircraft until you add it to your repairman certificate. That's right. You must have the FAA add this new or additional aircraft to your certificate if you want to perform the annual condition inspection on that machine.

Repairman Certificate (LSA) - Maintenance Rating

You can also do the annual condition inspection if you hold a *repairman certificate (light sport aircraft)* with a

Chapter 6 - Federal Aviation Regulations: How FAR Can We Go?

6-53

Requirements for Doing Maintenance or Inspections on Light Sport Aircraft

Special Airworthiness Certificate

Experimental

Special Light Sport

Amateur Built (LSA-definition)

Maintenance	Inspections	
Anyone	**A&P**	R^{EXP} must be primary builder of aircraft

Experimental Light Sport (ELSA)

Maintenance	Inspections		
Anyone Fig. 81A	$R^{LSA}+I$ must own aircraft	$R^{LSA}+M$ must be trained in "category" of aircraft	**A&P**

Maintenance		Inspections	
$R^{LSA}+M$ must be trained in "category" of aircraft	**A&P**	$R^{LSA}+M$ must be trained in "category" of aircraft	**A&P**

maintenance rating (Figure 81A and 81C) in the airplane category. You don't need to own the aircraft to do this inspection with this type of repairman certificate, either. Why? As you'll soon see, this type of repairman certificate requires a great deal more training to obtain than that required for the inspection rating. With more training comes more privilege. Thus, the FAA allows you perform the annual condition inspection on any ELSA (not just the one you own) as long as the aircraft falls within the category of aircraft on which you were trained.

A&P or Appropriately Rated Repair Station

Of course, any licensed *airframe and powerplant* mechanic (Figure 81A and 81D) or appropriately rated repair station can do the annual condition inspection, too.

Obtaining the Repairman Certificate and Ratings

To obtain a repairman (light sport aircraft) certificate with an inspection rating, you must attend a FAA approved 16-hour training course and pass a knowledge test at the end of the course. To obtain a repairman (light sport aircraft) certificate with a maintenance rating, you must attend a FAA approved 80- to 120-hour training course for the category of aircraft on which you intend to work (i.e., airplane, weight-shift, glider, etc.), as well as pass a knowledge test at the end of the course (see, I told you it was more extensive).

Keep in mind that an inspection rating on your repairman certificate allows you to perform the annual condition inspection on an ELSA *that you own*. Unlike the repairman certificate (experimental aircraft builder), you aren't required to have built the airplane to perform the annual condition inspection. You are only

$R^{LSA}+I$ = repairman (light sport aircraft) with an *inspection* rating

To obtain a repairman (light sport aircraft) certificate with an *inspection rating*, you must take an FAA approved 16-hour training course for the same class of ELSA that you own and you can only do the annual condition inspection on the aircraft that you own. **Fig. 81B**

$R^{LSA}+M$ = repairman (light sport aircraft) with a *maintenance* rating

To obtain a repairman (light sport aircraft) certificate with a *maintenance rating*, you must complete an FAA approved rating course for the category of aircraft on which you desire to work. This course consists of 80 to 120 hours of training. The course allows you do the annual condition inspections on ELSAs and SLSAs, the 100-hour inspection on an SLSA, as well as perform the maintenance and repair on any SLSA, if authorized by the aircraft manufacturer. **Fig. 81C**

A&P = airframe and powerplant mechanic (or FAA certified repair station)

This is an FAA issued certificate that requires both practical and knowledge tests as well as many hours of actual hands-on experience. Licensed A&P mechanics can work on almost anything that flies. **Fig. 81D**

required to own the airplane, meaning that you might have purchased it from someone, purchased it as a kit and built a little bit of it or none of it. This is one reason why some people obtain a repairman certificate with an inspection rating, then deregister their SLSA. In doing so they convert its airworthiness certificate to the ELSA sub-category, allowing them to do their own maintenance as well as annual condition inspection. This may saves a great deal of money on mechanics, but only if the work is done properly, right?

Fig. 82

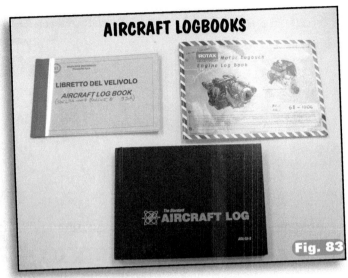

Fig. 83

FAR 91.327 Aircraft Having a Special Airworthiness Certificate in the Light-Sport Category: Operating Limitations

The special airworthiness certificate also includes the a sub-category named *light-sport* aircraft. These are typically production model aircraft made by manufacturers who comply with ASTM consensus standards in the creation of that aircraft. These types of aircraft are called SLSA or *special light sport aircraft*, and they meet the definition of light-sport aircraft discussed on page 6-2.

SLSA are limited to sport and recreational flying. They can, however, be used as rental aircraft, to conduct flight training and to tow gliders or unpowered ultralights (see FAR 91.309). These activities can be performed for compensation or hire by an appropriately rated pilot (glider towing requires at least a private pilot certificate and instructing requires at least a sport pilot instructor's certificate).

Owner or Operator - One reason flying a special light-sport airplane can be considered a relatively low-risk mechanical activity (compared to other activities involving machines) is that the FAA has a relatively strict maintenance policy on these aircraft. The FAA requires the *owner* (the person who has legal title to the aircraft) or the *operator* (this can be the person who operates the flight school) to ensure that the aircraft is properly maintained and inspected. Now, this doesn't mean that the owner or operator has to personally do the maintenance on these airplanes, nor does it mean the pilot must do this maintenance, either. It means that the person who owns the airplane or the person who causes the airplane to be operated (such as the flight school that rents the airplane for flight training), is responsible for ensuring the airplane is maintained and inspected properly.

Required Inspections - To be considered airworthy, a special light sport aircraft is required to have an annual *condition inspection* (Figure 82) within the preceding 12 calendar months. In addition, if the SLSA is used for hire

or to conduct flight instruction for hire, then the airplane must have had a 100-hour inspection within the preceding 100 hours of time in service (known as the *100-hour inspection*). Unlike the 100-hour inspection requirement for an ELSA, the annual condition inspection also counts as the 100-hour inspection on a SLSA. The 100-hour inspection must be entered in the aircraft maintenance records (Figure 83).

Who Can Perform Maintenance on an SLSA?

Since the special light sport aircraft is a manufactured aircraft (and not an experimental aircraft), the maintenance on this aircraft can only be performed by:

- a certificated *repairman (light sport aircraft)* with a *maintenance* rating in the *category* of aircraft for which the holder has completed training, which is the *airplane* category in this instance (Figures 84A and 84B), or
- an A&P mechanic (Figures 84A and 84C), or
- an appropriately rated repair station.

Who Can Perform the Annual Condition or The 100-Hour Inspection on an SLSA?

The annual condition inspection and the 100-hour inspection performed on a SLSA can only be conducted by:

- a certificated *repairman (light sport aircraft)* with a *maintenance* rating in the *category* of aircraft for which the holder has completed training, which is the *airplane* category in this instance (Figures 84A and 84B), or
- an A&P mechanic (Figures 84A and 84C), or
- an appropriately rated repair station.

Always Use a Good Mechanic

Chapter 6 - Federal Aviation Regulations: How FAR Can We Go?

6-55

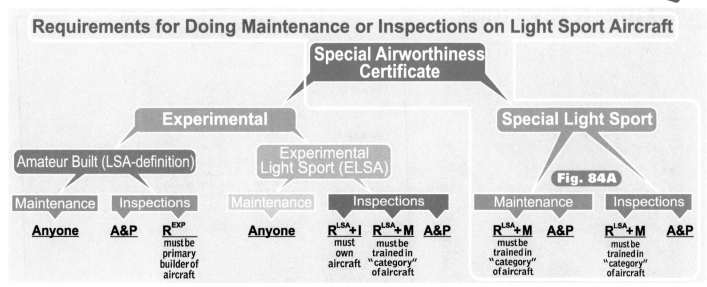

Requirements for Doing Maintenance or Inspections on Light Sport Aircraft

Fig. 84A

Safety Directives -
When a particular mechanical problem occurs with a special light sport aircraft, the airframe and engine manufacturer may issue something known as a *safety directive*. The safety directive is provided to the owner or operator of the aircraft (typically via the internet), since either of these individuals are responsible for ensuring that the aircraft is maintained and inspected properly. The owner or operator is responsible for complying with this directive and correcting any specified unsafe conditions (such as replacing a part that have been known to fail or inspecting some aspect of the machine that might fail). Service bulletins (Figure 85) are issued by the manufacturer to improve aircraft safety. As of this writing (2-7-14), they are not mandatory (unlike *safety directives*), but obviously should be heeded.

$R^{LSA}+M$ = repairman (light sport aircraft) with a *maintenance* rating

To obtain a repairman (light sport aircraft) certificate with a *maintenance rating*, you must complete an FAA approved rating course for the category of aircraft on which you desire to work. This course consists of 80 to 120 hours of training. The course allows you do the annual condition inspections on ELSAs and SLSAs, the 100-hour inspection on an SLSA, as well as perform the maintenance and repair on any SLSA, if authorized by the aircraft manufacturer.

Fig. 84B

A&P = airframe and powerplant mechanic
(or FAA certified repair station)

This is an FAA issued certificate that requires both practical and knowledge tests as well as many hours of actual hands-on experience. Licensed A&P mechanics can work on almost anything that flies.

Fig. 84C

Who can perform the work required by a safety directive? If the manufacturer doesn't specifically specify who can complete this work then it's reasonable to assume that it can be done by anyone allowed to perform maintenance on an SLSA.

Be aware that it is possible for the owner or operator to correct the specific condition listed in the safety directive in a manner that's different from that mentioned in the directive. This is permitted as long as the manufacturer issuing the safety directive concurs with this action. In other words, instead of replacing a wheel bearing, the manufacturer may instead permit periodic inspections to ensure the bearing's integrity

It's also possible for the owner or operator to obtain a waiver from the manufacturer regarding the provisions of the safety directive. For instance, suppose the safety directive of your

Fig. 85

A LETTER OF AUTHORIZATION

COSTRUZIONI AERONAUTICHE
TECNAM

May 1, 2009

TO WHOM IT MAY CONCERN

Subject: *TECNAM AUTHORIZATION*

Tecnam authorizes:

Chesapeake Sport Pilot, LLC, 210 Airport Road, Stevensville, MD 21666, to install the following equipment in P2002 Sierra, serial number 258, as proposed by Chesapeake Sport Pilot, LLC as long as Chesapeake Sport Pilot, LLC installs the equipment in accordance with all manufacturers' installation instructions and all modifications comply with all current FARs and complies with all applicable ASTM standards.

Authorization to perform: LSA Repairman – Maintenance Airplane, A&P mechanic, or an FAA Repair Station.

Nose
- Tire - Aero Classic 4.00-6
- Tube - ACST 13x5.00-6

Mains
- Tire - Condor 500x5
- Tube Leak Guard 500x5

Authorization Signature   **Fig. 86**

special light-sport airplane (which was originally equipped with wheels and floats) says you must inspect your machine for salt water corrosion (or hitchhiking mackerel) every 50 hours of flight. Let's also say that you have permanently removed the floats as allowed by the manufacturer. It's clear you aren't landing on water any more (if you are, you'll probably only doing it once). Therefore, you might negotiate with the manufacturer for a waiver on this particular safety directive.

Major Alteration/Repair - Suppose you desire to make a major alteration or repair to your SLSA. Perhaps you want to add a bigger generator, repair a windscreen or install a gun turret for flights over rough neighborhoods. If this is an experimental aircraft, then you wouldn't need anyone's permission to perform this work. (You may, however, be required to notify the FAA about the

repair or alteration to ensure that your aircraft still complies with the experimental certification requirements.)

On the other hand, if you're operating an SLSA, then all work must be done in accordance with the airplane or engine manufacturer's standards for that aircraft. This may mean the work must be done by either an A&P, an approved repair station or a repairman (light sport aircraft) with a maintenance rating. The repairman, in this instance, may be required to have completed specific training or have prior experience before being allowed to perform specific major alterations or repairs as per FAR 65.107. The repairman may also be required to obtain a letter of authorization (LOA) from the manufacturer to perform the specific alteration or repair (Figure 86). Any major alteration or repair must be documented in the aircraft log books as per FAR 91.417.

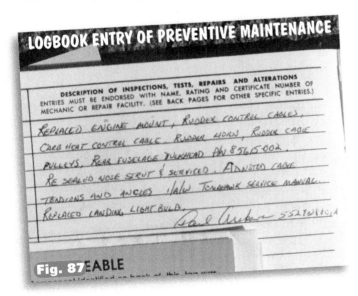

LOGBOOK ENTRY OF PREVENTIVE MAINTENANCE

Fig. 87

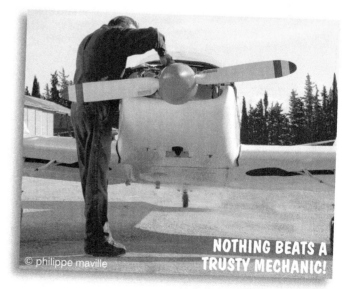

© philippe maville

NOTHING BEATS A TRUSTY MECHANIC!

Chapter 6 - Federal Aviation Regulations: How FAR Can We Go?

6-57

The 16 Greatest Lies in Aviation

1. I'm from the FAA and I'm here to help you.
2. Me? I've never flown with less than the minimum visibility.
3. We will be on time, maybe even early.
4. Pardon me ma'am, I seem to have lost my jet keys.
5. I have no interest in flying for the airlines.
6. I fixed it right the first time, it failed for other reasons.
7. All that turbulence spoiled my landing.
8. I'm a member of the mile high club.
9. I only need glasses for reading.
10. I broke out at minimums.
11. The weather is going to be all right; it's clearing to VFR.
12. Don't worry about the weight and balance—it will fly.
13. If we get a little lower I think we'll see the lights.
14. We shipped that part yesterday.
15. This plane outperforms the book by 20%.
16. We in aviation are overpaid, underworked and well respected.

Preventive Maintenance - There are times when a person who holds a sport pilot certificate but not a repairman certificate or A&P license is allowed to do preventative maintenance on an SLSA. Of course, preventive maintenance doesn't mean major overhauls and airframe repairs. Preventive maintenance typically implies that you can do things like changing sparkplugs, replenishing hydraulic fluid, and servicing landing gear and wheel bearings on your SLSA. However, what you can or cannot do in terms of preventative maintenance is spelled out in Appendix A of FAR 43. Additionally, the FAA requires you to have received training on that action before performing the maintenance. This can be from a local mechanic or other sources.

If you're doing preventive maintenance on your airplane, you're required to complete specific paperwork. This entry must include the signature, certificate number and kind of certificate held by the person approving the work (that could be you or the person doing the work). A description of the work must be entered in the aircraft maintenance records as shown in Figure 87.

FAR 91.411/413 Altimeter And Transponder Inspections

If you want to operate your transponder (Figure 88A) then it must be tested and inspected within the preceding

TRANSPONDER/STATIC SYSTEM INSPECTION

Fig. 88B

Fig. 88C

AIRCRAFT LOG

Transponder

Fig. 88A

24 calendar months and found to comply with the appropriate regulations (FAR 91.215 on page 6-45 specifies the airspace in which it must be operated). Completion of this inspections is shown in the aircraft logbook (Figure 88B). As an aside, Figure 88B also shows that the transponder has also had a inspection of its associated altimeter and altitude reporting equipment. The inspection must be logged in the aircraft maintenance records (Figure 88B). This inspection is only necessary if the airplane is operated under instrument flight rules in controlled airspace. Yes, an appropriately equipped light sport airplane (when allowed by the manufacturer) can be flown under instrument conditions but not by someone without an instrument rating.

National Transportation Safety Board Regs

The National Transportation Safety Board (NTSB) is the agency responsible for aircraft accidents, incidents and overdue aircraft. Under certain conditions, you may have to notify them or file a report if you are involved in an aircraft accident in which any person receives serious injury or the aircraft receives substantial damage. Part 830 of the Board's regulations governs the reporting of accidents, incidents, and damage to aircraft, cargo, mail, or injury to required crewmembers.

NTSB 830.2 Definitions

It's important that you know the definitions of serious injury and substantial damage, since many of your reporting obligations depend on deciding whether someone has sustained a serious injury, or an aircraft has sustained substantial damage.

The NTSB has five specific definitions for a serious injury. Looking at them closely, they appear to be what you might see at any hockey game. A *serious injury* is any injury that:

1. Requires hospitalization for more than 48 hours, commencing within 7 days from the date the injury was received.

2. Results in the fracture of a bone, except simple fractures of the fingers, toes or nose (such as what you get if you miss our first loan payment to a guy named Vinny).

3. Causes severe hemorrhages, nerve, muscle, or tendon damage.

4. Involves any internal organ.

5. Involves second- or third-degree burns, or any burns affecting more than 5 percent of the body surface.

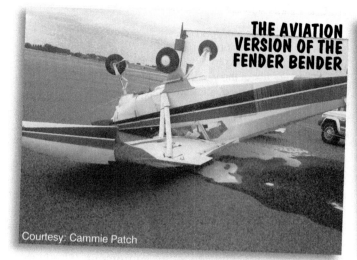

THE AVIATION VERSION OF THE FENDER BENDER

Courtesy: Cammie Patch

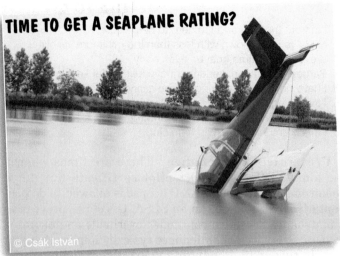

TIME TO GET A SEAPLANE RATING?

© Csák István

Substantial damage is defined as damage or failure that adversely affects the structural strength, performance, or flight characteristics of the aircraft and which would normally require major repair or replacement of the affected component. The following are NOT considered to be substantial damage for the purposes of this part:

1. Engine failure or damage limited to an engine if only one engine fails or is damaged.

2. Bent fairings or cowling, dented skin, small puncture holes in the skin or fabric

3. Ground damage to rotor or propeller blades and damage to landing gear, wheels, tires, flaps, engine accessories, brakes, or wingtips.

An *accident* is an occurrence associated with the operation of an aircraft which takes place between the time any person boards the aircraft with the intention of flight and all such persons have disembarked, and in which any person suffers death or serious injury, or in which the aircraft receives substantial damage.

An *incident* means an occurrence other than an accident, associated with the operation of an aircraft, which affects or could affect the safety of operations.

NTSB 830.5 Immediate Notification

The operator of an aircraft must immediately and by the most expeditious means available notify the nearest NTSB field office when an aircraft accident or any of the following listed incidents occur:

1. Flight control system malfunction or failure.

2. Inability of any required flight crewmember to perform his or her normal flight duties as a result of injury or illness.

3. Failure of structural components of a turbine engine excluding compressor and turbine blades and vanes.

4. In-flight fire.

5. Aircraft collide in flight.

6. Damage to property, other than the aircraft, estimated to exceed $25,000 for repair or fair market value in the event of total loss (i.e., you land on a Mercedes).

(7) Release of all or a portion of a propeller blade from an aircraft, excluding release caused solely by ground contact.

(8) A complete loss of information, excluding flickering, from more than 50 percent of an aircraft's cockpit displays known which you know as your primary flight display (PFD), primary navigation display (PND), and other integrated displays.

(9) An aircraft is overdue and believed to have been involved in an accident.

NTSB 830.10 Preservation of Aircraft Wreckage, Mail, Cargo and Records

This regulation basically says that if you are the operator of an aircraft involved in an accident or incident, it's your job to protect the wreckage and everything associated with that wreckage until the NTSB arrives and assumes responsibility. Avoid disturbing the wreckage. Do so only if it's necessary to help persons injured or trapped, to protect the wreckage from further damage, or protect the public from injury. If you need to move the wreckage or anything associated with it, make notes, take photographs, or draw sketches to detail its original condition.

NTSB 830.15 Reports And Statements to Be Filed

The operator of an aircraft must file a report *within 10 days* after an accident or *after 7 days* if an overdue aircraft is still missing. A report on an incident for which immediate notification is required shall be filed *only as requested* by an authorized representative of the Board.

Those are some of the important regulations necessary for flying safety. Of course, some of you may be thinking there's only one thing more boring than studying the FARs and that's listening to golf on the radio. OK, let me make this a little more exciting for you by introducing you to our next subject: Airport Operations.

Postflight Briefing #6-1

Sport Pilots Who Fly Aircraft Having Standard Airworthiness Certificates

As a sport pilot, you are restricted to flying airplanes that meet the technical definition of a light sport aircraft (LSA). As we've already discussed in this chapter, there are many different types of airplanes with *standard airworthiness certificates* that qualify as LSAs, such as the Piper J-3 Cub (Figure 89 through Figure 92), Aeronca Champ, Luscombe 8A and so on. If you elect to own or operate any of these airplanes, then you must adhere to the maintenance regulations pertaining to aircraft in the standard airworthiness category. While these regulations aren't really all that different from those previously covered, there area few differences that we should examine. Keep in mind that these regulations were written for those holding a private pilot certificate (or higher) who are not restricted to aircraft with limited weight, performance and seating.

FAR 91.407 Operations After Maintenance, Preventive Maintenance, Rebuilding or Alteration

This regulation states that no person may operate any aircraft that has undergone maintenance, preventive maintenance, rebuilding, or alteration unless it has been approved for return to service by a qualified mechanic or repairman and a maintenance record entry is made in the aircraft's logbooks. This usually means someone with an A&P license has to do the work on this airplane then follow up by making the required endorsements in the propeller, airframe and/or engine logbook as appropriate (Figure 93). Sorry, but endorsing an article of your clothing in lieu of a logbook won't meet FAA standards for an endorsement. If it did, then you could brag that an FAA inspector demanded proof of proper maintenance and you had to give him the shirt off your back to keep him happy.

THE PIPER CUB IS CLASSIFIED AS A LIGHT SPORT AIRCRAFT

Fig. 89

© Gekon - Fotolia.com

THE LUSCOMBE 8A IS CLASSIFIED AS A LIGHT SPORT AIRCRAFT

Fig. 90

Courtesy: General Aviation News

THE AERONCA CHAMP IS CLASSIFIED AS A LIGHT SPORT AIRCRAFT

Fig. 91

© Chris Connor

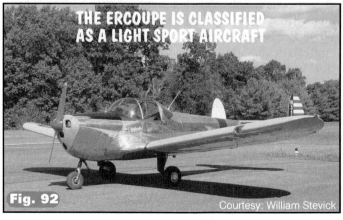

THE ERCOUPE IS CLASSIFIED AS A LIGHT SPORT AIRCRAFT

Fig. 92

Courtesy: William Stevick

PROPELLER, AIRFRAME AND ENGINE LOGBOOKS

Fig. 93

Major Alteration or Repair

This regulation also states that no person may carry another person (other than crewmembers) in an aircraft that has been maintained, rebuilt or altered in a manner that may have appreciably changed its flight characteristics, or substantially affected its operation in flight, unless that airplane is test flown. Huh? Me? A test pilot?

That's right. The regulation states that an appropriately rated pilot with at least a private pilot certificate (not a sport pilot certificate) must fly the aircraft, make an operational check of the maintenance performed or alteration made, and log the flight in the aircraft records (Figure 94). Welcome to test pilot school. Be sure an ask for medical, dental and a helmet.

As a sport pilot you won't be able to do the flight test necessary to return this aircraft to service. Therefore, if you decide to attach search light with a Batman light signal to the top of your Piper J-3 Cub, you'll need to have this approved by an A&P mechanic. Then, before carrying passengers in your Bat Plane, you'll need to find someone with at least a private pilot license to test fly the machine for you (perhaps someone named, Robin?).

Preventive Maintenance

As a sport pilot, you may not do preventive maintenance on an aircraft in the standard airworthy category (SAA). Preventive maintenance in this instance is strictly limited to those holding a private pilot certificate or higher. No exceptions. Sorry grease monkey, but no grease today.

FAR 91.409 Inspections

As a sport pilot, if you elect to operate an aircraft issued a standard airworthiness certificate, then it must have had an inspection within the preceding 12 calendar months by a qualified mechanic (think A&P here) and been approved for return to service. This is typically called the *annual inspection* (Figure 95) and it must be logged in the appropriate maintenance logbooks.

In addition to the annual inspection, a 100 hour inspection is sometimes required. If an aircraft is being used for flight instruction for hire, that aircraft must have had an inspection within the preceding 100 hours of time in service. This is known as a 100 inspection (who names these things?) and is usually less intensive than a typical annual inspection. On the other hand, if you had an annual inspection, then this counts as a 100-hour inspection. Why? Because the annual inspection is much more thorough than the 100-hour inspection. The 100-hour inspection must also be entered in the aircraft maintenance records (Figure 96).

As a practical matter, it's not unusual for airplane owners to elect to voluntarily have some type of non-regulatory modification made to their airplane. This could be a wing modification kit or electrical system upgrade, for example. In these instances, given the amount of work to be done (and duplicated), it may be economically wise to have the mechanic do whatever extra work is necessary to comply

LOGBOOK ENTRY OF PREVENTIVE MAINTENANCE

Fig. 94

LOGBOOK ENTRY OF THE ANNUAL INSPECTION

Fig. 95

LOGBOOK ENTRY OF THE 100-HOUR INSPECTION

Fig. 96

AIRWORTHINESS DIRECTIVE COMPLIANCE

Fig. 97

with the annual or 100 hour inspections. After all, there's nothing that says you can't do the annual or the 100 hour inspection every month or 10 hours, respectively. As a final note, an airplane with a standard airworthiness certificate can exceed the 100 hour inspection time limit by 10 hours if it is necessary to reach a place where the inspection can be done.

FAR 91.417 Maintenance Records

Since we've been talking about the maintenance logbooks, you should know that this isn't a voluntary thing. The FARs require that each registered owner or operator of an aircraft must keep records of aircraft maintenance. I'm speaking of the *annual inspection*, the 100-hour inspection, any major alterations or repairs or the completion of other required maintenance. This regulation pertains to the owner or operator or any aircraft, regardless of what type of airworthiness certificate it has (this means you sport pilots).

While special light sport aircraft have safety directives to handle special, and sometimes unexpected issues with aircraft, airplanes with standard airworthiness certificates have something similar, which is known as an AD or *airworthiness directive*. When a particular mechanical problem occurs with on these airplanes the FAA may issue an AD, which is sent to the owner or operator of the aircraft. AD compliance is mandatory and it's the owner or operator's responsibility to provide the maintenance required by that AD. When the mechanic completes this maintenance (only an A&P can do maintenance on airplanes with standard airworthiness certificates), an entry is made in the aircraft logbooks identifying the AD as having been complied with (Figure 97).

So there you have it. If you're a sport pilot flying an airplane with a standard airworthiness certificate (that falls into the LSA category, of course), then you must comply with these regulations.

Postflight Briefing #6-2

Experimental Exhibition Aircraft

Bob Comperini

The *experimental-exhibition* category is the type of certification most commonly associated with *war birds*, and other antique aircraft that are *exhibited* or flown at airshows and fly-ins.

As with the other types of experimental certification, as long as the aircraft meets the definition of a light-sport aircraft (as defined in 14 CFR 1.1), it can be flown by a sport pilot.

The experimental-exhibition category has no *51% rule*, as experimental amateur-built aircraft do. Experimental-exhibition has been commonly used to register aircraft (often, former *ultralight trainers*), when the applicant could not prove that at least 51% of the aircraft was amateur built, which of course, would make that aircraft ineligible for the experimental amateur-built category. Experimental-exhibition was often used to register aircraft that were built by the factory. The Interplane Skyboy is one example of an airplane that was often built by the factory, and certificated in the experimental-exhibition category.

As it is with the other types of experimental aircraft, any maintenance, repairs, and alterations on experimental-exhibition aircraft, can be performed by anyone. The required annual condition inspection can be performed by an A&P, or an FAA repair facility. There are no repairman certificates available for this type of aircraft.

There are three major differences between experimental-exhibition aircraft, and aircraft in other experimental categories:

(1) There is no way to obtain a repairman certificate for this type of aircraft. Potential owners might have difficulty locating an A&P mechanic willing to perform the annual condition inspection on an experimental-exhibition aircraft, especially, if the aircraft is an *ultralight* type vehicle.

(2) Experimental-exhibition aircraft still have prohibitions against flying over densely populated areas or in congested airways, except for a few circumstances. Experimental amateur-built, and experimental light sport aircraft (E-LSA) have more relaxed operating limits that allow flight into these areas, as long as a safe altitude is maintained.

(3) There are other operating limit restrictions that are unique to experimental-exhibition aircraft. The aircraft is normally restricted to a 300 nm radius from its home base, unless previously authorized by the FAA. In addition, owners must also file an annual *program letter* with the FAA, listing the fly-ins, airshows, etc. that the owner intends to *exhibit* the aircraft at. With this letter, you're not asking for *permission* to fly to these events. Instead, you are meeting your obligation to inform the FAA of your intentions to do so each year. Unfortunately, this is just one of the quirks of this certification category.

By Bob Comperini
Designated Pilot Examiner (SP-Airplane)
www.fly-ul.com

Postflight Briefing #6-3

Why Are NASA Forms a Pilot's Best Friend?

The reports sprinkled throughout this book are from the Aviation Safety Reporting System (ASRS). Staffed with controllers, flight surgeons, aviation lawyers and pilots from every aviation arena, they analyze safety related reports from pilots and controllers.

If you have been involved in a less-than-safe situation or feel you have accidentally been in violation of an FAR, immediately complete and mail a NASA ARC Form 277B or fill out the electronic version for submission (Figure 90). Always have one or two of these forms in your flight bag or glove box.

The NASA form should be thoroughly completed, using additional paper as necessary. Typed is great, handwritten is okay. They'll accept cranberry juice on birchbark, but attempt legibility. Before the strip at the top of the report is removed to de-identify you from the report, one of their experts may call for further clarification.

These folks have been doing this since the 70s without a breach of confidentiality, so rest easy. They even black out all names, places and times from the report body, like a war-time letter. When NASA has a full understanding of the incident, they separate the time-stamped top portion, returning it to you. It is important to keep this portion! Read on.

FAA Advisory Circular 00-46D affirms and clarifies the principles underlying the establishment of ASRS and the responsibilities of NASA in its administration.

The filing of a report with NASA concerning an incident or occurrence involving a violation of the FARs is considered by the FAA to be indicative of a constructive attitude. Such an attitude will tend to prevent future violations. Accordingly, although a finding of a violation may be still be made, neither a civil penalty nor certificate suspension will be imposed if: (1) The violation was inadvertent and not deliberate; (2) The violation did not involve a criminal offense or accident nor action which discloses a lack of qualification or competency; (3) The person has not been found in any prior FAA enforcement action to have committed a violation since initiation of the ASRS of the Federal Aviation Act or any regulation promulgated under that act; and (4) The person proves that, within 10 days after the violation, he or she completed and delivered or mailed a written report of the incident or occurrence to NASA under ASRS.

This information (without your identity) will be used to correct problems within our aviation system. Portions of reports are used in the newsletter, CALLBACK. Reading ASRS reports can be a positive learning experience. Learning from others' mistakes is less painful and less expensive.

NASA ARC Form 277 may be obtained from a FSS, tower, FAA office or your flight school. If you need a supply for your club or flight office write to: FAA, Aeronautical Center, Distribution Section, AAC-45C, P.O. Box 25082, Oklahoma City, OK 73125.

You can also submit your NASA ARC form via the internet. Visit the ASRS web site at the address shown below and follow the links for electronic submission.

For a free monthly copy of CALLBACK write to: CALLBACK, NASA Aviation Safety Reporting System, P. O. Box 189, Moffett Field, CA 94035. Visit NASA's home page at: http://asrs.arc.nasa.gov/.

THE ASRS FORM

Fig. 97

NASA's aviation safety reporting form can be downloaded directly from their web site and physically mailed. Or it can be downloaded, filled out then submitted electronically via the internet.

Chapter Seven

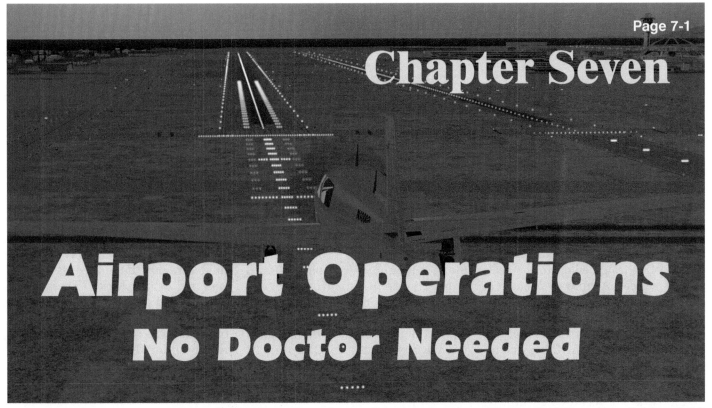

Airport Operations
No Doctor Needed

Have you ever wondered what all those small trucks at airports—the ones with the flashing yellow lights—do? I thought I knew. For a long time I was convinced they brought sandwiches to the student pilots who became lost on the airfield. After all, even students need sustenance while attempting to navigate from taxiway to runway to parking spot.

An airport's signage and markings are one situation where consistency makes for confidence, and the FAA lends a helping airfoil by specifying in great detail how airport runways, taxiways, and other aircraft movement areas are to be laid out, marked, and lit. While it's not quite true that if you've seen one airport you've seen 'em all, there *is* a method to the apparent madness. As with a Buck Rogers secret decoder ring, you just have to decipher what's in front of you.

Let's take a look at the airport in Figure 1. The airport is graced with two runways capable of handling takeoffs and landings in four different directions (two directions on each of two runways, for the geographically and mathematically challenged).

If we assume that the airport in Figure 1 is an airport with an air traffic control tower, and since controllers get so upset when you land on a different runway from the one *they* had in mind, it's helpful to know that runways come with numbers, which are always large and painted in white. Runway numbers and their markings help distinguish them from the airport's nonlanding surfaces. The runways in Figure 1 are numbered 8, 26, 21 and 3.

You think they just make those numbers up, don't you? I had a student who thought runway numbers were based on some sort of speed limit or seismograph record. Uh huh. There's a method to the madness. The numbers represent the first two digits of the runway's actual three digit magnetic direction.

THE AIRPORT LAYOUT

Fig. 1

Can someone get me a sandwich?

True north pole

Magnetic north pole

Runways numbers are angles with respect to the magnetic north pole (where the compass points) and not the true north pole (the earth's axis).

Speaking of Runways

There are three ways to say anything. The right way, the wrong way, and the runway. So

Let's learn the runway. In order to sound like a pilot, you need to know that real pilots like runways so much they always say each digit in a runway's name separately. Thus *Runway 26* become *Runway Two Six* when spoken. *Runway 3* is *Runway Three*.

There's actually a reason the numbers are spoken in this manner. English is the international language of aviation. Every tower handling international traffic must, by treaty, have at least one English-speaking controller on duty at all times. In order to avert international chaos, as well as crashes, it has been agreed that a certain controlled English vocabulary will be what everyone speaking Aviation English uses. Part of the deal is that instead of having to learn all the numbers from 0 to 360 in English, only the numbers 0-9 will be used in referencing runways and headings. That's how Runway 21 comes to be *Runway Two One,* and why headings are given as three single digits, rather than *one hundred seventy five*.

Essentially, a runway's numbers are its direction, rounded off to the nearest 10 degrees. A runway oriented at 211 degrees becomes Runway 21 (pronounced *runway two one* when speaking to controllers and other aviation-savvy people). A runway pointed 076 degrees becomes *Runway eight* (rounding up).

There are two sides to almost every issue, and two ends to every runway. With rare exceptions (usually having to do with terrain), you can theoretically land or take off from either end. This means each piece of runway pavement has numbers on each end. Those who are way ahead of me will realize these numbers, when expressed as three digit figures, differ by a value of 180. Makes sense, since the two directions are 180 degrees apart.

All runway angles are oriented to the magnetic north pole, where the magnetic compass points, and not the true north pole, where Santa Claus (a pilot) lives. When your airplane is

pointed down any runway, the airplane's magnetic compass should approximately indicate that runway's direction. Figure 2 shows what the compass and the directional gyro might look like when aligned with Runway 26. In Chapter 13 you'll learn more about magnetic and true direction. For now, just remember this when operating at an airport: wind direction, landing direction and any headings ATC asks you to fly are all based on magnetic direction.

Runway Lighting

Painted white runway markings are easy to identify during the day, but what about at night? Don't look for Day-Glo orange any time soon. The airport has an image to maintain. Besides, the airport would become a magnet for rock stars and flower-painted VW buses.

The answer at night is light. As the sun sinks slowly into the west, the airport often lights up like one of those Disneyland Main Street parades. All kinds and colors of lights, some flashing and some steady, are there to amuse and confuse you. Think of it as color-coded hints and you'll be on the right track.

White lights, shown in Figure 3, border both sides of the runway. Called runway edge lighting, these lights are spaced 200 feet apart. Controllers turn these lights on between sunset and sunrise or when the visibility is poor.

The beginning of the runway is announced with green threshold lights, while the far end of the runway is lit in red. It's an appropriate color to indicate you are running out of

usable landing surface (only tractors, bulldozers, and dune buggies beyond those red lights, please!). These lights actually lead a dual life. On one side they're green; on the other, red. Think about it for a second. The beginning (or threshold) of one runway is the end of another. The lights on the threshold of Runway 21 are also at the terminus of Runway 3.

What I've described so far is the basics of runway lighting, which you will encounter at almost any airport that supports night operations. It can and does get a lot fancier. Keep in mind that, while sport pilots are not allowed to fly at night, it's still possible for you to fly past sunset up to evening civil twilight (i.e., sunset may be 8:07 and evening civil twilight may be 8:36). This means that airport lighting is still an issue to you and you need to know something about it.

THE RUNWAY'S MAGNETIC DIRECTION

Go Ahead, make my day!

Both the heading indicator and the magnetic compass show the magnetic direction when pointed down the center of Runway 26.

Fig. 2

BASIC RUNWAY LIGHTING

Runway Edge Lighting
White lights

Fig. 3

Runway End Lighting

Red on this side indicates the end of the runway.

Green on this side indicates the runway threshold.

While gathering aviation experience, you're sure to come across airports with sophisticated lighting. In fact, airports with precision instrument runways can have such detailed lighting that it's possible to mistake it for a prairie fire. Some runways have centerline lighting, with embedded lights running the entire length of the runway centerline. Some have brilliant sequenced flashing strobe lights leading to the runway threshold. Others have touchdown zone lighting that looks like a gigantic Christmas tree was squished into the first 3,000 feet of the runway.

Taxiway Markings

There are few things as pitiful as a pilot on the ground, even in the daytime. The King or Queen of the Airways can easily become the Lost Platoon when the gear hits the ground. It is a common misconception that pilots are endowed with some superior ability to find their way around airports. This is demonstrably untrue. Most pilots can find a vending machine blindfolded, but many of us have trouble getting from the runway to the tiedown spot at an unfamiliar airport. Pilots and their airplanes have been extracted from some very unusual places (like the time a fellow pilot accidentally taxied into a secret military hangar at a combo civil/military airport. It obviously wasn't much of a secret, since they were in the habit of leaving their doors open.)

Figure 4 shows a drawing of taxiway markings from an airport chart. Taxiway D (Delta) parallels the north side of Runway 8L-26R and Taxiway C (Charlie) parallels the northwest side of Runway 3-21. There are several intersecting taxiways with individual phonetic names.

Bravo, Charlie

Remember our international English lesson a bit ago? Here's Part 2.

Pilotspeak includes a phonetic alphabet. Some letters and numbers can sound a lot like others, especially when spoken over an aviation radio by a non-native speaker of English. The phonetic alphabet is there to save the day. It permits unambiguous communication. It's also what verbally distinguishes pilots from those controlling other types of moving vehicles.

Every letter in the alphabet has a phonetic pronunciation. By speaking the word, instead of the letter, pilots make themselves heard and understood under some pretty non-optimal conditions. It's easy to mistake *B* for *C*, or *E*, but there's little chance of mixing up *Bravo, Charlie,* and *Echo.*

After a surprisingly short time, you will speak phonetic like a native.

A	Alpha
B	Bravo
C	Charlie
D	Delta
E	Echo
F	Foxtrot
G	Golf
H	Hotel
I	India
J	Juliet
K	Kilo
L	Lima
M	Mike
N	November
O	Oscar
P	Papa
Q	Quebec
R	Romeo
S	Sierra
T	Tango
U	Uniform
V	Victor
W	Whiskey
X	Xray
Y	Yankee
Z	Zulu
1	WUN
2	TOO
3	TREE
4	FOW-er
5	FIFE
6	SIX
7	SEV-en
8	AIT
9	NIN-er
0	ZEE-RO

At larger airports, and even at smaller ones when ground traffic or construction exists, it's not unusual for a tower controller to offer a complex taxi clearance. Here's such a clearance: "November 2132 Bravo, taxi to Runway 21 via Charlie, southwest to Delta, turn left; cross Runway 21, left on Golf, hold short of Runway 21 at Golf." Students normally respond to this clearance with a, "Huh?" If you had an airport chart out you could easily navigate from position A1 to position A2 in Figure 4 without getting lost. Figure 5 is an airborne view of the airport in Figure 4. Many varieties of airport charts (similar to the one in Figure 4) are available to make airport ground navigation easier.

TAXIWAYS AT A TYPICAL AIRPORT

Fig. 4

Control tower 709'

Elev 600'

Elev 652'
Elev 636'

Elev 637'

I'm not leaving till someone brings me a sandwich!

Taxiways, each having their own name, allow variable access to the different runways.

Chino airport in Figure 4 as seen from the air.

Runway 8R and 8L

Runway 21

Runway 3

Runway 26R

Runway 26L

Fig. 5

TAXIWAY MARKINGS
All taxiway markings are in yellow.

Black letters on yellow show intersecting taxiways.

Double yellow taxiway edge line

Fig. 6

Yellow letters on black identifies the taxiway you're on.

Yellow taxiway center line

A Tern for the Worst!

The copilot was flying and I was working the radios. Approach Control cleared us for the approach. At 1,500' we had a bird strike. Evidently I did not change over to tower frequency, since the bird distracted me. The first time we recognized that we had landed without a clearance was when Ground Control said, "The tower says you're cleared to land." As captain, I should have made sure we were cleared to land.

ASRS Report

TAXIWAY LIGHTING

Taxiways may have blue edge lighting.

Fig. 7

Green centerline lighting identifies the center of the taxiway at some airports.

Taxiways are identified by a continuous yellow line with parallel double yellow lines on the outer edges of the taxi surface (Figure 6). Taxiway names are shown by small signs (Figure 6). Placed along the side of the taxiway, these signs consist of yellow lettering on a black background. Signs containing black lettering on a yellow background indicate the position of intersecting taxiways. Arrows indicate the relative direction of these intersecting taxiways. At night, many (not necessarily all) taxiways have blue omnidirectional sideline lighting (Figure 7). At some airports, taxiways may have embedded green centerline lighting.

One time I caught an empathetic and sensitive student of mine weaving between the embedded green taxiway lights. I thought she was having a Nyquil flashback until I found out that she was afraid of damaging either the lights or the tires. You won't hurt the lights or the tires, but feel free (if you wish) to keep the nose wheel a few inches to the side of the embedded lighting.

As a pilot you must be able to identify the point where the taxiway ends and the runway begins. This transition is identified by four yellow lines—two solid and two dashed—crossing perpendicular to the taxiway and running parallel to the runway (Figure 8). These markings are known as *runway hold markings*.

If the two solid lines are on your side, then, at a tower-controlled airport, a clearance is required to enter the runway. If the double broken dashed lines are on your side, then you should cross those lines to clear the runway and enter the taxiway. (From now on we'll assume that a *controlled airport* is one having an operating control tower.)

Assuming you have just landed and are taxiing off the runway, you should taxi across the double broken dashed lines and clear the runway. The FAA assumes that your airplane hasn't cleared the runway until the entire airplane (down to the last rivet) is on the other side of those broken double yellow lines. The rea-

son for this is to prevent the tails of long airplanes (like a stretched DC-8) from poking out onto the runway. This could make landing quite challenging for another pilot and possibly give him or her an extra EKG blip.

At airports without an operating control tower (meaning the airport has no control tower or the tower has shut down for the night), entering an active runway is done at the discretion of the pilot. (From now on, an airport having no control tower or one at which the tower is not in operation will be referred to as an *uncontrolled airport*.) In this instance, you should hold short of the runway, behind the solid taxiway-hold lines. Taxi onto the runway only when it's

RUNWAY MARKINGS

White numbers on red indicate mandatory hold points for all tower controlled airports. They indicate that you're about to taxi onto a runway (possibly an active one!).

Fig. 8

I know I can cross those lines. I'm just not into it right now!

Runway-hold markings consisting of four yellow lines: two are solid & two are dashed. At a controlled airport, a clearance is required to cross these lines when the double-solid yellow lines are on your side.

An *enhanced taxiway centerline* consists of broken yellow lines bordering a taxiway line. They indicate that you are approaching a runway hold line.

If the broken double-yellow lines are on your side, you may cross them and enter the taxiway thus moving clear of the runway area.

ADDITIONAL RUNWAY MARKINGS

Some airports have holding position markings for taxiways and taxiway intersections consisting of a single yellow dashed line ex-

Protection of the runway safety area prevents collisions between taxiing and landing airplanes.

RUNWAY SAFETY AREA

On reverse side of this sign

Fig. 9

You should cross the broken double-yellow lines when they're on your side so as to clear the runway safety area.

This is a holding position sign for the runway safety area. An ATC clearance is required to cross the solid yellow hold lines when you're at an airport with an operating control tower.

This is a holding position sign for Runway 15.

clear of traffic and no airplanes are on a short final (getting ready to land). In other words "look carefully before taxiing onto the runway." The last thing you want is for someone to do a touch and go on you. And making another pilot go around won't win you too many friends at the airport. It's also a good idea to broadcast your intentions on something known as the Common Traffic Advisory Frequency (CTAF) when no tower is in operation. This lets other pilots in the traffic pattern know what you're doing. More on this later.

Another way to identify where the runway begins is the presence of a white-on-red sign next to the dashed and solid double yellow lines (Figure 8). These information billboards are called *runway holding signs,* though they don't actually hold anything. They exist to inform you when you're about to enter an active runway. They also indicate the runway direction. In Figure 8, *30-12* indicates Runway 30 is to the left and Runway 12 is to the right (in other words, go to the left to find the beginning of Runway 30, etc.). At controlled airports, these signs are your cue to hold your position unless a clearance has been given to enter or cross the runway. Figure 9 shows a single runway holding sign indicating that the taxiway intersects the beginning of the takeoff runway.

At uncontrolled airports, the runway hold signs indicate that you can proceed across or onto the runway when you've assured yourself no traffic conflict exists (an airplane preparing to take off or land is most definitely a conflict). At a tower-controlled airport, these signs are coupled with the double solid and dashed taxiway-hold lines, providing ample warning that you're crossing into the action area.

Holding position markings for a taxiway, consisting of a single dashed yellow line as shown in Figure 9, are installed at some airport. When a tower controller instructs you to hold short of a taxiway intersection, you should stop so that no part of the airplane crosses the dashed yellow line.

Some airports may have taxiways that interfere with the runway safety area, as shown in Figure 9. Taxiway Delta is located directly behind the beginning of Runway 15. Airplanes landing on Runway 15 could approach low enough to present a problem to both the approaching and taxiing airplane. This is more likely to be a problem for big airplanes, but the rules take into account the worst-case scenario. Holding position signs for this peripheral runway are shown by white on red lettering. The term *15APCH* next to the solid double yellow lines indicates a mandatory hold point at tower controlled airports (this means any aircraft on the following taxiway might affect aircraft on approach to Runway 15). On the opposite side of the runway, on taxi-

way Delta, on the back side of the runway hold sign, is a runway safety area sign (normally only found at only tower controlled airports). This consists of the same marking shown on the taxiway (double solid and dashed lines). These signs can be used as a guide in deciding when to report back to a controller that you are clear of the runway. Remember, at uncontrolled airports pilots must decide for themselves whether to enter or cross a runway.

It's difficult, but not impossible, for pilots to accidentally taxi onto an active runway at a tower controlled airport. One pilot at a very busy airport taxied right into the middle of an active runway and just sat there (probably waiting for one of those yellow trucks to bring him a sandwich). Completely confused about the tower's directions and unwilling to ask for clarification, he stopped his airplane while a jet was on final approach. The tower controller said, "32 Bravo, do you know where you are?" The pilot replied, "Burbank Airport?" The controller said, "Yes, that's good, but do you see that big Boeing 707 out there on final approach headed directly for you?" The pilot replied, "Yes." "Do you want him to do a touch and go on you?" The pilot replied, "No." The controller said, "Then you'd better get off his runway." The pilot, not wanting to get bounced on by a Boeing 707, immediately exited the runway.

RUNWAY SURFACE MARKINGS

A relocated threshold is identified by taxiway markings. You must land beyond the white threshold bar.

Bob?

Large yellow crosses indicate that this runway is closed.

A displaced threshold is indicated by white arrows. You can use this area for taxiing and taking off but not for landing.

Yellow chevrons indicate that this portion of the runway is unusable.

A

B

Fig. 10

and said, "Hey! Look what you did to our runway! You put divots in it. Geesh!" The only way they could get the airplane out was to completely strip it down to barebones metal, making it light enough to take off without further runway damage. The same could not be said for the pilot's career. (See Postflight Briefing #7-2 for more information on airport lighting.)

Airport Beacons

Airports have rotating beacons to make them easier to find at night. Civilian airports with runway lights have a two-color rotating beacon that alternately flashes green-white, green-white... Military airports, on the other hand, have rotating beacons that alternately flash green-white-white, green-white-white (the two white lights flash very quickly). A lighted heliport has a rotating beacon that flashes green-yellow-white. I mention the heliport lighting because if you try to land at a heliport I can guarantee the runway will be extremely short.

Figure 11 shows Taft Kern County airport with a small star (point A) near the airport symbol. This star indicates the presence of a rotating beacon at the airport. Elk Hills airport (point B) doesn't have a star; therefore, no rotating beacon is present (and the airport doesn't have runway lights either). Figure 12 shows the actual rotating beacon found at many airports.

Additional Runway Markings

Just because there is concrete in the shape of a runway doesn't mean that it can be used for landing. Some runways have yellow chevrons painted on them (Figure 10, position A). This signals that the surface is unsuitable for either taxiing, taking off, or landing. It's basically an airplane no man's land. Don't use any portion of this area. It might be off limits because the surface won't support the weight of an airplane even for taxiing, let alone landing, or because the surface is otherwise unsuitable. Planes that venture onto chevrons can find themselves up to their axles in asphalt, trapped like a gigantic fly on a No-Pest strip.

White arrows pointing in one direction form what is called a *displaced threshold* (Figure 10, position B). This is a runway area that is not to be used for landing, but on which you can taxi, take off, or roll out after landing. Displaced thresholds often exist as part of a noise abatement effort. By forcing you to land farther

down the runway this causes you to maintain a higher altitude on the approach than you would if landing at the very beginning of the runway. A displaced threshold can exist for other reasons, such as the presence of a surface that will support the weight of an airplane, but not the impact of an airplane landing. (There's a big difference. I know this since one of my instructors used to call out Richter scale values following my touchdowns.)

I won't mention any names, but on occasion professional airline pilots have been known to land at the wrong airport, with a full load of passengers. Nothing like bringing your own audience to a *faux pas*. Several years ago, a pilot did this at an east coast airport. He accidentally landed at a small training field with nothing but itty-bitty Cessnas and Pipers fluttering around the pattern. As he touched down and came to a stop, his wheels punched holes in the thin runway surface. He knew he was in trouble when it took full power just to taxi. A few of the locals came out

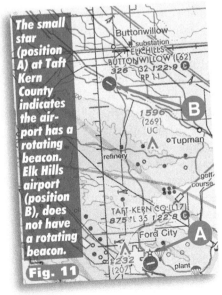

The small star (position A) at Taft Kern County indicates the airport has a rotating beacon. Elk Hills airport (position B), does not have a rotating beacon.

Fig. 11

An Airport's Rotating Beacon
(some beacons are omnidirectional capacitor-discharge devices that flash instead of rotate)

Fig. 12

Rotating beacons (some flash instead of rotate) are normally on between sunset and sunrise. If an airport's beacon is up and running during daylight hours, it means that the airport is below basic VFR conditions (ceiling less than 1000 feet AGL and/or visibility less than 3 miles). Of course, if the visibility is that bad you probably can't *see* the beacon until you've violated all kinds of airspace, but they turn it on anyway. In such conditions, a special VFR clearance is required if Class B, C, D, or E airspace exists at the airport (see Chapter 9 for more info on special VFR operations).

The Traffic Pattern

If you've ever seen moths dancing around a light bulb, you'll understand why airports have traffic patterns. If it weren't for some organization, airplanes might fly frenetically over, above and to the side of runways, vying for a position to land. Fortunately, it's not like that. We have traffic patterns that impose a respectable and safe order on the flow of traffic at airports. These pat-

terns are usually rectangular in shape with each portion having a specific name, for easy identification (Figure 13).

All airports—controlled and uncontrolled—have traffic patterns. At controlled airports, air traffic controllers manage the flow of aircraft. This becomes especially important when the airports are extremely busy. While it's obvious that airports such as Los Angeles, Chicago, and New York need towers, there are many general aviation airports that also have a very heavy volume of traffic. At such airports, pilots simply fly the established traffic pattern while controllers verbally coax them into an orderly sequence.

At airports with less activity, it's difficult to justify establishing an air traffic control tower. At these non-tower airports, pilots typically fly the airport's traffic pattern on their own. They are left to their own devices in deciding their landing direction and sequence among other aircraft in the pattern.

If the idea of a lot of pilots flying around near an airport without someone telling them what to do raises a few questions, then you have at least a modicum of common sense. Believe it or not, things work out remarkably well because pilots are reasonably adept at following rules. Much of aviation depends on there being a high degree of predictability. Knowing what pattern another pilot is flying or is likely to fly is the key to making the system work for everyone.

That's why the concept of the *traffic pattern* is so important. The traffic pattern represents a very standardized way for pilots to depart from or land at an airport. If everyone does what they're supposed to do in the traffic pattern, then everybody's actions become quite predictable. Once you know where you fit in the sequence of traffic, you will know what is going on and when it is your turn to take a particular action.

THE TRAFFIC PATTERN
Fig. 13

Decision Point (for turn to base leg) **D**

Downwind leg **C**

Crosswind leg **B**

E

Wind direction

A

F

Base leg

Final approach

Upwind leg (parallel & offset) **G**

Departure leg

THE TRAFFIC PATTERN Fig. 13 Repeat

Decision Point (for turn to base leg) — D
Downwind leg — C
Crosswind leg — B
Wind direction
E
Base leg — F
Final approach
Upwind leg (parallel & offset) — G
Departure leg
A

Left Wing Pilots

Traffic patterns are, unless posted otherwise, made with a series of left turns. This is referred to as flying *left traffic*.

Given a choice, pilots generally favor left turns because their visibility is better when the airplane is tilted toward the side they're sitting on. This is another example of a way in which flying is completely unlike driving. In a car, no matter which way you turn, your visibility from the driver's seat is pretty much the same. An airplane, however, operates in three dimensions. All things being equal, a pilot would rather have things rolling his or her way when it comes to turns.

Let's take a closer look at the airport traffic pattern, and what you will do once you're in one.

Traffic Pattern Components

Traffic patterns are rectangular in shape and consist of six segments: *departure leg, crosswind leg, downwind leg, base leg, final approach* and *upwind leg* (Figure 13).

Airplane takeoffs are made into the wind, and the takeoff flight path is thus called the *departure leg* (point A). After takeoff, you have two major choices—you can either depart the airport traffic area, or you can *remain in the pattern,* which means you will fly a prescribed path, come around, and land on the runway you just departed from. This is done by pilots who enjoy very short flights, as well as by pilots who are practicing landings. From time to time, we pilots remain in the traffic pattern in order to polish our skills and minimize the explanations to passengers for our occasional bad landings.

If you're remaining in the pattern, a turn (generally a left turn) to the *crosswind leg* (point B) will be made when the airplane is beyond the departure end of the runway and within 300 feet of the traffic pattern altitude. This portion of the pattern is called the crosswind leg because the flight path is perpendicular to the runway and generally crosswise to the wind direction (one time I asked a student what leg he was on in the traffic pattern. He replied, "I'm on my right leg, but plan on using my left leg once the right one gets tired" (I, of course, immediately asked if anyone had delivered him a sandwich lately).

As the airplane continues its climb, another 90 degree turn is made. This places the airplane parallel to the runway and traveling opposite to the direction of landing. This is called the *downwind leg* (point C) because your direction is with the wind. Throughout the upwind, crosswind and even a part of the downwind leg, the airplane continues to climb until reaching traffic pattern

altitude. This altitude varies from one airport to the next because of terrain, obstruction and noise concerns. Expect traffic pattern altitudes to range from 600 to 1,500 feet above the airport elevation, typically averaging about 1,000 feet AGL. The downwind leg is flown approximately 1/2 to one mile out from the landing runway. This keeps you comfortably close to the runway. In the event of an engine problem, you can glide to a safe landing.

You continue downwind until passing a point abeam the beginning of the landing threshold of the runway. Then it's another 90 degree turn and you're on *base leg* (point E). From here you make one more 90 degree turn, onto *final approach* (point F). The *upwind leg* (point G) is flown parallel to the runway in the direction of landing. It's often used during go-arounds or overflights to avoid departing traffic.

Assuming traffic isn't a factor, it's convenient and practical to start your turn onto base leg when the landing threshold appears 45° between the wing and the tail of your airplane. In other words, as you look out the left window (Figure 14, point D), the threshold appears to be at a 45° angle to the left of the wing (or midway between the wing and the tail). This provides you with a symmetrical, rectangular-type pattern and gives you enough distance from the runway to make a comfortable approach.

Aviation is one place where it is not good to become a homeboy or homegirl. Some student pilots fudge by using familiar landmarks on the ground to tell them when to make

THE TRAFFIC PATTERN Fig. 14

Decision point (for turning) — D

When the runway appears midway between the wing and your tail, this is a good time to think about turning onto your base leg.

TURNING ONTO BASE LEG

Normal turn point for base leg

Base leg turned early

Fig. 15

Normal final approach path

Final approach path that's high because base leg turned early

their turns. This is bad because it leads to a lack of flexibility. If you need the local Burger Boy restaurant to land, what will you do when you go to a new airport? There's nothing more pitiful than a pilot who can only fly to and from his or her home airport comfortably!

I've seen student pilots come absolutely unglued when they weren't allowed to turn base at "their" landmark. You will *not* always be able to turn base or final at an ideal time, and the ability to make adjustments is crucial. When traffic is heavy, you may have to fly the downwind leg for some distance past the airport before turning base leg. In fact, I was once in a traffic pattern with 19 other airplanes. One pilot was so far downwind that the controller called and asked, "45 Charlie, what time zone are you in now?"

Base leg is a point of transition for landing. It's the place where important adjustments are made in the airplane's speed and landing configura-

TURNING BASE TO FINAL

A modified turn from base to final

A square turn (90°) from base to final gives you time to assess your glide path and the effects of any crosswind.

Fig. 16

tion. This is why, even when there is little or no traffic, you should avoid turning base too early, as shown in Figure 15. Things happen mighty fast as you approach the runway. You want to give yourself enough time to adjust your airspeed, flaps, and glide-path. The descent for landing is normally started on base leg and continues throughout the final approach.

The *final approach* (sometimes just called *final*) is a critical part of the landing sequence. Generally, a square turn from base onto final approach is best (Figure 16). This provides you with enough time to observe your airplane's descent path and alignment with the runway. You can observe and correct for the effect of crosswinds on the airplane if you give yourself a reasonably long final approach. During the final approach, the airplane's glide path can be adjusted (using flaps, slips, or S-turns), making it easier for you to land on any selected runway spot.

When turning from base leg onto final approach, you have an additional opportunity to correct your glide-path (Figure 17). Let's assume that you are making a power-off approach from the base leg. After turning base, you retard the power and commence a descent. Your objective is to land on the runway numbers (the ones at the beginning, not the end of the runway—unless you want a sandwich!). If you're too low, you can cut short the turn from the base leg to final approach as shown in Figure 17A. Flying path 1 allows you to fly less distance during the descent, thus increasing your chances of making the runway numbers. Path 2 is longer, and path 3 is a nice square turn onto final.

If you're too high, you can deliberately overshoot the turn onto final approach giving you more distance to cover during your descent as shown in Figure 17B. Another option is to S-turn on final as shown in Figure 17C. S-turns are simply a series of alternating turns left and right of the direct glide path. Since the shortest distance between any two points is a straight

line, anything you do to fly *other* than a straight line lengthens the trip. Assuming a constant rate of descent, taking the long way home will allow you to lose more altitude.

S-turns, coupled with forward slips and use of flaps, provide you with several ways of adjusting your glide-path. This knowledge becomes especially important when a precision landing is necessary, such as on a short field or in the event of an engine failure when you generally get only one opportunity to hit the safe landing spot you've chosen. With a little practice you will be able to put the airplane down in the precise place you want. (We won't discuss forward or side slips in this book. Any good aviation procedures book should have information on this.)

PATTERN ADJUSTMENTS

A

Path 1
Path 2
Path 3

If you're attempting a power-off glide, you can purposely modify your pattern (the distance you travel) to allow you to make the runway.

B

Another way of modifying the distance you travel is to purposely overshoot your turn to final.

C

Another very effective way to modify your pattern is to make S-turns while on final approach. This is also very effective if you're following slower traffic ahead.

Fig. 17

Crabbing in the Pattern

No, this isn't what happens when your instructor doesn't get enough sleep, though it definitely describes how the instructor, the tower, and other pilots will act if you don't learn how to take account of the wind and adjust for its effects on your airplane.

The path your airplane traces over the ground is called its *ground track.* If you sit there fat, dumb, and happy with your compass showing a 165° heading, you will track a 165° heading over the ground from any given point only when there is no wind (or the wind blows directly on your nose or tail).

Think of the wind as being a giant hand. Because the airplane doesn't have its feet on the ground, it gets pushed around by the wind. Depending on how much wind there is and what angle the hand is pushing from, the effect can be anywhere from slight to considerable.

The only way to create a straight ground track is to compensate for whatever wind there is by pointing the airplane's nose (slightly or more so, depending on conditions) into the wind (Figure 18). If you head the plane to the right a bit, and the wind pushes to the left a bit, everything balances and you make your intended straight line over the ground. The term "crabbing" comes from the fact that crabs walk in a direction other than the one where they're facing.

CORRECTING FOR WIND DRIFT WITHIN THE TRAFFIC PATTERN

Fig. 18

In positions A & C the airplane crabs (points) into the wind to maintain a rectangular ground track in the traffic pattern. The stronger the wind, the greater the crab angle needed to fly a rectangular ground track.

It's called crabbing because the crab points one way and moves another, just like airplanes A and C.

Who are you looking at?

Crab moves this way

Crab points this way

How do you know the precise amount to crab? You simply make a slight turn (say 5° or 10° at first) into the wind, level the wings and watch the results. If the airplane is crabbed properly, it will make a rectangular ground track about the runway as shown by the dashed line in Figure 18. The airplane's ground track is now perpendicular to the runway, as flown by Airplane A. Airplane C is crabbed to the left, into the wind, to maintain the desired ground track while on base leg. Of course, if the wind is not directly aligned with the runway you'll have to crab on all five

segments of the traffic pattern to maintain a rectangular ground track (Figure 19).

If you let yourself get pushed around by the wind, you won't be where you're supposed to be. This is a particular problem in the traffic pattern. Remember a while ago I said predictability was important? Other pilots and the tower expect you to fly a traffic pattern that tracks straight on each leg, and crabbing to take account of the wind is the only way to do it.

Entering the Traffic Pattern

So far we've been talking about taking off and staying in the pattern, and we've been talking about flying at a tower-controlled airport. What happens when you are arriving at an airport to land, and there's no tower to issue instructions?

Before entering the traffic pattern at uncontrolled airports, you are expected to observe the flow of traffic and conform to the traffic pattern in use. In other words, you shouldn't be going in a direction different from everyone else. Doing so is not polite, smart, safe, or sanctioned. So, avoid doing this unless you want to end up on one of those TV shows like *Cops, 48 Hours Mystery* or *America's Most Wanted.*

CROSSWIND CORRECTION WITHIN THE TRAFFIC PATTERN

Fig. 19

Because of the wind direction, the airplane must be crabbed in all positions, (A, B, C, and D), to maintain a rectangular traffic pattern.

TWO MISSES...

Having my own small airplane at a private strip gives me a privilege few people get to enjoy, of being able to fly when I please. I always do a complete preflight before moving the airplane; however, this time I was preoccupied with worldly matters during my check. I taxied out, did a quick runup, and headed for the blue. After climbout, I wanted to turn left but was unable. Then it struck me. How stupid. I had forgotten to remove the wooden wedges used as rudder gust locks. Fortunately, a large open field near my runway provided ample room to land in any direction I desired by using ailerons only. It was an uneventful landing. A rather embarrassed but wiser pilot removed the gust locks.   **ASRS Report**

Forget the elevator lock, rather than rudder locks, and you will find yourself with even less control. A proper pre-takeoff check for freedom and direction of movement is imperative. Not doing so, this pilot missed his second chance to catch his walk-around foul.

...AND A HIT

"If I have been interrupted for any reason, or feel that my full attention has not been given to the task of an aircraft preflight walkaround, I will start again from the beginning." (Ahh, Grasshopper can learn much from this wise man.)

Dave Gwinn
Airline pilot, CFII, aviation educator and author

OK, you want to do what's right. How do you find out what that is? You need two pieces of information in order to figure out a traffic pattern—the runway in use, and the direction of turns in the pattern (left or right traffic).

The runway in use is normally determined by the wind direction. With rare exceptions, you take off and land *into* the wind. The exceptions (very rare) would be situations where the airport is situated in such a way that you can only land in one direction no matter what the wind (this generally has to do with terrain obstruction or other geographical oddities).

You don't need a weatherman to know which way the wind blows. You do, however, need either a wind sock or a report from the ground.

Wind socks look like brightly colored nets for capturing butterflies on steroids (See Figure 24, position A). They are supposed to be easily visible from the air. This is one of those aviation secrets, but I'm going to tell because you've been nice enough to read this far. Wind socks are *not* usually easy to spot, and when they are, it isn't always easy to figure out what they're telling you. In theory, the fat end is facing into the wind and the

narrow end is pointed toward the end of the runway where you'll land. This is most easily seen while standing on the ground next to the wind sock. Trying to discern it while 1,000 or more feet in the air, traveling 120 miles an hour and keeping the airplane upright, is a bit more of a challenge.

There is often an easier way to get the info. Many uncontrolled airports have what is called a *unicom* (short for *universal communications*). This is an authorized frequency on which someone—usually the operator of one of the refueling and repair operations (fixed base operators, or *FBO's* in pilotspeak)—provides information on the wind and traffic pattern directions. The unicom information is advisory in nature only. Unicom operators are *not* air traffic controllers. They cannot issue commands, sequence traffic, etc. though they will usually advise you if there are other aircraft in the pattern or inbound.

Another option is a *multicom* frequency. This is a frequency approved for air-to-air use. Other pilots in or around your destination airport will generally help out with information on request.

If information is not available from either unicom or multicom, then you have to take clues from wherever you can on wind direction (smoke, waves on a lake or ocean), and should refer to the *segmented circle* located at the airport for directions on the type of traffic pattern to fly.

Segmented circles are often constructed of large white blocks, bricks or ground paintings. Figure 20 shows how a segmented circle looks from the air. These circles contain several additional items to help you decide upon the proper runway for landing as well as the appropriate traffic pattern to fly (I'll show you how to interpret the segmented circle shortly).

THE SEGMENTED CIRCLE

The segmented circle as seen from the air over an airport.

Fig. 20

Segmented circles are segmented so they are easier to identify at higher altitudes. If you are unaware of the proper traffic pattern, simply fly over the airport and look for the segmented circle. The proper way to do this at uncontrolled airports is to overfly the field, above traffic pattern altitude and observe the indicator. Usually 1000 feet above the established traffic pattern altitude is sufficient to avoid the flow of airport traffic. In other words, if the traffic pattern altitude is 700 feet AGL and you're an additional 1,000 feet above that, this puts you at 1,700 feet AGL. At this altitude, you can easily observe the segmented circle without unexpectedly bumping into people who are minding their own business and trying to land.

At controlled airports, air traffic controllers will inform you of the runway on which to land and the appropriate traffic pattern to be flown. Some people are just born do-it-yourselfers, and they want to determine for themselves the lay of the land. It is often very helpful to see which way the runways run before attempting a landing, especially if visibility is less than optimal. In fact, I prefer that students unfamiliar with the complex taxiway and runway layout of an airport overfly the field and observe its runway and taxiway layout before attempting to enter the pattern. Things can get

pretty confusing down close to the ground and the overflight helps orient you to a runway direction. Once you gain a little experience, you can plan on skipping this overflight and enter the downwind at a 45 degree angle. To overfly a controlled field for a preliminary "look see," just ask the controller for permission to overfly at whatever altitude you want that is safely above the traffic pattern. Such a request will almost always be approved.

If you really want to take a look first, before even engaging the controller, keep in mind that Class D airspace normally ends at 2500 feet AGL. You can overfly at any altitude above that boundary without the need to tell anyone what you're doing. Then, when you're ready to enter the traffic pattern, you simply establish and maintain communication with the tower and enter the pattern (more later on how to call the tower and what to say). Remember, we're talking about overflying an airport in Class D airspace here, not Class C or B airspace, which extends to higher altitudes.

A few years ago, a student pilot got hopelessly lost on a solo cross country. He spotted a controlled airport and commenced circling the field a few hundred feet above the tower. Fortunately, the pilot knew enough to transmit on the emergency frequency of 121.5 MHz. The tower heard a transmission that went like this, "Will the tower that has a small airplane circling above it, with me in it, please identify yourself." The tower replied, "This is Long Beach airport. What are you doing up there?" The pilot replied, "I'm lost. Well, I was lost; but thanks to you, I think I just found myself." They cleared him to land on Runway 25 Left. When the pilot said he wasn't familiar with the runways, the tower said to pick out any piece of asphalt at the airport and land on it (of course, I'm sure all the controllers were placing bets on what kind of sandwich this pilot liked).

The Segmented Circle

The segmented circle shown in Figure 21 contains several useful pieces of information, once you know how to read the hieroglyphics. Attached to the segmented circle (A) are the landing strip indicators (D) and the traffic pattern indicators (B and C). The landing strip indicators are aligned with and represent the airport's runway(s). These are shown by the two strips (D) located on either side of the segmented circle. Attached to each end of landing strips are the traffic pattern indicators (B and C). Because of this combination, the landing strip and traffic pattern indicators take on an L shape when viewed from the air.

Basically, the traffic pattern indicators (B and C) point to the side of the runway on which the traffic pattern is flown. For instance, pilots

THE SEGMENTED CIRCLE

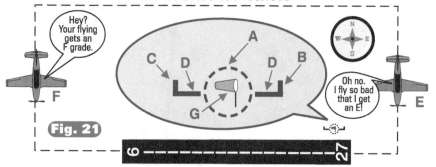

The segmented circle has several elements associated with it. These may include the landing-strip indicator (D); the traffic pattern indicator (B and C) and some form of wind or landing indicator (G) usually found inside the circle (A). According to the segmented circle's information, left traffic is made to Runway 9 with a wind from the east (Airplane F) and right traffic is made to Runway 27 with a wind from the west (Airplane E). Of course, pilots land into the wind whenever possible. The wind or landing indicator identifies the appropriate runway on which to land (G).

TRAFFIC PATTERN INDICATORS (Multiple Runways)

Fig. 22

I'll teach you to land on Bob!

A
B
C
D

The landing strip & traffic pattern indicator informs the pilot that the pattern for:
Runway 18 (A) is left traffic,
Runway 21 (B) is right traffic,
Runway 3 (C) is right traffic and
Runway 36 (D) is right traffic.

landing on Runway 27 should make their pattern to the north of the airport, since the traffic pattern indicator (B) is on the north side of landing strip (D). This results in Airplane E making right traffic for Runway 27

Actually Heard at the Airport...

Situation: A student pilot was on final approach to land with a Cessna jet (called a Citation) following close behind.

Tower: "Cherokee 43511, keep your speed up and make the first turnout, Citation to follow."

Cherokee 43511: "Hey, what did I do wrong?"

(all right turns). Pilots landing on Runway 9 should, likewise, make their pattern north of the runway as shown by traffic pattern indicator (C). Consequently, Airplane F makes left traffic (all left turns) to Runway 9.

Where two or more runways exist, multiple L shaped bars may protrude from the segmented circle as shown in Figure 22. Landing on Runway 3 requires a right hand traffic pattern; Runway 21, a right hand pattern; Runway 18, a left hand; and Runway 36, a right hand pattern.

What happens if no landing strip indicators or traffic pattern indicators protrude from the segmented circle, as shown in Figure 23? Is this a sign of airport vandalism? No. Segmented circles without these indicators imply that you should fly a standard left hand traffic pattern for the runway in use. Left hand traffic is considered standard and pilots should make all turns to the left in

the absence of other indications. Right hand traffic patterns, by default, are considered to be non-standard patterns.

Wind and Landing-Direction Indicators

Knowing whether it's a right or left hand traffic pattern is one thing, but what about deciding which way to land? Within the segmented circle you'll normally find some type of wind or landing direction indicators. Either one of these help you select a runway for landing that's most nearly aligned with the wind. We want to land into the wind whenever possible. It slows our touchdown speed and makes landings safer as well as easier.

Three types of indicators are used to identify the proper direction for landing. The first two are known as wind direction indicators and the last is called a landing direction indicator.

Go Around

You can always go around,
If it don't look right coming down.
Don't wait until you're sideways,
Maybe sliding on the ground,
You can always go around.

Ken Dravis
Singer, Songwriter, Pilot

THE SEGMENTED CIRCLE (indicating standard, left-hand traffic)

The landing strip & traffic-pattern indicators are missing from the sides of the segmented circle.

6
27

When neither landing-strip nor traffic-pattern indicators are shown along with the segmented circle, make all turns in the pattern to the left.

Fig. 23

The first type of wind direction indicator is the wind sock, which I discussed earlier. It's a big help—if you can see it. Study Figure 24A, so you'll at least know what you're looking for.

The *wind tee,* shown in Figure 24B, is another means of determining landing direction. This device looks like a little airplane. It's free to rotate around its base and is aerodynamically constructed so the small airplane points into the wind. Sometimes the device isn't free to rotate and airport personnel manually place it in the proper direction of landing. Either way, you can determine the appropriate landing direction by imagining the wind tee as a small airplane pointing in the direction (or nearly so) that you should land. Simply land on the runway most nearly aligned in the direction the wind tee points. The wind tee in Figure 24B suggests a landing on Runway 9 would head you into the wind.

A more direct means of determining landing direction is with a *tetrahedron* (this isn't a prehistoric dinosaur). Figure 24C shows what appears to be an arrow located within the segmented circle. This is a tetrahedron (a four sided object—three sides on top and one side on the bottom) and is technically called a landing-direction indicator instead of a wind indicator. It's a three dimensional structure that's usually free to rotate about its base. When it can rotate freely, it points into the wind; when it can't, it is also manually rotated by airport personnel to point in the appropriate landing direction. Determining landing direction is simply a matter of landing on the runway most nearly aligned with the direction the tetrahedron points (children seen playing on the tetrahedron should arouse suspicion as to the actual direction in which to land).

The tetrahedron should be used with caution when the winds are light or calm. These things are large hunks of wood or metal, not ballerinas. It takes at least a modest puff of wind to move one. It's a good rule in general aviation to treat all information with a high index of suspicion until you can confirm it in another way. I've had students who were crabbing 60° into the wind while insisting it had to be coming from another direction because they'd heard it on the radio or seen it on the tetrahedron. The airplane is the ulti-

LANDING & WIND DIRECTION INDICATOR — Fig. 24

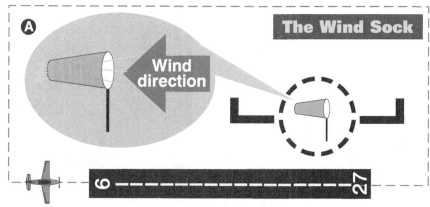

The wind cone (or wind sock) aligns itself parallel to the wind. The small end or opening points downwind and the big end (the opening) is upwind. To decide on wind direction, simply look at which way the small end points. This is the direction the wind is blowing. You'll land into the wind.

The wind tee looks like a small airplane placed on a swivel. It's free to rotate into the wind. Think of its shape as an airplane that points in the direction you should land (into the wind). The wind tee may be manually rotated by airport personnel to identify the proper landing direction. It may also be tethered, unattended and completely inaccurate! Use caution when using it to assess landing direction.

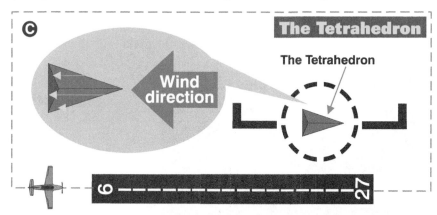

The tetrahedron points in the direction you should land (or it is manually pointed in the direction you should land). It is mounted on a swivel and can pivot, and like the wind tee, its reliability is questionable during light winds.

A wind sock and a tetrahedron side by side.

ENTERING & DEPARTING THE PATTERN

Fig. 25

Enter the traffic pattern at a 45 degree angle (A) to the downwind leg about midfield (B). When departing an airport, make either a straight out (C) or a 45 degree turn in the direction of the pattern (D) when reaching pattern altitude.

mate authority on what's really happening!

Some airports have a designated *calm wind runway* (usually the runway that's less noise sensitive). Under calm wind conditions, airport personnel may manually point the tetrahedron in the direction of the calm-wind runway. Be sure and maintain special vigilance during landings at uncontrolled airports when the winds are calm. This is necessary for two reasons. First, another pilot might have chosen another runway, since the wind didn't enforce its will. Second, keep in mind that *calm* doesn't necessarily mean *none,* so be prepared for the possibility of a breeze from any angle.

Many times the landing or wind direction indicators aren't aligned with any specific runway. This means a crosswind exists at the airport. In these conditions, pick a runway that's most nearly aligned with the wind. With a little practice you'll have no difficulty handling these crosswind landings. Honest!

The 45° Entry Point

Once you know the direction of the landing runway and the appropriate traffic pattern to use, you're ready to enter the pattern in an organized way. The best way to do this is to enter the traffic pattern in level flight at a 45° angle to the downwind leg at the approximate midpoint of the runway, as depicted in Figure 25, point A. This doesn't have to be exactly 45° but it should be close.

This angle of entry allows you to more easily see traffic on the crosswind and downwind legs of the traffic pattern. Seeing these airplanes makes it easier for you to blend into the flow of traffic. A 45° entry also makes it easier for other airplanes in the pattern to see and blend in with you. Of course, if it's a controlled airport, tower controllers will usually advise you of traffic in the pattern. Once again, keep in mind that *predictability* is important. The controllers expect you to make a standard pattern entry, at the standard pattern place. They don't like surprises very much, perhaps because they're responsible for what happens on their shift (they're concerned too!).

Aim to enter the pattern abeam the midpoint of the runway (point B). And always enter the pattern at the specified pattern altitude for that airport. This allows everyone to be at the same height, making it easier to see other airplanes. If no traffic pattern altitude is established, it's usually best to fly the pattern at 1000 feet AGL if no tower is available to advise otherwise.

I do want to make it clear that we're talking about an entry at a 45° angle and not a 45° bank to the downwind leg. I gave a phase check to a student pilot who didn't quite understand this. We were approaching the pattern when I reminded him to use a 45° entry. He immediately rolled the airplane into a 45° bank (then he asked me for a sandwich). How novel! I'm just glad the FAA doesn't recommend a 90° entry!

It should come as no surprise to you that the majority of midair collisions occur within five miles of an airport at an altitude of less than 3,000 feet AGL (79% in one study). Makes sense, since that's where the majority of the airplanes are. The same study found nearly half of all midair collisions occurred within 5 miles of an airport at an altitude of 500 feet or less AGL (49% to be specific). This is a common altitude for base leg and final approach, isn't it? A word or three to the wise should be sufficient here. *Pay close attention.* Look with your eyes and ears (i.e., listen for the call and position of other aircraft).

Departing the pattern also requires that you avoid interfering with traffic entering and remaining in the pattern. Figure 25, points C and D, depict two common methods for departing an airport. First, a departure can be made straight out as in position C. A 45° turn on the pattern side of the runway (the left side of Runway 30 in this case) is also recommended after the airplane has reached traffic pattern altitude. Of course, if there are parallel runways, noise sensitive areas, or obstructions, then you should follow the recommended procedures for departing that particular airport. These recommended procedures are sometimes found posted near the departure end of the runway (Figure 26). They may

An airport's recommended departure procedure.

PLEASE FLY QUIETLY
TURN CROSSWIND AT
HAWTHORNE MALL
FLY DOWNWIND OVER
EL SEGUNDO BLVD.

Fig. 26

The Airport/Facility Directory describes an airport's departure procedures.

SANTA MONICA MUNI(SMO)   3 E   UTC 8(7DT)   N34 °00.95   W118 °27.08   LOS ANGELES

AIRPORT REMARKS: Attended continuously. PPR for dual wheel acft in
excess of 60,000 pounds certified maximum ldg weight, ctc arpt
manager 310–458–8591.   Helicopter flight training ops prohibited,
helicopter ops apch boundry at midfield at or above 900 MSL. No
touch/go, stop/go, or low apch permitted on Sat, Sun, holidays,
weekdays SS–1500Z ‡. Noise test on 122.85. Continuous noise
ordinance in effect ctc noise office prior to arrival
310–458–8759/8692   or 310–434–2640.   Noise abatement
procedures: Pure jet and stage II (with/without hush kits)
prohibited. Maximum noise limit 95.0 senal all acft. No engine
starts or departures except PPR lifeguard flights 0700–1500Z ‡
Mon–Fri and 0700–1600Z ‡ weekends. PPR ex–military acft ctc
arpt manager 310–458–8591.   VFR departures Rwy 21 turn left
10 ° at end of rwy then turn right 225 ° to over–fly golf course W of
arpt. No crosswind turn until reaching Lincoln Blvd (1 mile W) and
out 800 ft MSL. If departure pattern, no turn before reaching
shoreline. Rwy 03 departure no turn prior to freeway located 1

Helipad H1: 40 X 40

Fig. 27

also be found in a useful document known as the *Airport/Facility Directory* (the *A/FD* as it's affectionately known to pilots) as shown in Figure 27. More on the *A/FD* in Chapter 16.

CTAF (Common Traffic Advisory Frequency)

The airports you'll land at and depart from will be either controlled or uncontrolled. Operations at controlled airports are accomplished by communicating with an air traffic controller. We'll discuss how to do this shortly. For now, let's examine the proper communication techniques when operating into or out of an uncontrolled airport (remember, this is an airport without a control tower or one whose tower isn't in operation).

At uncontrolled airports, pilots are not required to use their radio to communicate with other traffic during takeoff or landing. Simple see-and-avoid vigilance is considered satisfactory. Common sense, however, dictates using a radio if one is on board. Airplanes with radios tuned to the same (common) frequency can broadcast their intentions to each other while operating in the traffic pattern. This makes the airport a safer and more harmonious place.

At many uncontrolled airports a frequency known as the *Common Traffic Advisory Frequency* (CTAF) is available for pilots to communicate their intentions and receive information during takeoff or landing. It's called *common* simply because all pilots communicating at a particular airport use that frequency. The CTAF may be either a unicom, multicom, FSS (Flight Service Station), or tower frequency (if the airport has a tower but it's not in operation at the time).

Getting from Overhead to Over There

Many student pilots overfly an uncontrolled airport and take a look to see what's where. Then they say "OK big fella', now how do I get from way up here to over there for a standard 45° entry?"

ENTERING THE PATTERN

There are two common ways to enter the traffic pattern at an uncontrolled field from overhead. You can observe the segmented circle at 2000 feet AGL then fly from A to B to C to D, then inbound to the runway at a 45 degree angle (D to E). Another way is to start at 2,000 feet AGL and fly from A to F to G to H to D. The descent from 2,000 feet AGL to traffic pattern altitude is started from D to E. Traffic and terrain permitting, the descent can be done earlier at the pilot's discretion (from G to H, H to D or C to D.

Fig. 28

Some of the more creative students might think about flying to the entry spot at several thousand feet above the pattern altitude and diving into the pattern (after one too many reruns of *Tora, Tora, Tora*). This earns a Swiss cheese sandwich, for having enormous holes in their judgment.

Here are two options. Overfly an uncontrolled airport at a *minimum* of 2000 feet AGL to observe the runways and traffic pattern indicator. Once you've identified the runway you'll be using, fly parallel to the runway direction and off to one side as shown in Figure 28. Flying from A to B allows you to keep the runway in sight out of your left window. When the airplane is beyond the crosswind leg (point B), make a left 90° turn. This allows you to keep departing traffic and pattern traffic in sight.

Make sure you keep your eyes out for high performance airplanes departing the runway. These aircraft climb like a big hungry bat whose sonar is locked on the moon. It's no problem if you maintain a good scan, as pilots are supposed to do at all times.

Continue beyond the downwind leg until reaching point C. You can start your descent here or start it at point D as you turn toward the midpoint of the runway. Descend so as to enter the traffic pattern at traffic pattern altitude. Point D is chosen far enough from the runway to lose the excess altitude you had while overflying the airport. On the return to the airport, enter the downwind at a 45° angle, at traffic pattern altitude. Adjust your flight path, speed or timing to follow any traffic in the pattern or entering the pattern.

Another method is to fly from A to F while keeping the runway in sight out your left window. Point F is chosen far enough from the airport to keep the runway visible over your right shoulder as you fly from F to G to H. You can start your descent to traffic pattern altitude at position G, which is beyond the downwind leg

These methods of pattern entry allow you to keep the airport in sight at all times. The same procedures apply to a right hand traffic pattern. These procedures also work at tower controlled airports when the controller hasn't provided you with specific instructions on how to enter the traffic pattern. Always make it a point to enter the pattern at traffic pattern altitude—no higher and no lower.

CTAFs are found in several aviation publications as well as being printed on aeronautical sectional charts.

While a unicom frequency can also be the CTAF, this is not always the case. At airports with towers, the tower frequency will usually be the CTAF that's used when the tower isn't in service. Most airports with a tower will also have one or more unicom frequencies; these are *not* CTAFs, but they can be used to obtain airport and runway information from the provider. (See the *A/FD* or the aeronautical chart for this frequency.)

Using Unicom and Multicom For Information

If you're landing at an uncontrolled airport, at about 10 miles out it's time to talk, using the CTAF.

If the CTAF is a unicom station, the following phraseology is appropriate:

"Corona Unicom, Cessna two one three two Bravo is 10 miles southeast descending through 3,000 feet landing Corona, request wind and runway information Corona, over."

At airports without an established unicom station, you may ask for landing advisories from traffic that may already be in the pattern. On the CTAF simply state:

"Sun Hill traffic, Cessna two one three two Bravo is 10 miles southeast descending through 4,000 feet landing Sun Hill, request landing advisories Sun Hill, over."

Without an operating control tower to help inform pilots of each other's position, the CTAF is used to make position reports while in the pattern. In addition to the call 10 miles from the airport, report your position entering the pattern, when downwind, on base and on final approach. This keeps other airplanes at the airport apprised of your whereabouts. Since there may be another airport in the vicinity on a similar unicom or multicom frequency, state the airport name during these transmissions. For instance, the following is a typical report for such an airport:

"Corona Unicom, Cessna two one three two Bravo entering left downwind for Runway 25 for touch and go at Corona." Notice that you announce whether you're making left or right traffic. This provides an opportunity for everyone to yell at you if you're going the wrong way.

You should also broadcast your intentions on the CTAF when departing an uncontrolled airport. Make a broadcast before taxiing and on the runway before departure. The following self-announce phraseology should be used, "Sun Hill traffic, Cessna two

Finding Out What's Common

A CTAF isn't much good unless it's common knowledge. If a unicom *can* be a CTAF, but it isn't always a CTAF, how are you supposed to know what's what?

There are several ways to determine the CTAF for any airport.

Since you will always have a navigational chart on board (that's a polite hint, a request, and a plea all rolled into one), look at it. The information is printed there. The chart depiction in Figure 29 shows how Circle Town is presented on an aeronautical sectional chart. The small reverse-bold "C" under the airport tells you that 122.8 MHz is the CTAF.

The Airport/Facility Directory is another handy resource. It will tell you the CTAF. If there's no tower, but a unicom frequency exists, that fact appears in the *A/FD*, as shown in Figure 29. The following frequencies are usually reserved for unicom: 122.7, 122.8, 122.725, 122.975, 123.0, 123.050 and 123.075 MHz.

Fig. 29

If there's no tower or unicom frequency being used as the CTAF, are you left speechless? Nope. Just tune your aviation radio to 122.9. This frequency is referred to as multicom, because it's shared by many pilots at many places. It's sort of the pilots' airport party line frequency, and is used primarily for communications at airports with no tower, FSS or unicom. Without a unicom (or tower or FSS), the only airport information you're likely to receive will come from other pilots flying the pattern.

An aeronautical sectional chart excerpt (Figure 30) shows that 122.9 is the CTAF for Jordan airport. Figure 30 shows an *A/FD* excerpt of Jordan airport indicating that no unicom, tower or FSS is available at the airport (all these are missing from the communications line). By a process of elimination, you know it has to be multicom.

Fig. 30

one three two Bravo, at Bob's Bean Palace (this is your location on the airport), taxiing to Runway 25, Sun Hill."

"Sun Hill traffic, Cessna two one three two Bravo departing Runway 7, departing the pattern to the (direction) climbing to (altitude), Sun Hill"

Just because there is no tower doesn't mean that you should use nonstandard phraseology. I heard one pilot call the control tower and say, "Man in the tower this is the man in the bird, I'm ready to go so give me the word."

The controller responded, "Man in the bird this is the man in the tower, you talk funny, the delay's an hour." The moral to this story is save the poetry for smoky midnight cafes. Avoid slang and stick with accepted word usage. Remember that *predictability* is important. Other pilots and controllers expect to hear certain information in a certain order.

There are airports without an established CTAF. Normally, these are private (PVT) airports, as shown in Figure 31. This doesn't mean that you have to be a private pilot to use it, either. It just means that it's privately owned and you should seek permission from the owner if you want to land there.

When landing at a private airport, broadcast your intentions on 122.9 MHz. This is the frequency for air-to-air communications at airports without a control tower, FSS or Unicom. If you're landing at a non-privately owned airport without any CTAF listed in the *A/FD* or on a sectional chart, also use 122.9 MHz to broadcast your intentions.

Fig. 31

On Being an Air (Man or Woman) of Few Words

Learning to speak well on the radio is one of the most important piloting skills you can acquire.

Speaking well means speaking clearly and using *standard phraseology* to say the most with the least number of words.

The quickest route to being a royal pain in the prop is to be long-winded on the radio. I've heard pilots who had more hems than a recycled party dress. A few tips that will make you a microphone pro:

• Your initial callup in most cases should consist of who you are calling (Kennedy Tower, Alabaster unicom), and your call sign. I've heard pilots do a 60-second monologue only to be told "Stand by" because the controller was busy.

• Be patient. When you call a tower or ground controller, he or she can be talking to another controller on the phone (the *landline* in controller terms), working another frequency, or otherwise occupied. If you don't get an instant reply, wait 10 to 15 seconds before calling again.

• Listen before talking. Some pilots feel they have to start talking as soon as they tune in a frequency. Make certain you aren't in the middle of someone else's conversation. You will not be popular if you *step on* other pilots by talking over them.

• Think before talking. Don't key the microphone and then start pondering what to say. Key your brain first.

The airwaves are a very limited resource. You're sharing a frequency with a lot of other people who may also need to communicate. Be considerate by being concise and precise.

So far we've discussed operations at uncontrolled airports. Uncontrolled airports require that you, on your own, identify the wind direction, runway landing direction as well as the appropriate traffic pattern to fly. At controlled airports (those with operating control towers) the air traffic controller provides you with this information. This information includes traffic pattern direction, runway to use, directions to fly as well as position reports to make when approaching the airport. An important point to remember is that you must establish two-way radio communication before entering the controller's airspace (Class C or D) or obtain a clearance if it's Class B airspace.

(ATIS) Automatic Terminal Information Service

At many controlled airports there is a recorded broadcast of airport information known as *Automatic Terminal Information Service (ATIS)*. This service, which is pronounced *A-TIS*, provides noncontrol information to help relieve frequency congestion. In other words, ATIS keeps the controller from having to repeat the same airport information (ceiling, wind, visibility, etc.) over and over again to pilots landing or departing the airport.

Figure 32A shows the sectional chart depiction for Long Beach airport. The control tower (CT) frequencies are 119.4 and 120.5 MHz; 119.4 MHz is the CTAF (indicated by the reverse bold "C" after the frequency) and is used whenever the tower isn't in operation. The ATIS frequency is 127.75 MHz. Figure 32B shows where ATIS information is found in the *Airport/Facility Directory*. There's even a phone number available if you are so inclined to call and listen to the ATIS before departure. When approaching Long Beach or any other airport with an ATIS, you should listen to the ATIS broadcast when you're approximately 25 miles from the airport. If you're departing the airport, you should listen to the ATIS broadcast prior to contacting the tower for taxi instructions. A typical ATIS broadcast might sound like this:

"This is Long Beach airport information Hotel, 1300 Zulu weather.

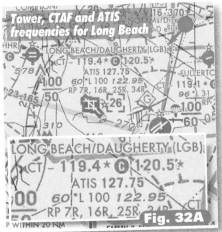

Tower, CTAF and ATIS frequencies for Long Beach

Fig. 32A

CALIFORNIA

LONG BEACH (DAUGHERTY FLD) (LGB) 3 NE UTC-8(-7DT) N33°49.07′ W118°09.10′ LOS ANGELES

clsd—CTAF. Rwy 12-30 HIRL lighted during hours tower clsd. REIL Rwy 12, Rwy 25R, and Rwy 25L, MIRL Rwy 07L-25R, HIRL Rwy 07R-25L, CL TDZL lgts Rwy 12-30 not avbl when ATCT clsd. VASI Rwy 25R and PAPI Rwy 25L opr 1500-0600Z‡ only. VASI Rwy 12 and PAPI Rwy 30 opr continuously. NOTE: See Special Notices — Air Carrier Operations Vicinity of Long Beach (Daugherty Fld), CA.
WEATHER DATA SOURCES: ASOS (562) 424-0572.
COMMUNICATIONS: CTAF 119.4   ATIS 127.75 (562) 595-8364   UNICOM 122.95   **Fig. 32B**
Ⓡ SOCAL APP CON 124.65
Ⓡ SOCAL DEP CON 127.2
LONG BEACH TOWER 119.4 (Rwy 30 apch, Rwy 12 dep) 120.5 (Rwy 12 apch, Rwy 30 dep) (1415-0745Z‡)
   GND CON 133.0   CLNC DEL 118.15
AIRSPACE: CLASS D svc 1415-0745Z‡ other times CLASS G.
RADIO AIDS TO NAVIGATION: NOTAM FILE HHR.
   SEAL BEACH (L) VORTACW 115.7   SLI Chan104   N33°47.00′ W118°03.29′   278° 5.3 NM to fld. 23/15E.
      HIWAS.
   BECCA NDB (LOM) 233   LG   N33°45.40′ W118°04.64′   301° 5.2 NM to fld.
   ILS 110.3 I-LGB   Rwy 30.   Class IT.   LOM BECCA NDB. Unmonitored when twr clsd. MM unmonitored.

Thirteen hundred scattered, measured ceiling three thousand broken, visibility 4 smoke and haze, wind 230 at 10. Altimeter 30.04. ILS Runway 30 in use. Landing and departing on Runways 30 and 25L. Contact Ground Control on 133.0. For Runway 30 contact tower on 119.4. For Runway 25R contact tower on 120.5. Inform the controller on initial contact you have information Hotel."

Once again, predictability is paramount. ATIS broadcasts always contain the latest weather sequence, active runways and other pertinent remarks in that order (ceilings and visibilities are not broadcast when they are above 5,000 feet and more than five miles). The first few times you hear one of these beasts, it sounds like a transmission from Mars. You soon figure out that it's always airport name, followed by the phonetic designator, followed by the time, etc. In addition to basic weather and frequency information, the ATIS broadcast may have other important tidbits tagged on at the end such as taxiway closures, temporary restricted areas, birds in the vicinity, etc. One time the ATIS said there was a large, 200 foot crane south of the airport. My student looked over and said, "Wow, now that's a big bird!" (I immediately liberated the sandwich from his hand.)

ATIS broadcasts are updated when any significant change occurs at the airport or upon the receipt of any official hourly or special weather information (typically received from

electronic weather sensing devices). Each new recording gets the name of the next phonetic alphabet letter in order. Delta becomes Echo, Hotel becomes India, etc.

One time I called the controller and told him we had information Delta. He replied, "32 Bravo, how can you have Delta when we've just issued information Bravo?" I thought about my mistake and said, "Well, we have a psychic on board." The controller, with a bit of humor, said, "Well, what does that psychic say about your chance of getting touch and goes today?" As you can see, controllers are intelligent people, often with a very sharp sense of humor.

Listening to the ATIS may not be as much fun as tuning in the Superbowl, but it can be a lot more helpful. From the ATIS you can find out if the airport is VFR or IFR (VFR

meaning that you can fly and IFR meaning that you can't as a sport pilot); what direction you will be landing; whether there are any problems on the ground or special procedures (such as newly installed large obstacles around the airport like a construction crane or advertising balloon) and whether you have to take into account a nasty crosswind, etc.

At about 15 miles out, it's talk time. If you're approaching an airport in Class D airspace, you'll make your initial call to the tower controller. If you're approaching an airport within Class C airspace, you'll make your initial call to the radar approach control facility responsible for that airspace. An early call means you have more time to establish communication in the event the frequency is congested or the tower controller's workload prevents an immediate response to your initial call.

Oh boy! You're in Big Trouble Again!

Is that a tower? I didn't know this airport had a tower! That explains those colored lights I saw on final approach. It also explains why that car kept following me...until I lost him. Let's see, my instructor, Rod, said if I'm in trouble, I should take out my logbook and erase everything with his name on it....

Your initial contact with any air traffic controller should contain the following information:

1. The name of the facility you're calling.

2. Your full aircraft call sign as filed in your flight plan (if you filed a flight plan).

3. The type of message to follow, or your request, if it's short.

4. The word *over* if required.

When contacting Long Beach Tower, your initial should sound like this:

"Long Beach Tower, Cessna two one three two Bravo, 15 miles southeast at 3,500 feet for landing, information Whiskey received, over."

The tower might reply with:

"Cessna two one three two Bravo, this is Long Beach Tower, make right traffic for Runway 7 right. Report entering downwind."

I was sitting at the local flight school when a student came back from a cross country to a busy tower-controlled airport. He was obviously flustered so I asked him what the problem was. He said, "I tuned in the tower frequency and they never stopped talking. All they did was blab, blab, blab. I couldn't get a word in edgewise and finally had to return home." I asked him to point out the tower frequency on the chart. Guess what? He pointed to the ATIS frequency (between taking big bites out of his sandwich). His instructor had never taken him to an airport with

Speaking When Spoken To

When a controller speaks, you are expected to acknowledge the communication orally. The acknowledgment consists of nothing more than the last three letters of your call sign. If the tower says "Cessna two one three two Bravo, report turning final" your reply is "32 Bravo."

There is one situation in which a longer reply is *mandatory*. When a controller issues instructions to taxi to but not enter a runway, you *must* acknowledge with your call sign and the fact that you understand you are to hold short of the runway. It might sound like this:

"Cessna two one three two Bravo, hold short of Runway 21."

"Cessna two one three two bravo, will hold short Runway 21."

an ATIS, so he knew nothing about it. I suppose if the tower ever asked him if he had the ATIS (sounds like "A - TIS") he might of thought they were talking about some sort of tropical skin rash.

Pilot Control Of Airport Lighting

At a few very busy airports the runway edge lights are kept on from sunset to sunrise. Figure 33 shows a sectional chart excerpt of Hogeland airport. Notice that next to the numbers "3138" (this is the airport's elevation above sea level) there is the letter "L." This indicates that lighting (specifically—runway edge lighting) is in operation from sunset to sunrise.

At many airports, though, you get to turn the lights on yourself. No, it doesn't take really long arms. In fact, all you need is a short thumb, because you can activate the lights by clicking the microphone.

Figure 34 shows a sectional chart excerpt of Turner airport. An asterisk (*) next to the lighting symbol (the "L") on the sectional chart means *lighting limitations exist*. In this instance, the limitation refers to the fact that "pilot control" of airport lighting is in use (available) at this airport. So don't expect to see Turner's airport lights on at night unless you or another pilot activated them. Figure 35 shows an excerpt from the *Airport/Facility Directory* for Turner, indicating that pilots should activate the MIRL (medium intensity runway lighting) on the CTAF of 122.9 MHz. The words, "ACTIVATE," followed by the specif-

ic type of lighting system, indicate that pilot control of airport lighting exists at that airport. The *AF/D*, not the sectional chart, is where the appropriate frequency for lighting activation is found. (The "*L" symbol may also mean lighting is available on *request* or the lighting is *part time*. If it's available on request, the *A/FD* will identify who to contact for light activation. Always check the *A/FD* if you see the "*L" symbol.)

Three different intensities of runway edge lighting (high, medium and low) are available at many airports. To activate runway lighting from the cockpit, key (click) the microphone button on the appropriate CTAF frequency. How many times should you click it? If all three intensities of lighting exist at an airport, simply click the mike 7 times within 5 seconds for the high intensity runway lighting (HIRL), 5 times within 5 seconds for the medium intensity runway lighting (MIRL) and 3 times in 5 seconds for the low intensity runway lighting (LIRL). Once activated the lights will stay on for 15 minutes.

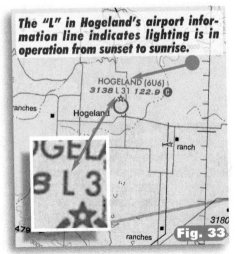

The "L" in Hogeland's airport information line indicates lighting is in operation from sunset to sunrise.

The "*L" in Turner's airport information line indicates lighting limitations exist (in Turner's case the limitation is for pilot controlled lighting). Check the A/FD for more info.

Light of My Life

According to one reliable source, this really happened.

A pilot who flew freight at night got to be familiar with the controllers at the numerous airports where he made stops.

Slightly bored with the repetitious nature of his work, he liked to key the microphone and say "Guess who?" to the controllers as his first callup.

One night the tower controller at a small airport was just waiting for his opportunity. Right on time came "Guess who?"

The tower controller turned out the airport lights, and said "Guess who? Guess where!!"

If you're approaching the airport at night and it's approximately 15 minutes since you've last activated the lights, you might want to re-click the microphone the appropriate number of times to reactivate them for an additional 15 minutes. Personally, I re-key the microphone the appropriate number of times when I'm on final approach just to make sure the lights don't go off by surprise. Imagine being on short final when the airport disappears. Not only will this make you nervous, but imagine what it'll do to the passengers.

Figure 35 shows only MIRL is available at Turner (look after the word "ACTIVATE" at point A). Keying the microphone more than 5 times in 5 seconds will only activate the medium intensity setting since it doesn't have high intensity capability.

If HIRL lighting exists and it's too strong for your eyes (some pilots say you can cook chicken on the bulbs of those high intensity lights), simply re-key the mic 3 or 5 times within five seconds to step down the lighting system to lower intensity lighting (if it is available). The FAA suggests that, when approaching an airport, you should key the microphone 7 times in 5 seconds just to activate all the airport's controlled lighting. After this, you can re-key the mike and lower the lighting intensity (if MIRL or HIRL are installed) or deactivate other lighting systems (VASI, REIL, PAPI, approach lights) that may be wired into the control system (more on these other lighting systems shortly).

The *A/FD* excerpt in Figure 35, point B also shows a Precision Approach Path Indicator (PAPI) is wired into the pilot controlled lighting system at Turner (I promise, I'll cover the PAPI shortly, honest!). Make it a point to activate airport lighting when close to the field. Activating the system at high altitudes far from the airport might needlessly activate another airport's lighting systems. It may also change another pilot's light system settings while on approach.

At some airports there are two small stroboscopic lights near the runway's threshold. These are called *Runway End Identifier Lights*. The acronym is *REIL*, pronounced like the word *real*. REIL lights help identify the beginning of the runway threshold, making it easier to see.

Highway to Heaven

On final with gear down and full flaps, I noticed a movement out of the corner of my eye. Another aircraft was turning final ahead and to our left. We took evasive action and went around. The aircraft took forever to get off the runway and we thought we might have to go around again. We didn't, but on short final, right before we landed, the pilot of the other aircraft said, "Tower, were you trying to call me?" We decided that we ought to talk with this pilot about the close call. He was apologetic. His excuse was that he had his personal tape player headset on and couldn't hear the tower over the music. **ASRS Report.**

New pilots are sometimes surprised at how hard it can be to spot an airport from the air, day *or* night.

Re-keying the mike button may allow you to step down or turn off the REIL system. At one airport, a tower controller called a pilot on approach and asked him if he wanted the REIL lights activated. The pilot replied, "Well, how can I tell the difference between the real lights and the imitation ones?" It wouldn't have surprised me if the controller said, "Well, I guess that all depends on what kind of sandwich you're having."

Visual Approach Slope Indicator (VASI)

Under poor visibility conditions or at night, the lack of outside visual clues sometimes makes a determination of the proper landing glidepath difficult. Fortunately there is something known as a *Visual Approach Slope Indicator* (VASI) that provides you with a visual clue as to the proper glidepath to fly. (By the way, VASI is pronounced *VAZ-eee*. It is not something in which you put flowers).

A VASI usually consists of two pairs of lightbars along the side of the runway (it's often called a *two bar VASI* for this reason). The two VASI bars are usually 500 to 1,000 feet from the approach threshold as

The word **ACTIVATE** in the A/FD excerpt for Turner indicates MIRL (Medium Intensity Runway Lighting) is available (point A). The PAPI (Precision Approach Path Indicator) is also wired into the pilot controlled lighting circuitry (point B).

Rod Machado's Sport Pilot Handbook

shown in Figure 36. These lights project either a red or white color, depending on your altitude. The colors are constant and don't actually change within the box. What changes is your height, which allows you to look at the VASI from different angles and see different colors.

When you are below the proper glideslope, both VASI bars show red. Some pilots remember that this signals trouble by thinking of it as *Red over red, you'll conk your head.* Level off until you see red over white. Red over white means that you're above the glidepath for the bar closest to you and below the glidepath for the bar farther away. This is a complicated way of saying you're on the glidepath that will plunk you down halfway between the two bars. A good way to remember this is *Red over white, you're all right.* Of course, if you're too high, both bars will show white. A good memory aid for this is *White over white, you'll soon be out of sight.* Increase the

THE 2-BAR VASI
(Visual Approach Slope Indicator)

A "red over red" indication on the VASI means you're below glide path. Think, "Red over red, you'll soon conk your head."

A "red over white" indication on the VASI means you're on the proper glide path. Think, "Red over white, you'll be all right."

A white over white indication on the VASI means that you're above the proper glide path. Think, "White over white you'll soon be out of sight."

Fig. 36

descent rate until the upwind bar turns red. You can expect the VASI's red and white bars to transition through a pink color as your altitude in relation to the proper glideslope changes.

If you see flashing red over flashing white, then you're making an approach to a police car. Now you're in really big trouble (besides, it's not natural for the VASI bars to chase other cars down the highway).

VASIs are visible from 3 to 5 miles during the day and up to 20 miles or more at night. You can count on safe obstruction clearance for 10° either side of the runway centerline when using the VASI. Obstruction clearance is guaranteed for a distance up

to 4 miles out along the centerline of the runway (Figure 37). If, however, you're nearing your turn onto final approach, it's best not to start a descent using the VASI until you are aligned with the runway. Personally, I wouldn't start my descent until aligned with the runway even if I was within 10° of the runway centerline. You never know what's out there, and I'm not about to turn my airplane into some sort of probe whose mission is to find a newly installed obstruction.

Keep in mind that regulations require you to fly at or above the glideslope when approaching a runway equipped with a VASI in Class B, C and D airspace. Be cautious about

THE 2-BAR VISUAL APPROACH SLOPE INDICATOR

VASI PROTECTED AREA

The VASI provides you with obstacle clearance for plus or minus 10 degrees either side of the runway centerline for 4 nautical miles.

THE 3-BAR VASI
(Visual Approach Slope Indicator)

Smaller aircraft use the lower glidepath giving them a 3 degree glideslope.

Larger aircraft use the higher glide path giving them a 3.25 degree (or higher) glideslope.

Fig. 38

THE 3-BAR VASI

High (3.25°) glide-slope

Low (3°) glide-slope

Fig. 39

I'm the captain and I'm on the glidepath!

We're the passengers in the cheap seats and we're below the safe glide path. Now we know why first class seats are more expensive.

When flying the lower glideslope (he should be on the upper one), the captain of this airliner is on glidepath while the rest of his long-bodied airplane is below glideslope. This is why many large aircraft use the high glideslope for landing.

3-Bar VASI

Some of the larger air carrier airports have a 3-bar VASI. This exists to serve the jumbo jet crowd, as shown in Figure 38. Problems arise in long-bodied aircraft when the captain is on a safe glideslope but the passengers behind him or her are not, as shown in Figure 39. If pilots of jumbo jets landed this way, obstructions in the flight path might intrude on passengers seated in row 38 through L (lavatory).

Three-bar VASI's have two glideslopes. One is angled at 3° and is identified by a bar combination of red/red over white as shown in Figure 38. The higher glideslope is angled at approximately 3.25° (1/4 degree steeper than the lower glideslope). Long bodied aircraft use this and see a color combination of red/white over white. VASI glideslope angles vary depending on the obstructions located along the approach path. It's possible to have VASI glideslopes as steep as 4.5°. Even if you're in a Cessna 152 pretending to be a Boeing 747, it's best to use the lower glideslope to avoid steep descents. Look for red/red over white as the appropriate on-glidepath indication for this lower (3°) glideslope.

making premature descents below the glideslope. In addition to safety, VASIs aid in keeping pilots from descending over noise-sensitive areas along the flight path.

Precision Approach Path Indicator (PAPI)

The precision approach path indicator (*PAPI*, pronounced *PAP-pee*) is another version of a visual glideslope indicator, as shown in Figure 40 (no, it's not that nice guy who's paying for your flying lessons either—that's your *pappy*). The PAPI uses red and white signaling colors in an arrangement of four horizontal lights to identify the correct glidepath. These four horizontal light units appear to change color as your glidepath varies. If you're above a 3.5° glide slope, the PAPI shows all four light units as white. When on a 3° glideslope the right two lights are red and the left two lights are white. When below a 2.5° glideslope, all four light units show red. A pink transition between

lights doesn't exist as it does with a two- or three-bar VASI.

PAPI
Precision Approach Path Indicator

RED

Below a 2.5 Degree Glide Path

WHT. RED

On a 3 Degree Glide Path

WHITE

Above a 3.5 Degree Glide Path

Fig. 40

TRI-COLOR VASI

Amber- **above glideslope**
Green- **on glideslope**
Red- **below glideslope**

The Tri-Color VASI is a single-light unit whose projected colors change in appearance based on your relation to the glideslope.

Fig. 41

Tricolor VASI

The tricolor VASI is not as common as the two- and three-bar VASIs. It normally consists of a single light unit projecting a three-color visual approach path into the final approach area of the runway (Figure 41). Red is the *below glideslope* indication. The *above glideslope* indication is amber, and the *on glideslope* indication is green. When the airplane descends from green to red the pilot may see a dark amber color during the transition. Tricolor VASIs have a useful range of approximately one-half to one mile during the day and up to five miles at night.

Pulsating VASI Systems

The last type of the fairly common VASI systems is the Pulsating Light Visual Approach Slope Indicator (PVASI, Figure 42). A pulsating VASI consists of a single light unit projecting a two-color signal to pilots

PULSATING VASI SYSTEM

Above glide slope
On glide slope
Pulsating White
Steady White
Steady Red
Pulsating Red
Below glide slope
Slightly below glide slope

Fig. 42

in the final approach area. If you are above the glide slope, you'll see a pulsating white light. A steady white light appears when you're on the glide slope. If you're below the glide slope, you'll see a steady red indication. If you descend further below the glide slope, you'll notice a pulsing red light. The pulsating rate increases the further the airplane is above or below the desired glide slope. The useful range of this system is approximately four miles during the day and up to ten miles at night (depending on the visibility).

Wake Turbulence

One of the unseen hazards of flight is something known as *wake turbulence*. This can be any form of airplane-generated disturbance of the atmosphere. The most common and hazardous type of wake turbulence is known as *wingtip vortices*. Wingtip vortices pose quite a hazard to other airplanes. An airplane caught in wake

Fig. 43   **WINGTIP VORTICES**

Low pressure on top of wing

The vortices remain spaced a bit less than a wingspan apart, at altitudes greater than a wingspan above the ground, and drift with the wind.

High pressure underneath wing

As the airplane moves forward, air spirals outward, upward and inward from underneath to on top of the wing creating cylindrical shaped wingtip vortices.

turbulence can experience a rolling motion so severe that there isn't enough control capacity to fight it. Wake turbulence can roll a small plane inverted and, quite frankly, passengers often become very upset when suddenly placed upside down in an airplane.

If that's not enough, the rolling motions and turbulence produced by the vortices can damage aircraft components. This doesn't mean that your airplane is necessarily going to go to pieces upon encountering vortices, but it's a risk not worth the gamble.

Wingtip vortices come not from somebody's shoes, but as an unwanted byproduct of lift. Wingtip vortices are generated by the differential pressure which exists over and under the wing's surfaces (Figure 43). High

pressure air under the wing attempts to sneak over the tip of the wing, toward the low pressure air above. The wing's vortex starts from under the wing, moves outward, then upward and inward toward the fuselage. The vortex appears to coil or rotate while trailing behind the wing of a moving airplane.

Generally, the heavier the airplane, the stronger the wingtip vortex (there are a few exceptions to this). In other words, the vortices produced by a fully loaded Boeing 747 are a lot stronger than those of a fully loaded Piper Cub. The reason is that the pressure differential between the top and bottom of the 747's wing is a lot greater than the pressure differential of a Piper Cub's wing. After all, the 747 has a lot more to lift. A greater difference in pressure implies air at the wingtip rotates faster.

When an airplane's gear and flaps are retracted, there is a tendency to produce stronger vortices. An airplane in this no-gear-and-flap configuration is said to be *clean* (no, this isn't a newly washed airplane). Couple a cleanly-configured airplane with slow airspeed and you've got a condition that normally produces the strongest wingtip vortices. Slow speed means a higher angle of attack, which results in a greater lift differential between the bottom and the top of the wing. Any large airplane that's flying heavy, clean and slow could produce more serious wingtip vortices.

As a small-airplane pilot, you must watch out for airplanes that produce hazardous wingtip vortices. Some are

WINGTIP VORTEX PRODUCTION

A

Wingtip vortex end where the airplane touches down.

Wingtip vortex begin where the airplane leaves the runway.

Fig. 44

B

Plan to lift off before this point, where the jet lifted off the runway.

Vortex production stars here.

Wingtip vortices begin at the point where the heavier airplane lifts off the runway (to be precise, vortices begin when the nose wheel lifts off the runway). Make sure you lift off long before this point and avoid flying directly into the path of the vortices. You may need to turn left or right to avoid the vortices.

C

Vortex production stops here.

Plan to land beyond this point after the jet clears the runway (don't land on the jet!).

When landing behind a heavier airplane, plan to land beyond the point where the airplane touched down. And make sure you don't sink into the the vortices while on the approach.

famous, or infamous, as generators of these horizontal tornadoes. Beware of Boeing 747, 757 and 767's, and DC-10's. Even other large airplanes try to avoid the vortices of these mammoth jumbos. But don't be deceived by the airplane's size. Lear jets, although small in size, can produce serious wingtip vortices.

Always remember that wingtip vortices are a byproduct of lift. The moment an airplane's wheels leave the ground, lift is being generated and vortices are produced. So expect vortices at and beyond the point of airplane rotation, as shown in Figure 44B. Likewise, as soon as the airplane's wheels touch down, wingtip vortice production stops (Figure 44C).

If you are departing behind a larger airplane, it's best to lift off before the point where that airplane raised

its nose (rotated) and commenced climbing. Once off the ground, avoid flying into the flight path of the departing airplane as shown in Figure 44B. In a small airplane with limited performance, it's unlikely you will climb above the glide path of the larger airplane. Turn right or left to avoid climbing into the larger airplane's departure path (and its vortices), as shown in Figure 44B. Let the tower controller know what you're doing (if departing a controlled field).

The unique thing about wingtip vortices is that they tend to descend at a rate of several hundred feet per minute and normally level off at 500 to 1,000 feet below the generating airplane (Figure 45). They also tend to remain a little less than a wingspan apart and drift with the wind. It's *always* wise to avoid the area 1,000 feet below any large airplane. So maneuver laterally (preferably upwind) to avoid flying below and behind these large aircraft.

While vortices diminish with time as well as with atmospheric turbulence (this helps chop them up and disrupt their rotational energy), they remain a threat for many minutes after the passage of a large airplane. Vertical separation of at least 1,000 feet below the airplane is considered safe by the FAA. Personally, I'd recommend you avoid flying directly beneath and parallel to the flight path of a large transport airplane even if you're more than 1,000 feet below it (vortices can remain formed 8 to 10 nautical miles behind an airplane). It never makes sense to thumb your nose at any in-flight hazard.

VORTEX MOVEMENT

Flight Path

500' to 1,000'

Avoid this entire area!

Trail about 8 - 10 miles

Wingtip vortices descend at several hundred feet per minute, tend to level off at 500' to 1,000' below the generating airplane and can trail for as much as 8-10 nautical miles behind.

Fig. 45

Tower, we can't move. Looks like we got one of those little toy airplanes blocking us.

Will the small airplane blocking the jet tell us what you're waiting for?

Our wind-up key!

Be prepared for vortices to drift when crosswinds exist at the airport. Figure 46(A) shows the typical behavior of a drifting vortex near the surface. When vortices sink to within 100 to 200 feet above the ground, they tend to move sideways at a speed of 2 to 3 knots. A crosswind will decrease the sideways movement of the upwind vortex and increase the movement of the downwind vortex as shown in Figure 46B. Expect the upwind vortex to remain over or near the touchdown zone if a light crosswind component of 1 to 5 knots exists.

A light quartering tailwind can move the vortices forward into the touchdown zone as shown in Figure 46C. You must be especially cautious because this increases the possibility of lingering vortices in the touchdown area. Be especially cautious when departing on close, parallel runways when a large airplane is upwind of your runway as depicted in Figure 46D. The vortices may drift directly into your flight path.

Another area of concern is when a larger airplane makes a low approach, missed approach or a go-around and flies directly over your airplane during the climbout. This is most common on parallel, closely spaced runways. It's also a problem on runways that intersect at a small angle. If you experience such an event and feel the airplane will pass less than 1,000 feet over your airplane during the go-around, move out from under the airplane's flight path. Your job is to protect you and your passengers. Call the tower and explain that you'd like to turn right or left in the interest of wake turbulence avoidance (if it's critical, turn first, talk later). I have never been refused a request to do something in the interest of "safety."

In many cases ATC will issue a "caution wake turbulence" warning when such a hazard presents itself. Even if ATC issues no warning, adjust your flight path as necessary to prevent encountering these dangerous wingtip vortices.

WINGTIP VORTEX DRIFT

When the vortices of larger aircraft sink close to the ground (within 100 to 200 feet), they tend to move sideways over the ground at a speed of 2 or 3 knots if no wind is present.

Vortex movement near ground—no wind present

A crosswind will decrease the sideways movement of the upwind vortex and increase the movement of the downwind vortex. Thus a light wind with a cross-runway component of 1 to 5 knots could result in the upwind vortex remaining in the touchdown zone for a period of time and hasten the drift of the downwind vortex toward another runway.

Vortex movement near ground—with crosswind

A tailwind condition can move the vortices of the preceding aircraft forward into the touchdown zone. The light quartering tailwind requires maximum caution. Pilots should be alert to large aircraft upwind from their approach and takeoff flight paths (especially when the runways are closer than 2,500 feet).

Use caution, vortex might drift onto your runway.

And always be prepared for the unexpected. One of my friends in a Cessna 421 (a twin-engine airplane) was cleared for takeoff when a small rabbit pulled out on the runway. He radioed the tower that he couldn't takeoff until the rabbit moved. The tower replied, "The rabbit on the runway is now cleared for takeoff. And Cessna 421, you're cleared for takeoff too, caution wake turbulence from the departing rabbit." This is what happens when tower controllers have a lot of free time on their hands.

ATC Wake Turbulence Separation Requirements

For the purposes of wake turbulence separation minima, ATC classifies aircraft as *heavy*, *large* and *small*.

Heavy aircraft are aircraft capable of takeoff weights of more than 255,000 pounds regardless of their weight during any particular phase of flight. *Large* aircraft are aircraft of more than 41,000 pounds maximum certified takeoff weight up to 255,000 pounds. *Small* aircraft are aircraft of 41,000 pounds or less maximum certified takeoff weight. (For the purposes of an aircraft type rating, a *large* aircraft is one weighing more than 12,500 pounds.)

Be especially alert to the word *heavy* when used by transport-type airplanes. This means the airplane can weigh over a quarter of a million pounds. And don't be fooled by the words *small* either. A Falcon 50 jet is a three-engine business jet that packs tremendous wake turbulence potential and it is classified as a small aircraft under these definitions.

If you're *landing* your small airplane behind a heavy *jet* (or a Boeing 757, notorious for its dangerous wingtip vortices), ATC will ensure that at least a six mile separation exists between you and that heavy jet (or five miles for a B757) by the time it crosses the runway threshold. If you're *following* (not landing behind) a heavy/B757 jet, ATC will keep you either 1,000 feet below or at least five miles behind the big fellow. These distances tell something about how smaller airplanes are affected by wingtip vortices. And if ATC provides *traffic* information, issues a *visual approach clearance* or asks you to maintain *visual separation* from an airplane and you accept these instructions, then you immediately become responsible for your own distance and wake turbulence separation.

When departing directly behind a heavy/B757 jet or when your projected flight paths will cross, ATC provides a two minute wait for wake turbulence (or the five mile separation mentioned above). ATC may state, "2132 Bravo, hold for wake turbulence avoidance." The controller can't waive these holding times for you. Nor should you want him/her to, either. Doing so is about as risky as accidentally honking your horn while riding behind a Hell's Angels biker gang.

Taking off from a runway intersection poses significant hazards if a *large* or *heavy* aircraft has just departed. Your departure path could put you directly into this airplane's descending vortices. Controllers *request* a 3 minute wait for wake turbulence separation in these instances. You can waive the hold time if it's a large aircraft but not if it's a heavy/B757 jet. Then again, this isn't always a wise thing to do even if you're wearing a helmet.

WHERE TO PLACE THE FLIGHT CONTROLS WHILE TAXIING IN A QUARTERING HEADWIND

Left quartering headwind

Fig. 47

The wheel is turned into the wind (to the left) which moves the left aileron up and keeps the left wing (upwind wing) from lifting. The elevator is held in a neutral position.

WHERE TO PLACE THE FLIGHT CONTROLS WHILE TAXIING INTO A QUARTERING TAILWIND

In a left-quartering tailwind while on ground, move the controls as if you were diving with the wind–wheel forward and to the right.

Left quartering tailwind

Fig. 48

The wheel is turned with the wind (to the right) which moves left aileron down. This keeps the left wing (upwind wing) from lifting as the wind pushes down on this aileron. Elevator is pushed forward so that the wind pushes down on the tail instead of pushing it up and tipping the airplane to the right or left.

Taxiing in Crosswind Conditions

Strong crosswinds present quite a challenge when landing as well as when taxiing. I've always felt much more comfortable flying an airplane than taxiing one. Why? Airplanes were meant to fly; cars were meant to taxi. Frankly, airplanes are a little awkward on the ground. It's possible, with a strong enough wind, coupled with a mishandling of the flight controls, for an airplane to tip over resulting in wingtip or propeller damage. If, however, you know how to position your flight controls to compensate for these strong crosswinds, your airplane will always remain upright.

When taxiing in strong winds, the proper placement or movement of the flight controls helps keep downward pressure on the airplane's wings. Remember, wind wants to lift the wing up. Your job is to keep it forced downward until you're ready to fly.

When taxiing into a quartering headwind in a tricycle-gear airplane, turn the ailerons into the wind and put the elevator in a neutral position (Figure 47). This forces the upwind wing downward. Keeping the elevator neutral (instead of back or forward) keeps the nose from coming up or going down and exposing more wing surface to the wind. If you are in a taildragger, position the ailerons in the same way but keep the elevator stick pulled full aft. This keeps the tailwheel stuck to the ground for more effective steering.

Quartering tailwinds are handled a little differently. Do you remember when you rode your first tricycle as a child? When you fell (and I know you did), you fell forward to the right or left. Tricycles are unstable in this direction. Unfortunately, a quartering tailwind tends to push in the direction the airplane's most unstable. Therefore, the ailerons should be positioned so that the upwind aileron is deflected downward (Figure 48). This aileron position allows the quartering tailwind to push downward on the upwind wing instead of lifting it and tipping the airplane. Applying down elevator allows the wind to push the tail down. A downward push on the tail means that the airplane is less likely to roll forward to the right or left. With quartering tailwinds, think of moving the control as if you are diving with the wind. This helps you to properly place the aileron and

elevator controls. If you're in a taildragger and have a quartering tailwind, keep the elevator well forward to prevent that tail from lifting.

Knowing how to handle yourself around an airport is important. This chapter provides you with much of the information you'll need to successfully cope during your first solo and continuing operations. But don't be surprised if something new arises. After all, isn't that what makes flying so novel? New experiences imply new learning.

A while back, Long Beach airport had a spectacular airshow with displays of several large aircraft. One of these was a C5A Galaxy aircraft—one of the largest transports in the world. As the show ended these large airplanes readied themselves for departure. A student pilot was number one in position on Runway 30 for departure. He was listening on 119.4 MHz—the tower frequency. Behind him was a C5A Galaxy whose pilots were listening on both the tower (119.4) and ground control (133.0) frequency. The C5A pilot had forgotten to load a jeep. So the pilot called

ground control (unbeknown to the student) and requested permission to load it right there on the taxiway, while holding in the number two position for takeoff.

C5As load their equipment by raising the nose of their airplane and sticking out a large metal pallet that looks like a big tongue. As the student pilot looks behind him he sees something his instructor never told him about. The student calls the controller and says, "Hey tower, what's that guy doing?" Before the tower could respond the C5A pilot says, "Hey little buddy, we're going to eat you." The student says, "Tower, what's he going to do?" The tower replied, "Well, it sure does look like he's going to eat you, 32 Bravo!" The student pilot in that small Cessna made one of the fastest takeoffs ever recorded in Long Beach history.

Having covered airport operations at controlled and uncontrolled airports, we'll discuss the specifics of radio communication in the next chapter.

Postflight Briefing #7-1

LAHSO (Land And Hold Short Operations)

At some controlled airports, LAHSO (Land And Hold Short Operations) provides visual signage for you to *land and hold short* of intersecting *runways, taxiways* or other *designated points on a runway*. Two solid yellow lines followed by two rows of dashed yellow lines along with runway number identifiers on each side depict the designated LAHSO hold point as shown below. For instance, in the figure below,

you're in Airplane B and are landing on Runway 8. ATC clears you to land but instructs you to hold short of Runway 15 for crossing traffic, a Boeing 767 (Airplane A). This means that if you accept the LAHSO clearance, you can't use the full length of Runway 8. You should land and exit by the first convenient taxiway short of the LAHSO hold lines. If you can't exit the runway, then hold at the LAHSO hold lines. A LAHSO clearance doesn't preclude a rejected landing (a go-around). If this is necessary, then go around, but maintain safe separation from other traffic and promptly notify the controller. A ceiling of 1000' and 3 miles visibility is required for a LAHSO clearance. Student pilots should not participate in the LAHSO program. The available landing distance on a LAHSO runway is found in the *A/FD*. It's very important that you give the controller a *full readback* of the LAHSO clearance. This lets the controller know that you know what's expected of you. And, if you need the full length of the runway, then don't accept the clearance. Remember, you're the PIC!

LAND AND HOLD SHORT OPERATIONS (LAHSO)				
CITY/AIRPORT	Airport/Facility Directory excerpt	LDG RWY	HOLD–SHORT POINT	MEASURED DISTANCE
			CALIFORNIA	
BURBANK/BUR		08	15/33	3,550 feet
		15	08/26	4,250 feet

Some airports have LAHSO lights, that consist of a row of pulsating white lights installed across the runway at the hold short point. These lights, when installed, will be on at all times that LAHSO is in effect.

These numbers (white on red) represent the intersecting runway referenced in the LAHSO clearance.

Yes, 8, that's the number of bounces allowed on this particular runway. That other guy is using the runway you want!

Yellow LAHSO Lines

Yellow LAHSO Lines

4,250 feet

3,550 feet

7-29

Postflight Briefing #7-2

ADDITIONAL AIRPORT & RUNWAY LIGHTING & MARKINGS

B On precision instrument runways edge lighting is yellow for the last 2,000 feet or ½ the runway length, whichever is less.

L Vehicle roadway markings define path for vehicles that are also intended for airplane operations (checkered and solid lines used).

N Dashed double yellow taxiway edge lines define taxiway area where adjoining pavement is intended for use by aircraft such as an apron or holding area.

E In Pavement Green/Yellow Taxiway Centerline Lighting

Roadway Stop Line **M**

Red Stop Bar Lights Used on Illuminated Taxiways **J**

Ramp, Apron Area (non-ATC controlled no clearance required to move in this area)

O Movement And Non-movement Areas

Non-movement Area This Side Of Solid Yellow Line

ILS Critical Area Hold Lines **I**

Movement This Side Of Yellow Dashed Line

A Runway Edge Lighting

K No Entry Sign

C Runway Threshold Lighting

F Flashing Yellow Runway Guard Lights

D Blue Taxiway Edge Lighting

G In-pavement Yellow Clearance Bar Lights

H Geographic Position Markings

ILS Critical Area Lines

Alternating yellow and green lights from the runway centerline to the holding position.

The ILS (instrument landing system) critical area is identified by double-double solid yellow bars. When the weather is poor and pilots are flying instrument approaches (one of which is called an ILS approach), then No Controller might protect the ILS critical area, meaning that your airplane shouldn't cross these double-double lines unless you're instructed to do so. This prevents your airplane from interfering with the navigation signal used by pilots flying instrument approaches. Since the weather is quite poor when the ILS critical area is in use, you probably won't be flying and thus won't have a reason to use these lines. It's nice to know about them, nevertheless.

Postflight Briefing #7-3

THE RUNWAY STATUS LIGHT SYSTEM (RWLS)

The RWLS is a fully automated system (using multiple airport sensing devices) that provides runway status information to pilots on final approach as well as to pilots during taxi and when holding in position for takeoff. The RWLS is based on red illuminated lights that tell pilots to either stop or remain stopped until a runway conflict is resolved. The operation of this system depends on your transponder being on at all times when departing the parking area and until engine shutdown.

Runway Intersection Lights (RIL)

• Flush mounted, one-directional red lights just like THLs (see below).

• Lights directed toward arriving end of runway and extend for 3,000 feet in front of aircraft approaching intersecting runway.

• RILs end at LAHSO light bars or the hold short line for intersecting runway.

• RILs illuminate for departing aircraft or aircraft in position to depart when there is high speed traffic operating on intersecting runway. Once traffic passes intersection, the RILs will extinguish.

• RILs illuminate for aircraft that has landed and/or is rolling and there is high speed traffic on intersecting runway that's within 5 seconds of meeting at intersection. Once traffic passes, the RILs will extinguish.

• If you observe RILs illuminate, you will stop before LAHSO bars or the hold short line for the intersecting

Takeoff Hold Lights (THL)

• Flush mounted lights directed toward arriving end of runway at line-up-and-wait point.

• THLs extend for 1,500 feet in front of holding aircraft.

• When illuminated (red color), THLs signal pilot that takeoff is unsafe because runway is occupied by another aircraft or vehicle.

• Once other aircraft or vehicle exits runway, red THL lights extinguish.

• When you observe red THLs illuminate, you should stop or remain stopped and contact ATC for a resolution if your clearance is in conflict with the lights.

• NOTE: When THLs extinguish, this is not a clearance for takeoff!

Precision Approach Path Indicator Lights

Final Approach Runway Occupancy Signal (FAROS)

• When activated, the PAPI lights flash or pulse to indicate to the pilot on final approach that the runway is occupied and may be unsafe for landing.

• PAPI lights will stop flashing or pulsing when traffic moves outside of the runway hold short lines.

• If PAPI lights are flashing, you must look for and acquire runway traffic at 500 feet AGL. At 300 feet AGL you must contact ATC for a resolution.

• If PAPI continues to flash (as you go below 300 feet AGL) then you must immediately execute a go-around.

RELs consist of one light before the hold line followed by a series of evenly spaced lights to the runway edge. One additional light is located in line with other lights at runway centerline

NOTE: The RWLS system uses Airport Surface Detection Equipment (ASDE). If you are operating at any airport with ASDE, then your transponder should be on "ALT" mode at all times when moving on the airport surface.

Runway Entrance Lights: REL

• RELs are flush mounted, one-directional red lights directed toward the pilot at the runway hold line.

• RELs turn red when activated, indicating that high speed traffic is on the runway or an aircraft is on final approach within the designated activation area.

• When departing traffic on Rwy 26 reaches 30 knots, all intersection RELs ahead of the aircraft turn red then extinguish 3-4 seconds before aircraft reaches RELs.

• When aircraft landing on Rwy 26 is one mile from threshold, all RELs on Rwy 26 illuminate. Lights extinguish 3-4 seconds before aircraft approaches RELs.

• Pilots would see RELs illuminating then extinguishing in relation to airplane or vehicle operating on runway.

• If you observe RELs illuminated red, you stop at hold line or remain stopped (regardless of what your clearance says) and contact ATC to ask why your clearance is in conflict with illuminated lights.

RIL, THS and REL are in-pavement flush lights. These lights have no distinct color when not illuminated; they are bright red when lit. ATC can adjust the settings of these lights to one of five brightness levels. Never cross illuminated red lights! Red means stop, so stop!

Postflight Briefing #7-4
GROUND REFERENCE MANEUVERS

Gettin' Down With the Ground

When does reference to the ground become important during flight training? If you answered, "When the pilot is close to it," then you've just found the second best answer. The very best answer is, *when a pilot tries to put his or her airplane on the ground*. I'm speaking of putting the airplane on the runway during a landing, of course. A landing is nothing more than the ultimate ground reference maneuver, and it's the primary reason we practice to gain proficiency in the following two maneuvers.

The Rectangular Course

One of the venerable ground reference maneuvers that all pilots learn is called the *rectangular course*. Its purpose is to show you how wind affects your operations in the airport traffic pattern and that's the reason I'm presenting it here.

You'll enter the maneuver at a 45 degree angle to the downwind leg (position 1). From here you'll turn and fly parallel to a previously chosen rectangular course (position 2), remaining a small horizontal distance from the course boundary. The horizontal offset chosen is primary determined by the steepness of the bank required while turning from one course leg to another.

Fig. 49

On the turn from downwind to base leg (position 3) your groundspeed is the maximum experienced throughout the entire maneuver. Therefore, to remain the same distance from the course boundary, you'll initiate a steep bank that gradually transitions to a medium bank during the turn. Because you must crab into the wind to maintain the desired ground track, you must turn more than 90 degrees during downwind to base transition.

On the turn from base leg to final, you'll start with a medium bank then transition to a shallower bank angle since your groundspeed decreases as you turn into the wind. The base to upwind turn is less than 90 degrees since no crab angle is necessary on the upwind leg. When initiating a turn from upwind to crosswind, you'll start with a shallow bank then transition to a medium bank as your groundspeed increases slightly when turning away from the headwind. The turn here is less than 90 degrees. Finally, on the turn from crosswind to downwind, you'll turn more than 90 degrees and go from a medium bank to a steep bank as your groundspeed increases with the turn downwind.

S-Turns Across a Road

S-turns across a road looks like you're using the "catch and release" method of holding a heading. Actually, this is another one of those great ground reference maneuvers that sharpens your skills by having you fly half-circles on each side of a road that's perpendicular to the wind. You'll enter the maneuver by flying downwind (position 1). At position 2,

your groundspeed is at its maximum, so you'll need the steepest bank angle to begin the turn. At position 3, the bank is shallower and the airplane crabs into the wind to maintain the lower half-circle track. At position 4 the wings are level as you cross the road and the groundspeed is at a minimum for this maneuver. You'll begin a shallow bank at this point, and maintain the half-circle track by crabbing the airplane into the wind through position 5. From position 5 to position 6, the bank angle increases to its maximum with an increase in groundspeed.

Become proficient at this maneuver and no one will ever doubt your flying skills.

Postflight Briefing #7-5

AVOIDING RUNWAY INCURSIONS

The FAA is very concerned about something known as runway incursions. They don't want airplanes to bump into each other (and not because airplane's don't have bumpers, either). Runway incursions are events involving the unauthorized presence of an aircraft, vehicle or person on a protected area designated for the landing and takeoff of aircraft. According to the FAA, approximately 65% of these incursions are caused by pilots, three-quarters of the 65% are caused by general aviation pilots. Let's see how we might avoid this problem.

Tower controlled airports have their airport surface divided into movement areas such as taxiways and runways, and non-movement areas such as ramps, aprons, etc. (See Postflight Briefing 7-2, position O.) The movement area is found on the solid side of the parallel "solid yellow, dashed yellow" line

and is controlled by the tower. You must obtain a taxi clearance before entering this area. A clearance is not necessary to taxi on the dashed side of the parallel "solid yellow, dashed yellow" line (the non-movement area). This area is not controlled by ATC.

When operating out of an unfamiliar airport, you should check the *Airport/Facility Directory* supplemental pages for the *airport diagram* and the *hot spots* page. The *hot spots* page describes any recognized hot spots for your airport (Figure 51). These are areas designated by the letters *HS* followed by a reference number on the airport diagram. Hot spots are enclosed by open circles or polygons on the airport diagram and are areas which are complex or confusing areas of taxiway or runway intersections offering increased risk of runway incursions for the unaware. Make sure you look closely at these areas before taxi and before landing. At John Wayne airport, for instance, HS 2 is an area between parallel runways where pilots have been known to turn off one runway and directly onto another without a clearance (Figure 52).

Once you're familiar with any hot spots that exist you'll want to use the airport diagram (Figure 53) to plot your assigned or planned taxi route to the departure runway. That's right. Run your finger along the route you were assigned as if it's a miniature airplane (just don't make the engine noise...unless you really want to).

If at any time you become uncertain about your position or the instructions you were given, ask ATC to say them again or request *progressive taxi instructions* (meaning that ATC will give you step-by-step taxi instructions).

ATC will normally give you a clearance to the departure runway. If ATC tells you to hold short of the runway, then you are required to read back all runway *hold short* instructions to the controller, verbatim. If you want a career in standup comedy, this isn't the place to start it. Be serious, be clear, be accurate with your readback. When cleared to a runway, I set the heading bug (on the DG) to the number of the departure runway. This helps ensure that when ATC clears me onto the runway, I'm actually on the correct runway (some runways intersect at a small angle and it's possible to confuse one with the other if you're not careful). Speaking of being cleared onto the runway, ATC no longer uses the term *taxi into position and hold* for departing airplanes. Instead, the phrase *line up and wait* is now used because it offers less chance of misinterpretation. And if you're waiting on the runway and don't hear anything from ATC for 90 seconds, call them and remind them of where you are. Yes, controllers are people too, and they can forget about you.

Whatever you do, don't taxi onto a runway unless you've been given clearance to do so. Period! Doing so becomes extremely dangerous if that runway is being used by another airplane. This is the reason that pilots are requested to illuminate all external airplane lights when crossing any runway (landing and taxi lights, nav lights, strobe lights, etc.). It simply makes it easier for other airplanes to see you just in case you aren't where you're supposed to be or someone else isn't where one of you should be. And when you line up and wait on the runway at night, do so a little to the left or right of the centerline. This makes your airplane easier to identify (and avoid) on the runway at night.

So keep your eyes open, ask ATC for clarification when necessary, and before you start taxiing, always use your airport diagram to make certain you know where you're going and how you are going to get there.

Chapter Eight
Radio Operations
Aviation Spoken Here

Controllers are real people, just like you and me.

I'm telling you this before we start talking about talking on the radio because the people you will usually be talking to on an aviation radio are controllers. For some reason the simple act of communicating with one strikes terror in the heart of most student pilots. Even lawyers become speechless when asked to push and talk.

Radios make us nervous because we're afraid of embarrassing ourselves. Mouthing a mistake when speaking to controllers who sound like radio announcers seems unbearable. It's voices like those of the controllers that got Noah into boat building and gave Moses the 10 Commandments.

It never fails to amaze me how normally-loquacious people can become completely tongue-tied when confronted by the microphone in an airplane. I've had student pilots who, on their first attempt at radio work, just moved their mouths without emitting a sound, kind of like a large goldfish at feeding time. I usually set a 30 second limit on such behavior for my students or they'll hyperventilate.

There are actually several factors at work here simultaneously. First, new pilots usually have their brains pretty well tied up with the mechanics of handling the airplane. They literally have trouble flying and talking at the same time. Second, there is a definite aviation language, and at first it does sound quite foreign. Nobody wants to say the *wrong* thing, so some student pilots hope to get around it by saying *nothing*.

It won't work. Communication is crucial, especially in today's increasingly-controlled airspace. I'm convinced that learning to fly might be the cure for teenagers who spend too much time on the phone. Nothing will shut them up quicker than telling them they have to talk.

Students, and even experienced pilots, often find it difficult to believe controllers will be nonjudgmental. As a result, it's easy to become self-conscious about our radio behavior. In fact, most controllers are eager to help beginners, and they'll do everything they can to assist you, including slowing down a bit if you ask.

Visit the tower and meet some real controllers. You'll see for yourself. As a courtesy, call in advance. Don't just show up and start banging on the tower. Given enough notice, they might let you plug in and listen to traffic under their control (but don't for a second think they'll let you control a few airplanes, even if you have Nintendo experience). As an added bonus, you'll gain some real insight into how the air traffic control function operates, and what can (and can't) be done and seen from the controller's perspective.

THE AIR TRAFFIC CONTROL TOWER

Radio Technique

Using the radio is no great mystery. When transmitting, move the mic close to your mouth (Figure 1). Don't slobber on it. Don't lick it. Just hold it close and speak in a normal voice. Whatever you do, don't yell. You'll blast the headset off the controllers' ears.

Unlike telephones, aviation radios cannot transmit and receive at the same time. To transmit, simply push the microphone button and speak. To listen, you must let go of the button. With headsets, the process is the same. You simply push the *transmit button* to speak, and release it to listen. This button, sometimes called the *push-to-talk switch,* or *PTT,* is usually located on the flight control column as shown in Figure 2. Be careful. Sometimes the electric pitch-trim switch is located next to the radio's push-to-talk switch. One of my students accidentally confused these switches in the traffic pattern. Every time he called the tower, the airplane's nose dropped.

Many women and some men have high-pitched voices. The excitement

Move the headset mic close to your mouth when transmitting.

Fig. 1

The push-to-talk switch is usually located on the joystick or control yoke.

Fig. 2

of flying, mixed with the anxiety of talking to controllers, tends to raise such a voice an octave or two. Radios often provide another boost in pitch. You've now gone ultrasonic, and your voice is probably causing bats to fly into walls or killing cockroaches for hundreds of miles in every direction.

To avoid being cited by the SPCA, and shunned by others on the airwaves, it's a good idea to develop a *radio voice* that is deliberately lower

in pitch. Emulate those deep-toned FM DJ's from late night radio. You may not believe this, but a controller once told me that he turned down a pilot's request for radar service (something it is within a controller's discretion to do under certain circumstances) just to keep this guy's screeching voice off the frequency.

The secret to sounding like a pro on the radio is knowing what you want to say, saying it in the shortest, most efficient manner, then getting off the microphone. Brevity is the hallmark of an experienced pilot. Follow Rod Machado's Linguistic Legerdemain Law which states:

- Speak low
- Tell' em only what they need to know
- Let go

Practice this by having your instructor write out on 3x5 cards all of the common communication statements you're likely to encounter. If you're operating at a controlled airport, these exchanges might include calls to ground control, to the tower for departure, to the tower for entry into the pattern, etc. Operating at an airport without an operating control tower, these statements might include departing advisory, traffic pattern position calls, etc.

How do you get good on the radio? Practice! Purchase a little VHF receiver (you can get them real cheap) and listen to the tower. Make recordings and listen to them over

Shhhh.

Over the years I've witnessed some unusual cockpit behavior relating to the radio. Once, while sitting in the runup area (a place where the engine and airplane are checked and readied for takeoff), I overheard the following exchange between a student and a tower controller who had a quick mind and wonderful sense of humor. The instructor was coaching his student on proper use of the radio when the student apparently keyed the microphone (pushed its button to transmit) before the instructor was finished giving directions. The following conversation in its entirety was transmitted over the airwaves:

Student (whispering): "What do I say? What do I say?"

Instructor (whispering): "Tell him you want to take off."

Student (in loud voice close to mike): "I want to take off."

Student (whispering): "What do I do now?"

Instructor (whispering): "Nothing. Let go of that button, dummy."

The controller, after hearing all this, decided to have a little fun.

Tower controller (whispering): "What do I say? What to I say?"

Same controller pretending to be another person (whispering): "Tell him he's cleared for takeoff."

Tower controller (in loud voice): "You're cleared for takeoff."

Tower controller (whispering): "What do I do now?"

Same controller pretending to be another person (whispering): "Nothing. Let go of that button, dummy."

Listen to Learn and Learn to Listen

Learning good radio work is part and parcel of being a good pilot. One of the fastest ways to learn is to listen (that's a good general rule). Invest in a small battery-operated radio that receives aviation frequencies. Then listen to the tower controllers. Listen to the ground controllers. Listen to the ATIS. Listen whenever and wherever you can (in some urban areas you can pick up a dozen or more frequencies throughout the city; in other places you'll have to get near the local airport to listen in).

You can teach yourself to talk, too. Just don't do it on the radio. I know one person who used to practice in the shower. He'd give himself clearances to taxi, then acknowledge the transmission. He'd clear himself for takeoff, give himself permission to change frequencies, then he'd call up approach control and ask for in-flight traffic advisories, carefully providing his call sign, position, altitude and request. On some of his coast-to-coast shower flights his skin got a bit shriveled, but he was *very* good on the radio (especially while flying in the rain).

As in much of aviation, practice really does make perfect.

and over again. You can learn to listen and interpret at a rate 10 times the rate of normal speech with a 40% distortion of the transmission (to a student, this is exactly what controllers sound like). All it takes is practice.

If you find the controllers talking too fast for you, tell them you're a student pilot. When driving down the road and seeing an automobile with *student driver* written on the side, don't you watch it a little closer than the other cars? If it's swerving all over the place, you're sure to keep an eye on this target. Tower controllers do the same thing with student pilots.

I prefer that all my students inform ATC they are *students* by saying, "Tower, this is November 2132 Bravo, ready for takeoff, student pilot." At a local airport in California, I had a student with me who mentioned to the controller that he was a student pilot. Replying without missing a beat the controller said, "Hey, don't worry, I'm a student controller. We can mess each other up." Be advised, some controllers have a wild sense of humor.

VHF Transmissions

Aviation transmissions are usually on the very high frequency (VHF) portion of the radio spectrum. Like most things in life, this has its good and less-good points. Operation in this frequency range minimizes

interference from atmospheric static and can provide excellent range. The downside is that the range is limited by the *line of sight* nature of VHF signals. There must be an unobstructed path between the transmitting antenna and the receiving antenna in order to communicate (Figure 3). While lower-frequency signals will bend and bounce, VHF is strictly point-to-point. Line-of-sight limitations are one of the biggest problems pilots face in communicating. The solution is to climb. The higher you are, the less chance there is of some obstacle interfering with your radio's reach.

The Federal Communications Commission (FCC) assigns frequencies ranging from 118.0 MHz to

135.975 MHz for aviation use. (*Hertz* is the international unit for frequency. One *Hertz* is one cycle per second. One *megahertz*, abbreviated MHz, is one million cycles per second.) VHF radio frequencies are spaced at 25,000 Hertz (.025 MHz) intervals: 118.000, 118.025, 118.050, etc. All radio frequencies have six digits even though it's not apparent that we're using all six of them. For instance, the frequency of 118.0 MHz is actually 118.000 MHz and 118.05 is MHz is actually 118.050 MHz.

If you're using a handheld microphone, please be careful about where you place it. When it's not in use, put the mic on the hook where it belongs. When it's not being used, don't lay it between your legs. One pilot put the mic between his legs while landing at a very busy airport. Everything after that he said with a thigh. From base to landing, this mic man radiated his landing commentary to the world—and blocked the frequency for everyone else. All the tower heard was, "I can't believe it, what a bad landing, I'm so messed up, I'm really messed up, UH-OOOH!"

Realizing what had happened, the pilot put the microphone back where it belonged. The controller said, "Aircraft that's messed up, please repeat your call number." The pilot came back with, "I may be messed up, but I'm not that messed up."

VHF LINE OF SIGHT TRANSMISSION

Fig. 3

I can hear the tower perfectly, geesh!

I can't hear the tower!

I'm not gonna be a rug in his den.

VHF (very high frequency) transmissions are "line of sight," meaning that there must be no obstacles between the transmitting and receiving stations. Airplane A has line of sight with station C, airplane B doesn't. Therefore, if the pilot of airplane B is having trouble receiving or transmitting, he or she should climb.

What Is This VOR You Speak of?

Before GPS (yes, there was such a time) the most common form of electronic navigation was known as VOR (*Very high frequency Onmi directional Radio range*) navigation. Today, most light sport airplanes use GPS and aren't equipped to navigate using the many VOR ground-based transmitting stations located across the country. Figure 4, position 1 shows the typical VOR ground-based station on a sectional chart. Position 2 shows the VOR frequency box containing the specific frequency (114.8 MHz) you'd tune into your airborne VOR equipment to receive the ground-based VOR navigation signal. Position 3 is the VOR compass rose that provides a reference for each of the 360 radials and courses projected by the ground-based VOR station.

Despite not navigating via VOR stations, they are still useful to you as a sport pilot. As you'll soon see, the VHF frequencies listed above the VOR frequency box (Figure 5, position 4) can be used to communicate directly with the nearest Flight Service Station to obtain weather and flight plan information. Additionally, when the Flight Service Station provides enroute weather, this is often defined geographically with reference to the positions of several VOR stations. Having a sectional chart showing these VOR stations allows you to understand how the weather affects you.

Fig. 4

Fig. 5

of certain heavy metal bands). Once the volume level is set, you simply push the button in to deactivate the squelch mode.

Talking the Talk

College professors sound like college professors; engineers sound like engineers; and pilots sound like pilots. If you are going to be a pilot, you will want to talk the talk. It won't do much in terms of providing lift for the airplane, but it will provide considerable lift for the pilot. If you hear the controller laughing hysterically after you've said something, it doesn't improve your pilot self-image (by the way, they don't really laugh hysterically).

As I've pointed out earlier, aviation has its own language. *Avspeak* consists of acronyms, special vocabulary, and particular shorthand ways of saying things. Much of this has evolved because of the need to communicate on the radio, where it's essential to communicate a lot while saying little.

You'll learn avspeak as you go along, but I want to provide a few basics so you can start sounding good from the get go.

The first and most important item is identifying yourself. Remember, controllers can't see you over the radio, and they hate guessing games.

Radio Equipment

Figure 6 shows a radio typical of those found in most general aviation airplanes. The control at position A consists of a small knob on top of a bigger knob. These knobs are used to select the frequency seen in the window (C). On some radios, there are two windows; the *active frequency* (the one you're currently transmitting and receiving on) is on the left; the window on the right shows the *standby frequency*. Pushing a button (D) swaps what's in the two windows. This arrangement allows you to select a frequency and keep it in standby until needed. Even better, it keeps the frequency you just signed off of handy in case nobody is home when you call on the new frequency (sometimes controllers hand out the wrong frequency, or pilots mishear what they're told).

Button B is the on/off/volume control. Turning it clockwise turns the radio on and increases the volume. Of course, if nobody is talking it's difficult to know how loud is loud

enough. Pulling the volume button all the way out usually activates the *squelch mode*. The squelch provides a pilot with the sound of static, which can be used to set the volume level (young student pilots will notice that this static is very similar to the tunes

Fig. 6

Frequent Flyer Frequencies

The following is a partial list of common aviation communication frequencies. You don't have to memorize all of these, though you should commit the ones **in boldface** to memory, because they're people you need to communicate with for critical information or at critical times.

118.0 to 135.975 MHz - Air Traffic Control general frequency range

121.5 MHz - Emergency frequency and ELT's

121.6 to 121.9 MHz - Ground control at tower airports

122.1 MHz - FSS receive-only and transmit other frequency

122.2 MHz - FSS common enroute frequency

122.7 MHz - Unicom at airports without an operating control tower

122.725 MHz - Unicom at airports without an operating control tower

122.75 MHz - Air-to-air communications (private fixed wing aircraft)

122.8 MHz - Unicom at airports without an operating control tower

122.9 MHz - Self-announce on Multicom at airports with no tower, FSS or Unicom

122.925 MHz - Multicom, forestry management and fire suppression, fish and game management and protection and environmental monitoring and protection

122.95 MHz - Unicom at airports with a control tower or FSS on field

122.975 MHz - Unicom at airports without an operating control tower

123.0 MHz - Unicom at airports without an operating control tower

123.025 MHz - Air-to-air communication general aviation helicopters

123.05 and 123.075 MHz - Unicom at airports without an operating control tower

123.3 MHz - Aviation instruction, glider, hot air balloon (not an advisory service)

123.5 MHz - Aviation instruction, glider, hot air balloon (not an advisory service)

You'll have to tell them who you are. Actually, they're not interested in who *you* are; they want to know the number of the airplane they're talking to. Controllers don't really talk to people, they talk to airplanes. So don't expect statements like, "OK Bob, cleared to land Bob, and Bob, contact ground control after you've cleared the runway. Have a good day Bob."

Suppose your aircraft number is N794CT and you want to call an ATC facility. Using the phonetic alphabet I described in Chapter 7, your call would be:

"Ontario Approach, this is Cessna seven niner four Charlie Tango, over."

The prefix *N* is dropped when the aircraft manufacturer's name or model number is stated. After initial communication is established, ATC may use an abbreviated call sign and refer to your aircraft by the prefix N and your last three digits or letter. In the above example, ATC may refer to you as *November four Charlie Tango*, or more commonly just *four Charlie Tango*.

Knowing how to refer to yourself on the radio is a good starting point in learning to talk avspeak. By the way, most aircraft have their call sign posted on a small placard somewhere among the instruments, or right above them. Many pilots fly multiple aircraft — especially instructors — so it's handy to be able to look and know who you are at the moment!

When informing ATC of your altitude, aviation phraseology should be used in the following manner (I'll assume that you are flying below 18,000' MSL):

If your altitude is 6,500 feet, state this as *six thousand five hundred*.

If your altitude is 10,500 feet, state this as *one zero thousand five hundred*.

If you're referring to a frequency like 125.6 MHz, it's properly stated as *one two five point six*. Decimals are identified by the word *point*.

Over is often used at the end of a transmission, although it is not essential if the context and pattern of your communication makes it obvious when you're done talking. When you use *over* at the end of your statements, it means that a reply is expected. It's also an effective way of telling the receiving party that you're done talking. If we were to use such language at a cocktail party, there would be much less confusion about

Tower, I Don't Know Who I Am...

A student reported downwind during a slow traffic morning at Riverside airport. The small plate with the airplane's identification number had fallen off the panel and he couldn't remember his aircraft call. The transmission went like this:

Student: "Ah Riverside tower, this is November... ahhh, ahhh, ahhh, I don't know who I am."
Tower: "Whoever doesn't know who they are, what's your name if you have one?"
Student: "My name is Bob, I'm at your airport and I still don't know who I am."
Tower: "We know who you are. You are Bob and you're cleared to land, over."
Student: "Tower, this is Bob, I understand I'm cleared to land. Thank you."
Tower: "Ah Bob, after landing, you're cleared to taxi to your destination so you can find yourself, over."
Student: "This is Bob, roger, wilco."

A wise man says, "Pilot who doesn't know who he is, probably doesn't know where he's at."

who's still talking. "Well Bob, how are you doing, over?" "To tell you the truth Frank, I'm not sure, over."

The word *roger* is used to let the transmitting party know their transmission has been received. It should not be used to answer a question requiring a *yes* or *no* answer. Speaking of *yes* and *no,* these become *affirmative* and *negative* in avspeak. Once again, the goal is to create clarity and eliminate (as much as possible) any chance of confusion. *No* can sound like too many other words when said over an aviation radio, which degrades speech considerably (no matter how silver-tongued you are). *Yes* could be *I guess,* or *What a mess.*

When the tower says to do something and you agree that you can and will accept the instruction, the proper response is *wilco,* which means you have received the message, understand it and *will comply.* Sometimes pilots are a little lazy and use *roger* instead of *wilco.* I can assure you that the words *roger dodger* are not part of the aviation communication lingo, so please don't use them. If you're carrying around any leftover CB lingo, get your ears on for a second good buddy, and listen up. Drop it, lest you become the laughingstock of the aviation airwaves.

Flight Service Station is a nice name, but a bit long for throwing around on the radio. That's why we call a Flight Service Station *Radio.* Hawthorne FSS becomes *Hawthorn Radio* on a radio call.

Other ground stations have their own nomenclature:

Airport unicom ..... *Corona Unicom.*

EFAS - Enroute flight Advisory Service (Flight Watch) ..... *Hawthorne Flight Watch.*

Air Traffic Control Tower ..... *Lambert Tower.*

Ground Control ..... *Boise Ground.*

Clearance Delivery ..... *Ontario Clearance Delivery.*

Approach Control ..... *New York Approach.*

Departure Control .... *St. Louis Departure.*

Air Route Traffic Control Center ..... *Miami Center.*

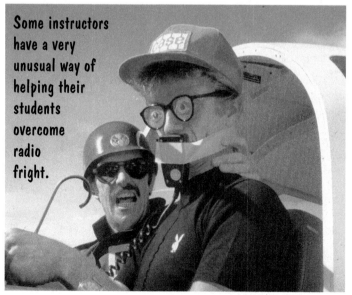

Some instructors have a very unusual way of helping their students overcome radio fright.

Then there's the matter of time. Pilots have lots of it. *Zulu* or *UTC (coordinated universal time)* time is the time in Greenwich, England. Who cares? You do, because many aviation times are stated as Zulu (or Z) times. Weather reports are stated in Zulu time, and the flight plans you file will give departure and arrival times in Zulu time. By using a clock in one place, pilots who sometimes cross large amounts of space in a relatively brief period don't wrestle with local time zones and conversions. When it's 0300 Zulu, it's 0300 Zulu *everywhere in the world,* although what it comes out to be in *local time* varies.

Another type of pilot time is the 24-hour clock (like that used in the military). In this system, the hours of the day are numbered from 1 to 24; 1 a.m. is 0100 hours, and 1 p.m. is 1300 hours. Local time is expressed on the 24 hour clock in aviation. Of course, this can be a bit of a mystery to non-aviators. One time I was on my way out of a parking garage. The young attendant looked at my ticket, subtracted 1300 (1 p.m., when I'd entered) from 1500 (3 p.m., when I was leaving) and announced the bill as 200 hours times $3/hour, for a total of $600. No checks or credit cards accepted (ouch!).

There's lots more avtalk to learn, but this will get you started.

Controlled Airports

As you learned in Chapter 7, some airports have control towers and others don't. The purpose of a control tower is to manage the flow of traffic into and out of the airport. The government usually installs a control tower when there is enough traffic to justify its existence. You can reasonably assume that an airport graced with a tower is (or has the potential to be) a busy place.

Most towers are staffed by at least two controllers at any time—one to control airborne traffic, and one to control ground traffic (and perform other duties). The ground controller is responsible for seeing that planes don't have any unexpected meetings on the ground, and that they don't intrude unexpectedly onto runways. That's why pilots are required to call and obtain permission—a *clearance*—before taxiing the airplane beyond specific areas at a controlled field.

When making your initial call to ground control, you will usually have listened to the ATIS recording. You'll tell the controller you have *information Bravo,* and he or she will clear you to taxi to the runway or some intermediate point. If it's a very large airport, you might be given a specific routing via particular taxiways.

Ground control frequencies are usually between 121.6 MHz and 121.9 MHz. After landing, it's not unusual to hear the controller say, *32 Bravo, contact ground point niner.* They're assuming that you know the beginning part of the frequency is *121* for 121.9 MHz. I realized how confusing this could be when one of my students, having just landed, taxied off the runway when the tower controller said, "32 Bravo, contact ground point six." He sat there, twirling the radio's frequency dial. I said, "Bob, what are you doing?" He replied, "I'm trying to get these first three numbers to go away." I immediately loosened his tie, thinking it might be restricting the flow of oxygenated blood to his brain.

After you've landed and taxied off the runway, don't automatically switch from tower to ground control frequency. Wait until you've been advised by the tower controller to do so. The tower controller may need you to maneuver on the taxiway to make room for other airplanes. If you're on a different frequency, you won't hear these instructions.

Some busier airports have an additional person in the tower known as a

clearance delivery controller (we'll explain more about this controller later in this chapter). Essentially, he or she is the person providing you with detailed instructions on how to depart that airport's airspace (typically Class C or B airspace). These instructions are essential when specific routes or departure procedures are necessary for traffic management.

Control Tower Communications

Figure 7 shows how control tower frequencies are portrayed on an aeronautical sectional chart. Columbia Regional's control tower frequency is 119.3 MHz. The *(CT)* identifies this as the tower frequency. The ATIS is found on 128.45 MHz. There is a unicom station at the field on 122.95 MHz (this is the unicom frequency for an airport with a control tower or

FSS on the field). You can call for fuel, transient parking availability, or other general information on the unicom frequency. It's usually staffed by one of the large FBO's (fixed based operators) having fuel services on the field. The small star next to the control tower's frequency means this tower is in operation only part time (usually closed from late evening until early morning).

At the bottom of every aeronautical sectional chart is a listing of the towers' hours of operation, ground and tower frequencies, ATIS frequencies, as well as ASR or PAR radar information for each airport, as shown in Figure 8. (ASR—Airport Surveillance Radar and PAR—Precision Approach Radar are services that provide radar guidance to the very beginning of the runway.) Columbia Regional's tower is in operation from 0700 to 2300 local time (7

Control tower frequency on a sectional chart follows the letters CT.

Fig. 7

Tower information is shown on a tab of the sectional chart.

CONTROL TOWER FREQUENCIES ON KANSAS CITY SECTIONAL CHART

CONTROL TOWER	OPERATES	TWR FREQ	GND CON	ATIS	ASR/PAR
BILLARD NF	0700-1900	118.7 257.8	121.9		
COLUMBIA REGIONAL	0700-2300	119.3*	121.6	128.45	
DRAKE	0600-2200	128.0 371.9	121.8	133.1	
FORBES	0545-2200	120.8 255.9	121.7 275.8	128.25	ASR
FORNEY AAF	0830-1630 MON-FRI	125.4 241.0		118.7 237.5	

Fig. 8

a.m. to 11 p.m.). Operational hours of the tower can also be found in the Airport/Facility Directory (more on this later in the chapter).

Figure 9, position A shows that Austin-Straubel airport has a Flight Service Station located on the field (position B). (The FSS is a place where you get weather information and file flight plans). On top and to the right of the dark-lined blue box (position C) is a frequency of 122.55 MHz. This is the frequency for Green Bay FSS.

Let's say you wanted to contact Green Bay FSS while in flight in order to have the FSS specialist update your VFR flight plan. You'd simply transmit and receive on 122.55 MHz and say, "Green Bay Radio, this is Cessna 2132 Bravo on one two two point five five, Green Bay VOR, over." (A VOR is a ground-based navigation station.) Notice that we tell the FSS specialist what frequency we're using. Why? Unlike most tower controllers, the FSS specialist is often monitoring several frequencies that broadcast and receive over a large geographic area. If you don't announce which one you're on, the specialist might have to try five buttons before finding you.

Flight Service Station Frequencies

Figure 10 shows a heavy, solid-line box (position A) near McKellar-Sipes Regional airport (position B). When you see a heavy-line box, it usually indicates the name of the nearest FSS, as well as stating the standard frequencies for communication. Above the heavy-lined box is a single frequency: 122.65 MHz. This frequency can be used for direct communication with the FSS.

A heavy-lined box (point A) indicates the name of the nearest FSS (Jackson) and that standard frequencies of 122.2 and 121.5 MHz (as well as those shown above the box) are available for communication with FSS even though these frequencies aren't listed.

Fig. 10

In addition, the heavy-lined box also implies that 122.2 MHz (the common FSS frequency) and 121.5 MHz (the universal emergency frequency) are available and monitored.

What about communicating with the FSS when you are far away from the nearest FSS location? Figure 11 shows how this might be done. Position A is the location of a VOR, which is a ground-based navigation station. Position B shows the frequency box for this VOR. Underneath the VOR's frequency box the words *San Diego* are listed in brackets. This is the controlling FSS for this VOR and the area around the VOR (most VORs are monitored for proper operation by FSSs).

To communicate with the FSS directly, simply transmit and receive on 123.65 MHz (the frequency listed on top of the box at position C). Even though you might be many miles away from San Diego, you'll be able to speak with them through a transmitter and receiver in the area. In other words, the transmitter and receiver near the Julian VOR are connected by a telephone line (or satellite connection) directly to San Diego.

Another means of communicating directly with the nearest FSS is shown in the Waycross VOR frequency box of Figure 12. The 122.1R above the box (position A) means that the Macon FSS (listed under the box) receives (that's what the *R* stands for—

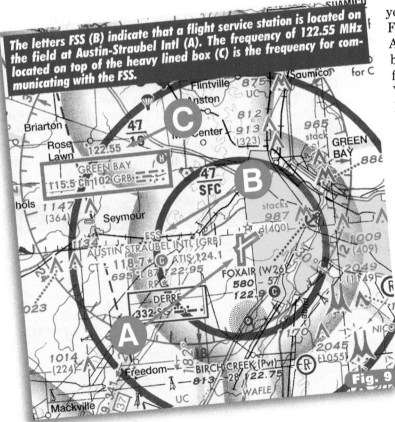

The letters FSS (B) indicate that a flight service station is located on the field at Austin-Straubel Intl (A). The frequency of 122.55 MHz located on top of the heavy lined box (C) is the frequency for communicating with the FSS.

Fig. 9

You can communicate with the nearest FSS (San Diego in this case) on the frequency listed above the VOR frequency box (123.65 MHz) as show by position C.

Fig. 11

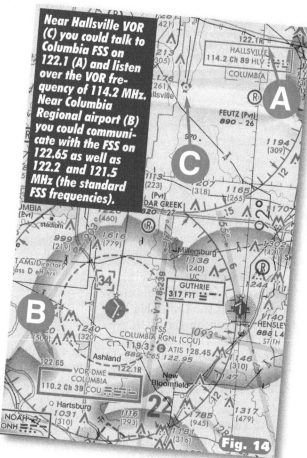

Near Hallsville VOR (C) you could talk to Columbia FSS on 122.1 (A) and listen over the VOR frequency of 114.2 MHz. Near Columbia Regional airport (B) you could communicate with the FSS on 122.65 as well as 122.2 and 121.5 MHz (the standard FSS frequencies).

Fig. 14

don't look for an *R* on the radio dial) on this frequency. To communicate with Macon, you'd simply transmit on 122.1 MHz and listen on the VOR frequency of 110.2 MHz. Your transmission should go something like this: "Macon radio, this is 2132 Bravo, on one two two point one, listening Waycross, over." The FSS specialist would immediately know which transmitter to use. You simply turn the VOR receiver volume up and listen to the FSS on the VOR frequency while transmitting on 122.1 MHz.

You won't find the frequency 122.1R listed above a VOR's frequency box if that VOR station has no voice receiving capability. Figure 13 shows a line underneath El Dorado's VOR frequency. Underlining usually means someone is trying to attract your attention to something. A line means no voice is available on this frequency. (That's why I don't have a mustache. My wife said, "With a nose that big, why underline it?")

Figure 14 further clarifies the distinction between a heavy-lined and a thin-lined VOR frequency box. This figure shows two VOR boxes: the thin-lined VOR box for Hallsville (position A) and the thick-lined VOR box for Columbia (position B). The heavy-lined box tells us that 122.2 MHz and 121.5 MHz

The R next to the 122.1 (A) indicates that you can talk to the Macon FSS on 122.1 MHz but must listen over the VOR frequency of 110.2 MHz. This allows communications with the FSS via some form of remote communication outlet.

Author's Insert Here

Fig. 12

A line underneath the VOR frequency (A) shows that no voice capability exists on that frequency. You won't find an R next to any frequency for FSS communication in these instances.

Author's Insert Here

Fig. 13

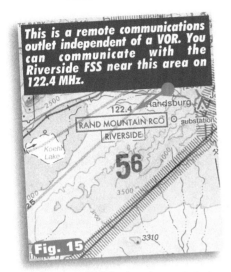

This is a remote communications outlet independent of a VOR. You can communicate with the Riverside FSS near this area on 122.4 MHz.

Fig. 15

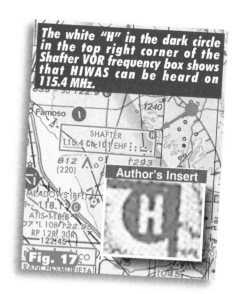

The white "H" in the dark circle in the top right corner of the Shafter VOR frequency box shows that HIWAS can be heard on 115.4 MHz.

Author's Insert

Fig. 17

are also available in that vicinity. Near Hallsville VOR you could only communicate with the Columbia FSS on 122.1 and listen on the VOR frequency of 114.2 MHz. In the vicinity of Columbia (position B) you could use 122.65 MHz as well as 122.2 MHz and 121.5 MHz for FSS communication.

Figure 15 shows an RCO (remote communication outlet). This is a communication outlet separate from a VOR. The Rand Mountain RCO is a remoted transmitter and receiver that connects you to a distant facility. In this instance, you can communicate with the Riverside FSS through the RCO even though you're some distance away. If you were near this

site you would simply dial 122.4 MHz on your communications radio and make the following call: "Riverside Radio, this is Cessna 2132 Bravo, on one two two point four, listening Rand Mountain, over." Give the FSS specialist a few seconds (perhaps even a minute or longer) to establish communication. Be patient. These FSS folks may be talking with other pilots who you can't hear because they're on a different frequency.

Not knowing how to find and use all the communication frequencies available is a little like not knowing what all the dials and buttons in the cockpit do. Not smart. Not safe. Not fun. It's very comforting to have someone to call on when you're not certain what the weather's doing up ahead, or if your engine starts sounding a bit unusual a million miles from anywhere. Modern communications capabilities mean you will rarely be out of calling range of *someone*, as long as you know how to read the available information and put it to use.

HIWAS and ASOS/AWOS

Sounds like the two guys Simon and Garfunkel wouldn't let into their band, doesn't it? Figure 17 shows the Shafter VOR frequency box with a little "H" in the top righthand corner. When you see this, it means that HIWAS Hazardous In-flight Weather

Advisory Service), when available, can be heard on the listed VOR frequency.

HIWAS is a continuous broadcast of in-flight weather advisories. *Weather advisory* can be a polite way of saying you should probably be thinking about where you'd like to park the plane. One thing you will soon learn in aviation is that the FSS will never tell you *don't go*, or *land*. They don't make decisions for pilots. Hints, yes, but no decisions. They just provide information, and leave it to your common sense to act in a way that will preserve your hide and that of your ever-trusting passengers.

Switch Hitter

We'll be discussing the use of VOR equipment for navigation a bit later, but it has a non-navigation feature you need to know about. Figure 16 shows a typical VOR receiver in the airplane. It has a switch with three positions: OFF, VOICE, IDENT.

Every VOR transmits a three-letter, Morse code identifier which permits you to confirm that what you see in the frequency window is what you've got. To receive the VOR's Morse code identification, you simply switch to the *IDENT* position. In this position, the Morse code is emphasized and voice transmissions (if any) can be heard weakly in the background.

The *VOICE* position is used to move voice transmissions to center stage and quiet the Morse code. This is the position in which you leave the switch whenever you are receiving or are expecting to receive voice transmissions over the VOR's frequency.

Typical VOR Navigation Receivers

Fig. 16

The reverse bold A in a circle within the VOR frequency box shows that ASOS/AWOS weather information can be heard on the VOR frequency.

Fig. 18

Mayo Emergency

Several years ago, a pilot had an emergency. In his anxious state, he forgot the word *Mayday*. He got as close as he could, yelling, "*Mayonnaise, mayonnaise, mayonnaise.*" Someone (probably from the Mayo clinic) responded immediately.

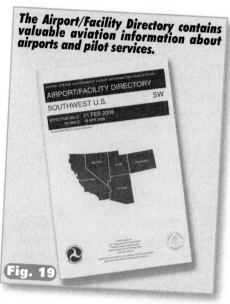

The Airport/Facility Directory contains valuable aviation information about airports and pilot services.

Fig. 19

If something is happening on the HIWAS frequency, you should be all ears. You'll learn more about this in the weather chapter. For now, when you suspect bad weather, leave the VOR volume up slightly so you can listen to any broadcast of weather hazards.

Figure 18 shows a VOR frequency box having a black circle with a white "A" (a reverse-bold "A") inside. This indicates that the ASOS or AWOS "one minute" weather information associated with the airport nearest the VOR (Sheboygan, in this instance) can be heard on Falls' VOR frequency. While you'll learn more about ASOS and AWOS in Chapter 12, it's important to know that you can listen to the local airport weather

Can't Raise the Controller On the Radio?

1. Check for stuck mic.
2. Check frequency—try another frequency or facility.
3. Check connections/plugs on mic.
4. Try another mic.
5. Check circuit breakers.
6. Check facility hours of operation
7. Use spare handheld radio.
8. In the air—look for light gun signals.
9. On the ground—shut down, phone tower.

information at Sheboygan on 110.0 MHz. This information is broadcast minute to minute (thus the reason it being called the "one minute" weather information), and it may contain information on ceiling and sky cover, visibility, precipitation and so on.

The Emergency Frequency

121.5 MHz is the international emergency frequency. Whether you're flying in Florida or France, Iowa or Italy, a call on 121.5 will usually get you help.

There is a tremendous bond between people in the aviation community, especially in times of trouble. A pilot declaring an emergency is entitled to—and receives—the undivided attention and assistance of anyone and everyone within radio range.

This doesn't mean you *must* be having an emergency to use 121.5. This frequency can be used if you know of no other frequency on which to communicate with someone, though it should be used that way as a last resort. You should be able to figure out another frequency that will permit you to communicate with someone, leaving 121.5 available for a pilot who has an emergency.

If you *do* have an emergency, 121.5 MHz is the frequency to use. Of course, this assumes you are not talking to someone else at the time of the emergency, such as a tower con-

troller, radar controller or FSS specialist. In this instance, it's obviously best to stay with the person to whom you're speaking.

The international distress call is *Mayday* repeated three times. This will get the attention of everyone listening on *any* frequency (it goes without saying that the words, "ahh-hhhhhhh!, ahhhhhhh!, ahhhhhhh!," screamed loudly into the microphone will also get someone's attention, but it's not as professional). Having said the magic word, you just sit back and wait. Usually help will be at hand (or ear) in microseconds. Someone will usually come on the frequency and say, *Aircraft transmitting Mayday, please identify yourself.* After that, you identify and explain the nature of the problem. We'll talk more about emergencies when we get to transponders.

The Airport/Facility Directory

The *Airport/Facility Directory* (*A/FD*), shown in Figure 19, is a booklet published every 56 days by the National Oceanic and Atmospheric Administration (NOAA). This is kind of a guidebook for pilots. Instead of listing tacky motels and hot nightspots, the *A/FD* contains valuable information on airports, seaplane bases, heliports open to the public, communications data, navigational facilities, certain special notices and procedures, and even information on parachute jump areas and areas having glider operations. Figure 20 shows a sample excerpt from the *A/FD*.

Why would you want to know where parachute jump areas are? There's a good reason. You don't want to hit or come close to hitting one of these folks. It's bad enough they've already fallen out of an airplane; you certainly don't want to frighten them. For a *skydiver,* as they like to be known, seeing an airplane coming at them is sort of like seeing a food processor from the inside, with the blade set to *dice.* You will find that most pilots are appalled at the thought of deliberately jumping out of a perfectly good airplane. They can't get past the notion that the first part of the word *parachute* sounds like *perish.*

Let's talk about the *A/FD* excerpt below. Area 1 in Figure 20 gives runway information. Unless otherwise stated, left traffic is assumed for the runway. Area 2 identifies the frequencies for ATIS, unicom, approach and departure control, tower, ground, clearance delivery and pre-

ATC RADAR SYSTEM

He's drawing a moustache on your mom's picture right now.

Your airplane is seen as a blip on the controller's radar scope.

Fig. 21

taxi clearance delivery. This section contains almost every frequency you'd need for the airport. The times these facilities operate are usually given in Zulu time.

Area 3 describes the airspace in which the facility is situated. This becomes important when you're attempting to determine the type of ATC service you can expect when arriving or departing this airport. As you'll soon see, each class of airspace (B, C and D) offers a different type of service.

The *A/FD* will be covered in additional detail in later chapters. For now, understand that it is a valuable

aid in finding information about specific airports and their services. Each *A/FD* booklet covers a different region, usually consisting of several states. The value of the *A/FD*'s information far, far exceeds its very modest cost. You can subscribe and have the *A/FD* mailed to your door as soon as it's published. The *A/FD* is also available online for viewing and download at *naco.faa.gov.*

Radar and the ATC System

When you ask anyone what the word "radar" means, they're likely to say something about a popular TV show from the mid-70s and early 80s. Radar O'Riley knew what was going to happen before it occurred. In a vaguely similar way, Radar allows air traffic controllers to do the same. Through the use of microwave radar energy, controllers can identify solid objects (aircraft, for example) at great distances as well as determine their direction, speed and altitude (altitude if Mode-C transponder equipped). Radar lets controllers "see" far beyond the range of their eyes. Now, you can easily see the meaning behind the name Radar which stands for *radio detection and ranging.*

Radar works on the echo principle. Microwave energy pulses are sent out over an antenna arrangement, as shown in Figure 21. Some of the energy bounces back to the originating antenna, and is reported as a visual blip on a screen. Through the use of radar, controllers can identify solid objects (aircraft, for example) at great distances.

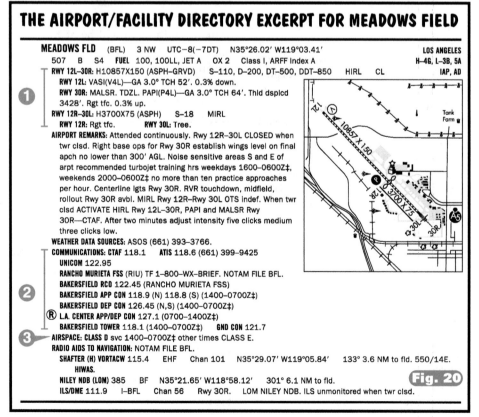

THE AIRPORT/FACILITY DIRECTORY EXCERPT FOR MEADOWS FIELD

MEADOWS FLD (BFL)   3 NW   UTC–8(–7DT)   N35°26.02' W119°03.41'   **LOS ANGELES**
507   B   S4   **FUEL** 100, 100LL, JET A   OX 2   Class I, ARFF Index A   H–4G, L–3B, 5A
RWY 12L–30R: H10857X150 (ASPH–GRVD)   S–110, D–200, DT–500, DDT–850   HIRL   CL   IAP, AD
  RWY 12L: VASI(V4L)—GA 3.0° TCH 52'. 0.3% down.
  RWY 30R: MALSR. TDZL. PAPI(P4L)—GA 3.0° TCH 64'. Thld dsplcd 3428'. Rgt tfc. 0.3% up.
RWY 12R–30L: H3700X75 (ASPH)   S–18   MIRL
  RWY 12R: Rgt tfc.   RWY 30L: Tree.
AIRPORT REMARKS: Attended continuously. Rwy 12R–30L CLOSED when twr clsd. Right base ops for Rwy 30R establish wings level on final apch no lower than 300' AGL. Noise sensitive areas S and E of arpt recommended turbojet training hrs weekdays 1600–0600Z‡, weekends 2000–0600Z‡ no more than ten practice approaches per hour. Centerline lgts Rwy 30R. RVR touchdown, midfield, rollout Rwy 30R avbl. MIRL Rwy 12R–Rwy 30L OTS indef. When twr clsd ACTIVATE HIRL Rwy 12L–30R, PAPI and MALSR Rwy 30R—CTAF. After two minutes adjust intensity five clicks medium three clicks low.
WEATHER DATA SOURCES: ASOS (661) 393–3766.
COMMUNICATIONS: CTAF 118.1   ATIS 118.6 (661) 399–9425
  UNICOM 122.95
  RANCHO MURIETA FSS (RIU) TF 1–800–WX–BRIEF. NOTAM FILE BFL.
  BAKERSFIELD RCO 122.45 (RANCHO MURIETA FSS)
  BAKERSFIELD APP CON 118.9 (N) 118.8 (S) (1400–0700Z‡)
  BAKERSFIELD DEP CON 126.45 (N,S) (1400–0700Z‡)
  Ⓡ L.A. CENTER APP/DEP CON 127.1 (0700–1400Z‡)
  BAKERSFIELD TOWER 118.1 (1400–0700Z‡)   GND CON 121.7
AIRSPACE: CLASS D svc 1400–0700Z‡ other times CLASS E.
RADIO AIDS TO NAVIGATION: NOTAM FILE BFL.
  SHAFTER (H) VORTACW 115.4   EHF   Chan 101   N35°29.07' W119°05.84'   133° 3.6 NM to fld. 550/14E.
  HIWAS.
  NILEY NDB (LOM) 385   BF   N35°21.65' W118°58.12'   301° 6.1 NM to fld.
  ILS/DME 111.9   I–BFL   Chan 56   Rwy 30R.   LOM NILEY NDB. ILS unmonitored when twr clsd.

Fig. 20

If all the system has to work with is the unadulterated bounceback of the radar signal, the blip is referred to as a *primary return* (which is not an election result). This would let a controller know *something* was there, but wouldn't provide much information beyond that.

Modern air traffic control is based on aircraft being equipped with *transponders,* which take the incoming radar beam, add coded information to it and return a stronger signal. This hyped-up bounceback is referred to as a *secondary return.* It permits the identification of a specific aircraft and the display on the controller's screen of a blip that is both brighter and more informative. For a further discussion of how ATC radar works, see Postflight Briefing #8-1 (page 8-21).

Transponders

On several occasions, I've mentioned the word *squawk.* This is official language for setting a specific, numerical code in the transponder or rotating the transponder's function switch to a specific selection. In other words if the controller told you to *squawk 2154,* you would set this code in the transponder's windows by twisting the number-code

VFR CODES SHOWN ON RADAR SCOPE

When you squawk the VFR code of 1200, it might be displayed several ways on the controller's radar screen. Different types of radar display this information differently. Either way, the controller can detect your airplane and advise others of your position and altitude (if Mode-C equipped and you're in the "ALT" position.)

1200 85

1200 85

Radar Screen

Fig. 24

SQUAWKING A CODE   Fig. 22

ATC told the pilot to squawk 2154. The pilot complies by dialing the numbers 2154 in the windows and making sure the function switch is set to the "ALT" position.

The transponder allows your airplane to be easily identified by air traffic control on their radar screen.

Fig. 23

selection knobs, as shown in Figure 22. Then you would turn the function selection switch to the *ALT* position. If the controller said to *squawk standby,* you would move the function-selection switch from the *ALT* position it normally rests in during flight to the *SBY* position (in a moment I'll explain what these positions do).

The transponder is a necessary component of the secondary radar beacon system. This little device has several interesting features. First, the typical transponder, shown in Figure 23, is called a 4096-code transponder because it has 4,096 code combinations that can be set in the windows. Radar controllers normally assign aircraft specific codes, but some codes are standard.

For instance, if you're flying VFR, whether you are talking to a radar controller or not, you should squawk the code 1200. This allows your airplane and the 1200 code (or a symbol representing that code—like an *x*) to appear on the controller's radar screen as shown in Figure 24. Traffic avoidance becomes easier when other airplanes, in contact with the radar controller, are alerted to your position.

The transponder's function switch has an *ALT* selection (meaning ALTitude). Unless ATC instructs otherwise, you should always operate your transponder in the ALT mode since your airplane most likely has something known as an encoding altimeter (a device that tags your altitude onto the signal and sends it along as part of the transponder's return). Selecting the altitude mode allows your altitude to show up with the airplane's data block on the controller's radar screen. Now the controller knows not only your position, but also your altitude. This makes it easier for him or her to inform other aircraft of your exact position. Operation in the altitude mode is also known as *Mode C operation*.

In fact, regulations require that if you have Mode C capability, you use it while squawking 1200 during VFR flights in controlled airspace. Sometimes controllers will ask you to *squawk altitude*. This means your transponder is probably being operated in the *ON* position and the controller wants you to turn the function switch one more click to the altitude (*ALT*) or Mode C position.

The transponder's *SBY* feature (Standby) is used to warm up the transponder and/or altitude encoder (not all transponders or encoders require warming up). It's like warming up a car before you drive away, except no exhaust is produced. Before takeoff, you want to operate in standby mode. As you taxi onto the runway for takeoff, switch the transponder on (the *ALT* position). On rare occasions, a controller may ask you to *squawk standby*. This most frequently occurs when your Mode C readout seems inaccurate and thus potentially confusing to controllers.

The *TST* or test feature temporarily activates the transponder's reply/monitor light to ensure the bulb is working and to adjust its brightness. The reply/monitor light flashes when the transponder is being interrogated by a ground-based radar unit.

Under the reply/monitor light is the *IDENT* (identification) button. This is pushed when the controller

This Buzzz's for You

Removed two wasps from the cabin during preflight. On takeoff at 100 feet a wasp flew into my vision and distracted me. I tried to hold altitude and prevent a stall as I pulled my wits together. It stung me on the hand as I waved it away. My flight path had diverted close to a skydiving operation so I made a sharp climbing turn away from the trees.

Preflighting the cabin doesn't mean just removing the gust lock. It takes only a minute for a small creature to move its home (in fact, a wasp can build a nest overnight). I assumed there were only two wasps. The next day I found a centipede under the step. I'm glad I'm looking harder now as I could have found him hidden in my plush sheepskin cover as I sat down.

Remember, no matter what's crawling down your leg, fly the airplane first. **ASRS Report.**

requests that you *ident*. Pushing this button makes the radar blip bloom temporarily, causing it to stand out, as shown in Figure 25. The ident feature is simply the transponder's way of saying to the controller, "Hey, look, I'm over here!"

Don't push the ident button unless told to do so by the controller. It's interesting to note that when the controller tells one specific aircraft to ident, sometimes another pilot, not listening carefully, pushes his ident button. As a student pilot, I accidentally did this a number of times. If other airborne students were like me, I'm sure the controller's radar screen probably lit up like fireflies at a recharging center. Certainly this makes it a little confusing for controllers.

The code 7700 should be used in the event of an emergency. Selecting this code in your transponder visually alerts the controller that you are in distress. Essentially, your data block lights up, making it easier for the controller to identify you, as shown in Figure 26. Students, lost on cross country flights, have set 7700 in the transponder and tuned 121.5 MHz (the emergency frequency) on their radios and asked for help. It usually doesn't take long before someone replies on this frequency and offers assistance (and you didn't even need to yell, *"Mayonnaise, mayonnaise, mayonnaise."* Of course if you're in an area where there is no radar coverage, the emergency transponder code won't be seen. This is one of the reasons why it's important to climb (if possible) when you're lost. It increases your chances of being seen on someone's radar as well as communicating with them.

VFR CODES SHOWN ON RADAR SCOPE

Fig. 25

When the controller asks you to "IDENT," you push the "IDENT" button once then let it go (no need to hold it in). Your airplane then becomes easier to identify on the scope since your blip either flashes or fills in and expands (depending on the particular radar).

ID

N2132B
120▲93

Radar Screen

THE EMERGENCY SQUAWK

If you squawk 7700 (in an emergency), the controller will see some symbol alerting him to your condition. This may be a flashing, expanding data block or the numbers 7700 with the letters "EMRG" underneath.

7700 EMRG

1200 85

7700 EMRG

7700 040

Fig. 26

Radar Screen

mine was lost and decided to land at the first uncontrolled airport he observed underneath his airplane. He taxied up to the gas pump, got out of his airplane and walked across the street to the hamburger joint to find out what town he was in. He asked the hamburger cook (the sliced protein thermal coordinator) how he pronounced the name of this place. The fellow looked at him and said, "BURR-GURR-KING." Ouch! After a few more questions and a Coke, he finally discovered where he was.

If you are hijacked, which is relatively rare in a Piper Cub, squawk code 7500 and tell your guest you can't go nonstop from California to Cuba. The 7500 code flashes a warning on the controller's radar screen. Of course the controller, seeing 7500 on the scope, won't say, "Hey 32 Bravo, why are you squawking the hijack code?" If the hijacker were listening, he might not be too happy with you and may request an impromptu wing walking demonstration. There is a certain protocol controllers follow when they see 7500. Usually they ask, "32 Bravo, verify squawking 7500?" In which case, if you are being hijacked, you calmly reply, "Ahhhh, ut, ahhhh, ughh, gulp, errrr, roger." Once it's established that the code selected is for real, you'll get some really incredible radar service, and a very nice landing reception with guests from the FBI, FAA, and local law enforcement agencies.

When I was a student, I was never lost. Temporarily unsure of my present position, perhaps, but never lost. These days it's more politically correct to call it *location challenged* instead of being lost (that's a joke). A friend of

Automatic Dependent Surveillance Broadcast

ADS-B or *automatic dependent surveillance broadcast* is a revolutionary new way of controlling air traffic and it will become mandatory for all aircraft operating in controlled airspace by January 1, 2020. The concept is simple. ADS-B equipped aircraft broadcast their precise position via a digital datalink along with their airspeed, altitude, direction of movement (up, down, right, left). Air traffic control or other aircraft with ADS-B can identify targets in real time for air traffic control to avoid a traffic conflict.

As a simplified example, consider an air-traffic control secondary radar. The radar measures the range and bearing of an aircraft. The bearing is measured by the position of the rotating radar antenna when it receives a reply to its interrogation from the aircraft. The range is measured by the time it takes for the radar to receive the reply. Unfortunately, the antenna's projected radar beam gets wider as the aircraft get farther from the antenna, thus making the measured position information less accurate.

An ADS-B based system, on the other hand, would listen for position reports broadcast by the aircraft. These position reports are based on accurate navigation systems, such as satellite navigation systems (e.g., GPS). The accuracy of the system is now determined by the accuracy of the navigation system, not measurement errors. The accuracy is unaffected by the range to the aircraft. With the radar system, detecting aircraft velocity changes requires tracking the received data. Changes can only be detected over a period of several position updates. With ADS-B, velocity changes are broadcast almost instantaneously.

The diagram to the right shows how ADS-B information is exchanged. A communications satellite helps provide voice capability between the aircraft and the ATC facility. The GPS satellite system provides position and altitude information and this information is relayed directly to the ATC facility via ground lines. Additionally, there is an airplane-to-airplane exchange of information (data).

Communications Satellite

GNSS Constellation

Downlink to ATC Center

AC to AC

A/C Position Speed, Etc. Info

Ground Link to ATC

Courtesy FAA

Another transponder code exists for pilots experiencing lost communications. (*Lost communications* means the radio has failed, not that you have lost your voice or have gotten yourself lost.) Squawking 7600 tells the controller that you've lost two-way radio capability. Normally, this code is used by IFR pilots experiencing communication failure (i.e., it's used by pilots flying in the clouds). VFR pilots, however, could also find it useful. For instance, if you were approaching an airport lying within class D airspace, in VFR conditions, with a failed radio, you might squawk 7600 hoping to get the attention of the tower controller. Even if the tower controller doesn't have radar, an observant radar controller, noticing the 7600 code on his or her screen, might alert the tower controller to your problem. In this instance, you would enter the pattern and look for the appropriate light signals from the tower (see FAR 91.125), as we discussed in Chapter Six.

When switching transponder codes, be careful to avoid switching through the codes 7500, 7600 and 7700. You don't want to trigger a false alarm on the controller's screen. Controllers have enough excitement in their lives just from the regular stuff some pilots do.

Fig. 27

Radar Services for Pilots

When you make contact with a radar facility and they identify you and provide in-flight advisories, the service is referred to as "flight following." It's an extra set of eyes that help you watch for traffic, and something you'll want to make use of as often as possible.

Men are notoriously reluctant to ask for directions when driving. I suppose if we had aerial gas stations, we'd still be reluctant to use them for directions. Manhood and directionhood seem intimately bound. Uncouple them when you get in the air, and ask the nice controller for *vectors to the airport* when you can't see because of poor visibility, or when you just can't find the darn thing.

He or she will be more than happy to help.

Flight following also provides you with the location of in-flight traffic. This becomes very helpful during hazy flight conditions or in and around busy airports. When using this service, controllers call out the traffic's position using the 12-hour clock, with the airplane's nose being 12. If the controller says, "Cessna 2132 Bravo, you have traffic at two o'clock, three miles," you start looking for traffic a bit to the right of the nose, as shown in Figure 27. If you see the traffic, inform the controller that you have "traffic in sight." If you don't see it, say, "negative contact." If you don't see it and are still looking, say to the controller "looking for traffic." In other words, don't sit silently after a controller calls traffic for you. A reply is mandatory, traffic permitting.

If the target airplane has Mode C capability (altitude encoder) then the controller will provide you with the airplane's altitude (otherwise, you'll be told *altitude unknown)*. The controller might say, "Cessna 2132 Bravo, you have traffic at eleven o'clock, four miles, southbound at 3,000 feet." This clarifies how much of a concern the target aircraft is to you. If you're at 4,500 feet, then you have reasonable separation. If you're at 3,000 feet, you really want to find that puppy—and sooner, rather than later. If the traffic is a factor for you, the controller will usually continue making these calls. You can sometimes get an approximate distance by listening to the rising tone and urgency of the controller's voice. At about high C, it's time to ask the controller to vector you out of harm's way.

If the traffic is not in sight, don't let the controller think you see it. Several years ago, late one evening, I heard a controller rapidly call three targets in a row for a pilot. Each time the controller said, "Cessna 2132 Bravo, traffic at..." the pilot immediately replied, "contact." Suspicious, the controller paused then said, "OK, traffic at twelve o'clock." The pilot immediately said, "contact." The controller said, "Hey, 32 Bravo, I was just kidding about that one." The pilot replied, "Hey, so was I."

Keep in mind that the controller has no idea which way your airplane is pointing. All the controller can visually discern on the screen is the path the aircraft is making across the ground (its ground track). If a strong wind exists, you will be crabbed into the wind. Your nose would point in one direction, while the airplane moved in another. Look at Figure 28. The controller sees you as having traffic at 12 o'clock. But you aren't pointed exactly where you're headed, so for you the traffic is going to be

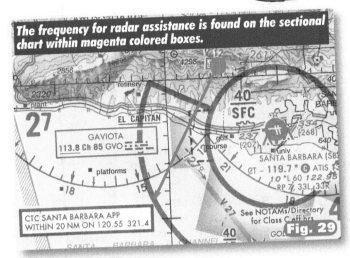

The frequency for radar assistance is found on the sectional chart within magenta colored boxes.

Fig. 29

found at two o'clock. When ATC calls traffic, you must look in the general area of the traffic advisory. In other words, you must look to the right or the left of the given position (we'll discuss this in greater detail in Chapter 16).

Radar Assistance to VFR Aircraft

Radar assistance to pilots is available in several different forms. These include:

1. Basic radar service
2. TRSA service
3. Class C service
4. Class B service

Basic Radar Service

Basic radar service is what we've been discussing. Radar controllers, on a workload permitting basis, provide VFR pilots with safety alerts, traffic advisories, limited radar vectoring and sequencing at specific terminal locations. The *primary* purpose of radar control is to provide control and separation for aircraft on instrument flight plans (IFR flights). Assistance to VFR pilots is also provided if the controller can do so without compromising the level of service to the IFR aircraft he or she is handling.

If you want basic radar service after departure, then inform ground control upon initial contact. If you're airborne and want radar vectoring to an airport, call Approach Control on the frequency listed on the appropriate aeronautical sectional or terminal area chart. For instance, if you were near Santa Barbara airport, as shown in Figure 29, you'd simply call approach control on 120.55 MHz. Give them your aircraft call sign, altitude, position (that's geographical and not whether you're sitting vertical or sideways in the airplane), type of aircraft, the transponder code you're squawking (if you're transponder

WIND EFFECT ON TRAFFIC CALLS

Because the wind is from the east, you're crabbed to the left while maintaining a south ground track. When you look for traffic in your 12 o'clock position, you don't see the target. You need to scan to the right and left of the 12 o'clock position to find the target.

From the controller's point of view, all he or she knows is that your airplane (blip) is moving southward.

Easterly wind direction

N
W — E
S

Target

The controller sees this target and alerts you to traffic in your 12 o'clock position.

Fig. 28

RADAR SCOPE

equipped), destination and your request. If you're arriving at an airport with ATIS, let the controller know that you've received the latest information. The call might go something like this:

YOU: "Santa Barbara Approach, Cessna 2132 Bravo."

SBA APPROACH: "Cessna 2132 Bravo, Santa Barbara Approach. Go ahead."

YOU: "32 Bravo is a Cessna 172, 4,500 feet over Gaviota VOR, squawking 1200, requesting vectors to Santa Barbara airport, information Whiskey received."

If you aren't planning on landing and just want radar traffic information only, your callup might go like this:

YOU: "Santa Barbara Approach, Cessna 2132 Bravo."

SBA APPROACH: "Cessna 2132 Bravo, Santa Barbara Approach. Go ahead."

YOU: "32 Bravo is a Cessna 172, 4,500 feet over Gaviota VOR, squawking 1200, transition to the north, requesting traffic advisories."

The frequency tab on the sectional chart indicates the appropriate frequencies and hours of availability for TRSA service.

CLASS B, CLASS C, TRSA, AND SELECTED RADAR APPROACH CONTROL FREQUENCIES		
FACILITY	FREQUENCIES ** §	SERVICE AVAILABILITY
ONTARIO/MARCH AFB CLASS C	127.25 318.2 (NORTH-NORTHEAST) 119.65 327.5 (NORTHEAST-EAST) 134.0 278.3 (EAST-SOUTH) 135.4 295.7 (SOUTH-SOUTHWEST) 125.5 351.1 (SOUTHWEST-NORTH)	CONTINUOUS
SANTA ANA CLASS C	121.3 263.1 (NORTHWEST-NORTHEAST) 124.65 343.9 (WEST-NORTHWEST) 132.7 380.2 (NORTHEAST-SOUTHEAST)	0615-2345 O/T CLASS G E 700' AGL & ABOVE
SANTA BARBARA CLASS C	120.55 321.4 (151°-329°) 125.4 397.9 (330°-150°) O/T 119.05 269.5 ZLA CNTR	0600-2300 O/T CLASS E
PALM SPRINGS TRSA	118.85 (NORTHEAST-SOUTHWEST) 126.7 (WEST-NORTH) 370.95 O/T 128.15 285.6 ZLA CNTR	0600-2300

Fig. 31

Terminal Radar Service Area (TRSA) Service

At certain busy airport locations a special type of airspace known as a Terminal Radar Service Area (TRSA) exists. Once widespread, TRSA's are rapidly fading from the aviation scene as they're replaced by Class C airspace.

Dark gray lines represent the borders of the Palm Springs TRSA as shown on an aeronautical sectional chart (Figure 30). For instance, position A shows the border of the Palm Springs TRSA. Position B shows the altitude limit for the TRSA in that area. It starts at 3,500 feet and extends vertically to 10,000 feet. If you're flying within the TRSA, you are encouraged to participate in TRSA service (although participation isn't mandatory). Figure 31 shows the frequency tab located on the bottom of every aeronautical chart. This tab lists the appropriate frequencies on which to call for TRSA service when you're approximately 25 miles from the TRSA-served airport. (We'll cover aeronautical sectional charts in greater detail in Chapter 10.)

TRSA service provides radar sequencing and separation between all participating VFR aircraft and all IFR aircraft operating within the airspace defined as the TRSA. Separation standards are based on one of the following: 500 feet vertical separation, visual separation between pilots or target resolution (a process controllers use to keep radar targets from touching—now that's a good idea isn't it?). (See Figure 32.) If you are asked to follow another aircraft into or out of the TRSA, you are responsible for maintaining a safe distance behind this aircraft. In other words, don't get close enough so that you can watch the in-flight movie in the other airplane. If you suspect wake turbulence could be a problem, give yourself more room. Even though ATC applies greater distances between large and small airplanes for wake turbulence separation, ask for more if you feel it's necessary. You *are* the pilot-in-command.

The borders of a Terminal Radar Service Area (TRSA) are shown on sectional charts by dark gray lines.

Fig. 30

TRSA SERVICE
(Sequencing & Separation between aircraft)

500' Vertical Separation

Targets prevented from touching on the controller's radar screen.

"Duchess 318, you have a Cessna 172 at 12 o'clock. Cessna 2132 Bravo, you've got at Beaver on floats at 1 o'clock at 2,500 feet. Beaver 43432, you are number one for landing at Carlsbad. Contact the tower on 119.4, over."

Fig. 32

Yes, hold the anchovies.

Here's an important caveat about TRSA service. As you're being vectored by ATC, be cautious about adhering to the required VFR minimums relating to clouds and altitude requirements. Remember, ATC's radar doesn't show clouds—clouds aren't solid and don't show up on the screen. The controller simply can't tell if the heading he or she gives you will put you in a cloud. Since you're not instrument rated, you can't be in the clouds. Avoid them! Immediately ask for an amended clearance—a new heading—if your present one will take you into a cloud. Even if ATC hasn't given you a new heading, turn as necessary to avoid flying into that cloud. The best thing to do is keep the radar controller advised of the weather conditions along your route if it looks like clouds or other obscuring phenomena are a problem.

Sometimes, when arriving or departing a TRSA, I prefer obtaining radar advisories from ATC, but not having the formal separation efforts that TRSA service entails. In this case I'll state *negative TRSA service* on my initial callup with approach control or ground control, as appropriate. This becomes especially important when departing. Suppose, barring any departure restrictions, you wanted a straight out departure after takeoff. We'll assume this heads you directly toward your destination. If you don't say, "negative TRSA service" on your initial callup, the controller might have you call Departure Control after takeoff. Now the radar departure controller, thinking you want TRSA service, could give you vectors that are anything but the shortest direction to your destination. These types of delays are most common at busy airports on busy days.

When departing the TRSA (or any other class of airspace), the controller will sometimes say, "Cessna 2132

CLASS "B" & "C" SERVICE
(Sequencing and separation)

"OK, Cessna 2132 Bravo maintain 4,000'. You'll be following a twin to the airport. Twin 23415, maintain 4,500 feet. You'll be following a Beaver ahead of you at 4,000 feet. Beaver 36531, fly heading 230 degrees and maintain at least 90 knots."

Fig. 33

I dunno. They're drawing pictures of me and they called me some sort of fish from the previous figure.

Bravo, radar service terminated." Don't take it personally. This either means you are leaving the boundaries over which the controller exercises control, or the controller is too busy to continue providing service. Either way, this is your clue to squawk VFR by setting the code 1200 in your transponder. Since you're no longer being given radar service, the controller has no need to keep you on a specific code or his or her frequency.

Class C Service

In Chapter 9, you'll learn more about Class B and C airspace. For now, understand that these airspace types belong to increasingly busy airports with operating control towers. Class C service provides basic radar service, separation between all IFR and VFR aircraft, and sequencing of the VFR arrivals to the primary airport as shown in Figure 33.

Class B Service

Class B service provides basic radar service, separation between IFR and VFR aircraft, and sequencing of VFR arrivals to the primary airport.

MERCED TOWER, THIS IS A/C 1234, RAMP 4. TAXI INSTRUCTIONS, PLEASE.

TOWER TO STUDENT PILOT IN A/C 1234—WE ARE UNABLE TO LOCATE YOU. WILL YOU PLEASE STAND UP IN THE COCKPIT SO WE CAN SPOT YOUR A/C?

HEH, HEH, IT NEVER FAILS.

SWITCHING TO "INTERCOM"

Cartoon by Bob Stevens   Reprinted with the permission of Mrs. Bob Stevens

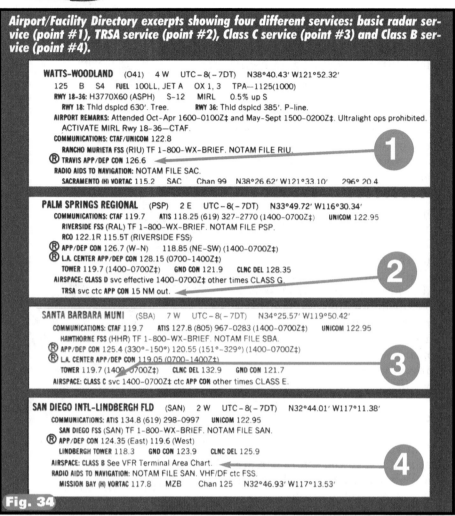

Airport/Facility Directory excerpts showing four different services: basic radar service (point #1), TRSA service (point #2), Class C service (point #3) and Class B service (point #4).

Fig. 34

If you want to know what stage of radar service is available at an airport, simply look in the *Airport/Facility Directory*. Figure 34 shows four A/FD excerpts indicating the individual services at an airport. Item #1 identifies an approach and departure control with a circled *R* next to the radar frequencies. This implies basic radar service is probably available at this airport. Item #2 shows TRSA service is available and that you should contact approach control 15 miles out from the airport for this service. Item #3 shows Class C service is available. Item #4 shows Class B service is available at this airport; you should look at the VFR Terminal Area Chart to determine how to make contact (this chart is discussed in Chapter 10).

Clearance Delivery

Some airports lying within class B or C airspace require you to have a *clearance* prior to departure. In this type of airspace you will generally be assigned very specific routing and altitude directions, as well as a frequency on which to make contact with a controller after a handoff from the tower.

Since you have to know before you go, that means getting a clearance from somewhere. The somewhere is called *clearance delivery*. A special frequency exists with a controller awaiting your call and request for a clearance. If there is a clearance delivery frequency, it will generally be part of the ATIS broadcast. The information can also be found in the communications section of the *A/FD*, as shown in Figure 35. At some less-busy airports, ground control functions as a clearance delivery.

When you contact clearance delivery, give them your complete aircraft number, tell them you have the current ATIS information, give them your destination and direction of flight, and tell the controller you're a VFR aircraft. A typical call may sound like this:

YOU: "Palm Springs Clearance Delivery, Cessna 2132 Bravo."

CLEARANCE DELIVERY: "Cessna 2132 Bravo, go ahead."

YOU: "Cessna 32 Bravo with information Hotel, VFR to Ontario, over."

A typical clearance out of a busy airport may sound like this:

CLEARANCE DELIVERY: "Cessna 2132 Bravo, after departure fly heading 230 degrees, climb and maintain 3,500 feet, departure control frequency will be 124.3, contact ground control on 121.9 when ready to taxi."

Fig. 35

It's customary to read back clearances to controllers to ensure the accuracy of the communication. Sometimes this makes pilots a bit nervous. Especially, if the controller spoke at 60 knots (fast!) with peak gusts to 90 knots (that's real fast!) and the clearance wasn't copied in its entirety. One fellow, after receiving a rapid fire clearance, picked up his microphone and said (very slowly), *Hey fellows, do you hear how fast I'm talking? Well, this is how fast I listen.* The controllers laughed and repeated his clearance slowly. If you have trouble understanding the clearance, ask the controller to slow down. One of these days some pilot is going to record his clearance with a portable recorder and play it back to the controller as his readback. I'm sure the controller, after hearing his own clearance, will say, *Hey, 32 Bravo, you're going to have to speak a little slower if you want me to understand any of that.* Gottcha!

Well, I've been promising you for quite a while that we're going to begin studying airspace. It's time to pay off on the promise. The next chapter is all about airspace and how it works. I hope you are ambitious enough to learn all you can about airspace. It's the one area in which I find pilots to be consistently in need of further study. Understanding how the airspace is arranged, and what you can (and can't) expect in each kind of airspace is absolutely vital to a safe flight.

Fasten your seatbelt. Here we go.

Postflight Briefing #8-1

How ATC Keeps An Eye on You

Radar is the air traffic controller's eye on the sky. A radar antenna sends out a microwave length radio signal. Encountering a solid object, these energy pulses bounce back to the originating antenna, where they are identified and converted to visual blips on a radar scope. One of my students said, "How can that same pulse

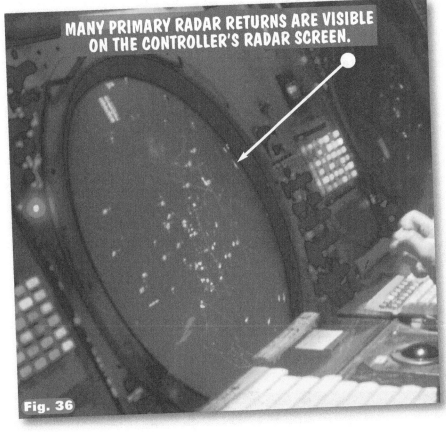

MANY PRIMARY RADAR RETURNS ARE VISIBLE ON THE CONTROLLER'S RADAR SCREEN.

Fig. 36

bounce off an airplane and return to the antenna if the antenna has rotated slightly?" My student didn't quite understand that electromagnetic pulses travel out and back at 186,300 miles per second (that's millions of miles per hour). A rotating antenna doesn't have much of an effect on the radar return. The target's distance from the radar antenna is determined by the signal's roundtrip time, based on the known speed of light.

Visual radar blips are called *primary radar returns* and are shown in Figure 36. Primary radar was the basis of early radar detection. But primary radar was inefficient since smaller targets (those with a less-reflective surface) were often difficult to identity. Weather (suspended water or ice) often interfered with target identification. With advances in technology, we now use something known as *secondary surveillance radar*. This system is known officially as the Air Traffic Control Radar Beacon System or ATCRBS.

Essentially, secondary surveillance radar is a separate system from primary radar because it uses an aircraft's transponder to identify

THE TRANSPONDER

Function selection switch

Reply monitor light

Number codes 0 to 7

SBY · ON · ALT
OFF · TST · IDENT

4 6 3 2

Identification button

Number code selection knobs

Fig. 37

A secondary radar return and its data block.

-70C
R348 450

N4600S
430C
486 432

Fig. 38

aircraft. A transponder is similar to the bell on a cow. Farmers hear the bell and know the location of the cow (which is also why cows can no longer play their favorite game called "let's sneak up on the other cows"). Transponders provide an electrical signal that the radar unit hears (receives) to determine your position.

Figure 37 shows a typical aircraft transponder. With the secondary radar beacon system, the ground-based radar sends out a coded signal which is received by the transponder, modified, then transmitted back to the radar unit where it's decoded by the ground facility. This allows ATC to identify your airplane among many other targets on the radar scope, based on the specific four-digit, discrete transponder code the controller assigned you.

If you are told to squawk a transponder code of "4312," you set those numbers in the code selection window, then turn the transponder function switch to the "alt" position. Controllers watching the scope might see your airplane as a secondary radar return in the form of a "blip" (also knows as a data block) with numbers along side as shown in Figure 38. These numbers might be 4312 (your assigned code) which makes it easy for the radar controller to identify you. Depending on the controller's type of radar equipment and the mode selected, the radar screen may show your groundspeed, altitude and aircraft call sign alongside the blip. Another advantage of the secondary system is that non-useful, scope-cluttering information can selectively be edited out.

Strangely enough, scope-clutter could be in the form of freeway traffic near the radar antenna. If it weren't for the secondary radar bea-con system, the controller might have to visually ignore these extraneous targets. These targets don't show up on the secondary beacon system's screen because they don't have transponders. Therefore, you'll never hear ATC say, "32 Bravo, you have a U-Haul truck at twelve o'clock, opposite direction, turn right for an avoidance vector; and watch out, those guys make wide right turns!"

Radar is truly ATC's eye on the sky. It permits large volumes of traffic to move safely and efficiently. Which is not to say ATC radar is perfect. Far from it. Most facilities are using sadly outdated equipment, driven by computers that should be in museums. A multibillion dollar upgrade effort in the mid-90s bogged down in bureaucratic inertia, and the FAA is now scrambling to find a way to bring its system up to snuff as quickly as possible.

Postflight Briefing #8-2

Proper Pattern Communication

Flight Instructors who've done an appreciable amount of instructing often develop their own list of pet peeves. One of mine involves radio communications, specifically the phrase, "Any traffic in the pattern please advise." It seems as if this phrase is used way too often at non-towered fields. For me, hearing it is like listening to fingernails on a chalkboard. When a pilot busts onto the frequency with this phrase, his radio call is likely to sound something like this, "XYZ traffic, Tecnam N2132B, 5 miles out. Any traffic in the area please advise."

Pat Brown

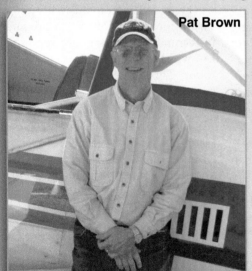

So, why is this so bad?

Well, it's lazy, unprofessional, and unnecessary. And, it invites chaos. Imagine if everyone within receiving range responded at the same time. Radios for miles around would squeal louder than teenage girls at a Justin Bieber concert! Had Captain Blabber simply listened for 15-20 seconds before talking, he might have heard position reports from aircraft in the traffic pattern, as well as from incoming and departing airport traffic.

So here's my recommendation. If you really feel you must ask for traffic advisories at non-towered fields, say this, "XYZ unicom, Tecnam 2132B, 10 miles west (I am assuming you know the direction from which you are coming), requesting airport advisory." If unicom replies with only the wind direction and active runway (which is the most common response), you can reply with, "Tecnam 2132B. Thank you. Is there any reported traffic in the area?"

The *Aeronautical Information Manual* contains an entire chapter on Air Traffic Control. A portion of that chapter deals specifically with the phrase, "Traffic in the area, please advise." Check it out for yourself in Chapter 4-1-9 (g.1) under *Self-Announce Position and/or Intentions*. At the end of that short paragraph, you'll see the following sentence, "Pilots stating, 'Traffic in the area please advise,' is not a recognized Self-Announce Position and/or Intention phrase and should not be used under any condition."

Pat Brown is co-owner and chief flight instruction at Houston Light Sport Aviation, Houston, TX. He holds airplane, instrument, and glider instructor ratings.

Chapter Nine

Airspace
The Wild Blue, Green and Red Yonder

In this chapter we're going to discuss how the airspace in the United States is constructed. We'll concern ourselves with the weather minimums and equipment requirements when flying in several varieties of airspace. I'll do my best to simplify the subject and make myself perfectly clear. (When one of my early flight instructors asked if he made himself perfectly clear, I wanted to run my hand up and down behind him and say, "Hey everyone, come here, look, Bob's perfectly clear now!")

Airspace rules sound and look worse than they are in practice. The fact of the matter is that 99% of the time 99% of the pilots will need to know only a handful of basics. Some of what you're about to read covers situations that, quite honestly, are *not* very prevalent. You need to be aware that certain rules exist, though, so you'll know when it's time to refresh your memory.

Bright student of aviation that you are, you might be asking yourself useful questions such as "Why?" Why is it so complicated, why are there so many rules, why do I care?

You care because the airspace structure is there to assure the maximum safety for everyone. Knowing where you can fly and under what conditions is essential to keeping yourself, your passengers, and lots of other people healthy and happy. You also care because I guarantee you that this material will show up on all the FAA sport pilot knowledge exams you take, both computerized and oral.

One more question. Why is the V-formation of ducks longer on one side than the other? Well, of course, one side has more ducks. Despite the asymmetric display, our fine-feathered friends are pretty good at keeping themselves from bumping into one another. They are their own air traffic control system. This is all the more remarkable when you consider that they have slightly less mental computing power than an Etch-a-Sketch.

Even if a few ducks were to collide, what's the worst that could happen? Some ruffled feathers? A headache, resulting in a duck coming in on a wing and a Bayer (I had to do that).

Pilots, on the other hand, can't afford a collision. Megatons of metal hurtling through the air at enormous speeds means any encounters will be of a very unfortunate type. Let's see how that can be avoided.

Eye See

Our modern airspace system has evolved to protect you (the pilot) from bumping into other aircraft and various solid objects (mountains, trees, antennas. etc.). This is accomplished by having rules that determine how and where you can (and can't) fly under given conditions. The rules vary depending not only on weather conditions, but also on the type of airspace in which you're flying. In order to maximize safety, the airspace has been divided into different types of areas, which generally reflect how busy that patch of airspace is and thus how demanding the flying is within it. Once upon a time, these had names like *airport traffic area,* and *terminal control area.* They've been renamed with snappy titles like Class A, B, C, D and E airspace. These are simple but they're not too descriptive. By whatever name, your job as a pilot is to know at all times what kind of airspace you're in and what its rules are.

Any time pilots are flying, they are operating under one of two primary sets of rules: visual flight rules (VFR) or instrument flight rules (IFR). Generally speaking, VFR flight is fair-weather flying based on the concept of being able to look out the win-

I think you better come with me!

dow and see any obstacles or other aircraft at all times. IFR is flight when clouds, fog, rain, dust and other kinds of natural phenomena reduce visibility. IFR flight is, of course, more demanding. It requires a private pilot license and an additional rating *(an instrument rating)* as well as additional equipment for the airplane. A VFR flight is a pretty hang-loose proposition. No flight plan is required (although it's suggested), you can get from hither to yonder via any route you want, and you don't need to talk to anybody except perhaps tower controllers at your departure or arrival airport.

IFR, on the other hand, is a tightly-controlled exercise. You file a flight plan prior to departure, in which you propose a very specific route, including altitudes, based on

electronic highways in the sky. You receive a *clearance,* which may contain modifications to your proposed route, and you follow it from takeoff to landing, communicating constantly with air traffic controllers on the ground. With rare exceptions, you are under constant radar surveillance.

The exact flight visibility and required distances from clouds for VFR flight vary, depending on the type of airspace in which you're flying. In other words, flying in busy airspace requires greater flight visibility and distance from clouds than flying in less-busy airspace. These minimum requirements, known as *basic VFR weather minimums,* allow you ample time to see and avoid other aircraft. See and avoid is the basis of all VFR flight. When you can't see and avoid, you're no longer flying VFR. Keep that in mind, please, because far too many needless accidents occur every year when pilots qualified only for VFR flight continue on into bad (IFR) weather and create business for a metal salvage dealer.

You might be wondering, "What keeps an IFR pilot from popping out of a cloud and bumping into a VFR pilot?" A VFR pilot, adhering to the minimum distance-from-clouds and flight visibility requirements, should have adequate time to see and avoid an IFR aircraft emerging from a cloud. That's why, in the types of airspace used by IFR pilots, the basic VFR weather minimums make collisions highly unlikely. This assumes, of course, that pilots are looking out their windows and making an effort to see and avoid other aircraft.

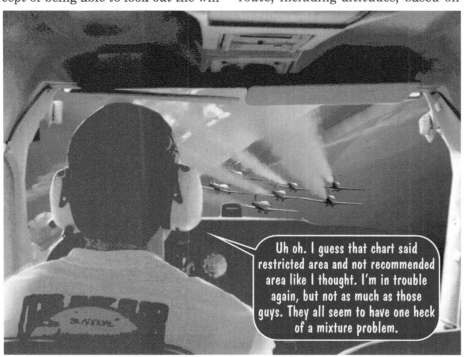

Uh oh. I guess that chart said restricted area and not recommended area like I thought. I'm in trouble again, but not as much as those guys. They all seem to have one heck of a mixture problem.

Controlled and Uncontrolled Airspace

Two basic types of airspace exist in the United States, *controlled* and *uncontrolled*. The major difference between the two can be distilled down to one very important point: controlled airspace is likely to be used by more aircraft (especially aircraft on IFR flight plans) than uncontrolled airspace. That's why controlled airspace typically has greater cloud distance and flight visibility requirements than uncontrolled airspace.

That makes sense, doesn't it? After all, if more airplanes use controlled airspace, the risk of a collision is higher. It's a numbers game. Greater flight visibility and cloud distance minimums make it more likely that pilots will see and avoid each other.

Uncontrolled airspace, on the other hand, is less active. It's normally found close to the surface, away from busy airports, and in areas devoid of airways (airways are the electronic highways in the sky I mentioned a few paragraphs ago, on which IFR flights are conducted and along which many VFR pilots also navigate). Since uncontrolled airspace is used less often, you can typically fly in this airspace with a lower flight visibility and cloud distance minimums.

If you've ever watched fish in an aquarium, you'll agree they swim around completely confused. If they think at all, it's to contemplate whether the Almighty is really an enormous nose that occasionally appears overhead and always precedes the sudden and inexplicable appearance of fish food falling from the sky. It's obvious that fish can't understand anything because they don't have the big picture. I don't want you to suffer the fish's dilemma. Let's take a look at airspace from the big picture perspective (just for the halibut).

The Big Picture

Figure 1 represents the big picture overview of the national airspace system. Don't be alarmed. This will all make a great deal of sense to you soon (and we won't need to do a Vulcan mind meld to get you through this). As you can see, the airspace is made up of several layers, shapes and sections. Each layer or section has a letter designation of either A, B, C, D, E, and G. Yes, I know, the *F* is missing. That's because there is no F-type airspace in the United States.

Because the people in charge didn't want any, that's why.

Class A, B, C, D and E is *controlled airspace.* Class G is *uncontrolled airspace.* Your job is to know the minimum flight visibility, cloud distance, aircraft equipment, and pilot qualifications for each class of airspace.

With the use of an aeronautical sectional chart and a little knowledge, it's easy to identify the weather minimums needed for any class of airspace. Just because the designations for airspace run from A to G (less F) doesn't mean we need to learn about them in alphabetical order, and a fair argument can be made that taking them out of order actually makes more sense.

Let's try this. We'll start with Class A (at the very top), then move on to Class E, then Class G airspace. There's a method to my madness (at least this portion of it). Class A airspace overlies Class E airspace, which, in turn, overlies Class G airspace.

Class A Airspace

Class A airspace consists of controlled airspace extending from 18,000 feet MSL up to and including 60,000 feet MSL (Figure 2). This airspace stretches from coast to coast with an additional 12 nautical mile extension over ocean waters.

Flight in Class A airspace requires that you have an instrument rating and be on an IFR flight plan. That's just one reason why we won't spend any more time on Class A airspace. You have to be a private pilot to earn an instrument rating, so Class A airspace isn't something in which you should be flying. Besides, the regulations specifically state that sport pilots aren't allowed to be in Class A airspace nor are they allowed to operate above 10,000 feet MSL (or 2,000 foot AGL, whichever is higher). So that's really all you need to know about Class A airspace. So let's move on to something much more relevant to you.

Class E Airspace

The airspace lying directly below Class A airspace is Class E airspace (Figure 3). Class E airspace overlies the 48 United States and Alaska (including a 12 nautical mile extension off the coastline).

Class E airspace is controlled airspace, implying that quite a few pilots are likely to use it. It's made up of airways, commonly flown routes, and those areas between busy airports.

You'll probably do the majority of your flying in Class E airspace, so let's cover it thoroughly. After all, if you use something regularly, you should know a lot about it, shouldn't you? Unfortunately, I have a friend who regularly eats at a Mexican restaurant but still doesn't know the proper Mexican names for food. He ordered a burrito and asked the waiter if it came with any Guatemala on it (it's actually called *guacamole).* The waiter said, "No, sir, but I do have some Nicaragua and conquistador that is mighty tasty." It pays to learn all about the things you use.

CLASS A AIRSPACE

Class A airspace starts at 18,000' MSL and extends vertically to 60,000' MSL. It extends offshore and overlies the waters within 12 nautical miles of the coast within the 48 states and Alaska.

Fig. 2

Alaska

Top of Class A 60,000' MSL

Base of Class A 18,000 MSL

18,000' MSL

18,000' MSL

Class A extends over water within 12 nm of the coast.

Why So High?

Why was 18,000 feet MSL chosen for the beginning of Class A airspace? When the airspace system was originally conceived back in the 1950's, designers thought few general aviation airplanes would fly above 18,000 feet MSL. At the time, private airplanes commonly went no higher than 15,000 feet MSL. Things have changed. We now have general aviation airplanes that climb like homesick angels and can easily ascend to 41,000 feet or more. Airspace operational specifications, however, haven't changed much since the 1950's.

Why does Class A airspace only go up to 60,000 feet? Similar reasoning applies. There weren't (and still aren't) very many commercial airplanes that can reach such lofty heights, though the late British Concorde jet did come pretty close to topping this altitude, while traveling at twice the speed of sound (that's why you can't hear the in-flight movie until two hours after you land—just kidding!). With the development of the Space Plane, it won't be long before this rule, too, is outdated.

CLASS E AIRSPACE

Class E airspace starts at 1,200 feet AGL (sometimes higher or lower) and extends up to but not including 18,000' MSL—the base of Class A airspace.

Fig. 3

Alaska

18,000' MSL

Base of Class A 18,000 MSL & top of Class E airspace

Base of Class E airspace at 1200 AGL

18,000' MSL

1,200' AGL

Class A extends over water within 12 nautical miles of the coast. Class E also extends to within 12 miles from the coast (not shown doing so in this graphic).

CLASS E AIRSPACE

Class E (controlled) airspace (green) generally begins at 1,200 feet above ground level (#1) and extends vertically up to but not including the base of Class A airspace. Within the area of the magenta faded border (#2), Class E begins at 700 feet AGL. Within the red dashed lines (#3), Class E beings at the surface. Therefore, it's surface-based Class E airspace in this area.

Base of Class A 18,000' MSL

Class A 18,000' MSL

Base of Class E 1,200' AGL

Class E starts at 1,200' AGL

Class E starts at 1,200' AGL

Class E starts at 1,200' AGL

#3 Class E starts at surface

#2

Class E starts at 700' AGL

Fig. 4 **#1**

Figure 4 provides a better understanding of the vertical structure of Class E airspace. This figure shows a plot of land over which lies Class E airspace. The Class E airspace in this figure starts at 1,200 feet AGL. Note that this is above ground level, not above sea level. Where there are hills or mountains, Class E airspace starts at 1,200 feet above the variable rising and descending surface as shown by position 1.

Class E airspace can also drop down to 700 AGL as shown in position #2. Class E airspace can also descend all the way down to the surface around an airport. When Class E airspace touches the surface, it's identified by a dashed magenta line in the shape of a circle, possibly with rectangular attachments, as shown at position #3. In just a while I'll explain why it drops to the surface and why this airspace is shaped the way it is. For now, our objective is to understand what Class E airspace means to you as a pilot. To do that, let's divide Class E airspace into two sections: a section at and above 10,000 feet MSL and a section less than 10,000 feet MSL.

Class E Below at and Above 10,000 Feet MSL

As you probably know by now, sport pilots are not allowed to operate above 10,000 feet MSL (or 2,000 feet AGL, whichever is higher). The FAA didn't create this restriction because they thought you were frightened of heights, either. The FAA assumed that there would be some degree of incompatibility between light-sport airplanes and the higher performance machines that actually operate at these altitudes. So instead of you getting buzzed in your SloMo-RX12 by the secret military's Aurora fighter, the FAA decided to keep light sport airplanes separate from the heavy metal folks.

Additionally, operating above 10,000 feet MSL does require additional knowledge that may be beyond the typical training a sport pilot receives. So consider anything above 10,000 feet MSL (and more than 2,000 feet AGL)

as private pilot territory. Nothing personal, here.

There is, however, Class E airspace existing at and above 10,000 feet MSL and extending all the way up to, but not including 18,000 feet MSL. There are also VFR weather requirements for flying at these altitudes, too. Since you won't be operating at these altitudes, I don't want to talk about these now, but in case you have an inquiring mind, you might want to know about them just so that you have an idea of what other pilots are doing and how it may affect you. I've placed a discussion on these requirements at the end of this chapter in Postflight Briefing #9-2. Please take time to read this once you understand the rest of this chapter.

Class E Below 10,000 Feet MSL

Before we begin our discussion of VFR weather requirements, keep in mind that as a sport pilot, the regulations say that you are always required to have a minimum of three statute miles flight or surface visibility, regardless of the type of airspace in which you're operating. You must also have visual reference to the surface whenever you're flying, too. That means you can't fly above a cloud layer where, when looking down, you can't see the ground. No matter what you read from now on, remember that three statute miles is the lowest flight or ground visibility you can have and still fly. Period! There are no exceptions to this rule.

Keep your speed up Bubba. I'm getting a feeling that we've entered the wrong airspace!

Figure 5 shows the VFR cloud distance and flight visibility minimums below 10,000 feet MSL. Any altitude in Class E airspace below 10,000 feet MSL requires that you fly at least 1,000 feet above, 500 feet below and 2,000 feet horizontally from any cloud formation. Three statute miles of flight visibility is also required. Here's Rod Machado's Airspace Simplification Rule #1: Since you're likely to see at least three Cessna 152's below 10,000 feet, let's encode the minimums in an easy-to-remember formula: 3V/152.

As I mentioned earlier, it's entirely possible that an airplane on an IFR flight plan could pop out of the side of a cloud that's close to you. Even though there is a 250 knot (288 MPH) indicated airspeed limit for all aircraft operating below 10,000 feet MSL, this should still concern you. Seeing a 250 knot airplane emerging from the side of a cloud could shock you as much as it would a pig seeing someone eating a ham sandwich. Maintaining a distance of no less than 2,000 feet horizontally from any cloud formation minimizes the risk of a collision. To repeat myself for a good cause, stay as far away from any cloud as you need to in order to feel really, really safe. Two thousand feet might not do it for you; it certainly doesn't for me. I prefer three, four or even five thousand feet (big feet too).

Why is a greater distance required above a cloud than below? Many high

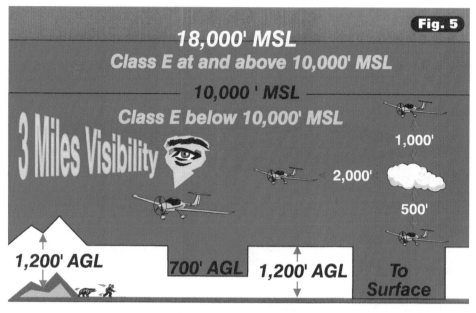

Fig. 5

18,000' MSL
Class E at and above 10,000' MSL

10,000' MSL

Class E below 10,000' MSL

3 Miles Visibility

1,000'

2,000'

500'

1,200' AGL

700' AGL

1,200' AGL

To Surface

performance airplanes typically climb faster than they descend. Small jet aircraft, like Learjets, can climb at several thousand feet per minute after takeoff (Learjets feel like someone strapped a little rocket onto your back). Being higher above the cloud tops helps reduce the risk that you will unintentionally become a hood ornament for a Learjet.

Pilots of jet aircraft, particularly big ones, rarely descend at thousands of feet per minute when they are below 10,000 feet MSL. Why? Trying to arrest a 6,000 foot-per-minute sink rate in a fully loaded Boeing 747 would take hundreds of feet. Boeing 747's (also known as "aluminum overcasts") have such inertia that descents

in excess of 1,000 feet per minute while close to the ground are done with great care. Since pilots generally descend at lesser rates than they climb, required distances below clouds are typically less than those above.

Class E Airspace Starting At 700 Feet AGL

When Class E airspace starts at 700 above ground level, it will be surrounded by a magenta faded line, as shown in Figures 6 and 7, position 1. Anywhere within this magenta faded area, controlled airspace starts at 700 feet AGL. An aeronautical sectional chart shows this magenta faded border (sharp on the outside, fading to the inside) quite clearly in Figure 7,

CLASS E AIRSPACE AT 700' AGL

Within the borders of the magenta faded area surrounding an airport, Class E (controlled) airspace starts at 700 feet above ground level (AGL) instead of the normal 1,200 feet AGL. The lower base of Class E airspace (i.e., 700' AGL), keeps airplanes flying instrument approaches in controlled airspace as they descend to the airport.

Base of Class E 18,000' MSL

Class E airspace

Class A 18,000' MSL

Class E starts at 1,200' AGL

Class E starts at 1,200' AGL

700' AGL

Carr Mem. Airport

Class E starts at 700' AGL

Fig. 6

Carr airport as shown on an aeronautical sectional chart. **Fig. 7**

CLASS E AIRSPACE AT THE SURFACE

Within the borders of the magenta (red) dashed line, Class E airspace descends all the way to the surface surrounding McComb-Pike airport. Since some instrument approaches bring pilots real close to the surface of an airport, this lower Class E surface area keeps them in controlled airspace during their descent.

Fig. 8

McComb-Pike airport as shown on an aeronautical sectional chart.

Fig. 9

position 1. Outside the border of the magenta fade, controlled airspace starts at 1,200 feet AGL.

Within the borders of the magenta fade, at and above 700 feet AGL, Rod Machado's Airspace Simplification Rule #1 applies. In other words, you need a minimum of 3V/152 for VFR flight.

Why would an airspace designer want to lower Class E airspace to 700 feet AGL around or near an airport? To keep VFR pilots from bumping into IFR pilots who are making instrument approaches.

The keyhole type extensions of Class E airspace starting at 700 feet AGL in Figure 6, position 2 identify descent paths followed by IFR airplanes during their instrument approaches. The keyhole slot is shown on the aeronautical sectional chart excerpt in Figure 7, position 3. IFR pilots on an instrument approach typically descend to altitudes of 700 feet AGL (and lower). They remain in Class E airspace during most of their IFR approach. If they see the airport, they land; if they don't see it, they fly off to another airport (hopefully one that has fewer clouds and better visibility).

Remember that in Class E airspace *below* 10,000 feet MSL, VFR pilots should be flying with no less than 3V/152. This means if an IFR pilot pops out of the clouds, there should be ample time for the VFR and IFR pilots

to see and avoid each other (IFR pilots are equally responsible to see and avoid whenever they are not in instrument meteorological conditions).

Some airports have instrument approaches that bring IFR pilots down closer than 700 feet AGL, as shown in Figure 8. There are airports allowing IFR pilots to come within 200 feet AGL or less while still in the clouds. Since controlled airspace helps VFR pilots see and avoid other pilots, these airports have Class E airspace lowered all the way to the surface. (There are other reasons why controlled airspace is lowered, but these are beyond the scope of this book.)

Figure 9 shows how surface-based Class E airspace is shown on an aeronautical sectional chart. A dotted magenta line defines the lateral boundaries of the controlled airspace surrounding McComb-Pike County airport (position 1). Airports without air traffic control towers use a magenta dashed line to represent this surface-based Class E airspace. (Airports with established control towers, as you'll see a little later, use blue-dashed lines to represent controlled airspace in contact with the surface around that airport.)

What does this surface-based Class E airspace mean to you as a VFR

WHICH WAY DOES THE MAGENTA AND BLUE FADE?

To learn about this non-faded area, see page 16.

The blue faded border (often seen in the western part of the US), indicates controlled (Class E) airspace begins at 1,200 feet AGL in the direction of the blue fade (the same direction my blue arrows point).

If you see only a magenta fade and no blue fade, just assume the area on the other side of the magenta faded border is Class E airspace starting at 1,200 feet AGL.

The magenta fades in the direction of the red arrows, indicating controlled (Class E) airspace starts at 700 AGL within the faded border areas.

Class E begins at the surface within the magenta dashed lines.

pilot approaching and departing McComb-Pike airport? It means Rod Machado's Airspace Simplification Rule #1 applies all the way to the surface within the boundaries of the magenta-dashed line. The only thing different here is that the controlled airspace normally existing at 700 feet or 1,200 feet AGL drops to the surface within the boundaries of the magenta dashed line.

---

*Here's Rod Machado's Airspace Simplification Rule #1: Since you're likely to see at least **three** Cessna 152's below 10,000 feet. You need **3** visibility, **1,000'** above, **500'** below and **2,000'** horizontally from any cloud formation. Let's encode the minimums in an easy-to-remember formula: **3V/152**.*

Additional Requirements In Surface-Based Controlled Airspace

There are two additional requirements when operating at an airport having *any* type of surface-based controlled airspace established for it (Class E in the case of McComb-Pike):

1. The reported ground visibility at the airport must be at least three statute miles. If the ground visibility isn't reported, then the flight visibility during takeoff, landing or when operating in the traffic pattern must be at least three statute miles. (The *flight visibility* is always determined by the pilot on the honor system.)

2. If a ceiling exists at that airport, it can be no lower than 1,000 feet AGL if you desire to operate beneath it. If you want to take off, land or operate in the traffic pattern, the ceiling (if one exists) must be at least 1,000 feet AGL or more.

A *ceiling* is defined as the height above the earth's surface of the lowest layer of clouds reported as *broken* or *overcast*, or any reported *vertical visibility* into obscuring phenomena. We'll be talking more about these terms in Chapter 12. For the moment, consider a ceiling as being anything in the sky you can't readily see through (like clouds for instance).

To summarize these requirements, remember this. To operate to, from, or at an airport within the boundaries of any surface-based controlled airspace, you need a minimum of three statute miles reported visibility (flight visibility if none reported) and no less than a 1,000 foot ceiling (if a ceiling exists). Let's symbolize these basic VFR requirements as *3V/1C*. (As you'll soon see, in addition to Class E, there are three other types of controlled airspace that can surround an airport at the surface: Class D, C and B.)

WHY 1,000 FEET WAS CHOSEN AS THE MINIMUM CEILING

If you think like a flight instructor (we're attracted to bright, shiny objects and trinkets that rattle), then you're probably wondering why 1,000 feet was chosen as the minimum ceiling for basic VFR within any surface-based controlled airspace. Well, as famed undersea explorer Jacques Cousteau says, "We do not know, but we shall soon find out." (Although, come to think of it, I've never actually seen him go into the water).

In Class E airspace, less than 10,000 feet MSL, you need to remain at least 500 feet below any cloud formation. Regulations also require that you remain at least 500 feet above the surface over a noncongested area. For the sake of rulemaking, the airport is assumed to be built around a noncongested area (you and I know that this isn't always true, but it's general enough to make this point). Adding the 500 foot minimum altitude requirement to the 500 foot minimum clearance beneath a cloud gives you a minimum ceiling height of 1,000 feet. These values are shown below.

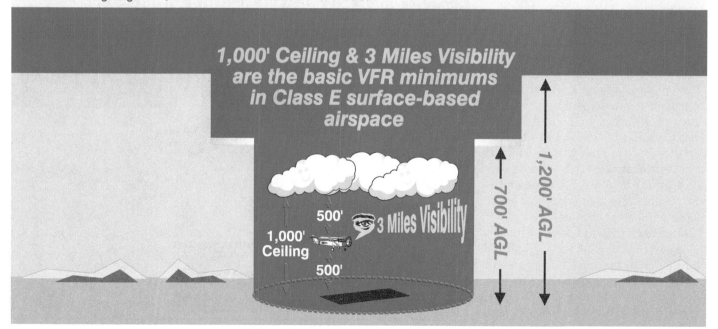

1,000' Ceiling & 3 Miles Visibility are the basic VFR minimums in Class E surface-based airspace

500' · 3 Miles Visibility · 1,000' Ceiling · 500' · 700' AGL · 1,200' AGL

The *A/FD* indicates that McComb-Pike's Class E surface area operates continuously.

Mc COMB-PIKE CO-JOHN E LEWIS FLD   (MCB)   4 S   UTC-6(-5DT)   NEW ORLEANS
    N31°10.71' W90°28.31'   H-5C, L-17D
    413   B   S4   **FUEL** 100LL, JET A   IAP
    RWY 15-33: H5000X100 (ASPH)   S-25, D-30, DT-60   MIRL
    RWY 15: PAPI(P2L)—GA 3.0° TCH 38'. Trees.   RWY 33: PAPI(P2L)—GA 3.0° TCH 46'. Trees.
    AIRPORT REMARKS: Attended 1400Z‡-dusk. For attendant and fuel after hours call 601-684-7070 or ctc FSS.
        ACTIVATE MIRL Rwy 15-33—CTAF. For MALSF Rwy 15 ctc FSS. Ground drops abruptly both ends Rwy 15-33
        starting 200' from thld.
    COMMUNICATIONS: CTAF 123.6   **UNICOM** 122.95
    Mc COMB FSS (MCB) on arpt. 123.6 122.4 122.2 122.1R. LC 684-7070 NOTAM FILE MCB.
    ® HOUSTON CENTER APP/DEP CON 133.5
    AIRSPACE: CLASS E svc effective continuously.
    RADIO AIDS TO NAVIGATION: NOTAM FILE MCB.
    (H) VORTAC 116.7   MCB   Chan 114   N31°18.26' W90°15.49'   233° 13.3 NM to fld. 440/03E. HIWAS
    FERNI NDB (MHW/LOM) 413   MC   N31°15.27' W90°30.63'   153° 5 NM to fld.
    ILS 109.1   I-MCB   Rwy 15.   LOM FERNI NDB. LOC unusable byd 25 degrees E of course.   **Fig. 10**

Here's Rod Machado's Airspace Simplification Rule #2: Taking off, landing, or operating in the traffic pattern of an airport having *any* type of surface-based controlled airspace requires basic VFR minimums of at least three statute miles visibility and, if a ceiling exists at that airport, it can be no lower than 1,000 feet. We'll symbolize this rule as 3V/1C. (There is one single exception to the 3V/1C rule and I've discussed it in Postflight Briefing #9-1.)

I specifically chose the words above to indicate that surface-based controlled airspace is established for a specific airport (usually the one in the center of that airspace). We call this the *primary airport*. Sometimes, other airports lie within the boundaries of the primary airport's surface-based controlled airspace. These are called *satellite airports* (think of them as orbiting the primary airport, although they really don't move!). As you can see below, the above simplification rule #2 also applies to satellite airports, with one exception.

Just because Class E airspace exists at the surface of an airport doesn't mean it stays that way 24 hours a day. In other words, the surface-based portion of that controlled airspace can revert back to Class E airspace starting at 700 or 1,200 feet AGL.

Normally, any type of surface-based controlled airspace requires a federally certificated weather observer or weather-observing system be present to make visibility and cloud height determinations. These weather observers or observing systems can be tower controllers, flight service station personnel, licensed weather observers, or federally certificated automated weather observing stations known as AWOS-3 (Automatic Weather Observing System). Some means of pilot-to-ATC communication is also required. Either direct communications with ATC, relayed communication through an FSS, or communication via a remote communication outlet is acceptable.

The official weather observer's hours of operation normally coincide with the hours during which the surface-based controlled airspace exists. I said *normally*, not *always*. The actual hours that surface-based controlled airspace exists are shown in the *A/FD* (*Airport/Facility Directory*) as shown in Figure 10. If the weather observer leaves before these hours, the surface-based airspace is still in effect. This is one reason why ground visibility might not be reported, yet three statute miles of flight visibility is still required for landing.

SATELLITE AIRPORTS LYING WITHIN THE PRIMARY AIRPORT'S SURFACE-BASED CONTROLLED AIRSPACE

Sometimes an additional airport (a satellite airport) lies within the surface-based airspace originally established for another airport (the primary airport). Port Angeles (to the right) is an example of such an airport. It lies within the Class E surface area established for Fairchild International airport. If Fairchild reports less than three miles visibility, a sport pilot may still operate into and out of Port Angeles as long as he or she has a minimum of three miles flight visibility (or ground visibility—if it's reported at the satellite airport). However, if Fairchild (the primary airport) reports a ceiling less than 1,000 feet AGL, then a sport pilot isn't allowed to operate anywhere within that surface-based controlled airspace. Simply stated, visibility is determined by pilots on the honor system but ceilings are determined by the official weather observer at the primary airport. This rule pertains to *any* type of surface-based controlled airspace (B, C, D as well as E).

As a sport pilot, you may see private pilots operating into or out of airports located with surface-based controlled airspace with less than three miles visibility. In these instances, the private pilots are operating on a *special VFR (SVFR) clearance*. A SVFR clearance allows private pilots to operate within surface-based controlled airspace with one mile visibility while remaining clear of the clouds. Sport pilots are permitted to use a SVFR clearance but only when the ceiling is less than 1,000 feet AGL, not when the visibility is less than three miles.

Port Angeles is a satellite airport located within the Class E airspace of another airport (Fairchild Intl.).

ARRIVING VFR AIRCRAFT SHOULD CONTACT WHIDBEY APPROACH CONTROL WITHIN 20 NM ON 118.2 286.0

CLASS G (UNCONTROLLED) AIRSPACE

Class G (uncontrolled) airspace starts at the surface and ascends upward until reaching the base of Class E (controlled) airspace. Class G airspace may extend upward to 700 or 1,200 feet AGL or even higher. Generally, Class G airspace contains fewer big and fast airplanes (except in the vicinity of certain airports). Therefore, the visibility and cloud clearance requirement is usually not as great as in controlled airspace.

Fig. 11

Monett airport lies in Class G (uncontrolled) airspace. Class E (controlled airspace starts at 700' AGL.

Fig. 13

Class G Airspace

We're about to do much ado about nothing.

Welcome to the short course on *Class G,* or *uncontrolled* airspace. This is a tiny sliver of airspace whose rules are thicker than its depth, and whose practical importance to most pilots on most occasions is vanishingly small unless you routinely fly from Point A to point B at or below 1200 feet above the ground.

While there are several types of controlled airspace (Class B, C, D and E), there is only one type of uncontrolled or Class G airspace. It's generally found below Class E airspace at altitudes less than 1,200 or 700 feet AGL. Figure 11 depicts Class G airspace. In fact, the only place near the surface where you *won't* find Class G airspace, is within the surface-based controlled airspace that surrounds an airport.

Think about Class G airspace as a thin layer of water resting over the entire, continental United States. In other words, any place other than an airport having surface-based controlled airspace must have a thin layer of Class G airspace lying on top of it. Those airports having surface-based controlled airspace in the United States couldn't possibly cover even 1% of the nation's surface (believe me when I say it's much, much less than that, but we'll use 1% anyway). Simple math indicates that over 99% of the United States surface area must have Class G airspace lying on top of it and extending vertically to 700 or 1,200 feet AGL. As you can imagine, Class G airspace within 700 or 1,200 feet AGL is quite common. That's why it's nice to know something about the basic VFR minimums in Class G airspace.

To understand what Class G airspace means to you, it's necessary to think back to the introduction of this chapter. Our airspace discussion revolves around the idea that controlled airspace is likely to be used by more aircraft (especially aircraft on an IFR flight plan) than uncontrolled airspace. Therefore, the basic VFR weather minimums are a little stricter in controlled airspace.

Have you noticed how the basic VFR weather minimums change with altitude? Generally, the lower you go, the less restrictive the weather minimums become. At low altitudes (say less than 1,200 feet AGL), fewer airplanes, and certainly fewer fast airplanes, fly close to the surface for long periods of time (except for taking off and landing at airports of course). There is less threat of a collision at these lower altitudes between airports.

With fewer airplanes flying long distances at low altitudes between airports, it's reasonable to conclude that the VFR weather minimums in these areas should be the least restrictive for sport pilots. That is precisely the case. In Class G airspace at and below 1,200 feet AGL, the basic VFR minimums are three statute miles flight visibility while remaining clear of all clouds as shown in Figure 12. We'll simplify this with the symbol *3V/COC*. (COC stands for clear of clouds.)

Monett airport, shown in the aeronautical sectional chart excerpt in

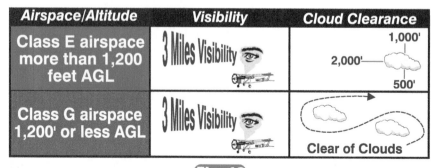

Airspace/Altitude	Visibility	Cloud Clearance
Class E airspace more than 1,200 feet AGL	3 Miles Visibility	1,000' 2,000' 500'
Class G airspace 1,200' or less AGL	3 Miles Visibility	Clear of Clouds

Fig. 12

Figure 13, position 1, is in Class G airspace. During the day you may depart or land at Monett with a minimum flight visibility of three miles, while staying clear of all clouds, as long as you remain at or below 700 feet AGL. Class E airspace starts at 700 feet AGL within the magenta faded borders above Monett (position 2). For flight above 700 feet AGL, within the magenta border's lateral limits, you must have the basic VFR minimums for Class E airspace operations below 10,000' MSL (3V/152).

Outside the lateral limits of the magenta fade, at what altitude does Class E airspace start? I hope you said it starts at 1,200 feet AGL, as shown in Figure 11. Let's assume you want to take off or land at Mt. Vernon airport (Figure 13, position 3). You can do so during the day with a minimum of three statute miles flight visibility and remaining clear of clouds (3V/COC) as long as you ascend no higher than 1,200 feet AGL. Climbing higher than 1,200 feet AGL above Mt. Vernon puts you in Class E airspace which requires 3V/152.

Most pilots do *not* routinely fly around at 1200 AGL or below. That's because most pilots realize there's not much margin of safety in case of engine failure when you're 1,200 AGL, there's a good chance of bumping into something tall (like a basketball player or TV antenna), and you probably couldn't convince the FAA that this met the standard for sensible altitude when over a densely occupied area. For these reasons, and many others, Class G airspace is not something in which you will spend a lot of your pilot life.

Figure 14 shows a basic summary of our basic VFR weather requirements. Once again, you must keep in mind that sport pilots are always restricted to flying with a minimum of three statute miles flight visibility. Nor can a sport pilot take off or land when the surface visibility is less than 3 statute miles, either.

We're almost done with our discussion on the basic VFR weather requirements. There's one more little item that we still need to cover. This concerns operations in Class G airspace more than 1,200 feet AGL but

---

Rod Machado's Airspace Simplification Rule #3:
*When flying in Class G (uncontrolled) airspace at or below 1,200' AGL during the day you're low enough to knock over **3 COC** machines (sounds like Coke). You need **3** miles visibility and must remain **c**lear **o**f **c**louds.*

---

less than 10,000 foot MSL. Yep, that's right. Class G airspace can extend above 1,200 feet AGL (all the way to but not including 14,500 feet MSL). This vertical extension is found on the west coast of the United States but is rare elsewhere. To better understand this requirement (you may be asked about it during your oral or knowledge exam), please take a look at Postflight Briefings #9-3 & 4.

Remember, the airspace designations and the basic VFR weather minimums for each are there for a reason—to protect you and other pilots. Rules are often created for just that purpose. In fact, that's why you now see little signs on Coke machines saying, "If you lose money in this machine, don't shake it, call the manager." Apparently people without much common sense were shaking the machines, causing them to tip over and squish these folks graveyard dead. (If you've been injured by a falling Coke machine, you probably shouldn't be flying an airplane. I always check for Coke imprints on the forehead before I fly with anyone.)

VFR REQUIREMENTS IN CLASS E AND CLASS G AIRSPACE

Shown above are the basic VFR weather minimums for Class E (controlled) airspace below 10,000' MSL. The VFR requirements above 1,200' AGL and below 10,000' MSL also apply to the controlled airspace extending to the surface. Additionally, a minimum of a 1,000' ceiling (if one exists) is also required for basic VFR in a class E surface area.

Operations in Class G airspace at 1,200 feet or less AGL require sport pilots to have three miles visibility (this is always the sport pilot minimum flight and ground visibility) and to remain clear of all clouds.

Fig. 14

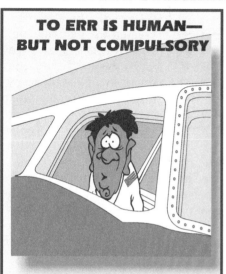

Reporting over XYZ (last foreign point before entering USA), the controller asked us to contact the American center on 125.65 and squawk 7500. We acknowledged and complied. Center asked me to confirm squawking 7500. I confirmed without it reminding me that this was the hijack code. The approach was curious in that we received (sort of), special handling. There didn't seem to be anybody else on the frequency and everything went very smoothly.

Tower asked us to roll out all the way to the end of the long runway, which seemed odd. I taxied off the runway and was surrounded by a phalanx of vehicles (police cars, airport vehicles, FBI, Border Patrol, M-16 carbines, sirens, lights, and customs people). The whole world was there to greet us. It was only when someone asked if I knew the meaning of Code 7500, that it dawned on me what had happened. It was then difficult to convince the authorities that the flight was in no way abnormal. Unfortunately, in the papers the next day they correctly spelled my name.

Our foreign controller friends could use a refresher on emergency codes like the one these company pilots received.

ASRS Report

Class B, C and D Airspace

The last three variations of controlled airspace are Class B, Class C and Class D airspace (all of which require additional training and endorsements for a sport pilot to enter). All three types of airspace start at the surface and surround those airports that have an operating control tower. Each class of airspace serves the single purpose of coordinating takeoffs and landings between individual aircraft. That's why an operating control tower is required. Geometric versions of these three different types of airspace are shown in Figure 15.

In Chapter 6 we referred to Class D and C airspace as having the shape of a single and double-stacked tuna can. We referred to Class B airspace as looking like an inverted wedding cake. Now it's time to upgrade this simile to an analogy.

It's safe to generalize here and say that the taller the airspace structure, the busier the airport with which it is allied. The word *busy* implies more as well as bigger and faster airplanes. A good way to understand how big and small airplanes operate within these three types of airspace is to think about fish. If you have goldfish, you put them in a small bowl. They certainly don't need a large living area. Sharks, on the other hand, need bigger aquariums. Whales need giant tanks. Airplanes are like fish, in that larger ones need more space in which to operate.

Think about these three airspace shapes as aquariums or water tanks (Figure 16). Class D airspace is small in comparison, meaning (most of the time) that smaller airplanes (goldfish) like Cessnas, Pipers and Beechcraft swim there. Class C airspace, being slightly larger, means that bigger and faster airplanes like Learjets and Boeing 737's (sharks) may be found there. Class B airspace (big tanks) means that aircraft like Boeing 747's and DC-10's (whales) may loom within this airspace. Let's examine each class of airspace starting with Class D (the goldfish bowl).

CLASS B, C, OR D AIRSPACE

An airport with an operating control tower can have either Class B, C, or D airspace at its surface. The Class of airspace depends on several factors: how busy the airport is, the types of airplanes using the airport, the number of IFR flights, the facilities available at the airport, etc.

There may be a few exceptions where a Class E or G surface area actually does have an operating control tower. These exceptions are minor and shouldn't ever concern you.

Class D Airspace

Class D airspace is controlled airspace starting at the surface of airports having an operating air traffic control tower (Figure 17 shows its dimensions). It's established to help air traffic controllers provide an orderly flow of traffic taking off or landing at airports within this airspace.

The blue dashed line surrounding Chico airport in Figure 18 (position 1) represents the lateral dimensions of Class D airspace. The radius of Class D airspace varies with individual airports and is individually tailored to the instrument approach procedure for which the controlled (Class D) airspace is established. It averages 4.3 nautical miles (5 statute miles). The top of the airspace cylinder generally extends to heights of approximately 2,500 feet AGL. The height also varies, depending on local needs. Position 2 in Figure 18 identifies the actual top of Class D airspace in hundreds of feet above sea level as shown by the bracketed value of 27 (2,700 feet MSL). As you can see, the 2,700 foot MSL top of Chico's Class D airspace is approximately 2,500 feet above its elevation of 238 feet MSL.

Class D airspace is established at airports having sufficient traffic to justify the presence of a control

AIRSPACE AS A FISH TANK

Think of different classes of airspace as fish tanks. The bigger the tank, the bigger the critter found within the tank. Similarly, larger classes of airspace usually contain larger airplanes. Of course, smaller fish (propeller airplanes) can also be found swimming in larger tanks.

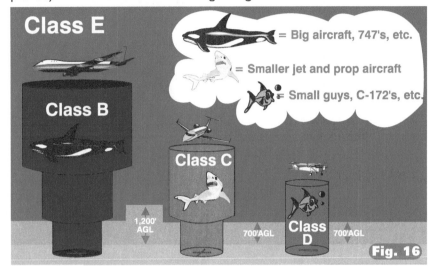

Fig. 16

tower. Normally, numerous general aviation airplanes are found taking off or landing at the primary airport within this airspace. The primary airport shown in Figure 18, position 3, (the one with the control tower) is usually found at the center of the blue dashed circle. This doesn't mean you won't find the occasional larger aircraft (shark or whale) at this airport. It does mean, however, that there may be quite a few smaller airplanes (goldfish) in the vicinity.

All aircraft operating within Class D airspace are required to establish and maintain two way radio communication prior to entering and when operating within this airspace. In other words, you must talk to the control tower before taking off, landing, or flying through this airspace. Of course, if you overfly Chico airport at more than 2,700 feet MSL, or operate beyond the lateral limits of the blue dashed line, you're not in Class D airspace and no communication is required. (See Chapter 6, FAR 91.129 for the precise definition of *establishing and maintaining communication.)*

DIMENSIONS OF CLASS D AIRSPACE

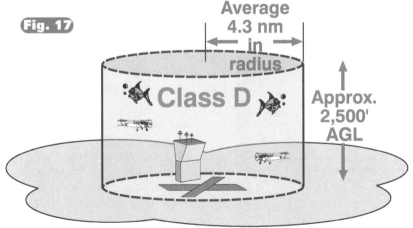

Fig. 17

Operating anywhere within the boundaries of Class D airspace requires that you establish and maintain communication with the Air Traffic Control tower prior to entering this airspace. While controllers don't provide separation between aircraft, they do provide sequencing as well as information about known air traffic.

CLASS D AIRSPACE AT CHICO

Fig. 18

Chico airport (Figure 26, position 3) is solid blue in color. This identifies the airport as having a control tower. Remembering this is easy, since blue is the color your face usually turns when you're attempting to understand what fast-talking controllers are saying. Communication with the air traffic controller is made on the tower frequency of 121.0 MHz shown next to the symbol CT (control tower). Realize that Class D airspace only exists when the control tower is operating. This means the control tower has someone in it. After all, there's no way you can establish communications without controllers (the night cleaning staff will not answer your calls). When the tower shuts down, the airport is treated like a non-tower (uncontrolled) airport.

Figure 19 shows an excerpt from the *A/FD* for Chico airport. Class D airspace is effective from 1500 to 0300 UTC. This is the same as the operating hours of Chico's control tower (0700 to 1900 local time), as shown on the aeronautical sectional chart's side panel in Figure 20. According to the *A/FD* (Figure 19, point C), when Class D airspace is not in effect, the airspace reverts to Class G airspace.

Figure 21 identifies the Class E airspace extensions added onto Class D airspace. As I've mentioned before, extensions of Class E airspace are added when it's necessary to keep IFR airplanes in controlled airspace during their instrument approaches.

> *This is the A/FD excerpt for Chico showing the effective hours of operation for Class D airspace (point A). Notice that these are the same as the operating hours of the air traffic control tower (point B).*

CHICO

CHICO MUNI (CIC) 4 N UTC–8(–7DT) N39°47.72' W121°51.51' SAN FRANCISCO
238 B S4 **FUEL** 100, 100LL, JET A TPA—See Remarks ARFF Index A H-1A, 2A, L-2G
RWY 13L-31R: H6724X150 (ASPH–PFC) S–63, D–100, DT–170 HIRL 0.5% up NW IAP
 RWY 13L: MALSR. VASI(V2L)—GA 3.0° TCH 54'. Rgt tfc (when twr clsd).
 RWY 31R: REIL. VASI(V4L)—GA 3.0° TCH 50'. Rgt tfc (when twr open).
RWY 13R-31L: H3005X60 (ASPH) S–25
 RWY 13R: Rgt tfc.
AIRPORT REMARKS: Attended 1530–0330Z‡. For fuel services after hours call 916–896–6122. TPA—1500(1262) jet/heavy acft opr E of fld, 1000(762) lgt acft opr W and E of fld. Rwy 13R-31L is part of an asphalt pad 3000'X1500'. When twr clsd ACTIVATE HIRL Rwy 13L-31R and MALSR Rwy 13L-121.0.
WEATHER DATA SOURCES: LAWRS.
COMMUNICATIONS: CTAF 121.0
 RED BLUFF FSS (RBL) TF 1–800–WX–BRIEF. (1400–0600Z‡). NOTAM FILE CIC.
 RANCHO MURIETA FSS (RIU) TF 1–800–WX–BRIEF. (0600–1400Z‡).
 RCO 122.1R 109.8T (RED BLUFF FSS)
Ⓡ OAKLAND CENTER APP/DEP CON 132.2
 TOWER 121.0 (1500–0300Z‡) GND CON 121.9 — **B**
 AIRSPACE: CLASS D svc effective 1500–0300Z‡ other times CLASS G. — **C**
RADIO AIDS TO NAVIGATION: NOTAM FILE CIC.
 (T) VOR/DME 109.8 CIC Chan 35 N39°47.39' W121°50.83' at fld. 220/16E. VOR/DME without voice when FSS clsd.
 NORDE NDB (LOM) **A** CI N39°53.22' W121°55.99' 132° 6.5 NM to fld.
 ILS 111.3 I- Rwy 13L LOM NORDE NDB. Unmonitored when twr clsd.
COMM/NAVAID REMARKS: Emerg frequency 121.5 not avbl at twr.

Fig. 19

Tower controllers give the impression of being pretty serious, yet most of them have a great sense of humor. For instance, one of our airport's more senior pilots had his false teeth fall out during a landing (he sneezed and flared at the same time and blew his teeth out of his mouth). The tower called but he couldn't reply. He finally got his teeth back in and said, "Tower, I'm sorry about the delayed response but my teeth fell out on landing. The controller said, "Well, you might think about pulling back on the wheel a little sooner next time." I think the controller also said, "and make sure you stay away from those Coke machines, OK?"

Weather Minimums For Class D Airspace

The weather minimums for Class D airspace are exactly the same as they are for Class E airspace below 10,000 feet MSL. Therefore Rod Machado's Airspace Simplification Rule #1 applies here. You need to maintain the VFR minimums of 3V/152—3 statute miles visibility, 1,000 feet above any clouds, 500 feet below clouds, 2,000 feet laterally from clouds—while airborne. Since Class D airspace is surface-based controlled airspace, Rod Machado's Airspace Simplification Rule #2 also applies. Taking off, landing or operating in the traffic pattern of an airport having any type of surface-based controlled airspace established for it requires a minimum of 3V/1C—3 statute miles visibility, 1000 foot ceiling.

As with Class E airspace, this is *reported* ground visibility. When it's not reported, the pilot must maintain at least three statute miles *flight visibility*. If weather conditions at that airport are less than three statute miles reported ground visibility or less than a 1,000 foot ceiling (if a ceiling exists), sport pilots are prevented from taking off, landing, or entering the traffic pattern within the surface-based portion of Class D airspace (and its Class E extension).

> *The operating hours of an air traffic control tower (Chico in this instance), are also found on the sectional chart's frequency tab.*

CONTROL TOWER FREQUENCIES ON SAN FRANCISCO SECTIONAL CHART

Airports which have control towers are indicated on this chart by the letters CT followed by the primary VHF local control frequency. Selected transmitting frequencies for each control tower are tabulated in the adjoining spaces, the low or medium transmitting frequencies are listed first followed by a VHF local control frequency, and the primary VHF and UHF military frequencies, when these frequencies are available. An asterisk (*) follows the part-time tower frequency remoted to the collocated full-time FSS for use as Local Airport Advisory (LAA) during hours tower is closed. Hours shown are local time. Ground control frequencies listed are the primary ground control frequencies.
Automatic Terminal Information Service (ATIS) frequencies, shown on the face of the chart are primary arrival VHF/UHF frequencies. All ATIS frequencies are listed below. ATIS operational hours may differ from control tower operational hours.
ASR and/or PAR indicates Radar Instrument Approach available.
''MON-FRI'' indicates Monday thru Friday.

Fig. 20

CONTROL TOWER	OPERATES	TWR FREQ	GND CON	ATIS	ASR/PAR
NAS ALAMEDA	CONTINUOUS	127.05 384.4	121.65 352.4	284.2	ASR/PAR
BEALE AFB	CONTINUOUS	119.4 276.15	121.6 228.4	273.5	ASR/PAR
BUCHANAN	0600-2200	119.7 123.9 257.8	121.9	124.7	
CASTLE AFB	CONTINUOUS	118.45 289.6	275.8	271.8	ASR/PAR
CHICO	0700-1900	121.0 239.3	121.9		
NALF CROWS LANDING	MON-FRI AS SKED	125.05 328.1			
NAS FALLON	0715-2245 MON-FRI 0745-1815 SAT	119.25 340.2	382.8	284.3	ASR/PAR

CHICO'S CLASS D AIRSPACE

Class D (blue cylinder) airspace starts at the surface of an airport with an operating control tower. It extends vertically to approximately 2,500' feet above the airport elevation. Chico airport, shown below, has an elevation of 238' MSL. This makes the top of the Class D airspace approximately 2,700' MSL ([27]). The radius of Class D airspace is approximately 4.3 nautical miles (but this varies from airport to airport).

Compare Chico's Class D airspace on this sectional chart excerpt below with the model to the left.

Fig. 21

During the day, you can usually tell if the primary airport is below basic VFR minimums by looking at the airport's rotating beacon. The beacon, which flashes white and green as it rotates, is normally activated at night to help identify an airport with runway lights. When it's activated during the day, it means that an existing ceiling is less than 1,000 feet or the visibility is less than three statute miles, or both. Either way, sport pilots are not allowed to operate into or out of the surface-based controlled airspace under these conditions.

Satellite Airports Within Class D Airspace

On occasion, another airport lies within the lateral boundaries of Class D airspace, as seen in Figure 22. Martha Lake airport (position 1), an uncontrolled airport, lies within the Class D airspace of Snohomish County airport (position 2).

If you're landing at Martha Lake, you need to establish and maintain two way radio communication with the primary airport (Snohomish Tower) prior to entering Class D airspace. If you're taking off from Martha Lake airport, you must establish contact with Snohomish tower as soon as practicable after departing.

Sometimes a special arrangement is made with the control tower concern-

ing satellite airports within its Class D airspace. This provision is known as a *letter of agreement*. It's somewhat like a prenuptial agreement that attempts to prevent the uppercuts, headlocks and general mayhem associated with divorce hearings. For example, a letter of agreement with the tower might allow pilots from a

particular flight school at a satellite airport to take off or land in a specific direction without first establishing communications with the tower. Unless you know that you are covered by this procedure, you should always establish and maintain two way radio communications with the tower prior to entering Class D airspace.

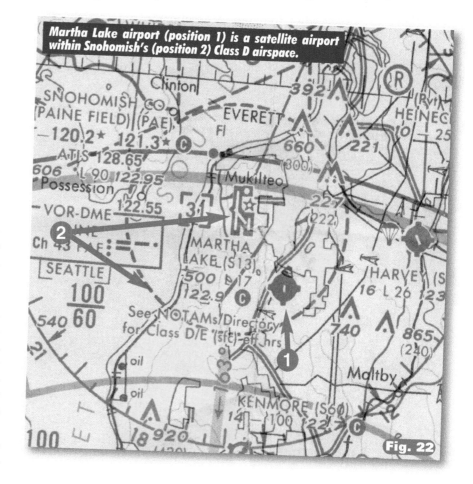

Martha Lake airport (position 1) is a satellite airport within Snohomish's (position 2) Class D airspace.

Fig. 22

Class C Airspace

Smaller jet-type aircraft (sharks) as well as propeller driven aircraft (goldfish) are normally found in Class C airspace. Radar services are available to ensure traffic separation between this mixture of fast and slow, IFR and VFR aircraft. An operating control tower (as found in Class D airspace) as well as radar approach control services are associated with the existence of Class C airspace. Figure 23 shows the typical dimensions of this airspace.

Class C airspace is geometrically shaped like two cylinders—a larger one on top of a smaller one (the double tuna can, remember?). The surface-based inner cylinder (the core surface area) extends upward to approximately 4,000 feet AGL and has a five nautical mile radius from the center of the primary airport. The upper cylinder (the shelf area) normally begins at 1,200 feet AGL and has a 10 nautical mile radius from the center of the primary airport. The upper limit of the top cylinder is generally found at 4,000 feet above the elevation of the primary airport. Remember, the Class C airspace fish tank is larger because it must hold sharks as well as goldfish. Dimensions of Class C airspace may vary depending on local terrain and traffic considerations.

Class C airspace is depicted on an aeronautical sectional chart by solid magenta rings surrounding the primary airport, as shown in Figure 24. Beale Air Force Base is the primary airport in this case. Positions 2 and 3 show both the inner and outer cylinders of this airspace. Elevation numbers (positions 4 and 5) show that the two sections of the outer cylinder start at 2,600 feet and 1,600 feet MSL respectively and extend vertically to 4,100 feet MSL (that's approximately 4,000 feet above Beale's airport elevation of 113 feet MSL).

DIMENSIONS OF CLASS C AIRSPACE

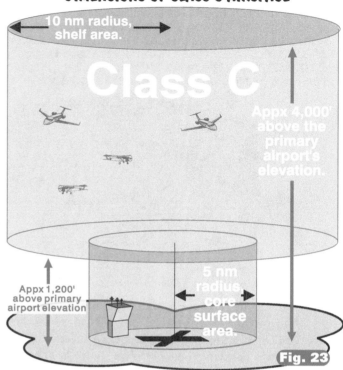

Fig. 23

Operating anywhere within the boundaries of Class C airspace requires that you establish and maintain communication with the appropriate ATC facility (usually Approach Control) prior to entering this airspace. ATC provides *basic radar service*, *sequencing* and *separation* between VFR and IFR aircraft. It also provides this same service within a 20 nm radius of the primary airport (often defined as the *outer area*). A mixture of faster ( ) and slower aircraft ( ) is common in Class C airspace.

Class C airspace at Beale Air Force Base as shown on a sectional chart. Position 1 shows the facility having jurisdiction over this airspace.

Fig. 24

BEALE'S CLASS C AIRSPACE STRUCTURE

Fig. 25

Because of higher terrain east of the airport, a section of the outer cylinder begins at a higher MSL altitude (position 4), yet it's still approximately 1,200 feet AGL. The inner cylinder elevation limits (position 6) extend from the surface (SFC) to 4,100 feet MSL. Figure 25 shows a 3-D view of Beale's Class C airspace.

Equipment Requirements To Operate Within Class C Airspace

If you are planning on entering Class C airspace (to land at any airport within the inner cylinder, or to fly through the area) you must establish and maintain two way radio communication with the appropriate ATC facility prior to entering this airspace. The facility you must communicate with is the one providing air traffic services for that airspace. Normally, this will be the local approach control facility for that area. Position 1 in Figure 24 shows the frequencies for the ATC facility having jurisdiction over this airspace.

Two-way radio communication is required in Class C as well as Class D airspace. In addition, operations within Class C airspace require a transponder with Mode C capability (an encoding altimeter). This transponder requirement also applies if you are flying anywhere above the ceiling and within the lateral boundaries of Class C airspace upward to 10,000 feet MSL. In other words, even though you're above the top of Class C airspace, as long as you are within its lateral boundaries and below 10,000 feet MSL, you need a transponder with an encoding altimeter.

Will The Flier Please Fly?

Do make it a point to have your radios in good working order when dealing with busy air traffic controllers. One pilot was attempting to call the tower for departure without much success. All the controller heard was, "Bzzzz, bzzzz, bzzzz." The controller said, "Aircraft calling the tower, your transmission is inaudible." Once again the controller heard "Bzzzz, bzzzz, bzzzz." This time the controller got upset and said, "Aircraft calling tower, get that radio fixed, you sound like a fly." Suddenly, from somewhere, the controller hears another pilot's high pitched voice saying, "Bzzz, bzzz, I am a fly, bzzz, bzzz." Never let it be said that pilots don't have a sense of humor.

ter. This helps keep ATC aware of potential traffic conflicts as pilots exit and enter the top of Class C airspace.

Class C Service

Within Class C airspace you'll receive Class C service. It's really first class service for Class C airspace. It means ATC provides you with basic radar service, sequencing to the primary airport, and separation of VFR aircraft from IFR aircraft.

Although *not shown* on the sectional chart, there is an *imagined* outer area to Class C airspace that's assumed to extend to a 20 nm radius from the primary airport. It's considered good operating practice (although not mandatory) to contact the approach control facility within 20 nm of the primary airport. This gives the controller more time for sequencing and separating you from IFR aircraft. (An aircraft doesn't need to be operating in the clouds to be considered an IFR aircraft. It need only be on an IFR flight plan, regardless of the weather conditions. IFR aircraft are in constant contact with ATC and these are the aircraft Class C service sequences you with and separates you from.)

Let's assume you're departing the primary airport within Class C airspace. Obviously you must establish and maintain two way radio communication with the control tower just as you did in Class D airspace. After departure, you must communicate as instructed by ATC while operating within this airspace. This means you'll probably be handed off from the tower to Departure Control when leaving the airport. The tower might say, "Remos 2132 Bravo, contact Bay Departure Control on 121.3." When departing the primary airport in Class C airspace, the ATIS will often require you to contact Clearance Delivery for departure instructions. Normally you will be given the departure control frequency, a transponder squawk code and instructions on how to depart the area (such as a heading or a route to be flown).

Satellite Airports Within Class C Airspace

Figure 24, position 7, shows that Hammonton airport is an uncontrolled, satellite airport within the inner circle of Beale's Class C airspace. You can depart a satellite airport without an operating control tower if you establish and maintain two-way radio communication with the appropriate ATC facility (usually approach or departure control) as soon as possible after departing. In other words, you may take off and, as soon as it's feasible, contact Sacramento Approach Control on one of the frequencies shown in the red tabbed box (position 1).

GOOD GRIEF, WILL SOMEONE TALK TO THIS GUY!!!

A small aircraft was observed maneuvering low within Class D airspace with no contact with the tower. The tower controller suspected the aircraft was NORDO (no radio) and was planning to maneuver traffic around it. Pilot finally called tower when entering downwind and was cleared to land on Runway 15L. Airplane landed on 15R, necessitating a go-around for another airplane on short final to 15R. After landing, the pilot said he was taking pictures and didn't know he was supposed to establish communications with the tower before entering Class D airspace. He THOUGHT he had landed on 15L. He said he didn't carry his private pilot license or medical certificate because it was getting wrinkled in his wallet.

That license should not get wrinkled during its possible suspension. Pilot might benefit by reading the FARs since he will probably have some spare time. **ASRS**

Variations in the Dimensions Of Class C Airspace

Figure 26 shows Class C airspace for Santa Barbara airport. A portion of the outer cylinder on the eastern side of Santa Barbara's Class C airspace is missing (no, this has nothing to do with UFO cattle mutilations). Steeply rising terrain east of the airport necessitated removal of this section.

The inner cylinder of Santa Barbara's Class C airspace is controlled airspace touching the surface. As we've previously seen with surface-based Class E airspace, a keyhole extension is sometimes necessary to accommodate instrument pilots making approaches into the airport. An extension of Class E airspace (position 1) is added onto the inner cylinder of Class C airspace at Santa Barbara (Figure 26). Within this small segment of the magenta dashed line, Class E airspace extends from the surface upward to the overlying shelf of Class C airspace (the overlying shelf begins at 1500 feet MSL in this case).

Weather Minimums For Class C Airspace

The weather minimums for Class C airspace are exactly the same as they are for Class D airspace and Class E airspace below 10,000 feet MSL. Rod Machado's Airspace Simplification Rule #1 applies here. You need to maintain the VFR minimums of 3V/152 while airborne. Since Class C airspace is surface-based controlled airspace, Rod Machado's Airspace Simplification Rule #2 also applies. Taking off, landing, or operating in the traffic pattern of an airport having *any* type of surface-based controlled airspace established for it requires a minimum of 3V/1C. As with Class D and E surfaced-based airspace, sport pilots should not be operating in these areas without 3V/1C.

Does Class C airspace exist continuously? Not necessarily. It's similar

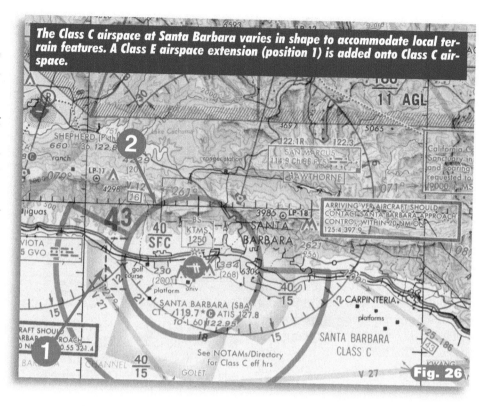

The Class C airspace at Santa Barbara varies in shape to accommodate local terrain features. A Class E airspace extension (position 1) is added onto Class C airspace.

Fig. 26

to Class D airspace in that it may exist only part time. The way to determine its effective hours is by refering, once again, to the *Airport/Facility Directory* as shown in Figure 27. The *A/FD* indicates that Santa Barbara's Class C airspace is in operation from 1400Z to 0700Z.

These are also the hours of operation of the control tower. Outside these times, the *A/FD* says that Class E airspace exists at the airport. Therefore, there is always some type of surface-based controlled airspace existing at SBA. That means that 3V/1C will always apply at SBA.

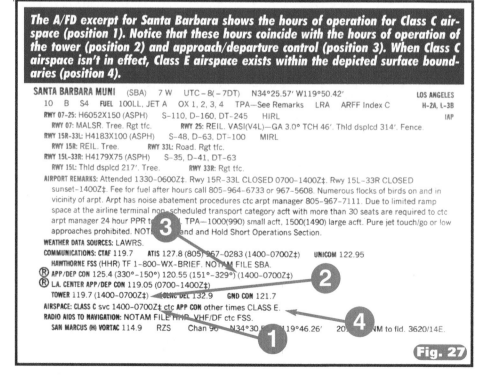

The A/FD excerpt for Santa Barbara shows the hours of operation for Class C airspace (position 1). Notice that these hours coincide with the hours of operation of the tower (position 2) and approach/departure control (position 3). When Class C airspace isn't in effect, Class E airspace exists within the depicted surface boundaries (position 4).

Fig. 27

Class B Airspace

Now let's talk about where the whales swim (747's, DC-10's, etc.). Airports like Los Angeles, Chicago, San Francisco, New York-JFK and others are home to these metallic sky mammals. Class B airspace is established to separate the whales from each other as well as from any small goldfish or sharks that might swim with them during takeoff or landing at the primary airport.

As we've already learned, the shape of Class B airspace is like an inverted wedding cake. It usually starts with a circular-based surface area surrounding the primary airport. Ever widening circular cylinders lie on top of lower cylinders, creating the inverted wedding cake (with a squished bride and groom) appearance, as shown in Figure 28.

CLASS B AIRSPACE

10,000' MSL

Class B

Fig. 28

Some Class B airspace structures have a corridor allowing flight that's exempt from Class B airspace entry requirements.

Class B airspace resembles an inverted wedding cake. Its multiple tier structure is designed to keep larger aircraft ( ) and small aircraft ( ) separated as they approach or overfly the primary airport. This is why an ATC clearance is required when operating anywhere within Class B airspace.

CLASS B AIRSPACE FOR DALLAS-FT. WORTH INTL. AIRPORT

Fig. 29

Class B airspace is designed to keep larger aircraft in a protective tank without unnecessarily restricting the movement of smaller aircraft below. Special extensions of the tank are nothing more than approach and departure paths into and out of the primary airport. These sections establish boundaries that prevent other aircraft from straying into the path of larger and faster aircraft.

Typically, Class B airspace has a radius of 15 to 30 miles from the primary airport and it extends vertically from the surface to 10,000 feet MSL. Figure 29 shows how Class B airspace for the Dallas-Ft. Worth International Airport (position 1) is displayed on an aeronautical sectional chart. The boundaries of Class B airspace are defined by solid blue lines surrounding the primary airport (position 2)

Position 3 shows that Class B airspace in the innermost ring extends vertically from the surface (SFC) to 11,000 feet MSL (DFW's Class B airspace is a little taller than normal. Most Class B airspace extends to about 10,000 feet MSL). Position 4 shows another section where Class B airspace starts at 3,000 feet MSL and extends to 11,000 feet MSL. Position 5 shows a section starting at 5,000 feet MSL and extending vertically to 11,000 feet MSL. Sections of Class B airspace may vary in altitude and shape to accommodate arriving and departing traffic (probably from airways or high altitude transitions).

An important thing to be aware of is that the rings and segments of Class B airspace are often made up of DME arcs and/or radials or bearings from local navigation stations. (DME, or *distance measuring equipment*, is an electronic instrument that tells you your distance from a navigation station, which is often a VOR.) For instance, the 207 degree radial from the Maverick VOR (position 6) makes up the line that identifies where the floor of Class B airspace changes from 4,000 feet to 3,000 feet on one of the inner rings (see the values circled in red at position 7). The arcs or rings of Class B airspace are determined by distances from the Maverick VOR (position 6). Since many airplanes have GPS capability, pilots can tell their position relative to the individual rings of this Class B airspace.

Requirements to Enter Class B Airspace

Now that you know what Class B airspace is and how it's depicted on an aeronautical sectional chart, you are inevitably curious about what it takes to swim with the big ones. First, in order to take off or land at an airport within this airspace, or to simply fly through the airspace, you must hold at least a sport pilot's license and be given instruction as per FAR 61.325 (an exception exists for student pilots who were given the instruction and appropriate logbook endorsements required as per FAR 61.94 and FAR 61.95).

Second, an ATC clearance is required before operating in Class B airspace. This clearance must be obtained from the ATC facility having jurisdiction over that area. Normally, it's the local approach and departure control serving the primary airport. This assumes you'll have a two way radio capable of communication with the appropriate ATC facility.

The communication requirement for Class B airspace is different than the communication requirement for Class C or D airspace. While you need only establish and maintain communication for Class C or D airspace, you need to obtain a *clearance* to enter Class B airspace. In other words, if you contact the controller to enter Class C or D airspace and that controller says, "Roger 2132 Bravo, stand by," you've established communication. You can enter that airspace. If, however, the controller in charge of Class B airspace says, "Stand by," this is most definitely *not* a clearance, You must remain on the outside looking in until permission is granted to enter the tank.

A typical clearance into Class B airspace will be:

"Remos 2132 Bravo is cleared to enter Class B airspace via direct to the Los Angeles VOR, maintain 5,500 feet while in Class B airspace."

Departing Class B airspace:

"Remos 2132 Bravo is cleared out of Class B airspace via radar vectors to MATWA intersection, climb and maintain 3,500 feet while in Class B airspace."

The arrival clearance would probably be provided by approach control and the departing clearance by clearance delivery or ground control. Sometimes controllers will clear you to a specific geographic location or an intersection as part of your clearance. These intersections, consisting of five letters, are usually shown on an aeronautical sectional chart. MATWA is the name of a typical intersection.

Fig. 30

One time, a pilot asked a controller (who was in a good mood) to "call MATWA" for him. (In avspeak, a request to "call" something means "Please tell me when I reach that spot, or when you want me to make that turn.") Without hesitation the controller said, "Here MATWA, here MATWA, here boy, whistle, whistle, whistle." Who said controllers don't have a sense of humor?

Third, a transponder with Mode C capability is also required. If for any reason the Class B airspace doesn't extend to 10,000 feet MSL, a transponder with Mode C capability is required when operating above the ceiling and within the lateral boundaries of Class B airspace.

It's interesting to note that while Class B airspace is controlled airspace, it actually has slightly less stringent VFR weather minimums (you knew there had to be one exception, right?). Three statute miles visibility is still required within Class B airspace. However, you only need to remain clear of clouds instead of the typical 1,000'/500'/2,000' distance minimums. The reason for this is that all aircraft operating within this airspace are being sequenced and separated while under ATC control.

There is little chance of another pilot popping out of a cloud and creating a collision threat to nearby aircraft. This cloud distance reduction prevents pilots from having to fly evasive headings (often to the surprise of ATC) while trying to maintain a minimum distance of 2,000 feet from any cloud.

Corridors And Circumnavigating Class B Airspace

Because of the numerous airplanes in, near, and around Class B airspace, you should be cautious when circumnavigating this area. Pilots often elect to fly underneath the floors or individual shelves of Class B airspace, thus avoiding the need for an ATC clearance. To enhance the opportunity for seeing and avoiding other aircraft, a speed limit is established in these areas. FAR 19.117C requires that pilots not exceed 200 knots indicated airspeed when operating below the lateral limits (or through a VFR corridor) of Class B airspace area (I don't think you have to worry about this in your airplane).

At a few locations, a VFR corridor has been implemented to assist pilots transiting the Class B airspace. Figure 30 depicts the LAX VFR corri-

dor. This opening or tunnel through the Class B airspace is called the *special flight rules area*. Basically, it is an exception to the Class B airspace that allows pilots to fly either north or south, directly over Los Angeles International Airport without having to meet some of the operational requirements of Class B airspace. You don't need a clearance to use this corridor. You may need to meet other requirements, such as having a VFR terminal area chart, specific navigation equipment, etc. Just follow the requirements listed on the VFR terminal area chart for the area's Class B airspace. (You'll learn about terminal area charts in Chapter 10)

More than one of these special routes may exist within the borders of Class B airspace. At the time of this writing, Los Angeles has two additional routes allowing passage through Class B airspace. Unlike the special flight area mentioned above, these require that you meet all the operational requirements of Class B airspace (i.e., FAR 91.131). Therefore, an ATC clearance is necessary, as well as minimum equipment and pilot qualifications.

Transponder and Mode C Within 30 NM of Certain Airports

In addition to the requirement for a transponder with Mode C capability in Class A, B and C airspace, FAR 91.215 also requires this equipment in other areas. Several airports listed in appendix D, section 1 of FAR Part 91 require a transponder with Mode C capability from the surface to 10,000′ MSL when operating within 30 nautical miles of that airport. You can tell if an airport requires this by looking at the aeronautical sectional chart. You'll see a magenta colored ring surrounding the primary airport listing this Mode-C requirement, as shown at Dallas-Ft. Worth International airport, Figure 29, position 8. The ring is slightly off-center from Dallas-Ft. Worth's Class B airspace, because the Class B airspace is centered at the Maverick VOR (position 6), while the ring is centered at Dallas-Ft. Worth airport (position 1).

Transponders and Mode C Above 10,000 Feet MSL

A transponder with Mode C is also required in all the airspace of the 48 contiguous United States and the District of Columbia when operating at and above 10,000 feet MSL, excluding the airspace at and below 2,500 feet AGL. I mention this just in case you decide to fly at precisely 10,000 feet MSL (which you can legally do as a sport pilot).

Transponders In Controlled Airspace

If your airplane has a transponder (and most do), the rules require that it be turned on (including the Mode C capability) any time you are operating in controlled airspace. This is to be done even when it's not required by the specific type of airspace in which you're operating. You should use the code assigned by ATC, or the VFR code (1200) when not in contact with ATC.

Transponder and Mode C Deviations

Occasionally, electrical equipment ceases to operate. It's possible that, one day, you might see a big puff of white smoke come from the transponder (and the inside of your cockpit could go to less than basic VFR minimums). The transponder has probably failed.

According to FAR 91.215, if you have a transponder lacking Mode C capability, you can request a deviation to operate within airspace requiring Mode C at any time. Such a request is made with the ATC facility having jurisdiction over that airspace (typically the tower or approach control have jurisdiction). If you have a transponder that is temporarily inoperative and you need to continue to your destination, just let the controller know of any intermediate stops you'll be making. He or she can OK the flight on the spot. If, however, your airplane doesn't have a transponder at all, a request must be submitted at least one hour in advance.

One day an air traffic controller at Van Nuys airport received a call from a hang glider using a handheld radio. This guy called up and said, "Van Nuys Tower, this is, ahh, hang glider Bob, over your airport for landing." The controllers didn't know what else to do, so they cleared him to land in the grass besides the runway. I mentioned to my friend that they should be glad I wasn't in the tower at the time. My friend asked why. I said that I would have made him go around!

The ADIZ (Air Defense Identification Zone)

The ADIZ is a boundary along the eastern and western coasts of the United States and the U.S./Mexican border and around land-based areas where national security is a concern. Unauthorized penetration of this zone is sure to arouse the suspicion of the military and/or drug enforcement agencies. Pilots penetrating the ADIZ without following proper procedures have been known to end up with a military jet escort for a portion of their flight. If you're thinking about either leaving the U.S., entering the U.S. or just entering any ADIZ, you must meet several requirements. A DVFR (Defense VFR) flight plan must be filed for coastal and domestic ADIZs and position reports must be made. A transponder (Mode C) and two-way

radio are also required (see the AIM for more information on ADIZ entry require-

ments and position reporting). For VFR entry into a land-based ADIZ you must have a transponder (Mode C), two-way radio and must file and activate a VFR (or IFR) flight plan then you must contact ATC to obtain a transponder code, maintain two-way communications at all times within the ADIZ as well as maintain your discrete transponder code until you have landed or are outside the ADIZ boundary. You must also close that VFR flight plan after landing.

THE BINGHAMTON TERMINAL RADAR SERVICE AREA (TRSA)

BINGHAMTON TRSA
SEE TWR FREQ TAB

Fig. 31

You would refer to the frequency tab on the edges of the aeronautical sectional chart to identify the appropriate approach control frequencies. Figure 32 shows the frequencies for the Binghamton TRSA. Any bearings shown are from the airport. If you're approaching anywhere within the bearings of 051° to 184° from the airport, you can contact Approach Control on 127.55 MHz. The *A/FD* (Figure 33) also contains this information.

If you're departing Binghamton, you can also elect to use the TRSA service. Usually the ATIS or the ground controller will provide you with the appropriate departure control frequency to use after departure.

In short, the TRSA is a good thing. It helps pilots approach and depart busier airports in a safer manner. Having ATC call traffic for you enhances safety. Pilot participation in the TRSA service is recommended, but not mandatory. If you happen to be talking to approach control (when approaching) or ground control and don't want TRSA service, you should state, "Negative TRSA service." There may be times when you want to fly your own (and perhaps more expeditious) route to the airport and

Terminal Radar Service Area

In Chapter 8 I briefly mentioned the *Terminal Radar Service Area* (TRSA). Let's fly by for a closer look at a type of airspace that's unusual by virtue of having nothing about it that's mandatory!

Recall that in a TRSA, ATC provides sequencing and separation between all participating VFR aircraft and all IFR aircraft. Figure 31 depicts a typical TRSA. Its boundaries are identified by a black line. TRSA's take on variable sizes and shapes but they usually contain a surface-based layer around the primary airport with one, two or more elevated cylinders of airspace. Altitudes for the different layers are shown within the individual rings as with Class B airspace.

Suppose you're approaching Binghamton airport and you want TRSA service (refer back to Chapter 8 for more detail on TRSA service).

THE SECTIONAL CHART'S FREQUENCY TAB

The frequency tab found on the sectional chart shows the approach control frequencies for TRSA service at Binghamton (position 1). These frequencies are based on the listed bearings from the primary airport (Binghamton in this instance).

Fig. 32

CLASS B, CLASS C, TRSA, AND SELECTED RADAR APPROACH CONTROL FREQUENCIES		
FACILITY	**FREQUENCIES ** §**	**SERVICE AVAILABILITY**
BINGHAMTON TRSA	127.55 242.7 (051°-184°) 118.6 397.2 (185°-050°) O/T 132.175 298.9 ZNY CNTR	0600-2400
ELMIRA TRSA	119.45 257.8 (098°-359°) 118.15 257.8 (360°-097°) O/T 133.35 372.0 ZNY CNTR	0600-2400

1

The A/FD also contains similar information about the Binghamton TRSA, frequencies based on bearings from Binghamton airport (position 1).

BINGHAMTON REGIONAL/EDWIN A LINK FLD
COMMUNICATIONS: ATIS 128.15
   BUFFALO FSS (BUF) TF 1-800-WX-BRIEF. NOTAM FILE BGM
   RCO 122.1R 112.2T (BUFFALO FSS)
Ⓡ APP/DEP CON 118.6 (185°-050°) 127.55 (051°-184°) (1100-0500Z‡)
Ⓡ NEW YORK CENTER APP/DEP CON 132.175 (0500-1100Z‡)
   TOWER 119.3 GND CON 121.9 CLNC DEL 125.05
AIRSPACE: TRSA svc ctc APP CON
RADIO AIDS TO NAVIGATION: NOTAM FILE BUF.

1

Fig. 33

Prohibited area P-47 shown on a sectional chart.

Fig. 34

THE SECTIONAL CHART'S SPECIAL USE AIRSPACE TAB

The sectional chart's special use airspace tab provides information on prohibited area P47.

SPECIAL USE AIRSPACE ON DALLAS-FT. WORTH SECTIONAL CHART Fig. 35

Unless otherwise noted altitudes are MSL and in feet; time is local.
Contact nearest FSS for information.
†Other time by NOTAM contact FSS

The word "TO" an altitude means "To and including:
"MON-FRI" indicates "Monday thru Friday"
FL – Flight Level
NO A/G – No air to ground communications

U.S. P–PROHIBITED, R–RESTRICTED, A–ALERT, W–WARNING, MOA–MILITARY OPERATIONS AREA

NUMBER	LOCATION	ALTITUDE	TIME OF USE	CONTROLLING AGENCY**
P-47	AMARILLO, TX	TO 4800	CONTINUOUS	NO A/G
R-5601 A	FORT SILL, OK	TO 40,000	CONTINUOUS	ZFW CNTR
R-5601 B	FORT SILL, OK	TO 40,000	CONTINUOUS	ZFW CNTR
R-5601 C	FORT SILL, OK	TO 40,000	CONTINUOUS	ZFW CNTR
R-5601 D	FORT SILL, OK	500 AGL TO 16,500	SR-SS TUE-SAT†	ZFW CNTR
R-5601 E	FORT SILL, OK	500 AGL TO 6000	SR-SS TUE-SAT†	ZFW CNTR
A-561	FREDERICK, OK	TO 4000	0700-2300 MON-FRI	NO A/G

have ATC provide only traffic information for you. At times like these, when it's real busy, TRSA service can entail extensive delay vectoring. In this instance you might say:

"Binghamton Approach, this is 2132 Bravo, negative TRSA service, request traffic advisories enroute to Binghamton airport, over."

When approaching and before entering Binghamton's Class D airspace, you'd cancel traffic advisories with approach control, then establish communication with Binghamton Tower and request landing instructions.

Conversely, when departing an airport, you can state, "Negative TRSA service" to the ground controller. This tells the controller that you want to fly your own route out of the airport.

You might be wondering why we have TRSAs when we have Class B and C airspace that seem to serve a similar function. TRSAs belong to airports that don't qualify for Class B or C airspace, yet have enough traffic to justify the presence of some sort of radar service.

A friend of mine was departing Ontario airport, in the Los Angeles area, when Ontario had a TRSA. He was heading 270° (west), toward the Pacific Ocean, and wanted to go to San Diego (south, to his left about 90°). He kept asking for a heading toward San Diego but the controller couldn't comply because of a traffic conflict. Finally, in frustration, my

friend said, "Ontario Approach, this is 2132 Bravo, I've been flying 270 for 10 minutes, can't I please have a more southerly heading?" The controller replied, "All right 32 Bravo, turn left to a heading of 269!" See what I mean? It gets busy sometimes.

Special Use Airspace

As if A, B, C, D, E and G weren't special enough, there are a few more special surprises out there in the air. *Special use airspace* is pretty much what it says it is—airspace that is set aside for a particular purpose. Some of it you can use, though with caution, while some of it is strictly off limits without specific permission.

Prohibited Areas – Prohibited areas are just that—areas where flight is simply prohibited. Figure 34 shows prohibited area P-47. This area is defined by blue-hatched lines within the prohibited area. Under the special use airspace section shown on the sides of the aeronautical sectional chart, Figure 35, there is a listing of different special use airspace segments as well as their limitations. P-47 extends to 4,800 feet MSL and is in continuous operation.

Like many things, *prohibited* is a somewhat relative term. Some prohibited areas function only during limited hours. Make the worst case assumption—that prohibited really means prohibited—and you can't go wrong. This is one of those situations where making a mistake will probably get you a bushel basket full of

trouble. Prohibited areas protect sensitive sites ranging from the White House to secret military installations. Unless you have a lot of free time on your hands, don't even think about trying to get permission to cross a chunk of prohibited airspace. Go around it!

Restricted Areas – Restricted areas are much more numerous than prohibited areas. Unlike prohibited areas, they restrict flights due to the unusual activities conducted within them. These areas often contain invisible hazards to aircraft such as the firing of artillery, aerial gunnery, guided missiles or, in the case of the restricted area in Figure 36, big rockets. Restricted areas are identified by blue-hatched lines similar to those defining prohibited areas. You can tell the difference by the listing of either a *P* or an *R* next to its identifying number.

Rockets are often fired from Vandenberg Air Force Base located in R-2516. There's nothing more unsettling than looking out your window and seeing yourself in formation with a Saturn-V rocket booster. The special use airspace section on the aeronautical sectional chart (Figure 37) shows R-2516 is in use continuously and extends to an unlimited height. *Unlimited* is really, really high so you can forget about climbing above it.

Before you can enter or fly through a restricted area, you need permission from the controlling agency (this is often obtainable through the local

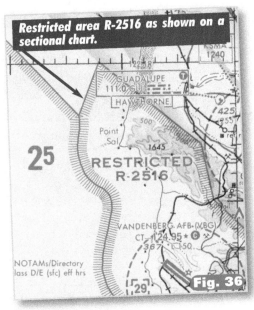

Restricted area R-2516 as shown on a sectional chart.

Fig. 36

Information on special use airspace (restricted areas in this instance) can be found on the sectional chart's special use airspace tab.

Note: Special Use Airspace (SUA) NOTAMS are issued when SUA is active outside scheduled/published times. NOTAMS to be discussed in last chapter.

SPECIAL USE AIRSPACE ON LOS ANGELES SECTIONAL CHART

Unless otherwise noted altitudes are MSL and in feet; time is local.
Contact nearest FSS for information.
†Other time by NOTAM contact FSS

The word "TO" an altitude means "To and including."
"MON-FRI" indicates "Monday thru Friday"
FL – Flight Level
NO A/G – No air to ground communications

U.S. P–PROHIBITED, R–RESTRICTED, A–ALERT, W–WARNING, MOA–MILITARY OPERATIONS AREA

NUMBER	LOCATION	ALTITUDE	TIME OF USE	CONTROLLING AGENCY**
R-2512	HOLTVILLE, CA	TO 23,000	0600-2300 †24 HOURS IN ADVANCE	ZLA CNTR
R-2513	HUNTER-LIGGETT, CA	TO FL 240	CONTINUOUS	ZOA CNTR
R-2515	MUROC LAKE, CA	UNLIMITED	CONTINUOUS	HI DESERT TRACON, EDWARDS
R-2516	VANDENBERG AFB, CA	UNLIMITED	CONTINUOUS	ZLA CNTR
R-2517	VANDENBERG AFB, CA	UNLIMITED	CONTINUOUS	NO A/G
R-2519	POINT MUGU, CA	UNLIMITED	CONTINUOUS	ZLA CNTR
R-2524	TRONA, CA	UNLIMITED	CONTINUOUS	HI DESERT TRACON, EDWARDS
R-2534 A&B	VANDENBERG AFB, CA	500 AGL TO UNLIMITED	CONTINUOUS	ZLA CNTR
R-2535 A&B	SAN NICOLAS ISLAND, CA	100,000	0600-2200 MON-FRI †24 HOURS IN ADVANCE	ZLA CNTR
W-60	OCEANSIDE, CA	UNLIMITED	INTERMITTENT	ZLA CNTR
W-61	MISSION BAY, CA	UNLIMITED	INTERMITTENT	ZLA CNTR
W-283	SAN FRANCISCO, CA	TO FL 600	0500-2100 MON-FRI	ZOA CNTR

Fig. 37

Air Route Traffic Control Center— ARTCC). Some restricted areas have designated hours or days of operation (as opposed to being active *continuously*). It's unlikely that you're going to get permission to enter a restricted area when it's in use.

Many times restricted areas aren't in use. The controlling agency for R-2516 is ZLA CNTR (Los Angeles ARTCC). Contact them for this permission. If you don't know how to establish contact with the center, call the nearest FSS for help in doing this.

Be cautious when flying in, near, or around restricted areas. A friend once unknowingly penetrated an active restricted area and saw red tracer shells whisking past his window. He had entered a gunnery range at a low altitude. Since they don't make bulletproof flight jackets (and seats), he felt pretty uncomfortable. Until bulletproof airplanes become popular, avoid flying in active restricted areas unless you have permission from the controlling agency.

In the early 1970s one of my students accidentally entered an active restricted area. He thought the top of the restricted area was 1,500 feet instead of 15,000 feet. A crease in his chart had rubbed off the last zero in 15,000. Upon entering the area, he scattered a covey of F-4s like frightened quail. The flight leader joined up on him and tried to give him hand

signals to switch to 121.5 MHz. My student simply thought the guy was waving at him so he waved back. Finally, out of frustration, my student pulled his power to slow down and assess the situation. Unable to maintain the slow speed, the jet sped off into the distance. The moral to the story is to get a new chart if wrinkles make it unreadable.

Warning Areas – Warning areas are another type of special use airspace where hazards may exist for pilots. Think of warning areas as restricted areas for airspace over which the U.S. doesn't have the right to impose a restriction because it's beyond the country's boundaries. These areas are identified by a blue-hatched line, similar to restricted and prohibited areas, as shown in Figure 38.

Warning areas contain hazards similar to those found in restricted areas (things that go *bang* in the night, and day; hyperactive fighter aircraft at low altitudes; and unescorted test rockets).

Penetration of a warning area when it's in use can be very interesting. The Aeronautical Information Manual states that warning areas may contain hazards to "non participating" aircraft. Participation, by the way, is on a strictly invitational basis, and you are not invited. It's best to avoid warning areas if at all possible. The special use airspace section on the sectional chart (Figure 39) shows that W-291 extends to 80,000 feet and is intermittently in operation. Calling the controlling agency listed (ZLA— Los Angeles Center) is a good idea if you're planning on entering this area.

Warning area W-291 shown on a sectional chart.
It usually extends from 3 nm outward from the coast of the United States.

WARNING W-291

See NOTAMs/Directory for Class D/E (sfc) eff hrs

Fig. 38

WARNING AREA INFO ON THE SECTIONAL CHART TAB

Warning area information on the sectional chart's special use airspace tab.

U.S. P–PROHIBITED, R–RESTRICTED, A–ALERT, W–WARNING, MOA–MILITARY OPERATIONS AREA

NUMBER	LOCATION	ALTITUDE	TIME OF USE	CONTROLLING AGENCY**
W-291	SAN DIEGO, CA	TO FL 800	INTERMITTENT	ZLA CNTR
W-412	SANTA CRUZ ISLAND, CA	TO 3000	CONTINUOUS DAYS	ZLA CNTR

Fig. 39

Alert Areas – Alert areas are shown on sectional charts to help identify areas where there is a high volume of pilot training or an unusual type of aerial activity. These areas are shown in a magenta color using the same symbolic hatching used by restricted, prohibited or warning areas. Figure 49 shows a typical alert area. Figure 50 shows the special use airspace box on the sectional chart that provides information on this airspace (the text used here is also magenta). You are not prohibited from entering an alert area, but as the name suggests, you should maintain added vigilance (remember, all pilots have a responsibility for collision avoidance). An alert area can be a place where a lot of student military drivers are practicing, but instead of cars they have airplanes that go hundreds of miles per hour. Got the picture?

Military Operations Areas – Known as a MOA (as in *mow-ahh*), military operations areas are designed to separate or segregate certain nonhazardous military activities from IFR traffic (outside of Class A airspace). Figure 42 depicts the military operations area outlined with a magenta hatched line. MOAs are often given names instead of numbers

(the military has always liked secret code names). Figure 43 shows the MOA airspace listing found on the aeronautical sectional chart. It lists altitude for all the MOAs. These are the MOAs' base altitude. All MOA's are assumed to extend vertically to FL180 (18,000 feet) unless stated otherwise. The Bakersfield MOA, according to Figure 43, consists of the airspace starting at 2,000 feet AGL and extending up to flight level 180, between the hours listed. The ZLA (Los Angeles Center) is the controlling agency for the Bakersfield MOA.

Unlike restricted or prohibited areas, a MOA doesn't restrict or prohibit the flight of VFR aircraft. You can enter a MOA without permission. I suggest, however, that you contact the nearest FSS and ask about the status of that particular MOA. If it's active (also referenced to as hot), I also suggest you contact the controlling agency prior to entry and ask for traffic advisories.

Be aware that you will find all types of military training activities within this airspace. It's possible that military pilots will be doing aerobatics, dog fighting (I don't know why they're so angry at dogs), or high speed runs (no military speed limit in

a MOA). The last thing you want to do is get in the way of a bunch of battle thirsty pilots who haven't seen combat in a while.

Take note of the red circle around Kern Valley airport in the Isabella MOA. The note attached to this circle (known as an *aerodrome traffic zone*) states that the MOA excludes the airspace below 1,500 feet AGL within the circle. In other words, you can do touch and goes in peace below 1,500 feet at Kern Valley. I had one student in a ground school class who suggested that if a military pilot were chasing you (they don't do that) you could make for the red circle. At least they can't go in there. I retorted that if he really wanted to get you, he'd be circling outside that circle until you made a break for your home field. Don't worry, the military guys are friendly, they don't chase us small guys—at least on purpose, anyway.

My recommendation is to avoid active MOA's when and where possible. Sometimes you have no choice but to fly through them. If so, do keep your eyes open. One student of mine claimed he discovered why they're called MOA's. Apparently, if you get frightened by a military jet while in one of these areas, you won't want to go back "no moah."

Military Training Routes (MTRs) – Military training routes are highways for military jet aircraft. They usually come in two brands: IFR or VFR military training routes. IFR military training routes are designed to be flown above 1,500 feet AGL. VFR military training routes exist at and below 1,500 feet AGL. Figure 44 shows how MTRs are depicted on an aeronautical sectional chart.

MTR's have the letters "IR" or "VR" identifying whether they are

Alert area A-220 shown on a sectional chart.

Fig. 40

ALERT AREA INFO ON THE SPECIAL USE AIRSPACE TAB

Alert area information found on the sectional chart's special use airspace tab.

W-106 C	TO 10,000	INTERMITTENT BY NOTAM	BOSTON CNTR
W-106 D	TO BUT NOT INCL 6000	INTERMITTENT BY NOTAM	FACSFAC VACAPES
W-506	TO FL 500	INTERMITTENT BY NOTAM	NEW YORK CNTR
A-220	TO 4500	0800-2200	NO A/G

Fig. 41

A military operations area (MOA) shown on a sectional chart.

Fig. 42

MOA INFO ON THE SPECIAL USE AIRSPACE TAB

MOA information found on the sectional chart's special use airspace tab.

MOA NAME	ALTITUDE OF USE*	TIME OF USE†	CONTROLLING AGENCY**
ABEL BRAVO	7000	0500-2200 MON-FRI	ZLA CNTR
ABEL EAST	5000 TO BUT NOT INCL 13,000	INTERMITTENT BY NOTAM	ZLA CNTR
ABEL NORTH	7000	0500-2200 MON-FRI	ZLA CNTR
ABEL SOUTH	7000	0500-2200 MON-FRI	ZLA CNTR
BAKERSFIELD	2000 AGL	0600-2200 MON-FRI	ZLA CNTR

Fig. 43

IFR or VFR routes. If either route has a four digit number next to it, it was designed to be flown at and below 1,500 feet AGL (i.e., VR1266). If the route has only three numbers next to it, it was designed to be flown above 1,500 feet AGL (i.e., IR216). Arrows point in the direction these routes are usually flown.

While you are not prohibited from flying along or near an MTR, it's a great idea to avoid them whenever possible. Consider that there are no speed restrictions for military aircraft along an MTR. Military jet air-craft may be flying at many hundreds of miles per hour just a few hundred feet off the ground, scaring all kinds of terrestrial-dwelling animals (groundhogs, ducks, mice, humans, etc.). Don't be one of them! A simple call to the nearest FSS will give you information on the status of MTR's in your area. In other words, the FSS should know whether the MTR is in use.

Temporary Flight Restrictions – When an unusual situation arises (natural disaster, events of high public interest, forest fires, national security, etc.) the FAA will often issue a TFR or *temporary flight restriction* for that area. Such a restriction helps protect persons or property on the surface, protect those providing disaster relief from the hazard of low flying sightseeing type aircraft, protect the President, Vice President or other public figures or provide a safe environment for space operations.

These temporary flight restrictions are usually issued in the form of a notice to airmen (NOTAM). NOTAMs designate an area and altitude in which the restrictions apply.

After the attack on September 11, 2001 numerous TFRs have been established for security reasons. This is one reason you need to check all NOTAMs during flight planning. TFRs are changing and new ones are being created frequently. Before every flight, check with the local FSS, or a reliable NOTAM internet source for TFR information about the area in which you'll fly. The following is a typical temporary flight restriction:

Flight Restriction - Julian, California due to fire fighting activity. Effective 1100 UTC August 28, 2009, until further notice pursuant to 14 CFR Section 91.137 (a)(1). Temporary flight restrictions are in effect within a three mile radius of the 20 DME fix on the 223 degree radial from Julian VOR at and below 4,000 feet MSL. San Diego FSS is the FAA coordinating facility.

Spaced Out

Now that we've charted the airspace, it's time to chart the charts. That means learning how to identify the symbology on aeronautical charts and use this information to help you navigate. Not knowing how to read an aeronautical chart is like having your limo driver show up wearing a neck brace—a very unsettling experience. So, fasten your seatbelts as we set off to discover how to make sense of those squiggles, squirts and markings on popular aviation charts.

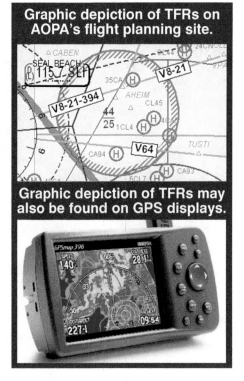

Graphic depiction of TFRs on AOPA's flight planning site.

Graphic depiction of TFRs may also be found on GPS displays.

Military training routes (MTR's) as shown on a sectional chart.

Fig. 44

SPECIAL VFR IN SURFACE-BASED CONTROLLED AIRSPACE

What happens if you want to land or depart McComb-Pike airport and the reported ground visibility is at or above three miles (always the minimum for a sport pilot) but the ceiling is less than 1,000 feet? Do you circle, eating a sandwich, until the cows come home or the clouds blow away? Not necessarily.

You can request something known as a *special VFR clearance (SVFR)* from the nearest ATC facility. This is permission to operate within the surface-based controlled airspace with less than a 1,000 foot ceiling. (For private pilots or those with a higher rating, it allows them to operate with less than a 1,000 foot ceiling and at least one mile visibility. Since you're a sport pilot, it's the ceiling and not the visibility reduction that applies to you.)

An SVFR clearance allows you to operate below 10,000 feet MSL down to the surface, within the lateral boundaries of surface-based controlled airspace (Class E in this instance at McComb-Pike) under the following conditions:

1. The pilot must have a clearance from ATC.

2. The reported ground visibility (by the official weather observer) must be at least three statute miles. If the ground visibility isn't reported, then the flight visibility must not be less than three statue miles.

3. The pilot must remain clear of all clouds and maintain three miles flight visibility (Figure 45).

Despite the lowered visibility that SVFR permits, this is considered a safe operation from the perspective of ATC. Since ATC is responsible for providing separation

between aircraft during SVFR conditions, they usually allow only one aircraft to operate within the lateral boundaries of the surface-based controlled airspace at any one time during SVFR operations. Remember, SVFR applies to any surface-based controlled airspace (Class E as well as B, C and D).

The whole purpose of SVFR is to get into or out of an airport that's surrounded by surface-based controlled airspace when the ceiling is less than 1,000 feet. That's why the SVFR clearance is only applicable within the horizontal boundaries of the vertically extended, surface-based airspace at that airport, as shown in Figure 45. The SVFR clearance is good below 10,000 feet MSL ATC assigns a lower altitude restriction.

SVFR is a very handy tool, and when used properly, a safe one. It is the answer to the phenomenon, observed by every pilot, that if there is one big fat cloud in the sky it will hang over the airport. You can use SVFR to depart or arrive at an airport when there are low clouds and the enroute weather is above basic VFR minimums for the airspace in which you'll fly.

Let's examine how you go about getting a SVFR clearance.

Obtaining an SVFR Clearance

Special VFR clearances are usually obtained by contacting the nearest ATC facility (tower, FSS, approach or departure control.) For instance, let's suppose the reported ground visibility at McComb-Pike is at least three miles but the ceiling is 900 feet AGL. You need to obtain an SVFR clearance if you want to depart the surface-based controlled airspace. You can obtain this clearance by calling the FSS located on the field at McComb-Pike (Figure 46). (The letters FSS indicate that a Flight Service Station is on the airport.)

The FSS specialist would contact the ATC facility in charge of the surface-based controlled airspace (Class E in this case) at McComb-Pike and obtain an SVFR clearance for you. Since no control tower exists at this airport, the nearest approach and departure control or air traffic control center will normally have jurisdiction over this airspace. The clearance may sound something like this:

"Remos 2132 Bravo is cleared to climb to VFR within the Class E surface area within 4 miles of McComb-Pike airport, maintain special VFR conditions until reaching VFR. Report reaching VFR."

When cleared for takeoff, you must maintain at least three miles flight visibility and remain clear of clouds within 4 miles of McComb-Pike. The assumption is that you will reach VFR conditions for the airspace outside the surface-based airspace structure. This is either 3V/152 when operating below 10,000' MSL in Class E airspace or 3V/COC in Class G airspace below 1,200' AGL.

Special VFR - 3 Miles Visibility (sport pilot) And Remain Clear of Clouds

10,000 MSL

Remain Clear Of Clouds

1,200' AGL
700' AGL

3 Miles Visibility

Fig. 45

McComb Pike's Surface-Based Controlled Airspace

If you were approaching McComb-Pike airport and the reported ground visibility was three miles but the ceiling was 900 feet, you could call the FSS and request an SVFR clearance into Class E airspace. The clearance might sound something like this:

"Remos 2132 Bravo is cleared into Class E airspace from the west, toward McComb-Pike airport, in special VFR conditions, maintain SVFR conditions until reaching McComb-Pike."

Once again, while the special VFR allows private pilots to operate with one mile visibility and remain clear of clouds in the surface-based controlled airspace, sport pilots are always limited to a minimum of three miles flight or reported ground visibility. There are no exceptions here. To a sport pilot, the special VFR clearance only allows him or her to operate with less than a 1,000 foot ceiling within the lateral boundaries of the surface-based controlled airspace. The assumption is that when pilots fly away from the airport, they will be in basic VFR conditions for the airspace in which they're operating.

To obtain a special VFR clearance when operating into or out of McComb-Pike airport, contact the flight service station that's located on the field at McComb-Pike.

Fig. 46

Postflight Briefing #9-2

CLASS E AT AND ABOVE 10,000 FEET MSL

Sport pilots are restricted to flight at and below 10,000 feet MSL (or 2,000 feet AGL, whichever is higher). Therefore, a few pilots might fly at precisely 10,000 feet MSL or up to 12,000 feet MSL (when operating within 2,000 feet AGL). For this reason and only this reason, I need to tell you about the VFR requirements for flying at and above 10,000 feet MSL in Class E airspace. Let's both agree that even though we may talk about operating above 10,000 feet MSL, you and I will both know that this means operating at or within 2,000 feet AGL.

To operate VFR in Class E airspace at and above 10,000 foot MSL you need the basic VFR minimums shown in Figure 46. You're required to operate at least 1,000 feet above, 1,000 feet below and one statute mile to the side (horizontally) of any cloud formation. You're also required to have a minimum of five statute miles of flight visibility at all times. These minimums make it easier for you to see and avoid other (and possibly faster) aircraft. Of course, as a sport pilot, if you're operating at exactly 10,000 foot MSL, you're not climbing above the cloud to avoid it. Instead, if you see a cloud directly ahead of you at 10,000 feet MSL, you must maneuver to the side of it by at least one statute mile (5,280 feet) or descend below it (in which case the *Class E Below 10,000 feet MSL* rule—coming up next—now applies to you).

Here's Rod Machado's Airspace Simplification Rule #1: If you're flying at and above 10,000' MSL, you could find fast jet fighters like the F-111. This reminds you that the minimum flight visibility is five (*F*) statute miles and the minimum distance above, below and to the side of a cloud is *111* or 1,000 feet above, 1,000 feet below and 1 statute mile to the side or. To make this easy to remember, just think 5V/111.

> *Rod Machado's Airspace Simplification Rule #1: If you're flying at and above 10,000' MSL, you could find fast jet fighters like the **F-111**. You need **5 miles Visibility, 1,000' above, 1,000' below and 1 mile** horizontally from any cloud formation.*

You may be wondering, "How do I know when I'm one statute mile to the side of a cloud?" Good question. You must take your best guess. The reason you are required to be one statute mile horizontally from a cloud at these altitudes is to prevent being hit by emerging IFR aircraft. If you're at or above 10,000 feet MSL and a jet (traveling at 450 knots) on an IFR flight plan pops out of a cloud, your entire vocabulary would be reduced to two words:

"Bad thing." Do you have any idea how scary it is to look out your window and see a jet coming directly at you at 450 knots? It's probably as scary as having Stephen King as a flight instructor. Being at least one mile to the side of a cloud provides you with a better chance of seeing and avoiding other aircraft.

One way to make a practical judgment on distance from clouds is to always ask yourself "If a jet were to pop out of there at about 500 knots right now, aimed directly at me, would I have time and space to do something about it?" With that thought in mind, you should always have sufficient clearance from clouds, and it will be a heck of a lot more than one mile.

Since there is no aircraft speed restriction at and above 10,000 feet MSL, jets and other fast flying aircraft typically move at or near their top speed. Over land, however, jet pilots must avoid flying faster than the speed of sound (if you're breaking the sound barrier in your Cessna Skycatcher, please send me a little note with information on what power setting you're using).

Postflight Briefing #9-3

CLASS G AIRSPACE ABOVE 1,200 FEET AGL

Class E airspace begins at 700 feet AGL within the magenta faded area as shown in Figure 48, position 1. Directly outside the magenta fade, Class E airspace begins at 1,200 feet AGL as shown by position 2. How do I know this? Because these positions are all surrounded by a blue-tinted line that fades in one direction and has a solid border on the other (position 3). The blue tint fades in the direction where Class E airspace begins at 1,200 feet AGL. This is shown by the direction of arrows marked by the number 4.

On the other side of the blue-tinted line, opposite the direction that it fades, is Class G airspace. Normally, Class E airspace begins at 1,200 feet AGL, but not in those areas shown at position 5. Here, Class G airspace actually rises vertically to more than 1,200 feet AGL, as shown by the direction of the white arrow pointing toward the area of position 5. In fact, Class G airspace in this area rises up to but not including an altitude of 14,500 feet MSL as shown in Figure 47 (this is an approximate 3-D representation of Figure 48).

Now, I must admit that Class G airspace extending more than 1,200 feet AGL is rare in the central and eastern United States. It is, however, more common in the western and north-cen-

3-D VIEW OF BISHOP'S AIRSPACE

The direction the blue tinted line fades indicates where Class E (controlled) airspace begins at 1,200' AGL. On the opposite side of the blue tinted line is Class G (uncontrolled) airspace from the surface, up to but not including 14,500' MSL.

Fig. 47

tral parts of the United States. The way to find it is by looking for the border of the blue tinted line on aeronautical sectional charts (Figure 48, position 3). On the opposite side of the blue fade, will be Class G airspace extending more than 1,200 feet AGL. Despite the presence of Class G airspace more than 1,200 feet AGL, it's a reasonable assumption that most of your flying will be done in Class E airspace.

OK, I've pushed you where no mammal has gone before, beyond normal vertebrate endurance. So why stop now? I have a few additional thoughts for you. We've already concluded that Class G airspace above 1,200 feet AGL is not very common. Why not make it all Class E airspace starting at 1,200 feet AGL over the entire United States? The reason is that air traffic control can't use some portions of the airspace above 1,200 feet AGL for IFR flights. In other words, there's no way to use the navigational facilities (VOR navigation for instance) because of restrictions imposed by other types of airspace, navigation station limitations or, as is frequently the case, by terrain-created signal limitations.

Class G airspace extending from the surface up to but not including an altitude of 14,500' MSL (area #5).

Blue tint fades in this direction.

No blue tint in this direction.

Fig. 48

There is an interesting point here. The highest mountain in the 48 contiguous United States is Mount Whitney, at 14,491 feet MSL. If you're at or above 14,500 feet MSL anywhere in the United States, you're not likely to have a problem with mountains interfering with navigational signal reception. That's why Class G airspace more than 1,200 feet AGL, extends up to, but not including 14,500 feet MSL as shown on the left hand side of Figure 49. At and above 14,500 feet MSL, it's Class E airspace (at least until reaching the base of Class A airspace).

On occasion, the floor of Class E airspace starts at altitudes higher than 1,200 feet AGL. See Postflight Briefing #9-5 for advanced information on this topic.

BASIC VFR MINIMUMS IN CLASS G AIRSPACE

Shown below are the basic VFR weather minimums within Class G (uncontrolled) airspace for three altitude levels: from the surface up to and including 1,200' AGL; from more than 1,200' AGL but less than 10,000' MSL, and at or above 10,000' MSL.

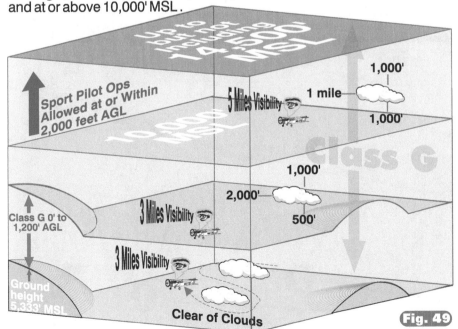

Up to but not including 14,500' MSL

Sport Pilot Ops Allowed at or Within 2,000 feet AGL

10,000 MSL

Class G

5 Miles Visibility — 1 mile — 1,000' / 1,000'

3 Miles Visibility — 1,000' / 2,000' / 500'

Class G 0' to 1,200' AGL

3 Miles Visibility

Ground height 5,333' MSL

Clear of Clouds

Fig. 49

VFR Weather Minimums For Class G Airspace

Figure 49 is a 3-D depiction of the VFR weather minimums for all Class G airspace. Notice that I have listed the basic VFR minimums for flight in Class G airspace at and above 10,000 feet MSL. That's because sport pilots are allowed to fly above 10,000 feet MSL but only when they remain at or within 2,000 feet AGL, whichever is higher. So, I'm burdening your brain with this information just in case you ever decide to fly that high.

As you can see, even in Class G below 10,000 feet MSL but above 1,200 feet AGL, the 3V/152 rules still apply here. Only the rules for daylight operations are shown here since sport pilots don't fly at night.

Of course, at this stage you're probably checking your forehead for a Coke machine imprint. It's not there, it just feels like it. I'm proud of you for sticking with this.

Postflight Briefing #9-4

VARIABLE FLOORS OF CLASS E AIRSPACE

The sectional chart excerpt (Figure 50) and its 3-D representation (Figure 51) depict several airways and their variable floors of controlled airspace. These are called Federal Low Altitude airways and are identified by a V (standing for the word *Victor)* followed by a number (position 1 in Figure 50). These are the routes pilots typically file on their VFR flight plans.

Of course, you don't have to fly these airways, just as you don't have to take major highways when you travel. You can take side streets (travel off airways in a direction of your choosing). Nevertheless, airways are convenient for flight planning. These low altitude airways are normally 8 nautical miles wide and begin at the base of the Class E airspace, continuing up to but not including 18,000 feet MSL.

Look at airways V-12 and V-538 (position 1 in Figure 50). The blue line fading toward the center of the airway indicates that controlled (Class E) airspace begins at 1,200 feet AGL within these borders. The solid blue wavy (serrated) symbols at position 2 indicate that the floor of controlled airspace (Class E) has changed within these symbols. Position 3 shows 7,500 feet MSL as the new altitude for the floor of this airway. Thus, the Class E airspace, within the area bordered by blue faded and wavy symbols, begins at 7,500 feet MSL instead of 1,200 feet AGL. Why raise the floor of controlled (Class E) airspace? Mountains in

HIGHER FLOORS OF CLASS E AIRSPACE

The blue serrated figure indicates that the base of Class E (controlled) airspace has changed. Within the borders of two or more serrated figures is an altitude value (shown in blue). This altitude (normally an MSL altitude) is the base of controlled airspace for that area. In the area listed below, the Class E airspace under Victor airway 538, is a section with a base of 7,500' MSL. A large mountain is responsible for raising the base of this airspace since, below 7,500' MSL, it would be difficult to receive the airway on your VOR equipment.

Fig. 51

the local area may make VOR reception unreliable below 7,500 MSL within these borders. Therefore, Class G exists below 7,500 feet MSL at and around position 3. Compare Figure 50 with its 3-D representation in Figure 51.

This sectional chart excerpt shows several airways having controlled airspace starting at some altitude other than the typical 1,200 feet AGL. Compare this chart with its 3-D representation above.

Fig. 50

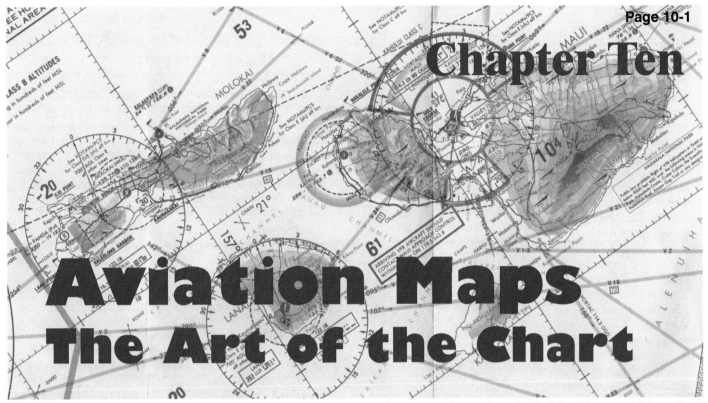

Chapter Ten

Aviation Maps
The Art of the Chart

Maps aren't something new. They began many years ago when one of our Neanderthal brothers or sisters first etched the location of a cave on a deerskin. This really upset the deer, of course, causing him to run away. That produced the world's first moving map display.

Many advances have come along since that time. We now draw maps on ground-up trees, which are easier to sneak up on than deer, come in several exciting shades, and leaf a good impression.

Maps are simply representations of the earth's surface and its topographic features—the bumps and holes that are mountains and lakes, hills and valleys, deserts and forests. In the case of aviation maps, there is also information about a variety of manmade features, such as cities, towns, roads, railroad tracks, and the other evidence of human existence. The challenge of mapmaking is to translate a three dimensional reality into a two dimensional map. Despite the age-old injunction about not fitting a round peg in a square hole, that's exactly what every mapmaker has to do. Like it or not, the earth is round and bumpy; maps are flat. Therein lies the rub.

A good map does several things at once. First, it minimizes the distortion that is inevitable in converting a 3-D world to a 2-D map. Second, it conveys at a glance crucial information. What's crucial? As a pilot you need to know where the land rises and falls (lest it rise up and smite thee), and what the major landmarks are, so you can figure out where *you* are.

Pilots use a wide variety of maps (or *charts*, as they are often called) to tell them where to go, or where they've been. Each type has specific information, and being able to select the right chart for the right job is an important pilot skill.

Cartoon by Bob Stevens

I HATE THESE UNANNOUNCED FLY-IN BRUNCHES!

Reprinted with permission of Mrs. Bob Stevens

THE LAMBERT CONFORMAL CONIC PROJECTION

Sectional charts and World Aeronautical Charts (WAC) are Lambert Conformal Conic Projections. A simplified view of their construction is shown in Figure 1A. Think of a light projecting and printing earthly surface features, as well as latitude and longitude lines, onto a conical surface. The conical surface is then flattened out in the form of a sheet as shown in Figure 1B.

This type of projection offers a relatively accurate representation of topographical features (lakes, towns, mountains, etc.). Additionally, errors in angular relationships are minimized. Straight lines drawn on the chart represent a great circle (the shortest distance between two points). The Lambert Projection also offers a relatively constant measurement scale over the entire chart which makes measuring distances easy and accurate.

The two standard parallels indicate the positions where the cone slices into the earth. No distortion occurs along these parallels. Additionally, areas north and south of the parallels experience little distortion.

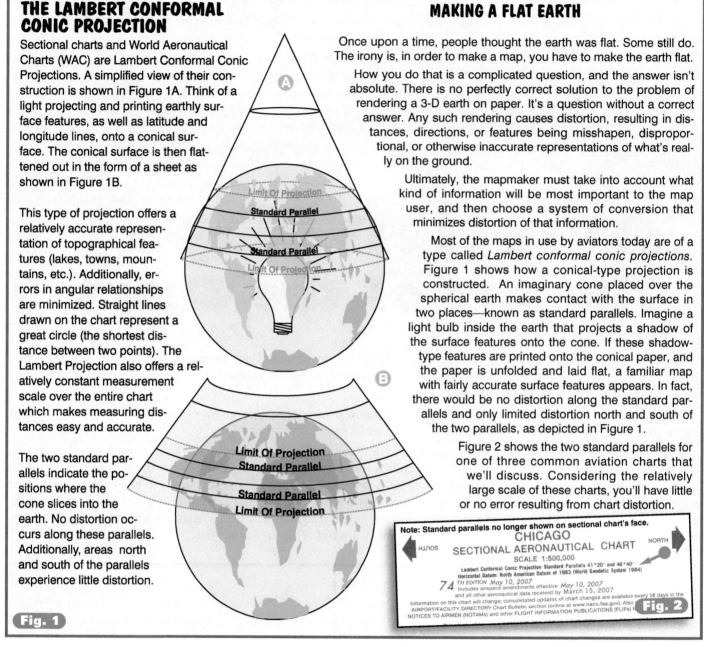

Fig. 1

Fig. 2

MAKING A FLAT EARTH

Once upon a time, people thought the earth was flat. Some still do. The irony is, in order to make a map, you have to make the earth flat.

How you do that is a complicated question, and the answer isn't absolute. There is no perfectly correct solution to the problem of rendering a 3-D earth on paper. It's a question without a correct answer. Any such rendering causes distortion, resulting in distances, directions, or features being misshapen, disproportional, or otherwise inaccurate representations of what's really on the ground.

Ultimately, the mapmaker must take into account what kind of information will be most important to the map user, and then choose a system of conversion that minimizes distortion of that information.

Most of the maps in use by aviators today are of a type called *Lambert conformal conic projections.* Figure 1 shows how a conical-type projection is constructed. An imaginary cone placed over the spherical earth makes contact with the surface in two places—known as standard parallels. Imagine a light bulb inside the earth that projects a shadow of the surface features onto the cone. If these shadow-type features are printed onto the conical paper, and the paper is unfolded and laid flat, a familiar map with fairly accurate surface features appears. In fact, there would be no distortion along the standard parallels and only limited distortion north and south of the two parallels, as depicted in Figure 1.

Figure 2 shows the two standard parallels for one of three common aviation charts that we'll discuss. Considering the relatively large scale of these charts, you'll have little or no error resulting from chart distortion.

The Aeronautical Sectional Chart

The sectional chart is a pilot's most common tool for VFR navigation. Figure 3 shows a typical sectional chart. It is one of 37 such charts covering the entire continental United States. Each one is issued with an effective date and an expiration date (Figure 4). Sectional charts are good for approximately 6 months, then reissued. It's very good practice to avoid using an outdated chart. While terrain doesn't move all that much (not even in California), airports, obstructions, navigational aids

and airspace can change. The last thing you want to do is attempt to navigate using a VOR that's been shut down or moved.

Many years ago a friend was using an old sectional chart (outdated by more than a year) for navigation to a Louisiana airport. The chart indicated the VOR (this is a ground-based navigation station) was located on the airport. Arriving over the VOR, all my buddy saw was swampland. He finally called the tower and asked them what happened to their airport. They said the VOR had been moved 15 miles north of the field seven

months earlier. He's lucky the FAA wasn't moving it the day he flew this cross country. (Imagine the confusion he'd feel at seeing a VOR cruising down the street on a flatbed truck!)

Cautious pilots know chart information can change within the 6 month publishing cycle. Fortunately, the *Airport/Facility Directory* provides you with information on these changes, as shown in Figure 5. The only way you can be completely assured a sectional chart (or any other aeronautical chart) is up to date is by checking the *AFD* for these changes.

A TYPICAL VFR SECTIONAL CHART

Fig. 3

EACH SECTIONAL IS ISSUED WITH AN EFFECTIVE AND AN EXPIRATION DATE

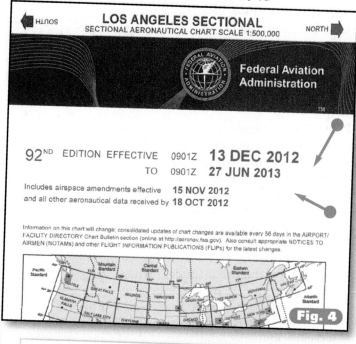

Fig. 4

The Airport/Facility Directory lists changes that affect aeronautical sectional charts.

AERONAUTICAL CHART BULLETIN

LOS ANGELES SECTIONAL
92nd Edition, 13Dec 2012

OBSTRUCTIONS
10 Jan 2013 Add obst 370 'MSL(250 'AGL), 33°00'45"N, 115°13'13"W.
7 Mar 2013 Add obst 4325 'MSL (400 'AGL), 34°37'22"N, 117°06'45"W.
Add obst 1992 'MSL (419 'AGL),33 °54'58"N, 116°44'55"W.
Add obst 1750 'MSL (440 'AGL), 33°44'16"N, 116°06'03"W.
Change windmill farm highest MSL from 998'MSL to 1750'MSL, 33°44'16"N, 116°06'03"W.
AIRPORTS
10 Jan 2013 Add SOUTHERN CALIFORNIA LOGISTICS ATCT frequency 282.225, 34°35'50"N, 117°22'58"W.
7 Mar 2013 Delete RABBIT arpt, 34°27'16"N, 117°01'35"W.
Add SOUTHERN CALIFORNIA LOGISTICS ATCT 282.225, 34°35'50"N, 117°22'58"W.
Add glider symbol at JACUMBA arpt, 32°36'57"N, 116°09'55"W.
NAVAIDs
10 Jan 201 3–7 Mar 2013 No Major Changes.
AIRSPACE

Fig. 5

A VFR sectional chart comes with its own mileage scale. Fig. 6

The sectional chart has a scale of 1 to 500,000. This means every inch on a sectional chart represents 500,000 inches on the actual earth. Fortunately, we can leave our rulers at home because sectional charts (and others) carry their own mileage scale, as shown in Figure 6. This scale is consistent for all sectional charts and equates to 1 inch=6.86 nautical miles.

A wise man says, "You shouldn't fly with strangers especially if they fly stranger than you."

World Aeronautical Charts (WAC)

I always thought they were called WAC (pro-nounced "whack") charts because that's the sound they made when military instructors used them to hit their students over the head (hey, I was wrong). Fourteen WAC charts cover the continental United States, Cuba and Puerto Rico, as shown in Figure 7. These charts have a yearly publication cycle (half as frequent as the sectional chart).

WAC charts have a scale of 1 to 1,000,000 (the precise ratio by which pilots exaggerate their adventures and war stories). These charts cover twice as much area per inch as does the sectional chart. They're useful for flight planning purposes when it's necessary to get a big-picture idea of terrain, navaids and special use airspace. Because of the smaller scale, this chart is particularly useful to pilots flying medium-speed aircraft at higher altitudes. When using this chart you should be cautious, since the increased scale limits charting detail. For instance, WACs don't show locations of Class E or D airspace, and only limited amounts of Class B and C airspace are shown. They do, however, show restricted areas (and other special use airspace), airways, terrain relief and other visual aids to navigation.

THE WAC OR WORLD AERONAUTICAL CHART

Fig. 7

THE VFR TERMINAL AREA CHART

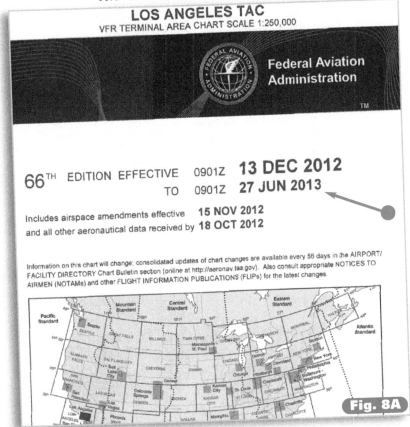

Fig. 8A

VFR Terminal Area Charts

I never liked the word terminal. It's a tad scary if you think about it. I once told a student I'd be taking him into a terminal area on our next flight. He didn't show up! Rest easy. Terminal areas are simply places with busy (such as Class B) airspace, usually with a major commercial airport right about in the middle. Many of these areas have a VFR terminal area chart associated with them (Figure 8A). The area covered by the VFR terminal area chart is indicated by a white bordering rectangular line on a sectional chart as shown in Figure 8B.

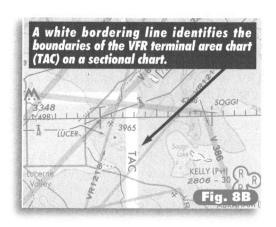

A white bordering line identifies the boundaries of the VFR terminal area chart (TAC) on a sectional chart.

Fig. 8B

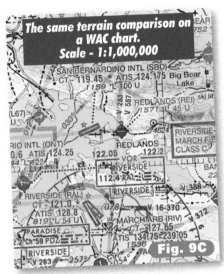

VFR terminal area charts are exceptionally detailed, with a scale of 1 to 250,000 (1 inch=3.43 nautical miles) which provides much more detail than sectional charts. These charts, revised once every 6 months, are very useful for pilots operating from airports within or near a major terminal area. For instance, they allow you to more precisely identify terrain features that help you physically avoid the shelf of Class B airspace. Figures 9A, 9B and 9C show a comparison of all three charts and their increasing information detail.

Topographical Information On A Sectional Chart

Topographical (ground) features on a sectional chart are of great value to the VFR pilot, if she or he knows what to look for. Pilotage is most often accomplished by use of the sectional chart, but learning to translate the shadings and markings on the chart into a mental picture and match it up with what's outside is definitely a learned skill. It's also a skill you definitely should learn.

Not all features are created equal, especially on a chart. The big stuff is pretty easy. Most of my students don't have a problem figuring out the Pacific Ocean. It's big, it's blue, and they've usually seen it before. Deciphering the contour features of a mountain or the alluvial fan of small streams takes a little more skill.

Here are some of the major topographical features you should be familiar with. Keep in mind that not all features on the ground are shown on the chart. What mapmakers show on the chart, however, is almost always found on the surface. (I say *almost always* because, over time, some landmarks disappear by erosion, construction, etc.)

Relief (the sloping of terrain) – Depicting three-dimensional hilly and mountainous terrain on a two-dimensional chart presents some difficulty. Mapmakers partially solve the problem with the use of contours to depict terrain elevations. Contours are lines joining areas of equal elevation—somewhat like the isobar on a weather map connecting areas of equal pressure. Figure 10 is an example of how contours depict terrain elevation.

TERRAIN CONTOUR LINES

Contour lines allow you to interpret terrain height and gradient above mean sea level on a sectional chart. The contour lines above are spaced at 500 foot intervals while other maps may use 100 or 250 foot terrain intervals.

Terrain contours on a sectional chart are usually spaced at 500 foot intervals as shown below.

Fig. 11A

Terrain Contour

This is what terrain on the sectional chart excerpt below looks like from the air.

Ridge

Valley

Fig. 11B

On a sectional chart, contour lines are spaced at 500 foot intervals, as shown in Figures 11A and 11B. Occasionally, contours may be shown at 250 foot, 100 foot or even 50 foot levels in areas of relatively low relief (slope). You can tell a lot about the slope of the terrain by examining the spacing between the contour lines in Figure 11A. Closely-spaced contour levels indicate rapidly rising terrain, while contours spaced farther apart indicate less precipitous terrain.

Color – An additional aid in determining the height and slope of terrain is color. Every sectional chart has a

terrain color bar on its front side (see Figure 12). The color bar shows a specific color representing the maximum and minimum elevations of terrain. These colors range from light green for the lowest elevation to dark brown for higher elevations. For instance, the dark yellowish-color shown at position A in Figure 12 represents terrain rising between 5,000 and 7,000 feet above sea level. Remember, a specific color doesn't precisely indicate the height of terrain, it indicates a range of altitudes (i.e., 5,000' to 7,000') through which terrain can be found in those areas. More precise indications of terrain are identified by something known as *spot elevations*.

Spot Elevation Symbols – Figure 13A shows a spot elevation used on VFR charts (Figure 13B shows the actual terrain features from the air). Normally, spot elevations (shown as *small* black dots) are chosen by mapmakers to indicate the high point on a particular mountain range or ridge. Next to the small black dot is the elevation of that spot above sea level. Remember, there can be several spot elevations in a local area. These spot elevations show heights of local peaks and don't necessarily represent the highest terrain in that area. The highest terrain located within an area bordered by lines of latitude and longitude (known as a *quadrangle*) is identified by a slightly *larger* black dot.

A small black dot represents a spot elevation that identifies high points on a mountain range or ridge.

Fig. 13A

Terrain from Figure 13A as seen from the air.

Fig. 13B

The terrain color bar on VFR charts helps identify terrain height and slope.

Fig. 12

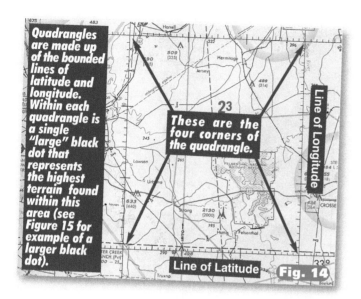

Quadrangles are made up of the bounded lines of latitude and longitude. Within each quadrangle is a single "large" black dot that represents the highest terrain found within this area (see Figure 15 for example of a larger black dot).

These are the four corners of the quadrangle.

Line of Longitude

Line of Latitude

Fig. 14

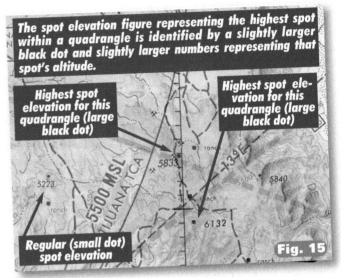

The spot elevation figure representing the highest spot within a quadrangle is identified by a slightly larger black dot and slightly larger numbers representing that spot's altitude.

Highest spot elevation for this quadrangle (large black dot)

Highest spot elevation for this quadrangle (large black dot)

Regular (small dot) spot elevation

Fig. 15

Spot Elevations Showing Highest Terrain – *Quadrangles* are the rectangular areas bounded by printed lines of longitude and latitude, as shown in Figure 14. Within each quadrangle there is a single *large* black dot. This dot is a special spot elevation figure that locates the highest *terrain* within that area and shows its height above sea level (see Figure 15). While there may be several spot elevation figures (small black dots) within a quadrangle, there will only be one represented by a larger black dot.

Maximum Elevation Figures (MEF) – Maximum elevation figures (MEFs) represent the highest elevation of terrain and other obstacles (towers, trees, etc.) within a quadrangle. Figure 16 shows the MEF value (point A) from the quadrangle containing the spot elevation identified by point B. The two-digit number represents the MEF value in hundreds of feet with the last two zeros missing. Figure 16 (point A), shows an MEF value of 6,700 feet MSL.

MEF values are slightly higher than the obstruction within the quadrangle it represents. How much higher? Cartographers (people who make maps) have a specific formula for figuring MEF values. To understand how this is computed, you must first understand that only manmade obstacles standing more than 200 feet AGL are generally charted. Those 200 feet or less are charted if they are considered critical by cartographers (i.e., in the vicinity of an airport). Cartographers then add a minimum of 100 feet onto the highest elevation shown on the chart. Then they round up to the nearest whole-number hundred value. Finally, they add an additional 200 feet for those manmade obstructions that may not be shown.

For instance, the MEF value in Figure 16 is 6,700 feet MSL (point A). The critical elevation figure for that quadrangle is 6,378 feet MSL (point B). Adding 100 feet onto 6,378 equals 6,478. Rounding this up to the nearest whole number hundred value equals 6,500. Adding an additional 200 for uncharted obstruction equals 6,700 feet MSL.

The MEF is calculated in a similar manner if a manmade obstacle standing more than 200 feet AGL is located on the highest peak in a quadrangle. In this instance, only 100 feet is added to the top of the obstacle, then this value is rounded up to the nearest whole number hundred value to calculate the MEF. The point here is the MEF is not the minimum altitude you should fly within this quadrangle. You should be at least a minimum of 1,000 to 2,000 feet higher (or more) than any MEF value shown along your route. This becomes especially important at night when it's difficult to see terrain or obstacles, even if these obstacles are lit (you don't want to hit one and light it up even more).

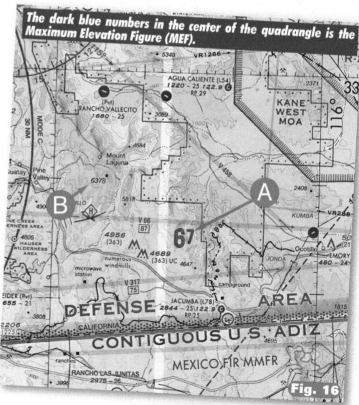

The dark blue numbers in the center of the quadrangle is the Maximum Elevation Figure (MEF).

Fig. 16

This symbol represents an obstacle standing less than 1,000' AGL.
Fig. 17A

This is what a similar obstacle may look like.
Fig. 17B

Symbols that look like large tepees are obstacles standing 1,000' or more AGL.
Fig. 18

Obstacles – At first glance, the item in Figure 17A looks like the tepee (or bingo temple) on an Indian reservation. It's not. This symbol represents obstacles standing less than 1,000 feet AGL. The bold number represents the height of the top of the obstacle above sea level. The number contained within the parentheses is the height the obstacle stands above ground level. If you're ever asked to find the height of the *base* of the obstacle above sea level, you only need to subtract the obstacle's AGL height from its height above sea level. (Be careful when taking a knowledge exam. Test makers have often graduated from "Trick Question Graduate School" and will try and confuse you with AGL and MSL values.) Figure 17B shows the same obstacle as seen from the ground.

Obstacles standing 1,000 feet and higher above ground level are portrayed by a more elongated obstruction symbol, as shown in Figure 18. The bold numbers and those within parentheses represent heights MSL and AGL, respectively. Sometimes these obstacles will have light-ray symbols emanating from the top of the obstruction symbol, as shown in Figure 19. This indicates the obstacle has a high intensity strobe lighting system associated with it. Sometimes an obstacle has the letters "UC" next to it, as shown in Figure 20. This means the obstacle is under construction. If the eventual height above ground that the obstacle will stand is known, it will be shown in parentheses (even though the building of the obstruction isn't completed).

Roads – Roads and highways make excellent VFR reference points, as shown in Figure 21A and 21B, and many pilots claim that *IFR* really stands for "I follow roads." Highways, especially major ones, are relatively easy to identify from the air. VFR charts often distinguish between single and multi-lane roads. Some major interstates even have their route numbers listed on the sectional chart.

The Perils of Opening a Chart Too Quickly in the Cockpit
SMACK!

Actually Heard!
A pilot calls the Flight Service Station and says:

Albuquerque Flight Service Station, this is Cessna 714 Sierra Bravo. I'd like to file a flight plan...depending on where I am.

Light rays emanating from an obstacle indicates the presence of high intensity strobe lights.
Fig. 19

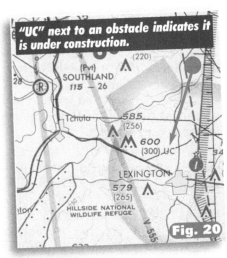
"UC" next to an obstacle indicates it is under construction.
Fig. 20

Roads are excellent visual checkpoints for navigation by pilotage.

Fig. 21A

The arrow points to the same road shown in Figure 21A.

Fig. 21B

Railroad Tracks – Railroad tracks (Figure 22A) are often relatively easy to identify from the air (see Figure 22B), especially if you're at a fairly low altitude. This is particularly true when a train lopes along the tracks (it's rare to see trains moving without tracks. If you see one, take a picture and send it to me—it's worth millions).

Wires – Power transmission wires and telephone lines are depicted on charts as shown in Figure 23A. These wires are usually a lot easier to see on the chart than they ever are from the air (Figure 23B). They're not very wide, and they tend to blend in with the terrain below, though you might have some success spotting the supporting towers. I'd be cautions about relying on them as my sole source of VFR landmarks or checkpoints for any cross country flight.

Shorelines, Rivers & Streams – Shorelines for coastal areas along with piers, wharves and jetties are excellent landmarks as shown in Figure 24A and 24B. Other large

Railroad tracks can make good checkpoints.

Fig. 22A

Railroad tracks from Figure 22A as seen from the air.

Fig. 22B

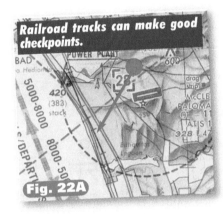

Power transmission lines are sometimes difficult to see from the air.

Fig. 23A

Power lines similar to those in Figure 23A.

Fig. 23B

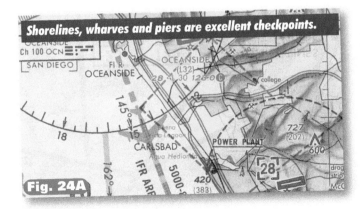

Shorelines, wharves and piers are excellent checkpoints.

Fig. 24A

Shoreline from Figure 24A as seen from the air.

Fig. 24B

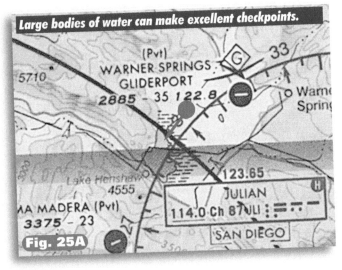

Large bodies of water can make excellent checkpoints.

Fig. 25A

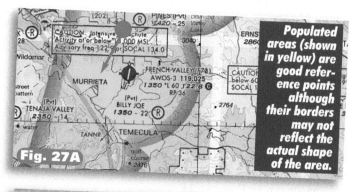

The same large body of water as seen from the air.

Fig. 25B

bodies of water make excellent landmarks as shown in Figure 25A and 25B. Of course, this assumes a drought hasn't made the shoreline unrecognizable. You'll probably have more difficulty in recognizing streams and small rivers from the air, as shown in Figures 26A and 26B. Frankly, unless you're using major rivers (the Colorado River for example), you'll be better off using larger bodies of water, roads or other references for VFR checkpoints.

Populated Areas – On sectional and VFR terminal charts, populated areas in the form of cities and large towns are outlined in yellow, as shown in Figure 27A. As long as you don't become too hung up on comparing the actual city to the yellow borders on the sectional, you'll find them a useful VFR reference point. Cities often grow faster than cartographers update their charting information. This can cause the city to have a very different outline than that shown on the chart (Figure 27B). Smaller towns and villages are shown by an empty circle (Figures 28A and 28B). These areas also make useful VFR landmarks. You'll find cities and towns even more useful at night, where their lights provide extremely helpful landmarks for VFR navigation.

Fig. 27A

Populated areas (shown in yellow) are good reference points although their borders may not reflect the actual shape of the area.

This is the populated area in Figure 27A as seen from the air. At night, city lights can make these areas easily identifiable from the air.

Fig. 27B

Streams and small rivers are sometimes difficult to identify from the air, especially when they're dry.

Fig. 26A

This is an airborne shot of Figure 26A. These small streams are not always easily identifiable from the air.

Fig. 26B

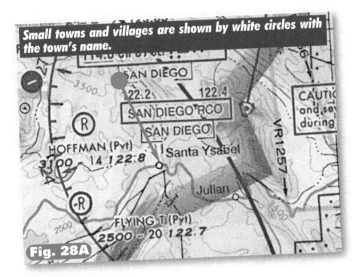

Small towns and villages are shown by white circles with the town's name.

Fig. 28A

The same small town in Figure 28A, as seen from the air. At night the light clusters from these towns make good checkpoints.

Fig. 28B

Airports colored in magenta don't have air traffic control towers.

Fig. 29

Airports colored in blue have air traffic control towers.

Fig. 30

Airports (magenta or blue) with hard surface runways longer than 8,069' take on a more realistic look.

Fig. 31

Airports – Frankly, there are few VFR reporting points better than airports. I like them for VFR navigation because I like having a place to land in the event of engine, weather or (human) bladder problems. Airports are divided into colors on the map (they are *not* really painted these colors, just like the states aren't painted the colors you saw on your junior high school maps). Magenta colored airports (Figure 29) don't have an air traffic control tower (ATCT). Those shown in blue have a tower (although it may not be in operation 24 hours a day—most aren't). Figure 30 shows an airport associated with an ATC tower. All recognizable runways, including closed runways, are pictured within the airport symbol, for visual identification.

Normally, both the magenta and blue airport symbols are circles unless the airport has a hard surfaced runway greater than 8,069 feet. In that case, cartographers place an enclosed box around the runway periphery, as shown in Figure 31.

A current aeronautical chart is a like a good aviation mechanic. It has the most up-to-date information to help you get to where you're going.

Airports with a solid circle (blue or magenta) have at least a 1,500' to 8,069' hard surface runway.

FALLBROOK
FALLBROOK (L18)
708 *L 21 123.05 ©
RP 36

Fig. 32A

This is the hard surface runway from Figure 32A as seen from the air.

Fig. 32B

Airports having other than hard surfaces at least 1,500' long or soft surfaces are shown by an open symbol.

KANE WEST MOA
excludes R-2510

SALTON SEA (SAS)
minus 84 – 50
122.9 ©
RP 7

OCOTILLO (L90)
60 – 42 122.9 ©
RP 9, 31

301

Fig. 33A

This is a typical soft surface runway seen from the air.

Fig. 33B

Some airports are restricted in that they are private and not open to public use. These airports are identified by the airport symbol containing the letter "R," if they have other than hard surface runways and the letters "PVT" if they have hard surface runways 1,500 to 8,069 feet long as shown in Figure 36.

Next to an airport symbol you'll find the airport data (Figure 37, position A). The official airport name is located above the control tower frequency (identified by the letters "CT"). Some airports have more than two control tower frequencies (this isn't for pilots who really like to talk, either.) Different frequencies are for use by aircraft approaching from different directions, or using different parallel runways (at very large airports). The Automatic Terminal Information Service frequency, which is listed, will provide the proper frequency. In lieu of the ATIS, other airports such as Chico (Figure 37, position B) have AWOS or ASOS installations that provide a repeating, one-minute automatic

Any airport having a darkened circle, with the runways in reverse-bold white, has a hard surface runway between 1,500 and 8,069 feet in length, as shown in Figure 32A and 32B. Airports with soft surface runways (grass, dirt, etc.) or with hard surfaces less than 1,500 feet long are shown by an open symbol without the runway(s) depicted (Figure 33A and 33B). Military airports with other than hard surface runways are shown by a double circle (Figure 34).

An open dot within a hard-surfaced runway configuration indicates the approximate position of a VOR located on the field, as shown in Figure 35. Airport symbols on VFR charts having four square protrusions around the airport indicate that fuel services are available during normal working hours (Mon.-Fri. 10 a.m. to 4 p.m., local time). (See Figure 35.)

The only thing worse than not having a current chart is having the wrong chart.

Bob, the reason we don't see a restricted area on this chart isn't because it's not current. It's because the chart is for a different state!

I hate it when that happens!

Military airports with other than hard surface runways are shown by a double circle.

BICYCLE LAKE AAF (BYS)
2350 – 95

Fort Irwin

Fig. 34

An open dot within a hard-surface runway configuration indicates the position of a VOR on the airport. Square protrusions indicate fuel services are available during normal business hours.

La Quinta

100
35

THERMAL (TRM)
minus 117 *L 70 123.0 ©

Fig. 35

Restricted airports (not open to the public) are shown with an "R" in the airport circle or by "PVT."

BLACKINTON (Pvt)
1156

BONDO

LAKE
WOHLFORD
1643

Escondido

(Pvt)
DESERT CENTER
559 – 42

Fig. 36

This figure shows typical airport data for a tower controlled airport. Next to the airport symbol you'll find airport data.

Fig. 37

This figure shows typical airport data for a nontowered airport. The letter "*L" with the asterisk indicates that runway lighting limitations exist (i.e., it may be available part time or on request. The best way to tell is to check the Airport/Facility Directory).

Fig. 38

recording of the local airport weather-er. (Read more about AWOS and ASOS in Chapter 12, page 12-13.)

The last line of information starts with the airport's elevation in dark bold numbers. An "L" following this number means lighting is available from sunset to sunrise. The next number is the length of the longest runway, in hundreds of feet (the useable runway may be less) and the unicom frequency. The letters "RP" followed by a number indicate the runway(s) that have a non-standard right hand traffic pattern.

Unicom stations at tower controlled airports usually provide fuel service while those at nontower airports usually provide traffic information (and may provide fuel service, too). Figure 38 shows the typical airport data for a nontower airport. Notice that the letter "*L" has an asterisk next to it. This means air-

port lighting limitations exist. Runway lights for night landings may be available part time or on request. Refer to the *A/FD* to find out more about the airport's lighting.

Airways – VFR airways (Victor airways) are depicted on sectional charts as shown in Figure 39. Each airway typically extends from one VOR to the next and is identified by its own unique number. These are the numbers used on a flight plan to describe your route of flight. A square box with a number inside shows the airway distance between VOR stations, in nautical miles.

VFR Checkpoints – Visual checkpoints are shown on sectional and terminal charts by a magenta flag (Figure 40). Their names are underlined and in bold capital letters. These are prominent landmarks visible from the air. Air traffic controllers may ask you to report your

position in reference to these landmarks when contacting them for landing. (See Postflight Briefing #10-1 for more information.)

A student pilot once approached a major psychiatric hospital, which was a designated visual checkpoint. He called the tower for landing instructions and said, "San Jose Tower, this is 2132 Bravo inbound from the north for landing, over." The tower replied, "Ahh, 32 Bravo, are you headed for the mental hospital." The student said, "No. Why? Is my flying that bad?" You must pay attention to these symbols.

Airborne Vehicle Symbols – In addition to airplane activity, other airborne vehicles use the airspace. Figure 41 shows those areas containing ultralight activities, hang gliders, gliders and parachutists (we'll consider parachutists airborne vehicles in this instance). The symbols simply remind you to be extra vigilant.

A Victor airway is identified by the letter "V" followed by its own unique number.

Fig. 39

Visual checkpoints are identified by a magenta flag.

Fig. 40

Airborne vehicle symbols identify ultralight, glider, hangglider, unmanned aerial vehicles and parachute areas.

Fig. 41

The boundaries of a National Park Service area, U.S. Fish and Wildlife Service area and U.S. Forest Service areas are shown by a solid blue line bordered by dashes. Pilots are requested to remain at least 2,000' above the surface of these areas.

Fig. 42

Park, Wildlife, Forest, Wilderness and Primitive Areas – Figure 42 identifies the boundaries of either a National Park Service area, U.S. Fish and Wildlife Service area or U.S. Forest Service Wilderness or Primitive area. Aircraft operating within one of these areas are often requested to maintain a minimum altitude of 2,000 feet above the surface within these areas (unless the chart specifically notes a different altitude). Maintaining these minimum altitudes prevents destruction or damage to our national wildlife. It also helps prevent people from thinking pilots are unconcerned about anyone but themselves. General aviation depends to a substantial degree on public tolerance for its existence, and disrupting the solitude of backpackers or annoying wildlife to death is not a defensible act.

Sometimes, of course, the wildlife defends itself. Many years ago, a fellow in Alaska decided wildlife wasn't all that sacred. He was piloting a helicopter when he spotted a grizzly bear. Descending to only a few feet above the grizzly, he taunted the beast with the helicopter's landing skid. In a surprise move (it was a surprise to the pilot) the bear rose up, grabbed the skid and retrieved his lunch from room service (if you know what I mean). Pay close attention to the minimum altitudes for these areas.

While there are many other symbols to discuss on the sectional chart, we've covered some of the most important ones. Take time to study the VFR charts in greater detail. With a little practice in chart symbol interpretation, you'll be able to fly anywhere using pilotage as your single navigational tool.

We've reached the Great Divide in our introduction to aviation. The next subject allows us to put our charts to use. After all, if you don't know how to navigate you're not likely to go anywhere (at least anywhere you intended to go) and charts will have little significance to you. In the upcoming chapter, we'll discuss the most common means of navigation. You'll find this chapter quite valuable since you'll need to have some knowledge of the subject before your instructor lets you zip off on solo cross country flights.

Postflight Briefing #10-1

GPS Identified VFR Checkpoints

Some VFR checkpoints are collocated with GPS waypoints as shown in Figure 43, positions A, B, C and D. The name of the checkpoint is listed above its five letter GPS identification . To navigate to any of these collocated checkpoints, just tune the five letter identifier into your GPS and proceed direct to the waypoint as shown in Figure 44.

In this instance, the GPS is set to track directly to the Queen Mary VFR checkpoint which is collocated with the GPS waypoint identified as VPLQM (Figure 44, position E).

Since it's not always easy to recognize these VFR checkpoints from the air, especially if you're from out of town, using your GPS to identify them make navigation much easier in these instances. The GPS also provides you with the ability to inform ATC of your position and distance relative to any of these checkpoints.

Fig. 44

Fig. 43

The Terminal Area Chart

The Terminal Area Chart (TAC) shown in Figure 45, is provided to show more chart detail in known high density traffic areas. Areas covered by the terminal area chart are identified as magenta shaded blocks on the front panel of the sectional chart (Figure 46, position A). Each block represents an individual terminal area chart. Inside the terminal area chart you'll find the detailed area coverage of these areas along with whatever VFR Flyway and special airspace information is available for that particular area of coverage.

For instance, the Los Angeles terminal area chart contains several navigation inserts that provide information on published routes through the Los Angeles Class B airspace (Figure 47) as well as the special flight rules area that provides easy transit directly across Los Angeles International airport (Figure 48). The VFR Flyway routes (Figure 49) shown on the chart are very useful when you're operating in a high density traffic area like the Los Angeles basin.

This chart helps you identify VFR flyways, which are designed to help VFR pilots avoid major controlled traffic flows. For instance, when departing Van Nuys airport (Figure 49, position B) to the west, it's probably wise to fly toward the Sepulveda flood control basin (position C) then follow the flyway found just south of the 101 Ventura freeway (position D). Flying at or below 3,500 feet then at or below 5,500 feet westbound should keep you out of major traffic flows (the routes with small blue arrows and accompanying altitudes). Ground references shown on the chart make visual navigation easy.

Chapter Eleven

Understanding Weather
Looking for Friendly Skies

© Nino Pavisic

Introduction

An airline pilot friend was seven miles from the airport on approach to Lambert Field in St. Louis when he made his first call to the air traffic control tower. "Lambert Tower, this is TWA 413, outer marker inbound, over." No reply from the tower.

"Lambert Tower, this is TWA 413, outer marker inbound, over." The tower controllers still didn't respond.

"Lambert Tower, this is TWA 413, how do you hear, over?"

Finally the tower controller replied, "TWA 413, this is Lambert Tower, please stand by, we're changing controllers down here" (meaning a controller shift change).

Not wanting to miss an opportunity, my TWA pilot friend replied, "Lambert Tower, this is TWA 413. Tell me, what do you folks use, Huggies or Pampers?" Everyone had a good laugh as the airliner landed uneventfully.

Isn't it interesting that tower controllers and pilots can get along with each other despite the tensions and anxieties of their jobs? Sure there are moments of frustration, but it ultimately works because of knowledge and understanding.

Knowledge and understanding is exactly what you need in order to cope with another relationship—the one you as a pilot must have with the weather. Unlike most relationships, this isn't one about which you have a whole lot of choice. If you fly, you will face weather, unless you confine your flying to outside the atmosphere. Learning about the weather, and your relationship to it, is what we're setting out to accomplish in this chapter. As a bonus, when you graduate from this chapter you will be able to really understand what the person on the Eyewitness News is doodling on the weather map.

Weather accounts for 25% of the aviation accidents and almost 40% of all aviation fatalities. Getting along with the weather machine is essential for safe, successful flying. As with all relationships, understanding the other party allows us to survive and thrive in a comfortable, safe atmosphere. Understanding meteorological forces begins with identifying how uneven heat distribution across the planet's surface creates weather.

Atmospheric Circulation

I will now teach you the basics of weather:

1. Air is heated unevenly by incoming solar radiation.

2. Heated air rises and moves.

That's it. The rest is just filling in the details. Class almost dismissed.

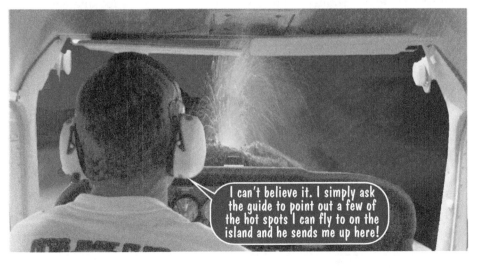

I can't believe it. I simply ask the guide to point out a few of the hot spots I can fly to on the island and he sends me up here!

And you thought learning about weather was difficult.

Uneven heating is the ultimate weather engine. It's what makes weather go. It causes rain, wind, thunder, clouds, and all the other excitement that makes up the weather show on earth.

Have you ever seen a cat on a metal roof in summer? There was once a play about it—Cat on a Hot Tin Roof. Instead of pussyfooting around, the animal stays on the move. Air does the same. It's air today, gone tomorrow, moving restlessly around the earth in a never-ending (and futile) attempt to evenly distribute heat. As the air moves, it creates the things we collectively refer to as *weather*.

For the sake of discussion, let's assume our earth doesn't rotate. (This is not true, just in case you're confused on the concept. I'll make the earth move for you in a minute.) Figure 1 shows how a portion of the earth at the equator receives a great deal more solar heat than the area near the poles. Equatorial air, resting over a warmer surface, is eventually heated from below, just like the cat's feet on a hot tin roof. The air becomes less dense, and rises. The engine is running.

Up to a certain altitude in the atmosphere (called the *tropopause),* temperature decreases with altitude. Therefore, our equatorial (heated) air rises until it finds air of a similar temperature near the tropopause (position A). Once it's at equilibrium with the air around it, the air stops rising, but it won't stop moving. Unable to ascend further, the air begins a journey north and south toward the poles, where it eventually cools and descends (position B). The airflow cycle in this simple illustration is complete when cold, descending polar air moves toward the equator, replacing the rising equatorial air (position C). This simple, single-cell circulation would be the way things were *if* (there always seems to be an *if*) the earth didn't rotate.

If the earth didn't rotate, this would be the end of our discussion on atmospheric circulation (and this chapter would be incredibly short). The earth, however, rotates, which literally introduces a new twist into the calculations.

SINGLE CELL AIR CIRCULATION FOR A NON-ROTATING EARTH

Solar heating of the equator causes air in contact with the earth to heat then rise and flow north and south. As it nears the poles, it cools, falls and flows in the opposite direction. This simple, single cell circulation is what would occur if the earth didn't rotate.

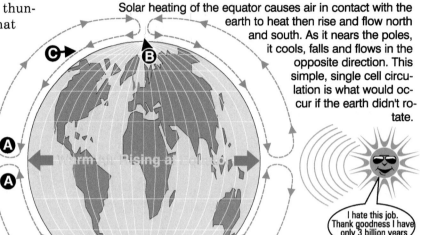

I hate this job. Thank goodness I have only 3 billion years to go.

Fig. 1

The Coriolis Force

When viewed from above the north pole, the counterclockwise rotation of the earth causes air to curve or twist to its right (relative to the terrain) in the northern hemisphere (and to the left in the southern hemisphere). No matter which way the air moves, it will have a right curve or twist added to its direction of motion.

Air is forced to curve by something known as the *Coriolis force*. This isn't a real force similar to that which you feel when a big thug punches you in the snoot. It's an apparent force. In other words, the earth rotates under a moving parcel of air which gives the air the appearance of being deflected to the right in the direction it was moving. What appears to be magic is actually sleight of land.

You can demonstrate the Coriolis force quite nicely as shown in Figure 2. Simply take an old record (Ethel Merman records are easiest to find since they sell like hotcakes—$2 a stack) and spin it in the direction the earth rotates (counterclockwise) as if you're looking down from over the north pole. Have a friend hold a ruler one-half inch above the rotating record. Take a piece of chalk and move

Parking problem? Nope. Strong winds did this!

IT'S AN ILL WIND

After landing at the cabin, I parked my airplane and walked a short distance. There was no wind, so I didn't tie my plane down. While away, the wind picked up within five minutes and turned my plane upside down. To prevent this occurrence pilots should always tie their plane down even if they are going to leave it only five or ten minutes. Very little damage was done. A lot of lost time could have been saved by just taking a minute to tie the airplane down.

ASRS Report

EFFECT OF CORIOLIS FORCE IN THE NORTHERN HEMISPHERE

To demonstrate the effect of the Coriolis force, draw several lines along a straight edge over a rotating record. Make sure record rotates in the direction shown, since this simulates the direction of earth's rotation as seen from over the north pole in the northern hemisphere.

As you can clearly see, the line always curves to the right in the direction of its motion because of the Coriolis force. A moving mass of air will also curve to the right in the direction of its motion in the northern hemisphere.

Fig. 2

Rotation

The earth rotates counterclockwise as viewed from above.

it along the straight edge of the ruler drawing a line on the rotating surface. Do it first from the exact center outward, as in position A. Then do it from the edge to the exact center, as in position B. Finally, do it in a sideways direction, as in positions C and D.

After each marking, notice how the chalk path curves. Each path is curved to the right in the direction the chalk moves. No matter which way you move that chalk, a right curve is apparently added to its motion. North of the equator, the Coriolis force curves the air to the right. South of the equator, the Coriolis force adds a left curve to the motion of the air. We'll limit our discussion to events in the northern hemisphere.

Little, if any, movement escapes the effects of the Coriolis force. One-way railroad tracks experience more wear on the right side of the track than the left. Rockets, planes, spitballs, boats and cars all, to some degree, experience the effects of the Coriolis force.

Remember, no matter which way the air moves in the northern hemisphere (right, left, sideways or diagonally), it will have an apparent right curve or twist added to it by the Coriolis force.

An easy way to remember this is to recall the movie *The Godfather*. You might remember Don Coriolis (actually it's Corleone). If things weren't going RIGHT he'd make them RIGHT, by doing the RIGHT thing. Perhaps Don Coriolis would grab a

tough guy's RIGHT arm and make him say "uncle," then talk to him about fish heads, RIGHT? Hopefully this makes it easier to associate the Coriolis force with a curve or twist to the RIGHT.

Now let's take a look and see how the Coriolis force alters the simple, single cell atmospheric circulation previously presented in Figure 1. In the northern hemisphere, rising warmer air is curved to the right in an easterly direction by the Coriolis force (Figure 3). Eventually, the high altitude rising air moves in an easterly direction and starts to bunch up, much like a freeway crowded with cars. This bunching up occurs most noticeably at about 30 degree north latitude. As the air rises, some of its heat is lost through radiation during the ascent.

SINGLE CELL CIRCULATION TO 30 DEGREES NORTH LATITUDE

Warm, rising air at the equator is curved to the right by the Coriolis force. As it travels northward at high altitudes, it cools and tends to bunch up at the 30 degree north latitude position. (warm, rising air also moves south of the equator, but we're only concerned about northerly air movement right now).

Fig. 3

60°

30°

0°

CIRCULATION OF AIR AT 30 DEGREES NORTH LATITUDE

Fig. 4

High altitude, northeasterly flowing air bunches up at 30° north latitude (position A). Some of this high altitude air continues northward (position B), while some of it falls, creating a permanent band of high pressure air around the globe at approximately 30 degrees of latitude (position C). The air at this latitude splits, some moving north (position D) and some moving south, back to the equator (position E).

MULTI CELL CIRCULATION OF AIR IN THE NORTHERN HEMISPHERE

Fig. 5

As high altitude air (position B) flows north, it finally reaches the North Pole (position F) where it cools, falls and flows southward (position G). The cold polar air flowing southward (position G) eventually makes contact with the warmer air flowing northward (position D). This warmer air flows up and over the cooler air, forming the polar front (position H). Three individual circulation cells are now apparent in both the northern and southern hemispheres (not shown here).

WIND BELTS OF THE NORTHERN HEMISPHERE

Surface winds, resulting from three individual circulating cells in the atmosphere, form three permanent wind bands across the northern hemisphere. Effects of the Coriolis force cause these winds to curve to their right in the direction in which they move.

Fig. 6

Both bunching up and cooling cause some (not all) of this air to slowly descend at the 30 degree north latitude location, shown in Figure 4, position A. Bunching up increases the air mass above and thus causes a higher surface pressure at the 30 degree latitude position. As the air descends toward the surface it warms, causing clear skies (usually) and warm surface temperatures. Some of this high pressure air flows southward toward lower pressure at the equator (position E). The rest of this warm, low altitude air at position D moves northward.

Some of the high altitude air that didn't descend at 30 degrees latitude continues to move northward toward the pole, as shown by position B in Figure 5. As it continues to cool, it falls, and travels southward from the north pole (position F). At approximately the 60 degree north latitude (position G), this southward-moving colder air meets the northward moving warmer air (position D). These two air masses have different temperatures, and thus different densities. We know that things with different densities tend not to mix. For example, crude oil and water have different densities and certainly don't mix (that's why California, with all its oil spills, now has three different types of beaches—regular, super and unleaded).

When very cold polar air bumps into cool tropical air, the result is a transition zone, shown at position H. This zone is known as the *polar front* (a front is simply a zone where air masses with different densities meet). Some of the northward-moving, cool air flows upward over the colder (denser) polar air (position H). This ascending air is carried northward, toward the pole, with the rest of the high altitude winds. Three separate cells of circulation are now evident. In a while, we'll discuss fronts and their movement. Right now, just notice how winds in these three cells are affected by the Coriolis force.

Figure 6 depicts a profile of these three individual circulation cells. Between 0 and 30 degrees latitude, the northeast tradewinds blow. From 30 to 60 degrees, the prevailing winds are westerlies, and from 60 to 90 degrees the winds are the polar easterlies.

Notice that meteorologists always talk about winds in terms of the direction they blow *from,* not to! Meteorologists do this because winds, like people, are better understood when you know their origins. If winds come from the north, they're likely to be cold; from the south, they're likely to be warm. If a mean looking guy comes from a bad neighborhood, you know a lot about him. If he said he not only grew up on the wrong side of the

3D MULTICELL CIRCULATION OF AIR

Fig. 7

Three wind belts are seen from above in 3-D perspective. Notice how warmer, northward moving air from 30° latitude (position A) confronts colder, southward moving air from the north polar region (position B). This confrontation is the source of much of the nasty weather we experience in the United States.

tracks, but grew up underneath them, you know he was a bad dude. Figure 7 depicts this circulation on a multidimensional level.

While the issue of air is weighing on your mind, let's see how it weighs on the earth.

Air Pressure and Vertical Air Movement

Air has weight. This weight exerts a pressure on the earth's surface in much the same way a professional wrestler exerts pressure on your body by standing on your chest (I hope this doesn't happen to you a lot). Changing the air's temperature, however, changes its density and the pressure it exerts on the earth's surface.

For example, along the equator there exist areas of warmer (less dense) rising air, as shown in Figure 8, posi-

tion 1. Rising air certainly wouldn't create as much pressure on the surface as descending air. After all, one moves upward while the other pushes downward. Warmer (less dense) rising air provides less push or pressure on the surface. We call large areas of warm rising air *low pressure centers*. Near the equator, it's quite common to find permanent belts of low pressure air wrapped around the earth.

Conversely, permanent high pressure areas exists at the poles (Figure 8, position 2). Colder (more dense) air descends, creating more pressure on the earth's surface. Now you know why cold air falls on your toes during those nocturnal refrigerator raids. Think of cold air as an anvil resting on your chest, as shown in Figure 9. Gravity pulls the anvil downward as it does with cold air, increasing the pressure on your body. Let's attach helium balloons to the anvil, making it lighter. Now the anvil moves upward (off your chest), in the same manner as rising warmer air moves upward off the earth's surface. Pressure at the surface decreases as warm air rises. Of course, as warm air rises, cold air moves in underneath to replace it. Thus, atmospheric circulation consists of high pressure air moving toward lower pressure air (Figure 8, position 3). This simple air circulation model is a fundamental key to understanding weather.

Now that you understand major wind patterns, it's time to examine exactly what makes the wind blow.

Getting Water in the Air

Weather (meaning clouds, rain, thunderstorms, etc.) wouldn't exist if there wasn't a means of putting water into the air. Television meteorologists would be forced to entertain their flock with hand-puppet shadows and benign patter. Nearly half of all pilot fatalities would disappear, and any remaining Flight Service Stations could be retrofitted as bowling alleys.

HIGH AND LOW PRESSURE CENTERS ON A NONROTATING EARTH

Fig. 8

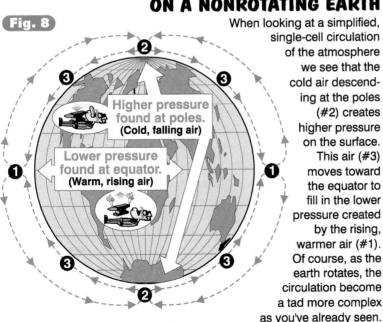

When looking at a simplified, single-cell circulation of the atmosphere we see that the cold air descending at the poles (#2) creates higher pressure on the surface. This air (#3) moves toward the equator to fill in the lower pressure created by the rising, warmer air (#1). Of course, as the earth rotates, the circulation become a tad more complex as you've already seen.

AIR MOVEMENT AND HOW IT AFFECTS SURFACE PRESSURE

Think of cold (heavier) air as an anvil that falls and increases the pressure on your chest. Similarly, cold air falls, creating more pressure on the earth's surface.

Fig. 9

Warmer (lighter) air, on the other hand, tends to rise like an anvil being lifted off your chest. You feel a reduction in pressure. Similarly, rising warmer air is felt by the earth as a lowering of pressure on its surface.

HELIUM, that's how you spell relief!

Weather is water. There's a good chance the room you're sitting in right now contains several pints of water suspended in the air. You can't see it, but it's there. It got there through one of two different processes: *evaporation* or *sublimation*. Either of these processes cause water molecules to absorb heat energy and enter the atmosphere.

Water exists in three states: solid (ice), liquid, and gas (water vapor). Changing from ice to water vapor (or water vapor to ice) while bypassing the liquid state is known as *sublimation*. For instance, snow or ice can sublimate directly from a solid to the gaseous state. This increases the water vapor content of the atmosphere, as shown in Figure 10.

A more common means of adding water to the atmosphere is through evaporation. As water molecules absorb heat energy, they eventually become energetic enough to jump into the air (Figure 11). More heat means more evaporation.

Given enough heat and a large enough water supply, the atmosphere can fill with water vapor. For a given temperature, however, the air can only hold a certain amount of water, just as a theater has only so many seats. The air is said to be *saturated* when additional water vapor is unable to enter the air. Saturated air is very much like the packed theater, in that no one else can get in without someone else leaving. The place is packed.

SUBLIMATION

Solid to gas

Gas to solid

Liquid stage is bypassed

Fig. 10

Sublimation occurs when a solid (ice or snow) turns directly into a gas (water vapor) or a gas turns directly into a solid. When the outside temperature is below the freezing point of water and the air is dry enough to begin with, water molecules will pass directly from icebergs, ice crystals or snow into the atmosphere.

EVAPORATION

Evaporation is the most common means by which water is added to the atmosphere. Solar heating causes water molecules to absorb heat energy. Given enough heat the water molecules eventually break free and enter the atmosphere.

Fig. 11

The Water Content Of Warm and Cold Air

Anyone who has spent time along the eastern coast of Florida or the Texas Gulf coast knows what humidity is. I once asked a friend what his summer visit to Houston was like. He replied, "Well, Rod, have you ever tried to breathe pound cake?" Apparently he found the humidity stifling. Why are summers usually more humid than winters?

Summers are generally more humid because the air is warmer to begin with. Warm air has the capacity to hold more water than colder air. Let's find out why.

To understand why warm air can hold more water vapor than cold air you need to understand a little quirk about water molecules. Unlike air molecules, water molecules like to cling to one another. This explains why you're more likely to find puddles of water than puddles of air on the ground. Water molecules are like aging, out of shape, one-too-many-Twinky-a-day prize fighters who always seem to grab onto each other in the 14th round (of course they might do this simply because they like each other).

Heating the air causes both air and water molecules to vibrate faster (Figure 12A). Water molecules that bounce and ricochet off each other with sufficient impact are less likely to stick together. Thus, you can put more water molecules into warmer air without them clinging to each other and forming clouds (*sky puddles*).

As the air cools, water molecules move slower and vibrate less (Figure 12B). Collisions between water molecules are now gentle enough to let

them stick together. These clinging water molecules now become visible in the form of a cloud. In other words, the water molecules can't remain as vapor (gas), so they return to the liquid state in the form of something visible (a cloud). Additional cooling allows the water droplets to grow in size, as shown in Figure 12C.

The process of water vapor becoming visible is called *condensation* and it results in the formation of fog or clouds. When water vapor condenses it means that the air is *saturated* and can't hold any more water in vapor form. Now you know why cold air can hold less water vapor than warm air. It reaches its point of saturation sooner.

Keep in mind that the process of condensation is the opposite of evaporation. When it comes to water, what goes around definitely comes around.

This explains The Mystery of the Sweating Glass. Why does a glass get damp on the outside when you pour cool lemonade in it on a hot summer's day? Hot air, carrying lots of

WATER HOLDING ABILITY OF WARM AND COLD AIR

Ⓐ In warmer air, water molecules (large circles) vibrate and move faster. Thus, they tend not to stick together (as they like to do). This allows more water molecules to enter the air before it becomes completely saturated with water vapor.

Ⓑ Cooling the air slows the speed and impact of colliding water molecules, allowing some of them to stick together, thereby returning to the liquid state in the form of a cloud (sky puddle). This leaves fewer unattached "invisible" water molecules in the now saturated air.

Ⓒ As cooling continues, the smaller droplets grow and merge into larger "visible" droplets of water. The colder air is still saturated, but even fewer water vapor molecules remain in the air. Thus, colder air can hold less water vapor than warm air.

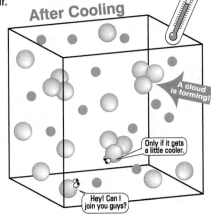

Warm, Unsaturated Air

After Cooling

After More Cooling

A cloud is forming!

Only if it gets a little cooler.

Hey! Can I join you guys?

Fig. 12   ◯ = Water Molecule   ● = Air Molecule

moisture, comes in contact with the cool surface of the glass. The suddenly-chilled air can't hold its water.

Do you recall your last flight on an air conditioned airliner? Cool, wasn't it? Dry, too. Very dry. Air conditioning cools the air and dries it, making your eyes feel like tiny shriveled prunes rattling around in oversized sockets (just like the last Tic Tac in the pack). Contact lenses dry and stick as if they've been arc welded to your corneas. This explains why several people on my last flight requested a ginger ale with a Visine chaser.

Two Ways to Cool Air

There are two ways to cool air and condense water vapor. First, you can put the air in contact with a cooler surface or environment. Second, you can lift the air and let it cool by expansion. Let's examine the first process.

Have you ever been to Minot, North Dakota in the winter? It's a beautiful place but it's memorably cold (a preacher friend says that's where you'll find all of God's frozen people). And that's why they call it Minot—you go there for one winter and you minot want to go back. Talk with anyone on those cold winter mornings and you'll see visible breath

shafts (clouds) coming from their mouth, as shown in Figure 13. Warm air from their lungs contains a lot of moisture. As this warm air comes into contact with the colder surroundings, the breath shaft becomes saturated with water vapor, condensation occurs, and a cloud forms. This is how clouds form by coming into contact with a cooler surface (an added benefit is that if the person speaking to you has bad breath, you can see it coming and take evasive action).

Fog formation is often based on air coming into contact with a cooler surface. Water vapor condenses, forming visible moisture in the form of clouds that touch the ground. But what about clouds that don't touch the ground? How do clouds form in the atmosphere?

If you lift air, you'll cool it. You'll have to go a bit farther than from your desktop to the top of your head to have any noticeable effect, so this isn't an experiment you can do at home. Rising air undergoes a decrease in pressure because of the decrease in weight (thus pressure) of the atmosphere above it. This is similar to the reduction in body pressure experienced when ascending from the

bottom of a swimming pool. Air molecules expand when they are subject to less pressure. Since there's no other source of energy available, the air molecules must use their own energy to expand. This slows them down, which results in a lower temperature. Air that rises always expands and cools. What happens to cooler air? It doesn't hold as much water as warmer air. Out it comes. This creates visible

HOW A CLOUD FORMS

On cold days a visible breath shaft is often seen when warm, moist air from the lungs is cooled by coming into contact with the cold, ambient (outside) air. As the air in the breath shaft cools, its water vapor condenses (returns to its liquid state), resulting in visible moisture in the form of a cloud (a mouth cloud).

Fig. 13

moisture, in the form of clouds, as shown in Figure 14.

In fact, air is not the only thing that expands as it ascends; the human body also does this. Decreasing air pressure with increasing altitude is one reason why flight attendants are told to wear looser clothing on the ground. Bodies expand slightly with altitude, making tight fits uncomfortable. I have never been trapped in pantyhose (honest!) but I understand it's very uncomfortable (hey, that's my story and I'm sticking to it).

Fortunately, the process of condensation is rather predictable. Without the amazing Kreskin or a Ouija board, we can still determine the temperature at which clouds begin to form. This is certainly a handy thing for pilots to know. Before we can do this, however, we need to know something about the percentage of water in the air, otherwise known as the relative humidity.

Relative Humidity

Relative humidity is not a description of your family who are all wet. It's a number that tells us how much water vapor the air is holding in relationship to how much it could theoretically hold at its current temperature.

Rush hour in Los Angeles, California helps us visualize this. At 3 in the afternoon, each moving automobile on the freeway is spaced about three car lengths behind the next. With greater space between vehicles, it's easy to slip in and move with traffic (especially when no weapons are involved). It might be said that the freeway currently holds only 25% (1 of a total capacity of 4) of the number of automobiles it's capable of holding. We might say the freeway's relative capacity is 25%.

But what happens at 5 p.m.? Space between automobiles decreases until bumpers are nearly touching. The freeway is now 100% saturated with cars. No more will fit. Nothing is moving. Its relative capacity is now 100%. If a car tries to get onto the freeway, another has got to go over the railing (Hey! It could happen!!).

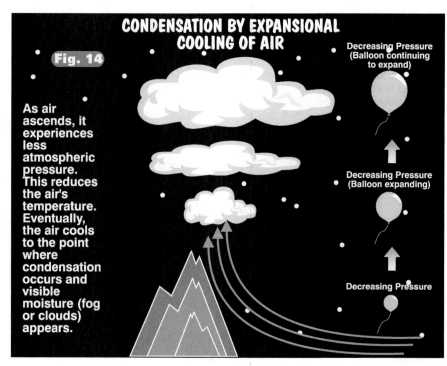

Similarly, evaporation or sublimation can add only so much moisture to the air before things reach a saturation point. And when the air is saturated, you're not going to coax any more water vapor into it. Evaporation or sublimation is just one way air becomes saturated, but it's not the most common way.

RELATIVE HUMIDITY

The parcel of warm air (A) is holding 50% of the water vapor it's capable of holding. We say its *relative humidity* is 50%. As the air cools, its capacity to hold water vapor diminishes. Water molecules begin to stick together, condense and return to the liquid state (form a cloud). Remember, if water molecules are leaving the vapor state for the liquid state, you're not going to get more water vapor into the air (and that is that). Eventually the air cools to the point where it can't hold any more water. The *relative humidity* has increased to 100% as shown by parcel B.

Warm Air: Relative Humidity - 50%

The container of air at this temperature can actually hold an additional 10 water molecules in the vapor phase (for a total of 20). Relative to the 20 that are possible, the *relative humidity* is 50%.

Cold Air: Relative Humidity - 100%   Fig. 15

As the air cools, its water holding ability decreases. Now it can't hold any more water in the vapor phase because the water molecules want to cling and form a cloud. Relative to this container, the relative humidity is now 100%.

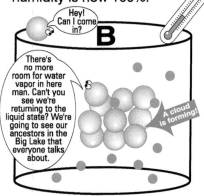

= **Water Molecule**   = Air Molecule

Fig. 16

The psychrometer is a device used to determine the dew point and relative humidity.

All Dew Determination

Dew point is determined by use of a wet and dry bulb thermometer—also called a psychrometer (Figure 16). Both are identical, mercurial thermometers. One measures air temperature; the other is encased in a wet sheath, permitting moisture to evaporate and cool the thermometer. Both thermometers are connected by small rope and are swung around for a few seconds. Then their temperatures are read.

Based on the readings from the two thermometers, the dew point, relative humidity and other measures can be calculated.

The first time I saw a weather specialist do this I thought he was a Bruce Lee protegee doing a nunchuka demo. In actuality, he swung them for a few seconds, took a reading, then retired with his data to the weather room.

It was a calculating move.

Cooling the air is the most common way for it to become saturated. Suppose air parcel A in Figure 15 contains only half the moisture it's capable of holding. We can say this parcel is 50% saturated, relative to the amount of moisture it can hold at its current temperature. Another way of expressing this is to say its *relative humidity* is 50%. The numerical value of 50% is relative to that particular parcel of air only.

What happens to the relative humidity when the air temperature decreases? Yes, the relative humidity goes up. It's just like the freeway losing a few lanes. It loses its capacity to handle traffic. When the temperature drops, the air loses its capacity to hold water.

As air parcel B in Figure 15 is cooled, its water molecules start clinging to one another and begin to return to the liquid state. The air eventually becomes saturated and can't hold additional water molecules with further cooling. Parcel B's relative humidity has now increased to 100%, condensation occurs, and water molecules are forced out of the air.

Notice that the actual amount of water (vapor and liquid) in parcel B didn't change. Only the ability of the air parcel to hold *additional* water vapor has changed.

While relative humidity informs us about the air's capacity to hold water vapor, it doesn't allow us to predict when clouds will form. After all, relative humidity just tells us the state of the air right now, not what it will be in the future. There is, however, a meteorological value known as the dew point which provides us with cloud-predicting ability.

The Dew Point

The *dew point* is the temperature to which a parcel of air must be cooled to become 100% saturated. It's a predictor of when condensation will begin for a particular parcel of air. Assume a meteorologist (that's a weatherperson, not an asteroid technician) says the air's dew point is 60 degrees Fahrenheit (F). If our thermometer shows the air's temperature is 75 degrees F, then we immediately know the air is not completely saturated. In other words, its relative humidity is less than 100%. But cool the air down to its dew point of 60 degrees F and the relative humidity increases to 100%. Condensation occurs, and fog or clouds form.

Meteorologists refer to the actual temperature difference between the temperature and the dew point as the *temperature-dew point spread*. Sounds like a nifty name for a Texas cattle ranch. The process of conden-

sation can actually begin about 5 degrees F (2.8 degrees C) *before* the air temperature cools to its dew point (otherwise stated as a temperature-dew point spread of 5 degrees).

Dew points are handy numbers for pilots to have for several reasons. It's important to understand that the dew point is a great indicator of the atmosphere's water content. High dew point temperatures indicate a lot of water in the air. Low dew point temperatures indicate little water in the air. The temperature-dew point spread also tells you whether the humidity is high or low.

Assume, for instance, you're planning a short flight to arrive at an airport about a half hour after sunset. Air temperature often drops noticeably at sunset—sometimes 10-15 degrees F (or more) within the first half hour. Your weather briefing shows the air temperature at the airport is 65 degrees F and the dew point is 55 degrees F. Would you anticipate any problems? Despite a 10 degree F degree spread between the temperature (65 degrees F) and the dew point (55 degrees F),

A wise man observes that all pilots should use their superior judgment to avoid situations that may require use of their superior skill.

Rod Machado's Sport Pilot Handbook

atmospheric cooling after sunset could easily drop the air's temperature to within five degrees of its dew point. That means fog or low clouds. Nothing is more frustrating for a VFR pilot than to navigate directly to where the airport should be, look down, and see the area covered by clouds.

Be aware that fog or low cloud formation can even occur with temperature-dew point spreads of as much as 6 degrees F. Also, water vapor condenses more easily when the air contains an abundance of airborne particles (also known as *condensation nuclei*). A large number of atmospheric particles makes it easier for very small particles of water vapor to collect, helping to form larger water drops. Airports downwind from an area of industry (smog = particulate matter) are more likely to have fog or low clouds form at larger temperature-dew point spreads.

Air in places like Los Angeles contains a lot of particulate matter. In the Los Angeles basin, it's not unusual for fog or low clouds to form at temperature-dew point spreads of 6 degrees F. Not only are there salt crystals from the ocean suspended in the air, but dust and photo-chemical smog are often available in abundance. As one friend said, "L.A. is a great place to be... if you're a muffler" (it is, however, a beautiful place... during a cease-fire).

Keep in mind the dew point varies with such items as geographic location and atmospheric pressure. It can change considerably during the day. A simple call to the Flight Service Station (FSS), accessing a computer weather program, calling an air traffic control facility, hearing the ATIS broadcast, or listening to an automated weather observation station, provides instant temperature-dew point information.

Condensation and Cloud Formation

If clouds are present, does that mean it's going to rain? Definitely not. But if you have rain, or some other form of precipitation (hail, snow, etc.), clouds are definitely nearby. If you're driving along and see water coming from the sky without clouds, there's a good chance that you've just hit a fire hydrant or driven under an elephant.

For significant precipitation to occur, clouds must generally be around 4,000 feet thick. Precipitation can take the form of rain, hail, snow, ice pellets or grains, or freezing rain. Essentially, precipitation is any or all forms of water particles, whether liquid or solid, that fall from the sky and reach the ground. It is distinguished from clouds, fog or dew in that it falls and makes contact with the earth's surface. When flying near any airport reporting precipitation of light or greater intensity, expect clouds to be at least 4,000 feet thick.

Lapse Rates and Temperature Inversions

Suppose your family acquires an electric hedge clipper, and you're an only child. The very next day, the family cat suddenly sports a new haircut. Does it take Sherlock Holmes to solve this mystery? Hardly. Most weather

SOLAR RADIATION AND HEATING OF THE ATMOSPHERE

The earth's atmosphere acts like glass to incoming solar radiation. It lets the sun's ray pass through while absorbing relatively little heat. This allows most of the solar radiation to be absorbed by the earth's surface.

Glass is cool to the touch.

Fig. 17

mysteries are equally easy to solve once you understand the relationship between lapse rates and temperature inversions.

The sun heats the earth. That's a fact. Very little of the sun's energy directly heats the air. That's also a fact. Then how does the air become warm? To incoming light, the atmosphere acts much like a pane of glass on a greenhouse (Figure 17). It lets solar radiation easily pass through without absorbing much heat itself. This heat is absorbed by the earth's surface. It's this heated surface that is primarily responsible for the atmosphere's heat content.

TEMPERATURE CHANGE WITH ALTITUDE

Air in contact with the surface is heated by conduction (touching). Closer to the surface, the air is warmer and, with an increase in altitude, the air cools. This change in temperature with a change in altitude is known as the "lapse rate."

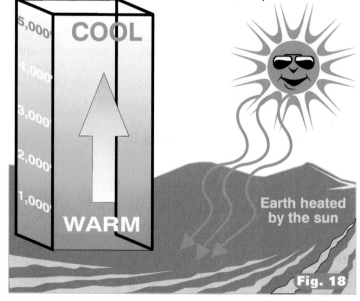

COOL

5,000'
4,000'
3,000'
2,000'
1,000'

WARM

Earth heated by the sun

Fig. 18

As we learned in the beginning of this chapter, it's the surface of the earth that heats or cools the air directly. On clear days, when the earth absorbs an enormous amount of heat, the air in contact with the surface is warmed by touching (Figure 18). As we move away from this heated surface, the air cools. We might say the temperature lapses or changes with an increase in altitude. Meteorologists call this the *temperature lapse rate*. It is one of the most important items in the science of meteorology.

No one can guess exactly how much the temperature will change with altitude. In fact, meteorologists don't know, and they're paid to make scientific guesses. A few people think it changes at a steady 3.5 degrees F (2 degrees C) per thousand feet, but that's not quite true. This is a misconception on the order of believing Pluto is a large dog orbiting the sun. There are many variables affecting the rate temperature changes with altitude.

To identify the rate of temperature change, weather specialists across the nation send up atmospheric test probes hooked to weather balloons twice daily. These probes, called radiosondes, provide information on wind, pressure, humidity and temperature.

TEMPERATURE PROFILE OF SUPERHEATED SURFACE AIR

Fig. 20

A left slope means the air cools as you ascend and warms as you descend

A right slope means the air warms as you ascend and cools as you descend

3:00 p.m.

11:00 a.m.

B A C

7:00 a.m. 9:00 a.m.

Altitude

Getting colder **Temperature** Getting warmer

A left sloping line indicates a temperature drop with altitude. Slope (A) and slope (C) both indicate the presence of a superheated layer of air close to the surface. The surface air of slope (C) starts off warmer because it's later in the afternoon. Above the surface, the air at slope (B) shows a normal lapse rate.

Using this information, meteorologists are able to determine an exceptionally important measurement called the *environmental temperature lapse rate*. This lapse rate is essentially a vertical temperature profile of the atmosphere.

Temperature change with altitude can vary considerably. It's anything but consistent. On a very hot day, the desert surface can reach temperatures of 150 degrees F, as shown in Figure 19 (it's so hot that small animals, standing too long in one spot, can be seen exploding right in front of you). Four to five feet above the surface the air temperature may be only 90 degrees F .

That's an incredible lapse rate! Airplanes entering this shallow, heated layer of air during landing might experience turbulence as well as a decrease in air density. The turbulence is caused by *thermals* or updrafts, which are small, rising parcels of warmer air that your airplane bumps into. This could make for a slightly less smooth landing if the pilot wasn't prepared (it's also a great excuse to use with passengers if you land hard).

EXTREME TEMPERATURE LAPSE RATES

On clear days over the desert, the surface can become extremely hot. The air resting next to the surface may also become quite hot. It's not unheard of for air temperature to be 150°F at the surface and 90°F at 5 feet AGL. Above 5 feet AGL, air temperature decreases at a more normal lapse rate.

85° F

500 Feet

90° F

5 Feet

150° F

Earth intensely heated by the sun

I hate it when this happens!

Fig. 19

Above the heated layer of air, this super lapse rate reverts to a rather normal, less dramatic temperature decrease with altitude. The depth (height) of this superheated layer can increase during the day as warm air from below rises and mixes with the cooler air aloft.

Figure 20 depicts several temperature-altitude plots for a clear day. At 11 a.m., the temperature plot tilts to the left immediately above the surface, showing a dramatic temperature drop with altitude (point A). This is the result of a super-high lapse rate found over very hot surfaces.

As altitude increases, the temperature decrease at a more normal, less dramatic lapse rate (point B). Later, at 3 p.m., the surface temperature starts off warmer and a quick temperature drop is even more noticeable because of intense afternoon heating (point C).

Temperature Inversions

While it's common for air temperature to decrease with height, sometimes the opposite occurs. There are many occasions when the temperature actually increases as you ascend. This is called a *temperature inversion,* since the normal-decreasing temperature lapse rate is turned upside down or inverted. There are two types of temperature inversions, a surface inversion and an inversion aloft.

Surface Inversion—The surface inversion, shown in Figure 21, is the most common type. It frequently forms around sunset and lasts until midmorning. A setting sun allows the surface temperature to drop quickly, especially on cloudless, calm nights. In the absence of a cloud cover, the

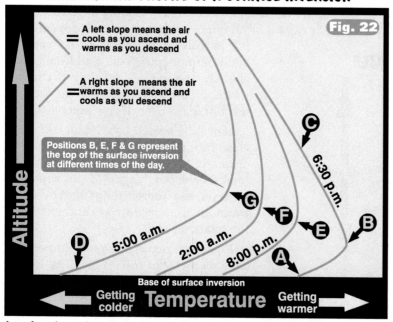

SURFACE BASED INVERSION

Altitude

Temp ➡

Top of Inversion

Bottom of Inversion

I knew I shouldn't have eaten that!

Air starts to cool again

Air becomes warmer

Air starts to get warm

Air next to ground is cool

Ground cools quickly as evening progresses

Fig. 21

A surface inversion occurs as the ground cools and the air next to it also cools. The air at altitude still contains heat from earlier in the day. With a further increase in altitude the air decreases in temperature.

earth cools quickly in much the same way a heated waterbed cools when the covers are left off. There is nothing above the surface to absorb the radiant heat (Clouds, somewhat like blankets, prevent rapid surface cooling. The water droplets in them absorb radiant heat from the surface. As they warm, they re-radiate this heat back toward the ground, which absorbs the heat energy again. This exchange continues all night long and keeps surface temperatures warmer than they would be on a clear night).

As the earth cools, the air next to it starts to cool. In situations where there is not a lot of mixing, the layer adjacent to the earth cools while the air above remains at or near daytime temperatures. The result is a temperature inversion.

TEMPERATURE PROFILE OF A SURFACE INVERSION

Fig. 22

A left slope means the air cools as you ascend and warms as you descend

A right slope means the air warms as you ascend and cools as you descend

Positions B, E, F & G represent the top of the surface inversion at different times of the day.

Altitude

C
6:30 p.m.
G
F
E
B
D
5:00 a.m.
2:00 a.m.
8:00 p.m.
A

Base of surface inversion

◀ Getting colder **Temperature** Getting warmer ▶

A surface inversion starts at the surface and is characterized by an increase in air temperature with altitude (a right sloping line). The top of the inversion occurs where temperatures resume their normal decrease with altitude (a left sloping line). As day progresses into night the top of the inversion increases in height, as shown by positions E to F to G.

The base of a surface inversion (where the temperature starts to increase with height) is located at the surface (I'm just making sure this is clear). The top of the inversion occurs where the temperature lapse rate resumes its normal decrease with height. Typically, the top of surface inversions occurs within a few hundred feet of the ground.

In case you think surface inversions involve sissy, wimpy little temperature changes, think again. Surface inversions can result in a temperature increase of 25 degrees F with a 250 foot increase in height above the surface (even larger temperature differences are possible).

Figure 22 shows several temperature/altitude plots for the late evening and early morning hours. At 6:30 p.m., a little after sunset in this profile, the temperature plot tilts to the right (position A). This means the temperature increases with an increase in altitude—up to a point—then the temperature plot bends back to the left (position B). Where the curve bends to the left, the air is the warmest (position B). This is the location of the top of the surface inversion. Above the inversion, the air has a normal (decreasing temperature) lapse rate (position C).

The 5 a.m. temperature plot tells a similar story. The plot line starts at the far left of the diagram, indicating the surface temperature has cooled noticeably during the late evening and early morning (position D). As night progresses, the top of the inversion occurs at progressively higher altitudes (points E to F to G) as the layer of colder surface air grows. (Remember, Figure 22 is a microview of the atmosphere. The altitude scale is in hundreds of feet.)

During winter, in parts of Alaska, surface inversions can be quite impressive. Air at the surface can be minus 45 degrees F, while at 200 feet AGL the air temperature can be minus 5 degrees F. This is a 40 degree F temperature increase in 200 feet—a very dramatic temperature change (somewhat like a Pompeian with a front row seat at the Mt. Vesuvius volcano trials). Long nights and short days contribute to this type of dramatic surface inversion.

Inversions with extreme temperature differences can cause pilots serious problems. Reports of very cold airplanes climbing into the warmer, moister air aloft warn of instantaneous frost formation on the windshield. This occurs in much the same way frost forms on a chilled drinking glass just removed from the freezer. Atmospheric moisture sublimates (bypasses the liquid state, going from gas in the atmosphere to solid on the glass) directly onto the aircraft's cold surface. At only a few hundred feet AGL, with no visual reference and no instrument rating, this has proven deadly to some pilots.

Without wind to mix the warm and cold air together, a surface inversion is more likely to form. Winds of about seven knots or greater can start mixing the warm and cold layers of air, causing the inversion to disappear. Little parcels of rising warm air (called *convective* currents because the motion is mostly vertical) from hotspots on the surface can help break up an inversion. This is why surface inversions forming over the desert seldom last past midmorning,

INVERSION ALOFT

Descending air aloft (usually from a high pressure area) is heated by compression. If this warmer air falls on top a cooler layer of air, an inversion aloft may form.

Air starts to cool again with altitude

Air warms up with altitude

Air cools with altitude

Fig. 23

which is the time when convective currents typically start forming and begin mixing the air.

I've always thought of convective currents as little, unruly children who run up and down stairs in the house breaking things up. Several years ago one of these little guys visited our place and tore things up. I told the little guy, "You better stop it or the devil is gonna get you!" He looked at me and said, "Why should I stop? I'm doing what he wants!" Ouch!

Inversion Aloft—The other type of inversion is called an *inversion aloft*. These inversions are caused by warmer air moving horizontally over colder air or by air aloft that is descending and heated by compression (Figure 23). Unlike surface inversions, these inversions are typically found at higher altitudes (thus the word *aloft*).

High pressure centers in the atmosphere consist of large masses of air descending at rates of hundreds to thousands of feet per day. As this subsiding air descends, it experiences the same effect divers experience when descending to the bottom of a swimming pool—an increase in pressure.

DATE WITH THE DUST DEVIL

It was the last pass spray run on an irrigated corn field. I started to pull up to clear the wires. A dust devil turned the aircraft nose down and to the left. I straightened the plane just before impact with wire. Damage: 18 inches of leading edge slapped with wire, paint scratched off nose bowl, 2 wires broke. These whirlwinds sometimes occur before a front moves through. They are 10' to 100' across and very powerful. Only way to keep out of them is to not fly when present. They are visible, except where the ground is wet— no debris for the whirlwind to pick up.

ASRS Report

An increase in air pressure produces an increase in temperature for the same reason dough becomes warm when it's kneaded (I'm not talking about the $dough$ everyone needs). Compressing dough (or air) increases its temperature. The harder the dough is squeezed, the warmer it gets. If this descending layer of warm air comes to rest on a cooler layer of air, a temperature inversion can form aloft. This type of inversion is sometimes called a subsidence inversion.

In the summer months, a subsidence inversion is more common in the western half of the country than in the eastern half. In particular, it's quite common on or near the Pacific Coast. When warm, high pressure air subsides (lowers) onto the cool, moist inflow of air from the ocean, an inversion aloft forms, as shown in the temperature-altitude profiles of Figure 24.

A pilot faces a decreasing temperature lapse rate when departing an airport beneath the inversion. The climb is initially made in cool air (position A). Upon entering

TEMPERATURE PROFILE OF AN INVERSION ALOFT

An inversion aloft is characterized by a temperature profile that starts decreasing at the surface (position A), increases (position B), then finally decreases again at the top of the inversion (position C). When air aloft is forced to descend (as in a high pressure area) it heats by compression. If warmer air comes to rest over a colder layer of air, an inversion aloft may form.

the bottom of the inversion the air becomes warmer as altitude is gained (position B). At the top of the inversion, a decreasing temperature lapse rate once again prevails (position C).

Effects of Temperature Inversions

Recently, a friend and I went flying in a hot air balloon. We departed immediately after sunrise and ascended through the cool, morning air. We rose so quickly it appeared that we were climbing at the best-angle-of-bag (if there were such a thing—there isn't). Suddenly, at approximately 1,500 feet AGL, the balloon ceased climbing (Figure 25A).

Reaching the base of a temperature inversion aloft nullified our lift. The middle or top of a surface inversion can produce the same effect on a balloon but at an altitude closer to the surface (Figure 25B). We just skipped along horizontally, beneath the base of the inversion, until more heat was applied to the balloon. In much the same way a temperature inversion impedes the ascent of a balloon, it can also prevent parcels of warmer air on the surface from ascending any higher.

Have you ever noticed smoke coming from a chimney in the early morning or evening hours? Sometimes this smoke ascends for a short distance then spreads out horizontally, as shown in Figure 26. The flattening of smoke is a sure indication of a temperature inversion (since it's often seen closer to the surface in the evening, it's probably a surface inversion).

EFFECTS OF AN INVERSION ALOFT AND A SURFACE INVERSION

VISUAL SIGNS OF AN INVERSION

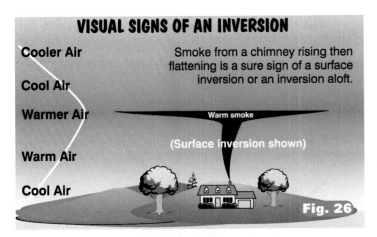

Cooler Air

Cool Air

Warmer Air

Warm Air

Cool Air

Smoke from a chimney rising then flattening is a sure sign of a surface inversion or an inversion aloft.

Warm smoke

(Surface inversion shown)

Fig. 26

Look for the flattening of smoke as one indication of a temperature inversion.

STRATUS CLOUDS ARE A SIGN OF A TEMPERATURE INVERSION

Surface Inversion

Cooler Air

Cool Air

Warmer Air

Warm Air

Cool Air

Stratus (straight type) clouds

Fig. 27A

Inversion Aloft

Cooler Air

Cool Air

Warmer Air

Warm Air

Cooler Air

Cool Air

Stratus (straight type) clouds

Fig. 27B

As warm parcels of air rise, expand and cool they may eventually form clouds. The inversion acts like a lid that keeps these rising parcels from ascending into the warmer air of the inversion. The parcels form clouds having *straight* tops, called s*tratus* clouds.

Stratus clouds close to the surface are generally good indicators of a surface inversion.

© Björn Schick - Fotolia

When cloud tops become stratus-like at higher altitudes (flattened), this probably indicates the presence of an inversion aloft.

POOR VISIBILITY IN AN INVERSION

Fig. 28

Temperature inversions act like a lid for pollutants.

A temperature inversion (surface or aloft) acts like a lid on the atmospheric pollutants beneath it. Unable to rise and disperse, the pollutants remain in a lower layer and restrict visibility.

Warm, rising puffs of smoke, much like a hot air balloon, cannot ascend through the warmer air of an inversion. In a very similar way, the presence of a temperature inversion acts to flatten cloud tops. Therefore, layer-type clouds (otherwise known as stratus or straight type clouds) are another visible indication of a temperature inversion, as shown in Figures 27A and 27B (more on stratus clouds later).

The inability of smoke, haze or pollution to move vertically and be carried away by winds at higher altitudes reduces the local flight visibility. This is especially true in areas of industry, as shown in Figure 28. Mexico City rests in a large valley and is notorious for its temperature inversions. Trapped pollution from the city can become so bad that asphyxiated birds have been known to fold their wings, croak, and just fall to earth. I wonder how many needless hours are spent plucking pigeons from sombreros?

What to Expect in an Inversion

The visible signs of an inversion should cue pilots to expect several possible flight conditions. First, temperature inversions mean an increase in the likelihood of cloud formation. Since cool air exists at the surface, the air might start to condense, forming fog or low clouds.

Second, visibility beneath the inversion can be quite low. Objects look farther away than they actually are. The mind equates something that is difficult to see with being farther away. A natural response to this situation is to get closer to the item you're attempting to see.

For example, under lower visibility conditions, pilots, thinking they are flying five miles away from the airport, are in all probability closer. They might be within the lateral limits of Class C or D airspace while thinking they're avoiding these areas. (In good visibility conditions, the opposite effect occurs. Pilots think they are flying closer to a specific point than they are and they tend to move farther away from a specific reference in good visibility conditions.)

Third, temperature inversions can indicate the presence of low-level windshear. An inversion can allow a warmer, faster layer of air aloft to move, unrestricted by surface friction (Figure 29). Since warmer and colder air have different densities, they tend not to mix (that's why fancy restaurants like Jacques en de Baux keep oil and vinegar salad dressing in separate bottles; they have different densities and don't mix). Given the proper conditions, the warmer air aloft can easily slip across the top of the cooler air, like skis on snow. Such a condition is conducive to the formation of a low level jet stream. This is where air, within a few hundred to a few thousand feet above the surface can be moving at speeds up to 100 MPH.

In the presence of an inversion, if surface winds are calm, and winds at a few hundred to a few thousand feet AGL are in the 25 knot range, be prepared for possible

WINDSHEAR IN A TEMPERATURE INVERSION

Fig. 29

Windshear in a temperature inversion can occur in the zone where warm air aloft and cold air below meet. The greater the difference in velocity between the warm and cold air, the greater the turbulence found in the shear zone (the warm and cold air in the shear zone don't mix well). It's possible to have sudden changes in airspeed when climbing or descending through windshear.

windshear. Windshear is a condition where the velocity of the wind changes drastically over a small distance vertically. It can occur at all altitudes and in all directions and result in a sudden loss of lift. Large crab angles on approach to an airport that's reporting calm surface winds are another clue to the presence of this windshear. In other words, if the tower reports the winds as calm, yet you're having to substantially crab to keep aligned with the runway, be prepared for strong windshear as you descend. I can think of no better time to add a few extra knots onto the approach speed for safety.

Fourth, temperature inversions indicate the presence of stable air. Stability is the tendency of the atmosphere to resist vertical motion. In much the same way an inversion impedes the vertical progress of a hot air balloon, it

STABLE AIR IN A TEMPERATURE INVERSION

Fig. 30

Stable air is air that suppresses vertical motion. In a temperature inversion, a warm bubble of air rises through the cooler air but can't rise into the warm air aloft (the bubble must be hotter than its surroundings for it to rise). Vertical air motion is suppressed. Therefore, temperature inversions are associated with stable air since they suppress the vertical motion of rising bubbles.

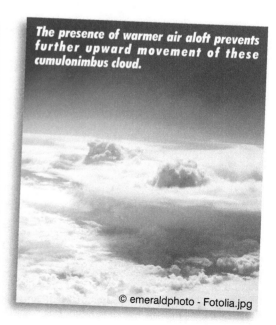

The presence of warmer air aloft prevents further upward movement of these cumulonimbus cloud.

STABLE AND UNSTABLE AIR

A warmer layer of air above a cooler layer of air is a stable condition. This is called a temperature inversion and it forms in stable air. These two layers don't want to change places. In unstable air, however, a warmer layer of air is found below a cooler layer of air. These two layers want to change places. This is an unstable condition and vertical motion (convection) occurs between these two layers.

also impedes the ascension of warmer air in the atmosphere, as shown in Figure 30. This is one of the most important points in the understanding of atmospheric stability.

Little parcels of warm air attempt to rise but they cannot ascend into the increasingly warmer layers of air aloft (just like the smoke stops rising when it hits warmer air aloft). This means the atmosphere becomes smoother, because the warm parcels of air stop rising. A smoother, more comfortable ride is the net result. This is especially true when you're flying within the warmer air that rests on top of the cooler air at the bottom of the inversion. At this point, there is probably very little air rising within the warmer air, and you are not likely to experience any turbulence.

Professional pilots know the most important tools for analyzing weather are visual clues, particularly haze layers, flattened cloud tops and smoke levels. These are all flags signaling the existence of a temperature inversion.

As the GPS is primary for navigational positioning, the thermometer is primary for meteorological understanding. Pay attention to the temperature when climbing or descending.

Perhaps Abraham Maslow summed it up very well when he said, "If the only tool you have is a hammer, then everything looks like a nail." The more tools in your toolkit, the better chance you'll have of building a complete picture of the weather at hand. One of the tools you'll most certainly want is knowledge of how slight changes in the lapse rate affect atmospheric stability.

Atmospheric Stability: Warm Over Cold, And Cold Over Warm

The atmosphere is stable when it resists the upward movement of air. It is unstable when it permits or amplifies this upward movement. In other words, stable air, if given an upward shove, sinks back to its original level. Unstable air, if shoved upward, continues to climb on its own.

Atmospheric stability can be roughly visualized in two different scenarios. Figure 31A consists of a warm layer of air resting on top of a colder layer of air. Do these two layers want to change places? In other words, will the cold air on the bottom want to rise up through the warm air on top? This is unlikely. Cold air is heavy (more dense) and warm air is light (less dense). The atmosphere is stable, since these two layers are content to remain where they are.

This explains why, after sunset, the air is usually stable. As the earth cools, so does the air resting next to it. An upper layer of the atmosphere remains warm from heat acquired during daylight hours. Cold (heavy) air is on the bottom and warmer (lighter) air on top, a very stable condition. We know this condition to be a temperature inversion and it explains why inversions are associated with stable air.

Figure 31B consists of a colder layer of air resting on top of a warmer layer of air. Does the warm layer of air on the bottom want to rise up through the colder air above? Do Golden Retrievers want to eat dinner? You bet. Warm air rises, cold air falls. It's sort of like sitting on a balloon in the bathtub (you're on your own if you try this at home). You know that balloon wants to rise, and it will at the first opportunity. Warm air surrounded by cooler air will do exactly the same thing (I can't predict what the Golden Retriever will do). Cold on top of warm is a very unstable condition.

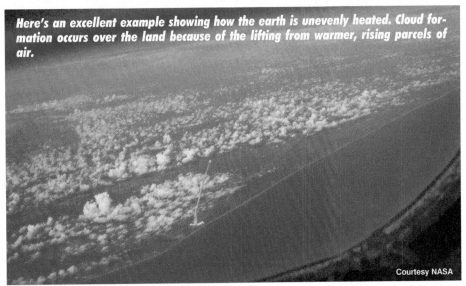

Here's an excellent example showing how the earth is unevenly heated. Cloud formation occurs over the land because of the lifting from warmer, rising parcels of air.

Courtesy NASA

As we've already seen with super lapse rates, a layer of air resting next to the heated surface of earth can become quite warm. The vertical motion of unstable air produces turbulence. It also produces good visibility as the rising air causes atmospheric mixing and helps disperse airborne pollutants.

The earth isn't heated evenly. The air next to the earth's surface isn't heated evenly either. If it were, then entire layers of air in the atmospheric environment would move up and down together. In reality, layers of air don't do this. What actually happens is that some chunks of air become hotter than others. These air parcels break off from the surface and ascend individually, as small blobs of variable sizes. Dust devils or isolated thunderstorms are often visual evidence of this happening. Glider pilots look for these rising columns of air with the same enthusiasm of young people on Spring break. So do hot air balloonists, who count on rising air for a free lift. Discovering one of these rising elevator shafts of air is their version of finding an engine in flight.

The Environmental Lapse Rate

I previously mentioned the environmental temperature lapse rate. This is the actual rate at which

Part and Parcel

When lifting occurs, only a small chunk of air —a parcel—is lifted. Nature moves a lot more parcels every day than U.P.S. In studying the weather, what we're really trying to figure out is, Who's shipping what to whom?

Parcels of air are made, not born. Something happens to lift a small section of the air in the environment upward. Lifting can be caused by a weather front, a mountain, or a hot spot on the surface.

The size of an air parcel varies. It can be a few feet across, or even miles in diameter. A parcel is this small portion of air that differs in temperature from its surroundings. Meteorologists use the parcel theory as a convenient way of explaining nature's behavior.

atmospheric temperature changes with altitude. Meteorologists also refer to the environmental lapse rate as the ambient lapse rate. These terms are used synonymously. I don't know why they don't just call it the real lapse rate, because that's what it is. Too simple, I guess.

No one can predict what this environmental lapse rate will be. If they could, meteorologists wouldn't need to send up radiosondes at locations around the nation twice a day.

Many aviation books will tell you the average lapse rate is 3.5 degrees F (2 degrees C) per thousand feet, and this number is often used in calculations. Even the FAA uses it. Fine and dandy, but I want you to know it

is as much a work of fiction as "Jaws or New York on $3 a Day." This 3.5 degree number is an average that conceals a huge amount of variation, both horizontally and vertically. The 3.5 degree figure might hold true for 10,000 or 20,000 feet, then change to a different rate; it might remain true for 50,000 feet straight up over a shopping mall in Topeka, but be different if measured 15 or 50 miles away (see Figures 31 A and B). The lapse rate is highly variable from place to place, time to time, and even moment to moment. You can guess at it, you can approximate it, but in the end if you want real information, you must measure it.

With an understanding of the environmental lapse rate under your seatbelt, you're ready to use your airplane's thermometer to obtain a rough approximation of atmospheric stability. On your next cross country flight, take vertical temperature measurements every thousand feet of climb. Ask yourself, "Am I climbing into air that's becoming warmer or colder?" If you're climbing into warmer air (a temperature increase with altitude), then a temperature inversion is present. This is a stable condition (see Figure 31A), and no fancy calculations or advanced thinking are necessary. Enjoy your flight.

If you're climbing into colder air (the temperature decreases with altitude), then atmospheric stability is dependent on how quickly the temperature decreases. If the air cools

The Meaning of Adiabatic Cooling

We've been speaking of air cooling from expansion as it's lifted, and heated by compression as it's forced downward. Meteorologists have a more precise word for this. It's called *adiabatic cooling* (or heating). Many pilots think that adiabatic is a Greek word meaning "you're not going to pass the weather portion of your written test." I can assure you it doesn't mean that. It literally means "without gain or loss of heat." In other words, adiabatic cooling or heating occurs without having to take heat away or add it to the parcel.

Expanding a parcel of air by lifting will move its molecules farther apart, keeping them from bumping into one another. Air molecules not being forced to bump into one another create less friction. Energy has been used in expanding the parcel, which causes the molecules to slow down a little. Thus, air temperature decreases. The parcel has cooled, yet no heat has been taken from it.

Conversely, compressing a parcel of air by downward motion moves its molecules closer together and increases their speed, which increases the air's temperature. No heat has been added to this parcel, yet it becomes warmed. Whenever you hear about adiabatic cooling or heating you can assume it involves the lifting or falling of air and the resultant temperature change.

EXPANSION AND COOLING OF RISING AIR

Fig. 32

* It's actually 5.4° F per thousand feet, but we'll use 5.5 since it makes the math easier.

4,000' 58°F

(-5.5°F) ↑

Step 2
Expansion moves the air molecules apart causing the air to cool at a predictable rate of 5.5° F per thousand feet.*

3,000' 63.5°F

(-5.5°F) ↑

2,000' 69°F

(-5.5°F) ↑

Step 1
Air parcel rises & expands

1,000' 74.5°F

(-5.5°F) ↑

Surface 80°F

As long as a rising parcel of air doesn't start to condense and form a cloud, it will cool at a rate of approximately 5.5°F per every thousand feet of altitude gain (it's actually 5.4°F/1000' but we'll use 5.5° for convenience). This is a constant that occurs everywhere on earth (similarly, as the unsaturated parcel descends it compresses and heats at a rate of 5.5°F per thousand feet altitude change).

quickly as you ascend, then the cold air is above you and the warmer air is below (see Figure 31B). You can be sure these two layers want to change places. Some instability is sure to be present.

Rising Parcels of Air

Let's consider those individual parcels of rising warm air we previously discussed. A warm parcel breaks away from the surface and rises into the cooler air aloft. As this parcel ascends it expands, as shown in Figure 32.

The air parcel expands much like a sealed bag of Fritos corn chips found in the back of your ascending airplane (eventually you reach the CFH or Critical Frito Height and the bag goes Frito-Nova). Frito bags, like air parcels, expand because atmospheric pressure decreases with a gain in altitude.

Basic physics decrees that as a parcel of air expands, it also cools. This is one of the reasons why using a spray-on deodorant early in the morning can cause you to moonwalk and make the Michael Jackson sound, "Eeeeooooowwwww!" The spray, which is rapidly expanding after being freed from its confinement in the can, cools quickly on its brief journey and forms a little glacier under your arm. A solitary parcel of air, moving vertically, also expands and cools with similar predictability.

Here is an amazing and crucial fact of atmospheric physics:

A rising parcel of air expands and cools at a constant rate of 5.4 degrees F for every thousand feet of climb as long as that parcel remains unsaturated (doesn't form a cloud).

Just to make the math a bit easier we'll round that figure off to 5.5 degrees. For all practical purposes, no mat-

ter where you are on earth (even the Bermuda Triangle!), if you lift a parcel of unsaturated air, it's going to cool at about 5.5 degrees F for every thousand feet of altitude change, as shown in Figure 32.

"But wait," I hear you saying, "Doesn't the rising parcel of air move through an atmosphere that also changes temperature?" Yes, it does. But the *rate* at which the atmosphere (the environment) changes temperature is, you will recall, inconsistent. It's inconsistencies that make things interesting, including the weather.

Suppose we measure the environmental lapse rate with the airplane's thermometer, as shown in Figure 33. Our thermometer shows a decrease in temperature as we gain altitude. Which will cool most quickly, the environment or the rising parcel of air? As the Kung Fu Master Cain would say, "Ahhhh Grasshopper, read on."

The airplane's thermometer in Figure 33 shows that, at this spot, at this time, there is a temperature decrease of 6 degrees F per thousand feet. The parcel, shown resting on the surface, rises because it is 1 degree warmer (at 71 degrees F) than the surrounding air (70 degrees F). This differential can be caused by the air parcel lying over a portion of the ground that is warmer, perhaps because it's paved, or because it's rock as opposed to the soil of surrounding areas. For whatever reason, there's a difference in temperature, and the air is on the move. Fasten your seatbelt and hang on tight.

ENVIRONMENTAL VS. RISING AIR PARCEL LAPSE RATES IN UNSTABLE AIR

Thermometer's measurement of outside air temperature

Rising parcel of air cools at 5.5° F/1000'

5,000' 40°F   43.5°F 5,000'

4,000' 46°F   49°F 4,000'

Environment cools at a rate of 6°F/1000'

3,000' 52°F   54.5°F 3,000'

2,000' 58°F   60°F 2,000'

Rising parcel of air cools at a rate of 5.5°F/1000'

1,000' 64°F   65.5°F 1,000'

Fig. 33

Surface 70°F   71°F Surface

Warm air bubble

A warm bubble of air at the surface starts to rise because it is 1 degree warmer than its environment. As the bubble ascends, it cools at the constant rate of 5.5°F per thousand feet. The environmental lapse rate (as measured by a thermometer in the airplane) changes 6°F per thousand feet. As the bubble rises it remains warmer than the environment. Thus, the bubble continues to climb indicating that the air in the environment is unstable.

Keep in mind that this air is going to cool off at 5.5 degrees per thousand feet, because that's a law and air is very law abiding. By 5,000 feet above the ground, it will cool to 43.5 degrees (5.5 [drop per thousand feet] × 5 [thousands of feet] = 27.5; 71-27.5 = 43.5). The surrounding air, meanwhile, has cooled to 40 degrees F (5 [thousands of feet] × 6 [degree F drop per thousand feet] = 30; 70-30 = 40).

As long as there is a temperature differential, our air parcel will keep moving. In fact, because the temperature differential is now greater than it was at ground level, the air packet will move even faster and accelerate its journey to equilibrium. When it gets there is all a matter of degree. The atmosphere depicted in Figure 33 is *unstable,* since it encourages upward motion of individual air parcels.

Let's examine a situation where the atmosphere is cooling at a lesser rate of, say, 3 degrees F per thousand feet (Figure 34). Same starting conditions, but this time look what happens at just 1000 feet AGL. The rising parcel has cooled to 65.5 degrees, or 1.5 degrees *cooler* than the surrounding air. It becomes a sinker that would be the envy of any major league pitcher. The South may rise again; the air won't, at least not far, because in this instance the atmosphere is *stable.*

The important fact you need to take away from this explanation is that the *environmental lapse rate determines the stability of the atmosphere.* Don't forget this concept. It's extremely important.

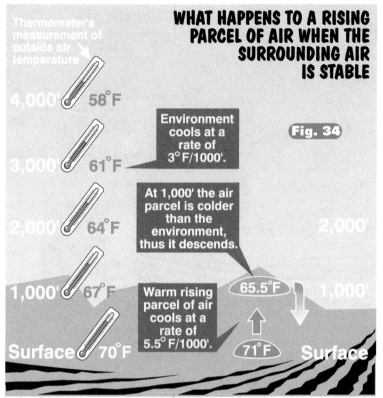

WHAT HAPPENS TO A RISING PARCEL OF AIR WHEN THE SURROUNDING AIR IS STABLE

Fig. 34

When the environment doesn't cool as quickly with an increase in altitude (i.e., remains warmer longer), it is more stable. In this example, the environment cools at only 3°F/1,000'. A warm, rising parcel of air cooling at an expected rate of 5.5°F/1,000' can only ascend to 1,000' before it becomes cooler than its environment. Thus, the environment (the surrounding atmosphere) is stable and the cooler air bubble now descends.

The next time you're on a flight, observe the thermometer during the climb. By noting the rate that temperature changes with altitude, you're measuring the environmental lapse rate in much the same way a rawinsonde does (no, you can't get paid for the information). If the environment cools quicker than 5.5 degrees F per thousand feet, as shown in Figure 33, then the atmosphere is potentially unstable, because a rising parcel of unsaturated air can't cool as quickly as the environment. You've located the stairway to heaven (but please don't play it for us).

If the environment cools at a rate less than 5.5 degrees F per thousand feet, or even becomes warmer with altitude (as in a temperature inversion), the atmosphere is potentially stable. A rising parcel of unsaturated air will cool more quickly than its surroundings and tend to fall back to earth, as shown in Figure 34.

If the environment cools at exactly 5.5 degrees F per thousand feet, then a parcel of air will have the same temperature as its surroundings if it's physically moved up or down. The atmosphere would be *neutrally stable.* In other words, a parcel will neither climb nor descend on its own.

Saturated Parcels of Rising Air

So much for unsaturated air. Now, let's get wet.

Once these rising parcels cool to within a few degrees of their dew point, condensation occurs and clouds form. Now things get really interesting, because when clouds form, heat is released as the water goes from vapor to visible moisture. Think about it for a second—what is an ice cube if not a big drop of water with the heat sucked out? Same goes for water that materializes out of water vapor. In the course of rearranging themselves in a new formation, the water molecules shed heat. You can take my word for it, or take three years of physics. Your choice. This *latent heat,* as the physics people call it, gets released into the atmosphere.

An air parcel that's busy chugging out clouds *doesn't cool as quickly* as one that isn't engaging in puffery. In fact, *saturated* parcels of air cool at rates between 2 degrees F and 5 degrees F per thousand feet, depending on how much water vapor (and thus how much trapped heat) was in the air to begin with.

Water Vapor and Instability

Memory Aid:
Mr. Bob has had too much coffee and is very unstable at the moment.

He makes himself stable by getting rid of the moisture (you figure it out).

If the atmosphere contains a great deal of water vapor, then the temperature of a *saturated,* rising parcel of air within the atmosphere might decrease at only 2 degrees F per thousand feet. This means the air parcel is being kept warm by the release of its latent heat as water vapor condenses (essentially, the parcel cools at a slower rate than its environment, making it want to keep rising). If the atmosphere contains very little water vapor to begin with, then a rising parcel of *saturated* air can decrease at a rate of as much as 5 degrees F per thousand feet.

A moist atmosphere is potentially more unstable than a dry one. Instability, however, is predicated on the condition that a rising air parcel within the atmosphere is lifted enough to reach saturation. This is why very moist air is called conditionally unstable air. It is stable as long as air parcels rising within it don't become saturated (i.e., form a cloud). The moment these parcels reach saturation, they can readily become warmer than their surroundings and start rising on their own. The atmosphere is then said to be unstable. Saturation is the *condition* upon which stability or instability is based.

Blowing In The Wind

Put a little water on your hand and blow on it, as shown in Figure 35. What does it do? It should cool your hand as the moisture evaporates (if it doesn't you've been eating too many Jalapeño peppers!). Heat, taken from your hand, is used in evaporating the saliva (that's why your hand feels cool—it lost some of its heat). Blowing simply accelerates this process. This heat (known as the *latent heat of vaporization*) is now trapped as energy in the water vapor above your hand. It's in a different energy state known as latent heat.

Try not to become overwhelmed by this concept of different forms of energy (energy states). Remember, whenever you put gasoline in your tank you're converting ancient vegetables and dinosaur lips into movement energy. Your automobile is nothing more than a fancy energy converting device much like that of the atmosphere.

Think of evaporation as a process opposite that of condensation. While evaporation puts *water* into the atmosphere, condensation gives the *water* back. If evaporation takes *heat* away, condensation must give *heat* back. The heat given back is known as *latent heat* (the *latent heat of condensation* to be precise). When water vapor condenses, latent heat is given back to the parcel, making that parcel slightly warmer.

Put a little saliva on your hand

Blow on saliva to accelerate the evaporation process

Fig. 35

Parcel of moist air forms above your hand, which contains heat taken from your hand and water from your saliva

Moist Air = Water + Heat

Spot on hand is now cool from heat loss during evaporation

Water — Heat — Water

MA

MA

MA

Rising moist air (MA) that forms a cloud is converted back into water (which becomes visible) and heat (which warms the cloud)

Figure 36 shows what happens when a rising parcel of air becomes saturated. Let's assume a parcel of unsaturated air is pushed up the side of a mountain. As it ascends, it cools at the unsaturated rate of 5.5 degrees F per thousand feet. The environmental lapse rate, as measured by our airplane's thermometer, also happens to be 5.5 degrees F per thousand feet. At 1,000 feet, this air parcel's temperature is the same as the surrounding air (its environment). It has neutral stability, since the parcel neither wants to rise nor descend.

Pushed aloft by The Force (the wind against rising terrain), at 2,000 feet the parcel cools to within a few degrees of its dew point and the moisture starts to condense. The parcel now becomes saturated. Latent heat is released, causing the rising air parcel to cool at a slower rate of only 3.5 degrees F per thousand feet. Push this baby up the mountain just a tiny bit more and a big difference in temperature will appear between the parcel and the surrounding atmosphere.

At 3,000 feet, the parcel has only cooled another 3.5 degrees F, while the surrounding air has dropped by 5.5 degrees. There is now a 2 degree F differential, and the air is about to do the locomotion. It rises on its own because it's warmer than the surrounding air. There may not be a free lunch, but there is a free ride. While the atmosphere was neutrally stable with respect to the unsaturated parcel of air, it is now unstable due to saturation of the rising parcel.

Clouds and Atmospheric Stability

By now you want to know what you know, and know why you care. You're ready to make a synaptic jump and begin contemplating some of the atmosphere's great mysteries.

Have you ever wondered why *cumulus clouds* (Figure 37) are associated with unstable air and *stratus clouds* (Figure 38) go with stable air? Maybe you've looked at clouds all your life and *not* known there was such an association. Chalk one up for learning and latent heat.

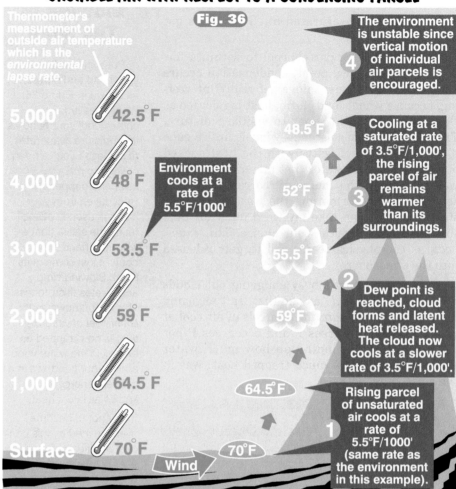

UNSTABLE AIR WITH RESPECT TO A CONDENSING PARCEL

Fig. 36

Thermometer's measurement of outside air temperature which is the environmental lapse rate.

5,000' 42.5° F
4,000' 48° F
3,000' 53.5° F
2,000' 59° F
1,000' 64.5° F
Surface 70° F

Environment cools at a rate of 5.5°F/1000'

4 The environment is unstable since vertical motion of individual air parcels is encouraged.

48.5°F

3 Cooling at a saturated rate of 3.5°F/1,000', the rising parcel of air remains warmer than its surroundings.

52°F
55.5°F
59°F

2 Dew point is reached, cloud forms and latent heat released. The cloud now cools at a slower rate of 3.5°F/1,000'.

64.5°F

1 Rising parcel of unsaturated air cools at a rate of 5.5°F/1000' (same rate as the environment in this example).

70°F Wind

A rising parcel of unsaturated air (i.e., no cloud forming) being moved up a mountain slope cools at the same rate as the environment (step 1). So far the atmosphere (the environment) is neither stable nor unstable; it's neutrally stable. When the parcel becomes saturated and a cloud forms (step 2), it releases its latent heat, which warms the body of the rising parcel (the cloud). Thus, the cloud remains warmer than its environment since this particular cloud parcel cools at only 3.5°F/1,000' (step 3). The parcel now rises on its own without the help of wind. The atmosphere is considered unstable since it encourages the parcel (once it's given a shove upward, of course) to rise.

Your Guess Is as Good as Mine

Point to Remember: Professor Bob Big Kahoona

Don't do anything crazy in an airplane or you'll end up on a daytime TV talk show like Oprah.

Meteorologists can predict the stability of the atmosphere by examining the environmental lapse rate, the amount of moisture in the air, and the opportunities for the air being lifted. While this isn't an exact science, they do fairly well with their predictions.

At least they are more accurate than seismologists (earthquake scientists). A friend from Ohio was visiting me in Los Angeles when a large earthquake struck. He remembered reading about what to do in a quake, so he ran under a door frame. The quake immediately stopped. He replied, "Hey, this stuff really works."

Geesh! I fell over laughing...in my newly sunken living room.

When an air parcel moves within unstable air, its direction is upward. Cloud formations tend to accumulate vertically, as you can see in Figure 37. Cumulus accumulate. As these clouds build, they eventually release their condensed water in the form of intermittent, showery-type precipitation. It's not unusual to see rain appear beneath a cumulus and, shortly thereafter, disappear.

Since cumulus clouds form in unstable air, there is a lot of vertical motion in the atmosphere. Dirt, dust, haze and other pollutants are drawn upward and redistributed to neighboring areas. That's why cumulus clouds normally correlate with decent-or-better visibility. All this vertical motion, of course, produces turbulence, which is a common phenomenon near or under cumulus clouds. Figure 37 also lists the conditions typically encountered when cumulus clouds are present.

When an air parcel moves in stable air, the resulting motion is more horizontal than it is vertical. The parcel of air doesn't develop the temperature difference with its environment that encourages vertical motion. If an air parcel is given a shove up the side of a mountain, it can eventually cool enough to condense and form a cloud. Then, when given an opportunity, the parcel of air sinks back to its original level on the other side of the mountain. During the process, stratus, or straight type, clouds develop, as shown in Figure 38.

CUMULUS CLOUDS ARE ASSOCIATED WITH:
1. Unstable air
2. Good visibility
3. Showery type precipitation
4. Turbulent conditions

Fig. 37

STRATUS CLOUDS ARE ASSOCIATED WITH:
1. Stable air
2. Poor visibility
3. Drizzle type precipitation
4. Smooth flying conditions

Fig. 38 © Björn Schick - Fotolia

Nearer My Cloud to Thee, But How High Are You?

Just how high up *is* that cloud? Good question. Sometimes you can get an ATIS answer, but there's a way to figure out for yourself the approximate height of the bottoms of cumulus clouds.

Because atmospheric pressure affects the dew point, the dew point will decrease approximately 1 degree F for every thousand foot altitude gain. Couple this with the understanding that a rising parcel of unsaturated air cools at a rate of 5.4 degrees F per thousand feet (2.5 degrees C per thousand feet), and you get the dew point and temperature converging at a rate of 4.4 degrees F per thousand feet.

So what? Well, when the temperature and dew point come together, water vapor condenses in the parcel and clouds form. To *estimate* the height of the cloud bases, simply find the difference between the temperature and dew point and divide this by 4.4 degrees F (or 2.5 degrees C if using Celsius). The number you get is the height of the cloud bases in thousands of feet.

This method of estimating is only reliable with cumulus clouds, since they are usually formed by lifting and thus subject to the effects of changing lapse rates.

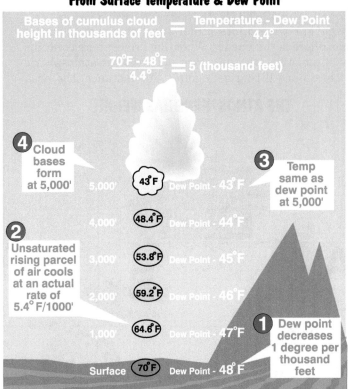

Determining Bases of Cumulus Clouds From Surface Temperature & Dew Point

$$\text{Bases of cumulus cloud height in thousands of feet} = \frac{\text{Temperature - Dew Point}}{4.4°}$$

$$\frac{70°F - 48°F}{4.4°} = 5 \text{ (thousand feet)}$$

④ Cloud bases form at 5,000'

③ Temp same as dew point at 5,000'

② Unsaturated rising parcel of air cools at an actual rate of 5.4° F/1000'

5,000'	43°F	Dew Point - 43°F
4,000'	48.4°F	Dew Point - 44°F
3,000'	53.8°F	Dew Point - 45°F
2,000'	59.2°F	Dew Point - 46°F
1,000'	64.6°F	Dew Point - 47°F
Surface	70°F	Dew Point - 48°F

① Dew point decreases 1 degree per thousand feet

You can estimate the bases of cumulus clouds by using the formula listed above. The dewpoint decreases approximately one degree Fahrenheit for every thousand feet of altitude gain. The actual temperature lapse rate in a rising air parcel for non saturated air is 5.4°F/1000'. Given this information, we can estimate where the temp and dew point will come close enough to form cloud bases (the 4.4° value in the denominator is the air parcel's lapse rate with 1° subtracted from it for a decrease in the dew point).

Stratus clouds are the result of water vapor condensing in air parcels that have little vertical movement. For instance, if the atmosphere becomes warmer with height (such as in an inversion), parcels of warm air are prevented from rising. Since these air parcels can't move vertically they tend to be flat on top, and any cloud tops present will take on a straight or stratified appearance. To see this in action in your very own kitchen, take a stick of cool but not cold butter in your hand and ram it into a plate, narrow-end first. Turn upside down, remove the plate, and you will have a fine model of a stratus cloud. Moving object meets immovable object. Squish. This is the Butterball explanation of stratus cloud formation, and no meteorologist has ever made it public. It is *not* a turkey.

It's no accident that stratus clouds often signal the presence of a temperature inversion. Limited vertical air movement in stable air means poor visibility. Pollutants, dust, dirt, and haze become trapped under the inversion much like dirt under a carpet. Any precipitation associated with stratus clouds is usually in the form of a continuous type of drizzle because stratus clouds typically contain smaller water droplets than those found in cumulus clouds and the clouds usually cover a wider area for a longer period of time. Figure 38 depicts the conditions typically found when stratus clouds are present.

Weather-wise pilots understand that water in the atmosphere is the enemy. When the atmosphere contains lots of moisture, there is great potential for atmospheric mischief once lifting gets going. For instance, the area

THE ATMOSPHERE HAS WEIGHT

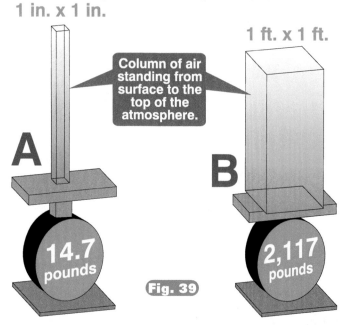

Air has weight. One square inch of air (scale A), standing from the earth's surface to the top of the atmosphere weighs 14.7 pounds. It also produces 14.7 pounds per square inch of pressure on the surface. A square foot of air (scale B), standing the same height weighs 2,117 pounds and produces 2,117 pounds per square foot of pressure on the surface.

NOW IS THE WINTER OF DISCONTENT

This problem is not restricted to wintertime, but seems to occur more frequently, and to be fraught with more serious consequences at that time of year. ALTIMETER SETTING, Kollsman Number, the old timers called it, but they meant the same thing: Station barometric pressure corrected to sea level. Elementary, you think. The voice in the speaker says, "Altimeter two niner four zero." So you turn the little knob until the numbers in the little window say "29.40." Don't you? Well, not always or we wouldn't receive any reports about it and we wouldn't have to deliver this sermon. If you set in the correct numbers, the altimeter tells you your altitude above sea-level. If you don't, it tells you something else, and that something else may turn out to be unhealthy.

Obtained ATIS. I mistakenly copied the altimeter setting as 30.59. We leveled at what we thought was 11.000'. The controller didn't advise us that we were at 10,000'. When we were given clearance to 3500' we descended and leveled off at 2500'. Controller advised we were at 2500'. We climbed back up to 3500' after resetting our altimeter. OVERLOOKED THE FACT THAT WE WERE GOING INTO A FAIRLY DEEP LOW PRESSURE SYSTEM. Fortunately, nothing serious happened this time.
ASRS Report

around Texas has a great deal of water vapor in the air (I should know, I go to Houston every summer for the humidity festival). The area around the Texas panhandle is called tornado alley because some of the world's nastiest thunderstorms swoop through this area. The Gulf of Mexico adds so much water vapor to the air that a fast moving cold front from the north often provides enough lift to create squall lines (lines of thunderstorms) hundreds of miles long. In other words, the fast moving cold front acts like a snow plow in that it scoops or pushes up large parcels of moist air that eventually become warmer than the atmosphere surrounding them. The results are thunderstorms that belch fire, hail, and electricity the like of which make a T. rex. dinosaur look like a sandbox sissy.

Understanding the difference in lapse rates between the environment and a rising parcel of air is perhaps the most important concept to comprehend. You're well on your way to being a real meteorological monster. Before you get too carried away with yourself, though, I must warn you that like most scientific models, the parcel concept is an attempt to make a simple statement about a remarkably complex real world. As a generalization, it works, and provides useful insights.

Differences in atmospheric pressure are just as important as temperature differences when it comes to making weather. For years you've listened to the nightly weather report and nodded when the weatherperson spoke of highs and lows. Now you're about to get the lowdown on what these terms *really* mean.

High and Low Pressure Areas

In a philosophy class I once took, the professor asked a very difficult question during our final exam. He really put the pressure on when he pointed to a chair at the front of the room and said, "Prove that that chair doesn't exist."

My buddy immediately asked, "What chair?" We laughed, the pressure was reduced and... and my friend failed. We speak of pressure metaphorically as compelling us to act or move in a certain, almost predictable way. Atmospheric pressure causes air to do the same thing—to move in a certain way.

As you might have noticed from our discussion of temperature and air parcels, there is a ceaseless, restless attempt to equalize any differentials in the atmospheric system. This

The tropical storm results from an enormous low pressure system.

AIR MOVEMENT FROM HIGH TO LOW PRESSURE WITHIN A VACUUM CLEANER

Fig. 40

LOW pressure created inside vacuum cleaner

??? High pressure air

A vacuum cleaner creates a low pressure center inside its container. Air outside the container exists at a higher pressure by comparison. This high pressure air rushes into the vacuum's hose toward the area of lower pressure dragging dirt along with it.

applies to pressure differentials, as well. Pressure differences are another way in which the atmosphere gets moved around, helping to create wind and weather.

Our atmosphere is composed of mega-billions of air molecules. There may even be more air molecules than the number of hamburgers cooked by McDonald's (but maybe not). Each air molecule is affected by gravity. This is why air has weight.

At the earth's surface, air pushes down with a pressure of 14.7 pounds for every square inch, as shown in Figure 39. That's a lot of pressure. The next time you tell someone that you're under a great deal of pressure, you won't be lying.

While gravity provides a constant tug on the air, the atmosphere still experiences variations in the pressure it exerts on the earth's surface. Sometimes, individual sections of air are forced upward or downward. Mechanical or thermal forces are often responsible for this movement. Regardless of the cause, small changes in atmospheric pressure can still be felt at the surface of the earth.

We've previously learned that air over the north pole is cooled and sinks. As the cool, descending air pushes on the surface, its weight is felt as higher atmospheric pressure.

Conversely, at the equator, air is heated by warm surface temperatures and rises. Rising air reduces the pressure it exerts on the surface, creating extensive areas of low pressure around the globe.

Variations in temperature, over water and land, cause changes in atmospheric pressure. Wherever there's a differential in the atmosphere, be alert, because I guarantee you *something* will happen to try and equalize it. In the case of pressure, the air moves from areas of higher pressure to areas of lower pressure. Moving air is what we call *wind*. You are probably the first person on your block (unless you live near a weatherperson) to truly understand what wind is.

Vacuum cleaners are wonderful inventions. They absorb dirt, dust, and small insects and do it by creating pressure inside the machine that's lower than the pressure outside, as shown in Figure 40. Air moves from the area of high pressure (outside the vacuum) to the area of low pressure (inside the vacuum), carrying the crud with it. Of course, it takes a motor and fan (which means noise) to do this. That's why my mother used to drive my dad crazy by vacuuming while he watched football. He'd become so upset that he would get up and move to another part of the stadium.

Sea and Land Breeze Circulation

Everyone knows it's usually breezy by the sea, but hardly anyone knows why.

Figure 41 shows a typical daytime sea breeze. Remember, it's called a *sea breeze* because that's the direction from which the air blows (from the sea). The sea breeze forms because land warms faster than water. Heating the land heats air lying next to it, causing the air to rise. This creates a small land-based low pressure area. Air rising over the land eventually cools by expansion and moves toward the ocean, where it begins to settle. It continues to cool (becomes heavier) as it makes contact with the cool water, thus forming an area of high pressure over the ocean. Higher pressure over the ocean forces air to move toward land, creating a breeze from the sea. A single-cell circulation pattern is established.

Later in the evening, after the land has had a chance to cool, airflow near the beach reverses direction (Figure 42). After sunset, the ocean retains more of the day's heat than the land. Land isn't generally heated to the depth water is, so it has less heat to lose and cools more rapidly. In the late evening hours, the low pressure center that was once over land is now over the water. High pressure now exists over the land where the air has cooled. A land breeze (blowing from the land) forms and airflow moves toward the water. The original single-cell circulation pattern is reversed.

HOW A SEA BREEZE FORMS

As land is heated by the sun during the day, the air next to the surface becomes warm and rises. Water takes longer to heat because water can absorb more solar energy before a temperature increase occurs. Therefore, during the day the ocean remains cooler than the land. Air over the ocean that's in contact with the cool water also cools and falls, creating higher pressure. Airflow is from the water toward the land, where the pressure is lower (thus it's called a *sea breeze*).

HOW A LAND BREEZE FORMS

The ocean heats to a greater depth than the land during the day. Thus, at night, the ocean remains warmer than the land. Descending high pressure air over the land moves toward the rising low pressure air over the ocean. Since the breeze is from land it's called a *land breeze*.

These two types of airflow—land and sea breezes—are miniature models of atmospheric circulation. Magnify them thousands of times and they become the large high and low pressure centers talked about by meteorologists.

Keep in mind that the terms *high* and *low* are relative. One man's ceiling is another man's floor. A low pressure center can exist simply because there are several higher pressure centers around it, as shown in Figure 43. Here's another way of thinking about the concept of pressure centers being relative to one another. You can spend a lot of time working out, pumping iron to look tough. Or you can just hang out with a bunch of sissies and weaklings and look tough by comparison. It's all relative. If the area surrounding a parcel of air becomes slightly cooler, this makes the central parcel of air warmer, thus lower in pressure by comparison. Air would then flow in the direction of this lower pressure, as shown in Figure 43.

Keeping It in Perspective

Keep high and low pressure areas in their proper perspective. High and low pressure centers are large masses of air—sometimes thousands of miles across—that descend and rise slowly, descending at rates from a few centime-

HIGHS AND LOWS

High and low pressure areas are measured by comparison. If the center of an air mass is slightly lower in pressure, it makes the surrounding areas higher in pressure. Similarly, if the surrounding areas are slightly higher in pressure, it makes the center area lower in pressure.　**Fig. 43** ters per second to thousands of feet per day. Within these slowly moving oceans of air, smaller air parcels move up and down, playing out any of the previously discussed stability scenarios.

It's important to remember that these high and low pressure oceans of air are the environments that smaller parcels of air move within. The environment is constantly changing (albeit slowly) because high and low pressure air moves. If the environment is slowly changing, atmospheric stability also changes. This is one reason why the atmosphere can be stable one day and unstable the next. *Tempest fugit,* and stability, too.

Highs and Lows on Weather Maps

On weather maps, high pressure and low pressure systems are represented by a series of contour lines (see Figure 44). High pressure centers are cooler and denser masses of air. Moving downward and outward, they rotate in a clockwise direction. Low pressure centers are typically warmer, less dense masses of air. Air moves inward and upward and rotates counterclockwise in a low pressure system. Right now you must be thinking, "Why does the air circulate counterclockwise in a low?" Hold onto your retrorockets Captain Midnight, we're going to cover that in detail on the very next page.

PRESSURE CENTERS ON WEATHER MAPS

Fig. 44

HIGH (clockwise)

1026
1023
1020
1017
1014
1011

LOW (counter clockwise)
1002
1005
1008

Isobars: Similar pressure along these lines.

1026 = **Barometric pressure in millibars**

Pressure centers on weather maps are created by barometric pressure readings from weather stations across the United States. The lines shown above are called *isobars*. The prefix *iso* means *equal* and *bar* represents *barometric pressure*. Therefore, anywhere along the isobar the pressure is the same.

This is what high and low pressure systems look like on a real weather map (known as the *Surface Weather Analysis chart*).

A wise man says, "Mother Nature very unfair. She often gives a pilot the test before she teaches the lesson."

These contour lines surrounding the highs and lows are called *isobars* (that's not an Italian ice cream cone, either). An isobar is a line connecting areas of equal barometric pressure. This is similar to the contour lines on an aeronautical sectional chart connecting areas of equal altitude. *Iso* means *equal,* and *bar* represents *barometric pressure*. Weather computers can automatically connect areas having similar surface pressure with lines. (People can do this, too, but people aren't used much to draw weather maps any more.) The result is a pattern like the one shown in Figure 44, which depicts atmospheric pressure distribution on a typical surface weather map.

Placed along each isobar in Figure 44 is a pressure value, stated in *millibars* (thousandths of a bar, which is the international unit of pressure). The isobar in the very center of the high pressure system depicted here connects all areas having a pressure of 1,026 millibars. Moving toward lower pressure (anywhere away from the high's center), the pressure decreases until the isobar connects pressure of 1,002 millibars in the center of the low.

Perhaps you've been feeling a little uncomfortable with Figure 44? Perhaps you wonder why the air doesn't flow directly from the high to the low as it does in a vacuum cleaner hose? Perhaps you have the latest copy of *Playpilot* hidden between the pages of this book and didn't think to ask this question?

Circulation in Highs And Lows: Going With the Flow

Air should flow directly from the high to the low because of something known as a *pressure gradient force*. This is the basic pushing force exerted on the air, causing it to move from a higher to a lower pressure, as shown in Figure 45A. Were it not for the Coriolis force, air would do just that. But it doesn't. As the descending high pressure air settles and spreads outward, the Coriolis force adds a right curve to its motion (Figure 45B). This explains the clockwise circulation shown in Figure 45E. The low pressure system, on the other hand, has air converging toward it. As air moves inward toward the center of the low, the Coriolis force also curves it to the right (Figure 45C). Eventually, the air is forced into a counterclockwise circulation around the low as shown in Figure 45D.

Because of these two forces—pressure gradient and the Coriolis forces—air circulation around a high or low flows parallel to the isobars instead of across them, as shown in Figure 45E.

Surface friction also has an effect on winds within 2,000 feet of the surface. This has a tendency to decrease wind speed as air is tugged on by mountains, trees and other terrain features. But as the air slows down it is less affected by the Coriolis force. This means the right curve added to the air diminishes slightly. This gives the wind the appearance of turning slightly left of the isobars within 2,000 feet of the surface, as shown in Figure 46. Over water, where there is less surface friction, wind curves left of the isobars by about 10 to 15 degrees. Over land, with greater friction, wind can curve 25 to 45 degrees left of the isobars.

Surface friction explains why weather maps depicting winds for high altitudes (more than 2,000 feet AGL) show isobars aligned differently

WHY AIR DOESN'T FLOW STRAIGHT

The pressure gradient (difference in pressure over distance) would cause air to flow *directly* from a high pressure area to a low pressure area if it were not for something known as the Coriolis force.

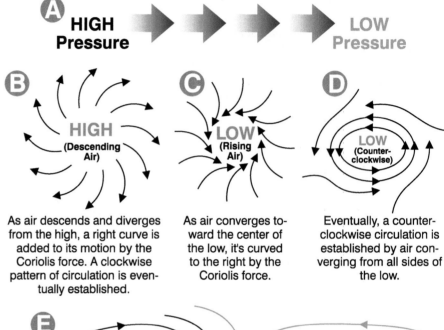

A HIGH Pressure ➤ ➤ ➤ LOW Pressure

B HIGH (Descending Air)

As air descends and diverges from the high, a right curve is added to its motion by the Coriolis force. A clockwise pattern of circulation is eventually established.

C LOW (Rising Air)

As air converges toward the center of the low, it's curved to the right by the Coriolis force.

D LOW (Counter-clockwise)

Eventually, a counter-clockwise circulation is established by air converging from all sides of the low.

E HIGH (Clockwise)　LOW (Counter-clockwise)

Fig. 45

Any parcel of air that moves is acted upon by two forces: the pressure gradient force (the push from high to low) and the Coriolis force (the right twist in the direction it moves). Therefore, instead of flowing straight air flows parallel to the isobars, rather than across them.

from maps showing surface isobars. Figure 47 depicts this difference with a constant pressure chart for 10,000 feet MSL and one for the surface.

As you'll see later, surface winds can give a false appearance of what the wind a few thousand feet above the surface is doing. Windshear is common when surface winds are calm and the wind at higher altitudes (a few thousand or even a few hundred feet AGL) is moving quickly.

Sometimes pilots are like surface winds—they give false appearances. There was a fellow who hung around our airport with a terrible reputation

for bragging. His mouth was so big that he could smoke a Duraflame log. He had the highest ratio of talking to listening in aviation, and claimed to have flown everything flyable. One day I asked him if he had some time in a tetrahedron (that's the big wind pointer resting on the ground). He said he had 30 or 40 hours in a tetrahedron. Must have been one that had hot air in it.

The Answer is Flowin' In the Wind

Sharp pilots on long cross country flights know how to take advantage of high altitude airflow to gain a tail-wind and avoid a headwind. On west-

EFFECT OF SURFACE FRICTION ON WINDS

Winds at 2,000'
or higher above the ground
flow parallel to the isobars.
Winds less than 2,000' AGL
are slowed slightly by surface
friction. Slower moving air isn't
as affected by the right twisting
effects of the Coriolis force.
Therefore, the air tends to flow
more directly away from the
high and more directly
toward the center of the
low. **Fig. 46**

Surface winds curve to the left
about 30° from the isobar direction

SURFACE WINDS VS. WINDS AT 10,000' MSL

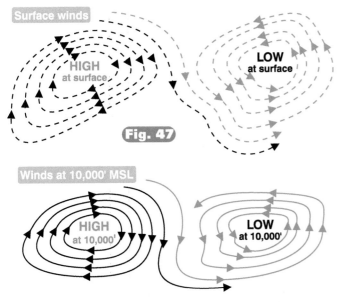

Examination of these wind patterns indicates that the surface
winds flow in a slightly different direction than winds at altitude
(10,000' MSL). Surface friction causes this difference to be 10° to
15° over water and as much as 25° to 45° over land with 30° being
typical (depending on how rough the terrain is).

TAKING ADVANTAGE OF HIGH ALTITUDE WINDS

Fig. 48

WIND CORRECTION ANGLES IN HIGHS AND LOWS

Fig. 49

Our airplane wants to maintain a ground track from A to B. Flying
toward a high pressure area requires a wind correction to the
right of the desired ground track (Airplane 1 and 2). Flying away
from a high is like flying toward a low. Thus, a left wind correction
is required (Airplane 3 and 4). Flying away from a low is like flying
toward a high, thus requiring a right wind correction angle (Airplane 5 and 6).

to-east flights, plan to fly north of the high and south of
the low as shown in Figure 48. You'll have a tailwind
most of the way using this method. On east-to-west
flights, plan on staying south of the high and north of the
low. This is called *pressure pattern flying*.

Pilots can tell whether they're approaching a high or
low based on the relationship between their wind correction angle and their ground track. For instance, in Figure
49 the airplane is flying a ground track from position A to
B. Airplane A flies into a high pressure area. Thus, in
positions 1 and 2, it needs a wind correction to the right
to maintain its ground track. As the airplane flies away
from a high, it must be flying toward a low. Approaching
a low requires an increasing left wind correction as
shown in positions 3 and 4. Flying out of a low, the air-

plane moves toward another high with the expected wind correction angle to the right of the ground track, as shown in positions 5 and 6.

You will always make a wind correction to the right when approaching a high, and to the left when approaching a low. If you ever want to determine the position of a low pressure center, simply stand with your back to the wind, rotate 30 degrees to the right (to compensate for the effects of ground friction) and stick out your left hand. It will point in the direction of the low, as shown in Figure 50.

As high pressure air descends, it eventually makes contact with the surface. Since it can't penetrate the ground, it spreads out in all directions. Meteorologists call this *divergence*. As we've already learned, the air spreads out away from the center of the high and the Coriolis force causes it to curve to the right, thus setting up a clockwise circulation.

ISOBAR SPACING AND WIND SPEED

Isobars spaced farther apart indicate a weaker pressure gradient with slower winds. A real weak pressure gradient is shown by a dashed line.

Isobars spaced closely together indicate that the pressure gradient (pressure change) is strong. High winds can be expected in this area.

HIGH

LOW

Fig. 51

DETERMINING THE LOCATION OF A LOW

Upper Winds

Surface Winds

Fig. 50

LOW

30°

30°

30°

Upper Winds

L O W

You can determine the location of a low pressure system by standing with your back to the wind and sticking out your left hand. Rotate 30° to the right to compensate for the wind's left shifting tendency due to surface friction. You're now approximately aligned with the isobars above the friction level. Your left hand now points toward the general location of the low pressure system.

Low pressure air converges near the center of a low. Having nowhere else to go as it converges from all directions, it begins to rise. Interestingly, convergence in the low accelerates the air. In much the same way a spinning ice skater picks up speed by bringing his or her arms in toward the body, wind speed in a low increases because air converges (is brought in) toward its center. This explains why wind velocities are generally higher around a low than a high.

Notice how the isobars are spaced in Figure 51. They are more closely spaced around the low than the high. Closely spaced isobars indicate a rapid pressure change. Rapid pressure changes mean faster winds. Isobar comparison around the high and low provides you with a good indication of wind speed in that system.

Weak pressure gradients (areas where there isn't much horizontal pressure change) are depicted with dashed lines, as shown above the high in Figure 51. Expect light winds in this area.

Weather Associated With Highs and Lows

In addition to wind direction and speed, high and low pressures centers have their own weather associated with them. As high pressure air descends, it tends to warm up slightly, decreasing the relative humidity. Clouds are less likely to form with decreasing relative humidity, and clouds that are present are likely to dissipate. Highs are generally associated with clear skies.

Lows, on the other hand, have rising air that expands and cools. If the air within the low approaches its dew point, condensation occurs. If this happens, clouds appear and the weather usually gets worse. Air that condenses in a low pressure system releases its latent heat, which adds to the heat content of the low pressure system. The low pressure area is now slightly warmer, causing it to rise faster. This further increases the chance that the weather in a low pressure area will continue deteriorating.

Remembering that you make a left wind correction when flying toward a low, you can use the Rule of L—left, low, lousy—to help remind you what weather to expect.

Keeping It in Perspective

Let's back off for a second in order to see the big picture. Large masses of air circulate around high and low pressure areas. Within these large masses, which heat or cool due to rising and falling air, individual parcels of air can in turn rise and fall, driven by changes in the environmental lapse rate.

Once again, you can see that the stability of the atmosphere is affected by several interacting variables.

Ridges and Troughs

Pressure patterns can take on rather unusual, elongated shapes. To the novice, they're just pretty; to the trained eye, they're pretty important. Figure 52

TROUGHS AND RIDGES

Fig.52

A trough is an extended area that's lower in pressure than the area on either side of it. Circulation is counterclockwise but not closed since the isobars aren't connected. A ridge is an extended area of pressure that's higher than the pressure on either side of it. Circulation is clockwise and, like the trough, isn't closed because the isobars aren't connected.

TROUGHS AND RIDGES

Ridge contains diverging air (moving downward)

Trough contains converging air (flowing into and up)

Fig. 53

A trough is a "V" or "U" shaped, extended area of low pressure. Think of it being similar to a valley or depression that draws air into it in much the same way a low pressure area draws air into it. This drawing-in or "convergence" causes air to ascend and, depending on its stability, might be the source of poor weather. A ridge, on the other hand, can be thought of as a "V" or "U" shaped, extended mound of descending, high pressure air. Good weather is usually associated with a ridge.

shows an extended area of a high and a low pressure center.

An elongated area of low pressure is known as a trough (pronounced *TROFF*). The pressure along this line is lower than the pressure on either side. Notice how the isobars show counterclockwise circulation at the trough line but don't form a closed circulation pattern. A trough frequently delineates the boundary between two different pressure centers. Just as pigs gather at a pig trough, storms gather at an atmospheric trough.

Perhaps the best way to think about a trough is to consider it, metaphorically, to be like a valley, as shown in Figure 53. The floor of the valley is lower than the mountains bordering it. Given the chance, water would easily flow into this valley. In a similar way, a trough allows air to converge (to flow into it). Of course, the air doesn't really sink into the trough, it just flows toward the lower pressure and rises. The concept of a trough simply makes it easier for meteorologists to visualize the way air flows.

An elongated area of high pressure is known as a ridge as shown in Figure 53. The pressure is higher along the center of the ridge than it is on either side. Think of a ridge as a mountain of piled up, heavy, descending air. The circulation of air along the isobars at a ridge line is clockwise, but the isobars don't form a closed circulation. In other words, they still have descending air but it doesn't follow typical clockwise circulation around a specific center point. Ridges exhibit characteristics similar to highs, with descending air and a minimum of cloudiness and precipitation.

But highs and lows are associated with more than the horizontal flow of air. These pressure centers attract or repel massive moving wedges of air known as frontal systems.

Frontal Systems

Several years ago a pilot friend lifted off in his small Cessna, failed to correct for a crosswind and drifted on a collision course toward the tower. The controller called and said, "Hey! Cessna 32 Bravo, what are your intentions?" My buddy replied, "I intend to avoid the tower...if I'm not too busy talkin' on the radio!" The pilot and the controller had a little confrontation. Likewise, air masses of different densities that bump into one another can also cause a confrontation. We call this confrontation a *front*, which is the battleground where these air masses meet.

Frontogenesis is about frontal formation (as *Genesis*, the first book of the Old Testament, is about how the universe formed). It's about two air masses, having different properties, that bump into one another and battle it out.

At first glance, you'd think the air would just sort of mix itself together and everything would even out. It doesn't work that way because the differences in temperature result in a difference in density. Things of different densities, such as oil and water, don't mix readily.

AIR MASSES AND SOURCE REGIONS

Maritime Polar (MP)
Cold and moist with a tendency to become very unstable when passing over warmer areas. Thunderstorms possible.

Continental Polar (CP)
Cold surface temperatures, low moisture content and, especially in its source region, has great stability in the lower layers.

Fig. 54

Maritime Tropical (MT)
Very humid, warm and often the most unstable air of all.

Continental Tropical (CT)
Dry, hot and unstable, but due to absence of water vapor, produces few showers.

The zone of transition between air masses of different densities is called a *front*. Think of it as the place where the weather action is, and often the place you as a pilot *don't* want to be. This is one kind of action you can definitely live without.

Frontal systems start with large air masses. These masses of air take on the characteristics of their source region (the land or water over which they form and originate). This occurs in much the same way people take on dialects of the local culture. I had a friend who spent 10 years in Texas and took on some of the local dialect. I still catch her saying, "fixin' to." I asked her if she was working on her instrument rating and she said, "I'm fixin' to." I replied with, "Well, then why don't you fix another one, that way you can be fixin' three." I'm lucky I'm not fixin' my tooth.

Fronts, like people, are often very different. Figure 54 depicts the source regions for the different air masses that affect weather in the United States. *Continental polar* air masses come from where Santa Claus lives— near the north pole. These are dry, cold air masses. *Maritime polar* comes from the same latitudes but the air is more moist because it originates over water. *Maritime tropical* air masses are born over heated, moist tropical waters, meaning they are hot and full of water vapor. This also means there is a tremendous amount of latent heat energy trapped inside the air (look out for thunderstorms). And *continental tropical* air masses are typically hot, dry, and unstable at low levels. The instability makes for bumpy flying but good visibility. Rain showers are virtually nonexistent as afternoon relative humidities drop to 10% or less.

Really Unusual Teaching Methods

There's nothing like letting a student experience the weather first hand. I always say, "To learn the weather, you gotta feel the weather." That's what I tell my students...when I can get a student.

The Polar Front

A cap of dense, cold air sits over the north polar region (Figure 55A). This undulating, amoeba-shaped mass of cold air comes from the cool air descending at the poles. Moving southward, this cap of cold air flows from the east, forming a band of winds known as the polar easterlies. The *polar front* is the zone between the cold polar easterlies and the warmer prevailing westerlies.

Several protrusions or waves of cold air occur along this frontal zone. There can be three to seven long waves existing globally at any one time. These long, protruding waves of cold air are anything but stationary. Plunging and retreating like the probing tentacles of an octopus, these waves advance southward in one area and retreat northward in another. It's this advance and retreat that we, as ground observers, experience as frontal movement.

THE POLAR FRONT

Polar cap in winter

Polar cap in summer

Fig. 55

The polar front consists of a cold cap of air centered over the north pole. Air over the pole descends and is cooled by a cold source region. Moving southward, this descending, high pressure air curves to the right, forming winds known as the polar easterlies. This mass of air is responsible for much of the weather we experience in North America. Cold air overtaking the warmer air of the westerlies forms steep-sloped cold fronts as shown by Globe A. Warmer air replacing receding cooler air forms shallow-sloped warm fronts as shown in Globe A. In the summer months the polar front doesn't extend as far south as it does in winter as shown by Globes B and C.

Fig. 56

FRONTAL TYPES

Icicles (triangles) represent the cold front and point in the direction it's moving (A). Half-suns or beads of sweat (B), represent the warm front and similarly point in the direction it's moving. A stationary front is indicated by icicles and beads of sweat on opposite sides of a frontal line (C). Beads of sweat and icicles pointing in the same direction indicate that the faster moving cold front has overtaken and undercut the slower moving warm air (D). This is called an *occluded front*.

An *occluded front* results when a cold front (A) overtakes the warm front (B). (See page L55.)

During winter, a long cold wave of this air can plunge down into the tropics, as shown in Figure 55B. A cold wave advancing southward in one area can allow the introduction of warm tropical air moving northward. Winter weather is characterized by a longer, more protruding polar front, as shown in 55B. The polar front is less wave-like in the summer (Figure 55C).

If you're really interested in how small storms form along the polar front see Postflight Briefing #11-1.

Different Types of Fronts

As a plunging long wave of cold air moves southward, it overtakes warmer, moister air. Hello, *cold front* (Figure 56, position A). Little blue triangles (think of them as icicles) represent the direction of cold front movement. Warm tropical air fills in the receding side of the long cold wave, forming a *warm front* (position B). Warm fronts are represented by red half circles (think of these as beads of sweat). As cold and warm fronts advance and retreat, weather constantly takes on new faces. Sometimes the warm and cold air butt up against one another and neither moves. This is called a *stationary front* (position C). Sometimes the cold front catches up to and lifts the warm air ahead of it forming an *occluded front* (position D).

Pressure falls as fronts approach. If you've ever spent time with a barometer, you will have seen this effect firsthand. It happens because fronts are often found along low pressure

FRONT FOUND ALONG A TROUGH

Polar Easterlies

Cold Air

Polar Easterlies

High

Low pressure trough:
isobars bend but are not enclosed

Fig. 57

Fronts are often found along low pressure troughs. According to our definition, a trough is an extended "V" or "U" shaped area of low pressure. Circulation in a trough is counterclockwise but not closed (i.e., the isobars don't connect). As you can see, the trough shown above meets these requirements. Because of the convergence in a trough, it's usually associated with bad weather (such as the cold front within it).

CONVERGENCE IN A LOW PRESSURE TROUGH

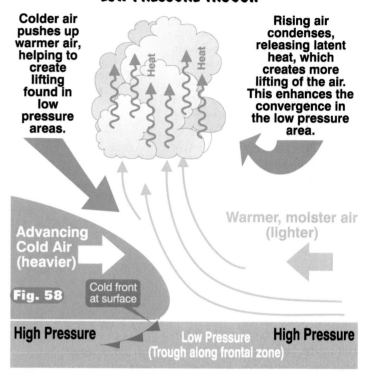

Colder air pushes up warmer air, helping to create lifting found in low pressure areas.

Rising air condenses, releasing latent heat, which creates more lifting of the air. This enhances the convergence in the low pressure area.

Advancing Cold Air (heavier)

Cold front at surface

Fig. 58

Warmer, moister air (lighter)

High Pressure   Low Pressure (Trough along frontal zone)   **High Pressure**

When birds and other airplanes are flying in the opposite direction, this should cause you concern.

troughs. Figure 57 depicts this process. Notice that the cold front lies along the border between two high pressure areas. As the front approaches, the pressure falls. It increases after frontal passage, since a high pressure area lies behind the front. But, why is the area along the front associated with a trough or area of low pressure?

Figure 58 shows the cold front air mass approaching a warmer air mass. Cold air is heavy, so it easily slips under the warmer air. As it does, it lifts the warmer air (which usually contains a lot of moisture). Given sufficient lift and lapse rate, it condenses and releases its latent heat. Heat released into the air enhances upward movement, intensifying the low pressure along the front. Simply stated, the frontal zone itself helps intensify the trough's low pressure. (While there are other reasons for trough formation, this gives you a basic understanding of how troughs form and what they do).

Remember, the trough is a line where the pressure is lower than on either side of the line, and where the isobars form a counterclockwise curvature but don't form a closed circulation. Along the cold front in Figure 57, the isobars are elongated diagonally in a downward and upward direction. Air flows in a counterclockwise circulation but it's not the typically smooth, circular flow of a low pressure center. In other words, the isobars look pinched and bent along the trough axis.

Polar cold fronts tend to move toward the low pressure trough, as shown in Figure 59. Keep in mind that high and low pressure centers move, so their associated

POLAR FRONT MOVES TOWARD LOW PRESSURE TROUGH

Fig. 59

High

Front Movement toward trough

High

Low pressure trough:

High

Front Movement toward trough

High

Low pressure trough:

Polar cold fronts tend to move in the direction of the low pressure trough. Think of the trough as drawing the frontal system into it as water might be drawn into a trough or depression on the earth's surface.

WIND SHIFT ACROSS A FRONT

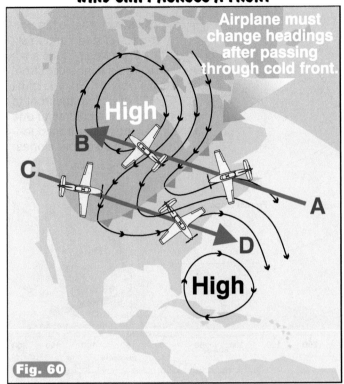

Airplane must change headings after passing through cold front.

High

High

B
C
A
D

Fig. 60

One of the indications of frontal passage is a wind shift. The airplane above, flying from position A to B and from C to D, must change its heading to the right to stay on course.

troughs move. You can think of the front being drawn along with the trough, much like a horse is drawn to a carrot (or as renter pilots are drawn to airplanes with broken Hobbs meters). There are many variables affecting the intensity of a low pressure trough—high altitude winds, intensity of upper-level convergence, latent heat of the air, to name just a few. Meteorologists go to school for many years to figure out how all these variables interact. So, if you can't predict the weather perfectly after reading this chapter, don't feel bad (the meteorologists can't either, and they paid for all that schooling).

Your job is to gain enough knowledge about weather to make some basic predictions. This is why I went to school to study psychology—to allow me to predict human behavior. A friend of mine used to work as a baggage handler for an airline when people used stairs instead of jetways to board airliners. During the boarding process, he delighted in making the passengers very nervous. He would walk over to the engine with a broom handle, hit the jet engine three times, then walk under the cockpit and yell, "OK, try it now." As I originally predicted, he's no longer working for the airline.

You'll become equally good at predicting weather by understanding a few basic weather principles.

Discontinuities Across a Front

Recall that a front is a boundary or transition zone separating air masses having different properties. As you cross a front, these properties change or become discon-

tinuous. When in an airplane, temperature is the most easily recognized discontinuity across a front.

Pilots flying across a front are likely to notice a sharper temperature change at lower altitudes than higher ones where air tends to become more homogenous. Since relative humidity varies with the moisture content of the air, as well as the temperature of the air, you should also expect changes in dew point with frontal passage. (My grandpa always got upset after cold frontal passage when we left the house door open. He'd yell, "Hey, I'm not paying to heat the neighborhood." You can probably tell that he desperately needed a course in thermodynamics!)

A change in wind direction and intensity is another good indication of frontal passage. Figure 60 shows an airplane flying from A to B across a cold front. On the east (right) side of the cold front the wind is from the left, requiring a left crab angle to maintain a straight ground track. On the west (left) side of the cold front the wind is from the right, requiring a right crab angle to maintain a straight ground track. Wind shifts from left to the right are an additional way pilots know they are crossing a frontal area. Direction of travel is irrelevant. Notice that a pilot flying from C to D still experiences a wind shift from left to right.

A stationary observer on the ground will notice a shift in wind with frontal passage. By the time the cold front in Figure 60 moves past position A, the wind will shift from a southerly (from the bottom of the page) to a northwesterly (from top of page) direction.

Aside from temperature, dew point, and wind shift, a falling then rising barometer is another good indication of frontal passage. As the front approaches, barometric pressure lowers. In other words, the altimeter settings for local airports along your flight path are reporting consistently lower altimeter settings. Altimeter settings rise as the high pressure air behind the front approaches.

WET PSEUDO ADIABATIC LAPSE RATE

The infamous aviation weather lecture has always been known to produce a carnival-like atmosphere in the classroom.

Cold Front Characteristics

A cold air mass overtaking a warm air mass is called a cold front. Cold air, being heavier than warm air, moves along the surface, pushing warmer air up in a bulldozer-type action. Because of its consistency and surface friction, the leading edge of the cold air tends to stick to the surface, forming a steeply sloped frontal edge, as shown in Figure 61. Faster moving cold fronts have steeper frontal slopes than slower ones.

Frontal steepness is relative. To me, a set of stairs leading up to a children's slide is steep. To a mountain climbing friend, the face of Yosemite's El Capitan is steep (at least that's what he told me in the hospital emergency room). Cold frontal slopes range on a meteorological scale of 1/50 (that's steep) to 1/150 (not too steep) and average about 1/80. A slope of 1/80 means that 80 miles behind the point where the cold front is at the surface, the top of the cold air would be 1 mile above the ground (Figure 61).

Figure 61 shows a cross sectional view of the cold front. The diagram is exaggerated for clarity, since the cold air is nowhere near as tall, relative to its length in this picture. A more realistic vertical versus horizontal view of this front is shown at the bottom of the diagram. With tops of cold air ranging up to 25,000 feet, the cold front occupies a relatively small vertical slice of the atmosphere.

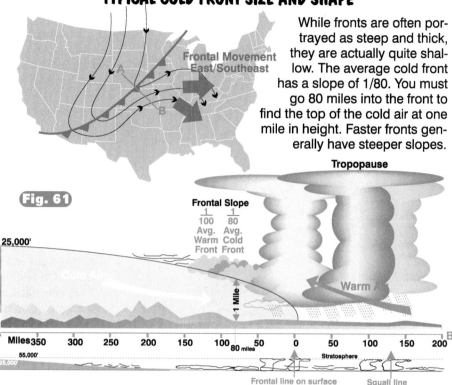

TYPICAL COLD FRONT SIZE AND SHAPE

While fronts are often portrayed as steep and thick, they are actually quite shallow. The average cold front has a slope of 1/80. You must go 80 miles into the front to find the top of the cold air at one mile in height. Faster fronts generally have steeper slopes.

In the Northern Hemisphere, strong cold fronts are usually oriented in a northeast to southwest direction and move toward the east and southeast, as shown in Figure 61. They are often followed by colder and drier weather. The cloudiness and weather associated with the front depends on the degree of stability and moisture content of the air mass ahead that's being lifted by the front.

Keeping It in Perspective

Earlier we talked about how parcels of air are lifted within their environment. Keep in mind that it's not the environment that's lifted, it's a parcel that's somehow pushed upward. Cold fronts provide an excellent means of lifting these parcels. Of course, the longer and steeper the front, the larger the number of parcels lifted. Therefore, the effects of stability or instability of the air are more widespread.

Two Types of Cold Fronts

Cold fronts can be divided into two general types: fast-moving and slow-moving.

Fast moving cold fronts have been clocked in excess of 60 MPH, which means you can be doing the legal freeway speed limit in some states and get run over by a speeding cold front. On average, they usually move at half that speed. Their speed is generally faster in winter than in the summer months.

Most of the cloudiness and precipitation associated with a cold front is located along and ahead of the area where warm and cold air meet, as shown in Figure 62. Because of the cold front's high speed, this weather is often the most hazardous that pilots encounter. Couple a fast moving, steep-sloped cold front with

COLD FRONTS AND SQUALL LINES

Cb - Cumulonimbus (cumulus cloud with rain)
Cu - Cumulus cloud
As - Altostratus (higher stratus cloud)
Ns - Nimbostratus (stratus with rain)

Fig. 62

Descending Cold Air
25,000'

Rising Warm Moist Air

Miles 150   100   50   0   50   100   150
Front on Surface   Squall Line

Fast moving cold fronts may generate a line of thunderstorms up to and beyond 150 miles in advance of the actual front. This line of thunderstorms is called a *squall line* and contains some of the nastiest weather pilots can imagine.

SQUALL LINE THUNDERSTORMS

Squall line thunderstorms may form 30 to 180 miles ahead of the cold front

Squall Line Thunderstorms

Fig. 63

Pressure wave

Cold Front

Lift created by wave

Garden hose

For reasons not clearly known to meteorologists, squall lines sometimes form in advance of a rapidly moving cold front. One theory has it that the cold front and its pressure system might generate a wave form (also known as a *gravity wave*) that moves in advance of the actual front. This is similar to the wave generated when you shake a garden hose. The wave travels along the hose. In a similar manner, pressure waves might travel ahead of the cold front, generating lift and creating thunderstorms in the unstable air.

unstable, moist air and you have the possibility for cumulonimbus (nimbus means rain) clouds, scattered thunderstorms and rain showers in advance of the front, as shown in Figure 62.

Fast-moving cold fronts can generate squall lines 30 to 180 miles in advance of and parallel to the front, as shown in Figure 63. Squall lines are lines of thunderstorms containing some of the most turbulent weather known to pilots.

Some meteorologists speculate that an isolated wave form may cause prefrontal lifting in the warm, moist air preceding the cold front. Think of this prefrontal wave (called a gravity wave) as the form appearing in a long garden hose that's given a good shake. This ripple of energy moves along the hose. A wave of air, moving in advance of the cold front, can generate enough prefrontal lifting (lifting in advance of the actual front) to instigate squall line thunderstorm weather.

Cirrus Clouds

Cirrus clouds have a thin, white feathery look and often form in patches or narrow bands.

Cloud Families

Clouds are divided into four families: High clouds, middle clouds, low clouds and clouds with extensive vertical development. The first three families of clouds have further classifications based on the way they are formed. They are classified as either cumulus, stratus, nimbus (meaning *rain*) and fractus (meaning *fragmented*).

High clouds are the cirriform family: cirrus, cirrocumulus and cirrostratus. Their bases typically range from 16,500 to 45,000 feet. The middle cloud family contains altostratus, altocumulus and nimbostratus. Their bases range from 6,500 feet to 23,000 feet. The low cloud family contains stratus, stratocumulus and fair weather cumulus clouds. Their bases range from near the surface to 6,500 feet. Clouds with extensive vertical development have bases ranging from 1,000 feet or less to above 10,000 feet.

Cirrostratus Clouds

These clouds are transparent, whitish, smooth in appearance and often produce halos.

Altostratus Clouds

These clouds are grayish or bluish sheets or layers and are often thin enough to partially reveal the sun.

Nimbostratus Clouds

These clouds are gray, dark and often block out most of the sun. They are rain clouds.
© Ieiana - Fotolia

SLOW MOVING COLD FRONTS AND STABLE AIR

Warm Stable Air

20,000'

Cold Air

Stratiform Clouds

Warm Air

Miles 350 300 250 200 150 100 50 0 50 100 150 200

Slow moving cold fronts are likely to generate more benign weather than their faster moving cousins. With a shallower slope, less intense lifting occurs. If stable air is being lifted, stratiform type clouds may occur over a large area.

SLOW MOVING COLD FRONTS AND UNSTABLE AIR

Warm Unstable Air

20,000'

Cold Air

Cumuliform Clouds

Warm Air

Miles 350 300 250 200 150 100 50 0 50 100 150 200

Slow moving cold fronts are likely to generate significant weather when the air being lifted is unstable. Cumulus clouds are likely along the frontal line.

Stratiform clouds associated with stable air in a slow moving cold front.

Cumuliform clouds associated with the unstable air of a slow moving cold front.

Slow-moving cold fronts, on the other hand, generally generate less-hazardous weather. Slower moving cold air forms a shallower slope, with less intense lifting of air (see Figure 64). Precipitation and cloud formation occurs in a rather broad band behind the cold front's surface position. Because the lifting is less intense, stratiform clouds are more likely to form if the air is relatively stable. Fog can also form in the rainy area. Unstable air, on the other hand, forms cumulus clouds and thunderstorms. Either way, the weather is confined to a rather narrow band along the front, as shown in Figure 65.

Warm Fronts

Warm fronts are typically associated with the small wave patterns moving along the polar front, as shown in Figure 66. Retreating cool air in the upper part of a small frontal wave is replaced by warmer, moister air from the south. Being heavier and denser, the retreating cool air is tugged by surface friction as it moves. Warm front orientation is more north-south or northwest-southeast, with the frontal position moving in a northeasterly direction, as shown in Figure 66.

Tugging creates a long shallow slope over which warm air rises gradually as it replaces the cooler air.

WARM FRONTS AND MOIST STABLE AIR

Warm fronts consist of warmer air overriding and replacing cooler air in the retreating part of the wave cyclone. Warm front slopes are very shallow, thereby producing less dramatic lifting as compared to a cold front. Additionally, warm fronts move slower (about 15 MPH on the average). Warm frontal weather is, therefore, distributed over a larger area for a longer time.

Fig. 66

20,000'

Warm Moist Stable Air

Cirrus

Cirrostratus

Altostratus

Nimbostratus

Fog

Cool Air

A Miles Frontal Surface 100 200 300 400 500 600 700 800 B

Stratiform clouds associated with warm fronts and moist stable air.

© Mark Rasmussen - Fotolia

WARM FRONTS AND MOIST CONDITIONALLY UNSTABLE AIR

Embedded thunderstorms (viewed from space) associated with warm fronts and conditionally unstable air.

Courtesy NASA

Fig. 67

Embedded thunderstorms are likely to be found in warm fronts containing moist, conditionally unstable air. Widespread precipitation is also likely to be found ahead of the warm front which generates fog and low stratus clouds. The frontal zone is also likely to have extensive fog and stratus because of high humidities induced from precipitation ahead of the front.

Because cool air is reluctant to give way to lighter, warmer air, warm fronts usually move at 15 MPH or half the speed of the average cold front. Warm front slopes typically range between 1/50 to 1/200 with an average of 1/100. A shallower slope means that warm frontal weather is distributed over a larger area than that of a cold front.

If the rising warm air is moist and stable, stratiform-type clouds develop in the warm front. The sequence of cloud formation encountered in advance of the warm front is cirrus, cirrostratus, altostratus and nimbo-stratus. Precipitation increases gradually with the approach of the warm

Frontolysis

If you go in for electrolysis, you expect to see hair disappear (you should also expect to see a great deal of your money disappear). *Frontolysis* is the process of frontal dissipation.

Have you ever wondered where fronts go? (If you haven't then you're probably still reading that *Playpilot* magazine.) As air masses travel from their source regions, they are modified by the type of surface over which they move. The winds aloft determine the trajectories of these air masses. Sometimes an air mass will control the weather in a region for a while. These persistent weather conditions are known as air mass weather. Yet even while controlling the weather, they are continually being modified. Eventually, cold air masses heat up and warm air masses cool down. With time, their differences disappear and they blend in with the local environment. They become one of the boys, so-to-speak (hey, girls too!).

front and usually continues until it passes. This sequence is seen in Figure 66. It's not unusual to have thunderstorms embedded in the stratus cloud mass if the air being lifted by the warm front is warm, moist, and conditionally unstable, as shown in Figure 67.

Widespread precipitation ahead of a warm front often causes low stratus and fog to form. The precipitation raises the humidity of the cold air to saturation. This and other related effects produce low ceilings and poor visibilities over a wide area. The warm frontal zone itself often has wide areas with ceiling and visibility reports of zero (such a condition is called *zero-zero* in pilot talk, or *not with me in the airplane you don't* in passenger lingo).

If the retreating cold air has below-freezing temperatures, the precipitation can take the form of freezing rain or ice pellets (freezing rain accumulates quickly on airplanes making it very dangerous to pilots). This occurs because raindrops from the warmer air aloft freeze as they fall into the colder air below. In fact, freezing rain or ice pellets are usually good indicators that there's warmer air aloft.

Stationary Fronts

Sometimes the opposing forces exerted by air masses of different densities are of similar strength and little or no movement occurs between them. With little or no movement at the air mass boundary, a stationary front forms, as shown in Figure 68. Wind on either side of the boundary

blows parallel to the front rather than across it.

While stationary fronts are seldom (precisely) stationary, they usually move at a rate of less than 5 knots. The type of weather that forms is similar to that of a warm front, but it's less intense because very little lifting of warm air over cold occurs. An annoying feature of stationary fronts is that their weather patterns usually persist for several days, driving VFR pilots to new depths of frustration. Frankly, there's nothing worse than having bad weather persist for days as it often does in Europe. This is why the British definition of a UFO is called—the sun.

STATIONARY FRONT ON SURFACE WEATHER MAP

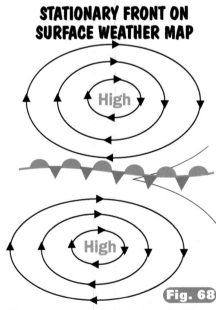

Fig. 68

When opposing air masses of different densities meet and no movement occurs, a stationary front forms. Wind on either side of the front blows parallel to the front's boundaries.

Thunderstorm Truth!

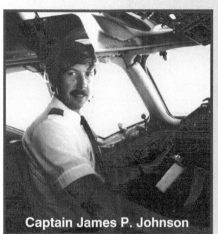

Captain James P. Johnson

Thunderstorms are a weather event that capture the attention of most aviators. Many pilots tell me that lightning is the most captivating feature. Lightning—the gunpowder of the Gods. It's nature's biggest spark. It's also nature's most deadly event.

Lightning kills 100-200 Americans every year. It kills more people in an average year than tornadoes, hurricanes and floods combined. Lightning strikes the earth over 14 million times a year. While its beauty can be truly striking, its striking power can be deadly.

Thunderstorm precautions should begin well before you get into your aircraft. As you know, a thunderstorm's gust front can affect a runway that is up to 15 miles away. As with gust fronts, so it is with lightning—the thunderstorm doesn't have to be overhead for lightning to strike. Lightning can discharge miles away from the thunderstorm into the rain-free area, where even patches of blue sky appear.

The mere presence of a thunderstorm near an airport should cause concern. As you study the storm, be aware that the most frequent cloud to ground lightning occurs just prior to the heaviest rainfall during the mature stage. Be cautious about disconnecting tie-down chains and other pre-flight activities at this time. Especially as you walk around a 20 foot lightning rod called the vertical stabilizer...
James Johnson, aviation meteorologist, Glenview, Illinois

Thunderstorms are one of Mother Nature's bad boys!

The Jet Stream

The *jet stream* is not a trout habitat funded by Boeing. The jet stream consists of one or more tubes of very fast moving air flowing west to east across the United States (other places, too, but we'll start close to home). The jet stream does several things (kind of like lowering your bird feeder to within 6 inches of the ground—now it's a combo bird and cat feeder). High altitude winds direct storm track movement across the United States, as well as providing tailwinds to pilots moving in an easterly direction.

It's kind of interesting to understand how jet streams form. If you share my interest, take a look at Postflight Briefing #11-2 for more information.

Thunderstorms

Thunderstorms are Mother Nature's bad boys.

Are we paying attention now? Good, because turbulence is unpleasant, rain is a pain, clouds make you crabby, but thunderstorms can and do cause pilots lots of grief. Along with ice, thunderstorms are something *every* pilot in *every* size of airplane is taught to avoid. It's not a question of "My plane isn't big enough to do that." In the case of thunderstorms, *nobody's* plane is big enough.

That's not to say that if you're caught in a thunderstorm, you are absolutely fillet of soul. Let's just say your survival opportunities languish.

A thunderstorm is one of the most impressive displays of raw power in existence. There are around 40,000 of these lightning-bolt, thunder-belching creatures roaming the planet on a daily basis. Your job is to avoid them.

If you could purchase a Mattel thunderstorm kit, it would include three items: moisture, unstable air, and some type of lifting force.

Moisture is a necessary ingredient of thunderstorms simply because it contains trapped energy, in the form of latent heat. The more moisture available in the air, the taller the thunderstorm monster can grow.

All the moisture in the world, however, won't help thunderstorm growth if the air is stable. A strong temperature inversion (very stable air) acts like a lid on cumulus clouds and stunts their growth. In the presence of unstable air, building cumulus clouds can heat up well beyond the temperature of their surroundings, creating conditions ripe for thunderstorm formation.

Finally, thunderstorms, like people, sometimes need a good kick in the pants (a push) to commence the growth process. A lifting force, in the form of wind blowing up a mountain, frontal lifting, surface heating or convective activity is often sufficient to start thunderstorm formation.

The (Not So Secret) Life Of a Thunderstorm

Thunderstorms have life cycles ranging from 20 to 90 minutes. They usually form in clusters of two or more cells, each in various stages of development. Thunderstorm cells have three stages: cumulus, mature, and dissipating. You can think of these as the beginning, middle, and end of a brief but very electric story. Let's examine each stage.

Cumulus Stage—The first stage of a potential thunderstorm is the cumulus stage. Although cumulus clouds don't always become thunderstorms, the initial stage is always a cumulus cloud, as shown in Figure 69A. Air parcels, given an initial shove by a lifting force (front, mountain or convective heating), form a small cumulus cloud in the unstable air. As the cumulus cloud grows, updrafts draw in more moist air from below. Latent heat is released as this moisture condenses. This makes the cloud warmer and accelerates its growth. The cumulus stage is characterized by updrafts that can be in excess of 3,000 feet per minute.

Have you ever heard of frozen birds falling from the sky? This is one of those "uh-huh, sure they do" stories that's true. Ducks (and other birds) flying beneath a building cumulus cloud can be drawn up into the cloud's belly. I'm sure the little guys have their power off and landing gear down, but they are unable to keep from ascending. They are promptly de-quacked, frozen solid, and spit out the top or side of the cloud, where they fall to earth.

Mature Stage—Thunderstorms are their nastiest when mature. This stage is characterized by updrafts, downdrafts, turbulence (sometimes severe), low level windshear, hail at times, ice, rain and lightning. This is the most dangerous stage of a thunderstorm's life cycle.

Toward the end of the cumulus stage, just before the mature stage, there is a lot of water in the cloud. The cloud droplets are very close together and give the cloud its crisp, well defined appearance. As more low level, moisture-laden air is drawn into the cloud, the condensation process continues producing additional cloud droplets in the updrafts. Pretty soon the cloud droplets begin bumping into each other and start combining, growing larger and larger. In fact, it takes about 1 million tiny cloud droplets to produce a respectable size rain drop. Gravity pulls on these droplets just as it does your airplane (and beltline). So, what's holding all of them up

The first sign of rain at the earth's surface indicates the beginning of the thunderstorm's mature stage.

Courtesy NASA

in the cloud? The only thing keeping the raindrops aloft is the updraft. As long as they are not too heavy, they are held aloft. The faster the updraft velocity, the larger the raindrops.

Eventually, a point in time is reached where the raindrops become so heavy that the updraft can no longer support their weight and they begin to fall. Yet, they're still growing as they collide with other cloud droplets. Once they get bigger than 5 millimeters, atmospheric drag breaks them apart into two smaller raindrops. Your first visual clue that the thunderstorm has reached the mature stage will be rain at the surface.

Falling water creates downdrafts, because rain drops tend to drag air along with them as they fall. The greater the rainfall rate, the greater the downdrafts. If you don't believe this, try an experiment the next time you're in your home-based karaoke club system—your shower. Run the water and notice how air currents swirl as droplets shoot from the shower head. This same principle is responsible for the downdrafts found within the cumulus cloud. With a combination of updrafts and downdrafts, the mature stage offers the greatest amount of turbulence and windshear. Hail is most likely to occur during this stage.

THREE STAGES OF THUNDERSTORM FORMATION

Fig. 69

LIFTING FORCES FOR AIRMASS THUNDERSTORMS

Heating of the earth creates convection or updrafts which provides a lifting force for airmass thunderstorm formation.

Ⓐ

Bob?

Ahhh, Bob's not here.

Earth intensely heated by the sun.

Air rising in a trough or a low pressure area can provide the necessary lifting for air mass thunderstorm formation.

Ⓑ

Trough

Fig. 70

Air rising orographically (over a mountain) can provide the lifting necessary for the formation of air mass thunderstorms.

Ⓒ

It's not unusual for thunderstorms to grow to 25,000 to 35,000 feet. In certain parts of the country they can tower to 50,000 to 60,000 feet, extending into the tropopause.

Airline pilots try to avoid being anywhere near thunderstorms. It's simply uncomfortable (and sometimes dangerous) for passengers. Consider that most airline lavatories have places to dispose of razor blades. How would you like to be shaving at 29,000 feet, hit turbulence, and come out looking like Van Gogh?

Dissipating Stage—Throughout the mature stage, downdrafts develop and updrafts weaken. Ultimately, downdrafts are all that's left in the once-mighty thunderstorm cell. But don't be fooled. Although aged on a meteorological scale, this geriatric cloud still packs a powerful wallop of gusts and turbulence.

The dissipating stage is often characterized by an anvil top (Figure 69C). Without continued vertical development, the thunderstorm's top is blown over by high altitude winds. The upper part of the cloud resem-

bles a blacksmith's anvil, which points in the direction the storm is moving. These same winds begin to disassemble the cloud's structure. With most of the water gone, the cloud is composed almost entirely of ice crystals, which changes its appearance. The crisp, sharp edges now look soft and fuzzy. Rain at the surface is now light.

Thunderstorm Types

The lifting action required for thunderstorm formation can be furnished by any of four sources: heating from below (creating convective currents), lifting by a front, air movement up a mountain, or convergence of air. Typically, thunderstorms form in air masses, in fronts, or over mountains.

Air Mass Thunderstorms—Air mass thunderstorms generally form within a warm, moist air mass and are not associated with fronts. They are usually classified as convective (heated from below) or orographic (mountain induced) thunderstorms. They are usually isolated and widely

scattered enough that pilots can safely navigate around them. The most important characteristic of an air mass thunderstorm is that it moves very slowly, making it relatively easy to avoid. What makes them tricky is that they are very hard to forecast.

During the afternoon or early evening, land masses can provide enough heating for air to begin rising and condensing. Figure 70A illustrates this process. With enough moisture and instability, thunderstorms form. Troughs or areas of decreasing pressure can also provide the necessary lifting for thunderstorm formation, as shown in Figure 70B.

Orographic Thunderstorms—Orographic thunderstorms occur when moist, unstable air is forced up mountain slopes, as shown in Figure 70C. When heating from below works in conjunction with other lifting forces (orographic lifting for instance), air mass thunderstorms tend to increase in frequency, especially during afternoon and early evening.

Sometimes thunderstorms are scattered along mountain peaks and safe passage around them is possible. When the conditions are right, however, you can have entire mountain ranges obscured by orographic thunderstorms. It's not unusual to have violent thunderstorms preventing passage for substantial distances in mountain ranges such as the Rockies.

Frontal Thunderstorms—Because fronts vary in slope and speed, thunderstorms associated with them vary considerably in intensity. Faster moving fronts usually produce the nastiest thunderstorms.

Thunderstorms associated with cold fronts are normally the worst, except for those found in squall lines. Both of these are associated with movement. Frontal thunderstorms usually form in continuous lines, as shown in Figure 71, and are relatively easy for pilots to identify.

Problems arise for pilots when thunderstorms extend along the frontal line. Circumnavigation is often impossible since the frontal line can extend several hundred miles and be packed with thunderstorms. The pilot's best option is to park the airplane, have a soda, and tell tall tales to older and wiser pilots waiting on the surface for frontal passage. I've done this on several occasions when thunderstorms loomed along my flight path. One time I landed at Garden City, Kansas (a real small town) and decided to rent a car to tour the neighborhood until the weather cleared. I walked into the car rental shop and said, "Ma'am, I'd like to rent a car." The agent said, "Ahhh, Bud's got it."

Thunderstorms can also be found in warm fronts. The gentleness of warm frontal lifting produces stratiform type clouds. These clouds can hide thunderstorms, as shown in Figure 72. These hidden pilot pokers are called *embedded thunderstorms*. Embedded thunderstorms are not easily visible to pilots. Fortunately, because of the

FRONTAL THUNDERSTORMS

Tremendous lifting occurs along the boundaries of a fast moving cold front. Given unstable air and a fast moving cold front, you could have thunderstorms stretching for hundreds of miles ahead of the front. This may require that you either sit out the storm or plan an extensive deviation (best to sit it out!).

shallow lifting, thunderstorms associated with warm fronts are usually the least severe of all frontal-type thunderstorms.

Warm occlusions can also produce thunderstorms. Rapid lifting of warm air occurs along the upper cold front, which sets off thunderstorm development, as shown in Figure 73. These thunderstorms are usually more severe than those found in warm fronts. And, in a similar fashion, they are usually embedded in stratiform clouds.

EMBEDDED THUNDERSTORMS

Embedded thunderstorms are likely to be found in warm fronts containing moist, conditionally unstable air. They present a problem in that you may fly under the stratus clouds of the warm front and encounter extensive areas of downdrafts associated with the thunderstorms. Fortunately, thunderstorms associated with warm fronts are the least severe of frontal thunderstorms.

THUNDERSTORMS IN A WARM OCCLUSION

The rapid lifting of warm air by the upper (overriding) cold front can set off thunderstorm development. This type of thunderstorm is usually more severe than those found in warm fronts and has the additional hazard of being embedded (hidden) by the stratus cloud mass.

BUCKLE UP—TIGHTLY

In cruise flight while enroute I was enjoying a normal flight on a nice VFR day. With the autopilot engaged, the last I recall was dialing up the VOR/DME about 60 miles out. My groundspeed was 180 knots. I awoke 5.8 miles north of the VOR at 6,500 feet. I had encountered light chop, then a severe area of clear air turbulence. My seatbelt was not as tight as it should have been and when encountering the turbulence, I was thrown up against the ceiling of the aircraft striking my head on the overhead console. When I regained consciousness, I had a small gash on my forehead. Moral: keep the belt tight.
ASRS Report

SQUALL LINE THUNDERSTORMS

Squall line thunderstorms may form 30 to 180 miles ahead of the cold front

Squall Line Thunderstorms

Fig. 74

Pressure wave

Cold Front

Lift created by wave

Squall line thunderstorms can form many miles in advance of a cold front.

Courtesy NASA

Squall Lines

As if one thunderstorm weren't enough (it is), these electric shows sometimes appear in extended lines —sort of a chorus line of trouble. Squall lines are associated with the most severe of weather conditions— large hail, destructive winds, tornadoes. Squall lines often develop 30 to 180 miles ahead of and roughly parallel to a fast-moving cold front, as shown in Figure 74.

Squall lines frequently accompany cold fronts, but a cold front is not an absolute requirement for their existence. Low pressure troughs, easterly waves, or atmospheric convergence can also produce squall lines.

Thunderstorm Turbulence

By now I hope you've gotten the idea that thunderstorms are *not* a party we wish to attend. Most thunderstorms have the capability to produce extreme turbulence, and up- and downdrafts that far exceed the capability of most light aircraft to cope. You do not ever want to fly *into* a thunderstorm, but with a little understanding and a lot of respect, you can often safely circumnavigate these airborne bullies.

One of the significant hazards produced by thunderstorms is something known as the *first gust,* which is illustrated in Figure 75. During the

mature stage, when rain begins falling from beneath the cell, a massive gust of cold air shoots down to ground level and spreads out in a horizontal direction. Winds of 20 to 50 knots and higher, within 150 feet of the ground, have been reported. Although most intense within 10 to 15 miles from the storm, the effects of these winds have been known to travel distances of 50 miles from the generating cell.

If you are on the ground (where you should be), the passage of a gust front resembles a miniature cold front. As it passes, the wind shifts and becomes strong and gusty; temperatures drop sharply; and because the air in the downdraft is cold and heavy, surface pressure rises. This cold air can linger close to the ground for several hours after the thunderstorm dissipates.

Seasoned pilots expect rapid changes in both wind direction and velocity. They watch for several signs of the first gust when thunderstorms are present. They keep an eye out for the first signs of rain beneath the cell. This usually indicates rapid changes in wind direction or velocity. Rising dust and flailing trees also indicate the presence of this gust. Before the arrival of a gust, the very best place to be is on the ground. Think carefully about taking off or landing in the presence of an anticipated thunderstorm. Sometimes it's better to wait for the storm to dissipate or move before taking off or to head for another thunderstorm-free

Fig. 75

THE THUNDERSTORM'S FIRST GUST

First gust, windshear, turbulence and rapid wind changes up to about 3,000' above ground level.

Roll Cloud

10 to 15 miles

Dust

Winds up to 100 knots at 150' AGL

Pilots may experience rapid changes in airspeed when encountering the first gust of a thunderstorm.

The first gust from a mature thunderstorm contains many hazards. With winds of 20 to 50 knots at 150 feet above ground level, this gust may cause dangerous airspeed changes close to the surface. Blowing dust, flailing trees and a sudden downburst of rain sometimes provide a visual clue to the presence of first gust hazards.

HOW VIRGA FORMS

Virga is rain that evaporates before reaching the surface. It's a sign of turbulence and severe downdrafts. Avoid it.

Fig. 76

Courtesy FAA

Cumulus Cloud

Altocumulus clouds (12,000' to 16,000') are known to produce virga.

Cumulus cloud produces rain.

Rain falls from a cloud into dry air (air with a large temperature-dew point spread).

Rain begins to evaporate.

Heat is taken from the air to evaporate water and air is now cold.

Cold air falls into warmer air and continues to accelerate downward creating very strong downdrafts.

Cold Air

airport for landing. Patience is the most often rewarded virtue in aviation.

Virga

Virga (variable intense rain gradient aloft) is virgin rain. It's called virgin because the rain doesn't touch the ground, as shown in Figure 76. Virga occurs when rain falls from a cumulus cloud (usually an altocumulus cloud) and evaporates before hitting the surface.

Think of virga as a "do not disturb" sign. As rain falls into the drier and warmer air beneath the cloud, it evaporates, as shown in Figure 77. You know it takes heat to evaporate water. Where does this heat come from? It comes from the air the rain falls through. This makes the air cold. The cold air falls, picking up speed as it descends. You can expect moderate turbulence and high-velocity downdrafts beneath virga.

My advice to you is to avoid flying directly underneath and near virga. You're thumbing your nose at the gods of turbulence and windshear if you do. If you see either virga or the downburst from a thunderstorm near the airport, I'd recommend making friends with your car until the phenomena dissipate.

Virga is "virgin rain" or rain that evaporates before being touched by the ground. It's sometimes associated with a severe downdraft phenomenon known as a "microburst." Microbursts produce downdrafts containing winds up to 150 knots that typically last from two to five minutes. Unlike a thunderstorm's downburst, which can cover areas of 10 miles or more, the microburst usually covers an area less than two and a half miles at the surface. An airplane attempting to take off into or land into a microburst might experience a temporary increase in indicated airspeed (A) as it flies into an increasing headwind. As it flies through the core of the microburst it may experience an increasing tailwind (B) which temporarily lowers its indicated airspeed.

Fig. 77

Wise man quote other wise man (Sun Tzu) who says, "Know the enemy (thunderstorms) and know yourself; in a hundred battles you will never be in peril."

Thunderstorm Avoidance

No one wants to get beat up. One time, while at school, a big sixth-grader came up, grabbed me and demanded my lunch money. I gave it to him and decided that would be the last time I'd hire on as a substitute teacher. What I needed was some form of defense, similar to what pilots need against thunderstorms. The best means of defense is avoidance.

Avoid thunderstorm cells by at least 20 miles (Figure 78). That may seem like a lot, but it isn't. Thunderstorm cells have tentacles of turbulence reaching out many miles. While turbulence is more frightening to pilots than it is structurally damaging to airplanes (assuming you're flying at or below maneuvering speed), it should be avoided. Besides, it bothers passengers and makes them think you don't know how to fly smoothly.

Flying between two cells is recommended only if enough distance separates them. Most pilots use a minimum of 40 miles separation between big cells for this minimum distance. Avoid flying directly underneath a thunderstorm cell. Once the cell becomes mature and rain falls, you can expect substantial downdrafts in the core of the rain shaft. Small airplanes don't have sufficient power to even think about out-climbing these downdrafts.

Lightning

Lightning is a phenomenon associated with every thunderstorm (without lightning you'd have no thunder). While not much of a problem during the day, it's a real thriller at night. The most important thing to understand about lightning is that it seldom affects airplanes in flight. What it does affect is you, the pilot. A reduction in night vision occurs when your pupils close as a reaction to the intense light display. It's not unusual for pilots to experience varying degrees of night blindness from lightning many miles away. Turning the white cockpit lights up as bright as

HOW TO AVOID THUNDERSTORMS

Fig. 78

20 Miles

40 Miles

20   20

Avoid

Dust

Come to think of it, that wasn't a good way to wash my airplane.

Avoiding thunderstorm hazards means that you stay at least 20 miles away from the side of any thunderstorm. Additionally, if you must fly between thunderstorms, make sure they are horizontally separated by at least 40 miles. Flying in the first gust or under the rain shaft of a thunderstorm is a very dangerous idea. Powerful downdrafts near a cumulus cloud could easily exceed the airplane's ability to climb safely.

possible is usually the best remedy for acclimating yourself to future flashes. This simply gets the eyes used to an elevated light intensity.

Turbulence and Windshear

Nothing bothers people more than an unsettling force they can't see. After all, isn't that what horror movies are made of? (Actually, the scariest part of the movie is that the producer took $7.00 from you.) Pilots experience the same thing with turbulence: it's there, but they don't know where. There are, however, several ways to anticipate and avoid turbulence and windshear. Let's start with an understanding of wind-

shear and find out when and where it might occur.

Windshear occurs when wind makes a rapid change in direction or velocity (or both). If you're standing by the roadside and a truck goes by, your pants or skirt start to wiggle. In one instant, the wind was calm; in the next, it changed in direction and/or velocity with truck passage. If it was a big enough and fast enough truck, the windshear might have ripped your pants clean off and taken a toupee along with it.

Windshear and its associated turbulence can become a factor during landing when winds flow over uneven terrain. Figure 79 shows how this

WINDSHEAR

Fig. 79

Wind   Wind

Be prepared for wind shear induced turbulence.

You should expect windshear and its associated turbulence when wind flows over uneven terrain, buildings and trees. If you suspect windshear while on approach, increase your approach speed a few knots above normal for better controllability.

can occur. Like water flowing over rocks on a creek bed, wind is upset, tumbled and churned as it flows over buildings, trees and other structures near the runway.

Often, windshear is hardly felt as more than a bump in low wind conditions. But given enough wind speed, say 10 to 15 knots, turbulence can be quite noticeable. Anticipating bumpiness, most pilots add a few knots onto their approach speed (perhaps 5 knots or more) for better controllability during landing. Of course, they'll make sure the extra speed doesn't cause them to run out of runway. Knowing where to expect turbulence prevents you from being shocked when it appears.

Convective currents are the most common form of turbulence you're likely to encounter in flight. As we've already seen, convective activity is often responsible for the start of thunderstorm formation. On a smaller scale, it becomes quite noticeable at low altitudes during approach to landing, as shown in Figure 80.

The uneven heating of land along your approach path causes variable concentrations of heated air near the surface. When the air is hot enough or when it's disturbed, heated air parcels rise, creating vertical currents of air. Air parcels cool as they rise, eventually falling back to earth.

TURBULENCE AND CLOUD FORMATION

Smooth

If the cumulus cloud tops are not too high, it's possible to climb on top to find smoother air.

Air generally stops rising at the top of a cloud because of the presence of an inversion. Thus, the air is smoother above the clouds.

Fig. 81

Turbulent

Cumulus clouds are visible indications of rising air. Flying underneath will generally be more bumpy than flying on top.

It's these rising and falling parcels that upset or disturb your glidepath.

Darker surfaces, such as plowed fields and paved roads, warm up quickly, producing rising currents of air. Conversely, green fields and small bodies of water remain cooler, creating downward currents of air. On approach, the glidepath you anticipate can require noticeable changes in pitch and power depending on the how strong the up- and downdrafts are.

The territory beneath cumulus clouds is a place that's almost guaranteed to give you the elevator effect (Figure 81). While not necessarily severe or extreme, it's often uncomfortable for passengers. Fair weather cumulus clouds are generally visible indications of rising and condensing air. The smoothest ride is generally found above these clouds. Of course, when cumulus clouds reach many thousands of feet in height, getting on top presents some difficulty for those airplanes without turbocharging. Therefore, circumnavigation of cumulus clouds is often the best means of avoiding turbulence.

Frankly, the only people who love turbulence are airline flight attendants. When it's bumpy, they don't have to serve food. This explains why flight attendants can sometimes be found in the back of the airplane jumping up and down, creating artificial turbulence.

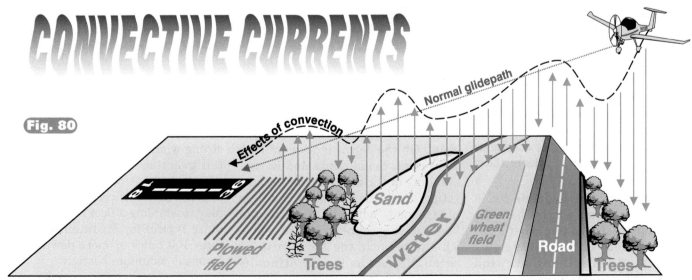

CONVECTIVE CURRENTS

Fig. 80

Effects of convection

Normal glidepath

Plowed field

Trees

Sand

Water

Green wheat field

Road

Trees

Convective currents caused by differences in terrestrial heating are quite common. Where different terrain exists, it's not unusual for pilots to experience considerable up- and downdrafts while on approach. Perceptive pilots can identify these convective currents by observing that plant life and water generally absorb heat and create downdrafts. Terrain, on the other hand, generally radiates heat and creates updrafts.

Mountain Waves

A mountain wave is not something you do from your airplane while flying over backpackers in the Rockies. A mountain wave is something much more interesting.

Throw a pebble in a still pond and wave patterns radiate outwardly, eventually traveling across the entire pond. If we move water over a pebble, a curve is added to the flowing stream. When air moves over a larger pebble—a mountain range for example—it also has a curve added to its motion, as shown in Figure 82. Given enough wind speed and large enough mountains, these wave patterns can travel hundreds of miles from their generating source.

Very stable air, moving above the level of surface friction, usually flows in a laminar or smooth, layered pattern. But when it encounters a large enough obstacle (a mountain range for example) a standing or mountain wave pattern is established in the mass of moving air. The standing wave is very similar to the wave that appears when a long rope is given a good shake at one end. The wave pattern appears to travel the length of the rope, eventually dissipating in a flip at the end. Mountain waves do something very similar.

As wind, usually with a velocity of 40 knots or more, encounters a sufficiently large mountain, a perturbation or shake-of-the-rope occurs. A wave pattern is induced in the once smooth-flowing (laminar) air. This pattern sets up a series of waves, in the downwind direction, with valleys and peaks that remain stationary. Given enough moisture in the stable air, condensation (from air cooling as it rises) occurs at the peaks of these waves.

Directly over the mountain top, a *pileus* or *cap cloud* occurs above the rough mountain surface (that's not Pontius Pileus either—wrong guy, wrong story). Farther downwind almond or lens-shaped clouds form at the wave crests. These clouds are called *lenticular clouds* because of their lens shape.

When very stable air moves across a mountain at velocities of 40 knots or more, a standing wave pattern may form. Similar to the shaking of a garden hose, airflow across the mountain sets up waves with crests and valleys. At the peak of this wave, the air is lifted, cooled and condensation occurs if there is sufficient moisture available. Lens shaped or *lenticular* clouds may form and appear to stand in one position. Underneath the lenticular cloud small rotor clouds may appear. Rotor clouds contain massive turbulence.

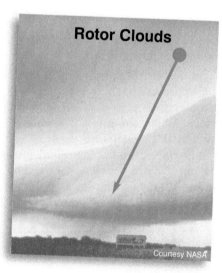

The formation of lenticular clouds is shown in Figure 82. As moist air rises on the upwind side of the wave, it cools and condenses, producing a cloud. On the downwind side of each wave crest, the air sinks and warms, resulting in the cloud droplets evaporating. Lenticular clouds differ from other clouds not only in shape, but because they appear not to move. This is because the air is rushing through them as they continually form on their western edges and evaporate away on their eastern edges. This is why they are sometimes called *standing wave clouds*.

When the air between the cloud-forming layers is too dry to produce clouds, lenticular clouds will form one above the other. Sometimes, when a strong wind blows perpendicular to a tall mountain range, the wave pattern extends up into the stratosphere. This produces a dramatic display resembling a fleet of UFO's. It is quite typical for mountain waves to form 100 miles or more downstream from the mountain barrier.

Directly underneath the lenticular clouds, a small *rotor cloud* can frequently be found at altitudes lower than the peaks over which the air flows. Rotor clouds result from the frictional effects of the surface and a lifting action from the rising crest of air. Air velocity is slowed near the surface, yet flows faster at higher altitudes. This adds a rolling motion to tubes of air, similar to the forward motion of a baker's rolling pin. Long cigar-shaped clouds form, each containing severe turbulence. These clouds are to be avoided like cooties were avoided in sixth grade. Violent turbulence will also be found in the up- and downdrafts associated with lenticular clouds.

Pilots must be especially cautious when flying near or around mountain waves. Many varieties of turbulence appear in these wave patterns. Keep in mind that mountain waves can and do form in dry air. The only problem is you can't see them. In other words, telltale lenticular clouds are not visible. With the lack of clouds in dry, fast moving air, pilots sometimes expect little or no hazard when approaching a mountain. Smart pilots, however, understand that winds in excess of 25 knots at mountaintop altitudes are sure to bring some degree of turbulence as well as up- and downdraft hazards.

Approaching a mountain on the windward side (the upwind side), as shown in Figure 83, you might find yourself climbing at several thousand

Fig. 83

Approaching the mountain on the windward side (the upwind side) you could encounter strong updrafts. On the leeward side (the downwind side), it's possible to encounter strong downdrafts that your airplane might not be able to out climb.

feet per minute with power completely reduced. While this produces one heck of a ride, it's not as dangerous as approaching a mountain from the leeward side (downwind side) with insufficient altitude.

Approaches to mountains with strong winds present should be made with caution, because the strong downdrafts can easily exceed the ability of a light airplane to climb. One way to minimize the risk if you are uncertain of conditions is to approach the ridge at a 45 degree angle. If downdrafts are encountered, you need only make a 90 degree turn to avoid the mountain instead of a 135 degree turn, as shown in Figure 84.

When attempting to cross a mountain over which high winds are blowing, you should approach the ridge on the leeward side at a 45° angle. If dangerous downdrafts are present, your turn away from the mountain is shorter than if you approached the ridge at a 90° angle.

Temperature Inversions And Windshear

Temperature inversions are common on the surface during clear, calm nights with little or no surface winds. Strong winds, however, can exist just above the inversion. Because air of different temperatures doesn't mix well, the warmer air on top tends to slide over the colder air below. This sliding, shown in Figure 85, becomes even more apparent when strong pressure differences exist, causing high wind speeds in the warmer air aloft.

If winds move in excess of 25 knots at 2,000 to 4,000 feet above the surface, you should expect windshear in the zone where the warm and cold air meet. Differences in wind velocities cause a tearing or churning of the air, producing eddies or turbulence in the shear zone. Pilots climbing or descending at slow speeds might find the windshear bad enough to induce a stall at low altitudes close to the ground.

If the inversion occurs within a few hundred feet above the ground, windshear can be a significant hazard. Imagine approaching an airport in a strong temperature inversion. Surface winds are calm at the airport, but you notice the winds at your altitude are quite strong. This often becomes apparent because of the rather large crab angle required

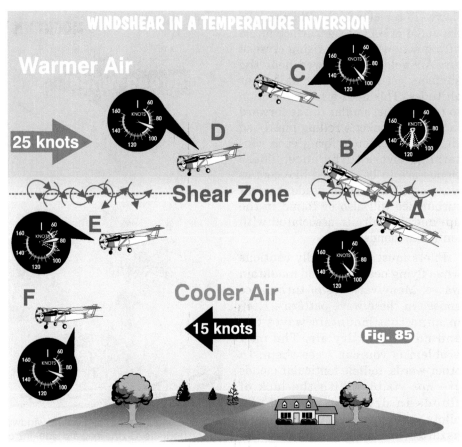

Windshear in a temperature inversion can cause sudden changes in your airplane's indicated airspeed. Airplane A is climbing through the inversion into an increasing headwind. At position B the indicated airspeed temporarily increases. As the airplane adjusts to the new wind direction, the indicated airspeed returns to normal at position C. Airplane D is descending into an increasing tailwind. At position E the indicated airspeed temporarily decreases, then returns to normal at position F. These indicated airspeed changes are more pronounced in heavier airplanes with large differences in wind speed.

to remain aligned with the runway. Noticeable differences between your airspeed and groundspeed is another clue to the possibility of windshear.

Suppose you encounter a sudden tailwind while descending through an inversion (Figure 85, D to F). Differences in wind velocity might cause you to lose a slight amount of airspeed as you descend into a tailwind (Airplane E). A sudden tailwind acts like a burst of wind from behind the airplane. Airspeed is momentarily lost until the airplane is accelerated by the tailwind, then it returns to the previous speed, as shown by Airplane F. This event becomes even more serious when the airplane is close to its stall speed and the temperature inversion is close to the surface. It's possible for the airplane to stall without sufficient room for recovery.

Suppose you were climbing through an inversion into a headwind as shown by Airplanes A, B and C. A sudden headwind, while climbing through the inversion, might cause a temporary increase in airspeed, as shown by Airplane B. While this isn't as serious as a loss of airspeed, the turbulence it produces can startle a pilot (no sense testing that triple bypass or a pacemaker's overdrive function if you don't have to).

Be cautious. Anticipate windshear within the first few hours after sunset. Also anticipate it before and after sunrise. These are the times when temperature inversions are most common. The presence of winds in excess of 25 knots above the inversion, with calm surface winds, is a good sign that windshear may be lurking. Add a few knots onto your approach speed to reduce the danger of a windshear-induced stall.

Actually Heard! Really!!

A pilot called in and said he was unsure of his position but he had a town in sight. Since they didn't have him on radar, the active controller told him to descend and look for the town's water tower, see what it said on the side, climb back up and tell him. Sure enough in about three minutes the pilot called back and said, "Approach, I found the water." The controller, looking rather pleased, asked, "And what did it say on the side?" The pilot replied, "It said, Seniors 1978."

Fog

Fog is a cloud that touches the ground. Fog comes in on little cat's feet, and casts its gloomy pall over the airport, putting an end to aviating for VFR pilots, and sometimes even for IFR-rated pilots. Fog is one of the most frequent causes of reduced surface visibilities and it's a real pain in the wings for VFR pilots.

Fog presents a serious problem because it can form in a very short time. I've seen airports go from three miles visibility to less than one-half mile in just a few minutes because of fog. Even David Copperfield would be hard pressed to make an airport disappear in as short a period of time. Many a student has raced an approaching fog bank to the airport only to lose the race. Figure 86 shows the reduced visibility experienced in fog.

Remember that the *dew point* is the temperature at which water will condense out of the air. It's a function of humidity, and the number is so crucial that it's one of the things you will hear on the ATIS broadcast. Small temperature-dew point spreads are conducive to fog formation. That's why fog is common in colder months. It can, however, form any time the air contains enough moisture, condensation nuclei, and cooling temperatures.

Unfortunately, there are a lot of ways to brew up a batch of fog. Cooling the air to its dew point is the

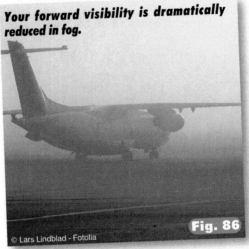
Your forward visibility is dramatically reduced in fog.
© Lars Lindblad - Fotolia
Fig. 86

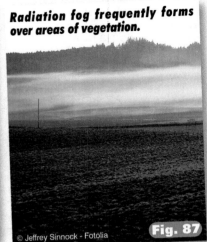
Radiation fog frequently forms over areas of vegetation.
© Jeffrey Sinnock - Fotolia
Fig. 87

most common means of fog production. Adding moisture to air near the surface also aids in fog formation. Precipitation from fronts is a common way moisture is added to the air. Fog is classified by the way it forms. Let's examine some of the different types of fogs.

Radiation Fog—This isn't the type of fog that forms near a nuclear power plant (we moved next to a nuclear plant and the farm across the street has 20 head of cattle. What bothers me is that the farmer only had 13 cows). *Radiation fog* is what happens when the ground radiates its heat away. On clear, calm nights, terrestrial radiation of heat cools the ground. This allows the air resting next to the surface to cool quickly. As air is cooled and approaches its dew point, water vapor condenses and forms a shallow layer of fog.

Radiation fog is very common at night and early morning hours. Figure 87 shows an example of radiation fog.

Areas of high humidity (rain soaked ground and vegetation) are especially conducive to the formation of radiation fog. This is why golf courses are common places for this type of fog. I've driven by these courses early in the morning and seen golf clubs popping out the top of a 6 foot layer of radiation fog. All you can see are funny little hats floating on the top of a 6 foot layer of fog.

I've even seen control towers standing above a shallow radiation fog layer at the airport. It's VFR for the controller but IFR for taxiing pilots. Bodies of water, despite their moisture potential, aren't a likely place for radiation fog to form. Bodies of water don't cool as quickly at night (compared to land), making radiation fog unlikely.

Winds up to about 5 knots tend to mix and deepen the layer of fog. Higher winds tend to disperse radiation fog. Solar heating of the earth after sunrise tends to dissipate radiation fog. Despite a fog layer, some solar heat makes it to the surface. This warms the ground, which helps dissipate the fog from below. Radiation fog also dissipates around its periphery first, where it's the thinnest. Of course, all this assumes a high altitude cloud layer isn't preventing a reasonable amount of solar heat from reaching the surface.

IT'S A LONG WAY TO A TIP-A-PILOT

The runway was tucked in close and parallel under a row of hills. The windsock was limp, giving no indication of the crosswind and turbulence higher up. Shortly after takeoff, I found myself fighting the turbulence with full and abrupt control movements. I heard my passenger remark that he didn't think my door was latched. It was good that I moved the throttle to its full-open position. My right hand was busy holding me in the seat. I hadn't fastened my seatbelt either!!! **ASRS Report**

HOW ADVECTION FOG FORMS

Fig. 88

Warm, moist air comes in contact with a cooler ocean surface, then condenses to form fog

Air warms and rises when it comes in contact with hot land

Warm Moist Air

ADVECTION FOG

Horizontal Fog Movement (Advection)

Lower Pressure (rising, warmer air draws fog inland)

Cooler Ocean Waters (perhaps caused by upwelling of colder water from below)

Land warmed by sun

Advection fog is very common near the coasts where it can move inland and quickly blanket an airport.

© JENNY SOLOMON - Fotolia

Advection fog, otherwise known as *sea fog* forms along coastal areas. When warm air comes in contact with cooler ocean waters, condensation can occur and form fog. Advection implies horizontal movement, thus this fog typically moves inland toward the area of lower pressure (caused by rising warm air from solar heating). Winds of 15 knots or more tend to lift the fog and form stratus clouds.

Some people speak of fog *burning off* rather than dissipating. I once told a student we could fly later in the morning after the fog burned off. He went home and told his mother he couldn't fly because there was going to be a fog fire at the airport. Geesh!

Advection Fog – Convection means to move something vertically; advection means moving it sideways. *Advection fog* is fog that forms elsewhere and comes to visit you. Sometimes called sea fog, advection fog is most common in coastal areas, although it can form in inland areas. As warmer, moist air comes in contact with the ocean's surface, air temperatures decrease and water vapor condenses. This process is shown in Figure 88. With slight heating, the pressure over land lowers, drawing advection fog inland. Advection means to move sideways, thus allowing this fog to live up to its name. Advection fog deepens when winds increase to about 15 knots. Winds above this speed tend to lift fog layers

into low stratus or stratocumulus-type clouds. (Stratocumulus clouds are a mixture of both stratus and cumulus clouds.)

Advection fog can form quite rapidly and cover extensive areas. Many a pilot has found only a deep white fog where the airport was supposed to be, even though the airport was reporting VFR conditions just a short time earlier. This makes you feel like you showed up at the airport gift shop before a commercial flight only to find them selling items from the luggage you just checked with the Skycap. Of course, plan B is to always have a fog-free airport nearby. Remember, good pilots always have a plan B and even a plan C.

Upslope Fog – When warm, moist air is forced up the slope of a mountain and condenses, it forms upslope fog. Technically, this cloud is considered fog because it touches the surface of the mountain. Upslope fog depends on wind for its existence. Therefore, it's not dependent on ter-

restrial cooling. This means that upslope fog can form under a higher layer of clouds that usually prevent terrestrial cooling. Expect to see upslope fog in the winter and spring on the eastern side of the Rocky Mountains.

Precipitation-Induced Fog – Warm rain, falling through cooler air can bring the air to the point of saturation, forming fog as shown in Figure 89. Commonly associated with warm fronts, it can occur in slow-moving cold fronts and stationary fronts. Couple this fog with the conditions that produce it—warm, cold and stationary fronts—and you get a double whammy of hazards.

Ice Fog – Ice fog forms under conditions similar to those that cause radiation fog except the air temperature is way below freezing. Instead of fog, you wind up with water subli- mating directly into the air as ice crystals. We're talking temperatures around -25 degrees F as being favor- able for its formation. This happens

Professor Bob Big Kahoona

Student Advection Fog

"Warm moist knowledge flowing over a cool dry brain."

PRECIPITATION INDUCED FOG

Precipitation-induced fog occurs when warm rain falls through cooler air and raises the humidity of the atmosphere to the point of saturation. It's usually associated with warm fronts but can occur in slow moving cold fronts and stationary fronts.

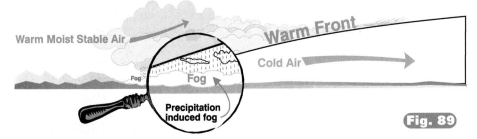

Warm Moist Stable Air

Warm Front

Cold Air

Fog

Fog

Precipitation induced fog

Fig. 89

mostly in the Arctic region but is not unknown in the middle latitudes. Ice fog can be quite blinding to someone when it refracts sunlight. If your instructor is sending you to the Arctic regions on your solo cross countries, you might want to check and see if he's upset with you over something.

Steam fog forms over a warm body of water.

© Sylvana Rega - Fotolia

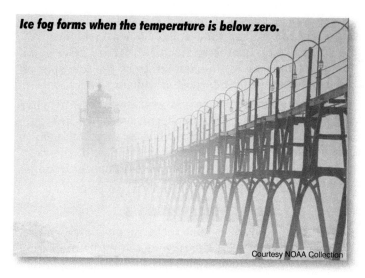

Ice fog forms when the temperature is below zero.

Courtesy NOAA Collection

Steam Fog – Anyone who has seen a heated swimming pool early on a cool morning has witnessed steam fog. As dry, cold air passes over a body of warm water, moisture evaporates rapidly from the surface. Condensation takes place as the cold air is quickly saturated. Water droplets often freeze, falling back into the water as ice crystals. Steam fog is quite conducive to low level turbulence and icing.

Weathering the Weather

Whether you like the weather or not, it's there, a force to be reckoned with. You don't need to get a Ph.D. in meteorology in order to be a good pilot, but you do need to understand and apply a basic knowledge of weather in order to fly safely.

Weather is a contributor to far too many aviation accidents. Most occur not because something came out of nowhere and smote the poor pilot, but because the pilot failed to properly anticipate what the weather would be, and plan accordingly.

Pilots as a group tend to be strong personalities. That's why they're called *pilots in command*. However, when it comes to the weather, a little bit of humility will go a long way toward keeping your skin (and that of your aircraft) intact.

"Know before you go," is the fundamental concept you need to come away from this chapter bearing. Keep in mind that you are legally *required* to obtain a weather briefing for all but the most minor of local flights. That should give you some sense of just how important it is to know what's in the sky before you put yourself there.

Weather is a fascinating subject, and one I think most pilots could profitably spend a lifetime schooling themselves in. Whatever you know, there's always more to learn. Take advantage of every opportunity to talk with flight instructors, Flight Service Station specialists, meteorologists, and others who can advance your education in how weather works.

WHOA NELLIE!!!

Normal approach and landing (wet runway). We could have taken any high speed turnoff but, because there was no apparent traffic immediately behind us, we asked permission to roll to the end. The response was, "OK, expedite to the end." Approaching the turnoff point at the end, I initiated brake application (unfortunately on the painted runway numbers) for final slowing (with allowance for the wet runway) for the turnoff. Braking was nil; came off brakes, tried easing into the turn with nosewheel steering. No reaction. Re-applied brakes; no response. Tried differential braking for pinwheel effect; no positive effect. Released brakes, straightened nosewheel, continued off the runway and 20° angle onto asphalt overrun. Informed Ground about possible/probable runway light strikes. Controller thanked us for the report and said they would check it out. Result: four lights struck. Should not plan to stop or turn on wet painted runway surfaces (even when grooved all the way to the end). A turnoff at one of the high-speeds would have prevented problem. At no time was there any flailing about or other gyrations of the aircraft. In fact, at the gate a flight attendant commented, "Nice landing." Unknowing is bliss, I suppose.

ASRS Report

Postflight Briefing #11-1

Advanced Weather Concepts

For those with a secret longing to challenge the local TV weatherperson, or perhaps just to gain that little edge you need to finally win a hangar discussion over why it's raining, I offer some more details on why the weather does what it does.

You won't need this to pass any pilot test administered by the FAA, but if you know and understand it, you might be able to get a job with the National Weather Service.

Wave Cyclones (Frontal Waves)

Not all fronts are found along low pressure troughs. Sometimes they form as small waves along one of the three to seven larger waves of the polar front. These smaller waves (also known as *wave cyclones* because they rotate in a counterclockwise manner) move along the polar front in an easterly direction. They are blown that way by the prevailing westerlies. Let's examine this process.

(The word *cyclone* indicates low atmospheric pressure having a counterclockwise rotation. Small wave cyclones are also simply called storms because they bring inclement weather).

Discontinuities along the polar front can appear and cause small wave cyclones (sometimes referred to as frontal waves) to form. Figure 90 (on the right hand page) depicts this process. Wave cyclones usually form in slow moving cold fronts or stationary fronts, as shown in Figure 90A. Airflow on each side of the stationary front is parallel to the actual front. Thus, there is little or no reason for the front to bend or twist.

Any small disturbance in the stationary frontal pattern, caused by uneven heating, irregular terrain or high altitude winds (the jet stream), can start a wave-like bend in the front, as shown in Figure 90B. If the wave-like bend is big (energetic) enough, warm air can start to rise over the retreating colder air. This often leads to condensation, and the release of latent heat into the atmosphere which intensifies the low pressure system (in other words, makes the air want to rise more quickly).

As the low pressure deepens, atmospheric pressure decreases. Counterclockwise circulation bends the front, which advances the cold air and forms a cold front, as shown in Figure 90C (position 1). As warmer air slides up and over the receding colder air, a warm front forms, as shown in Figure 90C (position 2). As fronts form, the entire wave cyclone (the storm) moves in an easterly direction, along with the prevailing westerlies.

Advancing cold air (cold front) usually moves faster than retreating cool air (the zone of which is the warm front). Think of the cold air as falling or sliding underneath the warm air. Things that fall are accelerated by

gravity. Retreating cooler air tugs at the ground as the warmer air slides up and over it. This tugging or sticking to the ground slows the advancing warm front. Retreating cool air acts like I did during my first visit to the dentist—I got splinters under my fingernails as my mother tried to tug me off the porch.

Figure 90D shows the faster moving cold front catching up, and overtaking the slower warm front. Meteorologists call this an occlusion and it is depicted by warm front and cold front symbols moving in the same direction.

Many parents have had the experience of taking their children to the orthodontist and hearing that little Bobby has maloccluded teeth. What the orthodontist is saying is that his teeth overlap. Translation? You pay megabucks (but little Bobby gets a great set of choppers). Since these fronts overlap, pilots find that an occluded front contains a combination of warm and cold frontal weather, as shown in Figure 90D (we'll discuss frontal weather shortly).

Once the occlusion forms, frontal movement slows down. The low pressure area diminishes in intensity because warm air is no longer rising and condensing over the colder air. In the final stage, shown in Figure 90E, the occlusion dissipates and the two fronts form a stationary front once again. Remnants of the low spin off and usually dissipate in forgotten whirling eddies.

Sometimes multiple storm systems (several wave cyclones) form along the polar front, as shown in Figure 91. It's not unusual for three, four or more of them to appear. These move eastward, with the flow of the westerlies and in the same direction as the high altitude jet stream (which blows from west to east).

Wave Cyclone Weather Patterns

Small frontal systems that occur in wave cyclone patterns offer a large scale mixture of the most interesting weather (a wave cyclone is the storm system that typically

STORM SYSTEMS MOVE EASTWARD

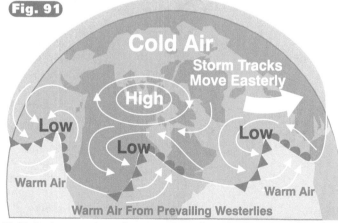

Fig. 91

Multiple storm systems (wave cyclones) can be found moving eastward along the polar front. Warm air from the prevailing westerlies and high altitude winds move these storms.

SHORT WAVE (STORM) FORMATION

Fig. 90

Frontal waves may form along a slow moving cold or stationary front.

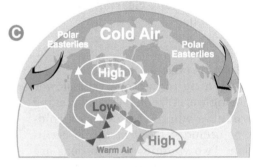

The jet stream or a geographical feature may cause a bend in the front.

Low pressure forms in the development of distinct cold and warm fronts.

The faster moving cold front eventually overtakes the slower warm front.

The frontal occlusion eventually dissipates.

contains fronts, a low pressure system and counterclockwise—cyclonic—circulation). Figure 92 shows one of these wave cyclones in full formation. North of the low pressure center, clouds lower and thicken, producing rain or snow usually lasting 12 to 24 hours. If the storm's warmer air is above you (along path A to B), precipitation usually takes the form of showers or snow flurries, depending on the temperature of the air below.

South of the low (along path C to D), you'll experience the approach of a warm front with lowering stratus, nimbostratus (stratus clouds with rain). With passage of the warm front, the weather clears and the air warms up. Finally the cold front arrives, typically bringing cumulonimbus clouds (these cloud types have the greatest turbulence) and thunderstorms. Following the cold front is cold air, clearing skies and gusty winds.

Cold Occlusions

In wave cyclones, cold fronts usually catch up to and overtake slower moving warm fronts. This overtaking produces what is known as a cold-type occluded front or a cold occlusion. Two varieties of occlusions are typical—cold occlusion and warm occlusion.

Cold occlusions occur when the air ahead of the warm front is less cold than the air behind the overtaking cold front, as shown in Figure 93. The cold front overtaking the warm front lifts the warm air up and over the retreating cool air. Essentially, the warm front is lifted entirely off the surface by the undercutting cold front.

The hollowed-out warm front symbols in Figure 93 represent the lifting of the warm front by the colder air. Weather ahead of the occlusion is similar to that associated with warm fronts, while weather near the surface position is similar to that of cold fronts.

As the occlusion develops, warm air is lifted higher and higher. Finally

WEATHER EXPERIENCED IN A WAVE CYCLONE

The upper part of this diagram (A to B) represents the north part of the wave cyclone. Warmer air is above you in this part of the wave, implying that you may experience showers or snow flurries, depending on the temperature of the air below. If you were stationary on the surface, south of the low, the fronts would pass from (C to D). The warm front passes first, followed by clearing skies, then the cold front and finally clearing skies and cold air.

COLD OCCLUSION

A cold occlusion occurs when the cold front overtakes and lifts up the preceding warm front. The warm air is lifted entirely off the surface by the cold front. Weather ahead of the occlusion is similar to that in a warm front. Near the surface, the weather is similar to that of a cold front.

the cloud system associated with the warm front disappears. The weather and cloud system now resembles that of a cold front. Cold occlusions form predominantly over continents or along the east coast and are more common than warm occlusions.

Warm Occlusions

Warm-type occluded fronts (or warm occlusions) are usually found in the northwestern United States. They begin with cold air masses from the Pacific overtaking a retreating colder air mass from the Arctic. Warmer air is caught in between these moving air masses. This process is shown in Figure 94.

The retreating Arctic air mass is colder than the approaching Pacific air mass. The Pacific cold front pushes the warmer air up and over the retreating Arctic air mass. The Pacific air mass is cool, but not as cold as the Arctic air mass, and it moves up the same slope as well. At this point the Pacific cold front becomes an upper cold front. Weather in the cross sectional area from (A) to (B), shown in the insert, is shown in Figure 94.

The structure of the warm occlusion in Figure 94, shows an open-type cold front symbol. This indicates the Pacific front is no longer in contact

WARM OCCLUSION

A warm occlusion occurs when the Pacific cold front pushes the warmer air up and over the retreating Arctic air mass. The Pacific air mass, not being as cold as the Arctic air mass, moves up the same slope. Weather associated with the warm occlusion is similar to that of a warm front, while tropical cold front weather occurs near the upper cold front boundary.

(Usually over west coast of continents)

Fig. 94

20,000'

Cumulonimbus

Cool Air

10,000'

Nimbostratus

Stratocumulus

Cirrus

Cold Air

Stratus

Fog & Rain

| A 150 | 100 | 50 | 0 | 50 | 100 | 150 | 200 | 250 | 300 | 350 | B |
| Miles | | | Warm Front Surface | | Upper Cold Front | | | | | | |

with the surface. Weather associated with a warm front occlusion has characteristics of both warm and cold fronts. The cloud sequence ahead of the occlusion is similar to that of a warm front, while tropical cold front weather occurs near the upper cold front boundary.

Are we having fun yet? Remember, it takes a lot of study to become intimately familiar with weather. It's not something you're expected to master before you become a sport pilot. The study of weather is an ongoing process for pilots. Try to learn a little about it every day. That way you won't be like the pilot who thinks stable air is something you find in a barn.

Postflight Briefing #11-2

How the Jet Stream Forms

To understand how the jet stream forms, we need to know something about the tropopause.

The tropopause is the boundary between the troposphere (where all our weather occurs), and the stratosphere (where very little weather occurs). This boundary surrounds the earth like skin surrounds an onion. The tropopause is shown in Figure 95. Temperatures decrease until reaching the top of the troposphere. Above the tropopause, however, temperatures remain steady and then start to increase.

The tropopause tends to bulge at the middle of the earth as a one-a-day Hostess Twinky man might bulge at the beltline. Normally, the tropopause is located around 30,000 feet MSL in the northern latitudes and bulges at the equator to altitudes of 65,000 feet MSL. It bulges because the warmer air near the equator expands slightly. As we move northward the air cools and shrinks slightly, thus lowering the height of the tropopause. The polar tropopause can vary, but will be typically found at 18,000 to 26,000 feet MSL.

Occasionally, breaks occur in the tropopause. Think back to the last time you witnessed a giant, big, big fellow sit on a waterbed (this guy's so big that when he gets on a scale it says, "Please, one at a time!"). You winced because this fellow's weight caused a large bend or bulge in the mattress. If it bulges too much and tears, water—under pressure—shoots out and swirls around the tear zone, as shown in Figure 96. Uneven weight distribution on the mattress causes a shearing or tearing effect in its thin skin.

In a similar manner, a strong vertical temperature gradient can cause large differences in pressure, resulting in a bulge or tear in the tropopause. Pressure differences occur because warmer air expands

THE TROPOPAUSE

The tropopause is like a thin skin covering the troposphere. It's found at lower altitudes over the poles and higher altitudes over the equator. Height varies because of the direct effects of air expanding by heating and shrinking by cooling.

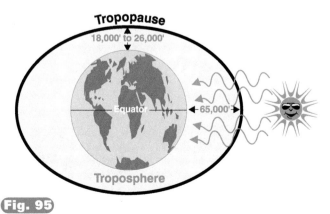

Tropopause

18,000' to 26,000'

Equator

65,000'

Troposphere

Fig. 95

WATERBED AND THE JET STREAM

When too much stress is applied to the mattress of a waterbed, it bulges then finally ruptures, sending water swirling in all directions. In a similar manner, too much stress on the troposphere (it's like a thin rubber mattress) can cause a rupture, allowing air to swirl. This can propagate something known as the jet stream.

Rupture

Waterbed

Fig. 96

and cooler air shrinks. Given enough vertical expansion and shrinkage in the troposphere, a break in the tropopause occurs. Air spills around the tear, as shown in Figure 97.

Figure 98 shows warm, tropical air rising at the break in the tropopause. This warm air circulates upward and northward toward the cold polar air. Then it circulates downward as it's cooled. As it circulates upward and downward, it's curved to the right by the Coriolis force. This gives the air a west-to-east rotating motion. The jet stream's tube of fast-moving air is further coaxed into a west to east motion by the prevailing westerlies.

Jet streams, which are usually found along or near the polar front, can have winds in excess of 250 MPH. If you could get your nonturbocharged Cessna Skycatcher up that high (you can't—take pictures if you do) and tried to fly against the jet stream you'd be able to fly it backwards at twice its normal speed!

Jet streams are important because they help meteorologists track the west-to-east migration of wave cyclones and their associated storms. These wave cyclones (and their associated low pressure systems), tend to follow the jet stream's winds at higher altitudes. In addition, jet streams can modify pressure centers near the surface.

Think of a jet stream as a ceiling fan that forces air earthward and forms a high pressure center. At other times, jet streams act like the ventilator fans found in our ceilings. These fans create a sucking action that creates a miniature low pressure center. Jet streams can increase low pressure centers on the earth's surface, modifying local weather patterns. The exact reasons for this are beyond the scope of this book (and most other books, too!). Suffice it to say that meteorologists pay very close attention to the jet stream when forecasting weather.

Studying the jet stream (admittedly advanced for a sport pilot) is like playing the slots in Las Vegas. Even if you don't win, it makes doing your wash a lot more fun. Playing with ideas about the jet stream makes studying weather a lot more fun because it helps explain many things that would otherwise seem a complete mystery.

THE JET STREAM

Think of the warmer air to the south standing taller than the colder air to the north. The differences in these heights stretch and eventually tear the tropopause in a manner similar to someone sitting on a water bed and stressing its mattress. At the point of tear, a large difference in temperature exists. This causes air to swirl in a circular manner as shown below. Warmer air rises upward toward the tropical or southern part of the tropopause. Then it cools and descends at the northern part of the polar tropopause. This circular motion is primarily responsible for the formation of the jet stream.

Fig. 97

JET STREAM MOVEMENT

The jet stream contains high speed, high altitude winds flowing from west to east. The flow of this stream normally follows the polar front and, at times, modifies the direction of polar frontal movement. It's not unusual to find winds from 150 to 200 MPH in the jet stream.

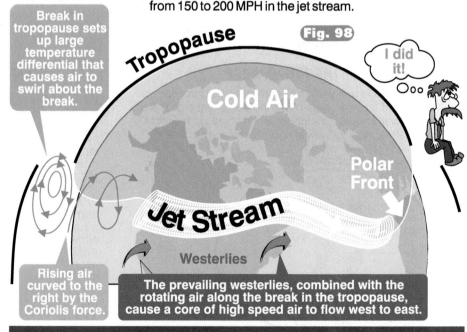

Fig. 98

Wisdom comes from experience, and experience from lack of wisdom.

Chapter Twelve

Weather Charts And Briefings

PIREPS, Progs & METARS

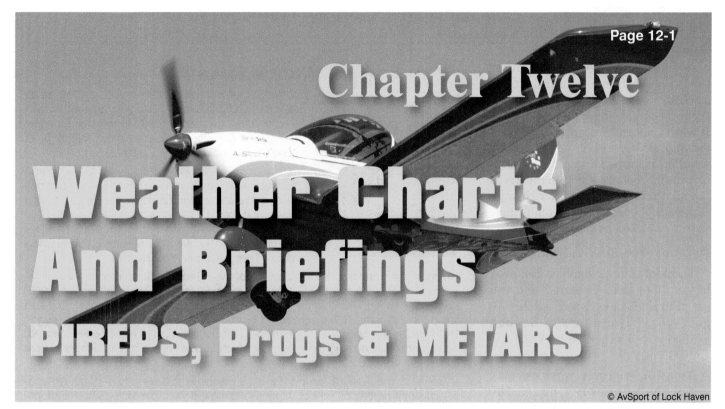

We all remember a few of the golden rules governing our earthly behavior: Do unto others as you would have them do unto you, judge not lest ye be judged, and always turn your wheel in the direction of the skid (the rules that are important to you may be a little different). Flying, too, has its golden rules, and they're not just bullion, because they often relate directly to the matter of keeping you and your passengers safe and happy.

That's never more true than when it comes to weather. As I hope you understood from reading Chapter 11, nature is not to be trifled with. Good pilots are not fearful, but they are certainly respectful. That's why one of the aviation golden rules is to always obtain a weather briefing before flying . . .anywhere, any time.

Some pilots think weather briefings are for sissies; others think they're just for cross country (long) flights. Both of these attitudes come from pilots who are flying with a fog bank between their ears.

It does *not* take the awesome force of a severe thunderstorm to make flying distinctly unfun and unsafe. Clouds, wind, fog, closed runways, unavailable navigational aids—these are just some of the things you will find out about in a preflight weather

briefing—but only if you get one. Any or all of these things can have a direct impact on any flight, no matter what its duration.

I distinctly remember preparing one day, while still a student, to do touch-and-goes. I anticipated only good weather. It was late morning and the skies were clear, without a hint of adverse weather. I knew it was a good day to practice landings for two reasons. First, all the seasoned instructors were away at a flight instructor seminar, so there was no one around to make fun of me. Second, the tower had switched the airport to right traffic and right turns were my specialty. Off I went.

Thirty minutes passed. The winds picked up substantially. Small cumulus clouds developed above the airport, causing turbulence and gusty conditions. I decided to quit early, before the local university called and complained about someone at the airport who kept popping the needle of their seismograph. Keeping the taildragger lined up on final was quite a challenge for an 18-hour student. I thought I did a great job, even though I swerved a little. Apparently the folks in the tower thought I swerved a lot. They called while I was on final and asked, "32 Bravo, are you in need of some assistance or should we just put on a little music?"

In the span of about 30 minutes the sky went from a beautiful blue to a white, cloud-dotted tableau with turbulence-bearing cumulus clouds. It wasn't a significant problem, but it did impress me with just how quickly weather changes. Obtaining a weather briefing before every flight keeps the pilot informed of weather changes that might be far more uncomfortable than what I experienced.

Aviation Weather Services

Think of a huge jukebox. No, even bigger than that. Press F7 and you get "Purple People Eater," while G10 gets you "There Ain't Enough Whiskey in Tennessee to Wipe the Ugly Off of You."

Aviation weather works pretty much the same way, though the titles aren't as interesting. You can obtain a staggering array of information from a large number of places. All you have to do is know which buttons to push. In fact, it's even better than the jukebox, because you don't have to deposit a quarter. Aviation weather services are, for the moment at least, free to pilots. Push the right buttons and *ka-ching*, out comes an hourly weather observation. Push again and *ka-ching*, there's your forecast, pilot reports, hazards, or NOTAMS (notices to airmen).

Lots of people from many agencies of the federal government, as well as

What's in an A?

When I tell new pilots there's such a thing as an *Automated* Flight Service Station, they tend to picture an unstaffed facility with synthesized voices. *Dave, I will give you the weather now. Please don't hang up, Dave. Dave, do you hear me?*

Once upon a time, when the nation was young and budgets were big, there were Flight Service Stations all over the place. You could walk right in, sit right down, and they'd let your briefing hang down. (This was literally true, because once upon a time PC—pre-computer—the weather reports came on long rolls of Teletype paper. Yes! Really!)

Today, the standard FSS is gone! Gone, I say! The FAA has replaced the hole-in-the-wall model with the AFSS, which is manned (and wo-manned) by Lockheed Martin. Lockheed Martin, as of this writing, has five large AFSS centers located around the country. These centralized facilities serve a huge area—did I say huge? The AFSS relies heavily on modern electronic wizardry. It's highly computerized, has telephone and radio tentacles that reach everywhere, and can access almost anything in an instant.

Gone are the clanking, cranky Teletype machines that used to print barely-readable weather reports on rolls of paper. Gone are the hand-generated weather maps.

What's not gone are the people. Despite its name, the Automated Flight Service Station is still staffed by very real folks whose expertise you'll learn to appreciate. While many pilots feel that the "local knowledge" has been lost because of the centralized nature of the new facilities, the people who staff them are information experts and certified weather briefers who can provide almost any kind of weather data you might want, and assist you in interpreting it correctly.

Though they're automated, the AFSSs depend on briefers to use that automation to your advantage before each and every flight.

A lot of time, money, and effort has been invested to gather and disseminate the information. None of it helps, though, if you don't make the call.

private individuals, have a hand in providing the weather services available to pilots. Among the participants are the Federal Aviation Administration, the Department of Defense, and several other groups and individuals, including a huge network of weather volunteers who provide hourly reports.

The main button that lets you rock 'n roll, is the Automated Flight Service Station (AFSS), run by Lockheed Martin. Dial (800) WX-BRIEF for a phone briefing, of contact the AFSS on its listed radio frequencies as shown in the *AF/D* excerpt (Figure 1), or log onto this site at: *www.1800wxbrief.com*. Either way you'll be connected to an AFSS facility serving up weather.

Figure 2 shows a typical Automated Flight Service Station. AFSSs offer a complete menu of prerecorded weather information accessible to anyone with a telephone or internet access.

Personal computers have become an increasingly popular way of obtaining a weather briefing. The Computer Science Corporation (CSC)

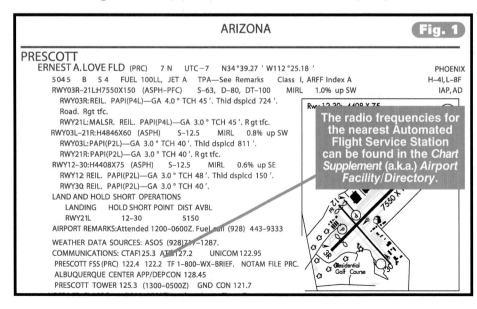

ARIZONA **Fig. 1**

PRESCOTT
ERNEST A. LOVE FLD (PRC) 7 N UTC–7 N34°39.27 ' W112°25.18 ' PHOENIX
 5045 B S 4 FUEL 100LL, JET A TPA—See Remarks Class I, ARFF Index A H–4I, L–8F
 RWY03R–21L:H7550X150 (ASPH–PFC) S–63, D–80, DT–100 MIRL 1.0% up SW IAP, AD
  RWY03R: REIL. PAPI(P4L)—GA 4.0 ° TCH 45 '. Thld dsplcd 724 '.
  Road. Rgt tfc.
  RWY21L: MALSR. REIL. PAPI(P4L)—GA 3.0 ° TCH 45 '. R gt tfc.
 RWY03L–21R:H4846X60 (ASPH) S–12.5 MIRL 0.8% up SW
  RWY03L: PAPI(P2L)—GA 3.0 ° TCH 40 '. Thld dsplcd 811 '.
  RWY21R: PAPI(P2L)—GA 3.0 ° TCH 40 '. Rgt tfc.
 RWY12–30:H4408X75 (ASPH) S–12.5 MIRL 0.6% up SE
  RWY12 REIL. PAPI(P2L)—GA 3.0 ° TCH 48 '. Thld dsplcd 150 '.
  RWY30 REIL. PAPI(P2L)—GA 3.0 ° TCH 40 '.
 LAND AND HOLD SHORT OPERATIONS
  LANDING HOLD SHORT POINT DIST AVBL
  RWY21L 12–30 5150
 AIRPORT REMARKS: Attended 1200–0600Z. Fuel cell (928) 443-9333
 WEATHER DATA SOURCES: ASOS (928)717–1287.
 COMMUNICATIONS: CTAF125.3 ATIS 127.2 UNICOM 122.95
  PRESCOTT FSS (PRC) 122.4 122.2 TF 1–800–WX–BRIEF. NOTAM FILE PRC.
  ALBUQUERQUE CENTER APP/DEPCON 128.45
  PRESCOTT TOWER 125.3 (1300–0500Z) GND CON 121.7

The radio frequencies for the nearest Automated Flight Service Station can be found in the *Chart Supplement* (a.k.a.) *Airport Facility/Directory*.

This is your typical Automated Flight Service Station (AFSS). The folks are very friendly and they have really good toys for weather watching.

offers a weather service called CSC Direct User Access Terminal Service (CSC DUATS), All you need is a personal computer, internet access and a web browser. Several commercial weather vendors sell software and access to either government or private weather databases. These programs even allow you to file your flight plan via computer. Some of these programs have flight planning capability, enabling you to plan your flight's time, distance, and fuel requirements based on the current winds and the airplane's performance characteristics (see Postflight Briefings #13-1 and 14-5).

For those with a computer, flight planning and preparation is easy, interesting, and informative. Best of all, you can save everything and either review it on the screen or print it out and take it along. One of the downsides of the oral weather briefing has always been the "Whatzat?" factor. This comes into play when you try to read your hastily scribbled notes after hanging up the phone.

There are other means of acquiring weather information. Newspaper weather forecasts, the Internet, the Weather Channel from cable television as well as public television news broadcasts all contain weather information of use, though none of these sources provides anything approaching a full weather briefing. Sometimes, though, all you need is one look at the weather map or the forecast to know it's no go.

The Telephone Briefing

As I mentioned earlier, it's no longer easy (or possible in most instances) to pay a visit to an actual flight service station facility. Yes, there are a few private weather service facilities that you might visit, but these aren't available to the average pilot. Nor are they really necessary, nowadays.

Today's pilot has at his or her fingertips more weather information than the average pilot could even imagine 30 years ago. I'm speaking of internet weather access via your mobile computing device (tablets, phones, pads, iThingy), or your desktop computer. We'll discuss this in more detail shortly.

Then there's the Automated Flight Service Station that can provide you with the same weather but dished up and a friendly and easily consumed format. You can call the nearest Lockheed Martin AFSS (or log onto their web site as reference on the previous page) to obtain your official weather briefing.

As a student pilot, that first call for a weather briefing might make you a little nervous. Most students have no idea of how they are supposed to act on the phone. This is why I have all my students listen to me on another line as I make a call to the AFSS. One of my students decided to try it for himself. He picked up the phone, dialed and got a briefer who said, "Hello, Los Angeles Flight Service, may I help you?" The student replied, "Ahhhhh, ahhhh, ahhhh, my instructor wants to talk to you, gotta go, bye," then he handed me the phone. His following calls were anxiety free once he realized how friendly the briefers were.

What's a Legal Weather Briefing?

You are legally required to have a weather briefing before any non-local flight.

Seems easy, until you ask yourself (or someone else) one simple question. What's a weather briefing, and who can give one?

The rules (FAR 91.103) state that "Each pilot in command shall, before beginning a flight, become familiar with all available information concerning that flight." Should something unpleasant happen, you will have a very hard time convincing the FAA that you didn't get a weather briefing because weather wasn't information that concerned you.

Until fairly recently, the only way to get anything approximating a weather briefing was to call a Flight Service Station. All such calls are recorded both manually and on tape, so it was always possible to prove a pilot was (or wasn't) properly briefed.

Many pilots now obtain a briefing via computer from one of several private weather services. Whether or not this constitutes a legal weather briefing for purposes of meeting the letter of the law depends on that service's ability to prove you actually obtained the weather.

If you obtain a weather briefing via computer, make sure the service you're using keeps a record of the briefing. Call them and ask, if you're not sure. If they don't, then it's best to leave a paper trail to protect yourself. Calling your friendly local (or not-so-local) FSS is a sure way to establish having received a briefing.

Besides, some of them have really great music-on-hold.

Just so you won't wind up with your tongue tangled behind your eye teeth, which would keep you from seeing what you're saying, let's walk and talk through a typical briefing.

We'll begin by dialing (800) WX-BRIEF. You will usually get a recording and a menu of selected items from which to choose. Be patient. The computer that's screening your call needs a little information before it can provide you with the appropriate weather service. For instance, it needs to know the state in which you're located so it can route you to the AFSS responsible for that area. You can respond to the nice synthesized computer voice by pushing buttons or with a verbal response (head nodding is not yet recognized by your phone or the computer). Eventually you'll be taken to a live briefer for your weather briefing.

Here's how it will go once you've gone live.

The FSS briefer says:

Good morning, this is Hawthorne Flight Service.

You respond by saying:

Good morning. I'm a student pilot and I need a standard briefing for a VFR flight.

Tell the briefer what kind of pilot you are and what kind of briefing you need, and the type of flight you're proposing to make.

By *kind of pilot,* I don't mean a good pilot or a bad pilot. I mean *student, sport, private, commercial* or *airline transport pilot.* Briefers are trained to tailor their briefing to the pilot's experience level.

A friend of mine called for a briefing once and told the specialist he was an airline transport pilot. Part of the briefing went like this: "... we're expecting logarithmic, neonocturnal katabatic perturbations in the magnetohydrodynamic ectoplasmic weather membrane..." Huh? What? My friend said, "Hey, I've got this piece of paper here with two boxes, one says *go* and the other says *stay.* Which one should I check?" The briefer laughed and they went through it all again—slowly.

Weather is responsible for over 25% of aviation accidents and 40% of its fatalities. Why are these percentages so high? It would be easy to put the blame on an inability to accurately forecast the weather. It's more likely the pilot didn't even check the weather. In one FAA study, 55% of the pilots involved in a weather related accident had no record of receiving a weather briefing. It seems more plausible that the real culprit is a pilot's inability to resist the urge to press on in the face of poor or deteriorating weather conditions. Known as "get-home-itis," this Lorelei of the air has probably caused pilots more grief than any other psychological pressure. Resisting the press to push on in bad weather is your greatest challenge as an aviator.

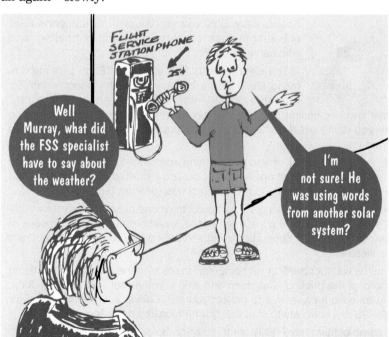

If you say *student pilot* they'll talk to you differently. For instance, the briefer will normally speak more slowly, usually using more precise terms. A friend who was a 747 captain for one of the now-defunct airlines (Pan Am) said he used to call the FSS for a weather briefing and always told the briefer he was a student pilot. He just liked to have a little fun at the briefer's expense.

Can you imagine the conversation? "This is the FSS, what can I do for you?" He replies, "Ah, yes sir, student pilot cross country today and I'd like a weather briefing." "OK, where are you going today?" He says, "Ahhh, Los Angeles to Japan." The briefer would pause, then reply, "Wow, this is your long cross country isn't it?" You can imagine what happened from there. It must have gotten real interesting when he wanted the briefer to give him the winds at 39,000 feet!

Briefings now come in three flavors, *standard, abbreviated,* and *outlook.*

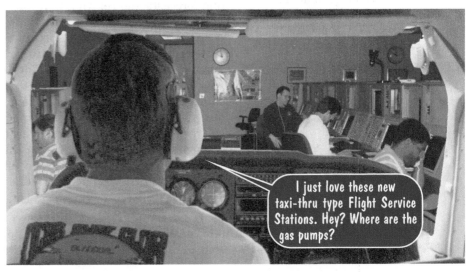

One good reason why you should always get a weather briefing before a flight!

© Steven Gibson - FOTOLIA

A *standard briefing* contains all the important weather and related items of concern. These items include adverse conditions, weather synopsis, current weather, forecast weather, forecast winds aloft, alternate routes if any and NOTAMS. NOTAMS include items concerning airports, navigation aids and hazards, all of which contain essential knowledge for safe flight. More on NOTAMS in Chapter 16.

A standard briefing is the entire enchilada. It's everything, and it assumes you have and know nothing. Always request a standard briefing if you haven't collected any weather information prior to your first call.

If you're calling to update or supplement previously acquired weather information, ask for an *abbreviated briefing,* and request the specific type of information you need. Each type of information has its own rate of change; METARs (hourly surface reports) change hourly, while TAFs (terminal aerodrome forecasts) are produced four times a day. If all you want is an update on the weather at your proposed destination, you don't need to sit through the entire enchilada.

Ask for an *outlook briefing* if you are calling the FSS for weather information six or more hours in advance of your proposed departure time. I usually do this the night before a flight to obtain a general idea about the weather the following day. It's difficult for meteorologists to predict weather accurately more than 24

hours in advance. An outlook briefing is only general information, intended to give you a notion of what's out there, and some sense of whether the weather is so bad (or good) that you should definitely cancel (or plan) your flight. A standard briefing is still necessary as departure time grows nearer.

Then tell the briefer that you'll be on a VFR flight (though the information is redundant in this case, since student pilots are *always* VFR, but it's a good habit to get into—later on you will perhaps be asking for a briefing for an IFR flight, which to the briefer is a whole different container of gumballs).

Say this the following way:

Cessna 1234 Bravo, a Cessna 172, Santa Monica to Santa Barbara via the coast. Departing Santa Monica 2230 Zulu, 1 hour plus 10 enroute at 4,500 feet.

Give the briefer your aircraft tail number or your name, the kind of airplane you're flying, the departure point, destination, the route of flight, your estimated time of departure, the estimated time enroute and the altitude at which you'll fly. At this point the briefer may express utter amazement at your preparation, because this information has to be extracted from most pilots in a process somewhat similar to pulling teeth. Briefers *really* appreciate it when you provide them what they need to get the job done for you.

Now get ready to copy. The briefer is about to do his/her thing. You will receive at least the following information *in this order (omitting items where there is no relevant information, of course):*

1. Adverse conditions

You will first be advised of major items that might cause you to say "Whoa, Briefer. That's enough. I thank you, my passengers thank you, good day and goodbye." This might include such things as runway closure at your departure or destination airport, 6-inch hailstones, a hurricane in progress, IFR conditions when you're not IFR rated, etc.

2. VFR flight not recommended

This is a warning that the weather is not great. The briefer will provide the reason ("Due to mountain obscuration in clouds and dense fog") and you will have to decide if it's reason enough not to attempt a VFR flight.

I just love these new taxi-thru type Flight Service Stations. Hey? Where are the gas pumps?

3. Synopsis

This is the general weather pattern covering the major weather systems and air masses influencing weather in the area where the proposed flight will take place.

4. Current conditions

Current surface observations for the departure and destination airports and pilot reports of enroute conditions.

5. Enroute forecast

The briefer will take you from departure and climbout through landing, summarizing the forecast for the period you'll be airborne. That's why the time of departure and time enroute are important information when requesting a briefing.

6. Destination forecast

The forecast weather for the estimated time of arrival (ETA).

7. Winds aloft

You will be given the winds at the altitude closest to your proposed flight altitude for which there are measurements, which is at 3,000 foot intervals through 12,000 feet. Some briefers will do minor math and interpolate, giving you something halfway in between the 6000 and 9000 figures if you're planning to fly at 7500 feet. I'll tell you how to do the math for yourself in a minute.

8. NOTAMS

Notices to Airmen (NOTAMS) are information of an advisory or cautionary nature. They can include everything from a runway being closed to a navaid being dysfunctional. The ones you'll hear most frequently have to do with navaids (VORs, primarily) that aren't working or are out of service.

A Note About NOTAMS

When there are significant and important changes in aeronautical information, you need to know about them. This becomes especially important when such information might affect the safety of your flight. NOTAMS contain information such as airport or primary runway closures, tower construction, changes in the status of navigational aids, radar service availability and other information essential to planned enroute, terminal or landing operations.

You can ask the Flight Service Station specialist for all pertinent NOTAM information during your weather briefing or just download them when you obtain your weather briefing from an FAA approved service provider, such as DUATS. (See Page 16-19, Chapter 16 for more information on NOTAMS.)

Runway Construction

Tower Construction

Courtesy FAA

Courtesy FAA

9. ATC delays

These will be pretty rare for pilots flying to anything other than major metropolitan airports. If you are headed for O'Hare or JFK, the briefer will tell you of any holds due to flow control or other measures designed to keep the traffic humming.

That's it.

Or is it? The briefer will usually conclude by asking you if there's anything else you'd like to know. Speak now or forever hold your wings, unless you call back. Now is the time to ask any questions you might have. Briefers are trained by the FAA to disseminate weather information. They're very skilled at reading charts and forecasts and relaying that information to pilots. They are not, however, meteorologists. They don't forecast weather. They only talk to you about it. And good talk it is! That's why briefers don't tell you whether to go or not. That decision is yours and yours alone. They will, however, tell you all about the highs, lows, squiggles and squirts comprising the aviation weather map. Listen to what they have to say. They do good work.

Briefers are sort of the Dear Abby of flightdom. They will answer almost any question (about aviation, that is; questions about your love life

should still be directed to Dear Abby). They'll tell you about Customs, search and rescue, ATC services, preferred routes, and why the computer will take a flight plan for one route and not another. They'll look up phone numbers (for aviation facilities, not for your Aunt Maude in Minneapolis), read the Class D NOTAMS, provide information about Military Training Routes, restricted areas, and other special use airspace.

They will do almost anything they can to get you almost any information you want about the aviation system. Just ask and ye shall receive.

Other Sources Of Weather Information

There is, the proverb says, more than one way to skin an airplane, and there are lots of other places to get information about which way the clouds blow.

NEWSPAPERS – My uncle liked his newspaper because he could swat the dog with it when the little fellow did something wrong. It's no wonder the newspaper started turning up wet (that also explains why the dog started chasing the paperboy). Nevertheless, the paper provides you with some valuable information about weather. Most newspapers publish a weather map showing major weather systems around the country, and many carry a satellite picture that helps provide a look at what the weather's doing. Weather-wise pilots study weather on a daily basis. Simply take the weather chart and/or satellite photo provided by the paper and examine it every day. These charts are a lot more accurate than they were several years ago. You'll be surprised how weather savvy you'll become with this small investment of time.

Telephone Information Briefing Service (TIBS) – *TIBS* is a continuous telephone briefing service consisting of prerecorded weather information. It's offered by automated flight service stations and provides weather briefings for an area or a route. It also provides airspace procedures and special aviation announcements. Using your Touch-Tone phone you can select from several weather menus of prerecorded information. You have the option, at any time, of transferring directly to a live briefer.

Cockpit Weather Uplink – A very useful innovation in aviation technology now allows you to receive uplinked weather information in the cockpit on your GPS moving map screen display (Figure 3).

The white "H" in the blue circle in the top right corner of the Julian VOR frequency box indicates HIWAS can be heard on 114.0 MHz.

Fig. 4

For instance, your iPad or Android tablet device might have flight planning software such as ForeFlight, WingX Pro, FlyQ, etc. With some additional equipment (ADS-B equipment, as discussed on Page Q37), this software allows your device to receive uplinked weather information for free. This uplinked weather contains many products including enroute and destination weather, NEXRAD radar imagery (this is similar to the same type of colorful weather imagery shown by your local weather man/woman on the evening news), station reports (METARs), winds aloft forecasts, and so on, all while in flight.

In addition, this flight planning software also works on your cell phone which makes it easy for you to have the same weather information available to you just before takeoff. And I do mean "just before takeoff" as part of your pre-departure engine runup check. Any chance of flying off into unexpected weather is highly unlikely with today's technology. In fact, you probably will never find yourself using the phrase, "Hey, where did that stuff come from?" except when you eat at an airport restaurant. How nice is that?

Hazardous In-flight Weather Advisory Service (HIWAS) – HIWAS is a continuous broadcast of in-flight weather advisories. HIWAS can be received over certain VOR and NDB stations (Figure 4). The purpose of HIWAS is to keep you abreast of any hazardous weather such as thunderstorms, icing, strong winds, etc. These advisories of hazardous forms of weather are sometimes called SIGMETS or AIRMETS and will be discussed in more detail later. The unique thing about HIWAS is that you can simply turn up the volume on your VOR and listen to this continuous weather broadcast while traveling to your destination. This keeps you informed without having to repeatedly contact the Automated Flight Service Station.

This portable Garmin GPS unit allows you to receive in-flight weather (NEXRAD imagery in this instance).

Fig. 3

In a geographical area where HIWAS has been implemented, you might hear a HIWAS alert on an ATC frequency (such as approach or departure control). The alert notice might sound like this:

"Attention all aircraft, monitor HIWAS or contact an Automated Flight Service Station on frequency one two two point zero or one two two point two for new Convective SIGMET information."

Upon hearing this one-time alert, you should make plans to contact the AFSS to find out if this information is applicable to you. At least listen to the nearest VOR over which HIWAS is broadcast for a description of the particular weather information contained in the alert notice.

As with all prerecorded in-flight broadcasts, HIWAS is not intended as a substitute for a specialist-provided briefing. Take advantage of these in-flight weather advisories by keeping the volume up slightly when using a HIWAS broadcasting navigation station. When you hear any voice transmission, turn up the volume to listen to the incoming broadcasts.

Enroute Weather Information – In addition to the weather information you have via any uplinked cockpit weather, you also have *radio weather*. This is the weather information you obtain by making a call to the Automated Flight Service Station on your radio. Yes, the company providing flight services is Lockheed Martin, but you can still refer to them as *flight service*. The universal frequency that all pilots can use to talk to a flight service station specialist is 122.2 MHz.

Fig. 5

Because flight service covers a rather large area, remote communication outlets have been established to assist pilots in reaching the AFSS specialist. Figure 5 depicts the area south and west of Albuquerque. While you can certainly use 122.2 MHz to contact the AFSS, it's best to use the specific frequency for the area in which you're flying. What's that frequency? While you'll learn more about this in the chapter on aviation charts, the best frequency to use in this instance is 122.5 MHz. It's shown above the blue box (position A) on the sectional chart excerpt in Figure 5. This is one of the frequencies that the AFSS has allocated for communicating with pilots this area. When you make your initial call on this frequency (you'll refer to the AFSS as *Albuquerque Radio*), the specialist in charge of that area will see a reference light activate on his/her weather

panel indicating that a transmission is being made on 122.5 MHz in that area. The specialist will respond to you on 122.5 MHz and provide you with whatever weather or flight plan information you need.

Pilot Reports (PIREPS) – One of the problems with the weather is that it changes. Weather forecasting is a game of catch-up that can never be won. The closest you can come is *pilot reports (PIREPS)*, which represent actual information on current conditions as reported by pilots in the air. These reports are made to the FSS, EFAS or an ATC facility, and they can be of immense assistance in helping you to make a go/no go decision, or to avoid problem areas once you're airborne.

When contacting EFAS or the FSS, in flight or before takeoff, you will usually be provided current pilot reports as part of the weather briefing.

Student Fantasy Panel: The way we'd love it to be!

A video of an airline captain that acts as your instructor and tells you exactly what to do.

Push this button to create a hole in the clouds with a laser beam.

Push to engage time warp that makes Hobbs meter run slower.

Push to engage audio filter that makes controllers sound like they're talking 10 times slower than they really are.

Push for holographic image that makes your airplane appear to land smoothly when you have an audience.

If they aren't forthcoming, ask for them. These reports give you a good idea how close to reality the forecast is.

In many instances, PIREPS have allowed me to make a decision to go when the forecast painted a very bleak picture. PIREPS become especially important in understanding what's happening in areas where weather reporting stations are few and far between. (Near the end of this chapter I'll show you how to decode PIREPS transmitted by the FSS.)

Whenever you contact the FSS, EFAS or ATC, give them a pilot report. Pilots don't do this often enough. Even if the weather is clear, report it. I make it a point to listen to the ARTCC (Air Route Traffic Control Center) whenever I'm on a cross country flight, whether or not I'm signed on for radar service. Believe me, if there's nastiness ahead, you'll hear it. My rule is that when the male pilots' voices hit a high C or above, it's time to re-evaluate my options. This is one of those cases where it's not just what they say, but how they say it, that counts.

Weather Reports

There are many weather reports available from the National Weather Service and private weather services to aid pilots in flight planning. Knowing what to ask for and how to use the information is an important pilot skill.

The available weather products are of two basic types: *observations* and *forecasts*. Observations are historical.

They are the weather conditions that occurred at the time the observation was taken. Forecasts are weather estimates for several hours (sometimes days) into the future. Like all estimates, weather forecasts are subject to change. Sometimes considerable change. If you've ever remodeled your house and remember what the original estimate was, and what you finally paid, you understand exactly what I'm saying.

Let's examine the weather reports you'll need for successful and safe VFR flight planning. Unless the weather report has the word forecast or prognosis in it, then it's probably an observation.

There are some pretty interesting inventions in the world, such as a pager that will summon you when your car is being burglarized, enabling you to get burgled *and* beat up in a single evening. There is, however, no contraption that will interpret the weather for you, though if you do a poor job of it you still might manage to get beat up.

You and only you are responsible for making your go or no-go deci-

sions. It takes training to make good weather decisions. Weather charts are part of this training. There are many times when you'll have access to weather charts without the benefit of an actual briefer. Knowing how to interpret these charts is very important.

Many of the following weather charts are on the sport pilot knowledge exam. I have added additional practical information where appropriate. You'll find that a few charts have partial legends accompanying them. These legends help interpret some (not all) of the chart's symbols. For purposes of the FAA knowledge exam, you'll need to memorize some basic chart symbology. As you'll soon see, many of the chart's symbols can be generalized to other charts. I'll specifically advise you when a chart's legend is available for a specific chart on the exam.

International Reports

Airplanes have helped shrink the world, and one of the results is an increasing demand for consistency internationally. This is particularly crucial in aviation, where pilots have the capability to cross numerous national borders within a few hours.

Because weather is so vital to flight safety, it was agreed internationally that consistency in reporting the weather was desirable. A pilot should be able to look at a weather report anywhere in the world and read it. That's why the U.S. now uses the International Civil Aviation Organization (ICAO) weather standard for reporting weather. This format provides a single global format known as METAR (METeorological

Reptile Rattles, Controller Tattles

Several years ago, a friend was working as a controller at Fullerton Tower in Southern California. She was looking at the surface aviation weather reports when she noticed the report for Tucumcari, New Mexico. It read "ROSNOT." She had never seen that particular acronym, so she called the FSS making the report. The phone rang and a briefer answered. She said, "What does ROSNOT mean?" He replied, "It means Rattlesnake On Step, No Observation Taken!"

Must have been a towering snake.

METAR WEATHER REPORTING FORMAT

METAR KINK 081955Z 32014G20KT 1/2SM R30R/2400FT DZ FG OVC006 13/12 A3004
SPECI KMKC 081936Z 20014G24KT 1/2SM R34/2600FT +SN BLSN FG VV008 00/M03 A2898
METAR KBOI 081953Z 23008KT 5SM SCT015 19/13 A2994 RMK SLP156 T01930128
METAR KLAX 081955Z 01013G20KT 3SM HZ SKC 18/11 A2995

Fig. 6

Aviation Report) and TAF (Terminal Aerodrome Forecasts) for weather reporting.

METAR (pronounced *ME - TAR* [as in YOU - JANE]) observations are taken hourly at many reporting stations located across the country. These reports indicate the weather conditions at the time the observation was made. Other than a pilot report, a METAR observation is as close as you can get to the actual weather conditions without sticking your finger out the window. Not only do these reports provide a current weather observation, they also allow you to sense a trend in the weather by observing several of the past hourly reports. Figure 6 shows a typical METAR for several airports (those reports preceded by the letters *SPECI* are special, unscheduled reports as a result of a significant weather change. An example would be when the ceiling goes above or below 1,000 feet or when the visibility goes above or below 3 miles).

When you first look at one of these reports, I'm sure it looks as convoluted and cryptic as Egyptian hieroglyphics. Once you learn the code, though, METARs are easy to understand, and learning the weather-code symbology from one report often makes the others much easier to learn.

You'll notice that these weather reports consist of abbreviations. This is a carryover from the days when weather was sent via Teletype, which was slow. Some personal computer software will automatically decode these abbreviations, providing you with a

To some the METAR looks as convoluted and cryptic as Egyptian hieroglyphics.

description of the weather in English (and many internet weather sites will also decode these for you, too). And no, you can't use your IBM or Apple computer on the knowledge exam to interpret weather symbols for you).

Interpreting the METAR requires an understanding of the individual sections contained within the report. Figure 7 is a breakdown of these individual sections. Let's take a closer look at each one.

To better help you understand the order in which a METAR presents the weather, take a look at the following acronym: STWVRWCTDA. This stands for *Should Tina Walk Vera's Rabbit Without Checking The Dog's Appetite?* Each letter represents a particular segment of the weather contained within the METAR as follows:

S	Station Identification
T	Time in Zulu or UTC
W	Wind Direction and Velocity
V	Visibility
R	Runway Visual Range (if reported)
W	Weather
C	Clouds
T	Temperature
D	Dew Point
A	Altimeter Setting

By remembering this acronym you'll be able to remember the general order in which the information is presented. Keep in mind that a METAR won't report what isn't happening, nor will it report a segment if the measuring equipment (such as a barometer) is not functional. By knowing what should be there, you'll easily identify any missing section. Let's jump into interpreting the METAR.

Station – The letter S in Figure 7 represents the first section of the METAR and is a four letter/number designation for the station or airport reporting this observation. KLAX is the designator for Los Angeles International Airport (*K* is the international designator that precedes all domestic U.S. location identifiers; Alaska locations start with *PA* and Hawaii locations start with *PH*). You'll learn some of these airport letter designations for your local area as you go along (besides, some of them are easy enough to guess). The only time you need to be really worried is if you're on an airline flight to Los Angeles and the Skycap checks your bag with a PKS (pak-e-stan?) tag—you'll never get it back.

Time – The letter T in Figure 7 is the date and time the weather observation was made. For instance, at KLAX, the observation was taken on the 8th day of the month at 1955 Zulu (also referred to as UTC or Coordinated Universal Time). Weather reports are always given in Zulu time. This is the time in Greenwich, England and not the time certain African tribes use. Using UTC calibrates all the weather reports to one time zone. All you need do is convert from UTC to your local time zone when interpreting weather reports. Refer to Chapter 13, page 13-4 to review converting between time zones.

Wind – The letter W in Figure 7 identifies the wind direction, velocity, and any gusts. The first three digits represent the wind direction in degrees relative to true north. The next two digits are the wind velocity in knots (as identified by the letters KT). The G followed by a number represents the wind gust in knots. For instance, a wind report of 31015G27KT says that the wind

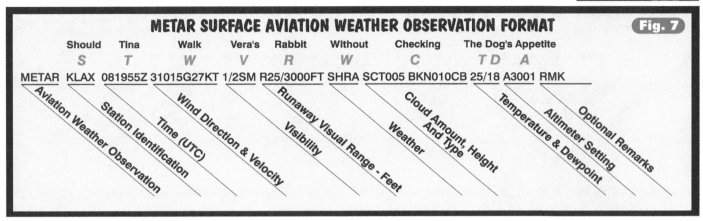

METAR SURFACE AVIATION WEATHER OBSERVATION FORMAT   Fig. 7

Should	Tina	Walk	Vera's	Rabbit	Without	Checking	The Dog's Appetite	
S	**T**	**W**	**V**	**R**	**W**	**C**	**T D**	**A**
METAR	KLAX	081955Z	31015G27KT	1/2SM	R25/3000FT	SHRA	SCT005 BKN010CB	25/18	A3001	RMK

Aviation Weather Observation — Station Identification — Time (UTC) — Wind Direction & Velocity — Visibility — Runaway Visual Range - Feet — Weather — Cloud Amount, Height And Type — Temperature & Dewpoint — Altimeter Setting — Optional Remarks

is 310 degrees at 15 knots with gusts to 27 knots. Gusts are reported when a 10 knot fluctuation occurs between the wind's peaks and lulls. A calm wind is reported as 00000KT. The letters VRB may be used if the wind speed is 5 knots or less. If the wind's direction varies by 60 degrees or more and the speed is greater than 6 knots, then variable wind direction values follow the reported wind. For instance, a 280V350 following the wind report indicates that the winds are 280 degrees variable to 350 degrees. The two extremes in direction will be included in clockwise order.

Visibility – The letter V in Figure 7 stands for visibility. Surface visibility is measured in statute miles and fractions thereof. A space divides whole miles and fractions and the letters SM follow the visibility to indicate *statute miles*. In Figure 7 the reported surface visibility is 1/2 mile. If you fly internationally, you should be aware that the U.S. is an exception in reporting prevailing visibility for the full 360 degree area of visibility rather than the *lowest sector* visibility, which is the international standard. In situations where visibility is very poor in one direction but fairly good in others, you can be mislead by what's prevailing, especially if you're flying in the area where visibility is low. (Significant differences in any sector from the prevailing visibility or a differing tower visibility will be stated in the remarks (RMK) section of the METAR.)

Runway Visual Range – The letter R in Figure 7 stands for RVR

(runway visual range). RVR is an electronically measured value used to determine the distance down a runway that a pilot can see high intensity runway lights. This shouldn't concern you until you become an instrument rated pilot. Nevertheless, understand that RVR is measured in feet. Figure 7 shows that the RVR along Runway 25 (R25) is 3,000 feet. The letters L, C or R that sometimes follow the runway number are designators for the left, center or right runway. The numbers following the slash indicate the RVR in feet (FT).

Weather – The letter W in Figure 7 represents the weather phenomena presently found at the airport. Figure 8 lists the weather codes used in reporting the weather phenomena. These codes contains five different columns. The first two columns contain qualifiers (intensity or proximity and a descriptor of the weather). The last three columns contain the actual weather phenomena, such as precipitation, obscuration, etc. Up to three separate groups of weather phenomena

may be included in the report; the most dominant weather is reported first. Precipitation (water products—rain, snow, hail—reaching the surface) are combined into a single group.

For instance, moderate rain and snow (these are two types of precipitation) present at the airport, is reported as SNRA (snow is the dominant precipitation and is reported first). Both are types of precipitation and are reported as one group. The absence of a + or - sign in front of the precipitation indicates that it's moderate in intensity.

Moderate rain, fog and funnel clouds are three separate groups of weather phenomena and are reported as three separate groups: RA FG FC. If light rain, fog, and volcanic ash were reported, it would look like the following: –RA FGVA. If light drizzle, hail and a sandstorm were reported it would look like the following: –DZGR SS (remember, light drizzle and hail—both are types of precipita-

WEATHER CODES

Qualifiers		Weather Phenomena		
Intensity or proximity **1**	Descriptor **2**	Precipitation **3**	Obscuration **4**	Other **5**
- Light	MI Shallow	DZ Drizzle	BR Mist (≥5/8sm)	PO Dust/sand whirls
Moderate (no qualifier)	BC Patches	RA Rain	FG Fog (<5/8sm)	SQ Squalls
	PR Partial	SN Snow	FU Smoke	FC Funnel cloud(s)/
+ Heavy	DR Low Drifting	SG Snow grains	VA Volcanic ash	
	BL Blowing	IC Ice crystals	DU Dust	+FC Tornado/ waterspout
VC means: in the vicinity	SH Shower(s)	PL Ice pellets	SA Sand	SS Sandstorm
(METAR: between 5 & 10 sm of observation point(s) TAF: between 5 to 10 sm from center of runway complex)	TS Thunderstorm	GR Hail	HZ Haze	DS Duststorm
	FZ Freezing	GS Small hail &/or snow pellets	PY Spray	
		UP Unknown Precip		Fig. 8

METAR SURFACE AVIATION WEATHER OBSERVATION FORMAT

Should	Tina	Walk	Vera's	Rabbit	Without	Checking	The Dog's Appetite
S	T	W	V	R	W	C	T D A

METAR KLAX 081955Z 31015G27KT 1/2SM R25/3000FT SHRA SCT005 BKN010CB 25/18 A3001 RMK

Aviation Weather Observation
Station Identification
Time (UTC)
Wind Direction & Velocity
Visibility
Runaway Visual Range - Feet
Weather
Cloud Amount, Height And Type
Temperature & Dewpoint
Altimeter Setting
Optional Remarks

This figure is repeated from the previous page for your convenience.

Fig. 7

tion—are grouped together). It would also be a hail of a weather report.

The obscuration or second section of the weather phenomena in Figure 8 is only reported in the weather grouping if the visibility is less than seven miles. The presence of smoke (FU) at the airport won't be listed in the weather grouping if the visibility is seven miles or greater.

In Figure 7, the letters SHRA represent showers (SH) and rain (RA). This is spoken as *moderate rain showers*. If it were light rain showers it would be abbreviated as -SHRA.

Clouds – The letter C in Figure 7 represents the cloud coverage, height, and type.

Cloud cover is either SKC (sky clear), indicating no clouds; FEW (reporting more than 0 to 2/8), SCT (scattered), representing coverage of between 3/8 and 4/8 of the sky; BKN (broken), which indicates the sky is between 5/8 and 7/8 covered by clouds; or OVC (overcast) which is complete sky coverage (8/8 coverage). (Automated reporting systems use the letters CLR to indicate no clouds are reported below 12,000 feet.)

A three digit number following the cloud coverage represents the height of the cloud base in hundreds of feet AGL. Three zeros indicates that the cloud height is less than 50 feet AGL.

Cloud types will be provided when towering cumulus (TCU) or cumulonimbus (CB) are observed.

Sometimes weather phenomena based at the surface hide all or part of the sky. This is considered an obscuration. When the sky is obscured and cloud details cannot be assessed, but information on vertical visibility is available, the cloud group is replaced by a

five character group. The first two characters are the letters VV followed by the vertical visibility in units of hundreds of feet. VV004 means the vertical visibility is 400 feet (ATIS reports will still broadcast the term *indefinite* 400 feet obscured).

Sometimes an obscuration doesn't obscure the entire sky. In this instance, partial obscurations are reported by the amount of obscuring phenomena (FEW, SCT, BKN), followed by three digits (i.e., BKN001). In the remarks, the obscuring phenomena precedes the amount of obscuration and the three digits (i.e., FU BKN001, which means that the smoke layer, at 100 feet AGL, is obscuring 5/8 to 7/8 of the sky.)

From our study of airspace, we know that a minimum of a 1,000 foot ceiling is required for operations within surface-based controlled airspace. In the METAR, the lowest layer of clouds reported as broken or overcast, or any reported vertical visibility into obscuring phenomena is considered the official ceiling.

In Figure 7, the METAR indicates the presence of a 500 foot scattered layer of clouds, a 1,000 broken layer of clouds (the ceiling), and CB's or cumulonimbus clouds are present.

REMARKS APPENDED TO METARS

Fig. 9

Remarks	Definition
Sky and Ceiling	
FEW CU	Few cumulus clouds.
BINOVC	Breaks in overcast.
LWR CLDS NE	Lower clouds northeast.
CIG 14V19	Ceiling variable between 1,400 feet and 1,900 feet.
Obscuring Phenomena	
FG7	Fog obscuring 7/10 of the sky.
BLSA3	Blowing sand obscuring 3/10 of the sky.
THN FG NE	Thin fog northeast from reporting station.
Visibility	
VSBY S1W1/4	Visibility south is 1 mile, west is 1/4 mile.
SFC VSBY 1/2	Surface visibility is 1/2 mile.

Remarks	Definition
Weather and Obstruction to Vision	
RAB30	Rain began 30 minutes after the hour.
RAE30	Rain ended 30 minutes after the hour.
OCNL DST LTG NW	Occasional distant lightning NW of reporting station.
T OVHD MOVG NE	Thunderstorm overhead, moving northeast.
Wind	
WND 27V33	Wind variable between 270 degrees and 330 degrees.
PK WND 33048/22 ("PK WND" is used whenever the peak winds exceed 25 knots)	Peak wind within the past hour from 330 degrees at 48 knots occurred 22 minutes past the hour.
Pressure	
PRESSR	Pressure rising rapidly.
PRESFR	Pressure falling rapidly.

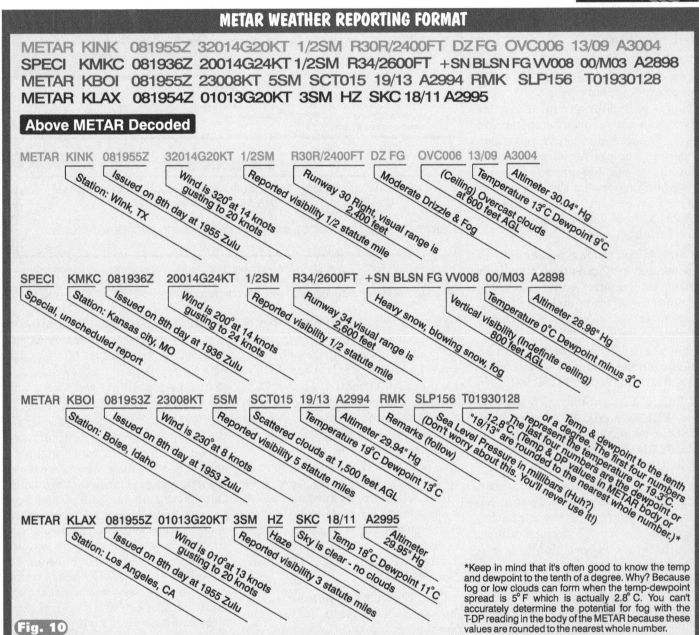

METAR WEATHER REPORTING FORMAT

METAR KINK 081955Z 32014G20KT 1/2SM R30R/2400FT DZ FG OVC006 13/09 A3004
SPECI KMKC 081936Z 20014G24KT 1/2SM R34/2600FT +SN BLSN FG VV008 00/M03 A2898
METAR KBOI 081955Z 23008KT 5SM SCT015 19/13 A2994 RMK SLP156 T01930128
METAR KLAX 081954Z 01013G20KT 3SM HZ SKC 18/11 A2995

Above METAR Decoded

METAR KINK 081955Z 32014G20KT 1/2SM R30R/2400FT DZ FG OVC006 13/09 A3004
- Station: Wink, TX
- Issued on 8th day at 1955 Zulu
- Wind is 320° at 14 knots gusting to 20 knots
- Reported visibility 1/2 statute mile
- Runway 30 Right, visual range is 2,400 feet
- Moderate Drizzle & Fog
- (Ceiling) Overcast clouds at 600 feet AGL
- Temperature 13°C Dewpoint 9°C
- Altimeter 30.04" Hg

SPECI KMKC 081936Z 20014G24KT 1/2SM R34/2600FT +SN BLSN FG VV008 00/M03 A2898
- Special, unscheduled report
- Station: Kansas city, MO
- Issued on 8th day at 1936 Zulu
- Wind is 200° at 14 knots gusting to 24 knots
- Reported visibility 1/2 statute mile
- Runway 34 visual range is 2,600 feet
- Heavy snow, blowing snow, fog
- Vertical visibility (Indefinite ceiling) 800 feet AGL
- Temperature 0°C Dewpoint minus 3°C
- Altimeter 28.98" Hg

METAR KBOI 081953Z 23008KT 5SM SCT015 19/13 A2994 RMK SLP156 T01930128
- Station: Boise, Idaho
- Issued on 8th day at 1953 Zulu
- Wind is 230° at 8 knots
- Reported visibility 5 statute miles
- Scattered clouds at 1,500 feet AGL
- Temperature 19°C Dewpoint 13°C
- Altimeter 29.94" Hg
- Remarks (follow)
- Sea Level Pressure in millibars (Huh?) (Don't worry about this. You'll never use it!)
- "19/13" are rounded to the nearest whole number. The last four numbers are the dewpoint or 19.3°C. (Temp & DP values in METAR body or 12.8°C. represent the temperature of a degree. The first four numbers Temp & dewpoint to the tenth.)*

METAR KLAX 081955Z 01013G20KT 3SM HZ SKC 18/11 A2995
- Station: Los Angeles, CA
- Issued on 8th day at 1955 Zulu
- Wind is 010° at 13 knots gusting to 20 knots
- Reported visibility 3 statute miles
- Haze
- Sky is clear - no clouds
- Temp 18°C Dewpoint 11°C
- Altimeter 29.95" Hg

*Keep in mind that it's often good to know the temp and dewpoint to the tenth of a degree. Why? Because fog or low clouds can form when the temp-dewpoint spread is 5° F which is actually 2.8° C. You can't accurately determine the potential for fog with the T-DP reading in the body of the METAR because these values are rounded to the nearest whole number.

Fig. 10

Temperature/Dew Point – The letters T and D in Figure 7 represent the reported temperature and dew point in degrees Celsius. This is reported to the nearest whole degree using two digits (i.e., 6 degrees C is reported as 06). Sub-zero values are prefixed with an M (e.g., 03/M02). In Figure 7, the temperature is 25 degrees C and the dew point is 18 degrees C.

Altimeter – The letter A in Figure 7 represents the altimeter setting for that location. The altimeter setting is always prefixed with an A, indicating the altimeter setting in inches of mercury. All four digits of the pres-

sure are listed. Simply insert a decimal after the second digit. In Figure 7, the altimeter setting is 30.01 inches of Hg.

At the end of the METAR, you will sometimes find supplementary information in the form of remarks (RMK). This is where the briefer can customize his or her weather observation by adding supplemental information. Figure 9 shows a few of these remarks (see the Aeronautical Information Manual or Aviation Weather Services Advisory Circular AC 00-45E for more information on remark codes). Don't be overwhelmed. Some of these codes are rarer than a wealthy flight

instructor. You'll learn them as you encounter them.

Figure 10 shows the decoding of the METAR presented in Figure 6.

Automatic Weather Observing Programs

Automatic weather observing stations will soon serve as the nation's primary surface weather observing network. These weather-watching computers-in-a-can transmit weather information (temperature, pressure, dew point, winds, cloud heights, etc.) directly to you in flight. We'll discuss two types of automatic weather observing systems: Automatic

Surface Observing System (ASOS) and Automatic Weather Observing System (AWOS).

ASOS – ASOS is sort of a hyperactive AWOS. In addition to basic weather measurements, it also reports precipitation and intensity, as well as the occurrence of freezing rain. Situated at airports and other observing points nationwide, these automated stations provide minute-by-minute reports on the ever-changing weather (you would officially report this as having received the *one-minute weather*).

One of the unique benefits of the automated system is that pilots can listen to computer-generated voice observations while airborne (some computer voices sound like Darth Vader with a cold). These transmissions are usually receivable within 25 nautical miles of an airport at a maximum altitude of 10,000 feet AGL.

Figure 11 shows an *AFD* excerpt for Wiscasset airport showing that ASOS observations can be heard on 135.725 MHz or heard by calling the listed phone number.

ASOS reports are similar to the METAR that we've already studied. There are, however, a few subtle differences. Automated stations cannot, for instance, report clouds above 12,000 feet. However, the ASOS will report *CLR* (meaning no clouds are reported below 12,000 feet) instead of the *SKC* value shown in the METAR. There could be a solid overcast at 15,000 feet, but the ASOS cannot identify it. Thus, it can't report it. Keep this little idiosyncrasy in mind whenever you see an observation annotated as AUTO, COR (for CORrected) or in the remarks you see AO1 or AO2 (the AO1 or AO2 indicates the level of sophistication of the precipitation discrimination sensors associated with the ASOS unit. AO2, being more sophisticated, can discriminate between different types of precipitation, i.e., rain, snow, etc.).

Remember, if you see or hear of something missing from a ASOS report, it doesn't mean it's not there. It just means that the ASOS unit can't or didn't detect it.

Airport/Facility Directory excerpt   **MAINE**

WISCASSET   (9B9)   3 SW   UTC–5(–4DT)   N43°57.67′
    68   B   S4   FUEL 100LL   TPA—1068(1000)
RWY 07-25: H3400X75 (ASPH)   S–22   MIRL
    RWY 07: PAPI(P4L)—GA 4.0°TCH 40′. Trees.   RWY 25:
AIRPORT REMARKS: Attended 1300Z‡–dusk. Fuel available 1400-2200Z‡ daily. For fuel after hours call
    207–882-6752. No touch and go ldgs Jun-Sep. PAEW S Rwy 25 safety zone. ACTIVATE MIRL Rwy 07-25; PAPI
    Rwys 07 and 25; REIL Rwy 25—CTAF. Rwy 25 REIL OTS indef.
WEATHER DATA SOURCES: ASOS 135.725 (207) 882-8094.
COMMUNICATIONS: CTAF/UNICOM 122.8

> *You can hear the ASOS (Automatic Surface Observation System) report on frequency 135.725 as indicated in the A/FD.*

Fig. 11

ASOS REPORTS   **Fig. 12**

METAR KABC 121355Z `AUTO` 21016G24KT 180V240 1SM -RA FG BKN015
    OVC025 06/05 A2990 RMK AO2 PK WIND 20032/25

METAR KINK 130900Z `COR` 03005KT 21/2SM +SHRA OVC015 15/14 A3000
    RMK AO2

The word *AUTO* or *COR* (for *COR*rected) appearing in the METAR indicates that this report was derived from some type of an automatic surface weather observation unit (ASOS, AWOS, etc.). When the ASOS report is augmented by a human observer, the word *AUTO* or *COR* is deleted.

Figure 12 shows two ASOS weather observations. You can tell these are automatic-type surface observations because the letters AUTO (meaning AUTOmated) and/or COR are located directly after the location of the date/time identifier. As you can clearly see, the ASOS observations are provided in the same format as the METARs we've already studied. There's nothing new to be learned here. Simply read the ASOS observations as you do the METAR. (See Figure 9 for a sampling of the codes for the remarks (RMK) found at the end of the ASOS (METAR) observation.)

The ASOS observation for KABC shows AUTO right after the date/time group and the letters AO2 in the remarks section. This indicates that no human oversight backed up or augmented the ASOS report. Some locations have a human observer augment the ASOS report. Whenever the human observer augments or adds to the ASOS report, the AUTO is deleted, because now it is a manual observation. However, the remarks section will still show either an AO1 or an AO2.

Personally, I am inclined to place greater faith in automated weather reports when a human being oversees the process. That's why I don't trust those automated blood pressure machines found at shopping malls and airports. I heard of a pilot who

put in his quarter, stuck in his arm and when his reading came up as 390 over 260, it wouldn't let him go until an FAA rep showed up (just kidding). Remember, machines can't detect all the weather.

AWOS – AWOS (Automatic Weather Observing System) are found at more and more airports across the country where weather reports were previously not available. Consisting of various sensors, a processor, a computer-generated voice system and transmitter, these stations broadcast minute-by-minute, real time, local weather information directly to pilots. AWOS/ASOS transmissions are receivable within 25 nautical miles of the transmission site, at or below 10,000 feet AGL. The transmissions can also be received on the airport. Frequencies for AWOS may be found near the airport data on the sectional chart, as shown in Figure 13, and in the *A/FD* as shown in Figure 14.

Four basic levels of AWOS stations are available:

1. AWOS-A reports only altimeter setting.

2. AWOS-1 usually reports altimeter setting, wind data, temperature, dew point and density altitude.

3. AWOS-2 provides the information provided by AWOS-1 plus visibility.

4. AWOS-3 provides the information of AWOS-2 plus cloud-ceiling data.

The frequency for AWOS is also shown on the sectional chart along with the airport information.

Fig. 13

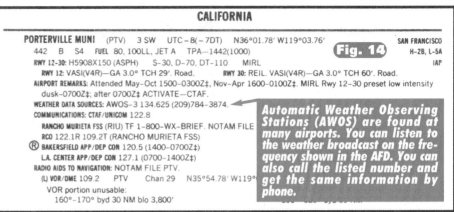

CALIFORNIA

PORTERVILLE MUNI (PTV) 3 SW UTC – 8(– 7DT) N36°01.78′ W119°03.76′   SAN FRANCISCO
442   B   S4   FUEL 80, 100LL, JET A   TPA–1442(1000)   **Fig. 14**   H–2B, L–5A
RWY 12-30: H5908X150 (ASPH)   S–30, D–70, DT–110   MIRL   IAP
  RWY 12: VASI(V4R)—GA 3.0° TCH 29′. Road.   RWY 30: REIL. VASI(V4R)—GA 3.0° TCH 60′. Road.
  AIRPORT REMARKS: Attended May-Oct 1500-0300Z‡, Nov-Apr 1600-0100Z‡. MIRL Rwy 12–30 preset low intensity
    dusk-0700Z‡; after 0700Z‡ ACTIVATE—CTAF.
  WEATHER DATA SOURCES: AWOS-3 134.625 (209)784-3874.
  COMMUNICATIONS: CTAF/UNICOM 122.8
   RANCHO MURIETA FSS (RIU) TF 1-800-WX-BRIEF. NOTAM FILE
   RCO 122.1R 109.2T (RANCHO MURIETA FSS)
  Ⓡ BAKERSFIELD APP/DEP CON 120.5 (1400-0700Z‡)
   L.A. CENTER APP/DEP CON 127.1 (0700-1400Z‡)
  RADIO AIDS TO NAVIGATION: NOTAM FILE PTV.
  (L) VOR/DME 109.2   PTV   Chan 29   N35°54.78′ W119°
   VOR portion unusable:
    160°-170° byd 30 NM blo 3,800′

Automatic Weather Observing Stations (AWOS) are found at many airports. You can listen to the weather broadcast on the frequency shown in the AFD. You can also call the listed number and get the same information by phone.

A typical ASOS or AWOS voice transmitted observation might sound something like the following:

"Denver, Denver Front Range airport, automated weather observation. One eight three three Zulu. Sky conditions six thousand five hundred scattered. Visibility greater than one zero. Temperature two two Celsius, dew point one niner Celsius. Wind three five zero at zero three (ASOS or AWOS winds received by radio are *magnetic* in direction). Altimeter two niner seven eight. Remarks, density altitude seven thousand five hundred."

Remember, just because it's a machine doesn't mean it won't make mistakes. The entire airport might be surrounded by clouds with a single, solitary hole over the ASOS or AWOS-3 weather unit. You can bet that little puppy reports *all clear*. The entire airport may be shrouded in fog while the ceilometer (cloud height measuring device) reports no clouds at the airport. Fortunately, the visibility would provide a clue to the presence of fog. When a human weather observer supplements mechanical weather observations, these problems disappear. Use a little common sense when using an automated observation of the weather on which to base your decisions.

Whither the Weather?

Having the current weather for airports along your route is valuable. But this is just one bean short of a hill if you're planning tomorrow's flight. Weather changes from day to day, hour to hour, minute to minute. It also changes while enroute. Pilots need a means of predicting this change.

Since pilots don't have crystal balls (no matter what they may claim), most of them look into the future through more conventional means such as one of several aviation forecasts that are available.

Terminal Aerodrome Weather Forecasts (TAF) – (also referred to as an *Aviation Terminal Forecast*) A terminal forecast sounds like it's the last weather you're ever going to get. Fortunately, this isn't what a TAF is all about. TAFs provide a description of surface weather expected to occur at an airport.

You would certainly invest one dollar to make a million dollars (we call this the Lotto), but you wouldn't invest half a million dollars to make one dollar. So why then would you risk half a million hours of the rest of your life just to arrive home an hour sooner in your airplane?

They are an excellent means of identifying the weather you can expect upon arrival at an airport. You can compare forecasts for airports along your route to obtain a better idea of how the weather is expected to change. When used in conjunction with METARs, TAFs provide you with a good idea of the present weather and how it's expected to change.

TAFs are forecast weather for a 24 hour period (30 hours for some locations) and represent the expected weather within a 5 statute mile radius of the airport's runway complex. They are issued four times daily (once every six hours starting at 0000Z). Much of the weather coding is similar to the METAR weather format (I knew that would make you happy). Since it's relatively simple to read, we won't need a memory-type acronym to interpret TAFs. If there are any major differences in the codes used by TAF compared to METAR, I'll let you know. Let's examine the TAF weather shown in Figure 15.

Station: (KLAX)

Same form and format as the METAR.

Date Forecast Issued: (091140Z):

The report was issued on the 9th day (09) at 1140 Zulu (UTC).

TERMINAL AERODROME WEATHER FORECAST (TAF)

```
TAF
KLAX 091140Z 0912/1012 22020KT 3SM -SHRA BKN020
     BECMG 0916/0919 33015KT
     FM100300 35014KT 2SM TSRA OVC015
     TEMPO 1006/1012 1SM +RA PROB40 1008/1009 1/2SM FG
```
Fig. 15

Time of Forecast: (0912/1012)

This forecast's date and valid times are shown by two four-digit numbers separated by a slash (0912/1012). The first four numbers represent the date and the time the forecast period begins (the 9th at 1200Z). The last four numbers represent the ending time of the forecast period (the 10th at 1200Z). The forecast is valid from 1200Z on the 9th to 1200Z on the 10th (a 24 hour period). If midnight UTC is the beginning time period of the forecast it will be coded as 00. If it is the ending time, it is coded as 24. Therefore, a 24 hour forecast beginning and ending at midnight UTC would be indicated as: 0900/1024.

Forecast Winds: (22020KT)

This is presented in the same format as the METAR. Figure 15 shows winds forecast to be from 220 degrees true direction at 20 knots. Calm winds are encoded as 00000KT and expected gusts are followed by the letter G.

Forecast Visibility: (3SM)

This is the prevailing visibility expected in statute miles, up to and including 6 miles. Expected visibilities greater than 6 miles are forecast as *P6SM* (*plus six statute miles*).

Forecast Weather: (-SHRA)

The same five categories used in a METAR are used in a TAF for reporting weather phenomena, as shown in Figure 8. The letters -SHRA represent only operationally significant weather that's forecast for the stated time period. In other words, light rain showers are forecast starting at 1200Z.

This figure is repeated from the previous page for your convenience.

TERMINAL AERODROME WEATHER FORECAST

```
TAF
KLAX 091140Z 0912/1012 22020KT 3SM -SHRA BKN020
     BECMG 0916/0919 33015KT
     FM100300 35014KT 2SM TSRA OVC015
     TEMPO 1006/1012 1SM +RA PROB40 1008/1009 1/2SM FG
```

Fig. 15

Forecast Cloud Conditions: (BKN020)

This is the same as the METAR format. In this example, broken clouds are forecast at 2000 feet AGL. As in the METAR, ceiling layers are designated by the lowest layer that's BKN, OVC or shows

DECODED TERMINAL AERODROME WEATHER FORECAST (TAF)

```
TAF
KLAX 101740Z 1018/1118 12020KT 4SM -RA OVC016
     FM101920 30015G25KT 3SM SHRA OVC015 PROB40 1020/1022 1/2SM TSRA OVC008CB
     FM102300 27008KT 5SM -SHRA BKN020 OVC040 TEMPO 1102/1105 00000KT 1SM -RA FG
     FM110800 VRB04KT 5SM -SHRA OVC020 BECMG 1112/1114 20010KT P6SM NSW SKC
```

Above TAF Decoded

KLAX 101740Z 1018/1118 12020KT 4SM -RA OVC016 **Fig. 16**

Station: Los Angeles — Issued on 10th day at 1740 Zulu — Forecast time beginning on the 10th at 1800Z ending the 11th at 1800Z — Wind forecast 120° at 20 knots — 4 statute miles visibility — Light rain — Overcast (ceiling) at 1,600 feet AGL

FM101920 30015G25KT 3SM SHRA OVC015 PROB40 1020/1022 1/2SM TSRA OVC008CB

Letters FM (meaning FroM) indicate significant change in weather expected on the 10th at 1920Z — Wind of 300° at 15 knots gusting to 25 knots — 3 statute miles visibility — Moderate rain showers — Overcast (ceiling) at 1,500 feet AGL — 40-49% probability between 2000Z & 2200Z (on the 10th) of 1/2 statute mile visibility with thunderstorms & rain with an overcast (ceiling) of 800 foot AGL & cumulonimbus clouds*

*CBs are the only cloud type forecast in the TAF

FM102300 27008KT 5SM -SHRA BKN020 OVC040 TEMPO 1102/1105 00000KT 1SM -RA FG

Letters FM (meaning FroM) indicate significant change in weather expected on the 10th at 2300Z — Wind of 270° at 8 knots — 5 statute miles visibility — Light rain showers — Broken clouds (ceiling) at 2,000 feet AGL & an overcast at 4,000 feet AGL — A temporary change between 0200Z & 0500Z (on the 11th) is expected with calm winds and one statute mile visibility due to light rain & fog

FM110800 VRB04KT 5SM -SHRA OVC020 BECMG 1112/1114 20010KT P6SM NSW SKC

Letters FM indicate another significant change in weather expected at 0800Z on the 11th — Wind variable in direction at 4 knots — 5 statute miles visibility — Light rain showers — Overcast clouds (ceiling) at 2,000 feet AGL — Between 1200Z to 1400Z (on the 11th) the weather is forecast to become: winds of 200 at 10 knots, plus 6 miles visibility and no significant weather & a sky that's clear

NEW! 30 Hour TAF Formatting

In its desire to remain internationally consistent, the FAA is adopting a 30-hour TAF format in lieu of its 24-hour cousin for 32 large airports in the United States (think Los Angeles, Denver, Chicago, etc.). The additional six forecast hours added to the TAF allow long-haul air carriers to better evaluate their flight planned routing. If you plan on landing at or near any of these 32 airports, you will now have an even better idea of the forecast weather.

TERMINAL AERODROME WEATHER FORECAST (TAF)

TAF
KLAX 091140Z 0912/1012 22020KT 3SM -SHRA BKN020
     BECMG 0916/0919 33015KT
     FM100300 35014KT 2SM TSRA OVC015
     TEMPO 1006/1012 1SM +RA PROB40 1008/1009 1/2SM FG

The date/time value 0912/1018 tells us that the TAF forecast period begins on the 9th day of the month at 1200Z and ends on the 10th at 1800 Zulu (30 hours total). Starting at 1200 on the 9th, you can expect winds of 220 degrees at 20 knots with 3 miles visibility and light rain showers. **BECMG** 0916/0919 tells us that between 1600Z on the 9th and 1900Z on the 9th, the winds will become (gradually, usually within a 2 hour period) 330 degrees at 15 knots. **FM**100300 tells us that on the 10th day, beginning at 0300Z, a rapid change in weather is expected (winds 350 degrees at 14 knots, 2 miles visibility with thunderstorms and rain with a 1,500 foot overcast. **TEMPO** 1006/1012 means a fluctuation in the weather (lasting less than 1 hour) will occur, resulting in a visibility of one mile and heavy rain. **PROB40** 1008/1009 indicates a 40 percent probability that, between 0800Z on the 10th and 0900Z on the same day, the visibility will fall to ½ mile in fog.

VV (vertical visibility) into an obscuration.

Expected Changes: (BECMG, FM, TEMPO, PROB)

When *gradual* changes in the prevailing conditions are expected (usually over a period not to exceed two hours), the abbreviations BECMG (becoming) is used. BECMG is followed by two, four-digit numbers separated by a slash. The first four digits indicate the date and time when the change is expected to begin and the last four digits indicate when it's expected to be completed. The weather conditions that follow are expected to change at a gradual rate over the depicted time period. Any weather condition forecast prior to BECMG that is not revised following the change time period is expected to remain the same. For example, our report showing *0916/0919* after BECMG means that, on the 9th (or 09) from 1600Z to 1900Z on the same day, the wind is expected to change to 330 degrees at 15 knots and all other weather is expected to remain the same.

FM is followed by a six digit number (the date and a four digit time value) that indicates the beginning time of a self contained portion of the forecast. This is used when a *rapid* (significant) change in weather (usually occurring in less than one hour) is expected. In our report, the sequence of FM100300 says that on

the 10th, from 0300Z the following weather conditions should occur: winds 350 degrees at 14 knots, 2 miles visibility, thunderstorms and rain and an overcast ceiling of 1,500 feet. Weather that's omitted in the FM group isn't significant to aviation. (Since FM implies "one" hour or less of time, it only needs a beginning date and time, thus six digits.)

TEMPO indicates that fluctuations (temporary and usually lasting less than one hour) from the predominant weather conditions are expected. TEMPO is followed by two four-digit numbers separated by a slash (1006/1012) giving the date and time period that these variations are expected. In our report, a temporary condition of 1 mile visibility and heavy rain is expected to occur on the 10th, between 0600Z and 1200Z.

PROB (PROBability) is used when the likely occurrence of any weather phenomena falls in the 30 to 39% (PROB 30) or 40 to 49% (PROB 40) range of expectation. If the probability of the condition is 50% or higher, the terms BECMG, TEMPO or FM will be used. In our report the sequence, PROB40 1008/1009 1/2SM FG indicates that, on the 10th, between the hours of 0800Z and 0900Z there is a 40 to 49% probability of 1/2 mile visibility in fog. Figure 16 shows a detailed analysis of an airport's TAF.

Remember, TAFs are issued once every six hours. Make it a point to check the latest TAF for the most current forecast information. I make it a point to check the METAR against the TAF. If the TAF said that this hour was to be clear but the METAR showed clouds, then that particular TAF might be too optimistic. I might then be less inclined to place a great deal of trust in its accuracy. Once something isn't right, you're disinclined to trust it. That's why I never trusted my uncle's communications skills. When I was young he told our neighbor to drop me off at the nursery on her way to work. For an entire day I sat, surrounded by plants and trees.

Area Forecasts (FA) – Remember the anxiety you felt when you went to a drive-in theater and drove off without unhooking the speaker? Five blocks away you heard, "Attention, attention, the snack bar will be closing in 15 minutes." OK, perhaps this never happened to you, but you might feel a similar sensation when looking at the area forecast. It consists of a lot of words without vowels. This is part of the carryover from those days when Teletypes were slow and words were abbreviated to speed things up. With just a little practice you'll be interpreting these reports as fast as Einstein whipping through nonlinear differential equations.

The *Area Forecast (FA)* is a general forecast, often covering a region that includes several states. It's your key to finding the expected weather enroute and at airports not having terminal aerodrome forecasts (not every airport has a terminal aerodrome forecast, which makes the area forecast your only forecasting tool). Figure 17 shows a typical area forecast.

> *The best way to determine the general forecast weather conditions over several states is with the area forecast.*

FAs are issued three times daily for six specific areas in the lower 48 United States. They are 12 hour forecasts with an additional 6 hour outlook. As with other weather reports and forecasts, times are in Zulu. Unlike the terminal aerodrome forecast, however, the area forecast presents its cloud heights in MSL rather than AGL (unless noted by an AGL or ceiling designation). This is logical, once you think it through, since the forecast isn't for a specific spot, but rather a huge area over which there is often considerable variation in terrain height. In the area forecast, a ceiling is identified by CIG (which means ceiling). Figures 18A and 18B show a few of the common contractions, definitions and variability terms used in the FA and other weather reports and forecasts.

The FA consists of four sections:

1. Communications and Header Section
2. Precautionary Statements Section
3. Synopsis Section
4. VFR Clouds and Weather Section

Let's examine the FA in Figure 17. The first section of the FA was issued for the Salt Lake City area (the C following SLC indicates that this forecast contains clouds and weather). This forecast was issued on the 26th day of the month (26) at 1045Z. Underneath this line is *SYNOPSIS AND VFR CLDS/WX* which tells you what's in this forecast, in case you don't already know. The next line states that the SYNOPSIS is valid until 0500Z on the 27th day of the month (270500). The line underneath indicates the CLDS/WX section is valid until 2300Z on the 26th (a 12 hour period from the time the forecast begins). Note that the syn-

opsis is valid for 18 hours while the VFR clouds and weather section is valid for only 12 hours. The OTLK (outlook) information is valid from 2300Z on the 26th to 0500Z on the 27th (that's a six hour period).

Following this are the states making up the forecast area. Idaho, Montana, Wyoming, Nevada, Utah, Colorado, Arizona and New Mexico are covered in this area forecast as shown in Figure 19.

As you can plainly see, often vowels are left out of the report to condense it for transmission (don't try to speak without vowels unless you enjoy sounding like a Klingon). Fortunately, weather briefers read it to you in real English (that's because Klingons don't get weather briefings—they go regardless of the weather). It's not, however, difficult to read once you've had a little practice. Since there are only five vowels (a, e, i, o and u for those long out of school), you can always just substitute until you get something that looks like an English word.

Fig. 17   **THE AREA FORECAST**

(Author's note: weather for NV, UT, CO, AZ and NM not shown)

```
SLCC FA 261045
SYNOPSIS AND VFR CLDS/WX
SYNOPSIS VALID UNTIL 270500
CLDS/WX VALID UNTIL 262300...OTLK VALID 262300-270500
ID MT WY NV UT CO AZ NM
```
COMMUNICATIONS AND HEADER SECTION

```
SEE AIRMET SIERRA FOR IFR CONDS AND MTN OBSCN.
TS IMPLY SEV OR GTR TURB SEV ICE LLWS AND IFR CONDS.
NON MSL HGTS DENOTED BY AGL OR CIG.
```
PRECAUTIONARY STATEMENTS SECTION

```
SYNOPSIS...CDFNT EXTDS FROM ERN MT ACRS SWRN MT AND
SWRN ID INTO NWRN NV INTO NRN CA.  BY 05Z...CDFNT WILL
EXTD FROM NWRN MN AND ERN SD ACRS CNTRL NEB AND SERN
ID INTO NWRN NV AND NRN CA.  UPR LVL LOW PRES SYS OVR
NRN NM WILL MOVE SLOLY SWD DURG PD.
```
SYNOPSIS SECTION

```
ID
NRN ID...SKC. OCNL SCT100 SCT CI.  OTLK...VFR.
CNTRL AND SRN ID...SCT100 BKN150.  TOPS TO FL200.  BKN CI
  ISOL -SHRA... MAINLY ERN SXNS.  BECMG 1723 OVR MAINLY ERN
  SXNS...BKN080-100 BKN150. TOPS TO FL200.  WDLY SCT -TSRA
  ...CB TOPS TO FL350...LWRG CIGS/VIS BKN030- 050/3-5SM.  OTLK...VFR.

MT
W OF DVD...SKC. OCNL SCT100 SCT CI.  OTLK...VFR.
SWRN MTNS...SCT100 BKN150. TOPS TO FL200.  BKN CI.  ISOL -SHRA.  BECMG 1723
  WDLY SCT -TSRA...CB TOPS TO FL350...LWRG CIGS/VIS BKN030-050/3-5SM.
  OTLK...VFR.
CNTRL AND ERN MT...SCT100 SCT-BKN150.  TOPS TO FL200.  ISOL -TSRA/-SHRA...CB
  TOPS TO FL310.  OTLK...VFR.

WY
MTNS AND WEST...SCT100 BKN150.  TOPS TO FL200.  BKN CI.  ISOL -SHRA.  BECMG
  1723 WDLY SCT -TSRA...CB TOPS TO  FL350...LWRG CIGS/VIS BKN030-050/3-5SM.
  OTLK...VFR.
ERN PLNS/FOOTHILLS...SCT150 SCT CI.  BECMG 1723 SCT100 SCT-BKN150.  TOPS
  TO FL200.  ISOL -TSRA/-SHRA DVLPG... CB TOPS TO FL350.  OTLK...VFR.
```
VFR CLOUDS AND WEATHER SECTION

The precautionary statements sections in Figure 17 is next. These statements are included in all area forecasts. Any IFR conditions or mountain obscuration that are present or expected to occur will be covered in something called an AIRMET (AIR METeorological advisory). As you'll soon see, these are advisories of significant weather phenomena and should be of concern to you. Keep in mind that hazardous weather (IFR, icing and turbulence) are not included in the area forecast. You must refer to AIRMETs and other in-flight Aviation Weather Advisories for this information (we'll discuss these shortly).

The next statement says that thunderstorms imply possible severe or greater turbulence, severe icing and low level wind shear and IFR conditions. The last statement indicates that all heights in the area forecast are MSL unless otherwise noted.

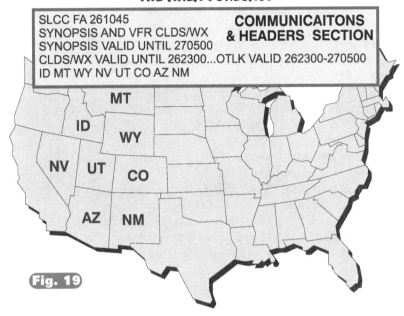

THE AREA FORECAST

SLCC FA 261045
SYNOPSIS AND VFR CLDS/WX
SYNOPSIS VALID UNTIL 270500
CLDS/WX VALID UNTIL 262300...OTLK VALID 262300-270500
ID MT WY NV UT CO AZ NM

COMMUNICAITONS & HEADERS SECTION

Fig. 19

Categories

Category	Definition
LIFR -	Low IFR - ceiling less than 500 feet and/or visibility less than 1 mile.
IFR -	Ceiling 500 to less than 1,000 feet and/or visibility 1 to less than 3 miles.
MVFR -	Marginal VFR - ceiling 1,000 to 3,000 feet and/or visibility 3 to 5 miles inclusive.
VFR -	No ceiling or ceiling greater than 3,000 feet and visibility greater than 5 miles.

Remarks appended to VFR items

Remarks	Definition
VFR CIG ABV 100	Ceiling greater than 10,000 feet and visibility greater than 5 miles.
VFR NO CIG	Cloud coverage less than 6/10 or thin clouds and visibility greater than 5 miles.
VFR CLR	Cloud coverage less than 1/10 and visibility greater than 5 miles.

Examples of categorical groupings

Example	Definition
LIFR CIG	Low IFR due to low ceiling only.
IFR F	IFR due to visibility restricted by fog.
MVFR CIG H K	Marginal VFR due both to low ceiling and to visibility restricted by haze and smoke.
IFR CIG R WND	IFR due both to low ceiling and to visibility restricted by rain, wind expected to be 25 knots or greater.

Fig. 18A

The synopsis section of the area forecast is simply the *big picture* of what's going on. It is a brief summary of the location and movements of fronts, pressure systems and circulation systems for an 18 hour period. Figure 20 shows how you might mentally picture this synopsis.

The VFR clouds and weather section contains a 12-hour specific forecast, followed by a 6-hour categorical outlook. This gives us a total forecast period of 18 hours. You'll find the VFR CLDS/WX section several paragraphs long. It's often broken down by states or by well known geographical areas. A general description of clouds and weather that cover an area greater than 3,000 square miles and is significant to VFR flight operations follows each of the listed geographical areas.

In order to interpret the area forecast, it's best to start with the synopsis

---

Contractions

Contraction	Designator	Definition
CLR	CLR	Sky clear
SCT	SCT	Scattered
BKN	BKN	Broken
OVC	OVC	Overcast
OBSCD	X	Obscured
PTLYOBSCD	-X	Partlyobscured
CIG	C	Ceiling

Fig. 18B

Area coverage of showers and thunderstorms

Adjective	Coverage
Isolated -	Single cells (no percentage)
Widely scattered -	Less than 25% of area affected.
Scattered -	25% to 54% of area affected
Numerous -	55% or more of area affected

Variability Terms

Variability terms are often included in the remarks and indicate how often a change might occur in ceilings, sky cover, weather, etc.

OCNL ... means *occasional* and indicates that there is a greater than 50% probability that the associated weather condition will occur, bit for less than 1/2 of the forecast period.

CHC ... means *chance* and indicates that there is a 30% to 50% probability that the associated weather condition will occur.

SLGT CHC ... means *slight chance* and indicates that there is a 10% to 20% probability that the associated weather conditions will occur.

section. Personally, I like this section best. Why? Because it's frank and to the point. I guess you could say that this is the place to get a *frank synopsis* (he was a great guy, wasn't he?).

According to the synopsis shown in Figure 20, a cold front (CDFNT) extends (EXTDS) from eastern (ERN) Montana across (ACRS) southwestern (SWRN) Montana and southwestern Idaho into northwestern (NWRN) Nevada into northern (NRN) California. By 0500 Zulu (the end of the outlook's valid time) the cold front will extend from northwestern Minnesota and eastern South Dakota across central (CNTRL) Nebraska and southeastern (SERN) Idaho into northwestern Nevada and northern California. An upper level (UPR LVL) low pressure system (SYS) over (OVR) northern New Mexico will move slowly (SLOLY) southward (SWD) during (DURG) this period (PD).

Once you've looked over the synopsis, forecast weather for individual states or specific locations in the VFR CLDS/WX section will make more sense to you. Figure 21 provides an interpretation for Idaho's weather.

THE AREA FORECAST   SYNOPSIS SECTION

SYNOPSIS...CDFNT EXTDS FROM ERN MT ACRS SWRN MT AND SWRN ID INTO NWRN NV INTO NRN CA. BY 05Z... CDFNT WILL EXTD FROM NWRN MN AND ERN SD ACRS CNTRL NEB AND SERN ID INTO NWRN NV AND NRN CA. UPR LVL LOW PRES SYS OVR NRN NM WILL MOVE SLOLY SWD DURG PD.

Cold Front

MT

WY

NV UT CO

Upper Low Pressure System

AZ

Fig. 20

Keep in mind that surface visibility and obstructions to vision are only included in the area forecast when the forecast visibility is expected to be six statute miles or less. Precipitation, thunderstorms and sustained winds of 20 knots or greater are always included when forecast.

HOW THE VFR CLOUDS AND WEATHER SECTION OF THE AREA FORECAST IS INTERPRETED

In northern Idaho... sky clear. Occasional scattered clouds at 10,000 feet MSL and scattered cirrus clouds CI (cirrus are high clouds). Outlook - VFR.

Central and southern Idaho...scattered clouds at 10,000 feet MSL, broken clouds at 15,000 feet MSL. Cloud tops to flight level 200 (20,000 feet). Broken cirrus clouds (located above). Isolated light rain showers (-SHRA) mainly in the eastern sections. Becoming by 1723Z, over mainly the eastern sections, broken clouds 8,000 to 10,000 feet MSL, with another broken layer at 15,000 feet MSL. Tops to flight level 200. Widely scattered thunderstorms and light rain showers, cumulonimbus tops to flight level 350 (35,000 feet), lowering ceilings/visibilities, broken clouds from 3,000 to 5,000 feet MSL and visibilities from 3 to 5 statute miles. Outlook - VFR.

THE AREA FORECAST   VFR CLOUDS AND WEATHER SECTION

ID
NRN ID...SKC. OCNL SCT100 SCT CI. OTLK...VFR.
CNTRL AND SRN ID...SCT100 BKN150. TOPS TO FL200. BKN CI ISOL -SHRA... MAINLY ERN SXNS. BECMG 1723 OVR MAINLY ERN SXNS...BKN080-100 BKN150. TOPS TO FL200. WDLY SCT -TSRA...CB TOPS TO FL350...LWRG CIGS/VIS BKN030- 050/3-5SM. OTLK...VFR.

Fig. 21

MT

ID

WY

THE WINDS ALOFT FORECAST

FB WBC 151745
BASED ON 151200Z DATA
VALID 1600Z FOR USE 1800-0300Z. TEMPS NEG ABV 24000

Fig. 22

AUTHOR'S NOTE: When the winds are expected to be in excess of 100 knots the first two numbers of the forecast are greater than 36. To find the direction, subtract 50 from the first two numbers (i.e., 73 - 50 = 23 [winds from 230 degrees]). Add 100 to the next two numbers to find the wind speed (i.e., 100 + 19 = 119 knots).

FT	3000	6000	9000	12000	18000	24000	30000	34000	39000
ALS			2420	2635-08	2535-18	2444-30	245945	246755	246862
AMA		2714	2725+00	2625-04	2531-15	2452-27	265842	256352	256762
DEN			2321-04	2532-08	2434-19	2441-31	235347	236056	236262
HLC		1707-01	2113-03	2219-07	2330-17	2435-30	244145	244854	245561
MKC	0507	2006+03	2215-01	2322-06	2338-17	2448-29	236143	237252	238160
STL	2113	2325+07	2332+02	2339-04	2356-16	2373-27	239440	730649	731960

Winds Aloft Forecasts (FB) – There are certain moments in your life that you just don't forget. A fellow once came up and said he was going to punch my nose in. I said, "Hey, don't you know that you never end a sentence with a preposition?" At that point he proceeded to punch in my nose.

Some folks are pretty tough, but no matter how tough you are as a pilot, you're never going to win a fight with the wind. The way to keep from being beat, however, is to know how fast and from what direction the wind blows. This is extremely important for planning proper fuel consumption, not to mention figuring out whether you'll get to your meeting on time. Fortunately, there is a forecast that provides you with an estimate of winds for up to 24 hours in advance. It's known as the *winds aloft forecast.*

Winds aloft forecasts are very useful to pilots. These forecasts are issued four times daily and are valid for either 6, 12 or 24 hours. Each forecast is issued with a valid time for its use. Figure 22 shows a typical winds aloft forecast.

Winds are forecast for true altitudes starting at 3,000 feet and additional 3,000 foot increments up to 12,000 feet (we won't worry about higher altitudes for the moment). Winds less than 1,500 feet above the reporting station's surface are not forecast. In other words if your airport lies at 5,000 MSL, the 6,000 foot winds aloft forecast will be blank for the area around the airport. Temperature is not forecast for altitudes within 3,000 feet of the surface.

Winds aloft are provided in knots and their direction is always in reference to true north as are other weather reports and forecasts. Figure 22 depicts the forecast winds at 6,000 MSL above AMA (Amarillo, Texas) as 2714. Unlike METAR or TAF, the first two numbers of this four digit value represent the wind direction in tens of degrees; you need to add a zero onto these numbers to get the wind direction. The last two numbers represent the wind's velocity. The wind at AMA is forecast to be from 270 degrees at 14 knots. At 6,000 MSL above MKC, the wind is forecast to be from 200 degrees at 6 knots with a forecast temperature of +3 degrees C.

The - or + after the winds represents a negative or positive temperature value that follows the four-digit wind value. Winds aloft temperatures are in degrees Celsius. At 9,000 feet MSL over DEN (Denver, CO), the winds are forecast to be from 230 degrees at 21 knots with a tempera-

ture of -4 degrees C. If winds are expected to be light and variable the identifier "9900" is used. This doesn't mean wind from 990, with no velocity (we can't have a wind with an unknown direction and no speed). Technically, it means that the winds are less than 5 knots. Calm winds are identified by 0000.

Forecast temperatures are useful for several reasons. Many pilots use them to predict where temperature inversions will be. Any time you see the forecast temperature increasing (or not decreasing as much) with altitude, you know you have a stable air situation. Warmer air aloft could act as a lid, trapping industrial pollutants.

If you want the winds at an altitude between those listed, it's time to interpolate, also known as meeting the numbers halfway. Break out the Cray supercomputer. Actually, the math is easy, and you can probably do it either in your head or on your fingers. If the altitude you'll be flying at is halfway between two forecast

A LESSON IN PILOT-DRAGGING

I decided to move the plane. Procedure: open the throttle to establish a fuel flow of 8 GPH with the primer pump, and when the engine starts, pull the throttle back to about 1100 rpm. I entered the plane, set the hand brake and followed the above procedures. The next thing I knew, I was on the ground and the plane was heading for a ditch. I remember hearing the engine start. The cabin door was not closed. The wind that day was 90° at about 20 knots with gusts up to 35. A gust must have lifted the right wing enough to cause me to lose my balance and tumble from the plane. I remember trying to stop the plane from rolling, but it just dragged me with it. In the future, I will secure my seatbelt and close and lock the cabin door every time I start the engine

ASRS Report

levels, the wind and temperature will be about halfway between the numbers given for those two levels. Add the two wind (or temperature) numbers together and divide by 2. Bingo. I told you it wasn't calculus. Actually, halfway is about all you'll ever need to figure; if you're closer than that to one forecast level or another, use it and you'll be close enough for rock 'n roll. If you believe there is a significant difference between the winds at 6,000 feet and the winds at 6,750 feet and that this can be forecast with great precision, then please call me about some low-lying land I have available in Florida.

One of the important items to check during cross country flight planning is the altitude that will provide the most favorable (or at least the least adverse) winds. After studying the winds aloft forecast, you can easily decide on an altitude giving you less of a headwind or more of a tailwind. Sometimes it's advantageous to spend additional time climbing in order to catch a tailwind.

Weather Charts: Getting The Big Picture

OK, you don't like numbers, and you're not real big on words. You bought this book *and* that copy of *Playpilot* you're holding for the pictures. Fortunately, when it comes to weather, you haven't been left out in the cold. Much of the complexity of weather makes a lot more sense presented as pictures, which is the way weatherpeople have been looking at the weather for decades. Even if you can't picture yourself reading charts, join me for a few moments and take a look at what you're missing.

There are a number of weather charts that can prove most informative. Accessing them was easy when there was a Flight Service Station on almost every airport corner. If you have a personal computer, the charts are now available from a variety of sources electronically (and in color), so you can brief yourself from the comfort of your home. And if you are

---

The weather depiction chart provides pilots with a broad overview (a bird's eye view) of weather conditions. It's an excellent place to begin your weather briefing and flight planning.

---

fortunate enough to be near one of the remaining Flight Service Stations, stop in for a look at some of the following charts. It's a great way to literally get the picture.

Weather Depiction Chart – The *weather depiction chart* (Figure 23) is prepared from METARs. It provides pilots with a broad overview (a bird's eye view) of weather conditions. It's

Fig. 23

THE PERSPIRATION FACTOR

I was descending from 6000' at night on a vector to the airport and was not using the autopilot. I had spent the day at the beach and had used a sunscreen product on my face at my doctor's recommendation. Apparently night flight has a "perspiration factor" because the sunscreen product ran into my eyes, causing them to sting. While trying to rub my eyes and use a handkerchief to stop the tearing, the airplane went off course by about 100°. I was able to recover quickly, with no damage other than to my pride. The sunscreen product contains a warning about not putting it in eyes, but I had not considered the possibility that perspiration could wash it into my eyes—at a very inconvenient time. Suggestions: try stick or waterproof sunscreen—it tends to stay put, or wear a hat and only put sunscreen below the eyes. **ASRS Report**

an excellent place to begin your briefing and determine the general weather conditions upon which to base your flight planning. The chart is issued every three hours, beginning at 0100Z.

The weather depiction chart has lots of good information. Perhaps most important is the graphic view it gives you of where VFR and IFR conditions prevail.

The weather depiction chart always comes with a means of decoding a few of its symbols. A decoding key is located in the bottom right hand corner of the chart. For instance, any area that is shaded is IFR (ceilings less than 1,000 feet and/or visibility less than 3 miles, position A). Contoured areas without shading are areas of marginal VFR (MVFR) weather with ceilings greater than or equal to 1,000 feet to less than or equal to 3,000 feet and/or visibility of 3 to 5 miles (position B).

Areas without contours are areas of VFR with ceilings greater than 3,000 feet and visibilities greater than 5 miles (position C).

Numbers and symbols surrounding the individual stations inform you about clouds heights, coverage and weather and obstruction to vision. A key for this chart's symbols is shown in Figures 24 and 25. (Note: only the code shown on the actual weather depiction chart is provided to you on the knowledge exam.) For instance, in the southeast corner of New Mexico (position D) the station circle is completely darkened in. Using the key in Figure 24, you can tell that the sky is overcast.

Cloud height is determined the same way it is with the METAR and TAF, by adding two zeros to the numbers underneath the station circle, as shown in Figure 25. This tells us that the height of the overcast with the numbers 60 under the station circle is 6,000 feet. Visibility and precipitation is shown to the left of the station circle. Our station has a visibility of 4 miles with thunderstorms (⚡) and rain showers indicated by the small black dot on top of the thunderstorm symbol.

Another nice thing about the weather depiction chart is that it shows the location of frontal systems using symbols similar to those on the surface weather map. Before your detailed flight planning begins, take a look at the weather depiction chart. Ask yourself these questions: Are there VFR or MVFR conditions in the direction I'm headed? Which way is the front moving? Which is more important, existence or essence? (Oops! Sorry, that's an optional question, no thanks to Sartre!). The

weather is sure to become worse in the direction of frontal travel.

The great value of the weather depiction chart lies in its frequency of issuance. You only get that advantage, however, if you're using the latest product. Just as you look on a box of cookies for the expiration date (don't you?), check when the weather depiction chart was issued. If it's stale, get another one.

WX DEPICTION PLOTTING SYMBOLS

PLOTTING SYMBOL	MEANING
◐ 8	Few clouds, base 800 feet, visibility more than 5 **Fig. 25**
▾ ◔ 12	Broken sky cover, ceiling 1,200 feet, slight rain showers, visibility more than 5
5 ∞ ◑	Thin overcast with breaks, visibility 5 in haze
▲ ◔ 20	Scattered at 2,000 feet, clouds topping ridges, visibility more than 5
2= ○	Sky clear, visibility 2, light fog
1/2 ≡ ⊗ 3	Total sky obscuration, visibility ½, fog, vertical visibility into obs 300 feet, fog determined by automated system
2= ⊗ 2	Total sky obscuration, vertical visibility into obs is 200 feet, visibility 2, light fog
1/4 ✱ ⊗ 5	Total sky obscuration, vertical visibility into obs is 500 feet, visibility ¼ intermittent snow
1 ⚡ ● 12	Overcast, ceiling 1,200 feet thunderstorms, rain showers, visibility 1

SYMBOLS FOR SKY COVER

SYMBOL	TOTAL SKY COVER
○	Sky Clear
◔	FEW - (more than 1/8 to 2/8)
◑	SCT - Scattered (3/8 to 4/8)
◕	BKN - Broken (5/8 to 7/8)
◖	Breaks in overcast
●	OVC - Overcast (8/8)
⊗	Total sky obscuration (8/8)
⊖	Missing cloud (or sky cover) observation or partial obscuration. **Fig. 24**

Radar Summary Chart – The radar summary chart, shown in Figure 26, is issued 16 times a day during a 24 hour period (some private weather services offer it 24 hours a day). It presents the location of radar echoes resulting from precipitation (usually water or hail) suspended in clouds. Since radar energy is incapable of reflecting off clouds, this chart does not directly show cloud locations, though you can surmise that where there's rain, there are clouds. The absence of a radar return, however, doesn't mean that there are no clouds. Radar energy goes right through a cloud. It takes *precipitation size* water drops to show up on radar in the form of a precipitation echo. If enough suspended water is present, the radar will show its location. Keep in mind that it also takes updrafts to suspend water. And strong updrafts are associated with thunderstorms. If the radar shows enough water, there's a strong possibility thunderstorms are present.

By examining the radar summary chart, you'll be able to determine the location of precipitation echoes, their intensity, intensity trend, configuration, coverage, echo tops, bases and movement. While this chart is primarily of value to the instrument pilot, it can also provide the VFR pilot with much useful information. (Read Postflight Briefing #12-2 for more information on radar and weather.)

Figure 27 provides you with a legend to interpret the symbols on the radar summary chart. This won't be available on the knowledge exam, so there are a few items you'll need memorize.

On the east coast of Florida near area C, there is a single, non feathered arrow pointing northeast with the numbers 05 near its tip. A single arrow represents an individual cell movement in the direction specified with a speed, in this instance, of 5 knots. The RW+ indicates rain showers with increasing intensity. On radar summary charts a + or - sign after the precipitation indicates the intensity trend of that precipitation. The tops of the echoes are 26,000 feet. Remember, this is the tops of the precipitation inside the cloud, not the cloud itself.

Area A indicates radar echoes moving east at 15 knots. The arrow has feathers, meaning that it's a line or area movement instead of just a cell (which is depicted as an arrow without any tail feathers). The arrow near area A has 1 1/2 feathers. Each feather represents 10 knots of speed. That's how you arrive at the conclusion that radar echo movement is easterly at 15 knots.

In area D, the radar return is moving northeast at 20 knots. Since it's a single arrow without feathers, this represents the movement of an individual cell. The highest top of the precipitation around area D is 30,000 feet, indicated by the *300* with an underline pointing to an area of echoes.

Whenever a severe weather watch is in effect, the affected area is surrounded by a dashed line, as shown in area B. A severe weather watch area can include tornadoes or severe thunderstorms, neither of which is an invitation to fly by in a small airplane—and believe me, when it comes to this kind of weather, *any* kind of airplane is "small."

As a VFR pilot, the radar summary chart is helpful because it provides clues on where the air is convectively

The absence of a radar return, however, doesn't mean that there are no clouds. Radar energy goes right through a cloud. It takes precipitation size water drops to show up on radar in the form of a precipitation echo.

active, or the weather is severe. The greater the suspended precipitation, the greater the intensity of the updrafts required to suspend it. When you have echoes with three contours (indicating intense or extreme echo intensity), then you have a greater chance of extreme turbulence and its associated problems.

The taller a thunderstorm, the nastier it generally is. Precipitation heights provide you with a rough idea of just how strong the echo or the areas of echoes is.

An additional source of information comes from the speed of the cells (or the areas of echoes). Faster moving echoes or cells are generally nastier. They usually contain more turbulence, precipitation, windshear, etc. Observe arrow feathers that provide cell or echo speed. Combine this with an observation of the height of a radar return. Shake gently, think carefully, and plan ahead. Consider whether you should go at all. If you do go, have a backup plan in case you can't comfortably reach your destination. That means having spare fuel on board. As Mark Twain once said, "It's better to be cautious 100 times than to die once."

HOW TO REPORT TURBULENCE		
INTENSITY	**AIRCRAFT REACTION**	**REACTION IN A/C**
Light	Turbulence that momentarily causes slight erratic changes in altitude and or attitude (pitch, roll, yaw). Report as light turbulence. OR... Turbulence that causes slight, rapid and somewhat rhythmic bumpiness without appreciable changes in altitude or attitude. Report as Light Chop.	Occupants may feel a slight strain against seat belts or shoulder straps. Unsecured objects may be displaced slightly. Food service may be conducted and little or no difficulty is encountered when walking.
Moderate	Turbulence that is similar to light turbulence but of greater intensity. Changes in altitude and/or attitude occur but the aircraft remains in positive control at all times. It usually causes variations in indicated airspeed. Report as moderate turbulence. OR... Turbulence that is similar to light chop but of greater intensity. It causes rapid bumps or jolts without appreciable changes in aircraft altitude or attitude. Report as moderate chop.	Occupants feel definite strains against seat belts or shoulder straps. Unsecured objects are dislodged. Food service and walking are difficult.
Severe	Turbulence that causes large, abrupt changes in altitude and/or attitude. It usually causes large variations in indicated airspeed. Aircraft may be momentarily out of control. Report as severe turbulence.	Occupants are forced violently against seat belts or shoulder straps. Unsecured objects are tossed about. Food service and walking are impossible.
Extreme	Turbulence in which the aircraft is violently tossed about & is practically impossible to control. It may cause structural damage. Report as Extreme Turbulence.	
Duration	Occasional—Less than 1/3 of the time. Intermittent—1/3 to 2/3. Continuous—More than 2/3 of the time.	

Note: Pilots should report location(s), time (UTC or Z), intensity, whether in or near clouds, altitude, type of aircraft and when applicable, duration of turbulence. Duration may be based on time between two locations or over a single location. All locations should be readily identifiable.

Fig. 28   ## THE LOW LEVEL SIGNIFICANT WEATHER PROGNOSTIC CHART

Low Level Significant Weather Prognostic Chart – A doctor told his patient that he had good news and bad news. The doctor asked which the patient wanted to hear first. The patient said, "Give me the good news first." The doctor said, "Well, you've got 24 hours to live." The patient said, "That's the *good* news? What's the bad news?" The doctor said, "I tried to call you yesterday."

Essentially, the doctor gave his patient a *prognosis* or a future outlook. While the terminal area forecast, area forecast and winds aloft forecast are all a textual prognosis of the weather, the *low level significant weather prognostic chart* does the same thing in picture form.

The low level significant weather prognostic chart—the *prog chart,* as it's usually referred to by those not wishing to carry supplemental oxygen—can be thought of as a graphic version of the area forecast, though it differs slightly from the written version, as shown in Figure 28. While the area forecast provides weather for one of six forecast areas in the United States, the prog chart provides a picture forecast for the entire U.S. The prog chart consist of four panels: The upper panels are 12 hour (left panel, A) and 24 hour (right panel, B) prognoses of significant weather from the surface to the 400 millibar pressure level (that's 24,000 feet). The lower panels (panels C and D) are 12 and 24 hour prognoses of surface weather (36 and 48 hour panels are also available at some locations). Prog charts are issued four times daily, approximately every six hours. These charts are now available in color via the internet as shown in Postflight Briefing #12-3.

A key, located between both upper charts, helps with interpreting the weather symbols. For instance, all areas surrounded by

PROG CHART SYMBOLS

Significant Weather Prognostic Symbols	
Depiction	*Meaning*
▽ / ℞	Moderate thunderstorms and rain showers (i.e., Thunderstorms embedded in an area of rain showers) covering >50-100% of the area.
• •	Continuous rain covering 30-50% of the area. (No shade indicates precipitation covers 30-50% of area.)
✱ ✱	Continuous snow showers covering >50-100% of the defined area.
'	Intermittent drizzle covering 30-50% of the area.
• •/▽	Continuous rain and rain showers embedded in an area of continuous rain covering 30-50% of the area. **Fig. 29**

Continuous precipitation is a dominant and widespread event and, therefore, shaded. Intermittent precipitation is a periodic and patchy event and unshaded. Areas with more than half coverage are shaded, and half or less coverage are unshaded.

STANDARD WEATHER SYMBOLS

Fig. 30

solid lines are areas with ceilings less than 1,000 feet and/or visibilities less than 3 miles (these are IFR conditions and the code is similar to that used on the weather depiction chart). Areas surrounded by scalloped lines are marginal VFR conditions consisting of 1,000 to 3,000 foot ceilings and/or 3 to 5 miles visibility. Areas outside scalloped lines are forecast to have ceilings greater than 3,000 feet and 5 miles visibility.

Panels A and B of the significant weather prog chart have zig-zag lines that show the location of the freezing level at the surface (panel A, position 1). Dashed lines on the same panel indicate freezing levels at altitude (panel A, position 1). Freezing levels are important for instrument pilots since they want to avoid flying in the clouds when the temperatures are

near or below freezing, lest they pick up ice on the plane and turn their aircraft into a giant Snowcone.

An additional and very useful feature of the significant weather prog chart is its forecast of turbulence. The long dashed line surrounding California, Arizona, and parts of New Mexico and Colorado indicates moderate or greater turbulence is forecast during the 12 hour time period (panel A, position 2). (Use the key between panels on prog chart.) Within the area surrounded by the long dashed line is the number *180* with what appears to be a *witch's hat* symbol above it and a small short diagonal line to the right. The 180 means this turbulence is forecast from the surface up to 18,000 feet. In the 24 hour significant weather prog (panel B, position 3) the 080 tells us that moderate turbulence is forecast for this area from the surface to 8,000 feet during the forecast time. A number to the right of the diagonal line (i.e., the "/" to the right of 080) states the base of the turbulence when it doesn't begin at the surface. By comparing the 12 and 24 hour significant weather prog, you can visualize the direction of weather movement during the next 24 hours. (Figures 29 and 30 show additional symbols used in this chart. These figures aren't provided on the sport pilot knowledge exam.)

The 12 and 24 hour surface prog (panels C and D) provides you with the expected location and movements of fronts, pressure systems, and their generated weather. The 12 hour surface prog (panel C) forecasts a low pressure center over northern Utah (panel C, position 4). The unshaded area within the solid line that circles

several western and northwestern states shows that the forecast precipitation will cover 30% to 50% of this area. The symbol (**/**) and its arrow pointing to the shaded area of the Utah low shows that continuous to continuous and moderate snow is forecast (use the key in Figure 30 to help with this interpretation). By comparing panels C and D, you see that the low is forecast to move northeastward into Wyoming. According to Figure 29, the shaded area surrounding the low indicates that the continuous snow (the precipitation) is still expected to cover >50% to 100% of the area during the latter part of the forecast period.

In the 24 hour surface prog chart, the east coast of Florida is expected to have continuous and moderate rain (three dots) and slight or moderate thunderstorms with rain indicated by the thunderstorm symbol ( ) with a single dot above (panel D, position 5). (I think a good thunderstorm symbol is a tiny picture of a pilot's face with his eyes bugging out and a Don King hairdo).

The area in the upper part of North Carolina (panel D, position 6) is expected to have continuous slight rain showers (two dots depict continuous rain and the dot above a triangle symbolizes slight rain showers). According to Figure 29, since the entire area is enclosed by a solid line, the precipitation is expected to cover 30% to 50% of the area.

By comparing panels C and D, it appears that the poor weather on Florida's western coast will move eastward. Panels A and B, however, suggest that all of Florida will still have ceilings of 1,000 to 3,000 feet and/or visibilities of 3-5 miles.

Why Flight Instructors Always Look Cool

Flight instructors always appear to look cool because we've been trained to sweat only on the right side of our face!

Flight Instructor

Student

Surface Analysis – The surface analysis chart (Figure 31) shows the location of pressure patterns and fronts. This chart is based on reported weather data and is issued every three hours. Individual reporting stations and their associated weather are depicted on the chart. Additional decoding information for the station model on this chart can be found in the FAA's *Aviation Weather Services* manual (AC 00 - 45G).

Even without a detailed understanding of this chart's symbology, you can derive some interesting information from it. Think of the surface analysis as a very large visual portrayal of hundreds of METARs (surface weather reports). Although this chart's information may be older than that of the individual METARs, it can provide you with a big picture of the weather for individual stations along your route. For instance, the chart shows the temperature/dew point spread over a large area. From this you can get a good feel for the likelihood of fog or low cloud formation before and after sunset. Orientation of the isobars and the pressure patterns gives you an idea of surface winds. Cloud coverage at the time the chart was constructed is identified by the fill of the individual station circles. In addition, you can determine the types of clouds existing enroute. Much, much more useful weather material exists on the surface analysis chart.

Personally, I like comparing the present location of pressure systems and fronts using the surface analysis with the predicted future locations on the 12 and 24 hour prog chart. This tells me where these fronts are now and where they're likely to be in the future. I think of this as being similar to the actions of professional boxers, who want to know where their opponent is and where he might move (personally, I've always thought of boxing as being similar to ballet, except that there are no leotards, no music, and the dancers get to hit each other).

THE SURFACE ANALYSIS CHART

Surface Analysis Chart

Fig. 31

In-flight Aviation Weather Advisories

Most people want to protect things that are of value to them. For instance, my parents used to have plastic covers on their living room furniture to protect it. My grandfather was different. He tried to make visitors wear plastic leisure suits instead of opting for covers. It didn't work too well (but our guests did lose weight). Pilots want to protect themselves while airborne. They do so by understanding what in-flight advisories are and how they're disseminated.

In-flight aviation weather advisories are forecasts that advise pilots of potentially hazardous weather—some of which might have been forecast, and some of which might have arrived as a complete surprise to everyone involved. These advisories are provided to the FSS and are normally included in your standard weather briefing. Always make it a point to ask the briefer for any in-flight advisories anyway. In-flight advisories may also be obtained during HIWAS broadcasts over specific VORs and NDBs. The AFSS also has a complete listing of in-flight advisories, therefore you may easily access

SIGMETS

SIGMET

DFWA UWS 051710
SIGMET PAPA 1 VALID UNTIL 052110
AR LA MS
FROM MEM TO 30N MEI TO BTR TO MLU TO MEM
OCNL SVR ICING ABV FRZLVL EXPCD.
FRZLVL 080 E TO 120 W
CONDS CONTG BYD 2100Z.

Fig. 32A

them in flight via a radio call. There are three types of advisories: Convective SIGMETS, SIGMETS, and AIRMETS.

SIGMET (WS) – A *SIGMET* is an advisory of non-convective weather (non-thunderstorm type weather) that is potentially hazardous to all aircraft, big and small. SIGMETs are issued when any of the following occur or are expected to occur: severe icing not associated with thunderstorms, severe or extreme turbulence or clear air turbulence (CAT) not associated with thunderstorms,

AIRMETS

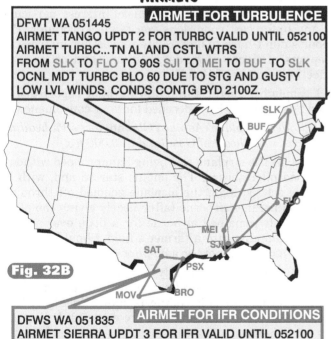

AIRMET FOR TURBULENCE

DFWT WA 051445
AIRMET TANGO UPDT 2 FOR TURBC VALID UNTIL 052100
AIRMET TURBC...TN AL AND CSTL WTRS
FROM SLK TO FLO TO 90S SJI TO MEI TO BUF TO SLK
OCNL MDT TURBC BLO 60 DUE TO STG AND GUSTY
LOW LVL WINDS. CONDS CONTG BYD 2100Z.

Fig. 32B

AIRMET FOR IFR CONDITIONS

DFWS WA 051835
AIRMET SIERRA UPDT 3 FOR IFR VALID UNTIL 052100
FROM SAT TO PSX TO BRO TO MOV TO SAT
OCNL CIGS BLO 10/VSBYS BLO 3 PCPN/F. CONDS
CONTG BYD 21Z THRU 03Z.

dust storms, sandstorms, and volcanic ash that lowers surface visibilities to less than 3 miles and, finally, any volcanic eruption (something we pilots are not trained to handle and don't want to see while it's occurring).

Any of these items certainly affects both large and small airplanes. SIGMETS are named by the phonetic alphabet using designators from November through Yankee, excluding Sierra, Tango and Zulu (these three are AIRMET designators). By knowing the specific phonetic name and number of a SIGMET or AIRMET, you can call the FSS or EFAS and determine if it has been canceled, continued, amended or updated. Figure 32A shows a typical SIGMET and the area it affects.

This SIGMET was issued for the DFW area at 1710Z on the 5th day of the month and is valid until 2110Z on the same day. The letters UWS (Urgent Weather Sigmet) are included in the first issuance of a SIGMET. SIGMETs have names for identification. This SIGMET is named Papa 1, indicating that this is the first SIGMET issued in that specific area. Issuances for the same weather phenomena will be sequentially numbered using the original name (Papa 2, Papa 3, etc.) until the phenomena end.

The SIGMET in Figure 32A is for Arkansas, Louisiana and Mississippi. From MEM to 30 miles north of MEI to BTR to MLU to MEM, you can expect occasional severe icing above the freezing level (remember, these three letter identifiers are all VORs in the affected area). The freezing level is from 8,000 feet eastward to 12,000 feet westward. Conditions continuing beyond 2100Z. (Four hours is the maximum forecast period of a SIGMET.)

AIRMET (WA) – *AIRMETS* warn of significant weather but describe conditions at intensities lower than those that trigger SIGMETs. They are intended for all pilots in the preflight and enroute phase of flight to enhance safety.

AIRMETs are issued once every 6 hours on a scheduled basis, with unscheduled amendments issued as required. Each AIRMET issuance contains current AIRMETs still in effect, significant conditions not meeting AIRMET criteria and an outlook for conditions expected after the AIRMET valid period. AIRMETs are valid for a period of 6 hours. They contain one or more of the following weather phenomena when they occur or are forecast to occur: moderate icing, moderate turbulence, sustained winds of 30 knots or more at the surface, ceilings less than 1,000 feet and/or visibilities less than 3 miles affecting more than 50% of the area at one time, as well as extensive mountain obscuration.

The upper portion of Figure 32B shows an AIRMET and the area it affects. It was issued for the Dallas/Ft. Worth forecasting area on the 5th day of the month at 1445Z. The *T* following DFW indicates the type of AIRMET. In this instance it means TANGO (for turbulence). AIRMET TANGO is updated and is valid until 2100Z on the 5th day of the month and applies to the area around Tennessee, Alabama and the coastal waters. The area described in the AIRMET is expected to have moderate turbulence below 6,000 feet MSL due to strong and gusty low level winds. These conditions are expected to continue beyond the AIRMET's valid time of 2100Z.

AIRMET SIERRA in the lower portion of Figure 32 is on its third update. The S following DFW indicates AIRMET SIERRA (which indicates IFR conditions or mountain obscuration).

The bordered area shown is expected to have occasional ceilings below 1,000 feet and visibilities below 3 miles in precipitation and fog. Conditions are expected to continue beyond 2100Z through 0300Z. If you're planning on doing any traveling to this area during the forecast time, you might think about doing it by car.

AIRMETs have fixed alphanumeric designators. If you see AIRMET SIERRA, this stands for IFR and mountain obscurations; TANGO stands for turbulence, strong surface wind and low level wind shear; and ZULU stands for icing and freezing level. Do you recall the precautionary statements section of the area forecast? It said to see AIRMET SIERRA for IFR conditions and mountain obscuration. This is why you always need to check for AIRMETs that may affect your flight.

Convective SIGMETs (WST) – Another version of the SIGMET is the *convective SIGMET* (WST). This is the granddaddy of in-flight advisories and present hazards to all aircraft. A convective SIGMET is an advisory associated with convective activity such as severe thunderstorms. Any convective SIGMET implies severe or greater turbulence, severe icing, and low level windshear. A convective SIGMET may be issued for any of the following items:

1. A line of thunderstorms at least 60 miles long with thunderstorms affecting at least 40 percent of its length,

2. An area of active thunderstorms affecting at least 3,000 square miles covering at least 40 percent of the area concerned and exhibiting a very strong radar reflectivity intensity or a significant satellite or lightning signature.

3. It is also issued for embedded or severe thunderstorm(s) expected to occur for more than 30 minutes during the valid period regardless of the size of the area.

Figure 33 is an example of a convective SIGMET. This SIGMET was issued on the 22nd day of the month at 1855Z. It is the 20th consecutive SIGMET (20C) issued on this day in the central U.S. The SIGMET references a line in the vicinity of GLD to CDS. It forecasts a line of thunderstorms developing by 1955Z and moving eastward at 30 to 35 knots through 2055Z. Hail to one and one-half inches is also possible. That's pretty serious weather. You better be on the ground wearing a hard hat and a roll bar if you experience hail that size.

Convective SIGMETs also contain an outlook. This is a forecast for thunderstorms that are expected to require convective SIGMET issuance during a time period 2-6 hours into the future. The convective SIGMET outlook in Figure 33 predicts isolated strong thunderstorms will

CONVECTIVE SIGMET

```
MKCC WST 221855          CONVECTIVE
CONVECTIVE SIGMET 20C      SIGMET
VALID UNTIL 2055Z
KS OK TX                  Fig. 33
VCNTY GLD-CDS LINE
FCST TO 2055Z
LINE TSTMS DVLPG BY 1955Z WILL MOVE
EWD 30-35 KTS THRU 2055Z
HAIL TO 1 1/2 IN PSBL.

OUTLOOK VALID 222055-230055
ISOLD STG TSTMS WILL DVLP OVER SWRN
KS THRUT FCST PD AS UPR LVL TROF
MOVS NEWD OVER VERY UNSTBL AMS.
```

develop over southwestern Kansas through the forecast period as an upper level trough moves northeastward over very unstable air.

Pilot Reports (PIREPs) – *Pilot reports* provide pilots with some of the best real-time weather information available. PIREPs provide an excellent means of finding current weather between reporting stations. The AFSS, as well as other ATC specialists, long for pilots to give reports of weather and other items of interest, particularly any unforecast conditions you might encounter. Pilot reports don't have to only relate to weather information. Reports of flocks of birds, balloons, and other items affecting flight are helpful.

I remember seeing the following pilot report distributed by a midwest FSS (decoded for your convenience):

Pilotless airplane (Aeronca Champ) last seen heading northeast of Goodland at 3,000 feet.

It seems the airplane was being handpropped without a qualified pilot aboard. The engine started and, with the throttle set too high, the airplane zoomed off through a field and became airborne (after nearly giving the pilot a crewcut). It remained airborne for a little over an hour before slamming into a farmer's field. Shouldn't this be called a *nonpilot* report or a *no-pilot-aboard* report?

Pilot reports are officially coded, then disseminated through the ATC system for use in flight planning. The official format for this coding is shown in Figure 34A. Figure 34B shows how PIREPs are encoded. Let's examine a few reports.

Figure 35 shows a typical pilot report. It reads: a routine PIREP (UA meaning *routine,* it doesn't mean United Airlines either; UUA means *urgent*)/ from Oklahoma City

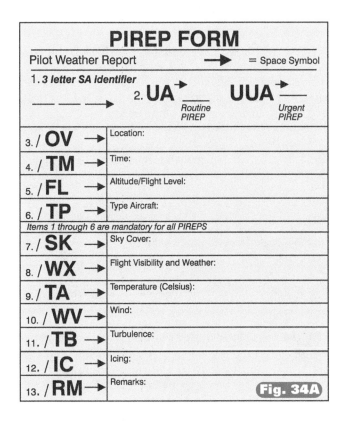

PIREP FORM

Pilot Weather Report → = Space Symbol

1. *3 letter SA identifier*

— — — → 2.**UA**→ __ **UUA**→ __
Routine PIREP / Urgent PIREP

3. / **OV** →	Location:
4. / **TM** →	Time:
5. / **FL** →	Altitude/Flight Level:
6. / **TP** →	Type Aircraft:

Items 1 through 6 are mandatory for all PIREPS

7. / **SK** →	Sky Cover:
8. / **WX** →	Flight Visibility and Weather:
9. / **TA** →	Temperature (Celsius):
10. / **WV** →	Wind:
11. / **TB** →	Turbulence:
12. / **IC** →	Icing:
13. / **RM** →	Remarks:

Fig. 34A

to Tulsa/ at 1800Z/ at 12,000 feet (FL means *flight level* and is used for any altitude)/ reported by a Beech 90. (The type of aircraft is important. If a 747 reported light turbulence it could mean moderate or severe for a small airplane.)/ the base of the first cloud layer is at 1,800 feet MSL broken with tops at 5,500 MSL (since a pilot reported this he or she is referencing the altimeter which displays height in MSL values. This means, for example, that if the ground elevation is 1,295 feet MSL, then the 1,800 foot MSL ceiling is 505 feet above ground.)/ the base of the second overcast cloud layer is at 7,200 feet MSL and tops are at 8,900 feet MSL/ and the weather is clear above the upper layer/ weather type: flight visibility is 3 miles in moderate rain/ temperature is -9 degrees Celsius/ the wind is from 080 degrees at 21 knots (pilots can determine wind direction and velocity from the cockpit by using sophisticated GPS and Loran systems)/ turbulence is *light* between 5,500 feet and 7,200 feet/ there was light to moderate rime icing between 7,200 feet and 8,900 feet.

Pilot reports are quite useful. They are, however, most meaningful when they are first issued. Conditions can change with time. Be very suspicious of pilot reports more than an hour old.

A TYPICAL PILOT REPORT (PIREP)

KTUL UA /OV KOKC-KTUL /TM 1800 /FL 120
/TP BE90 /SK BKN018-TOP055/OVC072-TOP089 /CLR ABV
/WX FV03SM RA /TA M9 /WV 08021KT /TB LGT 055-072
/IC LGT-MDT RIME 072-089.

Fig. 35

KEY FOR ENCODING PILOT REPORTS

1. 3-letter station identifier - nearest weather reporting location to the reported phenomena

2. UA - Routine PIREP, UUA is an urgent PIREP

3. /OV - **Location**: Use 3-letter NAVAID idents only
   a. *Fix:* /OV ABC or OV/ABC090025 (the first three numbers are the radial from the VOR and the last three numbers are the distance. In this example the PIREP concerns the area near the 090 degree radial of the ABC VOR at the 025 or 25 nautical mile position).
   b. *Fix to fix:* /OV ABC-DEF, OV/ABC-DEF120020

4. /TM - **Time:** 4 digits in UTC (Zulu) (e.g. /TM 0915)

5. /FL - **Altitude/Flight Level:** 3 digits for hundreds of feet, if not known use UNKN (e.g. FL085 is 8,500 feet and FL310 is 31,000 feet).

6. /TP - **Type aircraft:** 4 digits maximum, if not known use UNKN (e.g. /TP C150, /TPB747).

7. /SK - **Cloud layers:** Describe as follows:
   a. Cloud amount.
   b. Height of cloud bases in hundreds of feet.
   c. Height of cloud tops in hundreds of feet. If unknown, UNKN is used
   d. (e.g. /SK SCT038-TOP080)- means a scattered layer exists at 3,800 feet MSL and the tops are at 8,000 feet MSL. (Remember this is a pilot report and pilots use their altimeter to measure height above sea level so all reported clouds heights are MSL.)
   (e.g. /SK BKN-OVC055-TOPUNKN - means a broken to overcast cloud base starts at 5,500 feet MSL and its tops are unknown.

8. /WX - **Weather:** Flight visibility (FV) reported first in METAR format, precipitation, restrictions to visibility, etc. Standard weather symbols are used and intensity reported same as in METAR (e.g. /WX FV02SM -RA HZ means that the flight visibility is 2 miles in light rain and haze).

9. /TA - **Air temperature in Celsius:** If below zero prefix with an "M" (e.g. /TA M08). Temperature shall also be reported if icing is reported.

10. /WV - **Wind:** Direction and speed in 6 digits. Wind direction less than 100 degrees is preceded by a zero. (e.g. /WV 27045KT - means the wind is from 270 degrees at 45 knots.)

11. /TB - **Turbulence:** Use standard contractions for intensity and type (use CAT - Clear Air Turbulence or CHOP when appropriate). Include altitude only if different from FL, (e.g. /TB LGT-MDT BLW 060 - means that the turbulence is light to moderate below 6,000 feet MSL. A report showing /TB EXTRM means extreme turbulence is reported at the altitude identified in position 5 above).

12. /IC - **Icing:** Describe using standard intensity and type contractions. Include altitude if different than FL (e.g. /IC LGT-MDT RIME).

13. /RM - **Remarks:** Use free form to clarify the report. /RM LRG FLOCK OF GOOSEY LOOKING BIRDS HDG GNLY NORTH OF AIRPORT MAY BE SEAGULLS, FORMATION LOUSY AND COURSE ERRATIC....

Fig. 34B

Putting It All Together

The secret to successful flight planning is in anticipating the weather's behavior. Comparing one chart or forecast to another greatly enhances this understanding. Here's one way of making these comparisons (there are other ways, too!)

Surface Map and Weather Depiction Chart – Looking at the surface weather map tells you where the fronts and pressure systems are. Comparing this with the weather depiction chart provides you with a picture of what effects these fronts and pressure centers are having on surface weather. Figure 36 shows a typical comparison.

Weather Depiction Chart and Radar Summary Chart – With this comparison, shown in Figure 37, you get an idea of the convective activity associated with areas of IFR, MVFR and VFR conditions. If an area of MVFR conditions is associated with large, fast moving echoes (meaning thunderstorms), you might want to reconsider planning a flight in this direction. Thunderstorms mean turbulence and rain showers. Couple this with ceilings of 1,000 to 3,000 feet and visibilities of 3 to 5 miles, and you might be pushing your VFR flying luck. Keep in mind that the weather depiction chart will generally be a few hours older than the radar summary chart.

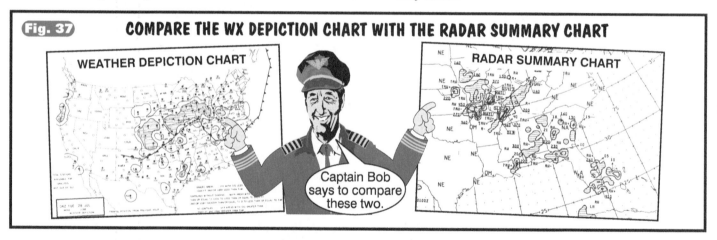

Area Forecast and Prog Charts – Since the area forecast is a textual description and the prog chart is a picture, comparison provides you with a complete, big picture description of forecast weather (Figure 38).

Weather Depiction and Prog Charts – Since the weather depiction chart shows the location of fronts and pressure systems, you can see which way these systems will move by comparing them against the 12 and 24 surface prog chart, as shown in Figure 39. You'll also get an idea about what kind of weather (IFR? MVFR? VFR?) will develop along the front by referring to the prog chart.

Fig. 39

COMPARE THE WEATHER DEPICTION CHART WITH THE PROG CHART

WEATHER DEPICTION CHART

SIG WX PROG CHART

Captain Bob says to compare these two.

METARs/Surface Map – Compare individual METARs with the surface weather map, as shown in Figure 40. This provides you with an understanding of surface weather around and between your departure and destination airports. If the surface weather map's reporting stations are all darkened-in along your route, this means you might be flying above a layer of clouds even though the destination airport is reporting clear conditions. Look at the isobars and, using your knowledge about clockwise and counterclockwise airflow around highs and lows, decide on a route that increases the likelihood of a tailwind. Remember, the surface weather map information can be up to three hours old.

Fig. 40

COMPARE THE METAR WITH THE SURFACE WEATHER MAP

SURFACE WEATHER MAP

METAR WEATHER REPORTING FORMAT

Captain Bob says to compare these two.

Finally, examine the winds aloft forecast for temperatures and the selection of a favorable cruising altitude. Then examine the convective SIGMETs for thunderstorms, SIGMETs for any severe conditions and any AIRMETs for IFR conditions, turbulence or pertinent icing conditions, as shown in Figure 41.

Fig. 41

REVIEW THE LATEST AIRMETS, SIGMETS, CONVECTIVE SIGMETS AND WINDS ALOFT FORECAST

AIRMETS, SIGMETS AND CONVECTIVE SIGMETS

WINDS ALOFT FORECAST

Captain Bob says to compare these two.

Sunny Side Up

A pilot's skill at handling weather is based on his or her weather sense. In other words, pilots must continually educate themselves about how weather works. Unfortunately, some pilots don't do this. I have a friend who is so weather insensitive he probably couldn't even tell you when it's sunny or rainy. This presents a special problem for him, since he is always forgetting where he left his sunglasses. It's not unusual for him to leave his glasses parked on top his head. One of these days he's going to have 3 or 4 pair up there, walk out into the sun, and start a little fire on his toupee.

Make it a point to check the weather every day, even if you're not flying. Call the FSS or PATWAS, look at the newspaper weather chart, check your personal computer (if you use DUATS, JEPPLINK or other service) or take a look outside and compare it to what happened yesterday. This is how pilots develop a weather sense. It's a sense that will offer you many years of safe flying.

Postflight Briefing #12-1

The Internet: More Weather Than You Can Imagine

The following statement summarized my experience with surfing. The closer you get to the beach, the shorter the sentences become. Hang ten and hang on. That was, until I began using an entirely different type of surfing called, "Surfing the Net."

Of course I mean *Internet,* the network of world-wide interconnected computer systems that talk with one another. Surfing the *net* has nothing to do with whales, water or wharves. It involves using your computer, its modem and the necessary software (a web browser) to browse the information stored in these interconnected computers. Of course, you only have access to information others want you to see. And there's a lot to see. In fact, the Internet is a wonderful place to learn about weather, as well as collect weather information for your flight. (The Web, or World Wide Web, is the graphical interface portion of the Net, for those folks who like to see what they're doing.)

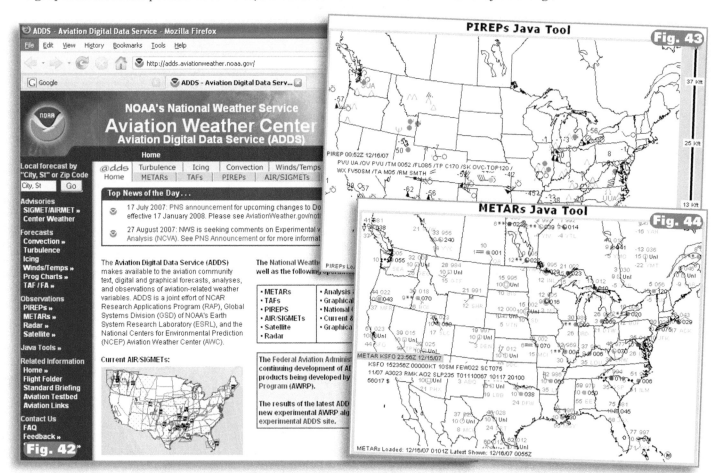

Aviation Digital Data Service is one of the most comprehensive sources for weather on the internet. One of its unique features is the interactive Java tool that allows you to move your cursor over an airport and immediately view pop-ups of textual weather in the form of PIREPS (Figure 43) and METAR/TAF weather (Figure 44).

Links of interconnected computers from universities, colleges, government sites and commercial companies from around the world are all available for you to access with your Web browser.

One of my favorite internet weather sites is the NWS Aviation Digital Data Service (ADDS) site at (http://adds.aviationweather.noaa.gov) as shown in Figure 42. Here, you can obtain nearly any weather you desire. You can also use the interactive Java tools (insert example, right side, Figures 43 and 44) that allow you to move your cursor over an airport and immediately see pop-ups of textual PIREP/METAR and TAF weather.

The Java tool also applies to other information such as AIR/SIGMETS, PIREPS and convective weather.

Without a doubt, one of the most interesting features on the ADDS site is the Flight Path Tool. In short, this Java feature allows you to select an area anywhere in the United States, move an altitude button slider and immediately identify the wind speeds, temps, humidity, icing, turbulence AIR/SIGMETS and PIREPS for your altitude and chosen location. If that wasn't enough, you can move another slider and identify these same phenomenon for up to 12 hours in the future. Amazing? Yes. Available? Yes. All you need is a computer and a browser.

AOPA's weather and flight planning page sites are excellent (Figure

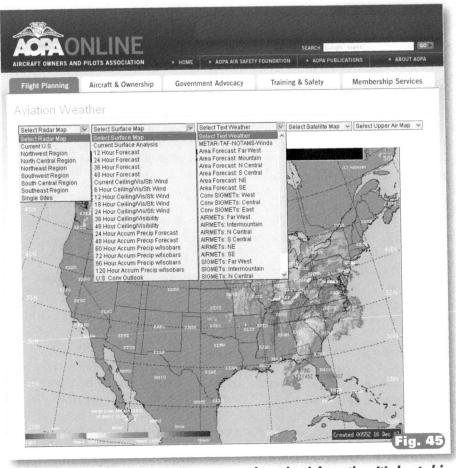

Fig. 45

AOPA's weather page is an excellent source of weather information. It's located in the "members only" section of AOPA's web site.

45). These are *member's only* locations, but this is simply another good reason to become an AOPA member.

A friend of mine who's Hawaiian is fond of saying, "Here today, gone to Maui." Which is true of some Web sites. They come and go. The above addresses were in good working order at the time of this printing. Keep in mind that while these sources offer excellent weather information, they don't necessarily constitute a legal weather briefing. They may not offer all the information necessary for preflight planning, such as NOTAMS. Use them as an additional service.

ARE YOU PREPARED?

Scene: Student and instructor are on a night, dual cross country flight:

Instructor: Turns down the panel lights, *"OK, you've just lost your lights; what are you going to do?"*
Student pulls out a flashlight.
Student: *"I get my flashlight."*
Instructor: *"The batteries are dead; now what are you going to do?"*
Student pulls out another flashlight.
Student: *"I get out my other flashlight."*
Instructor grabs next flashlight.
Instructor: *"The bulb is burned out on this one; now what?"*
Student pulls out yet a third flashlight.
Student: *"I use this flashlight."*
Chstructor: *"ALL your flashlights are dead. Now what?"*
Student: *"I use this glow stick."*
Instructor: *"Sighhhhh. Just fly the plane without any lights, OK?"*

Postflight Briefing #12-2

NEXRAD—Not Your Daddy's Weather

The revolution in modern avionics has made it possible for the average sport pilot to have access to in-flight cockpit weather that not long ago was only a dream. With the appropriate receiver, a moving map GPS display of the portable (Figure 46) or panel-installed variety and a subscription to one of several weather service providers, it's possible to have airborne access to all sorts of weather data. This includes METAR and TAF information, winds aloft, in-flight weather advisories, radar information and much more. In this chapter we've covered most of the types of in-flight weather available for uplink to the cockpit, but there's one weather product that deserves its own explanation. I'm speaking of NEXRAD or Next Generation Radar.

As a VFR pilot, NEXRAD becomes an extremely valuable source of weather information when making long distance cross country flights. Why? Because it shows you the location of suspended moisture, much like the radar summary chart does. Only NEXRAD does it in more detail and more often. Armed with cockpit uplinked weather, you're now in a much better position to avoid storm systems, areas of precipitation and so on.

Let's take a closer look at how NEXRAD weather information is generated.

Next Generation Radar

NEXRAD is a network of Doppler radars strategically located around the country and tied into a national network (Figure 47). While NEXRAD presents a normal multicolor rain rate display, its Doppler circuits can also depict whirling of droplets that pinpoints turbulence.

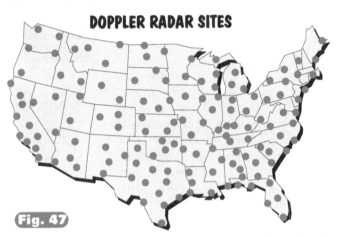

DOPPLER RADAR SITES

Fig. 47

The National Weather Service supports many Doppler radar sites across the United States.

NEXRAD is a combination of Doppler radar (WSR-88D to those who know) and conventional radar.

The WSR-88D radar works on the same principle as other radars except that Doppler radar spends more time listening than transmitting. (Airborne radar, for instance, transmits less than 1% of the time and spends 99%+ "listening" for the return of information). Doppler radar spends approximately *7 seconds* out of each hour of operation in the transmitting mode. The rest of the time (59 minutes and 53 seconds) is spent listening.

What does Doppler radar listen for? Like other radar, it listens for the return of the energy pulse it sent. The difference is that it also listens for any phase shift associated with this returning signal. "Phase shift" is a scientific way of saying that the pitch of a sound changes as it moves closer to or farther from the listener (human or radar). As a train approaches, the sound waves from its horn are compressed, making the pitch higher as the train gets closer. As the train passes, the sound waves from the horn are stretched, which lowers the pitch (Figure 48). This is the "Doppler shift," from which Doppler radar draws its name.

PORTABLE GPS UNITS CAPABLE OF PROVIDING UPLINKED WEATHER

Fig. 46

Uplinked weather is available with Garmin's 496 portable GPS receiver and a subscription to XM Weather. A company called Anywhere Map offers WX software for Pocket PCs/Palm PCs.

THE DOPPLER EFFECT

Lower Pitch Sound

Higher Pitch Sound

Fig. 48

Doppler radar listens for a phase shift to determine the motion of atmospheric particles. You experience a similar phase shift in sound when you listen to a passing locomotive.

WHAT RADAR DETECTS

REFLECTIVITY LEVELS

Wet Hail - Good

Rain - Good

Wet Snow - Good

Dry Hail - Poor

Dry Snow - Very Poor

WILL NOT REFLECT

Vapor

Ice Crystals

Small Dry Hail

Fig. 49

Radar energy reflects off some items better than others. Clouds don't reflect radar energy. It's the moisture in these clouds, in the form of rain, hail or snow, that produces a radar reflection.

The phase shift of the returning energy pulse allows Doppler radar to detect any change in velocity of an object, either toward or away from the radar. Particles moving toward the antenna impart a minute shift to higher frequencies; particles moving away from the antenna cause a shift to a lower frequency. The size of the object detectable by Doppler radar depends on the mode in which it's operating. The size of the object and what the particle is made out of also determine how much radar energy it reflects back to the radar screen. Ultimately, it's this reflected energy that determines the colored patterns you seen on your weather radar screen. Let's examine radar reflectivity sufficiently for you to make sense of these weather radar returns.

Radar Reflectivity (dBZ)

At the bottom of many NEXRAD weather charts is a color-number scale, consisting of numerical values paired with chart colors. These values are know as decibels of *reflectivity* or *dBZ* (also called the *reflectivity factor*).

A radar site sends out a pulse of energy, then looks to see what comes bouncing back. Energy is reflected, to varying degrees, by solid objects, as shown in Figure 49. The "object" can be your car, another airplane, or the droplets of water suspended in a cloud (remember, neither water vapor nor clouds reflect radar energy). The more water suspended in a cloud, the greater the radar energy reflected back to the radar antenna. This being science, the reality is of course more complicated than that, but for our purposes this explanation suffices. "Reflectivity" is the industry jargon and an acceptable way to describe radar returns.

It just so happens that the reflected radar energy can be an incredibly small amount or a very large amount, depending on the size the size of the water droplets and the number of them within the cloud (or if it's a cluster of cars, VWs versus Ford Explorers). The problem is

that it's often very difficult to talk about incredibly small numbers and very large numbers in the same conversation. It's like talking about distances that vary from one thousandth of an inch to hundreds of miles. The smaller values tend to lose their meaning (but they are still meaningful, of course). The *decibel* scale is well suited to describing such wide ranges in numbers. That's why radar reflectivity is calculated in decibels, or *decibels of reflectivity*, represented as dBZ (Figure 50, position A).

You're perhaps most familiar with the decibel scale from its use in measuring sound, either for your stereo or of a departing airplane that is being noise-monitored. I could tell you that a decibel is technically defined as the ratio of two numbers converted into a logarithm. I could, but I won't, so forget I said it. Nor did I say or admit to knowing that the *bel* in decibel honors Alexander Graham Bell, who developed the decibel scale. When speaking of someone's income and wealth, we can say he's either *poor, middle class, upper class,* a *millionaire* or a *billionaire.* The difference between being poor and being a billionaire is humongous. This scale lets you place any person on earth within one of five income slots for easy comparison. You just have to realize that there's a big numerical difference between one slot and the next. Think of decibel values in the same way. The difference between 30 decibels and 60 decibels is not just double, it's actually 100 times greater.

What Does dBZ Mean to Me?

So how should you interpret the different color codes you see in a NEXRAD presentation? The answer is simple. The larger the dBZ value, the greater chance of the suspended water in the clouds.

RADAR REFLECTIVITY SCALE ON A CHART

Fig. 50

Radar reflectivity values (dBZs) (position A) are often shown on the same chart or WX screen where NEXRAD information is displayed.

With enough suspended water in the atmosphere, it will eventually rain (Figure 51). A larger amount of suspended water (indicated by a higher dBZ value on the chart) suggests the presence of thunderstorms. As a general rule, weather radar returns with a steady dBZ value of 30 or less aren't associated with convective (storm producing) weather. These lower dBZ values, however, might be an indication of rain and reduced visibilities.

When the dBZ value increases to 40 or above, this is usually a good indication of thunderstorm activity. Remember, the dBZ value is calculated in decibels. Even a small increase in this value means a rather large increase in the return of radar energy. The jump from 30 to 40 dBZs indicates a tremendous increase in suspended water in the atmosphere. There's only one thing that will suspend that much water in the atmosphere—I'm speaking of updrafts, here—which is an indication of highly unstable air.

If the atmosphere is unstable enough to suspend a large amount of water sufficient to produce a 40+ dBZ reading, then thunderstorms are most likely involved (remember, thunderstorms initially form by the production of strong updrafts, also known as the cumulus stage). In Chapter 11, we learned to avoid thunderstorms by at least 20 nautical miles if we don't want to become like Elvis, or *all shook up*.

The general rule, therefore, is to suspect the presence of cloud coverage, reduced visibilities and precipitation where you see radar reflectivity values between 16 and 40 dBZs. Of course, you can't do more than simply "suspect" that poor weather will be present unless you combine the radar information with other weather information such as that from METAR, area forecasts, PIREPS, etc. Areas of 40 dBZ or greater on NEXRAD presentations not only suggest the presence of cloud coverage, precipitation and reduced visibilities, but should also be treated as thun-

Radar Reflectivity in dBZ

75 70 65 60 55 50 45 40 35 30 25 20 15 5 0 -5 -10 -15 -20 -25 -30

More suspended water in the air means stronger radar returns.

Less suspended water in the air means smaller radar returns.

NEXRAD RADAR #1 NEXRAD RADAR #2

Fig. 51

NEXRAD unit #1 shows that considerable water is suspended in the targeted clouds, so there is a high probability of bad weather associated with these radar returns. NEXRAD unit #2 shows that the examined clouds contain much less water, so there is less chance that these clouds will produce dangerous (thunderstorm-type) turbulence.

derstorms or storm areas and avoided by at least 20 nautical miles, unless other information leads you to believe that a closer proximity is safe. In other words, if you see a small, 40 dBZ radar return in one area of the radar presentation, you should treat that area and the area of lesser dBZ returns that are associated with it, as an area of thunderstorms unless you have information to the contrary. Of course, these are just general rules, but they're a good place to being when trying to make sense of NEXRAD information.

Another benefit of NEXRAD is that you can identify stationary storm systems or moving storm systems. When you can see poor weather on a cockpit screen, it should reduce the risk of flying into bad weather. It should also make it unlikely you'll be ambushed by a moving storm system, too. I can't emphasize this last value enough. On your cockpit weather display, you can easily seen moving storm systems in sufficient time to land, part the airplane and your derriere, and

let the storm system pass. You can even make an estimate of how long you'll stay parked based on how fast you see the storm system moving. Next to the invention of the TV remote, uplinked cockpit weather—specifically NEXRAD—is a VFR pilot's dream come true.

On the other hand, it's important to remember that NEXRAD information isn't presented in *real time*. That's because it takes the radar unit and the computer some time to process the weather information sufficiently to produce NEXRAD imagery. By the time you see it on your cockpit display (or on a paper chart), it can be from five to six minutes old. Measured in terms of the short lifespan of a thunderstorm, this is a long time.

Therefore, what you see on your cockpit weather display can be different from what you see through your airplane's windscreen. Nevertheless, the information is good enough, in my opinion, to allow you to make practical weather decisions. Keep in mind, however, that NEXRAD is only

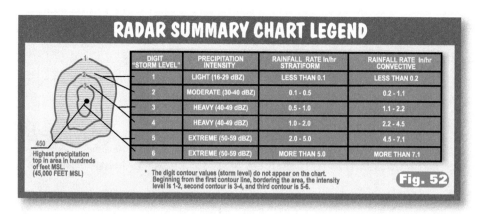

RADAR SUMMARY CHART LEGEND

DIGIT "STORM LEVEL"	PRECIPITATION INTENSITY	RAINFALL RATE In/hr STRATIFORM	RAINFALL RATE In/hr CONVECTIVE
1	LIGHT (16-29 dBZ)	LESS THAN 0.1	LESS THAN 0.2
2	MODERATE (30-40 dBZ)	0.1 - 0.5	0.2 - 1.1
3	HEAVY (40-49 dBZ)	0.5 - 1.0	1.1 - 2.2
4	HEAVY (40-49 dBZ)	1.0 - 2.0	2.2 - 4.5
5	EXTREME (50-59 dBZ)	2.0 - 5.0	4.5 - 7.1
6	EXTREME (50-59 dBZ)	MORE THAN 5.0	MORE THAN 7.1

450
Highest precipitation top in area in hundreds of feet MSL.
(45,000 FEET MSL)

* The digit contour values (storm level) do not appear on the chart. Beginning from the first contour line, bordering the area, the intensity level is 1-2, second contour is 3-4, and third contour is 5-6.

Fig. 52

The radar summary chart legend identifies 40 dBZs or more of reflectivity as a Level 3 or 4 radar return. It also identifies the same area as having "heavy" precipitation. When you hear either "Level 3" or "heavy" precipitation mentioned, suspect thunderstorms.

one of the many bits of information that you'll want to use in making weather decisions enroute.

Too Many Colors?

Previously, on page 13-24, you learned about the radar summary chart. Given your new understanding of NEXRAD, here's an additional dollop of Doppler information to stick in those cranial folds..

The radar summary chart previously studied on page 13-24 and its legend (shown again in Figure 52) identifies four different levels of radar returns in terms of precipitation intensity: *light, moderate, heavy,* and *extreme.* Each precipitation level is associated with a radar reflectivity (dBZ) value. We know

that thunderstorm weather is normally associated with a dBZ value of 40 or more, and is also referred to as a Level 3 or 4 radar return (one associated with heavy precipitation. Therefore, when you hear pilots talking about a Level 3 radar return or a controller talking about heavy precipitation, you know they're talking about an area that's likely to contain thunderstorms.

Sometimes, weather service providers use names instead of the more precise reflectivity values to indicate storm/precipitation intensity as shown in Figure 53.

As you can see, unless you knew that heavy meant 40 dBZ radar reflectivity values, you wouldn't quite know how to interpret what you're seeing on the radar screen. Some weather service providers use different color coding calibrations than the National Weather Service for their radar reflectivity values. This really doesn't matter as long as you know how those color codes are calibrated.

While there's a lot more to learn about weather radar, at least you've had an introduction to the basics. You can learn more about this topic by picking up a copy of *Rod Machado's Instrument Pilot's Handbook* or, if you want the inside (and more technical details), you can read about them in *Rod Machado's Instrument Pilot's Survival Manual.*

RADAR REFLECTIVITY IDENTIFIED BY TERMS

SEVERE   HEAVY   LIGHT

Fig. 53

Some NEXRAD charts or displays use terms instead of dBZ values to identify radar reflectivity. The important thing to keep in mind is that "heavy" should mean 40 dBZs (or more) of reflectivity (check with the service provider to be sure).

The "NEW" Lockheed Martin Flight Service Station
www.1800wxbrief.com

ACAS | EasyActivate™ EasyClose™ | Close Reminders | ATC Notices | SE-SAR

No one can say that the Lockheed Martin Flight Service Station isn't cutting edge. Here are a few of the newest services that are available to you when you register at www.1800wxbrief.com.

Since nearly everyone has email and a cell phone, you can register to receive several new flight plan and weather alerting services. Here are a few you should choose.

Adverse Conditions Alerting Services

ACAS provides preflight and in-flight alerts to your email client or cell phone prior to departure or while enroute (if your cell phone can receive while enroute). These alerts include information on TFRs, SIGMETs, AIRMETs, Airport/Runway closures, etc. This service is available for IFR and VFR flight plans.

Easy Activate and Easy Close Flight Plan Service

When you register for this service, you'll receive an email and/or text message with a link for opening a prefiled flight plan 30 minutes prior to your estimated departure time. You'll also receive similar messages 30 minutes after the ETA listed on your flight plan. This service is available for VFR flight plans.

Flight Plan Close Reminders

If you'd rather just have a reminder to close your flight plan (not active it), then this service allows you to receive an email and/or text message 20 minutes after the ETA listed on your flight plan. This service is available for VFR flight plans only.

ATC Notices

This service informs you via email (email only, no text messaging) if and when your IFR flight plan has been accepted by ATC. It also alerts you if ATC makes a change in your flight planned route. This service is for IFR flight plans.

Please note that when you register for these services on Lockheed's web site, you'll see terms such as MIFR, MVFR, ZFR and YFR. The first two terms refer to Military IFR and VFR flight plans (not marginal VFR or IFR as you typically use them). The last two terms are not used in the U.S. at this time. Set up an account today!

Postflight Briefing #12-3

Significant Weather Prognostic (Prog) Charts - Colorized Versions

If you've used the internet to look at weather charts, you know that they now come in living color. They're pretty, too. These colorized prog charts, produced by the National Weather Service, ultimately make it a bit easier to identify weather patterns on your computer screen.

For instance, panel A, position 1 shows that during the 12 hour forecast period, the area surrounded by solid red lines is expected to be IFR (see the legend between panels A and B). The thick yellow dashed line in panel A, position 2 indicates that moderate turbulence is expected from the surface to 15,000 feet MSL during the 12 hour forecast period.

The thin green dashed line in panel B, position 3 shows that the freezing level over central Oklahoma is expected to be 8,000 feet MSL during the 24 hour forecast period.

The solid, thick green line in panel C, position 4 shows a shaded area (it's also called a *hatched* area) in northern Indiana forecasting mixed precipitation (light snow showers) covering more than half the area.

The solid, thick green line surrounding the non-shaded (non-hatched) area in panel D, position 5 identifies an area where light snow can be expected during the 24 hour forecast period. Since the area isn't shaded (hatched), the snow can be expected to cover half or less of the bordered area.

The 12 and 24 hour low level significant weather prognostic chart consists of four panels: The upper panels are 12 hour (left panel, A) and 24 hour (right panel, B) prognoses of significant weather from the surface to the 400 millibar pressure level (that's 24,000 feet). The lower panels (C and D) are 12 and 24 hour prognoses of surface weather (36 and 48 hour panels are also available at some locations).

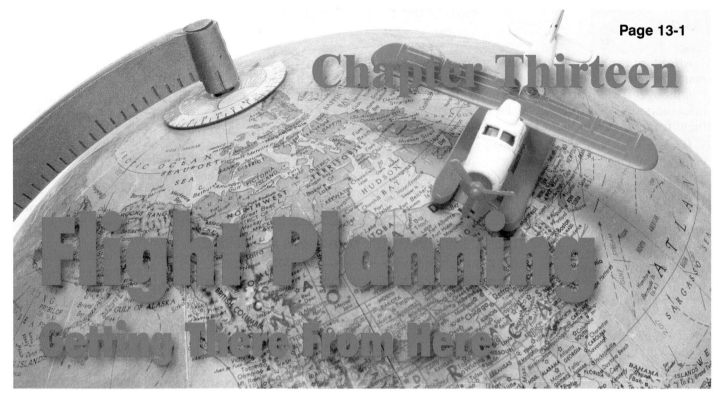

Chapter Thirteen

Flight Planning

Getting There From Here

Despite the navigational ease of certain cross country trips, some pilots still manage to get lost. There are two major islands off the coast of Southern California, Santa Catalina and San Clemente. San Clemente is approximately 57 miles off the coast and Catalina lies about half that distance.

Catalina is a popular fly-in spot for many pilots. San Clemente is a naval base not open to the public. Somehow, about twice a year, a pilot manages to land at San Clemente after mistaking it for Catalina. You might think the pilot would know something was wrong when it takes twice as long as expected to get to Catalina and the runway doesn't have the same numbers. Such details aside, some pilots manage the feat, often while in contact with the Unicom operator on Catalina Island (Catalina is a non-tower airport). The conversation usually goes something like this:

Pilot: "Catalina traffic, this is 2132B, I'm on final to land."

Unicom: "32B, I don't see you, but there's no reported traffic for Runway 24."

Pilot: "Catalina Unicom, this is 32B, a jet just strafed me."

Unicom: "32B, there are no jets in the pattern."

Pilot: "Then someone's flying one heck of a model airplane out here. I'm going to have to talk to somebody about that. It's dangerous."

Unicom: "32B, I don't see anyone flying model airplanes at Catalina."

Pilot: "Well, I just touched down and I bet it belongs to those two kids in Boy Scout uniforms walking over to my airplane with . . .uh, those guns. . .uh oh."

Mistakes happen. Contrary to popular lore, the military doesn't make you enlist for four years. They're pretty nice about it. Often they just talk with the errant pilot, show him all their guns and ammo,

then suggest he might want to reread the chapter on flight planning to avoid making the same mistake again.

To avoid having such a misadventure, or worse, let's invest a little time in acquiring some flight planning knowledge.

What is Flight Planning?

Sometimes students get very involved with the details of flight planning. Up to their elbows in calculators and scratch paper, they often lose track of the reason they're crunching numbers. There's a lot more to flight planning than just plotting a course.

The Original Global Positioning System

The original Global Positioning System (GPS) is nothing like its modern day counterpart. It didn't work too well as a navigational device. It did, however, help pilots fly coordinated by conking them in the head during slips in a left turn and skids in a right turn.

Flight planning is information management. Your job is to assemble, interpret, and put to use *all* the information needed to safely make a flight from Point A to Point B.

Here are just *some* of the reasons you flight plan:

● To know how to navigate from departure to destination

● To know if the weather presents any problems

● To know whether there is *any* condition (weather, equipment, runway availability) so adverse that you shouldn't go

● To make certain there is sufficient fuel on board, with an adequate safety margin, to reach your destination given the wind and other conditions enroute

● To enable you to file a flight plan, so that someone will begin looking for you if you don't reach your destination within a reasonable period

● To determine if you, as pilot-in-command, and the equipment (airplane and accessories) meet all the demands of a particular flight

● To identify any areas enroute or at your departure or destination that require special consideration (mountains), preparation (short fields), or equipment (engine pre-heat in extreme cold, for example)

● To find out if the airplane can safely carry the load of people and fuel you're planning on taking, and whether the weight can be loaded in such a way as to meet certain limitations (more on weight-and-balance a bit later)

● To know whether adequate fueling facilities will be available enroute and/or at your destination

● To calculate how long the flight will take, and to determine whether you, your passengers, or your airplane will need one or more stops enroute and if so, where those will be

● To determine whether the flight can be safely and successfully completed under conditions for which you are licensed and current. If you are not current for carrying passen-

gers at night, will you arrive at your destination before dark, with enough of a time margin to allow for unexpected headwinds? If you don't have an IFR rating, will the flight definitely be in VFR conditions? If conditions are marginal, are you comfortable and capable of handling the airplane in such circumstances?

Properly done, flight planning is like buying an insurance policy for you and your passengers. Done poorly, or not done at all, it exposes everyone involved to unnecessary risks.

Flight planning is not an enormously complex task. It's really just information gathering and some calculation. In fact, planning a flight is often a favorite task of pilots, who get to "fly" the flight once on paper and again in the air. Properly done, flight planning is like buying an insurance policy for you and your passengers. Done poorly, or not done at all, it exposes everyone involved to unnecessary risks.

Measuring Direction

Once upon a time, sailors set out with nothing more than the sun, stars, and their senses to guide them. Today, you're in a more fortunate position. As a pilot, you have a wide variety of means for determining where you are and where you're going.

Everything is somewhere. Keep that in mind next time you're lost. The challenge is in finding out where what you want *is*. Airports are in a fixed location (even in California, despite all the earthquakes). We describe the location of airports (and other things we want to find) by their position on an invisible grid of lines called *latitude* and *longitude,* as shown in Figure 1A. These lines are not actually painted on the earth, of course, but they are drawn on all navigational charts used by pilots. Lines of longitude run from the true north pole to the true south pole as shown in Figure 1B. Think of *longitude* as something running the

LATITUDE AND LONGITUDE LINES

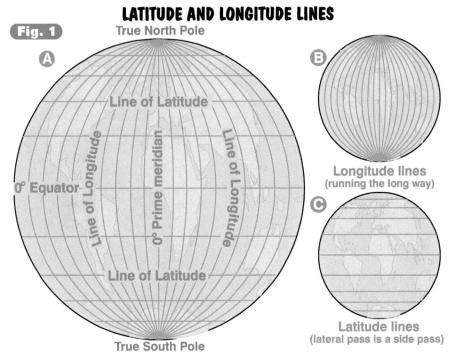

Lines of longitude run vertically, from the true north pole to the true south pole. Lines of latitude run horizontally around the globe. By knowing the latitude and longitude coordinates, you can pinpoint any place on earth with great precision. The 0 degree line of longitude, also called the *prime meridian,* runs through the center of Greenwich, England and the 0 degree line of latitude starts at the equator.

long distance from the top to the bottom of the earth. Longitude lines are also known as *meridians*.

Lines of latitude run sideways, like a sideways pass in football—a lateral pass. Lines of latitude are perpendicular to lines of longitude, as shown in Figure 1C. They run in an easterly and westerly direction around the earth and are longest around the equator.

Spaced one degree apart, 360 lines of longitude drop from the north to the south pole, striping the globe. The longitude line running directly through Greenwich, England is known as the *prime meridian* (the 0 degree longitude line). By convention, we start counting lines of longitude east and west from this point, as shown in Figure 2. To the left (west) of the prime meridian are 180 lines of longitude (including the prime meridian). To the right or east of the prime meridian are another 180 lines of longitude (also including the prime meridian)—360 in all. Longitude is stated as being a certain number of degrees *east* or *west* of the prime meridian.

MEASURING LATITUDE AND LONGITUDE

Longitude lines to the east and west of the prime meridian are called east and west longitude respectively. These lines meet on the opposite side of the earth at the 180 degree line of longitude. Lines of latitude run north and south of the equator and are called north and south latitude respectively. Lines of latitude start at 0 degrees at the equator and run to 90 degrees at the poles. Their angles are measured based on using the earth's center as an angular reference as shown below.

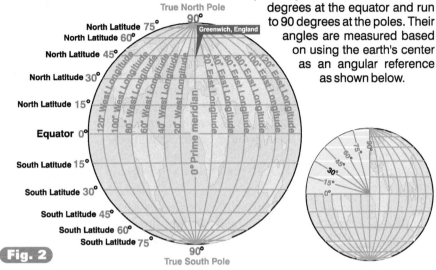

Fig. 2

You can see how the lines of longitude help us locate places on the earth. Africa's west coast, for instance, begins near the 20 degree west longitude line. Central Africa appears to lie on the 20 degree east longitude line. While longitude lines are helpful, they don't quite serve to nail down a position, since 20 degrees west can still be anywhere from up near the north pole to down near the south pole.

With the use of *latitude lines*, we can precisely locate our position. The zero degree line of latitude, otherwise known as the *equator*, is located at the midpoint of the earth. Spaced one degree apart, lines of latitude run parallel to the equator spaced north and south. Latitude lines north of the equator are called *north latitude* and south of the equator are called *south latitude*. They are sometimes called parallels because, unlike lines of longitude, latitude lines are parallel to each other, as shown in Figure 2.

If you were standing at the center of the earth, the angular distance from the equator to either pole would be one-quarter of a circle or 90 degrees. Lines of latitude run from 0 degrees at the equator to 90 degrees at the poles, as shown by the smaller globe insert in Figure 2. The 90

degree north latitude line is a tiny little circle (a dot) sitting at the true north pole. The 90 degree south latitude line is a small circle at the south pole (a point on a polar bear's nose).

The United States is located between 30 degrees and 45 degrees north latitude and 75 degrees and 125 degrees west longitude (see Figure 2). Any specific point on earth can be referenced by lines of latitude and longitude. Washington D.C. for example is located at approximately 39 degrees north latitude and 77 degrees west longitude. Soon we'll discuss how we achieve even more precise measurements with latitude and longitude, making it easy to find individual airports.

Time Measurement

A day is defined as the time it takes for the earth to rotate 360 degrees—one full rotation. With 24 hours in a day, the earth rotates 15 degrees every hour (15 degrees × 24 hours=360 degrees). If the sun were directly over the prime meridian in Greenwich, England, it would be noontime for the English locals.

Flight planning isn't a complex task. It is simply information gathering and some calculation.

But it would be very early morning for everyone on the U.S. west coast. In fact, for everyone on the west coast of California, the difference in longitude between their location and the prime meridian is 120 degrees. This makes the time difference approximately 8 hours (15 degrees per hour × 8 hours = 120 degrees).

It's a standard practice to establish time zones in the United States at 15 degree intervals, as shown in Figure 3. The center of each time zone is located on the 75th, 90th, 105th and 120th meridians. These zones are respectively called the Eastern, Central, Mountain and Pacific time zones. Each zone has one hour time difference (15 degrees/hour) from its neighbor. You would think the borders of different time zones would be straight lines running down the United States. Not so. Time zone borders usually consist of natural landmarks (rivers, canyons, etc.).

Local political reasons often explain why borders of each time zone are irregular rather than neat, straight lines.

When the sun is directly above the 120th, 105th, 90th and 75th longitude line, it's noon in these time zones. For example, when the sun is directly over the 90th meridian, it is noon, Central Standard Time. Under Daylight Saving Time, however, noon occurs when the sun is shifted 15 degrees to the left as an earthling looks up at it while facing south (to your right as you look at Figure 3). In other words, noon in the Central Daylight time zone occurs when the sun is located directly over the 75th longitude line, instead of the 90th. Daylight is *saved* since it's noon before the sun reaches directly overhead. The day appears to last longer because the afternoon is longer. Daylight Saving Time is in effect starting at 2 a.m. on the second

TO CONVERT FROM:	TO COORDINATED UNIVERSAL TIME
Eastern Standard Time	Add 5 hours
Eastern Daylight Time	Add 4 hours
Central Standard Time	Add 6 hours
Central Daylight Time	Add 5 hours
Mountain Standard Time	Add 7 hours
Mountain Daylight Time	Add 6 hours
Pacific Standard Time	Add 8 hours
Pacific Daylight Time	Add 7 hours
Yukon Standard Time	Add 9 hours
Alaska, Hawaii Standard Time	Add 10 hours
Bering Standard Time	Add 11 hours

Fig. 4

Sunday in March and ends at 2 a.m. on the first Sunday in November, except in a few areas such as Arizona, which never goes on Daylight Saving Time (as I said, local politics is a factor).

It's important to know about time zones for several reasons. First, the time listed on all weather charts is for Greenwich, England. This time is called Zulu or Universal Coordinated Time (UTC). For any weather chart to be meaningful, you'll need to know how to convert from the time in Greenwich (Universal Coordinated Time—UTC) to local time.

According to the conversion chart in Figure 4, if it's 1:00 p.m. (1300 hours) PST, what time is it UTC? The chart says to add 8 hours (1300 + 800 = 2100 hours). It makes sense to add 8 hours to find the time in Greenwich, England because it's always later there. If you're having trouble seeing how it's always later in England, examine Figure 5. When the sun is directly overhead in Greenwich, England (noon for them), it hasn't

TIME ZONES

Time zones are established at 15 degree intervals of longitude. When the sun is directly above the meridian, the time at points on that meridian is noon. Each time zone is one hour different from its bordering time zone.

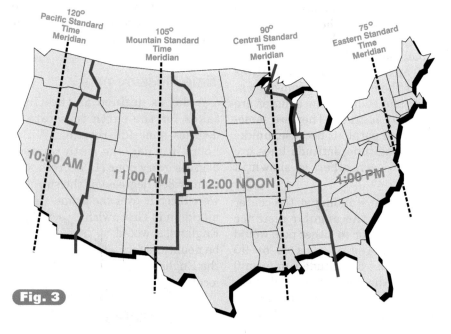

120° Pacific Standard Time Meridian

105° Mountain Standard Time Meridian

90° Central Standard Time Meridian

75° Eastern Standard Time Meridian

10:00 AM   11:00 AM   12:00 NOON   1:00 PM

Fig. 3

IT'S ALWAYS LATER IN ENGLAND

Fig. 5

True North Pole

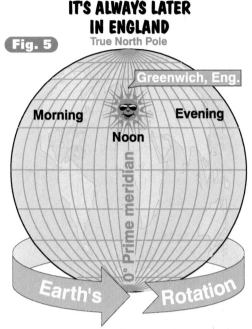

Greenwich, Eng.

Morning   Noon   Evening

0° Prime meridian

Earth's Rotation

Based on the way the earth rotates the time is always later in Europe. In other words, if it's morning in the United States it's noon in England. And if it's noon in England, then it's morning in the U.S. Thus, when you convert from local time to UTC, you must add hours; from UTC to local, you must subtract hours.

risen in the eastern sky of the U.S. It's still (very early) morning for us. Figure 4 is very useful for converting local time in any time zone to UTC when filing flight plans (all times on a flight plan are given in UTC).

While filing flight plans requires local-to-UTC conversion, interpreting weather charts requires the opposite conversion. For instance, suppose the valid time of a weather report is between 0800 Zulu (UTC) and 1600 Zulu. When would this chart be applicable to you in the Pacific Standard Time zone? To convert 0800Z and 1600Z to PST do the opposite of what the conversion chart in Figure 4 suggests. Simply subtract 8 hours from the Zulu time. This gives us a local chart time of 0000 to 0800 hours, or midnight to 8 a.m. Between the second Sunday in March and the end of first Sunday in November (Daylight Saving Time), you would subtract 7 hours instead of 8 hours.

Most aviation operations are expressed by using the 24 hour clock. Starting at 1:00 a.m. the time is referred to as 0100 hours or *zero one zero zero Zulu,* and 1:00 p.m. is called 1300 hours and spoken as *one three zero zero Zulu.* This count continues to the end of the 24 hour clock with midnight being 2400 hours.

WHO'S IN CHARGE HERE?

I was hired to fly a small airplane to an airport (about an hour away) to pick up the owner of the plane and return to base. The wind at destination was 15, gusting to 25. Being from the full-flap-for-every-landing school, I used 40 degrees and made an acceptable landing. Two men then boarded the airplane. As I taxied out, the one in the back seat asked why I had used full flaps. I asked if he was an instructor and he said yes. Since he was the customer, I remained polite and told him that was my technique. From there the flight went downhill. I filed IFR to get a direct flight back through Class B and Class C airspace in the smoother upper altitudes. As we climbed out, the gentleman in the back seat said there was too much wind at altitude and that I should cancel and go low around Class B and Class C airspace. Since he was the customer, I complied and for the next 1 1/2 hours fought to keep the aircraft on an even keel in moderate turbulence.

The customer then decided he didn't like the way I was navigating (direct) and told me to navigate to a VOR. Once again I bit my tongue and complied. As I got within ten miles of the VOR and now clear of Class B airspace, I set a direct course for home base and the gentleman in the back seat wondered why I wasn't picking up the VOR—four miles from the field (because it was not direct). With the continuous pounding of the turbulence and the continuous badgering from the back seat, all I wanted to do was land. The problem led to my not following my pre-landing checklist —I was too distracted. I had forgotten flaps until I realized that I wasn't as slow as I'd like to be. I was fast and sloppy arriving at the runway, killing power, dropping flaps, and fighting the gusty crosswinds all at the same time, trying to salvage a bad approach. I fishtailed and floated halfway down the runway before touching down. The landing was soft, just embarrassingly sloppy.

I was disgusted with myself for allowing the distraction to get me behind the airplane. The problem was that I was afraid to get the customer mad by exercising my pilot-in-command authority. Pilots in back seats must remember that the pilot flying is PIC and unnecessary distractions can cause problems. I suggest that pilots never fear exercising their PIC authority. Next time I get a back seat pilot I will give one warning as to who is PIC and further distractions will be treated as a violation of FAR 91.3!!!   **ASRS Report**

Try: "Sir, I prefer not to talk while flying, so that I may devote my full attention to a safe and comfortable flight. I will be happy to answer any questions after the flight." D.T.

A Matter of Degree: Longitude And Latitude On Sectional Charts

Individual lines of latitude and longitude allow us to precisely pinpoint any spot on a chart (like an airport). Figure 6 shows how we read these positions. Bob's airport lies directly between the 93rd and 94th lines of longitude (running up and down) and the 39th and 40th lines of latitude (running sideways). There's a great deal of real estate within a one degree boundary of longitude or latitude (see sidebar "Miles in a Degree"), so it's necessary to find a more precise means of determining a position.

Every degree of longitude and latitude can be broken down into 60 smaller segments called *minutes,* as shown by scale A and B in Figure 6. We won't think of minutes as a time reference. For our purposes, think of minutes on a sectional chart as being similar to the smaller markings on a ruler. They simply let you physically locate your position between lines of latitude and longitude with greater accuracy.

Imagine 60 smaller lines, each parallel to the 93rd and 94th lines of longitude, running up and down the chart. Were the lines really there, you couldn't locate *anything,* because you wouldn't be able to see the chart. To solve the problem, chartmakers place a small *tick* or line segment to one side, allowing you to see the subdivisions.

DEGREES, MINUTES AND SECONDS ON CHARTS

Lines of longitude run vertically up and down the chart. Their scale is identified in minutes by the orientation of the lines on scale A. Lines of latitude run horizontally across the chart. Their scale is identified by the lines on scale B. Between each whole line of latitude and longitude are divisions of minutes. Sixty minutes make up one degree of latitude or longitude and sixty seconds equal one minute (seconds are not depicted on sectional charts).

A BRIEF ON RELIEF

Enroute in a small airplane, the owner was in the right seat and I was in the left. The owner was flying and decided to land on a paved road to relieve himself (no cars in sight for miles, desolate). He landed, exited and returned. During the takeoff roll, at about 40-45 mph, we observed a vehicle appearing on the road in the distance. The pilot seemed startled and abruptly pulled back on the yoke, lifting the plane off. It then mushed back down on to the road's shoulder, hitting a bush with the right main gear, which was separated from the wing. The plane skidded to a stop, with damage to the bottom of the right wing and right landing gear. The pilot shut off the engine and we exited, uninjured. A normal takeoff could have been accomplished had the yoke not been prematurely pulled back because of the vehicle. Although the incident was far from any civilization, we probably shouldn't have landed on the road. A portable relief bottle, available in both women's and men's versions, makes a unique pilot gift and saves expensive airframe modifications, too! **ASRS Report**

The entire 30 minute longitude line, however, is there, helping give a rough division of the degrees of longitude, running up and down the chart. Scale A clearly shows these smaller line segments, which make it easy to identify your position in degrees and minutes. In the same way, each degree of latitude has smaller minute segments as shown by scale B, along with the 30-minute latitude line running across the chart between each degree of latitude.

For even greater accuracy, each minute of distance is broken down into 60 seconds (Figure 6, left side). Although it's not possible for chartmakers to show seconds on the chart, you can simply imagine their presence. The proper symbols for degrees, minutes and seconds are: °, ′, ″, and locations are written as 110° 15′ 10″.

As you can clearly see, Bob's airport lies halfway between the 93rd and 94th longitude lines. It's located

Miles in a Degree

How big is a degree, in statute miles? It depends.

There are degrees of latitude and degrees of longitude and the longitudinal lines converge as you head toward either pole. Measured in an east-west direction, there is more distance in a degree at the equator than higher or lower on the longitude "pole." If the reason for this isn't apparent to you, grab an orange or apple and inscribe (with pen or knife) some longitude lines. You'll readily see what I'm talking about. Then eat the fruit. It's good for you.

At the equator, there are 69.17 statute miles (sm) per degree of longitude. At 40 degrees north (about the midriff of the U.S.), a degree of longitude is 53.06 sm in width. Go to 85 degrees north latitude and it's only 6 sm between one degree of longitude and another. Go a bit farther north, to 89 degrees 30 minutes, and you can walk "around the world"—over all 360 lines of longitude—by going just 218 sm. Say hi to Santa.

Life is easier when measuring degree distance in a north-south direction, because nothing gets squished. Remember that the lines of latitude are sometimes called *parallels* because, yea verily, they are (pretty much) parallel (uniform in distance). That distance is 69.17 sm at the equator, varying by about 1/2 sm from the measurement at the extreme north pole (zero to one degree N, where it's 68.70 sm), and by about 1/4 sm from the measurement at 89-90 degrees south, where it's 69.41 sm. This slight variation reflects the fact that Planet Earth is not perfectly round. Call it 69 sm per degree of latitude and you won't get cited by the parallel police.

at 93° 30′ west longitude and 39° 30′ north latitude. Fred's airport is located at 93° 45′ west longitude and 39° 50′ north latitude. Hank's airport is located at 93° 20′ west longitude and 39° 25′ north latitude.

There's a good chance all your training as a student pilot will be done within the United States. If your instructor says to plan a cross country to Central America, she probably means somewhere in Kansas. Don't come back with a flight plan to Guatemala (it will make her real suspicious). Knowing that you'll always be flight planning for the U.S. helps, because it means you'll only need to consider west longitude and north latitude coordinates.

Which Way Is Up?

Anywhere in the United States, degrees of west longitude always increases to your left and degrees of north latitude always increases as you move up the chart. If you're looking for the 93° 30′ minute longitude point, and you find the 93° line of longitude, then the 30 minute line is to your left, not to your right. This same bit of wisdom applies to latitude. If you know where the 39° north latitude line is, then you know that 39° 30′ is above this line, not below it.

Fig. 7

Line of Latitude

Line of Longitude

A

D
39° 54' NL
93° 52' WL

Minutes of Longitude

Minutes of Longitude

Minutes of Latitude

E
39° 20' NL
93° 56' WL

F
39° 12' 45" NL
93° 55' 30" WL

B
39° 19' NL
93° 30' WL

C
39° 04' NL
93° 41' WL

Let's identify specific airports by their latitude and longitude coordinates on a real sectional chart. Figure 7 is a sectional chart excerpt for Kansas. At each corner of the page, the latitude and longitude coordinates are circled. Of course, the 40 degree mark at the top left of the page can only be the 40 degree north latitude line and the 94 degree mark can only be the 94 degree west longitude line (remember, this is in the U.S.). Halfway between whole lines of latitude and longitude are the minute lines. The vertical and horizontal running lines marked on the chart in position A are the 30 minute lines I mentioned before.

Take a look at Carrollton Memorial airport at position B in the bottom, center of the page. Carrollton lies on the 93° 30' line of longitude. What line of latitude does it lie on? Looking at my drawn-in scale to the right of Carrollton, it look like it lies at 39° 19' north latitude.

What is the latitude and longitude of Higginsville airport at position C? Higgineville is located at 39° 04' north latitude and 93° 41' west longitude.

What airport lies near the point defined by 39° 54' north latitude and 93° 52' west longitude? Yes, it's Longwood airport, located at position D.

Let's try one more. Identify the latitude and longitude location of Curtis airport, position E. It looks like Curtis is located approximately 3 minutes to the right of the 94 degree line of longitude, running vertically left of the airport. This would locate it at 93° 56' west longitude. Sometimes you have to just count individual minutes to the right or left from a whole line of latitude or longitude to find the minute value. The 5 and 10 minute marks are often difficult to see.

The latitude of Curtis is best found by counting down from the horizon-tal 30 minute line just above the airport. It looks like Curtis lies on the 20 minute north latitude line, giving it a coordinate of 39° and 20' north latitude. Can minutes be subdivided? Yes, they can be divided into an additional 60 small (very small) increments called seconds. They're too hard to see on this chart so the best you can do is estimate them. Lexington airport (position F) is located at 39° 12' 45" north latitude and 93° 55' 30" west longitude.

You're probably wondering why I'm making such a big fuss about the latitude and longitude coordinates for an airport. Well, it's important since the newer methods of navigation—Loran and GPS—all use latitude and longitude coordinates to determine airport position. You can usually navigate to an airport with your Loran or GPS equipment by dialing in the airport's three letter/number code.

You're probably thinking, "Oh, come on Rod. Why should I spend time learning about dead reckoning when I'll probably use my GPS, Loran or VOR to get me to my destination?" Stick with me for a few minutes, and you will learn to not just navigate but to understand what you're doing and why.

Figure 8 is an excerpt from the *AFD*. It shows the latitude and longitude coordinates of both airports as well as the airports' three digit codes (shown in parentheses).

Now that you have an idea about how to find airports on a sectional chart, we're ready to jump right into basic cross country navigation. But first, let me tell you about a friend of mine who had a golf ball hit his car's windshield. Surprisingly, he wasn't upset. He said it probably wouldn't have happened if he hadn't been driving on the golf course.

Isn't this like the pilot who got lost and actually said, "It probably wouldn't have happened if the wind hadn't been blowing that day"? You'll never need to worry about getting where you're going once you know the direction to aim the airplane and how to correct for wind. This is the essence of basic navigation.

Cross Country Navigation

As we saw before, there are several ways to get from one airport to the next. The most popular form of navigation is called *electronic navigation*. Devices such as VOR, Loran, GPS or VOR-based RNAV all allow you to navigate to your destination with relative ease.

You might also recall our discussion of pilotage, in which you read the features (natural and manmade) on the ground and compare them to the map to find your location. This is also used in combination with *dead reckoning,* a term that stands for *deduced reckoning* (and has no reference to what happens to pilots who don't know how to use it). Dead reckoning involves calculating the effects of wind and compass error on a plotted course. It is one of the most important forms of navigation. Why? Because it's the one form of navigation which requires you to understand

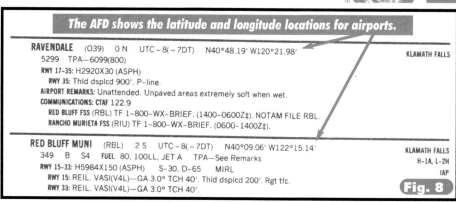

The AFD shows the latitude and longitude locations for airports.

RAVENDALE   (O39)   0 N   UTC–8(–7DT)   N40°48.19' W120°21.98'   KLAMATH FALLS
5299 TPA—6099(800)
RWY 17-35: H2920X30 (ASPH)
RWY 35: Thld dsplcd 900'. P-line.
AIRPORT REMARKS: Unattended. Unpaved areas extremely soft when wet.
COMMUNICATIONS: CTAF 122.9
RED BLUFF FSS (RBL) TF 1-800-WX-BRIEF. (1400-0600Z‡). NOTAM FILE RBL.
RANCHO MURIETA FSS (RIU) TF 1-800-WX-BRIEF. (0600-1400Z‡).

RED BLUFF MUNI   (RBL)   2 S   UTC–8(–7DT)   N40°09.06' W122°15.14'   KLAMATH FALLS
349   B   S4   FUEL 80, 100LL, JET A   TPA—See Remarks   H-1A, L-2H
RWY 15-33: H5984X150 (ASPH)   S-30, D-65   MIRL   IAP
RWY 15: REIL. VASI(V4L)—GA 3.0° TCH 40'. Thld dsplcd 200'. Rgt tfc.
RWY 33: REIL. VASI(V4L)—GA 3.0° TCH 40'.

Fig. 8

how the wind affects your airplane. There's no better education for a pilot than to have a mental picture of how wind affects an airplane. That's why I'll be placing the emphasis on dead reckoning and pilotage in this chapter.

You're probably thinking, "Oh, come on Rod. Why should I spend time learning about dead reckoning and pilotage when I'll probably use my GPS, Loran or VOR to get me to my destination?" Stick with me for a few minutes, and you will learn to not just navigate but to *understand* what you're doing and why. That will be worth its weight in airplane tires to you some day, no matter how you navigate. Understanding how compass errors and wind affects your flight has a profound effect on your ability to enjoy a lifetime of safe flying.

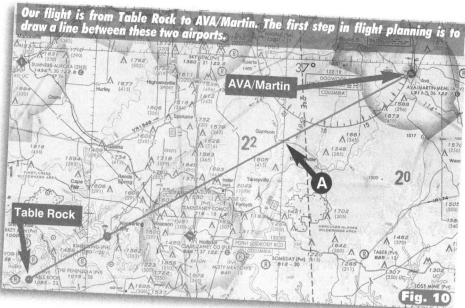

Our flight is from Table Rock to AVA/Martin. The first step in flight planning is to draw a line between these two airports.

Fig. 10

Our Trip

Let's start with the basics of how a course is plotted. The following are the six steps we'll use when planning a cross country flight based on dead reckoning navigation.

Flight Planning Step 1:
Draw a line between airports or checkpoints.

Flight Planning Step 2:
Determine the true course.

Flight Planning Step 3:
Determine the wind correction angle.

Flight Planning Step 4:
Determine the true heading.

Flight Planning Step 5:
Determine the magnetic heading.

Flight Planning Step 6:
Determine the compass heading.

While some if not all of your flights will use advanced forms of navigation (GPS, for instance), good pilots always keep these basic steps in mind on every flight. As we follow each of these individual steps, we will fill in a flight log (Figure 9). A flight log is a means of keeping track of navigational information, *not* something to use in your airplane's fireplace.

We'll only use a few of the sections in the flight log for this flight. Notice that the log starts with your checkpoints (item 1) and leads you to the TC or true course (item 7). Eventually, it leads to the CH or compass heading (item 13) which is also step 6 of our flight planning sequence. The point here is that the flight log provides you with a visual sequence of the basic steps you need to take to get to your destination airport. Let's fill it out as we proceed with each flight planning step.

Flight Planning Step 1—Draw a line between airports or checkpoints – The first step in cross country flight planning is to draw a line on the chart between our departure and destination airports. For this flight we'll assume we're departing Table Rock airport and our destination is AVA/Martin Memorial airport, as shown in Figure 10. We'll draw a line between the centers of each airport symbol. (If you're not planning a flight as a single, straight course between airports, then draw lines between turning points. Treat each straight segment as an individual course and apply the following steps to each segment.) Let's also insert these two airports as checkpoints in our flight planning form, as shown in Figure 11. (Ideally, we'd pick several checkpoints for every flight. For simplicity, however, we'll only use the departure and destination airport in this example.)

FLIGHT PLAN STEP 1: DRAW LINE BETWEEN CHECKPOINTS

Check Points	VOR Ident. Freq.	VOR Course (if applicable)	Altitude	Wind Dir./Vel. Temp.	True Airspeed	TC	WCA R+ L-	TH	V E- W+	MH	D	CH	Distance	GS Ground speed Est. Act.
Table Rock														
AVA/ Martin														

Fig. 11

Flight Planning Step 2—Determine the true course (the angle your flight path makes with the true north pole) – The first thing I like to do is to make a rough eyeball estimate of the course. From Table Rock to AVA, we're flying in a northeasterly direction (Figure 10). What do you think our course should be? Take a guess. I think it's somewhere around 50 degrees or so. These eyeball estimates are important, and should be a prelude to virtually every flight planning calculation. Don't go looking for an answer until you have some idea of what it should be. Believe me when I say that good pilots are always making mental estimates about time, distance, fuel consumption, etc. When one of these estimates doesn't jive with their paper calculation, they recheck their work (or put new batteries in the electronic flight computer). Follow this rule of guesstimating first and I guarantee you will avoid some remarkably embarrassing moments in your aviation activities.

Here's another of those handy rules of thumb—any flight in a right hand (easterly) direction requires a true course of somewhere between 0 degrees and 179 degrees. Any flight in a left hand or westerly direction requires a true course of somewhere

between 180 degrees and 359 degrees.

Figure 12 shows that we need to fly an angle of 60 degrees with respect to the true north pole on our flight from Table Rock to AVA. Conversely, for our return flight from AVA to Table Rock, we need to fly an angle of 240 degrees (the reciprocal of our original heading) with respect to the true north pole. An angle is defined as a course. Since this course is relative to the true north pole, we call it a *true course* (unlike some of the courses I had in college). This name allows you to understand the reference the angle is measured against. This is important because, as you'll soon see, there are magnetic courses and compass courses.

To measure the *true course,* find a line of longitude approximately halfway between the airports, as shown by point A in Figure 10. When measuring any true course on a sectional chart, it's best to pick a line of longitude halfway between your departure and destination as shown in Figure 10, point A. We do this because all the lines of longitude converge at the north pole and their angles subtly change as they converge. A halfway measurement point is more than accurate enough for navigation. Remember, we're launching light-sport airplanes

MEASURING TRUE COURSES

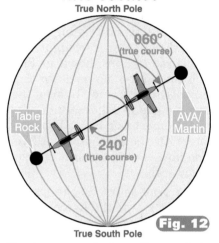

Fig. 12

Your true course is the angle your flight path makes with the true north pole. Since lines of longitude run up and down between the true north and south poles, we can simply measure the angle our flight path makes with the longitude line at the midpoint of our trip.

here, not cruise missiles. We only need to be accurate enough to be near the airport, not through the window of some terrorist hideout (Oops! Terrorists now want to be called *hostage administrators*).

Put a dot where the course line intersects this line of longitude. Figure 13, point A shows a closeup view of this intersection point.

Now you're ready to use a simple but effective tool called a *plotter* (see Figure 14). If this looks remarkably like a grade school protractor, that's because it's remarkably like a grade school protractor. The top or curved part of the plotter is for measuring course angles. In the bottom center of the curved section there's a small hole called a *grommet*. The bottom

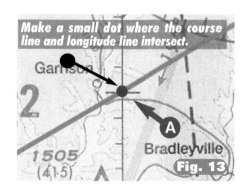

Make a small dot where the course line and longitude line intersect.

Fig. 13

The Basic Navigation Plotter

Fig. 14

part of the plotter has several scales used for measuring distances on charts. We will discuss the different parts as we use them.

Use the plotter's angle-measuring device to determine your true course. Place the plotter's straight edge over the course line as shown in Figure 15. Slide the plotter up or down the course line so the grommet is over the small dot we made in Figure 13. You're done! Wait, come back here. I mean you're done with the mechanics. All you have to do now is read the true course on the curved scale.

Your true course is the number that lies directly over the line of longitude at the top of the curved scale. This line is shown, close up, in Figure 16 (point A). It looks like 60 degrees is our true course for a flight from Table Rock to AVA/Martin Memorial. In other words, 60 degrees is the angle your flight path makes with respect to the true north pole. Since this is pretty close to our eyeball estimate of 50 degrees, we know it's an accurate (or at least plausible) measurement. Let's insert the true course of 60 degrees into our flight planning form (Figure 17).

The plotter in Figure 16 has two scales, an outside scale (point B) and an inside scale (point C). The outside scale (the one with the letter *E* next to it), suggests we use this scale if we're going east or from left to right—which we are. The inside scale (the one with the letter *W* next to it), suggests we use this scale if we're going west or from right to left. Using the inside scale you can easily see that the true course on our return flight is 240 degrees—the reciprocal of 60 degrees (180 degrees + 60 degrees = 240 degrees).

One word of caution! The numbers on both scales increase and decrease differently than your intuition might suggest. Moving 3 degrees to the left of the plotter's numerical value of 60 degrees yields 63 degrees, not 57 degrees, violating our notion that things always get smaller to the left and larger to the right. It's printed that way because of the way the plotter is used. Read the scales carefully when measuring courses.

Now you understand how to identify the direction of a course on a sectional chart. Next, we want to determine and correct for the effects of wind that might blow on our course.

To measure the true course, place the plotter's straight edge over the course line and then slide the plotter along this line until the grommet is over the small dot we previously made.

True course

Grommet (small hole)

Lay plotter along course line

Fig. 15

Your true course is the number lying directly over the longitude line at the top of the curved scale (point A).

Fig. 16

FLIGHT PLAN STEP 2: DETERMINE THE TRUE COURSE

Check Points	VOR Ident. Freq.	VOR Course (if applicable)	Altitude	Wind Dir. Vel. Temp.	True Airspeed	TC	WCA R+ L-	TH	V E- W+	MH	D	CH	Distance	GS Ground speed Est. Act.
Table Rock		▶				60°								66 kts
AVA/ Martin		▶												Fig. 17

Plotting Your Plotter Practice

For further practice, examine Box 1 below. The plotter shows a true course of 323 degrees when traveling up and to the left (use the W or *west* scale) and 143 degrees when traveling downward and to the right (use the E or *east* scale). If you are not careful, you might mistake 143 degrees for 157 degrees. Box 2 shows a true course indication of 27 degrees up and to the right (E scale), and 207 degrees down and to the left (W scale).

Two additional scales exist inside the plotter's two main outside scales, as shown in Box 3. The smaller, inner scales are useful for plotting courses in a north-south direction when no line of longitude exists near the course centerline. Simply place the base of the plotter along the course line and slide the grommet to a line of latitude, as shown in Box 3. The course number directly over the line of latitude (horizontal line) is your true course. This is shown clearly in Box 4. If traveling in a northerly direction, read the true course on N scale; in a southerly direction, use the S scale.

The plotter shows a true course of 323 degrees when traveling up and to the left (W scale) and 143 degrees when traveling down and to the right (E scale).

Box 1

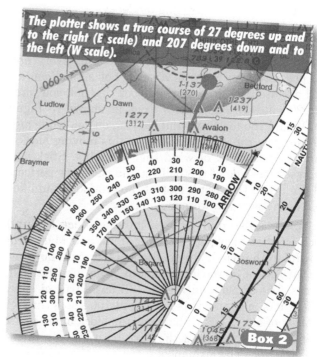

The plotter shows a true course of 27 degrees up and to the right (E scale) and 207 degrees down and to the left (W scale).

Box 2

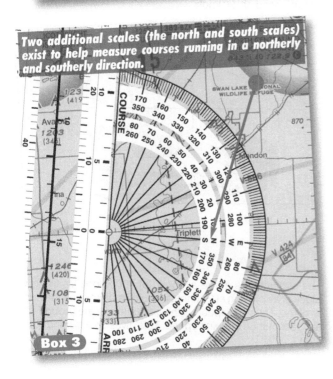

Two additional scales (the north and south scales) exist to help measure courses running in a northerly and southerly direction.

Box 3

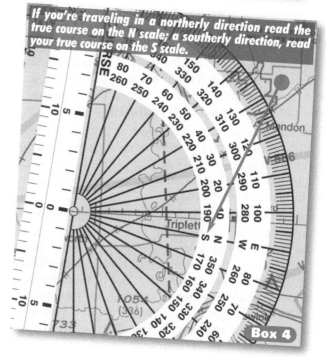

If you're traveling in a northerly direction read the true course on the N scale; a southerly direction, read your true course on the S scale.

Box 4

Flight Planning Step 3—Determine the wind correction angle – Before we can discuss how to correct for the effects of wind, let's review some basic principles about how wind affects your airplane in flight.

Without wind, all you'd have to do is fly the compass course and you'd get where you're going. Mother Nature (trickster that she is) is not so accommodating. Wind exists to some degree almost every time you fly. If it blew directly on your nose or tail, it wouldn't blow the airplane off course. Nature, however, is perverse in tooth and law, and most of the time the wind blows at some angle to your flight path. The effect, left uncorrected, is to blow the airplane off its intended course. Your job is to compensate for this drifting tendency.

If the wind is blowing from the north at 20 knots, we're saying the atmosphere is moving across the ground a distance of 20 nautical miles for every hour that passes. If you were in a small hot air balloon and lifted off into this large moving block of wind, you would drift 20 miles in one hour's time, as shown in Figure 18A. Would you feel any wind blowing on you while moving? No, you are stationary within this moving block of wind. It's the block of wind that's moving. Stick your hand over the side of the balloon and the air is perfectly still. In fact, if you didn't look at the ground it's unlikely you'd even know you were moving.

Airplanes also drift with a moving block of wind, which is what inspired the Peter, Paul and Mary song "Blowin' in the Wind." In addition to this drift, however, they also have forward movement generated by their engines. The airplane in Figure 18B has a true airspeed of 100 knots, meaning it is moving at 100 knots through the block of air. It just so happens the block of air is also moving at 20 knots, and they are both moving in the same direction. The airplane's speed over the ground is a combination of the wind and air speeds. Adding our wind speed to our true airspeed gives us a speed over the ground (groundspeed) of 120 knots.

The airplane in Figure 18C moves through the block of air at 100 knots. With the block of air moving at 20 knots in a direction *opposite* that of the airplane, we have a net groundspeed of 80 knots (100 – 20 = 80).

If winds blew exactly on the nose or the tail of the airplane, it would be easy to determine your groundspeed. But the wind usually blows at some angle to the intended flight path, making its effect on groundspeed a little more difficult to determine.

Even worse than its effect on groundspeed, which only represents a delay in reaching your destination, is the fact the wind is trying to push you where you don't want to go. This doesn't bode well for all those pilots who like ending up at the destination they had in mind (remember, it makes the passengers nervous if you keep landing at unknown airports to find out where you are). Fortunately, we can correct for the effects of wind direction and velocity on our flight path.

MOVING WITH A BLOCK OF WIND

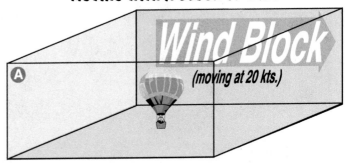

The balloon is drifting with a block of wind that's moving over the earth at a speed of 20 knots. Without any mechanical form of propulsion, the balloon has a groundspeed of 20 knots.

MOVING WITHIN A MOVING BLOCK OF WIND

The airplane has a true airspeed of 100 knots. It's flying within a block of air moving at 20 knots that blows directly on the tail of the airplane. Thus, the speed of the airplane over the ground is a combination of the wind speed and true airspeed, which gives us a groundspeed of 120 knots.

MOVING WITHIN A MOVING BLOCK OF WIND

The airplane has a true airspeed of 100 knots. It's flying within a block of air moving at 20 knots that blows directly on the nose of the airplane. Thus, the speed of the airplane over the ground is the true airspeed minus the wind speed. This gives us a groundspeed of 80 knots.

Fig. 18

COMPENSATING FOR DRIFT

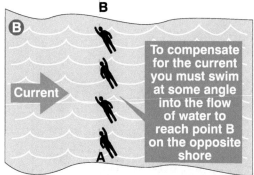

To prevent being carried downstream, a swimmer must swim at some angle into the flow of water. Airplanes must similarly fly (crab) at some angle into the wind to prevent being carried off course.

Fig. 19

The Effect of Water on a Swimmer – Suppose the swimmer in Figure 19A wants to swim across the river from point A to point B. Unless he swims at some angle into the flowing water, he'll be carried downstream to point C (or out to sea!). We'll call this the water correction angle (WCA). Figure 19B shows how angling into the current allows the swimmer to cross the river and arrive where he intended. Despite the fact our swimmer is pointed upstream, he actually travels directly across the river. Lights on? Camera. Action! Airplanes must do something similar when they travel in a stream of moving air.

The Effect of Wind on an Airplane – In Figure 20A, our airplane points in the direction of the desired course while flying with a left crosswind. Its track over the ground is a combination of the motion of the airplane and the motion of the air. The airplane is blown away from the desired course. The angle between the desired course and the actual ground track is called the drift angle. By determining the drift angle and correcting for it, you can fly a ground track exactly along the desired course, as shown in Figure 20B. Like our swimmer, you must head or point the airplane into the wind at enough of an angle to compensate for its effects. Instead of a *water correction angle,* we call this (remarkably) the *wind correction angle (WCA).*

Determining WCAs is where that fancy electronic flight computer you purchased will earn its keep. However, you really can't sense what the wind does to your flight path unless you visualize how it blows on your airplane. This is why I insist you initially use (or at least become familiar with) the venerable and trustworthy E6-B type computer to determine the wind's effect on your drift and groundspeed. (E6-B is an old military designation for the manual, slide type computer.)

Low Blow

In case you don't think it's all *that* important to have a good sense about how the wind affects your airplane, read on.

Several years ago I was returning to California from an Arizona airport on a moonless, pitch black night. I knew the wind was from the north (from my right), yet the VOR showed that a left wind correction angle (indicating a wind from the south) was necessary to remain on the desired course. As time passed, the left wind correction angle I needed to remain on course kept increasing. This shouldn't have been the case with a right (north) wind.

I eventually discovered that FAA maintenance technicians were working on the VOR station and hadn't removed its identification (giving the impression the station was in service). The work they were doing caused the VOR to produce an incorrect and misleading signal. If I hadn't understood the basics of how wind affects an airplane, I might still be looking for my destination.

Believe me, learning about dead reckoning navigation will serve you well in the future.

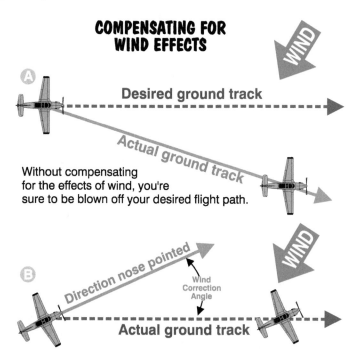

COMPENSATING FOR WIND EFFECTS

Without compensating for the effects of wind, you're sure to be blown off your desired flight path.

By pointing your airplane into the wind a small amount, your airplane tracks the desired flight path across the ground. The exact amount of angling into the wind is determined by use of your flight computer. This angle is called the WCA or Wind Correction Angle.

Fig. 20

I know I sound a little techno-regressed, but there is a reason I want you to use the manual computer before you start crunching numbers with your Cray Multimegabyte Handheld Captain Kirk Wind Computer. Trust me on this one. Besides, this argument is eternal and probably dates back to Confucius' mom telling him to put down that abacus and use his fingers for counting.

I'll walk you through the steps needed to use the E6-B for calculating a wind correction angle, but that's just the start of the calculations you can perform using this mechanical wonder. For an extended discussion of the workings and capabilities of the E6-B, please take the time to read Postflight Briefing #13-1. You'll need to know something about this to perform basic time, speed and distance computations on the front side of the E6-B.

From now on, we'll refer to the E6-B computer's two sides as the *wind side* and the *front side*.

Using the Wind Side of the Slide Computer – Here's the wind, and the performance information for our trip:

The wind as reported by the FSS for the altitude we'll fly is 020 degrees at 40 knots.

For this flight our performance charts say our true airspeed is 100 knots.

(In Chapter 14 you'll learn about how to use performance charts.)

The true course from Table Rock to AVA is 60 degrees.

Let's take just a second and visualize how the wind is affecting our airplane on this flight (see Figure 21). Notice that the wind is from 020 degrees. Our true course of 060 degrees means we're heading into a left quartering headwind. Common sense (always check for the presence of this when doing computations) indicates we'll need to correct to the left of 060 degrees in order to track the course line. It also indicates our groundspeed will be something less than our true airspeed of 100 knots, since the wind is blowing on the front of the airplane.

Given this, we have enough information to use our flight computer to determine two very important items necessary for all dead reckoning navigation: the wind correction angle (WCA) and our groundspeed. Let's take a look at the wind side of the E6-B type computer.

Figure 22 shows the basic components of the wind side of a typical E6-B computer. A rectangular sliding card fits inside the circular sleeve. The rectangular card has speed arcs with their appropriate values marked vertically along the centerline. It also has diagonal lines running up and down the card. The circular sleeve has a moveable inner scale that rotates about a center point (a small hole) known as the grommet. At the top of the circular scale is a small, white triangular reference point known as the *true index*.

THE WIND CORRECTION ANGLE

By pointing at an angle into the wind (to the left) Airplane A follows the course line we drew on the chart. The exact angle the airplane must point into the wind is called the wind correction angle (WCA). Without this correction, the airplane would drift in the direction of Airplane B.

Angles exaggerated for easier analysis

Fig. 21

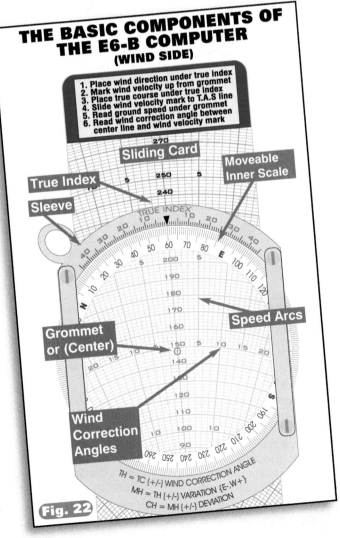

THE BASIC COMPONENTS OF THE E6-B COMPUTER
(WIND SIDE)

1. Place wind direction under true index
2. Mark wind velocity up from grommet
3. Place true course under true index
4. Slide wind velocity mark to T.A.S line
5. Read ground speed under grommet
6. Read wind correction angle between center line and wind velocity mark

Fig. 22

TH = TC (+/-) WIND CORRECTION ANGLE
MH = TH (+/-) VARIATION {E-,W+}
CH = MH (+/-) DEVIATION

At the top of the card are the six steps in solving wind problems.
Step 1: Place the wind direction under the index.
Step 2: Mark the wind velocity up from the center.

1. Place wind direction under true index
2. Mark wind velocity up from grommet
3. Place true course under true index
4. Slide wind velocity mark to T.A.S line
5. Read ground speed under grommet
6. Read wind correction angle between center line and wind velocity mark

The center (Grommet)

TRUE INDEX

Fig. 24

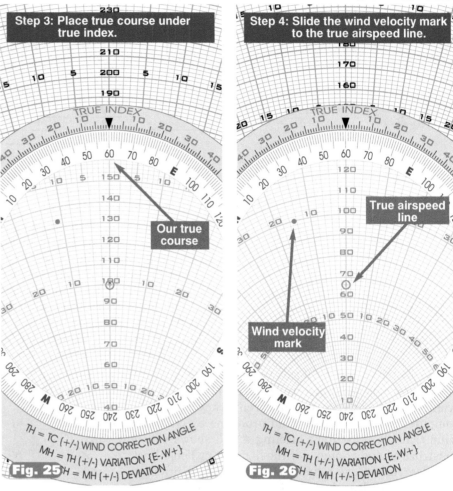

Step 3: Place true course under true index.

TRUE INDEX

Our true course

TH = TC (+/-) WIND CORRECTION ANGLE
MH = TH (+/-) VARIATION {E-,W+}
CH = MH (+/-) DEVIATION

Fig. 25

Step 4: Slide the wind velocity mark to the true airspeed line.

TRUE INDEX

True airspeed line

Wind velocity mark

TH = TC (+/-) WIND CORRECTION ANGLE
MH = TH (+/-) VARIATION {E-,W+}
CH = MH (+/-) DEVIATION

Fig. 26

Before starting a wind problem, it's best to slide the wind card until the 100 arc value is under the grommet.

Place grommet (the metal ring) on 100 arc for ease in marking wind velocities up from center.

Fig. 23

At the very top of the rectangular card in Figure 22 are a series of 6 steps used in solving a wind problem.

Before starting any problem, it's always best to slide the rectangular card up or down to place the card's 100 arc value under the grommet as shown in Figure 23. This makes it easier to do the measuring required. If your computer has been used before, the rotating circular scale probably has a complexion problem—lots of dots over its plastic face. If there are any pencil marks on this scale, it's best to erase them now or there's no telling what kind of bizarre answers you'll get for your wind problems.

Step one says to place the wind direction under the *true* index. Rotate the inside plastic circle until 020 degrees is under the *true* index (Figure 24, position 1).

Step two says to mark wind velocity up from the center (the center is the grommet). Having placed the 100 arc under the grommet, simply count up the wind velocity along the given scale and make a mark (Figure 24, position 2). In our case the velocity is 40 knots (now do you see why I had you place the 100 arc under the grommet? It simply makes it easier to count up to the specific wind value).

Step three says to place the true course under the *true* index, as shown in Figure 25. Notice that your wind mark is on the left side of the scale.

Step four says to slide the wind velocity mark to the TAS (true airspeed line), as shown in Figure 26. I simply move the cardboard slide upward until the wind mark is on top of the 100 knot true airspeed line (it's actually an arc because it's curved). You're done! Wait, wait, come back here (you've got to stop running to the airplane every time I say "You're done"). All you need do is read the groundspeed and wind correction angle off the computer.

Step 5: Read the groundspeed under the grommet.
Step 6: Read the wind correction angle under the wind mark.

Wind correction angle is 15 degrees left

Groundspeed: 66 knots

Fig. 27

FLIGHT PLAN STEP 3: DETERMINE THE WCA

Check Points	VOR Ident. Freq.	VOR Course (if applicable)	Altitude	Wind Dir. Vel. Temp.	True Airspeed	TC	WCA R+ L-	TH	V E- W+	MH	D	CH	Distance	GS Ground speed Est. Act.
Table Rock		▶		020 40	100 kts.	60°	15L°							66 kts.
AVA/ Martin		▶												

Fig. 28

Step five says to read groundspeed under center (the grommet). Figure 27 shows a closeup of the center position. The grommet lies directly over a groundspeed of 66 knots.

Step six says to read the wind correction angle between centerline and the wind velocity mark, as shown in Figure 27. Notice the small lines running diagonally down the sliding scale. Our wind mark falls on the 15 degree diagonal line to the left of scale. Our wind correction angle is 15 degrees to the left. This means that a 15 degree angle to the left should compensate for the wind and allow us to track directly along the course line we drew on the chart in Flight Planning Step 1. Let's list the wind correction angle in our flight log as shown in Figure 28. (I'll explain the significance of left and right WCAs in a moment.)

Now look how nicely all this ties together. Figure 29 is a comparison of our previous wind picture (Figure 21) and the computer's wind triangle. They're very similar, aren't they? That's because the computer actually solves wind problems by creating a small wind triangle. Postflight briefing #13-3 shows you how to construct a wind triangle for the flight from Table Rock to AVA/Martin. Please take a good look at this briefing. It's well worth learning how to do a wind triangle (I sound like Confucius' mom, don't I?). The reason we often don't construct wind triangles on charts is because it's easier to do them mechanically on the plastic face of the computer.

Flight Planning Step 4—Determine the true heading – The next item in our flight log calls for the TH or *true heading*. A heading is technically a course that's been corrected for wind. In other words, if you correct your true course for the wind correction angle, you obtain a heading that allows you to track directly along the course line you drew on the sectional chart. Given that our WCA is 15 degrees left, we need to subtract this from the true course to obtain the true heading for this flight.

Why subtract? Any time the airplane turns to the left, the numbers of the compass get smaller. A right turn causes the compass numbers to get larger. It seems when most things are turned to the right (including radio dials), their numbers increase. Turning the dial to the left makes things less or smaller. That's why left WCAs are *subtracted* from the true course to obtain the true heading.

The E6-B computer solves a wind problem by constructing a wind triangle (see Postflight Briefing #13-3). A wind triangle is a picture of how the wind affects your airplane. From it you can determine the WCA and airplane's groundspeed. An actual wind triangle is shown below. Notice the similarities.

Wind 020° 40 knots

Wind Correction Angle

AVA/ Martin

Direction nose pointed

A

A

Desired ground track (true course line)

A

Table Rock

Angles exaggerated for better analysis

Fig. 29

How True Airspeed Affects Your Wind Correction Angle

A 160 TRUE INDEX
15 degree WCA at 100 knots TAS

B 260 TRUE INDEX
7.5 degree WCA at 200 knots TAS

Item A (to the left) is the same problem as our flight from AVA to Table Rock. Item B, however, uses a new true airspeed for the computations. Notice that the wind mark in item B is over the 200 knots TAS arc. This gives us a new wind correction angle of approximately 7.5 degrees instead of 15 degrees for 100 knots TAS.

It's important for you to understand that the faster you fly, the less the wind affects you by blowing you off course. Why? Because you don't spend as much time enroute. There is less time for the wind to blow you off course when you're flying faster. The groundspeed, however, still stays approximately 34 knots below the true airspeed.

Right WCAs are *added* to the true course to obtain the true heading. The flight log reminds you to do this by putting a (-) next to L and a (+) next to R. Our flight log shows that a true course of 060 degrees with a left WCA of 15 degrees gives us a true heading of 045 degrees as shown in Figure 30.

Now that we have a true heading, is this all we need to get to our destination? Not quite. While a true heading corrects a true course for the wind, it's not something you can fly on your compass. In other words, the angles we've measured so far are in relation to the true north pole. Your airplane's compass is called a magnetic compass (not a true compass) because it points to a different pole. In other words, the magnetic compass measures angles with the magnetic north pole, while we have measured angles on the sectional chart with respect to the true north pole. We're mixing kiwi fruit and papayas here (OK, apples and oranges). We need to correct the true heading for the difference (called *variation*) between these two poles. Let's find out how to do that.

Flight Planning Step 5—Determining the magnetic heading – It's been said that women love a man in uniform. I believe this to be a substantiated fact. In fact, my wife fell for me because of the uniform—she couldn't resist the scarf, merit badges, and compass. And no pilot should be without a compass, even if you're out of uniform. As I said before, the compass is our primary means of navigation. But a slight problem exists, because the compass points to a pole that is different from the true north pole.

Recall that lines of longitude converge at the true north pole. In earlier times this was known to you as Santa Claus' house. The true north

Is There an Untrue North Pole?

You might have noticed by now there are two north poles—the *true* north pole, and the *magnetic* north pole.

Once upon a time, just a few million years ago, both of these were in the same place, which is right where they should be, smack dab on top (or bottom, depending on your point of view) of the earth. When a compass needle pointed north (if there had been compass needles back then) it would have pointed to the one and only north pole.

Alas, things change. In the case of the magnetic pole, it began to wander around. Where a compass needle pointed as being north was no longer where the tippy top of the earth was. I won't worry your databank with a deposit on why the magnetic pole moves, but it has and it does and it is and it will.

What you as a pilot need to understand is that while east may be east, and west may be west (and never the twain shall meet), north isn't always north. *Magnetic north* is where the needle on a compass points. *True north* is where it always has been, the place where all the lines of longitude converge at a single point. The difference, at the moment, is a matter of about 1300 miles!

The angular difference between true north and magnetic north is referred to as *magnetic variation.* It varies for every location, and continues to slowly change. The current value can be found on your sectional chart.

Knowing the north pole isn't true should inspire some great country and western songs.

FLIGHT PLAN STEP 4: DETERMINE THE TRUE HEADING

Check Points	VOR Ident. Freq.	VOR Course (if applicable)	Altitude	Wind Dir. Vel. Temp.	True Airspeed	TC	WCA R+ L-	TH	V E- W+	MH	D	CH	Distance	GS Ground speed Est. Act.
Table Rock		▶		020 40	100 kts	60°	15L°	45°						
AVA/ Martin		▶												Fig. 30

and true south poles represent the spin axis points of the earth. The earth acts like a very large magnet (too big to put on any refrigerator), and has two magnetic poles (Figure 31). As I've previously stated, they are, unfortunately, not located in the same position as the true north pole. Lying just a little north of Hudson Bay, the *magnetic* north pole is separated by a distance of approximately 1300 miles from the *true* north pole.

The variation between these two poles presents a slight challenge in navigation. We measured our course with respect to the *true* north pole, but we must navigate using a compass that points to the *magnetic* north pole. Fortunately, the answer is simple—correct for the angular variation between the true and the magnetic north poles. This is easy to do once you understand that this variation changes depending on your geographic location.

Figure 32 depicts an airplane in three different locations across the United States. In position B, the airplane is located so the magnetic north pole is directly in

EARTH AS A GIANT MAGNET

The earth is essentially a very big magnet with north and south poles. Magnetic lines of flux run between the magnetic poles of the earth in the same way they run between the poles of a small magnet. Your compass points to the magnetic north pole while the earth rotates around an axis running between the true north and south poles.

Fig. 31

front of the true north pole. In this instance, both poles appear in line with one another, so there is no apparent variation in location between poles. Your true heading would be a magnetic heading at this location (a location with zero variation). You could simply fly the number you found with the plotter on the compass (assuming no wind and the compass is free of errors itself).

An airplane in position C views the magnetic north pole to the west (to the left) of the true north pole. We have what is technically known as *westerly variation* between poles. The airplane in position A sees the magnetic pole located to the east (to the right) of the true north pole. Airplane A experiences *easterly variation* between poles.

Clearly, the variation between poles depends on what part of the United States (or the world for that matter) you're in. Fortunately, we can correct for this variation since it's a known quantity dependent on your location. Figure 33 shows the angular variation between the magnetic and true north poles. If you were flying along the western part of Texas (Airplane C), the magnetic north pole would be 10 degrees to the east of the true north pole. Printed lines of

Fig. 32

MAGNETIC VARIATION DEPENDS ON YOUR LOCATION

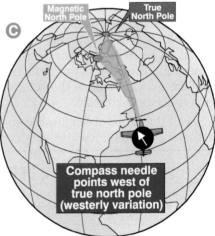

From this position on earth, the magnetic north pole appears to the east of the true north pole. Easterly variation is experienced in this area.

From this position on earth, the magnetic north pole appears to be aligned with the true north pole. No variation is experienced in this area.

From this position on earth, the magnetic north pole appears to the west of the true north pole. Westerly variation is experienced in this area.

Home Plate

Never leave your flashlight (with its magnetic clip) lying on the dash, next to the compass. Word has it that entire platoons of soldiers went the wrong direction in Vietnam when they held their compasses up next to their steel helmets to take a directional reading. Anything magnetic (and many steels) can affect the compass; keep such items away from wherever the compass is mounted.

A friend had a student who was worried that an anatomical problem might affect his navigation. He had a metal plate in his head (I think he installed it himself). I'm not sure if this would be harmful in terms of navigational accuracy, but it sure would keep him from losing his flashlight!

Another Way Of Looking at It

WHY WE SUBTRACT EASTERLY VARIATION AND ADD WESTERLY VARIATION

Our airplane is headed directly toward the true north pole. Its true course is 360 degrees. Its magnetic compass, however, says it's flying 340 degrees (it's flying at a 340 degree angle to the magnetic north pole). Thus, when we know our true course and we want to find our magnetic course (or heading), we subtract easterly variation from the true course. Subtracting 20 degrees of easterly variation from a true course of 360 degrees gives us our magnetic course of 340 degrees (the angle our airplane makes with the magnetic north pole).

In an area where the westerly variation is 20 degrees, our airplane makes a 0 degree angle (same as 360 degrees) with the true north pole, yet it makes a 20 degree angle with the magnetic north pole. Therefore, to find our magnetic course (or heading) when we are given westerly variation, we need to add this to the true course. Twenty degrees of westerly variation added to a true course of zero degrees give us a magnetic course of 020 degrees.

MAGNETIC VARIATION AND ISOGONIC LINES

Fig. 33

Isogonic lines (lines with equal variation) are shown for the United States. Anywhere along the depicted line, the angular variation between the true north pole and the magnetic north pole is the same (thus the prefix *iso* which means *the same as*). As you can see above, all the airplanes are headed toward the true north pole while their white compass needles are deflected an amount equal to the magnetic variation for that location.

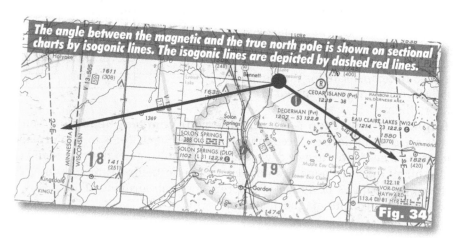

The angle between the magnetic and the true north pole is shown on sectional charts by isogonic lines. The isogonic lines are depicted by dashed red lines.

Fig. 34

variation shown on sectional charts are known as *isogonic lines* and are shown in Figure 34. They are spaced at increments of one degree and are marked for either east or west variation with an E or W respectively. *Iso,* like isobar, means *the same as*. *Gonic* is a Greek derivative meaning *angles*. Anywhere along an isogonic line, the angular variation between the poles is the same.

To the northwest of Florida, Airplane E (Figure 33), is on an *agonic line*. The prefix *a* means *no*. Along the agonic line there is no angular variation between the poles. Standing along this line, the true and magnetic north poles would be aligned with one another and no variation exists in this location. The isogonic lines aren't straight because of the many slight variations in the earth's magnetism (perhaps caused by too many heavy metal rock concerts in one area).

Now you're ready to correct the true heading for the effect of magnetic variation. You can do this by finding the closest whole number (not half degree) isogonic line nearest the center of your course line as shown in Figure 35. The magnetic variation is 2E or 2 degrees east. Our flight log in Figure 36 shows that easterly variation is subtracted from the true heading to obtain the magnetic heading. If we subtract the easterly variation of 2 degrees from our true heading of 45 degrees, this gives us a magnetic heading of 43 degrees.

If we had westerly variation, we would have added this to the true heading to obtain the magnetic heading. An easy way to remember this is to think, East is least, west is best. Least means *subtract,* best implies *add.* After correcting the true heading for variation, you now have an angle with respect to the magnetic north pole or a magnetic heading.

Now we at least have a number we can fly on our compass, right? Almost. There's one more thing to consider. What happens if the compass in our airplane is slightly inaccurate? In other words, what happens if the value it shows deviates slightly from the actual magnetic direction? We need to compensate for this deviation before we can set off on our cross country flight.

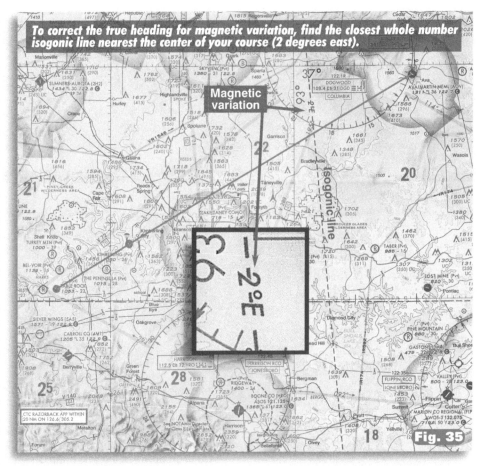

To correct the true heading for magnetic variation, find the closest whole number isogonic line nearest the center of your course (2 degrees east).

Fig. 35

FLIGHT PLAN STEP 5: DETERMINE THE MAGNETIC HEADING

Check Points	VOR Ident. Freq.	VOR Course (if applicable)	Altitude	Wind Dir. Vel. Temp.	True Airspeed	TC	WCA R+ L-	TH	V E- W+	MH	D	CH	Distance	GS Ground speed Est. Act.
Table Rock		▶		020 40	100 kts	60°	15L°	45°	-2°	43°				66 kts
AVA/ Martin		▶												

Fig. 36

Flight Planning Step 6—Determine your compass heading – Many instructors are fond of saying that compasses are devious devices. Occasionally, they lie. Some items in the airplane have a strong magnetic field that causes the compass needle to turn or deviate slightly, resulting in an error. If you think about it, the airplane has quite a few little things that can generate deviant magnetic fields—radios, lights, tools, magnetized metal parts, and flight instructors. Compass deviation is different for each airplane. That's why you will always find a *compass deviation card* mounted near the magnetic compass (Figure 37).

TYPICAL COMPASS DEVIATION CARD

FOR (MAGNETIC)	N	30	60	E	120	150
STEER (COMPASS)	O	28	57	86	117	148
FOR (MAGNETIC)	S	210	240	W	300	330
STEER (COMPASS)	180	212	243	274	303	332

Fig. 37

The compass deviation card is located on or near the airplane's magnetic compass.

Have you ever noticed a painted *compass rose* (these are not decorated flowers that point north) around the airport, much like the one shown in Figure 38? This isn't a sacred place where Druids go for a belly button alignment. It's much more practical.

Mechanics place the airplane in the center of this compass rose and point the nose in precise magnetic directions painted around the circle. All the airplane's equipment is turned on to obtain the maximum amount of potential magnetic interference. The actual magnetic direction is measured against the compass' indications. This process is known as *swinging the compass*. To the extent possible, adjustments are made to the compass to eliminate the discrepancies. Any remaining deviation between the actual magnetic direction and what the compass shows is recorded on the compass deviation card (Figure 37). This card will usually be found mounted directly beneath the compass.

Step 6 of cross country flight planning requires you to correct the magnetic heading for the compass deviation, to obtain a heading you can fly

The airport's compass rose allows calibration of the airplane's magnetic compass. With the airplane's electrical equipment on, mechanics can compare compass readings with known magnetic directions. Differences are logged on the compass deviation card.

Fig. 38

FLIGHT PLAN STEP 6: DETERMINE THE COMPASS HEADING

Check Points	VOR Ident. Freq.	VOR Course (if applicable)	Altitude	Wind Dir. Vel. Temp.	True Airspeed	TC	WCA R+ L-	TH	V E- W+	MH	D	CH	Distance	GS Ground speed Est. Act.
Table Rock		▶		020 40	100 kts	60°	15L	45°	-2°	43°	-2	41°		66 kts
AVA/ Martin		▶												

Fig. 39

on your compass. The compass deviation card in Figure 37 shows that if you wanted to fly a magnetic heading of 060 degrees, you'd need to steer a heading of 057 degrees on your compass. In other words, with a value of 057 degrees showing in the window of your compass, you'd actually be making an angle of 060 degrees with the magnetic north pole. The difference between the magnetic heading you want to fly and what's shown on the compass is the *compass deviation*. In this case, the deviation is -3 degrees.

As you see in Figure 37, the deviation can vary on different headings. What would the deviation be on a magnetic heading of 310 degrees? Since this values isn't listed, use the deviation for the magnetic heading closest to this value—in this case a magnetic heading of 300 degrees (closest to 310 degrees). This deviation is +3 degrees, so we'd fly 313 degrees on our compass. Correcting the magnetic heading for the deviation gives us the correct *compass heading*.

Since we want to fly a magnetic heading of 043 degrees, the closest value on the compass deviation card in Figure 37 is 030 degrees. The deviation on this heading is -2 degrees. So we will steer 041 degrees on the compass, thus making the 2 degree correction which lets us fly the desired 043 degree magnetic heading. Enter this compass heading in the flight log, as shown in Figure 39.

Whew. The flight log shows we have finally arrived at a heading to fly. This compass heading will take us from Table Rock to AVA/Martin, correcting for wind, magnetic variation, and compass deviation.

In these few short pages you've learned the basics of dead reckoning navigation. Of course, we haven't found distances nor used our calculated groundspeeds to estimate fuel consumption and time of arrival. We'll do that in a while. For now, understand that calculating

New Aviation Inventions

Here's a new device that's sure to become a top-of-the-line item for all air traffic controllers. It's a miniature water-cooled radiator that fits over a controller's lips and helps prevent them from catching fire as they deliver those megaspeed clearances.

the compass heading to be flown is an important part of every flight plan. If your flight has two or more legs (places where the course line drawn on the chart changes direction), then you'll need to calculate the compass heading for each leg. On longer flights, you might have several legs, with flight log items 6 through 13 completed for each leg. Once you get a little practice using the computer, you will do these calculations quite quickly.

The basic process of dead reckoning navigation from Table Rock to AVA/Martin involves finding a course, correcting it for wind to obtain a heading then following the steps listed below:

True heading......... 45 degrees

Variation............ -2 degrees east

Magnetic heading... 43 degrees

Deviation.............. -2 degrees

Compass heading.. 41 degrees

Did you notice the first letters of each line? They are TVMDC and they refer to the values of True heading, plus or minus the Variation equals the Magnetic heading, plus or minus the Deviation equals the Compass heading. Don't forget this letter sequence. It will help you remember how to convert a true heading into a compass heading. In fact, here is a great mnemonic to help remember this.

Tele

Vision

Makes

Dull

Company

Simply visualize yourself sitting in front of the TV planning a cross country flight while thinking. Figure 40 shows this process using a flow diagram that we'll use from now on.

You can also use the flow diagram in Figure 40 to obtain something known as the *compass course,* shown in Figure 41. A compass course is essentially a compass heading without the wind correction angle. Sometimes you will

want to make a short flight (well within the airplane's fuel range) that doesn't require elaborate navigational calculations. You plan to use VOR, Loran or GPS to take you to your destination and neither want nor need detailed flight planning and wind correction. That's fine. There's nothing wrong with this for those short-hop flights. You simply start off toward your destination using the magnetic course backed up with either pilotage or some form of electronic navigation. For longer flights that are sure to consume a lot of fuel, you need to do more detailed flight planning to determine groundspeeds and fuel consumption rates.

Figure 41 also helps you determine your magnetic course. Do you remember FAR 91.159, the VFR cruising altitude regulation? This regulation requires you to fly at even or odd thousand foot levels plus 500 feet, depending on your magnetic course. The magnetic course is easily determined by correcting the true course for the variation, as shown in Figure 41.

Return Trip From AVA/Memorial To Table Rock

Let's say we've spent enough money at the pilot supply shop at AVA/Martin airport and have decided to return home (before our airplane becomes too heavy for liftoff because of all the pilot toys—headsets, computers, flight cases—we've purchased). We call the FSS and they tell us the winds are from 350 degrees at 30 knots at all altitudes below 10,000 feet MSL. Let's follow the same six flight planning steps we performed before, and fill out our flight log as we go along. We'll use 120 knots for our true airspeed on the return flight to get home quicker and play with our new pilot toys.

Flight Planning Step 1—Draw a line between checkpoints – We've already done this in Figure 35.

Flight Planning Step 2— Determine the true course – The true course from AVA/Martin to Table Rock is the opposite of

FINDING THE COMPASS HEADING

Fig. 40

TC 60° (+/-) 15 L° equals the WCA TH 45°

TH = True Heading
V = Variation
MH = Magnetic Heading
D = Deviation
CH = Compass Heading
WCA = Wind Correction Angle

(+/-) V -2 E equals the MH 43° (+/-) D - 2° equals the CH 41°

FINDING THE COMPASS COURSE

Fig. 41

TC 60° (+/-) V -2 E° equals the MC 58° (+/-) D - 3° equals the CC 55°

TC = True Course
V = Variation
MC = Magnetic Course
D = Deviation
CH = Compass Course
WCA = Wind Correction Angle

Airplane on the downwind, for the third time, can you hear the tower?

OK, you're going to have to push the mic button, I can't hear you when you nod your head.

FLIGHT PLAN STEP 2: DETERMINE THE TRUE COURSE

Check Points	VOR Ident. Freq.	VOR Course (if applicable)	Altitude	Wind Dir. Vel. Temp.	True Airspeed	TC	WCA R+ L-	TH	V E- W+	MH	D	CH	Distance	GS Ground speed Est. Act.
AVA/ Martin				350 30										
Table Rock														

Fig. 42

SELECTING AN ALTITUDE AND TRUE AIRSPEED

Check Points	VOR Ident. Freq.	VOR Course (if applicable)	Altitude	Wind Dir. Vel. Temp.	True Airspeed	TC	WCA R+ L-	TH	V E- W+	MH	D	CH	Distance	GS Ground speed Est. Act.
AVA/ Martin			4,500	350 30	120 kts	240°								
Table Rock														

Fig. 43

what it was for the initial trip (which was 060 degrees). We'll put 240 degrees in our flight log form, as shown in Figure 43.

DETERMINING THE WIND CORRECTION ANGLE, STEPS: 1&2

1. Place wind direction under true index
2. Mark wind velocity up from grommet
3. Place true course under true index
4. Slide wind velocity mark to T.A.S line
5. Read ground speed under grommet
6. Read wind correction angle between center line and wind velocity mark

Wind dot

Fig. 44

At this point we can quickly determine the magnetic course to see what altitude (even or odd) to fly. Recall the letter sequence *TVMDC*. Correcting the true course (240 degrees) for the magnetic variation (2 degrees east—it hasn't changed from our first flight) we obtain a magnetic course of 238 degrees (240 degrees – 2 degrees E=238 degrees).

According to FAR 91.159, when flying a magnetic course of 180 degrees through 359 degrees, we need to fly at even thousands plus 500 feet (assuming that we'll be more than 3,000 feet AGL during the flight—we will be). Since AVA/Martin's altitude is 1,311 feet MSL, we can fly at 4,500 feet, 6,500 feet 8,500 feet, and so on. No sense wasting all that fuel in

climbing high for such a short flight. For the purposes of this example, let's fly at 4,500 feet MSL, putting us more than 3,000 feet above the surface (realistically, I'd probably fly at 2,500 feet MSL on this flight, meaning that I am not restricted by the hemispherical cruising altitudes). We'll add these values to our flight log, as shown in Figure 43.

Flight Planning Step 3— Determine the wind correction angle – Let's use our flight computer to do this. Using the wind side of the slide computer, set the computer's grommet on the 100 arc before starting a wind problem, as shown in Figure 44. Erase all the other wind marks from previous problems. I hope you used pencil, not indelible ink. Make it a point to use a soft lead pencil. Hard lead pencils require you to take running stabs at your computer to make any type of visible mark (besides, you could accidentally pole vault over your desk).

Step one says to place the wind direction under the true index. Rotate the inside plastic circle until 350 degrees is under the true index, as shown in Figure 44.

Step two says to mark wind velocity up from center (the center is the grommet). Having placed the 100 arc under the grommet, simply count up the wind velocity along the given scale and make a mark. In our case the velocity is 30 knots (Figure 44).

How Rod Determined That TV Makes Dull Company

I know for a fact that TV makes dull company. Television numbs the mind, deactivates dendrites and pickles personalities. In short, watch it long enough and you feel like you have an IQ a grade lower than bean dip.

My friend's grandfather used to watch TV so much he had a hard time distinguishing fantasy from reality. One time, during a football game, he started yelling at the TV quarterback. "Throw it to Winston you fool, throw it to Winston! Geesh! Can you believe that guy?" snapped grandpa. I looked over at him and said, "Ah, sir, calm down, calm down, they can't hear you." He looked at me for a second, then mumbled, "Yeah, I guess you're right. They've got their helmets on."

Step three says to place the true course under the true index as shown in Figure 45. Notice that your wind mark is now on the right side of the scale.

Step four says to slide the wind velocity mark to the TAS (true airspeed line), as shown in Figure 46. Simply move the cardboard slide upward until the wind mark is on top of the 120 knot true airspeed line (arc). You're done! All you need do is read the groundspeed and wind correction angle off the computer (see the next two steps)

Step five says to read groundspeed under center (the grommet). The grommet lies directly over a groundspeed of 127 knots.

Step six says to read the wind correction angle between the centerline and the wind velocity mark. Your wind mark falls on the 14 degree diagonal line to the right of scale. Your wind correction angle is 14 degrees to the right. This makes sense, since the wind is from your right and slightly behind you.

Let's insert our WCA and groundspeed in the flight log form (Figure 47). The rest of the flight planning is a snap.

Flight Planning Step 4: Determine the true heading – When we add the true course of 240 degrees to a right WCA of 14 degrees we obtain a true heading of 254 degrees, as shown in Figure 48.

Flight Planning Step 5: Determine the magnetic heading – Correcting the true heading for variation (TVMDC, remember?) gives us the magnetic heading. The variation of 2 degrees east hasn't changed on this flight. Our magnetic heading is 250 degrees (254 degrees – 2 degrees E=252 degrees). Let's insert this into our flight log as shown in Figure 49. And now for our last step.

Flight Planning Step 6: Determine the compass heading – Correcting the magnetic heading for compass deviation (TVMDC) gives us the compass heading. The compass deviation card shown in Figure 37 shows that for a magnetic

DETERMINING THE WIND CORRECTION ANGLE STEP: 3

1. Place wind direction under true index
2. Mark wind velocity up from grommet
3. Place true course under true index
4. Slide wind velocity mark to T.A.S line
5. Read ground speed under grommet
6. Read wind correction angle between center line and wind velocity mark

Wind dot

Fig. 45

DETERMINING THE WIND CORRECTION ANGLE STEPS: 4,5 AND 6

1. Place wind direction under true index
2. Mark wind velocity up from grommet
3. Place true course under true index
4. Slide wind velocity mark to T.A.S line
5. Read ground speed under grommet
6. Read wind correction angle between center line and wind velocity mark

Wind dot

Fig. 46

FLIGHT PLAN STEP 3: DETERMINE THE WCA (& GS TOO)

Check Points	VOR Ident. Freq.	VOR Course (if applicable)	Altitude	Wind Dir. Vel. Temp.	True Airspeed	TC	WCA R+ L-	TH	V E- W+	MH	D	CH	Distance	GS Ground speed Est. Act.
AVA/ Martin			4,500	350 30	120 kts	240°	14R							127 kts
Table Rock														

Fig. 47

FLIGHT PLAN STEP 4: DETERMINE THE TRUE HEADING

Check Points	VOR Ident. Freq.	VOR Course (if applicable)	Altitude	Wind Dir. Vel. Temp.	True Airspeed	TC	WCA R+ L-	TH	V E- W+	MH	D	CH	Distance	GS Ground speed Est. Act.
AVA/ Martin			4,500	350 30	120 kts	240°	14R	254°						127 kts
Table Rock														

Fig. 48

heading of 252 degrees (we'll use 240 degrees on the card since it's the closest to our magnetic heading) we

should steer 3 degrees more, which gives us a compass heading of 255 degrees (252 degrees+3 degrees=255

FLIGHT PLAN STEP 5: DETERMINE THE MAGNETIC HEADING

Check Points	VOR Ident. Freq.	VOR Course (if applicable)	Altitude	Wind Dir. Vel. Temp.	True Airspeed	TC	WCA R+ L-	TH	V E- W+	MH	D	CH	Distance	GS Ground speed Est. Act.
AVA/ Martin		▶	4,500	350 30	120 kts	240°	14°R	25°A	-2°	252°				127 kts
Table Rock														

Fig. 49

FLIGHT PLAN STEP 6: DETERMINE THE COMPASS HEADING

Check Points	VOR Ident. Freq.	VOR Course (if applicable)	Altitude	Wind Dir. Vel. Temp.	True Airspeed	TC	WCA R+ L-	TH	V E- W+	MH	D	CH	Distance	GS Ground speed Est. Act.
AVA/ Martin		▶	4,500	350 30	120 kts	240°	14°R	25°A	-2°	252°	+3°	255°		127 kts
Table Rock														

Fig. 50

degrees). Let's insert this value into our flight log form, as shown in Figure 50.

That wasn't too bad, was it? Believe me when I say this becomes real easy with just a little practice. Now that we know how to get to our destination, let's discuss how to obtain our expected time enroute and the amount of fuel we'll use in getting where we're going. We can do this using the groundspeed we've obtained during flight planning step 3 and the front side of our flight computer.

Planning an Actual Flight

Let's put your knowledge to practical use and plan a short cross country flight from Healdsburg to Nut Tree airport, as shown in Figure 51. We'll assume that due to solar flares and vacuum tube shortages all VORs in the area are inoperative, so the flight is to be conducted by dead reckoning and pilotage. This will be a simple, barebones flight plan. The objective is to give you a basic idea of how to make the calculations needed to put you over the destination airport.

Since we're planning on making this flight within the next few hours, we'll place a call to the Flight Service Station to obtain the weather and pertinent NOTAMS. If we were planning this flight for the following day we would call the FSS and obtain an outlook briefing. Before the flight, however, we would call to obtain a standard briefing and current NOTAMS.

Let's say the FSS gave us clear skies, no applicable NOTAMS, and the following winds aloft forecast for the station nearest our area:

3,000 feet—040 degrees at 12 knots

6,000 feet—070 degrees at 24 knots, temperature +1

9,000 feet—080 degrees at 31 knots, temperature –5

Now we're ready to draw the course line. Figure 51 shows a direct line between Healdsburg and Nut Tree airport. Whenever possible, I try and fly direct between airports. After all, that's what makes flying unique, isn't it? Unfortunately, direct flights are not always possible. Restricted

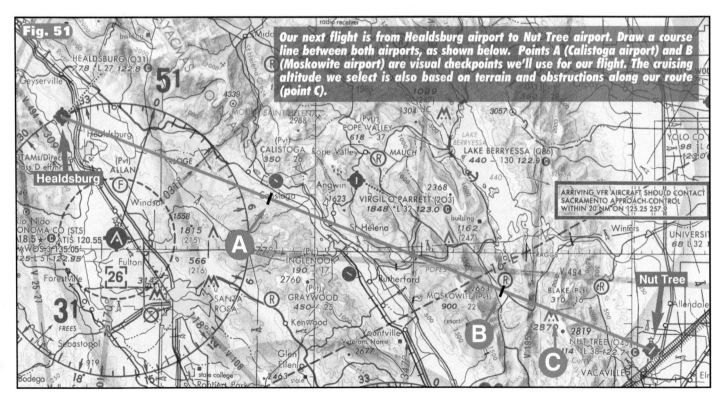

Fig. 51 *Our next flight is from Healdsburg airport to Nut Tree airport. Draw a course line between both airports, as shown below. Points A (Calistoga airport) and B (Moskowite airport) are visual checkpoints we'll use for our flight. The cruising altitude we select is also based on terrain and obstructions along our route (point C).*

Measuring the distance between airports is easily accomplished with the scale on the bottom of the plotter. Be sure and use the sectional chart scale and not the WAC chart scale. Measure from the center of one airport to the other in nautical miles.

Sectional chart scale

Total distance = 46.5 nautical miles

Total distance between Healdsburg and Nut Tree—46.5 nm

Fig. 52

areas, mountains, AND large bodies of water are just a few of the things that might break up a direct flight into separate segments or *legs*, each having different directions and distances. Look the route over carefully and decide if a direct flight is possible or if the route should be broken down into separate legs having different directions.

Cross Country Planning: Selecting a Route – Since there is no special use airspace and there are no major obstacles on our selected route, we'll fly directly to the destination. This is convenient since it allows us to apply our wind correc-

tion to a single route. If you choose several route segments, each having different directions, wind correction must be calculated for and applied to each portion. In other words, you must work separate wind computations for each leg of the flight on your flight computer (this is where an electronic computer comes in handy).

Cross Country Planning: Measuring the Distance – After drawing the route, I like to measure the total distance. I'm concerned about whether the airplane has enough fuel for the flight. Having a general idea of the airplane's range is important here (we'll discuss a per-

formance chart that shows the airplane's range under different power conditions in Chapter 14). Using the nautical mile scale on the bottom of the plotter, we find the total distance between Healdsburg and Nut Tree is 46.5 nautical miles, as shown in Figure 52. Obviously, there is no range problem here. If the total distance were 400.5 nautical miles, range would be a concern—especially if you have strong headwinds (and a small bladder). In that case you might elect to land at an airport(s) along the way to obtain additional fuel. While the FARs require 30 minutes reserve during the day (45 minutes at night), I make it a point never to be airborne with my tanks less than one-quarter full. This may be a bit conservative for some, but I've never had to turn an airplane into a glider because I ran out of fuel.

Cross Country Planning: Selecting Checkpoints – Even though our route is direct, we'll divide it up into segments. Our objective is to select visual checkpoints to aid us in navigation along the route. Yes, dead reckoning will surely point us in the proper direction of Nut Tree, but monitoring checkpoints along the route allows us to make small corrections for variations in winds during the trip (believe me when I say that winds can and do vary). I've chosen two checkpoints along the route, as shown in Figure 51 (points A and B).

BEEP—BEEP

While returning from a pleasure flight, I experienced an engine problem that caused a loss of power. After checking the engine instruments, engine and propeller controls, fuel gauge and selector valve, I decided to land the airplane immediately. A suitable roadway was selected. Upon touching down, I saw a small automobile pull out of a side street and proceed down the road ahead of me. To avoid hitting the car, I veered to the left, where the wing encountered three small mailboxes. At this point, the aircraft passed the small car and the right wing went up and over the full length of the automobile. Both aircraft and automobile stopped. The driver of the car jumped out, chastised me for not using my "horn," looked to see if there was any damage to his car, which there was not, got back in the car and promptly drove away.
ASRS Report

Try and pick checkpoints separated by 10 to 15 miles. You can pick more if you wish, but I don't suggest picking fewer. Select checkpoints you're sure are easily visible from the air. A little flying experience will quickly teach you what can and can't be seen from an altitude of 5,000 or 10,000 feet. You'll find that some shapes and colors stand out much better than others. Narrow things of neutral color, such as power lines, are hard to see. When selecting checkpoints, ask yourself, "Could I see this from a mile away on the ground?" Remembering that 5,000 feet is about a mile high, you'll have some idea of whether a given checkpoint is a sensible choice.

I've chosen Calistoga airport (point A) and Moskowite airport (point B) for our two checkpoints. Given the short distance of this flight, two checkpoints are sufficient. You don't have to chose checkpoints you will fly directly over. In fact, sometimes it's better if they are a little to the side of the flight path (preferably to the left side, since that's where you're typically

INSERTING TC, VARIATION & DISTANCE INTO THE FLIGHT LOG

Check Points	VOR Ident. Freq.	VOR Course (if applicable)	Altitude	Wind Dir. Vel. Temp.	True Airspeed	TC	WCA R+ L-	TH	V E- W+	MH	D	CH	Distance	GS Ground speed Est. Act.	Time Airborne ETE	ATE	GPH Gallons Per Hour Used Remain
Healdsburg																	
Calistoga						110°			-16°				16.5				
Moskowite						110°			-16°				18				
Nut Tree						110°			-16°				12				
Totals																	Fig. 53

The true course on our flight from Healdsburg to Nut Tree is 110 degrees (point A). The magnetic variation near our route is 16 degrees east (point B).

Fig. 54

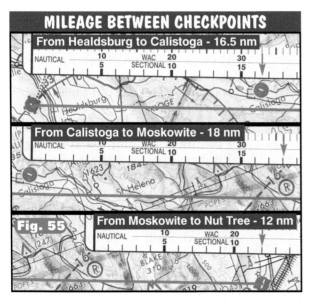

MILEAGE BETWEEN CHECKPOINTS

From Healdsburg to Calistoga - 16.5 nm

From Calistoga to Moskowite - 18 nm

Fig. 55

From Moskowite to Nut Tree - 12 nm

seated). At night, cities or heavily traveled freeways or highways make great checkpoints, since you can't identify much else in the dark (highways have BLS —Buick Lighting Systems!).

Cross Country Planning: Input Information – Figure 53 is a typical flight log used for cross country flight planning. I've inserted the three separate legs into the log along with the true course for each leg (it's the same for all legs) and distances between legs. Figure 54 shows how we measured the true course for this flight. Point A shows the line of longitude intersecting the easterly (E) plotter scale at an angle of 110 degrees. This is our true course. Point B shows a variation of 16E for our flight. Figure 55 shows the mileage for each of the three legs. All this information can be placed in our flight log, as shown in Figure 53.

Cross Country Planning: Chose an Altitude for the Flight – What altitude should you choose for this flight? There are several factors to consider when selecting an altitude. First, if your flight takes you over mountainous terrain, plan on flying at least 2,000 feet or more above the ground. Over nonmountainous terrain, a lower altitude AGL is acceptable. If you're planning on receiving a VOR station for navigation, the higher you fly, the better the reception you'll obtain. Don't expect VOR reception for more than 25 miles if you're 1,000 feet AGL or less. Higher altitudes also mean higher true airspeeds and the possibility of favorable winds.

INSERTING CRUISING ALTITUDE INTO THE FLIGHT LOG

Check Points	VOR Ident. Freq.	VOR Course (if applicable)	Altitude	Wind Dir. Vel. Temp.	True Airspeed	TC	WCA R+ L-	TH	V E- W+	MH	D	CH	Distance	GS Ground speed Est. Act.	Time Airborne ETE	ATE	GPH Gallons Per Hour Used Remain
Healdsburg		▶	5,500			110°			-16°				16.5				
Calistoga		▶	5,500			110°			-16°				18				
Moskowite		▶	5,500			110°			-16°				12				
Nut Tree		▶															
		▶															
		▶					Fig. 56										
		▶															
Totals																	

Figure 51, point C shows obstructions at 2,870 feet MSL. These appear to be the highest obstructions along our route. Another consideration is the hemispherical cruising altitude rule. FAR 91.159 requires that flights conducted at more than 3,000 feet AGL must be flown at odd thousand + 500 foot altitudes while on a magnetic course of 0 degrees through 179 degrees. While on a magnetic course of 180 degrees through 359 degrees, you must fly even thousands + 500 foot altitudes.

DETERMINING THE WIND CORRECTION ANGLE STEPS: 1 AND 2

1. Place wind direction under true index
2. Mark wind velocity up from grommet
3. Place true course under true index
4. Slide wind velocity mark to T.A.S line
5. Read ground speed under grommet
6. Read wind correction angle between center line and wind velocity mark

wind direction

Mark wind dot 22 knots up from center

Fig. 57

DETERMINING THE WIND CORRECTION ANGLE STEPS: 3 AND 4

1. Place wind direction under true index
2. Mark wind velocity up from grommet
3. Place true course under true index
4. Slide wind velocity mark to T.A.S line
5. Read ground speed under grommet
6. Read wind correction angle between center line and wind velocity mark

True course

Wind dot

Fig. 58

From our flight log sheet in Figure 53, the magnetic course is easy to find. Simply subtract the variation (it's east so it's least) from the true course to obtain a magnetic course of 94 degrees (don't bother to write the magnetic course down, since we only use the value to decide on cruising altitudes). We need to fly an odd-thousand foot altitude + 500 feet. Our choices are 3,500 feet, 5,500 feet 7,500 feet, etc. Let's choose 5,500 feet. This will be a relatively short flight, and the time needed to climb to 7,500 feet would more than likely wipe out any small gain we might expect from increased true airspeed. Figure 56 shows our log sheet with cruising altitudes inserted (even though we'll be climbing to our cruise altitude from Healdsburg, we'll leave 5,500 feet in the first altitude block).

Cross Country Flight Planning: Finding the Compass Heading – Finding the compass heading requires us to find the wind correction angle on our computer. To do this we need the winds for our altitude as well as the airplane's true airspeed. We'll select 100 knots true airspeed for our flight. Performance charts (to be discussed in Chapter 14) allow us to determine what our true airspeed will be, based on a selected power setting and atmospheric conditions.

Finding the winds at our altitude requires just a bit of lower math. Referring back to our briefing (page 13-27), we know we have the wind direction and speed for 3,000 and 6,000 feet. Notice that the difference between the winds at 3,000 and 6,000 feet is 12 knots (nice how that happened eh?). This means the wind velocity increases 4 knots per thousand feet. The winds at

INSERTING COMPASS DEVIATION INTO THE FLIGHT LOG

Check Points	VOR Ident. Freq.	VOR Course (if applicable)	Altitude	Wind Dir. Vel. Temp.	True Airspeed	TC	WCA R+ L-	TH	V E- W+	MH	D	CH	Distance	GS Ground speed Est. Act.	Time Airborne ETE ATE	GPH Gallons Per Hour Used Remain
Healdsburg		▶														
Calistoga		▶	5,500'			110°			-16°				16.5	83 kts.		
Moskowite		▶	5,500'			110°			-16°				18	83 kts.		
Nut Tree		▶	5,500'			110°			-16°				12	83 kts.		
		▶														
Fig. 59		▶														
Totals																

4,000 feet must be 16 knots. At 5,000 feet they must be 20 knots. Between 5,000 and 6,000 feet the winds must be 22 knots. Wind direction also changes, by about 10 degrees per thousand feet. Using the same means of interpolation, you'll find the wind direction at 5,500 feet to be from 065 degrees. At 5,500 feet the winds must be from 065 degrees at 22 knots.

Now we're ready to solve a wind triangle problem on the flight computer.

Figure 57 shows the wind side of the computer with steps 1 and 2 completed. Figure 58 shows steps 3 and 4 completed. Our wind correction angle is approximately 9 degrees to the left and our groundspeed (under the grommet) is approximately 83 knots (differences between computers can easily result in a +/- 1 knot or +/- 1 degree variation). Let's fill in our flight log with the information to obtain our compass heading, as shown in Figure 59 (the compass deviation card in Figure 37 shows a deviation of -4 degrees for a magnetic heading in the vicinity of 90 degrees).

Cross Country Flight Planning: Estimating Time Enroute and Fuel Consumed – The next step in flight planning is to use our groundspeed to estimate the time enroute between checkpoints. If you haven't already done so, now is a good time to study Postflight Briefing #13-1 to learn how to use the front side (time, speed and distance side) of the E6-B flight computer. Given a groundspeed of 83 knots, we can approximate our *estimated time enroute* or *ETE* between checkpoints. Figure 60 shows the front side of the computer with the speed reference (the kitty cat's nose) pointing to 83 knots—our groundspeed. It takes approximately 12 minutes to cover the first 16.5 nautical mile leg. It takes 13 minutes to cover the next 18 nautical mile leg and 8.5 minutes to cover the last leg (we'll round off to the closest 30 second mark). Based on an expected fuel consumption of 8.5 GPH (gallons per hour—obtained from a performance chart you'll learn about in Chapter 14), Figure 61 shows the calculation of our fuel burn based on the time we can expect

Fig. 60

ESTIMATING TIME ENROUTE AND FUEL CONSUMED (See Postflight Briefing #13-1 to learn how to use this side of the E6-B computer).

Fig. 61

between checkpoints. We'll insert the rest of this information in our finished flight log as shown in Figure 62.

The total column at the bottom of Figure 62 represents only a *rough estimate* of the fuel used and time required between Healdsburg and Nut Tree. We haven't taken into consideration the extra fuel used in preparation for takeoff, during the climb, or the slower airspeed when climbing. These are important considerations, and are even more significant (as a percentage of the whole) on a short

INSERTING TIME/DISTANCE/FUEL INFO INTO THE FLIGHT LOG

Check Points	VOR Ident. Freq.	VOR Course (if applicable)	Altitude	Wind Dir.	Wind Vel. Temp.	True Airspeed	TC	WCA R+ L-	TH	V E- W+	MH	D	CH	Distance	GS Ground speed Est.	GS Act.	Time Airborne ETE	Time Airborne ATE	GPH Gallons Per Hour Used Remain
Healdsburg		►																	
Calistoga		►	5,500'	068	22	100 kts.	110°	-9°	101°	-16°	85°	-4°	81°	16.5		83 kts	12 min.		1.7 Gal.
Moskowite		►	5,500'	068	22	100 kts.	110°	-9°	101°	-16°	85°	-4°	81°	18		83 kts	13 min.		1.8 Gal.
Nut Tree		►	5,500'	068	22	100 kts.	110°	-9°	101°	-16°	85°	-4°	81°	12		83 kts	8.5 min.		1.2 Gal.
		►																	
		►										Fig. 62							
		►																	
Totals														46.5					4.7 Gal.

flight. Some pilots have their own formula for determining how much extra fuel they use when climbing. I've heard pilots say just add an extra 1.0 to 1.5 gallons of fuel for the engine start, taxi, takeoff and climb. Frankly, this estimate is only meaningful for specific airplanes and specific conditions you're familiar with. There is a better way to find your true fuel consumption for the flight. It involves a little more work, but it's worth the extra precision you obtain in your flight planning. Let's examine a more precise method of estimating time and fuel consumption.

Figure 63 is a time, fuel and distance to climb performance chart (you'll see this in the performance chapter but I want to introduce it to you now). Two columns are very important to us: the *time to climb from sea level* column and the *fuel used from sea level* column. At a slower climb speed of 73 knots indicated airspeed (KIAS), it takes approximately 10 minutes to climb from sea level to 5,500 feet (since Healdsburg is at 278 feet MSL, we'll assume a sea level pressure altitude starting point). I interpolated this time by simply observing the times to climb between 5,000 and 6,000 feet. The same process yields an estimate of approximately 2.5 gallons of fuel used during this climb. With this information, you can now complete a more detailed and accurate flight log. Let's do this.

A More Accurate Flight Plan

Based on a slower climb airspeed of 73 KIAS (we'll assume IAS = TAS for the climb), I know the wind will have a different drift effect on my airplane than it would at my cruise speed of 100 KTAS, so I'll add another checkpoint to my flight log, as shown in Figure 64. The additional checkpoint is called the "top of climb" reference. I expect to reach my cruise altitude before reaching my first visual checkpoint, so I've placed the "top of climb" checkpoint before Calistoga airport. Now we must work an additional wind computer wind problem based on the slower airspeed during climb (see Figure 65). Remember, the winds are the same, only the airspeed varies. Our groundspeed is 55 knots during the climb and the wind correction angle is approximately 12 degrees to the left (this reaffirms that at slower speeds the airplane must crab at a larger angle into the wind).

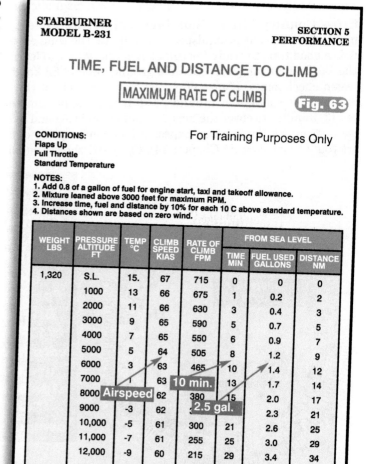

STARBURNER MODEL B-231

SECTION 5 PERFORMANCE

TIME, FUEL AND DISTANCE TO CLIMB

MAXIMUM RATE OF CLIMB Fig. 63

For Training Purposes Only

CONDITIONS:
Flaps Up
Full Throttle
Standard Temperature

NOTES:
1. Add 0.8 of a gallon of fuel for engine start, taxi and takeoff allowance.
2. Mixture leaned above 3000 feet for maximum RPM.
3. Increase time, fuel and distance by 10% for each 10 C above standard temperature.
4. Distances shown are based on zero wind.

WEIGHT LBS	PRESSURE ALTITUDE FT	TEMP °C	CLIMB SPEED KIAS	RATE OF CLIMB FPM	FROM SEA LEVEL		
					TIME MIN	FUEL USED GALLONS	DISTANCE NM
1,320	S.L.	15.	67	715	0	0	0
	1000	13	66	675	1	0.2	2
	2000	11	66	630	3	0.4	3
	3000	9	65	590	5	0.7	5
	4000	7	65	550	6	0.9	7
	5000	5	64	505	8	1.2	9
	6000	3	63	465	10	1.4	12
	7000	1	63		13	1.7	14
	8000		62	380	15	2.0	17
	9000	-3	62			2.3	21
	10,000	-5	61	300	21	2.6	25
	11,000	-7	61	255	25	3.0	29
	12,000	-9	60	215	29	3.4	34

(overlay labels: **Airspeed**, **10 min.**, **2.5 gal.**)

Let's take this new WCA and groundspeed and see how they apply to our flight log (Figure 64).

During the climb from Healdsburg to our cruise altitude, we'll fly a compass heading of 78 degrees, as shown on the first line of Figure 64. What we need to know is how much distance we'll cover in 10 minutes (the time our chart showed was required to climb to 5,500 feet). This is the distance to be placed in position A. We can figure this out by using our computer to determine how much distance we cover in 10 minutes at 55 knots, as shown in Figure 66. It looks like we'll cover approximately 9 miles during the climb. We put this value in position A of our flight log. Since the distance to Calistoga from Healdsburg 16.5 miles, this means that 7.5 miles is left to fly at cruise speed (position B).

The next calculation is how much time it takes to cover 7.5 nautical miles at 83 knots—the rest of the distance to our first visual checkpoint (Calistoga). Figure 67 shows that it takes approximately 5.4 minutes to cover 7.5 miles at 83 knots. We'll put this information in position C of our flight plan.

The last item we must determine is how much fuel we use during the 5.4 minute cruise segment when we're consuming fuel at a previously determined rate of 8.5 GPH. Figure 68 shows that .77 gallons are used for this 5.4 minute segment. We'll put this information in position D of our flight log.

INSERTING TIME/DISTANCE/FUEL INFO INTO THE FLIGHT LOG

Check Points	VOR Ident. Freq.	VOR Course (if applicable)	Altitude	Wind Dir. Vel. Temp.	True Airspeed	TC	WCA R+ L-	TH	V E- W+	MH	D	CH	Distance	GS Ground speed Est. Act.	Time Airborne ETE	ATE	GPH Gallons Per Hour Used Remain
Healdsburg		▶	↑	065 22	73 kts.	110°	-12°	98°	-16°	82°	-4°	78°	A?	55 kts	10 min.		2.5 Gal.
Top of climb		▶	5,500'	065 22	100 kts.	110°	-9°	101°	-16°	85°	-4°	81°	B?	83 kts	C?		D?
Calistoga		▶	5,500'	065 22	100 kts.	110°	-9°	101°	-16°	85°	-4°	81°	18	83 kts	13 min.		1.8 Gal.
Moskowite		▶	5,500'	065 22	100 kts.	110°	-9°	101°	-16°	85°	-4°	81°	12	83 kts	8.5 min.		1.2 Gal.
Nut Tree		▶															
		▶															
		▶								Fig. 64							
Totals													46.5				

Based on a slower 73 knots climb speed, we have a groundspeed of approximately 55 knots and a wind correction angle of 12 degrees to the left during the climb.

Our computer shows that during the 10 minute climb, we'll cover approximately 9 miles at the climb groundspeed of 55 knots.

It takes 5.4 minutes to cover 7.5 miles at a cruise groundspeed of 83 knots (7.5 miles is the distance left to our first visual checkpoint after reaching our cruise altitude).

At 8.5 GPH, we'll use .77 gallons of fuel for the 5.4 minute cruise segment.

Our completed flight log is shown in Figure 69. Note the small note I've added at the bottom right of the flight log. It says that note #1 of the performance chart in Figure 63 states we should add 1.4 gallons of fuel for engine start, taxi and takeoff. A total flight time of approximately 37 minutes and fuel consumption of approximately 7.67 gallons is estimated for this flight.

It's a good idea to compare the fuel estimate

OUR COMPLETED FLIGHT LOG

Check Points	VOR Ident. Freq.	VOR Course (if applicable)	Altitude	Wind Dir. Vel. Temp.	True Airspeed	TC	WCA R+ L-	TH	V E- W+	MH	D	CH	Distance	GS Ground speed Est. Act.	Time Airborne ETE	ATE	GPH Gallons Per Hour Used Remain
Healdsburg			↑	065 22	73 kts.	110°	-12	98°	-16°	82°	-4	78°	9	55 kts.	10 min.		2.5 Gal.
Top of climb			5,500	065 22	100 kts.	110°	-9	101°	-16°	85°	-4	81°	7.5	83 kts.	5.4 min.		.77 Gal.
Calistoga			5,500	065 22	100 kts.	110°	-9	101°	-16°	85°	-4	81°	18	83 kts.	13 min.		1.8 Gal.
Moskowite			5,500	065 22	100 kts.	110°	-9	101°	-16°	85°	-4	81°	12	83 kts.	8.5 min.		1.2 Gal.
Nut Tree														Performanch chart says add 1.4 gal. for start, taxi and takeoff.			1.4 Gal.
Totals													46.5				7.67 Gal.

Fig. 69

against what really happens in order to see how well the process is working, and whether any of the fixed amounts you're using (such as the rate of fuel burn at cruise, or the amount allowed for startup, taxi, and takeoff) need to be adjusted. Keep in mind that any such numbers are averages, and your number may vary.

While it would be nice to think everything can be measured with great precision, the fact of the matter is your fuel burn will not be accurate to the tenth of a gallon. In fact, there can be several gallons variation in your estimate of fuel onboard based on the size of the fuel tanks and how close to the top the line person (the petroleum-molecule-fluid-allocation person) fills them up. It pays, however, to plan as precisely as possible, while keeping real-world considerations in mind. Do not ever try and stretch your flight based on the fact that by a paper calculation, you "should have" a few gallons of fuel left. Always be aware of the imprecision of these seemingly-precise calculations, and fly conservatively.

Flight planning can be a lot of fun, but I don't want you to think it must be this detailed for short flights. If I'm heading to a local airport 10 miles away that I'm very familiar with, I check the weather and NOTAMS, preflight the plane, make sure I have full fuel and go. It's that simple. It's reasonable to say that the farther away from the airport you fly, the more detailed the flight planning that's necessary. Make no mistake about it, even experienced pilots who slack off on their flight planning get to fly gliders (airplanes with fuel exhausted engines).

Final Words on Electronic Flight Computers

An explanation on the use of the electronic flight computers hasn't been included for a very good reason—they're easy to use. Many of these wonderful little devices are menu driven, making it unbelievably easy to solve wind, time, distance, and fuel problems.

We worked on the mechanical computer so you would know the principles. With that in hand (and in mind) you can feel more confident in the use of an electronic computer, where it's easy to crunch numbers without understanding what they mean. I am all for technology, but only if you understand what it's doing for you.

Quite frankly, I am simply amazed at all the wonderful little devices available for people nowadays. A friend's grandfather purchased a $1200 hearing aid. He claims it has call waiting!

Postflight Briefing #13-1

The Mechanical Flight Computer

Figure 70 shows the most common mechanical flight computer in use today. It's often referred to as the *E6-B computer* and is a device you should become familiar with.

Patented by Lieutenant Phillip Dalton on June 30th, 1936, the E6-B has become one of the most familiar items in all of aviation (E6-B was probably a military designation). You might be wondering why I recommend learning to use a mechanical flight computer when there are so many wonderful electronic computers on the market. There are two reasons. First, it's important that you understand the principles behind the calculations, and the E6-B shows the facts in a way electronic computers can't. Second, you can *always* get a useable calculation from an E6-B. No dead batteries, bad circuit boards, inoperative LCDs, or other electronic maladies.

Putting on a Happy Face

The E6-B does not, at first glance, present a friendly face (Figure 70). Numbers upon numbers, scales upon scales, windows within windows—any of these could cause your blood pres-

OUR SIMPLIFIED MECHANICAL FLIGHT COMPUTER

Fig. 71

THE STANDARD MECHANICAL E6-B TYPE COMPUTER

Fig. 70

Unlike our simplified version, this is what an actual E6-B computer looks like.

sure to rise so fast that if it weren't for your skin, you'd be a fountain. It's even created mental vaporlock in some students, whose heads spin so fast after one look that they feel like a termite in a yo-yo. It would do little good for me to say, "Don't worry, it will all make sense to you soon." So, let me do something better. Figure 71 shows a simplified version of this computer.

I have taken out all the confusing items on the computer's face, leaving just the basics. You are welcome to photocopy this figure, cut out the white internal ring and paste it (with removable paste) over the internal, moveable ring of your computer (you may have to expand or shrink the photocopy to make it fit). After a short time practicing with this cleaned-up, moveable inner ring, you can pull it off and the original computer's complexity won't be so overwhelming. (Caution: Only use this photocopy to become familiar with the face of the computer. It's not meant for use outside of Postflight Briefing #13-1. Many important items have been removed.)

Another option is to make a photocopy of Figure 71, carefully cut the white inner ring from the black outside ring and construct a temporary,

HOW TO MAKE YOUR OWN PAPER-TYPE MECHANICAL COMPUTER

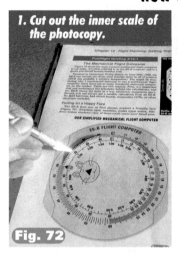

1. Cut out the inner scale of the photocopy.

Fig. 72

2. Paste outer portion on piece of card stock.

3. Place inner scale as shown and pin it in the middle.

PLACE PIN HERE

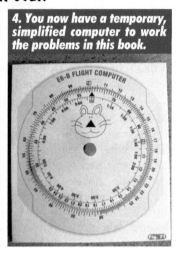

4. You now have a temporary, simplified computer to work the problems in this book.

paper computer to practice with, as shown in Figure 72. Either way, this cleaned-up computer is much easier and more enjoyable to use during the learning process.

Dance of the Decimals: The Number Scale

In Figure 71, the inner (white and moveable) ring is matched up against the outer (fixed) ring. The numbers on both scales match one another. Find the number 10 on the very top of the computer's inner or outer ring. Moving clockwise around both scales, the numbers increase in value. To the right of 10 is 11, 12, 13 and so on all the way to a value of 90, which is a full digit left of 10. These numbers can represent any value you want.

These ropes appear to be equal in length. The one with the knot, however, is actually longer when unraveled.

Fig. 73

We could let the number 10 equal 100. Then the digits to the right would be 110, 120, 130 and so on. Or we could let 10 equal the value of 1.0. The number to the right would then be 1.1, 1.2, 1.3 and so on. It's very important that you stay with the same numerical category of values you start with when solving a computer problem (i.e., 1s, 10s or 100s). If you are letting the value of 10 on the scale equal 100, don't let the value of 11 equal 1.1. It should represent a value of 110.

Miles on the Menu: Converting Nautical And Statute Miles

Two forms of distance measurement are used in aviation: nautical miles and statute miles. Statute miles are normally used for measurement of visibility, while nautical miles are more often used in navigational computations. You will find that most airspeed indicators on newer airplanes use knots (nautical miles per hour) instead of (statute) miles per hour, but there will be situations where it's necessary to convert from one type of mile to the other.

A nautical mile is a distance of 6,076.1 feet. A statute mile is a distance of 5,280 feet. The conversion factor is 1.15. In other words, a nautical mile is equal to 1.15 statute miles. Another way of saying this is that one nautical miles is longer than a statute mile. To convert nautical

miles to statute miles, simply multiply it by 1.15. For example, 20 nautical miles equals a distance of 23 statute miles (20 x 1.15 = 23). To convert statute miles to nautical miles simply divide the statute mile value by 1.15 (23 statute miles/1.15 = 20 nautical miles).

Here's how to remember the difference between nautical and statute miles. Think of two ropes that appear to be equal in length. One rope, however, has a knot in it, as shown in Figure 73. If we let the length of the rope without the knot equal a value of one, then, the knotted rope also appears to be the same length. But when the rope with the knot in it is unraveled, it's actually longer than the other rope (1.15 times longer). This makes sense, since a nautical mile is 1.15 times longer than a statute mile. So, when you compare equal values of nautical and statute miles, remember that the value with the knot (nautical) in it is actually longer or bigger.

There is an easy way to convert nautical and statute miles using the E6-B computer. On the computer's outside ring, there's a conversion arc (Figure 74). Simply put the mileage value you want to convert under the STAT or NAUT arrow on the inside ring, then follow the arc across and read the equivalent mileage value on the same inside ring. In Figure 74, a value of 6.6 nautical miles is set on the inside ring under the NAUT

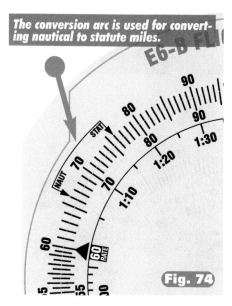

The conversion arc is used for converting nautical to statute miles.

Fig. 74

This is how we convert 90 nautical miles to statute miles.

103.5 sm

90 nm

Fig. 75

Numbers on the inside or outside scales can represent many values.

Fig. 76

arrow. The STAT arrow points to 7.6 as the statute mile equivalent value.

Let's convert 90 nautical miles to statute miles. Figure 75 shows this conversion. Place 90 under the NAUT arrow on the inside ring and read the statute mile value under the STAT arrow on the same ring. Ninety nautical miles equals 103.5 statute miles. I (or the FAA, on a test) might ask you to convert 103.5 statute miles to nautical miles. You would place 103.5 under the STAT arrow and read the nautical value of 90 miles under the NAUT arrow.

Be careful when reading numerical values on the computer's inside or outside ring when "marks" instead of actual "digits" are used to represent

the scale's values. For instance, in Figure 76, between 250 and 300 on the inside ring, there's just not enough space to place whole number values (i.e., 26, 27, 28 and 29). These whole number values are represented by longer slashed lines. Between each longer slashed line are smaller lines representing an increase in value of .2, 2 or 20. As you can see, point A represents either .254, 25.4 or 254 depending on the original value we started with.

Try converting 276 statute miles to nautical miles. Figure 77 shows this process. Placing 276 under the STAT arrow gives you 240 nautical miles. Of course, if the statute mile value was 27.6 then the nautical value

would be 24. Remember to keep with the same value of 1s, 10s or 100s. In other words, 27.6 statute miles wouldn't be 240 nautical miles. This is part of the common sense needed when solving these problems.

There is a mileage scale at the bottom of your plotter (Figure 78). Both statute and nautical mileage scales are available for easy use. If you don't have your flight computer with you and can't remember how to convert nautical and statute miles, you can easily do it on the matched scales on the bottom of the plotter. Simply find the statute mile value on the plotter's statute scale and move to the opposite nautical scale to read the nautical mile value. It doesn't get any easier than that.

Converting 276 statute miles gives us 240 nautical miles. Remember, 24 can be 2.4, 24, 240 or 2,400. You must stay with the same value in ones, tens or hundreds that you start with.

276 sm

240 nm

Fig. 77

Another way of converting statute and nautical miles is to use your plotter. Simply find the comparative nautical or statute scale (most plotters have them) and read the conversion value on the opposite scale.

Fig. 78

Time, Distance and Speed Computations

Computing time, speed and distance is a necessary skill for all pilots. After all, how can you estimate the fuel you'll use if you don't know how long it will take you to get somewhere? The following formula should be committed to memory:

Speed = Distance/Time

This formula states that your speed is the ratio of the distance traveled over the amount of time it takes to travel that distance. If you have any two of these three items in the formula above (the speed, time or distance), you can determine the third. For instance, if you know how much distance you traveled in a certain amount of time, you can determine your groundspeed. If you know your groundspeed, you can tell how much time it will take to travel a certain distance or you can tell how much distance you'll travel in a certain period of time.

Think about this carefully. We always measure our speed in either miles per hour or knots (which is nautical miles per hour). If you're doing 60 miles per hour, you'll travel 60 miles in one hour. That's one mile per minute, since there are 60 minutes in one hour. At 120 miles per hour you'll travel 2 miles per minute. These are handy numbers to keep in mind.

Whenever the word *per* is used in arithmetic (as in miles per hour or nautical miles per hour), it represents some sort of ratio. If I went 120 miles per hour it means I traveled 120 miles in 60 minutes. Such a ratio is represented as follows:

$$\frac{120 \text{ miles}}{60 \text{ minutes in an hour}} = 120 \text{ miles per hour}$$

Your computer is nothing more than a mechanical device for picturing a ratio. You're going to be amazed how easy this little device is once you understand how ratios are shown on the computer's face. For example,

The face of the mechanical flight computer has three areas of concern. The white moveable ring is the inside scale and the fixed portion of the computer is the outside scale. The small black triangle, which we'll call the "kittycat's nose," is the hour index.

Fig. 79

setup your computer as shown in Figure 79. From now on we'll refer to the white, moveable ring as the inside scale and the fixed outer ring as the outside scale.

Which scale of the computer has the greatest distance around it? Yes, the outside scale has a larger circumference, thus the greatest distance. All distance values will be found on the outside scale. That's the memory aid. Distance refers to the outside scale and this is where you look to find any distance values.

What do the hands of a clock do? Yes, of course, they tell time, but they also move. Which scale of the computer moves? The inside scale moves.

As a memory aid, the inside scale of your computer is where you'll find all your time values. Any value other than time (such as distances) will be shown on the outside scale.

Notice there is a blackened triangle on the inside scale that looks like a kittycat's nose in Figure 79. This is the hour-index since it represents a time value of 60 (60 minutes in an hour). From now on we'll call the hour-index the kittycat's or cat's nose. With the cat's nose (the hour index) pointing to 120, we've set up a ratio. What we're saying here is that we went 120 miles (distance on the outside scale) in 60 minutes (time on the inside scale). Many similar ratios can be shown on the computer's face.

By setting the kittycat's nose to the "per" value of 120 miles "per" hour, we see that it takes 30 minutes (position A) to travel 60 miles.

Problem 1—At 105 MPH (cat's nose) we cover 35 statute miles (outside scale) in 20 minutes (inside scale).

Fig. 80

Fig. 81

For instance, we know intuitively that at 120 MPH, we will travel 60 miles in half an hour. Find the 30 minute mark on the inside scale (time) in Figure 80. Opposite the 30 minute mark you'll find 60 miles on the outside scale (distance) as shown by position A. Position B shows a ratio of 16 miles per 8 minutes. Position C shows a ratio of 24 miles per 12 minutes and position D shows a ratio of 40 miles per 20 minutes. All these ratios represent a speed of 120 miles per hour. If you have any two of the three variables of speed, time, or distance you can find the other on the computer's face.

One last thing before we start solving problems. What do kittycats do? I hope you said they PER. No, that's not a typo, I meant PER. Now, this is not the purr we're familiar with, but it sounds the same, doesn't it? As a memory aid, we'll say that the kittycat's nose always points to the PER value you're working with. In other words it points to miles PER hour, nautical miles PER hour or, as you'll

soon see, gallons PER hour. Remember, you'll always be working with some PER value when doing speed, time and distance computations.

Now you know where to find speed, time or distance variables. Time is on the inside scale, distance is on the outside scale, and speed (per quantities) is on top of the cat's nose. These ratios are shown in the center of the computer, for your reference (Figure 80).

I like using these types of symbols to solve problems as long as they make sense. Several years ago in a Mexican restaurant, the restroom doors read *matador* and *bull*. Now, those are confusing symbols. I didn't know what to do. Fortunately, the cat's nose is a lot simpler to use. Let's solve a few problems.

Problem 1

If your speed is 105 miles per hour, how much distance will your airplane cover in 20 minutes? To solve this problem ask yourself which of the three variables (speed, time, dis-

tance) you have and which one you are looking for. You have speed and the time. What you want is the distance. First, point the cat's nose at the per value of 105 miles per hour as shown in Figure 81. Since time is always found on the inside scale, find 20 minutes on the inside scale. Opposite the time you see a value of 35 on the outside scale. You'll cover 35 statute miles in 20 minutes at 105 MPH. You can also say that at 105 knots you will cover 35 nautical miles in 20 minutes.

Once you find an answer, you must always make certain it makes sense. Since at 120 MPH you travel 2 miles per minute, at 105 MPH (close to 120 MPH for an estimate) you should have a distance/time value somewhere near 2 to 1. A value of 35 miles in 20 minutes is close enough to confirm your numbers are accurate. After all, if you arrived at an answer of 350 miles, you know this wouldn't be correct unless you were captain of the Starship Enterprise.

Fig. 82

$$SET\ MPH\ (KTS) = \frac{DIST\ (OUTER)}{TIME\ (INNER)}$$
$$SET\ GAL/HR. = \frac{TOTAL\ GAL\ (OUTER)}{}$$

Fig. 83

$$SET\ MPH\ (KTS) = \frac{DIST\ (OUTER)}{TIME\ (INNER)}$$
$$SET\ GAL/HR. = \frac{TOTAL\ GAL\ (OUTER)}{TIME\ (INNER)}$$

Fig. 84

Problem 2

If we travel 7 miles in 4 minutes, what is our speed? The value you're looking for is the *per* value and it will be found on top of the cat's nose (on the outer scale), as shown in Figure 82. Simply set 7 miles (distance) on the outside scale over 4 minutes (time) on the inside scale and read what the cat's nose (per-index) points to. Your speed according to Figure 82 is 105 MPH, which is the same speed as in our previous problem.

Problem 3

At 138 MPH, how long will it take to travel 81 miles? First, what does common sense tell you about the answer? Obviously, it will take you less than one hour or 60 minutes, correct? After all, in one hour at 138 miles per hour, you'd travel 138 miles. The value you're looking for is located on the inside (time) scale. Figure 83 depicts this problem. Set the cat's nose (per index) to 138. On the outer (distance) scale you'll find 81 miles and underneath that value you'll find a time value of 35 minutes. Of course, it's possible to interpret this as either 3.5 minutes or 350 minutes, but neither of these alternatives makes sense.

Problem 4

At 90 knots, how much distance will you cover in 15 minutes? By now you know that the value you're looking for (distance) is on the outside scale. Set the cat's nose (per-index) to 90 and read the distance value on the outside scale over the 15 minute time mark on the inside scale, as shown in Figure 84. You obtain a value of 22.5 miles. This makes sense in that 60 knots is one mile per minute and 120 knots is 2 miles per minute, so 90 knots should be somewhere in between, or 1.5 miles per minute. At 15 minutes, you should travel one and a half times this amount, or 22.5 nautical miles.

Problem 5

What is your groundspeed if you traveled 13 nautical miles in 10 minutes? Figure 85 shows how this answer is derived. Rotating the inside (time) scale so 10 minutes is underneath the distance of 13 miles on the outer (distance) scale leaves you with the cat's nose (per index) pointing to a groundspeed of 78 knots.

I might have also asked what the groundspeed is if you traveled 130 nautical miles in 1 hour and 40 minutes. Directly under the 10 minute mark is the 1:40 mark. Since 1:40 is

100 minutes, you could set this time directly under 130 nautical miles, giving you a groundspeed of 78 knots.

Problem 6

What distance will you cover in 9 minutes at a groundspeed of 172 knots? Figure 86 shows how this answer is derived. Setting the cat's nose (per index) to 172, and locating 9 minutes on the inside (time) scale gives you a value of 26 miles on the outside (distance) scale. Of course, this can't be 2.6 miles, nor can it be 260 miles. Your answers must always make sense.

$$SET\ MPH\ (KTS) = \frac{DIST\ (OUTER)}{TIME\ (INNER)}$$

Fig. 85

Problem 6—At 172 knots (nose) we cover 26 miles (outside) in 9 minutes (inside).

172 knots

Time

Distance

Fig. 86

Problem 7—At 158 knots (nose) it takes 9.5 minutes (inside) to travel 25 nautical miles (outside).

158 knots

Time

Distance

Fig. 87

minutes or 1:30). In one hour and 30 minutes you'll use 13.5 gallons of fuel.

Fuel problem 2

If your airplane consumed 21 gallons of fuel in 2 hours and 30 minutes (2:30), what was your rate of fuel consumption? We are looking for the *per* or gallons per hour value, which will be found on top of the cat's nose. Set 21 gallons on the outside (fuel burned) scale over 150 minutes (2:30) on the inside (time) scale as shown in Figure 89. The cat's nose (per index) points to 8.4 gallons per hour fuel consumption rate.

Fuel Problem 3

With a fuel consumption rate of 15.6 gallons per hour, how long can you fly with 90 gallons of fuel on board? Common sense tells you the answer is going to be somewhere around six hours. Set the cat's nose (the per index) to 15.6 as shown in Figure 90. Finding 90 gallons on the outside (fuel burned) scale gives you a time value of approximately 345 minutes (read the time scale carefully). You could divide 345 minutes by 60 to obtain the hours flyable or you could look underneath the minutes scale to find the hours scale. The hours scale is simply easier to use when dealing with large minute values.

Problem 7

How much time will it take to travel 25 nautical miles if your groundspeed is 158 knots? Figure 87 shows how this answer is derived. Set the cat's nose (per-index) to 158 and find 25 miles on the outside (distance) scale. Underneath it is a time value of 9.5 minutes.

Fuel Consumption Problems

Finding fuel consumed is very similar to finding speed, time and distance on the computer. The PER value with fuel consumption is gallons PER hour. Instead of distance

on the outside scale, you'll find the fuel consumed. Of course, time is always found on the inside scale. Let's work a few problems.

Fuel Problem 1

If your fuel consumption is 9 gallons per hour, how much fuel will the airplane consume in 1:30 (one hour and 30 minutes)? You don't even need a computer for this one, do you? First, set the cat's nose to the *per* quantity, as shown in Figure 88. The amount of fuel burned will be on the outside scale directly above the time value on the inside scale (90

Fuel Problem 1—At 9 GPH (nose), for 1 hour and 30 minutes (inside) we use 13.5 gallons (outside).

9 gph

Fuel used

Time

Fig. 88

Fuel Problem 2—If we used 21 gallons (outside) in 2:30 (inside), our rate is 8.4 GPH (nose).

8.4 gph

Time

Fuel used

Fig. 89

Fuel Problem 3—At 15.6 GPH (nose), with 90 gallons of fuel (outside), we can fly for 345 min or 5:45 (inside).

Fuel used

Time

15.6 gph

Fig. 90

Postflight Briefing #13-2

FINDING DENSITY ALTITUDE, TRUE AIRSPEED AND YOUR TRUE ALTITUDE

Finding Density Altitude

You can use the computer to find density altitude if you have two variables: the pressure altitude and the outside air temperature. Figure 91 shows a density altitude computation scale on a typical flight computer. If you set the outside air temperature on scale A, opposite the pressure altitude on scale B, you can read the density altitude at the window located on scale C. This is a handy way to easily compute density altitude without using a fine-lined graph.

In Figure 91, the outside air temperature at a sea level pressure altitude is 15 degrees Celsius, which is standard temperature at sea level. Under these conditions, pressure altitude is equal to density altitude. A sea level or zero density altitude value is shown at the window located on scale C.

With an outside air temperature of +10 degrees Celsius at a pressure altitude of 10,000 feet, what is the density altitude? Sliding +10 degrees Celsius over a 10,000 foot pressure altitude in Figure 92, you see that your density altitude is 11,700 feet.

To find your density altitude, set the outside air temperature (scale A) over the pressure altitude (scale B). Read the density altitude in the density altitude window (scale C). (Make sure you set the temperature and pressure altitude on the appropriate temp/pressure scale. This is often the scale on the right side of the E6-B and it's usually labeled as the "airspeed correction scale.")

Fig. 91

Finding True Airspeed

Using the same procedure for finding density altitude, you can easily find your true airspeed on the face of the flight computer. Figure 93 shows your computer with an outside air temperature of -12 degrees Celsius with a pressure altitude of 5,000 feet (scale A). The true airspeed (TAS) is read on the outside scale opposite the calibrated airspeed (CAS) on the inside scale. We'll use indicated airspeed (IAS) in lieu of calibrated airspeed since they are not that much different at cruise airspeeds. An IAS of 115 knots, produces a TAS of 120 knots as shown by position B. Suppose your IAS is 120 knots. What is your true airspeed under the same condition? Position C shows an IAS (same as CAS for our purposes) of 120 knots on the inside scale, giving you 125 knots TAS on the outside scale.

Finding Your True Altitude

In the chapter on flight instruments, we discussed true altitude. Altimeters read our height above sea level when they are corrected for nonstandard pressure and temperature. Typically, however, we don't correct the altimeter for variations in temperature since these variations aren't normally that large. Nevertheless, under certain conditions, temperature can cause a rather large error. Let's do a true altitude computation on the computer.

Here are the conditions:

1. Your aircraft is flying at an indicated altitude 9,500 feet.

2. The altimeter setting is 30.42 inches of Hg.

With an outside air temperature of +10 degrees Celsius and a pressure altitude of 10,000 feet, a density altitude of 11,700 feet exists.

Fig. 92

3. The outside air temperature is -20 degrees Celsius.

What is your true altitude?

Step 1: Find your pressure altitude.

To find the pressure altitude, the altimeter must be set to 29.92 inches of Hg and the face of the altimeter read (i.e., the indicated altitude read). Since we don't have an altimeter knob to twist, we'll use our previous knowledge of how the altimeter works to determine pressure altitude. Moving the numbers down from 30.42 inches to 29.92 inches is a change of .5 inch of Hg. This means the hands move down 500 feet, and the pressure altitude is 9,000 feet.

Step 2: Place the pressure altitude under the temperature in the computer's altitude computation window (the window on left side of the E6-B's face).

Figure 94, position A shows the temperature of -20 degrees Celsius placed over a pressure altitude of 9,000 feet.

Step 3: Read the true altitude over the indicated altitude on the inside scale (we'll assume that *indicated altitude* is the same as *calibrated altitude* for all these examples. See Glossary for definition of CAL. ALT.).

Figure 94, position B, points between the circled abbreviations for true altitude (TRUE ALT.) on the outside scale and calibrated altitude (CAL. ALT.) on the inside scale (we'll use indicated altitude instead of calibrated altitude). Finding 9,500 feet indicated altitude on the inside scale at position C, we see that our true altitude is 8,900 feet as shown directly opposite on the outside scale. Under large differences in pressure and temperature from standard, it's not unusual for indicated altitude to differ substantially from true altitude. Under these extreme conditions you should consider flying a little higher than normal on your cross country flights if you're planning on being close to terrain. This caveat is especially true for night flight.

There are many more things your computer can do for you. They are beyond the scope of this book, but I would recommend that you purchase a mechanical flight computer and study its manual. You're going to be surprised at how versatile this simple little machine really is.

! BUENO !

When traveling south of the border, don't leave your E-6B in the airplane. It can be a useful tool for money conversion. Just place the current peso rate on the outside scale opposite the 10 on the inside scale. Leave the scales in this position. When converting pesos to dollars, find the peso amount on the outside scale, and read the dollar amount on the inside scale. It's great for shopping, dining and bartering. Que bueno!

Jan Peterson, CFI

To find your true airspeed, use the same procedure for finding density altitude. Match the outside air temperature against the pressure altitude (position A). Read the CAS (calibrated airspeed) on the computer's inside scale (use IAS if you don't have calibrated) and read your TAS opposite this value on the outside scale (position B).

Fig. 93

You can find your true altitude by correcting the indicated altitude for non standard temperature. We'll use the altitude correction window of the E6-B (don't use the density altitude and airspeed correction window). First, place the outside air temperature under the pressure altitude (position A). Second, read true altitude on the computer's outside scale opposite indicated altitude (use CAL. ALT.) on the inside scale (position C).

Most E6-B type computers have two temp/pressure windows. One is for finding true altitude, the other is for finding true airspeed and density altitude.

Fig. 94

Postflight Briefing #13-3

CREATING A WIND TRIANGLE

Let's construct a wind triangle for the flight from Table Rock to AVA/Martin Memorial, shown in Figure 95. Our true airspeed is 100 knots (as determined by the airplane's performance charts) and the wind is from 020 degrees at 40 knots (as given by the Flight Service Station). The true course along our route is 60 degrees. Let's use a wind triangle to determine our expected groundspeed and wind correction angle for this flight.

Step 1—The first step in construction of a wind triangle is to draw a line between the departure and destination airports on the sectional chart as shown in Figure 95.

Step 2—Next we want to visually represent the wind with a line of a

Representing the wind with a line requires you to draw the line at the same angle the wind blows from (020 degrees). You can use your plotter to draw a line 20 degrees offset from true north (use a line of longitude). Run this line though the destination airport. Let each half-inch (or any length/speed unit of your choice as long as you stay with that unit) represent 10 knots of wind. Therefore, make the line 4×1/2 inch long or 2 inches to represent 40 knots of wind.

Fig. 96

specific length and direction. The wind is from 020 degrees at 40 knots. Winds given by the FSS are angled with respect to the true north pole. In other words, they are always in a true direction. Simply draw a line

angled at 20 degrees to true north, running through the destination airport, as shown in Figure 95, point B. Figure 96 helps you understand how to draw a line at this angle. This line represents the wind direction.

The first step in the construction of a wind triangle is to draw a line between the departure and destination airports (line A). The next step is to visually represent the wind's direction and velocity with another line (line B).

True course = 60 degrees

We'll let each half-inch of the rule equal 10 knots of wind speed

Fig. 95

What we need to do now is find some way of representing the wind's velocity with this line. The easiest way is to let the line's length represent the wind's speed. Let's arbitrarily make 1/2 inch equal to 10 knots of wind (we could use any value we want, this is simply a personal choice for this example). Since our wind velocity is 40 knots, make the line 2inches long (4 x 1/2"). I like to mark outward on the line in one-inch intervals, starting at the center of the airport, as shown in Figure 95. From this picture you can easily see the wind is a headwind blowing from your left. This single picture already allows you to visualize that your groundspeed will be slower than your airspeed and you'll have a left wind correction angle.

Step 3—Since we've represented the wind's direction and velocity by a line of a specific length pointed in a specific direction, we need to do the same with the airplane's speed and direction. The final step requires you to take the ruler, put one end up against the tail of the wind line, as shown in Figure 97, position A. Next, count outward along the ruler to a value of your true airspeed or 100 knots. Since we've already agreed that 1/2 inch equals 10 knots, measure outward 5 inches (10 x 1/2" = 5") as shown by point B on the

ruler. Finally, pivot the ruler about point A until the true airspeed dot (point B on the ruler) is in contact with the course line at position C. Draw a line from C to the tail of the wind arrow at point A. You're done! That's it! You've got yourself a completed wind triangle depicted by points C, A and AVA/Martin airport, as shown in Figure 98.

The angle between the true airspeed line (position C to position A) and the course line (position C to AVA/Martin) is our wind correction angle of 15 degrees. This represents how much the nose of the airplane must point to the left of the course to allow you to track directly along the selected course line from Table Rock to AVA/Martin. In other words, the nose must be pointed 15 degrees to the left of a true course of 60 degrees. You must head 45 degrees (60 degrees - 15 degrees=45 degrees) to fly parallel to the line drawn from Table Rock to AVA/Martin airport.

The length of the line, in inches, from position C to AVA/Martin is the groundspeed you can expect. Measuring this distance, as shown in Figure 98 gives you 6.6 inches. At 10 knots per inch increment, this equates to approximately 66 knots groundspeed.

Figure 99 shows the comparison between our completed wind triangle and the wind triangle made by the mechanical flight computer. Notice the similarity. Next time you use the mechanical computer, realize that you're simply creating a wind triangle.

Final Words on Wind Computations

Is it necessary to do hand draw a wind triangle before every flight? Absolutely not. Is it necessary to use a slide type or electronic computer to help determine the effect of wind on your airplane? Yes, I believe it is. You need to know how the wind will affect your fuel consumption and time enroute. This means some sort of wind computation is necessary.

The wind side of the mechanical computer shows that a wind triangle is also created that looks like our hand drawn version.

6.6 ½ inch increments = 66 knots groundspeed

15° WCA

Fig. 99

Postflight Briefing #13-4

This angle on the compass rose is your magnetic course.

Displaced Course Line

Course Line

Fig. 100

An Alternate Method of Flight Planning

Another method of flight planning allows you to determine the *magnetic course* directly by displacing the course line through the center of a VOR compass rose. Find the nearest VOR compass rose and run a line parallel to the course line through its center, as shown in Figure 100. Your magnetic course is found on the compass rose. In the case of Figure 100, our magnetic course from Potters eastward is 100 degrees. Simply correct the magnetic course for compass deviation to get the compass course and you're on your way with no further corrections (assuming no wind exists).

If wind does exist, you can correct the winds (which are in true direction) for magnetic variation to obtain winds from a magnetic direction (simply add or subtract the variation from the true winds as appropriate). With your E6-B computer, use winds from the magnetic direction along with the magnetic course (instead of the true course) to find the wind correction angle (WCA). Apply the wind correction angle to your magnetic course, correct this for deviation and you end up with a compass heading for your trip. Why do it this way? If pilots often fly VOR airways (which are magnetic courses) it's sometimes easier to convert the true winds to a magnetic direction, then solve for the WCA and groundspeed.

Postflight Briefing #13-5

Flight Planning/Weather Briefings by Computer

We all know someone who's technically challenged. I have a friend like that. He purchased a camera and was happily showing it off when I asked him what kind of "lux" value it had (lux is a measure of the camera's light sensitivity). He replied, "I think it's a Dee-lux." Oh well. If you don't have a fear of things technical, you're in for a treat.

It's the computer age. Knowing how to use one has many benefits. In addition to providing sophisticated means for shooting down Klingons and wasting time, a computer allows you to obtain a complete and legal weather briefing and other essential preflight information, all from the comfort of your home.

You can do things such as file a flight plan, close a flight plan, obtain weather maps and NOTAMS, see temporary flight restrictions, use a flight planner to help select routes, determine mileage and much more. You can also obtain plain language interpretation of things like METAR, TAF and other weather reports. Best of all, the service is free. Whoa! Pick yourself up, and stow that credit card. That's right, for exactly no outlay of money, you get access to highly sophisticated software that provides state-of-the-art flight planning services.

While there are many wonderful flight planning software programs available, I recommend that you begin by using AOPA's real-time FlyQ flight planner (free to all AOPA members—if you're not yet a member, you should join). It can be found on AOPA's web site (www.aopa.org).

Before you can begin using AOPA's flight planner, you need to obtain a DUAT access code and password. DUAT is *not* you and a flight instructor singing a song together. It's your free ticket to flight planning information. Several years ago, the FAA authorized the establishment of the Direct User Access Terminal (DUAT). Under this program, the government supports the dissemination of weather information via two providers: CSC (call 800/345-3828 or visit www.duats.com) and DTC (call 800/243-3828 or visit www.duat.com). It's through these service providers that you're able to use AOPA's flight planner to access weather and NOTAM information.

Begin by filling out the appropriate pilot information in the FlyQ intro page, including your new DUAT access code and password. Click OK when done. Next, fill out the Aircraft information dialogue box that opens and click "Next" to begin flight planning.

Now you're ready to rock, or flight plan to avoid the rocks, if you will. Let's choose a practice flight from John Wayne airport (KSNA) in Southern California to Reid-Hillview airport (KRHV) in Northern California (Figure 101, position A).

Fig. 101

Begin by clicking the Create/Edit tab in the upper part of the Plans dialogue box (Figure 101, position A). Fill in the departure airport identifier and the destination airport identifier (if either airport has numbers in its identification, then don't place the "K" value in front of the airport identifier). Choose the appropriate date and time for departure, along with the type of route you'd prefer to fly. You can choose either an *airway* routing or a *GPS direct* routing. If you choose the airway option, the flight planner will automatically choose an airway routing for you. We'll also use a cruise altitude of 10,500 feet for this flight. Once done, click OK and the a magenta flight planned route will automatically appear (Figure 101, position B). The Create/Edit dialogue box now shows the individual intersections, VORs or waypoints that make up your routing (Figure 101, position C).

The magenta line represents your airway route from John Wayne to Reid-Hillview. At this point, if you decide that you want to fly an alternate route instead of the one given, click and drag the magenta course line to any intersection, VOR or fix (or waypoint), as necessary, to fly any route desired. See what nice things AOPA does for you here?

The really special part about being able to modify your route is that you can move the route line around any temporary flight restrictions (TFRs) present on the chart,

Now it's time to obtain the weather for this flight. You'll do this by clicking the weather tab at the top of the flight planner (Figure 101, position D). When you do, the Weather Types dialogue box opens as shown in Figure 102. There are several weather types you can choose from here. The winds aloft chart is a good example (Figure 103).

Wonderful as electronic flight planning is, don't let it make you lazy about examining *and understanding* the weather and route information. You always want to keep your head in the game, and have a gut feel for the routes, headings and altitudes you've chosen. There are two reasons for this. First, even computers can hand you the wrong information if there are programming errors, bad data, or other glitches. Catching those things is *your* responsibility. Second, unless you've manually gone over the entire route, you won't have this information at your fingertips and you won't have the extra bit of mental insurance that's so much needed if and when you have to make an important decision about navigation.

While there's quite a bit more to this wonderful software, I'm reluctant to make this book any bigger. At least you understand the salient features of the online flight planning software.

I don't want to give you the impression that flight planning software is your key to rest and relaxation when it comes to creating manual flight logs, as we learned to do in this chapter. That would be a very wrong impression. First, the flight planning you'll initially do is based on dead reckoning and pilotage. This means picking personalized checkpoints off the chart, inserting them in the flight log, then making all the calculations necessary to fly the flight. You can't learn how to do this if you let the flight planning software do the work for you. This is why you should learn all the basics first, then let the flight planning software assist you in making a more complete flight plan with weather overlays and weather chart generation. Remember, you must learn to walk before you run (or taxi before you fly). So please don't skip the basics of flight planning just to spend more time in that lounge chair.

In regard to this book being big, let me just say that it's built that way for safety. In the event you can't clear the trees on the end of a runway during takeoff, let's hope you have my book on board. By opening the window and throwing out the book, you could get an extra 500 feet per minute of climb rate. Now *that's* a safety advantage.

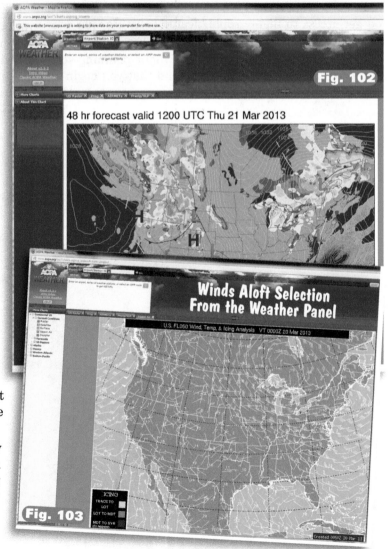

Prog Chart Selection From the Weather Panel

Fig. 102

48 hr forecast valid 1200 UTC Thu 21 Mar 2013

Winds Aloft Selection From the Weather Panel

U.S. FL050 Wind, Temp, & Icing Analysis   VT 0000Z 20 Mar 2013

Fig. 103

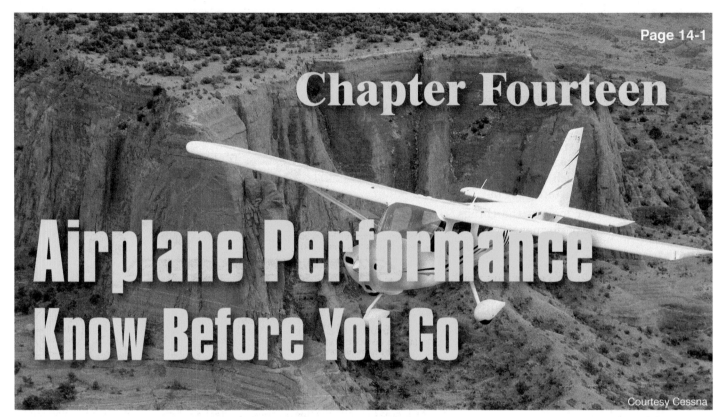

Chapter Fourteen

Airplane Performance
Know Before You Go

Courtesy Cessna

"Skycatcher 2132 Bravo, this is Departure Control, please squawk standby. There's a problem with your transponder," said the controller.

"What's the problem?" asked the pilot of the Cessna Skycatcher.

"Well, we show your airplane climbing through 19,500 feet doing 320 knots," replied the controller.

The quick thinking pilot with an excellent sense of humor replied, "Oh no, that's right. We just had our engine overhauled." Now that's real performance! Except, of course, that it was *unreal* performance. The controller could easily predict that no Skycatcher on (or off) Earth was capable of doing 320 knots *or* climbing to 19,500 feet.

Airplane performance *is* predictable. Unlike psychics, pilots don't need crystal balls or Quija boards to make performance estimates that are very close to the mark. An airplane's takeoff, climb, cruise and landing performance is easily estimated from a variety of charts found in the Pilot's Operating Handbook (POH), which is as much a part of the aircraft's equipment as the wings. (If you don't see either the wings or the POH, better ask about it).

Your job is to know how to use the performance charts. As you'll soon see, all airplane performance is based on one very important item—air density. That's because the thickness of the air flowing over the wings or into the engine determines how well the airplane performs (or fails to perform).

Air Density

Airplanes are remarkably similar to people in that both experience decreased performance in less-dense air. Anyone who's ever hiked to the top of a high mountain knows how human performance decreases. One trip up El Capitan at Yosemite and you feel like you're the big, bad wolf, huffing and puffing as though you were trying to blow a house down.

Airplanes, too, are air-breathing machines, and they respond much as you do to lowered air density. The more air molecules flowing over the airplane's wing, the greater the lift developed. Anything that thins the air reduces the wings' ability to generate lift.

Airplane engine performance is affected in the same way. Powerplants require air to run. Anything reducing the amount of air the engine swallows diminishes its power output. Less power equals less performance. No fancy mathematics here. It's really quite simple. To fly without understanding this important relationship is about as wise as having the three little pigs invite the wolf in for a spot of tea, which would certainly give new meaning to the term "pig out."

Let's take a closer look at the things which affect airplane performance.

Height

As we discussed in an earlier chapter, the higher you go, the less frequently you—or your airplane's wing—will run into air molecules, because they are fewer and farther between with increasing altitude. This is another way of saying that the *air density* is less. Fewer air molecules are available to move past the wing, so lift is reduced and performance is decreased. Expect higher altitudes to provide you with slower acceleration, longer ground runs, and shallower climb profiles, as shown in Figure 1.

Heat

Heat is also notorious for reducing the performance of airplanes. Heated air is much less dense than colder air. Expect slower acceleration, longer takeoff runs, and shallower climb profiles on hot days, as shown in Figure 2.

Humidity

High humidity also reduces airplane performance by thinning the air. Wait a minute, you say! How can adding moisture to air make it thinner? Moist air is lighter (thus less dense) because water molecules are actually lighter than air molecules. Mind you, I said water molecules, not water, which is obviously a lot heavier because of the density. If you've ever tried to carry a bucket of steam (it rises because it's lighter than air), you've had direct proof that moist air is less dense than dry air. By itself, moist air isn't much of a problem. This is why most performance charts make no correction for humidity. Nevertheless, in combination with height and heat it could put your airplane dangerously close to those trees at the end of the runway.

The very best way to think of all this is to remember that you should avoid joining

HEIGHT AND AIRPLANE PERFORMANCE

An increase in altitude has an adverse effect on airplane performance. Higher altitude means thinner air, which reduces the wing's ability to develop lift as well as reducing the engine's power output. Higher altitudes are associated with a longer ground run, a reduced rate of climb and a shallower climb angle. The likelihood of climbing over obstacles at the departure end of the runway diminishes at this decreased air density.

Fig. 1

HEAT AND AIRPLANE PERFORMANCE

An increase in temperature has an adverse effect on airplane performance. Warmer air means thinner air which reduces the wings' ability to develop lift as well as reduces the engine's power output. Warmer temperatures bring longer ground runs and shallow climb angles.

Fig. 2

Flare when you hear the crickets.

Dave Rossi

HUMIDITY

An increase in humidity produces an increase in density altitude, but it's not often dramatic. Increasing the relative humidity of standard temperature air from 50% to 100% often doesn't increase the density altitude by more than 100 to 150 feet. Now, if the air is significantly above standard temperature, then the increase in density altitude can be as high as 600 feet.

For example, if the air temperature at 5,000 feet is 80 degrees F with a 0% relative humidity, then the density altitude is approximately 7,445 feet. Increase the humidity in the example above to 100% and the density altitude jumps to 7957 feet. That's an increase in 514 feet due to a 100% increase in relative humidity at these higher temperatures.

If you'd like to see for yourself how humidity affects density altitude take a look at Richard Shelquist's density altitude calculator page at (http://wahiduddin.net/calc/calc_da_rh.htm).

aviation's 4-H club. Because if you have height, heat and humidity, you have heck to pay (ahhh, those 4 H's!). Any one or a combination of these factors can turn an airplane into a car by keeping it from becoming airborne.

If you want to avoid ending up on the Oprah Winfrey show, don't do weird, strange things in your airplane, like taking off with a lot of height, heat and humidity.

"OK, Rod," I hear you saying, "how much is *a lot?*" Good question. The effects of height and heat are all combined into one very important calculation called *density altitude*.

Density Altitude

Taking off at an airport near sea level usually results in good acceleration and climb performance. The elevation has no effect on performance, temperatures are usually moderate, and the humidity is generally not too high. If we take off from an airport situated at 100 feet MSL, the airplane performs quite well.

Suppose, however, that it's an extraordinarily hot day at our 100 foot MSL airport. Will the airplane perform well? No. Because of the high heat, the air might have a density equivalent to an altitude around 3,000 feet. The term *density altitude* describes how dense the air feels to the airplane, regardless of the airplane's present height above sea level. Density altitude is an extremely important term for you to understand.

In the previous example, even though the airplane was physically at 100 feet MSL, in terms of *airplane performance* the airport has a density altitude of 3,000 feet.

In Chapter 5, I mentioned that pressure altitude was the reference to which airplane engineers calibrate their performance charts. Pressure altitude is what the altimeter indicates when 29.92 inches Hg is set in the altimeter's Kollsman window. In addition to the pressure altitude reference, engineers also calibrate many of their performance charts to a standard temperature of 59 degrees F (15 degrees C) at sea level.

Engineers call the conditions of 29.92 inches Hg and 59 degrees F (15 degrees C) at sea level *standard conditions*. Since you must have a starting point or reference when calibrating the performance of airplanes (and their instruments), standard conditions at sea level is a good starting place. For example, when you ask the teacher how your son Bobby is doing in school, he or she normally compares his performance to that of a previous year. The teacher might say, "Well, compared to last year, Bobby is doing better." If the teacher said, "Well, in reference to all forms of animal and plant life on this planet, little Bobby is holding his own against most species of protozoa," then Bobby is in trouble. Standard temperature and pressure conditions are simply a reference point where a baseline of performance is established.

Of course, if standard conditions existed at sea level all the time, we wouldn't have to worry about changes in air density and its effects on airplane performance. Unfortunately, Mother Nature doesn't like constant, standard conditions (that's why a tornado is similar to a divorce or an earthquake—one of them is going to get your house).

Let's assume you're at an airport at 4,000 foot MSL and standard conditions exist at sea level. Let's also assume that temperatures decrease at 3.5 degrees F (2 degrees C) per 1,000 feet (by now you know that while this is the engineer's standard lapse rate and is used for instrument calibration, it is seldom the actual lapse rate found in the environment). Under these conditions, the temperature at 4,000 feet should be 45 degrees F (4x3.5=14 and 59-14=45 degrees F). Suppose it's really hot,

HIGH FRIGHT

I was on a night, scenic VFR flight with a passenger. After one hour my passenger was trying to eat popcorn and talk, but it was all "gibberish." My altimeter was indicating 11,500' and holding steady. However, I noticed a steady rate of climb indication of 120 fpm, and an 11,000' mountain off the wing appeared unusually small. I contacted Approach and asked for Mode C readout. They informed me that Center read me at 19,700' MSL. The controller recommended rapping on the panel. I began a descent for home airport and banged on the panel above the altimeter. It immediately jumped to 16,400 and was moving again. I should have noticed a shallow climb with the other instruments. However, I hadn't had any sleep for 36 hours and thought I was doing a nice job of maintaining my eastbound cruise altitude of 11,500.

ASRS Report

say 100 degrees F (38 degrees C) at 4,000 feet (this is definitely a non-standard temperature). Is the airplane going to perform like it normally would at 4,000 feet? Definitely not. In fact, the airplane is going to perform more like it's at 7,500 feet (I'll show you in just a moment how I arrived at this value).

Because of the higher than normal temperature, the air has a density altitude—a performance altitude, if you want to think of it that way—of approximately 7,500 feet. Think of density altitude as you do personal debt. Whenever debt increases, bad things happen; when debt decreases, good things happen. Increasing density altitude decreases airplane performance; decreasing density altitude increases airplane performance.

Density Altitude Example No. 1 – Finding the density altitude is easy with the density altitude chart in Figure 3. Along the bottom (horizontal) axis is a temperature scale with Fahrenheit and Celsius markings. Rising diagonally upward from left to right are pressure altitude lines. On the left side of the chart is the density altitude reading along the vertical scale. If you know the pressure altitude and the air temperature for your location, you can easily find the density altitude. Let's see how this works.

Assume your outside air temperature (OAT) is 80 degrees F (27 degrees C) and the pressure altitude is 7,000 feet. Referring to Figure 3, find 80 degrees F (27 degrees C) on the bottom, horizontal scale and move upwards until reaching the 7,000 foot (diagonal) pressure altitude line. Make a mark at this point (position 1) and move horizontally to the left. The number on the left hand vertical scale is the density altitude. In our example the density altitude is 10,000 feet.

Density Altitude Example No. 2 – What is your density altitude if the pressure altitude is 3,257 feet and the OAT is 75 degrees F (24 degrees C)? First you must locate your pressure altitude between the diagonal lines on the density altitude

Fig. 3

DENSITY ALTITUDE CHART

Altimeter Setting (" Hg)	Pressure Altitude Conversion Factor
28.0	1,824
28.1	1,727
28.2	1,630
28.3	1,533
28.4	1,436
28.5	1,340
28.6	1,244
28.7	1,148
28.8	1,053
28.9	957
29.0	863
29.1	768
29.2	673
29.3	579
29.4	485
29.5	392
29.6	298
29.7	205
29.8	112
29.9	20
29.92	0
30.0	-73
30.1	-165
30.2	-257
30.3	-348
30.4	-440
30.5	-531
30.6	-622
30.7	-712
30.8	-803
30.9	-893
31.0	-983

chart in Figure 4. Locating the pressure altitude value of 3,257 is easy if you draw the intermediate values between the 1,000 foot pressure altitude lines. Simply draw the 3,500 foot pressure altitude value between the 3,000 and 4,000 foot pressure altitude lines, as shown in Figure 4. Now draw an intermediate value between the 3,000 and 3,500 foot pressure altitude line. This will represent the 3,250 foot pressure altitude value. Move up the 75 degree F (24 degree C) line until reaching the pressure altitude line of 3,250, as shown by position 2 (this is very close to the actual pressure altitude value of 3,257 feet). Go across to the left to find a density altitude value of approximately 5,000 feet.

At the end of this chapter in Postflight Briefing #14-1, I've included two different types of density altitude problems that show up on FAA knowledge exams. Unfortunately, one of the problems is more test oriented than it is practical in the real world. Don't ask me why test creators do this. It reminds me of some 8th century monk-scribe inserting words in an ancient text that eventually becomes the foundation of our modern English language. As the monk is writing the official word for sharp instrument with a handle that cuts your steak, he looks around, then mischievously inserts a K in the word knife. No one knows why he did this, but it's a done deed. We've got to live with it. Study Postflight Briefing #14-1 carefully during your final preparation for the knowledge exam.

Let's look at an even more meaningful example of how density altitude relates to airplane performance. Before we can do that we need to understand something known as service ceiling.

Fig. 4

DENSITY ALTITUDE CHART

Altimeter Setting (" Hg)	Pressure Altitude Conversion Factor
28.0	1,824
28.1	1,727
28.2	1,630
28.3	1,533
28.4	1,436
28.5	1,340
28.6	1,244
28.7	1,148
28.8	1,053
28.9	957
29.0	863
29.1	768
29.2	673
29.3	579
29.4	485
29.5	392
29.6	298
29.7	205
29.8	112
29.9	20
29.92	0
30.0	-73
30.1	-165
30.2	-257
30.3	-348
30.4	-440
30.5	-531
30.6	-622
30.7	-712
30.8	-803
30.9	-893
31.0	-983

Service Ceiling

Most POHs for individual airplanes inform pilots of the maximum height the airplane can be flown to before it ceases climbing (technically, the altitude at which the climb rate drops to 100 feet per minute). This height is known as the *service ceiling* (Figure 5). The service ceiling applies to a brand new airplane with a new engine. You can expect older airplanes to have service ceilings less than the book value. Figure 6 shows 14,625 feet as the service ceiling of a Cessna SkyCatcher 162. Of course, if the density altitude is close to or equal to that of the 14,625 foot service ceiling, the airplane will only climb at 100 feet per minute or less.

Density Altitude Problem No. 3 – Suppose you're flying a new Cessna 162 from an airport where the pressure altitude is 10,000 feet and the OAT is 94 degrees F (34 degrees C) (that's hot for an airport that high—better be careful!). What is the density altitude at that airport?

Use the density altitude chart (Figure 4) to identify where the 94

THE SERVICE CEILING

Fig. 5

14,625' MSL
(Service Ceiling)

10,000' MSL

5,000' MSL

An airplane reaches its service ceiling when its climb rate is reduced to 100 feet per minute or less.

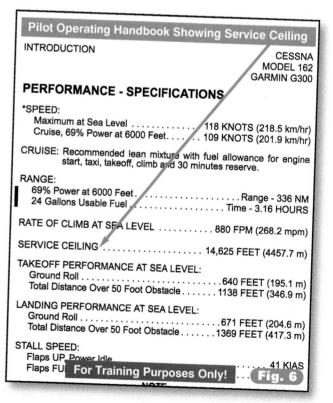

Pilot Operating Handbook Showing Service Ceiling

INTRODUCTION

CESSNA
MODEL 162
GARMIN G300

PERFORMANCE - SPECIFICATIONS

*SPEED:
Maximum at Sea Level . . . . 118 KNOTS (218.5 km/hr)
Cruise, 69% Power at 6000 Feet. . . . . . 109 KNOTS (201.9 km/hr)

CRUISE: Recommended lean mixture with fuel allowance for engine start, taxi, takeoff, climb and 30 minutes reserve.

RANGE:
69% Power at 6000 Feet. . . . . Range - 336 NM
24 Gallons Usable Fuel . . . . Time - 3.16 HOURS

RATE OF CLIMB AT SEA LEVEL . . . . 880 FPM (268.2 mpm)

SERVICE CEILING . . . . 14,625 FEET (4457.7 m)

TAKEOFF PERFORMANCE AT SEA LEVEL:
Ground Roll . . . . .640 FEET (195.1 m)
Total Distance Over 50 Foot Obstacle . . . . . . 1138 FEET (346.9 m)

LANDING PERFORMANCE AT SEA LEVEL:
Ground Roll . . . . .671 FEET (204.6 m)
Total Distance Over 50 Foot Obstacle . . . . . . 1369 FEET (417.3 m)

STALL SPEED:
Flaps UP, Power Idle . . . . 41 KIAS
Flaps FU **For Training Purposes Only!** . . . **Fig. 6**

TAKEOFF DEFINITIONS

Litfoff or
rotation point

Ⓐ Ⓑ Ⓒ

50'
Obstacle

|—— Ground roll ——|

|—— Total distance to clear a 50' obstacle ——|

The ground roll is the total distance required for the airplane to become airborne. The point where the airplane reaches 50 feet above the runway is the total distance required for the airplane to clear a 50 foot obstacle (supposedly placed at this precise point).

Fig. 7

degree F (34° C) line intersects the 10,000 foot pressure altitude line (position 3). Moving horizontally to the left you determine the density altitude to be 14,625 feet.

How will our airplane perform? Not well. Better get out your driver's license, since driving is what you'll be doing. The airplane, if it gets off the runway at all, will barely climb 100 feet per minute. You're going to scare quite a few people standing at the end of the runway. Take my word for it, if it's an older airplane, you'll never become airborne under the conditions in this example. And if it's a tired old airplane you'll notice something is wrong because it'll take full power to taxi (that's a joke. But it does emphasize how much the performance decreases).

Here's Machado's Service Ceiling Caveat: Never count on more than 75% of an airplane's posted service ceiling. This is, admittedly, a conservative estimate if the airplane is new, but a wise and realistic one if the airplane is old. By my numbers, I would expect a Cessna 162 to climb no faster than 100 feet per minute at a density altitude of 10,968 feet (75% of 14,625 feet).

Anything that makes the air thinner (lower pressure, high heat, high humidity) increases the density altitude. Anything making the air thicker (increasing pressure, low heat, low humidity) decreases the density altitude.

Machado's Whammo Density Predictor states: For a given pressure altitude, the density altitude increases by 1,000 feet for every 15 degree F (8.5 degree C) temperature increase. Given this, and knowledge of your airplane's service ceiling, you can easily estimate the amount your airplane's performance will decrease.

Performance Charts

As a kid, it was often difficult to predict whether my grandfather was being serious or just joking around. He was a card carrying prankster and proud of it. One time he called me over to his chair and said, "Did you know you were adopted?"

I was crushed and sighed, "You mean I was really adopted? Oh no!"

"That's right," grandpa said, "but they brought you back." Hah!

On another occasion (according to my mom), whenever I cried as a kid my grandfather would threaten to call Tibet and tell the authorities that he suspected I was the new Dalai Lama, knowing that they'd come and take me away. Everybody had a big laugh over that one, except me. To this day, whenever someone knocks at the door, I peep through the hole and yell out, "You aren't from Tibet are you? I was adopted so leave me alone."

Fortunately, while grandpa's antics were hard to predict, airplane performance isn't. That's because airplanes have performance

This type of activity dramatically reduces airplane performance. Nevertheless, credit must be given to the pilot who went out of his way to entertain his passenger on those long flights.

charts for all facets of their normal activities: takeoff, climb, cruise, landing, etc. Your success at predicting what will happen during these conditions is a matter of your familiarity with these charts. Machado's Ornithological Observation states: All things that fly should use performance charts except birds—since they don't have pockets.

Takeoff Concepts – Takeoffs are second only to landings for their excitement and challenge. While a takeoff may not be as spectacular for some pilots, in my view it requires just as much research and planning to do it well. Figure 7 shows a typical takeoff profile. At position A the airplane applies full power and accelerates down the runway. It eventually reaches liftoff speed at position B and *rotates,* which is a fancy word for *raises the nose to climb.* One time I forgot to tell a student what rotate meant. At the appropriate point during the takeoff, I looked at him and said, "OK Bob, rotate, rotate. He looked really confused. He thought he was supposed to twirl around somehow (perhaps as a bizarre takeoff ritual similar to the secret handshake some flight instructors use). The takeoff ground roll is the distance between A and B.

At position C, the airplane has attained enough height to clear a 50 foot obstacle. The distance between positions A and C is called the *total distance to clear a 50 foot obstacle* (don't you wish all definitions were that easy?). Obviously, the taller the obstacle, the greater the distance required between A and C.

Best Rate and Best Angle Of Climb Speeds

After the liftoff is made, you normally want to climb at a speed that will get you to your selected cruising altitude in the shortest possible time. There is one and only one such speed. It is, as I hope you remember from the discussion in an earlier chapter, called the *best rate of climb speed*—otherwise known as Vy.

Figure 8A shows how a climb at Vy might look. The best rate of climb speed will give you the largest upward deflection on the vertical speed indicator. In other words, you'll be able to gain altitude in the shortest possible time.

THREE CLIMBING AIRSPEEDS
Climbing at the best rate of climb speed (Vy)

Fig. 8

Vy: 79 kts   700 FPM

The best rate of climb speed (Vy) gives you the greatest altitude gain for a given amount of time. In other words, it gives you the largest deflection on your vertical speed indicator.

Climbing at the best angle of climb speed (Vx)

Vx: 69 kts   650 FPM

BIG ANGLE   Most altitude

⊢ For a given distance ⊣

The best angle of climb speed (Vx) gives you the greatest altitude gain for a given distance over the ground. In other words, it gives you the largest climb angle possible.

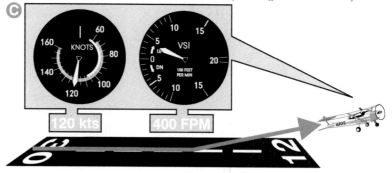

Climbing at a cruise climb airspeed (pilot's choice)

120 kts   400 FPM

A cruise climb is done with the pilot's choice of airspeed. When no obstacles are present, climbing at a slightly higher speed provides less climb rate yet provides better visibility and good engine cooling.

Sometimes climb angle instead of time is a concern during takeoff. Altitude gain for a given distance over the ground is a concern when an obstacle looms at the departure end. Watching an obstacle grow in your windshield is exciting in the way it's exciting to be a spotted owl at a lumberjack convention. If you want to gain the most altitude for a given distance over the ground, then climb at the *best angle of climb speed*, otherwise known as Vx. Figure 8B shows a climb profile at Vx. Notice that if the most altitude is gained by the time the airplane has arrived at the obstacle, this represents a very large angle of climb.

Even though the nose attitude is generally higher at Vx, the airplane won't have as large a rate of climb deflection on the VSI as it would at Vy (it will initially as you rotate, but then returns to a lesser value). The airplane still climbs at a larger angle because Vx is slower than Vy. With a slower forward speed, it gains more altitude per foot of forward distance, making the angle of climb quite large. In many cases, the airplane's POH recommends small flap settings to facilitate a short-field climb over an obstacle.

The easiest way to remember the difference between Vx and Vy is to ask yourself which one, the Y or the X, has more angles? The X has more angles making it the best angle of climb speed (Vx). By default, Y, with fewer angles, becomes the best rate of climb speed.

Vx and Vy Change With Altitude

The best angle and best rate of climb speeds change slightly with altitude and weight. Since the airplane's ability to climb is predicated on excess thrust (power), changing altitude or changing weight (or both) changes the amount of excess thrust (power) available for a climb. This, in turn, affects the speeds at which Vx and Vy occur.

Figure 9 shows a typical rate of climb (ROC) vs. true airspeed graph under full throttle conditions. The curve identifies the ROC for different airspeeds at a specific altitude. At full throttle (assumed to be maximum power) there is no rate of climb at point Z since all the airplane's power is used to achieve maximum forward speed.

As the airplane slows to point C, parasite drag decreases and the excess thrust (thrust not used to overcome drag) has been converted into a rate of climb. Continued slowing of the airplane further reduces the ROC because of the increasing induced drag. At point Y, the airplane has no ROC since all the airplane's power is used in overcoming an enormous amount of induced drag. (This is *operating behind the power curve,* as described in Chapter 2.)

RATE OF CLIMB VS. TRUE AIRSPEED GRAPH

Fig. 9

ROC Curve (Rate Of Climb)

Tangent Line

Vx - Best angle of climb 69 kts

Vy - Best rate of climb 79 kts

The full throttle rate of climb (ROC) curve depicts a zero rate at point (Z)— the point of maximum level forward speed and point (Y)—the power-on stall speed. Where the tangent line contacts the ROC curve at point A, the airplane attains the maximum altitude gain for a specific forward velocity, otherwise knows as the best angle of climb speed (point B at 69 knots). The maximum rate of climb is achieved at point C. The speed for the maximum rate of climb is found at 79 knots at point D.

The sea level, best rate of climb is found at point C. Dropping directly downward to point D identifies the Vy speed for this particular airplane. A tangent line from the bottom left corner of the graph contacts the sea level ROC line at point A. At this point, the airplane experiences its best angle of climb. Dropping downward from point A to point B identifies the airplane's speed for Vx.

Why the tangent line? Mathematically, when the beginning of this line is anchored at the graph's origin (the 0 FPM, 0 airspeed point), it has the steepest slope (largest angle upward) where it contacts the ROC curve at point A.

As you can see, Vx is a little less than Vy. As altitude increases, the indicated airspeed for Vx increases slightly while the indicated airspeed for Vy decreases slightly, as shown in Figure 10. Think about it this way: The smaller one (Vx) gets larger while the larger one (Vy) gets smaller as altitude increases.

Vx AND Vy CHANGE WITH ALTITUDE

Fig. 10

Best Angle of Climb (Vx)

Best Rate of Climb (Vy)

The indicated airspeed for the best angle-of-climb (Vx) increases with an increase in altitude. The indicated airspeed for the best rate-of-climb (Vy) decreases with altitude. The point at which they meet (point A) is the altitude where the airplane can no longer climb. This is known as the *absolute ceiling.*

Cruise Climb Speed

Most of the time, it's preferable to climb at some speed slightly above Vy. This is often called a cruise-climb speed and it provides you better forward visibility during the climb, as shown in Figure 8C. On hot days it also keeps the engine cooler, preventing overheating and possible detonation. The choice of cruise-climb speeds is a matter of pilot preference.

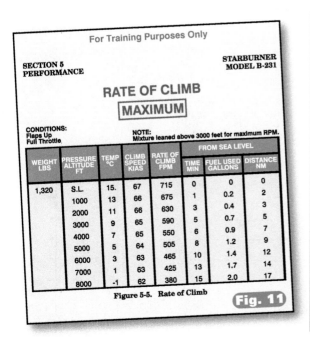

Figure 5-5. Rate of Climb

Fig. 11

How Do They Figure Out All This Stuff?

Having found out about the stork and babies, you are now perhaps wondering where performance charts come from.

They come from actual flight data gathered by the airplane manufacturers, using experienced test pilots and new airplanes. This is something to keep in mind, because there are few mere mortals who are as adept as a full-time test pilot at coaxing full performance from an airplane, and there are few airplanes that perform as well as they did when they were new or nearly new.

Just so you don't leave here with any illusions, they do *not* test to get the information for every single point on any chart. A certain amount of what's there is by interpolation, the same way you've learned to figure out what the winds are between altitudes where there are published data.

Always keep in mind that performance charts reflect a new airplane, flown by a professional pilot, under optimal conditions. *Your mileage,* as they say on the car stickers, *may vary.* So may your landing roll, rate of climb, and all the other things in the charts. Add a safety margin, especially when you are just getting to know an airplane.

Figure 11 shows the rate of climb chart available for some airplanes. This chart is for a small two-place trainer. Notice that the rate of climb decreases with an increase in pressure altitude and that Vy is found at a slower indicated airspeed (KIAS) at higher altitudes. (KIAS stands for *knots of indicated airspeed.*) Under the rate of climb column are several temperature columns with variable climb rates. Considering how airplane performance varies with air density, it shouldn't come as a synaptic shock that the rate of climb varies with temperature.

Many POHs don't show the slight increase in the indicated airspeed for Vx with an increase in altitude because the increase is usually small. These handbooks do often show the change in Vx with a change in airplane weight. Figure 12A is a short field takeoff distance chart. Section 1 (expanded) shows the variable Vx speeds under the 50 FT column. Notice that these speeds decrease with a decrease in airplane weight (Vy also decreases with a weight decrease).

Remember, at higher altitudes your climb angle at Vx is going to be much less than it would at sea level despite the fact that you're at Vx. So give yourself plenty of extra margin if attempting to climb over an obstacle off the departure end of a high altitude airport.

Also remember that the airplane is going to climb at less of a rate or angle with the gear down. That's why, on retractable gear airplanes, we retract the gear as soon as it's safe after departure (usually when there is no runway left on which to land). Flaps are sometimes used for takeoff when suggested by the POH. The important thing to keep in mind about flaps is that they usually shorten the ground run but reduce the angle or rate of climb (not always, but sometimes. Check your POH to determine if they do). They should be retracted after liftoff when the airplane has accelerated to the recommended climb speed.

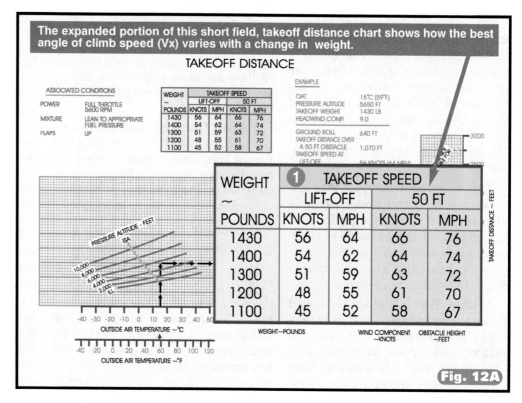

The expanded portion of this short field, takeoff distance chart shows how the best angle of climb speed (Vx) varies with a change in weight.

WEIGHT	① TAKEOFF SPEED			
~	LIFT-OFF		50 FT	
POUNDS	KNOTS	MPH	KNOTS	MPH
1430	56	64	66	76
1400	54	62	64	74
1300	51	59	63	72
1200	48	55	61	70
1100	45	52	58	67

Fig. 12A

Fig. 12B

⑦ TAKEOFF DISTANCE

⑧ ASSOCIATED CONDITIONS

POWER	FULL THROTTLE 5600 RPM
MIXTURE	LEAN TO APPROPRIATE FUEL PRESSURE
FLAPS	UP

WEIGHT ~ POUNDS	TAKEOFF SPEED			
	LIFT-OFF		50 FT	
	KNOTS	MPH	KNOTS	MPH
1430	56	64	66	76
1400	54	62	64	74
1300	51	59	63	72
1200	48	55	61	70
1100	45	52	58	67

EXAMPLE

OAT	15°C (59°F)
PRESSURE ALTITUDE	5650 FT
TAKEOFF WEIGHT	1430 LB
HEADWIND COMP.	9.0
GROUND ROLL	640 FT
TAKEOFF DISTANCE OVER A 50 FT OBSTACLE	1,070 FT
TAKEOFF SPEED AT	
LIFT-OFF	56 KNOTS (64 MPH)
50 FT	66 KNOTS (76 MPH)

Takeoff Distance Chart

All airplanes have some takeoff and landing performance charts. Figure 12B is a typical example of a takeoff distance chart. With your first glance at this chart, you probably feel as confused as a farsighted Venus flytrap that's just ripped the fly off someone's pants. Not to worry! I'll explain how to use it (the chart, not the flytrap).

This chart provides you with the takeoff ground roll under variable airplane and airport conditions. It also provides the best angle of climb speeds based on various weight conditions. Learning how to use this chart is best done by example.

A Hint When Using This and Other Performance Charts – Many performance charts require that you slide up and down calibrated lines on the chart when moving from one reference point to the next.

Movement along these lines should be proportional, not parallel. Figure 13 provides you with a good idea about how to do this. In those cases where a performance chart's calibrated lines are close together or appear parallel, then move parallel to these lines.

Takeoff Distance Example No. 1 – Using the takeoff distance chart in Figure 12B, what is your ground roll and distance to clear a 50 foot obstacle based on the following conditions:

OAT: 59 degrees F (15 degrees C)

Pressure altitude: 5,650 feet

Takeoff weight: 1,430 pounds

Headwind component: 9 knots

First, find 59 degrees F (15 degrees C) on the bottom of the chart in section 1. Move directly up to the 5,650 foot pressure altitude line (section 2). You'll have to estimate where 5,650 feet pressure altitude is, just like you did with the density altitude chart in

Figure 3. Use the following method. The 5,000 foot pressure altitude line is halfway between 4,000 and 6,000 feet. Draw a hair-thin proportional line between these altitudes. It stands to reason that the 5,650 foot pressure altitude line is a little above a point halfway between the 5,000 foot line and the 6,000 foot line. Now move horizontally to the right, directly over to the dark, vertical reference line in section 3. As you move horizontally on the chart simply follow the nearest grid line to avoid making mistakes.

In section 3, we'll correct for weight. Since your weight is 1,430 pounds, you should move downward proportional to the diagonal weight lines (see Figure 13) until reaching a weight of 1,430 pounds, then you'll move horizontally to the right until reaching the next reference line in section 4. If your weight was the same as that directly underneath the

MOVING ALONG THE DIAGONAL LINES OF A CHART

When moving along the sloping line of a performance chart, make sure you move proportionally (up or down) the line. In other words, don't parallel the nearest line as you move. Try to remain the same (proportional) distance between lines.

The line remains proportionally 2/3rds from the bottom as it slopes down.

Fig. 13

reference line at position 3 (or 1,475 pounds, for example), then you'd move horizontally to the reference line at position 4.

Now it's time to correct for a headwind or tailwind component. We have a 9 knot headwind component, so we'll move down, proportionally, to the nearest diagonal line until reaching a 9 knot wind component value, shown on the bottom scale of section 4. From this point we'll move horizontally to the right, toward the next reference line. If we had a tailwind value we'd move up and proportionally to the nearest sloping dashed line until reaching the appropriate wind component value. Then we'd move horizontally to the right toward the reference line.

At the reference line in section 5 we can determine our takeoff ground roll by moving horizontally toward the right. The numerical value of approximately 640 feet, listed at section 6, is our takeoff ground roll. This is only our ground roll, not the distance required to clear an obstacle at the end of the runway.

If an obstacle exists at the end of the runway, we can determine how much horizontal distance is required to clear that obstacle. Let's assume we have a 50 foot obstacle at the end of the runway. Move up and proportional to the diagonal line nearest section 5 until reaching the 50 foot height mark on the bottom scale (obstacle heights are calibrated by the scale at the bottom of section 5). When reaching the obstacle height shown horizontally along the bottom of the chart (50 feet in our case), look horizontally to the right to find that 1,070 feet of horizontal distance is required to clear that obstacle (section 6A). Keep in mind that this is just to clear the obstacle. Your tires should just scrape the top of that obstacle, possibly thumping some bird on the head (maybe that's how bald eagles got bald?).

There are several other interesting things you should know about this chart. First, in section 7, there is a list of takeoff speeds for different weights. At 1,430 pounds we want to lift off at 56 knots. If there is an obstacle at the end of the runway then we want to climb at a speed of 66 knots for that weight. Variable weights require different liftoff and obstacle climb speeds.

Second, section 8 lists all the associated conditions this chart is based on. Machado's Inverse Law of Chart Conditions says: The notes on a performance chart will be of value to you only when you forget to read them. Notes at the bottom of performance charts are the fine print of aviation. Always make it a point to read all the conditions listed in this section of a chart. There are many little variables affecting airplane performance listed

in this section. Notice that the mixture must be leaned to the appropriate fuel pressure during takeoff. This assures maximum power is developed. Also, the flaps must be fully retracted. Additionally, full throttle must be used and the expected RPM with the throttle fully opened is 5,600 RPM. Just because you've moved your throttle fully forward doesn't mean that the engine is guaranteed to generate the maximum amount of power, especially if carburetor ice or a fuel flow restriction is present. You can only be sure you're generating the desired power if your RPM reads close to 5,600 on takeoff.

Takeoff Distance Problem No. 2 – Refer to Figure 12B and determine the ground roll and the total distance required for takeoff to clear a 50 foot obstacle based on the following conditions:

OAT: standard conditions

Pressure altitude: 4,000 feet

Takeoff weight: 1,400 pounds

Headwind Component: calm

Figure 14 shows how this problem is solved. ISA stands for *International Standard Atmosphere* and means the same thing as the term *standard conditions* used by U.S. engineers. Just find where the ISA line (standard temperature line) intersects the 4,000 foot pressure altitude line and move right horizontally to the next reference point. Approximately 530 feet are required for the takeoff ground roll and 925 feet of horizontal distance is required to clear a 50 foot obstacle. Be careful when you are moving horizontally across the chart. Make sure you move parallel to one of the horizontal grid-lines, thus minimizing the chance of error in chart reading.

Fig. 14

Fig. 15 Takeoff Distance Prob #3

Frankly, there is a time when you might use the standard temperature or ISA line when computing airplane performance. You may want to estimate how the airplane will perform at a given altitude without knowing the actual outside temperature (such as when making rough estimates as to the amount of weight—fuel, payload, etc.—that you can depart with). Simply find where the ISA line intersects the elevation of the departure airport. Since you don't know the temperature and pressure altitude, this gives you a rough way to anticipate airplane performance. Remember, this is only used as an approximation (I still have a feeling that some of those mischievous 8th century monk-scribes got loose from the monastery, became performance chart engineers and inserted these ISA or standard temperature lines in airplane performance charts).

Takeoff Distance Problem No. 3 – Refer to Figure 12B and determine the ground roll and the total distance required for takeoff to clear a 50 foot obstacle based on the following conditions:

OAT: 100°F

Pressure altitude: 2,000 feet

Takeoff weight: 1,320 pounds

Tailwind Component: 5 knots

Figure 15 shows how this problem is solved. The only significant difference with this problem is that a tailwind component exists. We must move upward, proportional to the dashed lines, in section 4 in Figure 12B. From there we proceed to the next reference line. A ground roll of approximately 600 feet is required and 1.000 feet of horizontal distance will be used to clear a 50 foot obstacle.

At this point you're probably wondering why the Federal Aviation Administration puts up 50 foot obstacles at all these airports. All these questions make it seem like obstacles are mounted on mobile dollies, towed to different airports (like the old MX missile program) and placed on the departure end of runways to test the skills of a pilot. Well, this isn't true, but it is interesting to consider that most of these obstacles are represented as trees. If that were so, it would seem logical that those obstacles would get smaller whenever pilots, ignorant about takeoff performance charts, depart that runway. In other words, they'd be 50 foot obstacles at first, then, the following week they'd be 46 foot obstacles, then 38 foot obstacles and so on. Eventually, the FAA would have to tow in a new obstacle. Fortunately pilots do a good job in avoiding obstacles.

A Different Takeoff Distance Chart – Figure 16 shows a takeoff distance chart for a small, two-place trainer. As with all performance charts, read the notes before doing any computations. Short field computations are based on 10 degrees of flaps, full throttle then brake release, specific runway conditions, and zero wind. Note #3 states that distances should be decreased 10% for each 9 knots of headwind. For tailwinds up to 10 knots, increase distances by 10% for each 2 knots.

If we're taking off on a dry, grass runway, instead of a hard surface, we need to increase distances by 15% of the ground roll. Grass creates drag and prevents acceleration of the airplane. (If there are groundhogs hiding in the grass, this might also

inhibit acceleration. You'll never see a chart that says to add 5% for each suspected groundhog). You'll notice there is no chart variation for different weights. That's because a small two-place trainer doesn't have much variation in its payload compared to a larger, multiseat airplane.

Takeoff Distance Problem No. 4 – Using Figure 16, determine the takeoff ground roll and distance to clear a 50 foot obstacle based on the following conditions:

Pressure altitude: 3,000 feet

Temperature: 20 degrees C

Tailwind component: 4 knots

Without correcting for the tailwind we obtain a ground roll of 1,000 feet and a distance to clear a 50 foot obstacle of 1,870 feet according to Figure 16. Note #3 on the top of Figure 16 states we need to increase our distances by 10% for each 2 knots of tailwind. Our calculated distances need to increase by 20%. Based on the computations in Figure 17 our expected ground roll becomes 1,200 feet and the horizontal distance to clear a 50 foot obstacle becomes 2,244 feet.

Takeoff Distance Problem No. 5 – Using Figure 16, determine the takeoff ground roll and distance to clear a 50 foot obstacle based on the following conditions:

Pressure altitude: 3,500 feet

Temperature: 10 degrees C

Headwind component: 18 knots

Notice that the pressure altitude is halfway between the 3,000 and 4,000 foot values. There are several ways to go about solving this problem and a little interpolation is necessary. Here's one way, as shown in Figure 18.

Determine the ground roll and distance to clear a 50 foot obstacle at 3,500 feet by adding the 3,000 and 4,000 foot values in the 10 degree C column together then dividing by 2. You should get 973 feet (rounded off) for the ground roll and 1,825 feet for the distance over a 50 foot obstacle.

We could stop here if it were not for the 18 knot headwind. Note #3 in

TAKEOFF DISTANCE
SHORT FIELD

Fig. 16

For Training Purposes Only!

CONDITIONS
Flaps 10 degrees
Full Throttle Prior to Brake Release
Paved, Level Dry Runway
Zero Wind

NOTES:
1. Short field technique as specified in Section 4.
2. Prior to takeoff from fields above 3000 feet elevation, the mixture should be leaned to give maximum RPM in a full throttle, static runup.
3. Decrease distances 10% for each 9 knots of headwind. For operations with tailwinds up to 10 knots, increase distances by 10% for each 2 knots.
4. For operations on a dry, grass runway, increase distances by 15% of the "ground roll" figure.

WEIGHT LBS	TAKEOFF SPEED KIAS		PRESS ALT FT	0°C		10°C		20°C		30°C		40°C	
	LIFT OFF	AT 50 FT		GRND ROLL	TOTAL TO CLEAR 50 FT OBS	GRND ROLL	TOTAL TO CLEAR 50 FT OBS	GRND ROLL	TOTAL TO CLEAR 50 FT OBS	GRND ROLL	TOTAL TO CLEAR 50 FT OBS	GRND ROLL	TOTAL TO CLEAR 50 FT OBS
1,320	50	54	S.L.	640	1190	695	1290	755	1390	810	1495	875	1605
			1000	705	1310	765	1420	825	1530	890	1645	960	1770
			2000	775	1445	840	1565	910	1690	980	1820	1055	1960
			3000	855	1600	925	1730	1000	1870	1080	2020	1165	2185
			4000	940	1775	1020	1920	1100	2080	1190	2250	1285	2440
			5000	1040	1970	1125	2140	1215	2320	1315	2525	1420	2750
			6000	1145	2200	1245	2395	1345	2610	1455	2855	1570	3125
			7000	1270	2470	1375	2705	1490	2960	1615	3255	1745	3590
			8000	1405	2800	1525	3080	1655	3395	1795	3765	1940	4195

Takeoff Distance Chart For Training Purposes Only!

Takeoff Distance Problem #4 Answer:
20% of 1,000' = (.20)x(1,000) = 200'
1,000'+200' = 1,200' Ground Roll
20% of 1,870' = (.2)x(1,870') = 374'
1,870'+374' = 2,244' to clear 50' obstacle.

WEIGHT LBS	TAKEOFF SPEED KIAS		PRESS ALT FT	0°C		10°C		20°C		30°C		40°C	
	LIFT OFF	AT 50 FT		GRND ROLL	TOTAL TO CLEAR 50 FT OBS	GRND ROLL	TOTAL TO CLEAR 50 FT OBS	GRND ROLL	TOTAL TO CLEAR 50 FT OBS	GRND ROLL	TOTAL TO CLEAR 50 FT OBS	GRND ROLL	TOTAL TO CLEAR 50 FT OBS
1,320	50	54	S.L.	640	1190	695	1290	755	1390	810	1495	875	1605
			1000	705	1310	765	1420	825	1530	890	1645	960	1770
			2000	775	1445	840	1565	910	1690	980	1820	1055	1960
			3000	855	1600	925	1730	1000	1870	1080	2020	1165	2185
			4000	940	1775	1020	1920	1100	2080	1190	2250	1285	2440
			5000	1040	1970	1125	2140	1215	2320	1315	2525	1420	2750
			6000	1145	2200	1245	2395	1345	2610	1455	2855	1570	3125
			7000	1270	2470	1375	2705	1490	2960	1615	3255	1745	3590
			8000	1405	2800	1525	3080	1655	3395	1795	3765	1940	4195

Fig. 17

Takeoff Distance Chart For Training Purposes Only!

Takeoff Distance Problem #5 Answer:
Ground Roll at 3,500' (925'+1,020')/2 = 973'
To clear a 50' obstacle:
973-(20% of 973') = (973')-(195') = 778' Ground Roll
1,825-(20% of 1,825') = (1,825')-(365') = 1,460' to clear a 50' obstacle.

WEIGHT LBS	TAKEOFF SPEED KIAS		PRESS ALT FT	0°C		10°C		20°C		30°C		40°C	
	LIFT OFF	AT 50 FT		GRND ROLL	TOTAL TO CLEAR 50 FT OBS	GRND ROLL	TOTAL TO CLEAR 50 FT OBS	GRND ROLL	TOTAL TO CLEAR 50 FT OBS	GRND ROLL	TOTAL TO CLEAR 50 FT OBS	GRND ROLL	TOTAL TO CLEAR 50 FT OBS
1,320	50	54	S.L.	640	1190	695	1290	755	1390	810	1495	875	1605
			1000	705	1310	765	1420	825	1530	890	1645	960	1770
			2000	775	1445	840	1565	910	1690	980	1820	1055	1960
			3000	855	1600	925	1730	1000	1870	1080	2020	1165	2185
			4000	940	1775	1020	1920	1100	2080	1190	2250	1285	2440
			5000	1040	1970	1125	2140	1215	2320	1315	2525	1420	2750
			6000	1145	2200	1245	2395	1345	2610	1455	2855	1570	3125
			7000	1270	2470	1375	2705	1490	2960	1615	3255	1745	3590
			8000	1405	2800	1525	3080	1655	3395	1795	3765	1940	4195

Fig. 18

Figure 16 says decrease distances 10% for each 9 knots of headwind. This means we must decrease both values by 20%. According to Figure 18 this gives us a 778 foot ground roll and 1,460 feet to clear a 50 foot obstacle.

Be careful when applying corrections for headwinds or tailwinds. You must remember to subtract takeoff distance values for a headwind and add these values for a tailwind. Headwinds decrease takeoff distances and tailwinds increase them.

Sometimes it will be necessary to interpolate for both pressure altitude and temperature when using these charts. If you find yourself close to any whole number value (for temperature or pressure) and feel it's difficult to interpolate, then use the larger, whole number value. This gives you a slightly longer takeoff and obstacle clearance distance but at least it errs on the conservative side.

Landing Distance Performance Charts

Remember as a kid watching movies in school (on days when the teacher didn't feel like teaching)? Sometimes the film would jam, and after straightening it out they'd run it backwards a bit so you didn't miss any morsels of knowledge.

We're about to do the same thing. A landing chart is a takeoff chart in reverse. Instead of launching over a 50 foot obstacle, you're assumed to be landing over one. Once again there's the distance over the obstacle to the point of touchdown, and there's a ground roll to account for.

LANDING DEFINITIONS

During landing, the ground roll is the distance required to stop the airplane once the wheels have made contact with the runway. The distance to land over a 50' obstacle is the total distance to cross over that obstacle, touchdown and come to a stop.

Fig. 20

Figure 19 shows a typical landing distance chart. Notice its similarity to the takeoff chart used in Figure 12B. This chart is used in exactly the same way as Figure 12B. Remember, we're just running the movie backwards.

Keep in mind these distances for landing over a 50 foot obstacle assume that you barely clear the obstacle, as shown in Figure 20. You may assume you will always clear an obstacle by more than just inches, but the chart doesn't assume that. To be practical and safe about this, add a few more feet onto the values shown in the chart. In other words, you shouldn't be landing with branches and twigs protruding from the wheelpants. Let's try the following problems.

Fig. 19

A LEAN MEAN FLYING MACHINE

Bob! You're sup-posed to lean with the mixture, not your body.

(Written as an ASRS report by a University flight instructor) *One item that is seldom mentioned in articles on fuel exhaustion and mismanagement deals with student pilots or low-time pilots on cross-country trips. In local area training, the instructors keep the mixture rich because of the varied power settings used and seldom mention or practice proper leaning procedures. So when the solo or low-time pilot is on a trip, under a relatively high work-load, they fail to remember to lean the mixture. (The fuel flow data used in flight planning always assumes a proper leaning of the mixture. Without leaning properly, the actual fuel consumption will be higher than expected and the result is possible fuel starvation.) Also, since local area flights are brief, the instructor and the student seldom (and sometimes never) switch fuel tanks. When the training is in an aircraft having a fuel selector with the option of "Both," there is even less incentive for the student pilot to develop the habit of switching fuel tanks.*

ASRS Report

Landing Distance Problem No. 1 – Using the landing distance chart in Figure 19, and based on the following conditions, determine the total distance required to land.

OAT: 32 degrees F

Pressure altitude: 8,000 feet

Weight: 1,300 pounds

Headwind component: 20 knots

Obstacle: 50 feet

Before using any performance chart, always read the conditions list-ed on that chart. Section 8 in Figure 19 lists the conditions under which the landing is conducted. Section 7 lists the approach speeds you should be using to obtain performance chart values for your landing. I also like how it lists *gear down* as one of the conditions. (Remember, if you forget to put the landing gear down, your landing distance will be cut by approximately 99%, but your mainte-nance bill will go up considerably!)

Figure 21 shows how I computed the answer. Notice the headwind components require that you slide down diagonal lines shown in section 4 of the chart. Sliding downward decreases your final distance value while sliding upward increases any landing value. You need 675 feet of horizontal distance to clear a 50 foot obstacle situated on or near the end of the runway. From the instant you cross the obstacle at 50 feet until the time you come to a stop on the run-way, you'll need 445 feet of distance. Of course this assumes, according to section 7, that at 1,300 pounds of weight, you cross the obstacle at an indicated airspeed of 55 knots. Any faster and the landing distance will increase.

Landing Distance Problem No. 2 – Using the landing distance chart in Figure 19, determine the total dis-tance required to land based on the following conditions:

OAT: standard

Pressure altitude: 2,000 feet

Weight: 1,150 pounds

Headwind component: calm

Obstacle: no obstacle

According to Figure 22, you'll need a 475 foot ground roll under these conditions. This is the distance required to stop from the time the airplane touches down.

		AT SEA LEVEL & 59°F		AT 2500 & 50°F		AT 5000 & 41°F		AT 7500 & 32°F	
GROSS WEIGHT LBS	APPROACH SPEED IAS, MPH	GROUND ROLL	TOTAL TO CLEAR 50 FT OBS	GROUND ROLL	TOTAL TO CLEAR 50 FT OBS	GROUND ROLL	TOTAL TO CLEAR 50 FT OBS	GROUND ROLL	TOTAL TO CLEAR 50 FT OBS
1,320	60	445	1075	470	1135	495	1195	520	1255

— LANDING DISTANCE —   FLAPS LOWERED TO 40 DEGREES - POWER OFF HARD SURFACE RUNWAY - ZERO WIND

NOTES: 1. Decrease the distances shown by 10% for each 4 knots of headwind.
2. increase the distance by 10% for each 60 degrees F temperature increase above standard.
3. For operations on a dry, grass runway, increase distances (both "ground roll" and "total to clear 50ft obstacle") by 20% of the "total to clear 50 ft obstacle" figure.

Fig. 23

A Different Landing Distance Chart

There are certain things you just never do. For instance, never put the word *yes* on a job application on the line that says *salary expected*. When being interviewed as a police officer candidate and asked why you want the job, you shouldn't say, "The lights man, I love all the lights. Whooo, whooo, whooo." There's one thing you never do when working with a landing distance chart. You should never assume that all landing distance charts are the same. These charts come in several shapes and flavors.

The chart shown in Figure 23 is another version of a landing chart. Once again, before using any chart, look at the notes and conditions listed on the chart.

Notice that note #1 says we must decrease distances by 10% for each 4 knots of headwind. We must increase distances by 10% for every 60 degrees F

temperature increases above standard. Standard temperatures are those listed next to the altitudes in each chart column. Sixty degrees is a rather large temperature jump. If temperatures are only 30 degrees F above standard, increase distances by 5%.

Notice that in note 3, landing distances on dry, grass runways increase all calculations by 20%. If dry, grass runways increase our takeoff distance, shouldn't they also decrease our landing distance? Not really. Braking is much less efficient on grass (even if you are conking gophers on the head). Delicate braking is required to slow the airplane, making stopping distances much longer. Read the note carefully! Let's try a few of these problems.

Landing Distance Problem No. 3 – Using the landing distance chart in Figure 23, and based on the following conditions, determine the total distance required to land over a 50 foot obstacle.

OAT: standard

Pressure altitude: 7,500 feet

Headwind component: 8 knots

Runway: dry grass

Based on pressure altitude of 7,500 feet and a standard temperature of 32 degrees F, our landing distance over a 50 foot obstacle is 1,255 feet. With a headwind of 8 knots we need to decrease our distance by 20% according to the chart note #1. This gives us a ground roll of 1,255 - (20% of 1,255)=1,004 feet. Our last correction is for a dry, grass runway. Note 3 states we must increase all distances by 20% of the total to clear a 50 foot obstacle distance. This gives us a final value of 1,004 + (20% of 1,004)= 1,204.8 or 1,205 feet.

Landing Distance Problem No. 4 – Using the landing distance chart in Figure 23, and based on the following conditions, determine the total distance required to land over a 50 foot obstacle.

OAT: 101 degrees F

Pressure altitude: 5,000 feet

Headwind component: calm

According to Figure 23, an altitude of 5,000 feet and 41 degrees F produces a distance over a 50 foot obstacle of 1,195 feet. Our temperature is 60 degrees F more than standard for that altitude. According to note #2, we need to increase our landing distance by 10%. This gives us a 50 foot obstacle clearance value of (10% of 1,195)+1,195=1,315 feet.

Never forget Machado's Calculation Canon: The most important part of the body to use in calculating takeoff and landing distance is the brain, not the wishbone.

Hmmm? For an obstacle this size the short field takeoff performance chart says not to use Vx. It says use V911 and keep my eyes closed.

Time, Fuel and Distance To Climb Chart

Another flavor of chart useful in flight planning is the time, fuel and distance to climb chart shown in Figure 24. As always, read all the notes before using the chart. Notice that the columns provide you with a climb speed (the best rate of climb speed, Vy), an expected rate of climb, the time it takes to climb, fuel used in gallons and distance covered (assuming zero wind). The chart shows how Vy decreases with an increase in altitude.

Climb Problem No. 1 – Using Figure 24, estimate the amount of time and fuel consumed to climb from sea level to 5,000 feet pressure altitude under standard temperature conditions.

This is a relatively easy problem to solve. First, look at the fuel used and distance values for the 5,000 foot pressure altitude row. This gives you 8 minutes and 1.2 gallons of fuel used. Adding .8 gallon of fuel per note #1, we find that we consume 2.0 gallons of fuel while taking approximately 8 minutes to climb once airborne. That's easy, so let's make it a little more practical and challenging.

Climb Problem No. 2 – Using Figure 24, estimate the amount of time and fuel used to take off and climb from an airport with a pressure altitude of 2,000 feet to 6,000 feet pressure altitude, when the temperature at the airport is 21 degrees C.

This problem requires us to subtract the difference in time and fuel consumed from 6,000 feet to 2,000 feet. This gives us a time to climb from 2,000 to 6,000 feet pressure altitude of approximately (10 minute - 3 minutes = 7 minutes). We also derive a fuel consumption of approximately (1.4 gallons - .4 gallons = 1 gallon).

The last thing we do is make a correction for the nonstandard temperature. Since 21 degrees C at 2,000 feet is 10 degrees C above standard temperature for that altitude, per note #3 we should increase both these values by 10%. Our time to climb value becomes (7 minutes + .7 minutes = 7.7 minutes). Our fuel-used value becomes (1.0 gallon + .1 gallon = 1.1 gallons). We do, however, need to add that .8 gallon according to note #1 for engine start, taxi and takeoff. This gives us a total fuel consumption of 1.9 gallons.

This is a very handy little chart to use. You'll find it very useful for cross country flight planning purposes. Although we didn't compute the distances covered during the climb, this is easily done using the same method described in Chapter 13, page 13-32, under the section titled: A More Accurate Flight Plan.

STARBURNER MODEL B-231 · For Training Purposes Only! · **SECTION 5 PERFORMANCE**

TIME, FUEL AND DISTANCE TO CLIMB

MAXIMUM RATE OF CLIMB

CONDITIONS:
Flaps Up
Full Throttle
Standard Temperature

NOTES:
1. Add 0.8 of a gallon of fuel for engine start, taxi and takeoff allowance. **Fig. 24**
2. Mixture leaned above 3000 feet for maximum RPM.
3. Increase time, fuel and distance by 10% for each 10 C above standard temperature.
4. Distances shown are based on zero wind.

WEIGHT LBS	PRESSURE ALTITUDE FT	TEMP °C	CLIMB SPEED KIAS	RATE OF CLIMB FPM	FROM SEA LEVEL		
					TIME MIN	FUEL USED GALLONS	DISTANCE NM
1,320	S.L.	15.	67	715	0	0	0
	1000	13	66	675	1	0.2	2
	2000	11	66	630	3	0.4	3
	3000	9	65	590	5	0.7	5
	4000	7	65	550	6	0.9	7
	5000	5	64	505	8	1.2	9
	6000	3	63	465	10	1.4	12
	7000	1	63	425	13	1.7	14
	8000	-1	62	380	15	2.0	17
	9000	-3	62	340	18	2.3	21
	10,000	-5	61	300	21	2.6	25
	11,000	-7	61	255	25	3.0	29
	12,000	-9	60	215	29	3.4	34

To Trust or Not to Trust

The only way to accurately estimate your airplane's actual fuel consumption is to observe what it does over numerous flights. Take note of how much fuel your airplane actually consumes under different conditions and compare this to the chart's estimated fuel consumption. At least you'll know how accurate your charts are.

Cruise Performance Chart

So far we have charts for predicting takeoff distance, landing distance, and time and fuel to climb. Now let's look at a chart to help compute enroute fuel consumption and expected true airspeed. This chart is the *cruise power setting chart,* shown in Figure 25.

Pressure altitudes are found on the left side of the chart with variable RPM settings for variable power conditions. This chart allows us to choose various percentage selections of BHP (brake horsepower) with which to operate. In other words, if the airplane has a 100 horsepower engine, this chart shows what percentage of those 100 horses are being used. This chart also allows us to refine our performance estimate by selecting from one of three different temperature columns, two of which vary from standard temperature by 20 degrees Celsius. Let's try a few problems.

Cruise Performance Problem No. 4 – Determine the expected fuel consumption and true airspeed for a flight at a pressure altitude of 4,000 feet at 2,300 RPM under standard conditions, using Figure 25.

Find the 4,000 foot pressure altitude column, then move to the 2,300 RPM value. Directly across is our expected true airspeed of 96 knots and fuel consumption of 5.1 gallons per hour at an expected power output of 63%. Are you wondering why we want to know how much power our engine is producing? In many airplanes, leaning of the mixture is recommended when the engine is producing less than 75% power. This chart lets you know when it's reasonable to lean the mixture for more efficient engine operations. It also provides information that might be required in computing values based on other performance charts.

CRUISE POWER SETTINGS

SECTION 5 PERFORMANCE

For Training Purposes Only!

STARBURNER MODEL B-231

CRUISE PERFORMANCE

Fig. 25

CONDITIONS:
1,320 Pounds
Recommended Lean Mixture (See Section 4, Cruise)

NOTES:
Cruise speeds are shown for an airplane equipped with speed fairings which increase the speeds by approximately two knots

PRESSURE ALTITUDE FT	RPM	20°C BELOW STANDARD TEMP			STANDARD TEMPERATURE			20°C ABOVE STANDARD TEMP		
		% BHP	KTAS	GPH	% BHP	KTAS	GPH	% BHP	KTAS	GPH
2000	2400				75	101	6.1	70	101	5.7
	2300	71	97	5.7	66	96	5.4	63	95	5.1
	2200	62	92	5.1	59	91	4.8	56	90	4.6
	2100	55	87	4.5	53	86	4.3	51	85	4.2
	2000	49	81	4.1	47	80	3.9	46	79	3.8
4000	2450				75	103	6.1	70	102	5.7
	2400	76	102	6.1	71	101	5.7	67	100	5.4
	2300	67	96	5.4	63	96	5.1	60	95	4.9
	2200	60	91	4.8	56	90	4.6	54	89	4.4
	2100	53	86	4.4	51	85	4.2	49	84	4.0
	2000	48	81	3.9	46	80	3.8	45	79	3.7
6000	2500				75	105	6.1	71	104	5.7
	2400	72	101	5.8	67	100	5.4	64	99	5.2
	2300	64	96	5.1	60	95	4.9	57	94	4.7
	2200	57	90	4.6	53	89	4.4	52	88	4.3
	2100	51	85	4.2	49	84	4.0	48	83	3.9
	2000	46	80	3.8	45	79	3.7	44	77	3.6
8000	2550				75	107	6.1	71	106	5.7
	2500	76	105	6.2	71	104	5.8	67	013	5.4
	2400	68	100	5.5	64	99	5.2	61	98	4.9
	2300	61	95	5.0	58	94	4.7	55	93	4.5
	2200	55	90	4.5	52	89	4.3	51	87	4.2
	2100	49	84	4.1	48	83	3.9	46	82	3.8
10,000	2500	72	105	5.8	68	103	5.5	64	103	5.2
	2400	65	99	5.3	61	98	5.0	58	97	4.8
	2300	58	94	4.7	65	93	4.5	53	92	4.4
	2200	53	89	4.3	51	88	4.2	49	86	4.0
	2100	48	83	4.0	46	82	3.9	45	81	3.8
12,000	2450	65	101	5.3	62	100	5.0	59	99	4.8
	2400	62	99	5.0	59	97	4.8	56	96	4.6
	2300	56	93	4.6	54	92	4.4	52	91	4.3
	2200	51	88	4.2	49	87	4.1	48	85	4.0
	2100	47	82	3.9	45	81	3.8	44	79	3.7

Since this chart doesn't have detailed calibrations for various temperatures, what do you do if the temperature is only slightly different from the values listed in one of the three vertical temperature columns? The answer is to pick the temperature column closest to the actual air temperature.

Cruise Performance Problem No. 5 – Using Figure 25, determine the expected fuel consumption for a flight at a pressure altitude of 5,500 feet at 2,400 RPM under conditions 14 degrees C colder than standard for your flight altitude.

We'll use the first temperature column, since 14 degrees C colder than standard is closest to its -20 degrees C below standard value. Notice that we're using 5,500 feet, which isn't shown on the chart. A little interpolation is necessary here.

Fuel flow for 6,000 feet at 2,400 RPM: 5.8 GPH

Fuel flow for 4,000 feet at 2,400 RPM: 6.1 GPH

From this you can find the fuel flow for 5,000 feet:

(5.8+6.1)/2=5.95 GPH at 5,000 feet at 2,400 RPM

Now, find the fuel flow for 5,500 feet at 2,400 RPM

This is the difference between the 5,000 foot and 6,000 foot values

(5.95 + 5.8)/2=5.87 or approximately 5.9 GPH (See Figure 26)

PRESSURE ALTITUDE FT	RPM	20°C BELOW STANDARD TEMP			STANDARD TEMPERATURE			ST % BH
		% BHP	KTAS	GPH	% BHP	KTAS	GPH	
4000	2450				75	103	6.1	7
	2400	76	102	6.1	71	101	5.7	6
	2300	67	96		63	96	5.1	6
	2200	60	91	5.95	56	90	4.6	5
5000	2100	53	86		51	85	4.2	4
5500	2000	48	81	5.87	46	80	3.8	4
6000	2500				75	105		
	2400	72	101	5.8	67	100		
	2300	64	96	5.1	60	95		

Fig. 26

Let's be real practical about this. Looking at the numbers, you can usually eyeball the correct value without much difficulty (even without interpolating). This is made much easier when chart values don't vary much between conditions. In other words, at 4,000 feet in this example we had a fuel flow of 6.1 GPH and at 6,000 feet we had 5.8 GPH. It's fairly easy to see that the value for 5,500 feet is closest to 5.8 GPH. In the real world this works fine. For FAA testing purposes you want to be as precise as possible. There is nothing wrong with taking liberties at estimating values as long as you know how to be precise when the need arises.

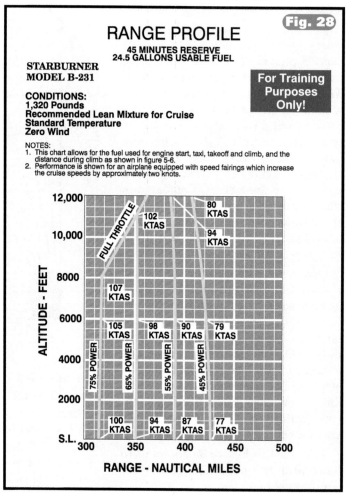

Endurance and Range Profile Charts

Figures 27 and 28 are two additional charts you might see. Figure 27 is a best-endurance chart and Figure 28 is a best-range chart. There are many times when knowing your endurance and range is of immense value. For instance, if I had to remain airborne until the weather cleared for landing, the endurance chart would be of immense value. I'd know how long I could afford to hang around while flying in circles before heading to another airport.

To use either chart, you need to know the percentage of power developed by the engine. Given that information, you can find your endurance and range for various altitudes. Just where will you find the engine's power output in percentages? From the typical cruise performance charts we've already seen in Figures 25 and 26.

If we were using 65% power, what would our endurance be at 8,000 feet? Simply find 8,000 feet in Figure 27 and move across to the 65% power line. Drop straight down and find an endurance of 3 hours and 36 minutes (5 divisions between hour marks=12 minutes per division). At 65% power, according to Figure 28, our range is approximately 354 nautical miles. Of course, assuming you've read all the conditions in both charts you'll know the range is based on no wind, and both charts yield numbers that include a 45 minute fuel reserve.

A wise man says, "On the ground it's OK to say the fuel tanks are half full. In the air, it's best to think of them as half empty. Optimism is not useful when calculating fuel consumption."

Crosswind Component Chart

The only pilots who don't have to worry about crosswinds are aircraft carrier pilots. They have a lot more to worry about than crosswinds. Their runway is always moving. How would you like to take off, then return to find your airport has moved to another location? And I bet you never have to worry about rolling off the end of the runway and getting run over by the airport. Compared to such challenges, crosswinds pale. For the rest of us, however, crosswinds are a factor, so we'd better learn how to figure them out.

Several of our performance charts require us to determine the amount of headwind or tailwind component in order to determine our takeoff or landing distance. You will also find in most POHs a value listed for the *maximum crosswind component* the airplane is capable of handling. This limit is usually a function of flight control limitations and pilot skill available for coping with the crosswind.

The chart in Figure 29 allows us to determine the headwind and crosswind components.

Crosswind Problem No. 1 – Assume you're departing on Runway 30, as shown in Figure 30. The tower reports a wind from 330 degrees at 40 knots. What are the headwind and crosswind components associated with this wind?

Runway 30 is aligned in a direction of 300 degrees. A wind from 330 degrees makes a 30 degree angle with the runway. It's reasonable to say that some of this wind imparts a headwind component and some a crosswind component (do you remember Bud and Ed from Chapter 2, the bottom of page 2-3? It's the same principle). To find exactly how much there is of each, ask yourself what the angle is between the wind and the nose of the airplane.

Obviously the wind is 30 degrees off the right of the nose. The chart in Figure 30 shows degree calibrations in increments of 10, in a right direction. Assume the zero degree mark represents the nose of the airplane.

Start the problem there. Find the 30 degree diagonal line (point A). This represents the angle the wind makes with the nose of the airplane. Slide down this 30 degree line until reaching the 40 knot wind velocity arc (point B). Now all you need to do is drop straight down to point D to determine the amount of crosswind blowing on the airplane. We have a right crosswind of 20 knots. To find the amount of headwind blowing on the airplane, simply move left horizontally to point C. This represents the amount of headwind blowing on the airplane. We have a headwind value of 35 knots. This headwind value is what we would use for any takeoff or landing performance computation.

THE CROSSWIND COMPONENT CHART

If the tower reports a wind from 330 degrees at 40 knots, you can find your headwind and crosswind components by finding the angle between the wind and the nose. That angle is 30 degrees. Find the 30 degree line (point A) and move downward to the 40 knot wind arc (point B). Move horizontally to point C to find the headwind component (35 knots). Drop straight down to point D to find the crosswind component (20 knots).

Crosswind Problem No. 2 – Based on Figure 29, what is the crosswind component you can expect if landing on Runway 18 with the tower reporting a wind of 220 degrees at 35 knots?

Use Figure 31. First ask yourself what the angle is between the wind and the nose. The difference between 180 degrees and 220 degrees is 40 degrees. Find the 40 degree diagonal line (point A) and slide down it until reaching the 35 knot wind arc (point B). You'll have to estimate where 35 is between the 30 and 40 arcs. Dropping straight down gives you a crosswind component of approximately 23 knots (point D). A headwind component of 27 knots also exists (point C). If your airplane was certified to handle a maximum crosswind component of 20 knots, would it be safe to fly? Probably not. This is another good reason to know how to use this chart.

Crosswind Problem No. 3. – Using Figure 29, determine the maximum wind velocity for a 30 degree crosswind if the maximum crosswind component for the airplane is 12 knots.

THE CROSSWIND COMPONENT CHART

If the tower reports a wind from 220 degrees at 35 knots you can find your headwind and crosswind components by finding the angle between the wind and the nose. That angle is 40 degrees. Find the 40 degree line (point A) and move downward to the 35 knot wind arc (point B). Move horizontally to point C to find the headwind component (27 kts). Drop straight down to point D to find the crosswind component (23 kts.).

The solution is provided in Figure 32. This problem requires us to work backwards. First, we know our airplane has a maximum crosswind component of 12 knots. Find this position along the bottom of the crosswind chart (point A). Move straight up until reaching the 30 degree diagonal line representing the wind's angle with the nose of the airplane (point B). At this point, ask yourself what wind arc you would be resting on if smaller wind-arc calibrations existed. Parallel this arc around to the end of the scale (either direction). The maximum wind velocity should be 24 knots.

THE CROSSWIND COMPONENT CHART

In the unfortunate event you happen to conk a prairie dog on the head during takeoff, this could affect your ground run. This isn't good (especially for the prairie dog!).

Suppose your airplane has a maximum demonstrated crosswind component of 12 knots. What is the maximum speed of a 30 degree wind that won't exceed this 12 knot limit? We can solve this problem by working backwards. Start with a 12 knot crosswind at point A and move upward till reaching the 30 degree angle line at point B. The 24 knot wind arc runs through this point as seen at the end of the arc (points C).

Crosswind Problem No. 4 – Using Figure 29, find the amount of tailwind expected with a 30 knot wind from 135 degrees when landing on Runway 27.

The crosswind chart can also be used to find tailwind and crosswind components quite easily. The same procedure applies, except that we must find the angle between the wind and the tail (since we're talking about tailwinds). Figure 33 shows this problem. If you have trouble finding the angle between the wind and the tail, draw (or find) a circular compass rose with the four major directions (N, E, S, and W) on it as shown in Figure 33.

Aligned with Runway 27 means you are pointed in a direction of 270 degrees. With wind from 135 degrees (remember, wind always blow from somewhere), you have wind that makes a 45 degree angle between itself and the tail. Simply go to the crosswind chart and find the wind components for a 30 knot wind offset at a 45 degree angle. Point A shows a crosswind of 21 knots. Keeping your original

THE CROSSWIND COMPONENT CHART

Tailwind component 21 knots

45°

Wind 135° at 30 knots

(270°)

If the winds are from 135 degrees at 30 knots and you're landing on runway 27 (270 degrees), what is the tailwind component during landing? Find the angle between the wind and the runway. The wind makes a 45 degree angle with the runway as shown by the compass rose to the right. Since the wind is blowing from behind the airplane, start at the bottom left hand corner of the crosswind chart and follow the 45 degree line up to the 30 knot arc. Move horizontally to the headwind scale (it tells us tailwind—that should be obvious) and downward to find the tailwind component of 21 knots (point A).

picture in mind, you'll recognize this as a left crosswind. Point B shows a headwind component of 21 knots; we know, however, that this is actually a tailwind component. The crosswind chart wasn't necessarily built to find tailwind components, but if you understand the principle involved, it can be done. This is not to encourage you to plan on taking off with a tailwind. Such behavior is rarely prudent unless the tailwind is pretty minor.

Making the Forces Be With You

During my youth, many a school counselor attempted to predict what I might do with my life. One counselor suggested life as a woodworker, then realized it meant handling sharp objects. No go. Another felt I would succeed at hubcap repair, but backtracked once he thought about how distracting all the bright, shiny objects would be.

Fortunately, my counselors didn't predict well. This may be because nobody *ever* predicts someone will grow up to be a flight instructor. That's an inherently unpredictable outcome.

As a pilot, you can't afford to predict poorly when it comes to airplane performance. You need to become very familiar with the performance charts—not only how to crunch numbers, but what those numbers really mean in terms of performance. Additionally, you need to understand the limitations these numbers impose on when and where flight can be safely undertaken.

Remember, performance charts are prediction charts. And good pilots never leave to chance what they can predict.

Postflight Briefing #14-1

Advanced Density Altitude

Advanced Problem #1

In the airplane, finding pressure altitude is as easy as being a lifeguard in a car wash. Simply place 29.92 in the altimeter's Kollsman window and read what the hands point to (the indicated altitude). This is your pressure altitude. Take the OAT and the pressure altitude and compute the density altitude by using the chart in Figure 34.

But how do you compute density altitude for an airport if you aren't there to set the altimeter to 29.92 inches of Hg and read the temperature? In other words, if you're reading the METAR for an airport and know the temperature and altimeter setting, can you still find its density altitude? Yes. Here's how. Let's start with a field elevation of 7,257 feet MSL.

To the right of the density altitude chart is a vertical column showing altimeter settings vs. pressure altitude conversion factors. Simply find the airport's current altimeter in the altimeter setting column and see what conversion factor must be applied to the altimeter reading to find pressure altitude. In other words, the altimeter should read the field elevation of 7,257 feet MSL with 30.20 inches of Hg set in the Kollsman window. Moving the window's numbers down to 29.92 would simultaneously move the hands downward (make the indicated altitude read less). The conversion factor specifies how much the hands would move downward.

Figure 34, position 1, shows that the conversion factor for an altimeter setting of 30.20 is -257 feet (you would add this value if it didn't have a "-" sign next to it). Subtracting 257 from 7,257 gives you 7,000 which is the pressure altitude. Take the OAT of 80 degrees F (27 degrees C) and a pressure altitude of 7,000 feet and, as shown by position 2 in Figure 34, the density altitude is 10,000 feet. Even though your airplane is at 7,257 feet MSL, it's going to perform like it's at 10,000 feet MSL.

Fig. 34

Advanced Problem #2

Notice the diagonal line labeled "standard temperature" running downward from left to right in Figure 34. Sometimes we want to know the standard temperature for a specific altitude when standard conditions exists at sea level. Find any spot where the standard temperature line intersects a pressure altitude line and drop straight down to the temperature scale. This reading is the standard temperature for that pressure altitude. For example, on Figure 34, find where the standard temperature line intersects the 4,000 foot pressure altitude line (position 3). Drop down to find the standard temperature of 45 degrees F (7°C) for that altitude. The same process works for all other pressure altitude values.

Suppose I ask you to find the density altitude if standard temperature exists at 4,000 feet pressure altitude. Simply find where the standard temperature line intersects the pressure altitude line on Figure 34 and move horizontally left to read a density altitude of 4,000 feet. You'll notice that whenever standard temperature exists at various pressure altitudes, the pressure altitude is always equal to the density altitude. I offer this only as an academic exercise, because standard temperatures seldom exist at various pressure altitudes. I have been flying since 1970 and I have yet to see more than a handful of days having standard temperatures at sea level that stayed that way for any significant amount of time.

Another important reason for offering this to you is because someone decided to put this type of question on the knowledge test (don't ask me why either).

Advanced Problem #3

What is your density altitude if the altimeter setting is 29.96 inches of Hg and the airport elevation is 3,293 feet with an OAT of 75 degrees F (24 degrees C)? First, you must find the

DENSITY ALTITUDE CHART

Altimeter Setting (" Hg)	Pressure Altitude Conversion Factor
28.0	1,824
28.1	1,727
28.2	1,630
28.3	1,533
28.4	1,436
28.5	1,340
28.6	1,244
28.7	1,148
28.8	1,053
28.9	957
29.0	863
29.1	768
29.2	673
29.3	579
29.4	485
29.5	392
29.6	298
29.7	205
29.8	112
29.9	20
29.92	0
30.0	-73
30.1	-165
30.2	-257
30.3	-348
30.4	-440
30.5	-531
30.6	-622
30.7	-712
30.8	-803
30.9	-893
31.0	-983

APPROXIMATE DENSITY ALTITUDE - THOUSANDS OF FEET

°C -18 -12 -7 -1 4 10 16 21 27 32 38 43
°F 0 10 20 30 40 50 60 70 80 90 100 110

OUTSIDE AIR TEMPERATURE

Fig. 34 Repeat

pressure altitude. With the altimeter setting in the altimeter window, the altimeter reads the true altitude (a field elevation of 3,293 feet MSL). The pressure altitude conversion for 29.96 inches of Hg is approximately halfway between that for 29.92 and 30.00, as shown in Figure 34, position 4. Since the correction factor for 29.92 is 0 and 30.00 is -73, use a value halfway between them, or approximately -36. Subtracting 36 from 3,293 gives us a pressure altitude of 3,257 feet.

Locating the pressure altitude value of 3,257 is easy if you draw the intermediate values between the 1,000 foot pressure altitude lines.

Simply draw the 3,500 foot pressure altitude value between the 3,000 and 4,000 foot pressure altitude lines, as shown by position 5 on Figure 34. Now draw an intermediate value between the 3,000 and 3,500 foot pressure altitude line. This represents the 3,250 foot pressure altitude value. Move up the 75 degree F (24°C) line until reaching the pressure altitude line of 3,250, as shown by position 6 on Figure 34 (this is real close to the actual pressure altitude value of 3,257 feet). Go across to the left to find a density altitude value of approximately 5,000 feet.

Advanced Problem #4

Suppose you're flying a new Cessna 162 from an airport located at 9,702 feet MSL. The altimeter setting is 29.60 and the OAT is 95 degrees F (35 degrees C) (that's hot for an airport that high—better be careful!) What is the density altitude at that airport?

Using the pressure altitude conversion table in Figure 34 you determine that it's necessary to add 298 feet onto the true altitude to obtain a pressure altitude of 10,000 feet (298+9,702=10,000). Using the OAT of 95 degrees F (35°C) and a pressure altitude of 10,000 feet gives you a density altitude of 14,700 feet.

Fig. 34 Repeat

Postflight Briefing #14-2

Higher Knowledge: Cruise Performance (time and fuel planning)

By Steve King

Steve King

FAA regulations (FAR Part 91) require that you plan your VFR flight to include enough fuel to get to the destination with sufficient reserve to fly for 30 minutes during the day and 45 minutes at night. Realistically, you need to allow substantially more than that to protect against running out of fuel. The following suggestions will help you make safer decisions about how far you can safely go between fuel stops.

1. Assume 5% (x .95) less cruise airspeed than what is shown in the POH charts. Then, calculate actual TAS in flight to compare with your estimate. When you do this comparison, note the aircraft weight, since it will affect the cruise speed a little, especially at higher altitudes/lower power settings.

2. Assume 20% (x 1.2) more fuel consumption (GPH) than what is shown in the POH charts. Then, calculate actual GPH after a flight (using takeoff to landing time) to compare with your estimate.

3. For fairly good conditions, plan on having 1.5 hours of fuel left when you land to refuel. For good to excellent conditions, less than 1.5 hours reserve might be adequate. If flying with a smaller reserve, compare your actual progress (actual elapsed time to checkpoints) with your flight plan. For adverse conditions, you should have at least a 2 hour reserve, possibly more. Consider the following when you make decisions about fuel reserves:

- Day or night? It's wise to add about 1 hour *additional* fuel reserve at night. Why? There are greater consequences associated with running out gas when it's dark. Additionally, the extra fuel reserve helps in case you have difficulty with navigation (pilotage, for instance, is more difficult at night). And, since weather hazards are more difficult to detect at night, you might need the fuel to deviate to another airport. Finally, consider that fewer places sell fuel at night. You might need to travel to find a place that sells it.

- Ease of navigation? Is there any chance of being lost enroute, or of having difficulty in finding the destination?

- How many airports are along the route so you can land if you are low on gas or are behind schedule?

- How many of those airports sell gas? (See #5 below.)

- How good is the weather? If the weather is somewhat marginal, it may become necessary to leave the planned route for things like flying around clusters of thunderstorms. This could add significantly to the planned distance and time. Diverting from a planned route also increases the possibility of becoming lost, especially if the weather is poor. You really want to avoid the possibility that you might be lost (thus not knowing where you could go to land) and be low on fuel and in poor weather *all* at the same time!

- How hazardous is the terrain over which you are flying? For example, how does flying over water, over mountains or over very remote areas compare to following a freeway?

4. To fly with as little as one-half hour fuel reserve (assuming that you have previously assumed 95% TAS and 120% GPH), you should have ideal conditions including:

- Daytime flight, planned to end well before sunset. (Watch for delays that could affect this.)

- Very easy navigation, like following a freeway, with careful navigation planning—integrating pilotage, dead reckoning and electronic navigation.

- Many airports along the latter third of your route, *with fuel available* (you can use these as alternate fuel stops in case you fall behind schedule, or the ideal conditions deteriorate). (See #5 below.)

- Excellent weather, with essentially no chance of any weather problems. (Make sure you monitor the weather through Flight Watch, etc., during flight.)

- Non-hazardous terrain that's within easy gliding distance of a freeway, airport, or dry lake at all times during the latter third of the flight.

5. Before planning to depend on an airport or an alternate fuel stop (especially the one during last third of the route), verify that you will actually be able to get fuel at that location, by phoning ahead. Then, before descending from cruise to land at an airport when your fuel level is low, call on Unicom to verify fuel availability. If they don't respond, you might be able to safely fly to a nearby airport to refuel even though you wouldn't have enough fuel to land at the first airport, then take off and fly to the second airport. When you phone, check the following:

- How late are they open? If you fall behind schedule and arrive late, what are the chances of getting fuel at that airport?

- Do they have the type of fuel you need? Will they accept your form of payment? Some places only accept cash, traveler's checks (some don't accept these, or only certain brands because of counterfeiting concerns), or their own oil company credit card (often Phillips 66).

Steve King is professor and department head of the Professional Pilot Training Program at Long Beach City College located in Long Beach, California. He has been a pilot since 1965, an A&P since 1966 and is a certificated flight instructor.

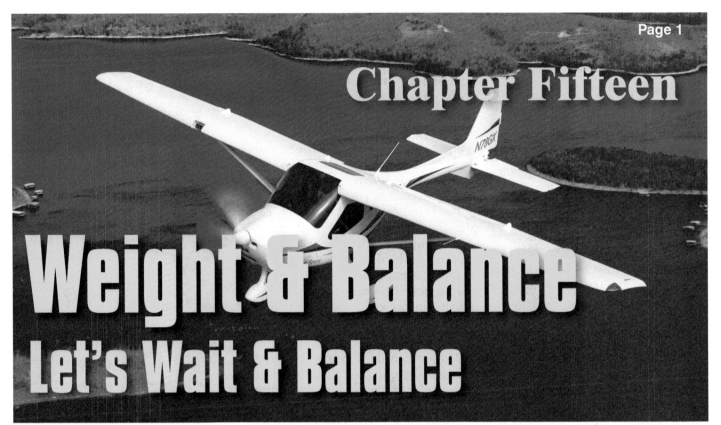

Chapter Fifteen

Weight & Balance
Let's Wait & Balance

All airplanes have limits on the maximum weight they can carry and where that weight is placed within the airplane. Within these limits, airplanes perform normally; outside of them, they behave erratically. Structural damage and in-flight stability are the two most important reasons why an airplane's weight is restricted, and why the weight must be distributed in a certain way. Calculating whether the plane is within its stated restrictions is referred to as doing a weight-and-balance calculation. It's a crucial part of your preflight planning.

Some pilots think the term is *wait and balance* and that it refers to time spent in the aviation medical examiner's office before he invites you in and asks you to jump up and down on one foot without having a heart attack.

A friend of mine found out the hard way what weight and balance really meant. Bob was a corporate pilot for a small Orange County firm. One day the boss wanted to take the company's A36 Bonanza on a ski trip. The plane was fully fueled when the boss arrived with enough ski gear to fill a 747.

Taxiing to the runup area, Bob turned the aft-heavy Bonanza into the wind and pressed the brakes.

Suddenly the nose started to rise—for no apparent reason. The airplane slowly and deliberately listed aft on the main gear. *Smack*. The nose pointed up, and the tail hit the ground.

Bob was thinking about how he might gain admission to the federal witness protection program. He was embarrassed for not having done a weight and balance computation before the flight. He was even more embarrassed at not having said "No"

to the obvious improper loading of an airplane. There was no telling how unsafe the airplane would have been had he taken off in this aft center of gravity condition.

Bob gave the airplane full power, righted it, taxied back to the tiedown area, and unloaded the aircraft. He refused to fly unless the plane was operated within the proper weight and balance limits. This was an embarrassing lesson, but one he would never forget.

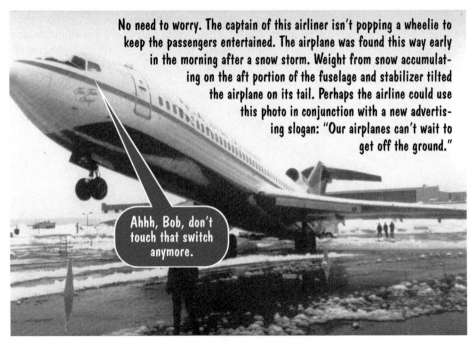

Ahhh, Bob, don't touch that switch anymore.

No need to worry. The captain of this airliner isn't popping a wheelie to keep the passengers entertained. The airplane was found this way early in the morning after a snow storm. Weight from snow accumulating on the aft portion of the fuselage and stabilizer tilted the airplane on its tail. Perhaps the airline could use this photo in conjunction with a new advertising slogan: "Our airplanes can't wait to get off the ground."

Excessive Weight And Structural Damage

Airplane wings are like bicycle tires in that both are designed to support a certain amount of weight. Too much weight could pop a bicycle's tire. Excessive weight can also damage a wing. Airplanes are designed to be flown up to a specific maximum gross weight. While it's possible to become airborne beyond this maximum certified weight, structural problems can arise when turbulence or high-G maneuvering enters the picture.

Think about it this way. If an airplane is certified in the utility category, it can withstand 4.4 positive Gs without structural damage. If this airplane has a maximum gross weight of 2,000 pounds, its wings are certified to withstand 4.4 times the maximum gross weight of 2,000 pounds or a total of 8,800 pounds. Distributing 8,800 pounds of force over the wings will bend them slightly. However, when the force is removed, the wings will flex back to their original position (this is good!).

Now, suppose you take off in the same airplane with a gross weight of 2,100 pounds. No doubt, the airplane easily becomes airborne when only 100 pounds over gross weight. But what happens if turbulence is encountered? If you experienced 4.4Gs, the airplane's wings must now support 9,240 pounds of weight (4.4 X 2,100). That's 440 pounds beyond the 8,800 pounds the engineers

planned for. You're now a test pilot and you are not getting hazardous duty pay. The risk of turbulence-induced damage has increased.

Flying beyond the maximum weight limits presents other problems. For instance, the stall speed increases at heavier weights. More weight requires the wings to move faster through the air before they can develop the minimum lift necessary to sustain flight. It takes more runway to attain this faster speed. The takeoff distance increases. You won't find a performance chart for "How much runway you'll need for takeoff when taking off over the maximum weight limit."

More weight also means less climb performance, higher fuel consumption, reduced range, higher landing speeds, longer landing distances. The list goes on and on. There is just no good reason to fly the airplane beyond its maximum gross weight limits. Pilots who insist on carrying all their friends in one airplane, regardless of their weight, should hang out with skinny people.

A friend of mine owned a small Cessna 150. This situation was unfortunate, since he weighed several hundred pounds (He was 370. That's incredible when you consider that 360 is a full circle). The only way he could fly the airplane and be within proper limits was to drain half the fuel from the tanks. This substantially shortened his range. Fortunately, his bladder was about the size of a BB and shortened range was never really a bother.

ALL OBJECTS HAVE A CENTER OF GRAVITY (CG)

Fig. 1

⊕ = Center of Gravity

I think I heard someone say Tartar sauce!!!

N2132B

Regardless of what the object is, it has a center of Gravity. A block of cheese, wrenches, tape cassette drives, and whales, as well as airplanes have a place where they would balance if picked up at that point. This point is known as the center of gravity.

Center of Gravity

The *center of gravity (CG)* of any object is the point where, if an imaginary finger lifted it, the object would balance (see Figure 1). For an object whose weight is evenly distributed along its length, such as a Popsicle stick, the CG is precisely at the center. For an object such as an airplane, where weight is *not* distributed evenly along its length, you have to calculate where the CG is.

Moving Moose

Many years ago, two hunters chartered an airplane to fly into the Alaskan wilderness for a hunting expedition. Two weeks later, when the pilot came to fly them out, he noticed the two large moose they shot and said, "I told you fellows that I could only take you and one moose. You'll have to leave the other one behind."

"But we did it last year in a plane this size," protested one hunter, "and the pilot gladly let us take both moose."

"Well, OK, if you did it before, then I suppose we can do it again," said the pilot. So the two moose and the hunters were loaded and the plane departed. Because of the heavy weight, the airplane struggled into the air. Barely climbing, the airplane was unable to clear the obstructing mountain—it crashed. Both men climbed from the wreckage and looked around. One hunter said to the other, "Where are we, anyway?" His companion looked around, and said, "I think we're about a half mile farther than we got last year."

If an airplane will return, unassisted, to level flight after its controls are disturbed, it is said to have *positive dynamic stability*. If the airplane won't return to its original flight configuration, and in fact keeps diverging farther from it in a series of oscillations, it is said to be exhibiting *negative dynamic stability*. Engineers tell us that for an airplane to be positively stable, its weight must not be concentrated too far aft. Weight concentrated too far forward may prevent sufficient pitch control to hold the nose up during landing. These forward and aft weight limits are known as the *center of gravity limits*, as shown in Figure 2.

Engineers know these limits because they have flight tested the airplane (while wearing parachutes) under variable load conditions. The results of this flight test information are provided to you in your airplane's weight and balance papers (always located in the airplane) or in an approved flight manual specifically modified for that airplane.

Beyond the aft CG limit, the airplane demonstrates negative dynamic stability in flight. For example, assume the airplane's weight is loaded within the allowable limits. If the controls are bumped as shown in Figure 3A, the airplane will oscillate up and down and eventually return to its previous level flight position. When the oscillations diminish in amplitude over time, it is a demonstration of positive dynamic stability. Now, assume the airplane is *not* loaded within its allowable limits and the controls are bumped, as shown in Figure 3B. The airplane exhibits negative dynamic stability because it moves farther away from its normal position.

Flying an airplane that is experiencing negative dynamic stability is about as safe as being the fourth crew member to beam down on a Star Trek show (you know something bad is going to happen to this person). Negative dynamic stability means you're always having to fight for control of your airplane. In extreme cases, you may not be able to get the airplane under control. You never want to operate under these conditions. Loading an airplane properly prevents this problem. If the airplane would balance on your finger anywhere between the forward and aft CG limits, it will be positively stable in flight (assuming also that the airplane's weight doesn't exceed its maximum allowable limit).

AN AIRPLANE'S FORWARD & AFT CENTER OF GRAVITY LIMIT

Forward CG limit

Aft CG limit

If the airplane's CG falls beyond its forward or its aft limits, it should be considered unsafe to fly.

CG limit exaggerated | Normal CG range

N2132B

⊕ = Center of Gravity

UNSAFE : SAFE : UNSAFE

Fig. 2

AIRPLANE STABILITY IN FLIGHT

Ⓐ **Airplane loaded within proper CG limits**
(positive dynamic stability)

Controls bumped

Amplitude of oscillations decrease

Fig. 3

Ⓑ **Airplane loaded outside proper CG limits**
(negative dynamic stability)

Hey! This is my demo flight!!!

Amplitude of oscillations increase

Controls bumped

An airplane loaded within its proper CG limits experiences positive dynamic stability. When the airplane is disturbed from level flight it pitches up and down with the amplitude of each oscillation decreasing as shown in position A. An airplane loaded beyond its aft CG limit experiences negative dynamic stability when it's disturbed from level flight. The amplitude of each oscillation increases as shown in position B. Airplanes loaded forward of their CG limit may not have sufficient pitch control to raise the nose during landing. Both conditions make the airplane difficult to control and unsafe to fly.

Longitudinal Stability

Longitudinal stability is the term used to describe the airplane's pitching motion. Since the airplane pitches about its lateral (sideways) axis, it's correct to say that *longitudinal stability* describes the airplane's pitching motion about its lateral axis.

Properly loaded airplanes are longitudinally stable. Any pitch away from a trimmed flight condition results in the airplane returning to its original pitch in a series of dampened, decreasing oscillations. The location of the CG with respect to the center of lift (see page 15-4) determines the airplane's longitudinal stability.

Lateral Stability

Lateral stability is the term used to describe the airplane's rolling motion. Since the airplane rolls about its longitudinal (long) axis, it's correct to say that *lateral stability* describes the airplane's motion about its longitudinal axis.

Airplanes with good lateral stability tend to favor a wings-level flight condition. They resist roll movement. Dihedral, weight placement and keel effect are common means of enhancing lateral stability (see glossary for the definition of *dihedral*).

AFT CG LOADING

In normal flight the center of lift is concentrated behind the CG. Since the airplane always rotates about its CG, the nose wants to pitch down.

Airplane wants to pitch nose down | Center of lift | **Fig. 4** Ⓐ N2132B

Airplane rotates about its CG | ⊕ = Center of Gravity

The tails on most airplanes help compensate for this nose down pitching tendency by creating lift in a downward direction.

Nose down pitch | Ⓑ Center of lift | Tail down pitch | N2132B

Lift by the tail (in the downward direction)

When the airplane increases its angle of attack (as when it slows), the center of lift moves forward along the wing. As long as the center of lift remains behind the CG, the airplane remains positively stable.

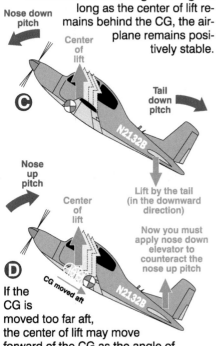

Nose down pitch | Center of lift | Ⓒ | Tail down pitch | N2132B

Nose up pitch | Center of lift | Ⓓ | Lift by the tail (in the downward direction) | Now you must apply nose down elevator to counteract the nose up pitch | CG moved aft | N2132B

If the CG is moved too far aft, the center of lift may move forward of the CG as the angle of attack increases. This makes the airplane unstable. It now wants to pitch up. You must apply nose down elevator. Under slow airspeed conditions, the nose may not want to go down (bad news!).

Note: All CG positions exaggerated for effect

Other CG Considerations

Negative dynamic stability isn't the only negative outcome of loading a plane outside its CG limits.

The lift an airplane develops is spread over the entire surface of its wings from the leading to the trailing edge. Like weight, lift can be thought of as being focused at one point called the *center of lift* (Figure 4A). (Also see the *Center of Lift* sidebar at the top of opposite page.)

Notice that the center of lift is located behind the CG. Since the airplane rotates about its CG, the wing's lifting force causes a constant nose-down tilting condition. This is why the tails of most airplanes (their horizontal stabilizers) are rigged to provide a downward force as shown in Figure 4B. A downward force on the tail compensates for the downward tilting force of the nose. This allows the airplane to remain controllable in flight (if you lost the tail in flight, you would lose control of the airplane).

As the angle of attack increases, the center of lift moves forward, toward the front of the wing as shown in Figure 4C. As long as the center of lift is behind the CG, the airplane still has a forward-pitching tendency. This is a good thing since this nose-downward pitching tendency acts to automatically reduce the angle of attack. The airplane naturally wants to keep itself away from high angles of attack where stalls occur. It also wants to automatically reduce its angle of attack in the event of a stall.

Moving the CG rearward, beyond the aft CG limit, is very dangerous. If the CG is too far aft, the center of lift, at high angles of attack, might move ahead of the CG, as depicted in Figure 4D. Now the airplane wants to pitch up and increase its angle of attack. You might have to apply a lot of forward elevator control to get the nose to pitch down. Under certain conditions (slow airspeeds and high angles of attack for instance) the airplane may not respond.

An aft CG condition can lead to violent stalls and flat spins. These

FORWARD CG LOADING

Airplane wants to pitch nose down | Center of lift | ⊕ = Center of Gravity | Ⓐ N2132B

CG is excessively far forward (exaggerated) | Large tail down force required to keep nose up

Nose down pitch becomes excessive | Center of lift | Ⓑ N2132B

CG is excessively far forward (exaggerated) | Airplane may not be able to generate sufficient tail down force to keep nose gear from hitting the runway first

When the CG is too far forward an excessive tail down force is required to keep the nose from pitching forward. While this may not present a problem in cruise flight, it may cause difficulty during landing. At the slower landing speeds, the elevator loses its effectiveness and can't compensate for the excessive nose down pitching. Nose gear damage is possible during the landing flare.

Fig. 5

are not good things. Fly like this and you'll feel like a chicken with the Colonel close behind. When flown within the proper CG limits, however, airplanes are perfectly safe. A pilot's job is to always make sure the CG remains within the limits.

An aft CG tends to give you lower stick forces, meaning that a slight touch on the controls causes a large, and sometimes uncontrollable oscillation of the nose. It's similar to the first time you drove a car with power steering—it's very easy to overcontrol. The airplane can be easily overstressed in this condition.

Airplanes loaded beyond the *forward* CG limit often fare no better. With the CG located ahead of the forward limit (Figure 5A), an excessive tail-down force is required to keep the nose up. During landing, as the airplane slows, there may not be enough airflow over the tail to generate this tail-down force. You might

THE CENTER OF LIFT

The center of lift is the point where the wing's total lifting force is concentrated. Think of it as the sum or the average of all the lifting forces spread across the wing (simulated by all the little black arrows). At low angles of attack the center of lift is found farther back along the wing as shown by wing A. As the angle of attack increases, all the little lifting forces move slightly. They tend to become more concentrated toward the front of the wing as shown by wing B. Therefore, as the angle of attack increases, the center of lift moves forward along the wing.

Airplanes are designed so that the center of lift always remains behind the center of gravity (assuming that your airplane is loaded properly). Since all objects rotate about their center of gravity, this causes the airplane to have a nose down pitching tendency. That's why the tail of an airplane must create a slight downward lifting force. This keeps the airplane from nosing end over end.

find yourself needing full, rearward elevator pressure just to keep the nose up during the flare (if it will stay up at all) as shown in Figure 5B. Excessive forward loading causes higher stalling speeds, decreased performance and higher stick forces.

Correct placement of the CG is obviously very important. But how do you measure its location? You can't go sticking your finger under an airplane and lifting it up every time you need to do a weight and balance. You can, however, use that dexterous digit to push calculator buttons or a pencil and find the CG through the magic of mathematics.

Just a Moment

To locate the center of gravity on an airplane you need to understand the concept of *moment* or tilting force. An airplane moment is different than a Kodak moment or a moment of time. A moment, as we're using the term here, is nothing more than a measure of the tilting force that weight imposes on an airplane. Figure 6A shows two 10 pound blocks placed on a plank at equal distances of five feet from the balance point. The plank is perfectly balanced (because of where the weights are placed). The plank's CG or balance point is located at the fulcrum (small triangle).

It's obvious that Block K causes the plank to tilt counterclockwise (to the left). Block R, on the other side of the plank, causes a similar tilt but in the clockwise direction (to the right). It's this tilting force that engineers refer to as the plank's moment. Since the plank balances, it should be obvious that the opposite tilting forces or moments caused by both blocks are opposite yet equal. They cancel out each other and the plank remains balanced at the fulcrum. Seeing is believing, but how do we prove this without actually performing the experiment?

We can prove that the plank is balanced by multiplying the individual weights by their distances from the fulcrum, then comparing these values. Before we

The result of multiplying the weight times its distance from a reference point (the fulcrum in this case) is the moment. A moment is the numerical value of the amount of tilt that an object produces. Block K and Block R both produce the same moment (tilting force) of 50 lb-ft in opposite directions about the fulcrum. Thus, the plank remains balanced.

do this, let's define a few terms. The word *weight* is self explanatory (it's what you measure with a scale). The distance that the weight is placed from the fulcrum is called the *arm*. The tilting force resulting from a certain weight being placed at a specific arm (distance) from the fulcrum is called the *moment*. To determine the moment, we simply multiply the weight times the arm. Figure 6B shows this formula.

At this point most people say, "Hey, you're using higher math, wait just a moment!" That's probably how they got the name for tilting force (not really). Many people treat math like the handle of a bathroom door. In their mind that handle is a Petri dish on a hinge—something to be avoided. Don't worry. The worst math you'll have to do is division (on the sport pilot knowledge exam you are welcome to use your calculator).

In Figure 6A, to obtain Block K's moment, simply multiply the weight of Block K times the arm (its distance from the fulcrum). You obtain 10 pounds × 5 ft=50 lb-ft of tilting force in the left or counterclockwise direction (we'll call this the negative direction). Do the same with Block R and you get 10 pounds × 5 ft=50 lb-ft of tilting force in the right or clockwise direction (we'll call this the positive direction), as shown in Figure 6B. It's obvious

MOMENTS ARE TILTING FORCES

This figure is repeated from the previous page for your convenience.

Fig. 6

The result of multiplying the weight times its distance from a reference point (the fulcrum in this case) is the moment. A moment is the numerical value of the amount of tilt that an object produces. Block K and Block R both produce the same moment (tilting force) of 50 lb-ft in opposite directions about the fulcrum. Thus, the plank remains balanced.

that both tilting forces or moments are equal and opposite in direction. This is mathematical proof that the plank balances at the fulcrum. (Since the moment is a product of a weight and a distance, the units of foot-pounds or inch-pounds follow its numerical value.)

Now let's make the problem a little more interesting (this is your instructor's way of saying I think you'll be stumped if I don't show this to you). Suppose we have two different weights located at different positions along the

MOMENTS ARE TILTING FORCES

Fig. 7

While Blocks P and Q have different weights, they produce the same moment about the reference point (the fulcrum). By multiplying their weights times their arms (distances from the fulcrum) you obtain a moment (tilting force) of 50 lb-ft for both blocks. Since the moments are equal but in opposite directions, the plank remains in balance.

plank as shown in Figure 7. Notice that the moments for Block Q are equal and opposite to the moments of Block P. The plank balances at the fulcrum. Despite the differences in weights and their positions along the plank, we can easily (with math) determine whether the plank will balance or tilt.

Now that you understand the concept of moments, let's find the center of gravity when the weights and moments are known. Figure 8A shows the same plank without a fulcrum. Our objective is to find where we should place the fulcrum so that the plank will balance. On the left side of Figure 8A is a datum line. This is nothing more than an arbitrary vertical reference line from which we'll measure our distances.

The datum line is easy to understand. For instance, I might ask you what your distance is from the Hawaiian island of Molokai (our datum reference). If you said 4,000 miles east, then I'd have an idea of your position. If you said you were 1,500 miles east of San Francisco (another datum reference) I'd still have an idea of your position, as long as I know which datum (or reference spot) I'm measuring from.

To find the center of gravity of the two weights in Figure 8A, we'll find the moment of Block Z about the datum line. Simply multiply Block Z's weight times its arm (its distance from the datum line—our new measuring reference). Do the same with Block W. These calculations are shown in Figure 8B. Remember, we're trying to find the point past the datum where these weights would balance if a finger or fulcrum were placed under the plank. Now add all the weights and moments up as shown in Figure 8B. These are the total weights and the total moments produced by these weights. Dividing the total moments by the total weights as shown in Figure 8C gives you the arm (distance) at which the plank balances. This distance is 10 feet to the right of the datum line. The arm represents the CG location of these two weights.

Notice how the CG is located in the same place in Figure 8D as it is in Figure 7. The general rule in finding the CG is to add up the individual weights, find the moments of these weights about the datum or reference line, then divide the moments by the total weight. This gives you the arm or the current CG location in inches or feet past the datum line. Finding the CG of an airplane is done in exactly the same way.

DETERMINING THE POSITION OF THE CG IN RELATION TO THE DATUM LINE

Fig. 8

(A)

Datum Line (Reference line)

Block Z
10 lb

Block W
5 lb

← 5 ft. →
← 20 ft. →

(B)

Weight x Arm = Moment
(weight) × (distance) = (twisting force)

Block Z's moment about datum line: (10 lb) x (5 ft) = 50 lb-ft ⟩+

Block W's moment about datum line: (5 lb) x (20 ft) = 100 lb-ft ⟩+

Total   15 lb   150 lb-ft

(C)

If: Weight x Arm = Moment, Then Arm = $\dfrac{\text{Total Moment}}{\text{Total Weight}}$

$\underset{\text{(new CG)}}{\text{Arm}} = \dfrac{\text{Total Moment}}{\text{Total Weight}} = \dfrac{150 \text{ lb-ft}}{15 \text{ lb}} = \underset{\text{(new CG)}}{\textbf{10 ft}}$

(D)

Datum Line (Reference line)

Block Z
10 lb

Block W
5 lb

← 5 ft. →
← 20 ft. →
← 10 ft. →

Center of gravity located here at 10 ft. from datum

A new reference point is chosen from which to measure the arm or *distance of weight placement* (section A). Called a *datum line*, both Block Z and W produce a specific tilting force about the datum line as in section B. When the total moment about the datum line of both Blocks (Z+W) is divided by the total weight of the blocks, the arm or center of gravity is found (section C). This new CG is located 10 feet past the datum or 5 feet past Block Z (similar to Block Q in Figure 7).

Talking on the Radio is More Frightening Than Doing Weight & Balance Problems

Talking on the radio can be a very uncomfortable experience. All you hear is a disembodied, deep, well modulated, resonant voice coming from overhead. And the last time someone heard that, it convinced him to build a boat (a big boat!).

When we push that mic button, it seems like our brain immediately disconnects from the nerves leading to our mouth and eyes. Our lips seem to flap like a fish on a pier, while nothing comes out. Sometimes our eyes seem to...

...bug out (their default position), and we can't think of a thing to say to the controller. Welcome to the club. Everyone experiences this at one time or another. Just remember, controllers are just like you and me. Just tell them you're a student and ask them to speak slower.

Nerves

Nerves

Some airplanes have datum lines located at the firewall or on the tip of the spinner, as shown in Figure 9. The datum line can be placed wherever the engineer chooses. It's a personal decision, much like how a flight instructor dresses (instructors are not snappy dressers, which explains why they are always asking their spouses, "Honey, does plaid go with a propeller hat?").

When datum lines are located at the firewall, then everything to the left of the datum line produces a negative value; and everything to the right, a positive value. For instance, oil, located to the left of a firewall datum line, produces a moment with a negative value. The negative moment must be subtracted from the total moments before dividing. Don't subtract the weight of the oil, since it is part of the total weight of the airplane.

We're almost ready to work an actual weight and balance problem. But first, we need to add a few more terms to your vocabulary:

1. *Maximum Takeoff Weight* – This is the maximum weight with which you can take off. This is sometimes referred to as the *maximum certificated gross weight* or *maximum gross weight*. The latter term is often shortened to *max gross* by pilots,

making it sound like it's someone they know. This weight is based on a structural limitation of the airplane.

2. *Empty Weight* – The weight of a standard airplane, including all nondrainable fluids (this includes unusable fuel, hydraulic fluid and nondrainable oil), all permanently installed equipment (radios, etc.). For some airplanes, the term *basic empty weight* might include engine oil. You should check your airplane's weight and balance information to specifically identify when oil is included in the basic empty weight. This information is always located inside the airplane and can be seen in Figure 10.

3. *Useful load* – The weight of the pilot, passengers, baggage, cargo, usable fuel and oil (if not included in basic empty weight). You can also think of the useful load as the difference between the maximum takeoff weight and the empty weight.

A very important formula to remember is:

The empty weight+the useful load=the gross weight

Aviation fuel weighs 6 pounds per gallon and oil weighs 7.5 pounds per gallon (watch out, that's per gallon, not per quart). It's important to know the exact weight of fuel since there are times when the airplane must be defueled to meet the maxi-

COMMON LOCATIONS OF THE DATUM LINE

The datum line is sometimes placed at the tip of the propeller spinner.

So this is what they mean by rentals half-off!

The datum line may also be placed at some arbitrary distance to the front of airplane.

The datum line may also be found at the firewall. **Fig. 9**

mum takeoff weight requirements. Many times airplanes are fueled the day or night before your flight. Deciding to carry an extra passenger or extra baggage the following day might require removing a certain amount of fuel from the tanks. The gas boy or girl (internal combustion liquid petroleum allocation manager) can do this.

THE AIRPLANE'S WEIGHT AND BALANCE INFORMATION

Fig. 10

Some Extra Weights

Two additional definitions may pop up from time to time. Keep them in mind.

A. *Maximum Ramp Weight* – During startup, taxi and runup, a certain amount of fuel is consumed. The maximum ramp weight includes this small fuel allowance with the assumption that, by the time the airplane is ready for takeoff, its weight will be at or below the maximum takeoff weight. This is not normally a consideration for small general aviation planes.

B. *Maximum Landing Weight* – The maximum weight approved for landing. This is also based on a structural limitation of the airplane. In other words, damage to the airframe is possible if a landing is attempted beyond this weight. For most smaller airplanes, the maximum landing weight is the same as the maximum takeoff weight. If an immediate return for landing were necessary after departure, you wouldn't need to concern yourself about possible weight-induced structural damage to the aircraft.

For example, if your airplane is 110 pounds over the maximum take-off weight, how much fuel must be drained to be within legal weight limits? The answer is approximately 18.3 gallons. Simply divide 110 by 6 pounds/gal of fuel.

Once you know the proper steps to take in solving a weight and balance problem, you'll whip right through the calculations. Believe me when I say it works. It's like using a sunblock with an SPF rating of 2,047. That stuff works! It not only blocks the sun, it makes it rain.

Don't Wait to Balance

Let's apply our new-found knowledge to solve the simple weight and balance problem shown in Figure 11A.

Figure 11A provides the airplane's empty weight along with the arm and moment associated with this weight. Figure 11B shows a visual representation of what the airplane loading might look like. The empty-weight arm is nothing more than the point where the weight of the empty airplane is concentrated (its CG). This arm is used in computing the empty-weight moment. Since the empty-weight moment is given to you in the airplane's weight and balance papers, you need not calculate it.

The pilot and front passenger weigh a combined 313 pounds. They will both sit at an arm (distance) of 39.8 inches aft of the datum. What moment do the pilot and passenger produce? Multiply their weight and arm together. You should get 12,457 lb-in. Fuel is next. We have 15.8 gallons of usable fuel on this flight. How much does that weigh? Multiply 15.8 times 6 pounds/gallon=95 pounds. The fuel tanks are located at an arm of 6.0 inches aft of the datum. What moment does the fuel produce? Multiply 95 pounds times 6.0 inches=570 lb-in.

To find the CG for the loaded airplane you must divide the total moments by the total weights. Remember, all three arms that are shown in the middle column of Figure 11A are only used in comput-

WORKING AN ACTUAL CG PROBLEM

A Fig. 11

	Weight (lb)	x	Arm (inches)	=	Moment (lb-in)
Empty weight	827.0		27.2		22,494
Pilot & front passenger	313.0		39.8		12,457
Fuel (15.8 gal.)	95.0		6.0		570
Baggage	31.0		60.4		1,872
Total	**1,266 lb**				**37,393 lb-in**

How far aft the datum is the CG located?

$$\text{Arm}_{(new\,CG)} = \frac{\text{Total Moment}}{\text{Total Weight}} = \frac{37,393\ \text{lb-in}}{1,266\ \text{lb}} = \textbf{29.5 in}_{(new\,CG\,aft\,datum)}$$

B

Datum Line

Front seat occupants

39.8"

Fuel

6.0"

Empty weight

27.2"

Baggage

60.4"

N2132B

CG

29.5"

Allowable forward CG limit (27.4") Allowable aft CG limit (32.5")

ing the moments. The arms aren't added since this would serve no purpose. The next time that you will use the concept of arm is when you divide the airplane's total moment by its total weight. The arm or distance is now the point where the full airplane would balance (i.e., its center of gravity).

Weight X Arm=Moment

Arm (CG)=Total Moments
⎯⎯⎯⎯⎯⎯⎯⎯
Total Weight

The total weight is 1,266 pounds. The total moments are 37,394 lb-in.

Divide the total moments by the total weight to get the CG arm (the distance from the datum where the weights balance). Dividing 37,394 by 1,266=29.5 inches—the center of gravity as shown in Figure 11B.

Considering that forward and aft CG limits are usually expressed in inches past the datum line, we can easily tell if the CG is within the appropriate limits for safe flight. Suppose the forward CG limit was set at 27.4 inches and the aft limit was 32.5 inches. In this instance, the airplane falls within the proper CG limits.

Bob attempts to honor the controller's request by extending his downwind leg.

Credit to Gwen Ledbetter for this joke.

A Different Type Of Weight and Balance Chart

One of the most popular weight and balance charts that exists for light sport airplanes is shown below (Figure 12). What makes this configuration so interesting is that there is no multiplication used in finding moments. The loading graph in Figure 12A has weights along the vertical axis and moments/100 along the horizontal axis. A reduction factor of 100 is used for the moments, but, as you'll see, you don't have to worry about using a reduction factor when using this format. To find the moments for specific weights, simply proceed horizontally along the weight lines. When reaching the desired diagonal line (for pilot, passenger, fuel or baggage) drop straight down to find the moments. That's easy!

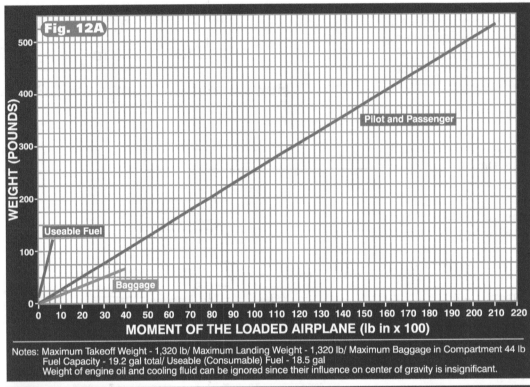

Notes: Maximum Takeoff Weight - 1,320 lb/ Maximum Landing Weight - 1,320 lb/ Maximum Baggage in Compartment 44 lb
Fuel Capacity - 19.2 gal total/ Useable (Consumable) Fuel - 18.5 gal
Weight of engine oil and cooling fluid can be ignored since their influence on center of gravity is insignificant.

When the total moments and weights are tallied, simply proceed to the center of gravity/moment envelope shown in Figure 12B. Compare weights and moments to see if they fall within the envelope. Using this simple format, you'll be able to do weight and balance problems while using only 50cc's of your turbocharged 1400cc brain.

Weight and Balance: Problem No. 1 – Using the airplane loading information shown in Figure 13A, determine if the airplane is within its proper CG limits. Figure 13B shows the solution for this problem. Figures 14A and 14B show the solution on the loading graph and CG/moment envelope.

This is a relatively straightforward weight and balance problem. Nothing tricky here. You should use caution, however, when calibrating moments from weights in Figure 12A. It's very easy to move up or down a line and end up with an incorrect moment. Watch the calibration for the individual chart lines. In Figure 12A, notice that each line along the weight (vertical) scale is calibrated in 25 pound increments while each line along the moment (horizontal) scale is calibrated in values of 2.5 (in-lb/100). In figure 12B, each line along the weight scale is calibrated in 10 pound increments while each line along the moment scale is calibrated in values of 5.0 (in-lb/100).

WEIGHT AND BALANCE PROBLEM NO. 1

Using the loading graph in Figure 12A and the center of gravity envelope in Figure 12B, determine if the airplane is within the proper CG limits based on the information below.

Fig. 13A	Weight	X Arm	= Moment-lb/in
E - Empty weight	827.0 lb	27.2 in	22,494
P - Pilot & front seat occupant	310 lb	39.8 in	....
F - Fuel (13 gallons)........................	78 lb	6 in	....
B - Baggage	20 lb	60.4 in	....

SOLUTION TO PROBLEM NO. 1

Step 1. Using the loading graph in Figure 12A, find the individual moments for the weights listed below. Remember that the weight of the oil and the engin cooling fluid is included in the airplane's empty weight for this airplane. (See note on at bottom of Figure 13B.)

Fig. 13B	Weight	X Arm	= Moment-lb/in
E - Empty weight	827lb	27.2 in	22,494
P - Pilot & front seat occupant	310 lb	39.8 in	12,338
F - Fuel (13 gallons)........................	78 lb	6 in	468
B - Baggage	20 lb	60.4 in	1,208

Step 2. Add the totals and divide the moment by 100. **Totals** 1,235 lb   365.1 **lb-in** / **100**

Step 3. Using the center of gravity/moment envelope in Figure 12B, match the total weights on the left vertical axis against the total moments on the bottom horizontal axis. Since both values meet at a point within the envelope, the airplane is within the proper CG limits for safe flight. Figures 14A & 14B show how I calculated the moments and made the CG determination.

Weight and Balance: Problem No. 2 – The next problem, in Figure 15A, requires you to determine the maximum amount of baggage that can be carried in the airplane after all the other items have been loaded. Solving this problem simply requires you to find the current loaded weight of the airplane and subtract that from the maximum allowable weight. The difference is the amount of baggage (or any other item you're interested in) that can be carried onboard. After you determine the allowable weight of baggage, you must make sure that carrying this weight still keeps the airplane within its proper CG limits. Figures 15B, 16A and 16B show the solution to this problem.

WEIGHT AND BALANCE PROBLEM NO. 2

Using the loading graph in Figure 12A and the center of gravity/moment envelope shown in Figure 12B, determine the maximum amount of baggage that can be loaded aboard the airplane for the CG to remain within the center of gravity/moment envelope.

Fig. 15A	Weight	X Arm	= Moment-lb/in
E - Empty weight	827 lb	27.2 in	22,494
P - Pilot & front seat occupant	340 lb	39.8 in	....
F - Fuel (18.5 gallons)......................	111 lb	6 in	....
B - Baggage	X? lb	60.4 in	....
Totals	1,278 lb		

Step 1. You can determine this value by finding the airplane's maximum allowable gross weight, which is 1,320 lb. I determined this by looking at the upper limit of the normal category CG/moment envelope in Figure 12B. Now subtract the present loaded weight from the maximum allowable gross weight to obtain (1,320 - 1,278 = 42 lb). The maximum allowable weight we can carry in the airplane without exceeding the airplane's maximum gross weight is 42 pounds. But you do need to be sure that this value doesn't exceed the baggage compartment's maximum allowable weight which, according to the note at the bottom of the loading envelope in Figure 12B, is 44 pounds.

Step 2. Now add the weight of the baggage (42 pounds) and its moment as determined from Figure 12A (calculated as shown in Figure 16A) to the totals you found in step 1. The baggage produces a moment of 2,536.8 in-lb. This gives you a total weight of 1,320 lb and a total moment of 392.28 lb-in.

SOLUTION TO PROBLEM NO. 2

Fig. 15B	Weight	X Arm	= Moment-lb/in
E - Empty weight	827lb	27.2 in	22,494
P - Pilot & front seat occupant	340 lb	39.8 in	13,532
F - Fuel (18.5 gallons)......................	111 lb	6 in	666
B - Baggage	42 lb	60.4 in	2,536.8
Totals	1,320 lb		392.28 lb-in / 100

Step 3. Using the center of gravity/moment envelope in Figure 12B, determine whether or not the airplane is within its proper CG limits. The intersection of the total weight and total moment fall within the loaded aircraft moment envelope as shown in Figure 16B.

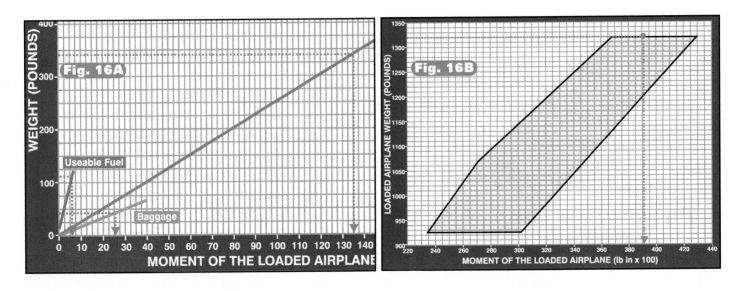

Weight and Balance: Problem No. 3 – Figure 17 is our final problem. This problem is similar to problem No. 2. Instead of finding the maximum amount of baggage that you can carry, this problem asks you to determine the maximum amount of fuel that can be carried aboard the aircraft for takeoff. It's solved in precisely the same way as problem No. 6. Solving this problem simply requires you to find the current loaded weight of the airplane without fuel and subtract that from the maximum weight allowable for that airplane. The difference is the amount of fuel that can be carried on board. You must, however, make sure that the fuel allowed by this calculation doesn't exceed the maximum amount of fuel that the tanks can hold. After you determine the allowable weight of fuel, you must make sure that carrying this weight still keeps the airplane within its proper CG limits. Figures 17, 18A and 18B show the solution to this problem.

Weight and balance is quite serious and necessary for safety. With modern day, handheld calculators, you should be able to do weight and balance problems for your airplane in seconds. Onto our last chapter: Pilot Potpourri.

SOLUTION TO PROBLEM NO. 3

Step 1. Using the loading graph in Figures 12A and B, you determine the individual moments for the weights listed to the right (except for the fuel which is our unknown). Figure 16A shows how these moments were derived.

Fig. 17	Weight	X	Arm	=	Moment-lb/in
E - Empty weight	827lb		.........in		22,494
P - Pilot & front seat occupant	360 lb		.........in		14,328
F - Fuel	X? lb		.........in		X?
B - Baggage	20 lb		.........in		1,208

Step 2. Add the totals ⟶ **Totals** 1,207 lb $\frac{380.30}{100}$ **lb-in**

Step 3. Using the upper limit of the center of gravity/moment envelope in Figure 12B, we determine that our maximum allowable gross weight is 1,320 lb. Subtracting 1,207 lb from 1,320 lb allows us to carry 113 lb of fuel, which is equal to 18.8 gallons. The problem is that the airplane is limited to carrying 18.5 gallons of useable fuel, which weighs 111 pounds. So, despite the weight and balance allowing us to carry 18.8 gallon, the answer to the question is actually 18.5 gallons based on the airplane's fuel tank limitations. According to Figure 12A, 111 pounds of fuel produces a moment of 666 lb-in.

Step 4. Adding the fuel weight and its moment to the totals in step 2 gives us a new total weight of 1,318 pounds and a new total moment of 386.96 lb-in/100.

Step 5. Using the center of gravity/moment envelope shown in Figure 12B, we determine that the center of gravity is within proper limits for safe flight.

Postflight Briefing #15-1

Now that you have an understanding of the basic principles of weight and balance, you might want to consider working a few different types of weight and balance problems using charts from airplanes larger than your typical light sport airplane. Why? It turns out that a few of these problems are still showing up on your sport pilot knowledge exam. The practice, however, will certainly help you understand different types of weight and balance charts.

Fig. 19 USEFUL LOAD WEIGHTS AND MOMENTS

 A OCCUPANTS

FRONT SEATS ARM 85		REAR SEATS ARM 121	
Weight	Moment 100	Weight	Moment 100
120	102	120	145
130	110	130	157
140	119	140	169
150	128	150	182
160	136	160	194
170	144	170	206
180	153	180	218
190	162	190	230
200	170	200	242

B USABLE FUEL

MAIN WING TANKS ARM 75		
Gallons	Weight	Moment 100
5	30	22
10	60	45
15	90	68
20	120	90
25	150	112
30	180	135
35	210	158
40	240	180
44	264	198

 C BAGGAGE OR 5TH SEAT OCCUPANT ARM 140

Weight	Moment 100
10	14
20	28
30	42
40	56
50	70
60	84
70	98
80	112
90	126
100	140
110	154
120	168
130	182
140	196
150	210
160	224
170	238
180	252
190	266
200	280
210	294
220	308
230	322
240	336
250	350
260	364
270	378

D AUXILIARY WING TANKS ARM 94

Gallons	Weight	Moment 100
5	30	28
10	60	56
15	90	85
19	114	107

E *OIL

Quarts	Weight	Moment 100
10	19	5

*Included in basic Empty Weight

Basic **Empty Weight** ~ 2015

F MOM / 100 ~ 1554

MOMENT LIMITS vs WEIGHT

Moment limits are based on the following weight and center of gravity limit data (landing gear down).

G

WEIGHT CONDITION	FORWARD CG LIMIT	AFT CG LIMIT
2950 lb (takeoff or landing)	82.1	84.7
2525 lb	77.5	85.7
2475 lb or less	77.0	85.7

15-15

Fig. 20   **MOMENT LIMITS vs WEIGHT (Continued)**

Weight	Minimum Moment 100	Maximum Moment 100	Weight	Minimum Moment 100	Maximum Moment 100
2100	1617	1800	2600	2037	2224
2110	1625	1808	2610	2048	2232
2120	1632	1817	2620	2058	2239
2130	1640	1825	2630	2069	2247
2140	1648	1834	2640	2080	2255
2150	1656	1843	2650	2090	2263
2160	1663	1851	2660	2101	2271
2170	1671	1860	2670	2112	2279
2180	1679	1868	C 2680	2123	2287
2190	1686	1877	2690	2133	2295
2200	1694	1885	2700	2144	2303
2210	1702	1894	2710	2155	2311
2220	1709	1903	2720	2166	2319
2230	1717	1911	2730	2177	2326
2240	1725	1920	2740	2188	2334
2250	1733	1928	2750	2199	2342
2260	1740	1937	2760	2210	2350
2270	1748	1945	2770	2221	2358
2280	1756	1954	2780	2232	2366
2290	1763	1963	D 2790	2243	2374
2300	1771	1971			
2310	1779	1980	2800	2254	2381
2320	1786	1988	2810	2265	2389
2330	1794	1997	2820	2276	2397
2340	1802	2005	2830	2287	2405
2350	1810	2014	2840	2298	2413
2360	1817	2023	2850	2309	2421
2370	1825	2031	2860	2320	2428
2380	1833	2040	2870	2332	2436
2390	1840	2048	2880	2343	2444
			E 2890	2354	2452
2400	1848	2057	2900	2365	2460
2410	1856	2065	2910	2377	2468
2420	1863	2074	2920	2388	2475
2430	1871	2083	2930	2399	2483
2440	1879	2091	2940	2411	2491
2450	1887	2100	A 2950	2422	2499
2460	1894	2108			
2470	1902	2117			
2480	1911	2125			
2490	1921	2134			
2500	1932	2143			
B 2510	1942	2151			
2520	1953	2160			
2530	1963	2168			
2540	1974	2176			
2550	1984	2184			
2560	1995	2192			
2570	2005	2200			
2580	2016	2208			
2590	2026	2216			

Figures 19 and 20 (previous page) provide you with information that might come from a typical airplane. As you'll soon see, doing a real weight and balance is easier than it looks.

Figure 19 provides us with the moments for the variable weights of occupants, usable fuel, baggage, auxiliary fuel and oil (oil for this airplane is included in the basic empty weight). The bottom right hand corner (Block G) informs us about the forward and aft CG limits for variable weight conditions. What's nice about this chart is that, in many instances, it's often not necessary to do multiplication to find the moments. For example, assume you wanted to find the moment of the front seat occupants weighing 320 pounds (that's two people, not one big guy!).

Look in the weight column in Block A and find the moments for any weight combinations that add up to 320. For instance, 120 pounds produces a moment of 102 and 200 pounds produces a moment of 170. Adding these together gives you a moment of 272.

Notice that Block A shows that all the moments are divided by 100. Why? This is known as a reduction factor and it makes large moments easier to work with. Since the front seat arm is 85 (you can assume the distance is in inches), multiplying 85 inches × 320 pounds=27,200 lb-in of moment. When divided by a reduction factor of 100 we still arrive at a moment of 272 lb-in (27,200/100 = 272).

Of course, when you're done computing all the moments, you'll want to multiply the total moments by 100 to be able to compute the actual CG. (Or you can move the decimal two places to the right—it's the same thing).

Suppose the weights are between the values shown in the columns, such as 295 pounds. There is no moment value listed for 295 pounds The best way to handle this is do the math and simply multiply the weight times the arm for that location to get the moment (remember the reduction factor of 100).

The same procedure for finding moments is used for rear seats (Block A), usable fuel (Block B), baggage or 5th seat occupant (Block C), auxiliary wing tank fuel (Block D) and oil (Block E). Remember, the weight of the oil and its moment are included in this airplane's basic empty weight. Therefore, don't include oil in this weight and balance problem.

Block F provides you with the basic empty weight and its moment divided by the reduction factor of 100. Block G informs you of the forward and aft CG limits for variable weight conditions.

> *To avoid becoming complacent during the preflight, try doing your walkaround opposite to the direction in which you normally do it..*

OK, let's try it.

Basic Weight and Balance: Problem No. 1 – Using the weight and balance information in Figures 19 and 13, and the loading information given below, determine if the airplane's weight and balance is within safe limits.

Front seat occupants .... 320 pounds

Rear seat occupants .... 295 pounds

Fuel (main wing tanks) ...... 44 gallons

Baggage .... 56 pounds

Before you start, let's remember the big picture here. What you're going to do is find the tilting force produced by all the individual weights to be carried on the airplane by using the Useful Load Weights and Moments chart (Figure 19). Then you'll add all these weights together and add all the moments together. Take these two sums over to the Moment Limits vs. Weight chart (Figure 20). This chart lets you determine if the combination of total weight and total moments allows the airplane to operate within its allowable CG limits.

Now don't worry. I'm going to walk you through this first problem in great detail as shown in Figure 21. Not only will I show you how to proceed, step-by-step, but I'll give you a visual representation of what the loaded airplane would look like in Figure 22. OK, are you ready? Now go to Figure 21 and follow each step in the solution of this problem. Return here when you're done.

Now that wasn't too bad was it? I'm going to show you how to make solving this type of problem even easier. But first, here are a few additional points to remember when doing this type of problem.

To compute the moment of the front seat occupants you need to refer to Figure 19 (Block A, section #1) and find the moments for 200 pounds and 120 pounds, then add these together. You do this because there is no posted moment for 320 pounds. The weight of the baggage isn't listed in Figure 19 (Block C). You can find its moment, however, by multiplying the arm (140) by 56 pounds. When preparing to divide the total moments by the total weights, don't forget to move the decimal of the total moments over two places to the right to compensate for the reduction factor of 100.

The result of Figure 21 (step #9) shows that at a weight of 2,950 pounds we have a CG of 83.4 inches. Figure 19 (Block G) indicates that we are right at the maximum gross weight of the airplane for takeoff or landing. At a weight of 2,950 pounds our CG of 83.4 inches falls within the posted forward and aft limits. We are legal and safe to fly. Figure 22 shows a pictorial representation of how this airplane is loaded.

What if our totaled weights were different than the limits shown in Figure 19 (Block G)? Fortunately, the Pilot's Operating Handbook or the plane's weight and balance papers come with a moment-limit vs. weight chart to help determine if the airplane is within weight and balance limits. Figure 20 shows such a chart. This

WEIGHT & BALANCE PROBLEM NO. 1

Fig. 21

Determine if the airplane's weight and balance are within safe limits. (Use Figure 19 & 20.)

Pilot & front seat occupants.......	320 lb
Rear seat occupants..................	295 lb
Fuel (6 lb/gal)...........................	44 gallons
Baggage.................................	56 lb

These are the numbers you should have computed.

Step 1: See Figure 19(F) to find the basic empty weight and its moment.

Step 2: See Figure 19(A1) to find the moment for 120 lb and 200 lb of front seat occupants.

Step 3: See Figure 19(A2). Since the exact weight of our rear seat occupants doesn't appear in the table, we must multiply their weights times the arm of the rear seat (121"). This gives the moments of the rear seat occupants.

Step 4: See Figure 19(B) to find the moment for 44 gal. of fuel (note: don't forget to use the listed weight of the fuel (264 lb). (i.e., Don't list the gal. in the weight column.)

Step 5: See Figure 19(C) to find the moment for the baggage. Since no moment is listed for 56 lb, multiply this times the arm of 140" & divide by 100 to obtain the moment of the baggage.

Step 6: See Figure 19(E) The note says that oil is included in the basic empty weight, so we don't need to do anything here.

Step 7: Add the total weight and the total moments. You don't need to add the total arms since this is meaningless.

Step 8: Move the decimal place of the total moments two digits to the right to correct for the reduction factor of moment/100.

	Weight	X Arm	= Moment/100
E - Empty weight (basic).................	2,015 lb	.........in	1,554.0
P - Pilot & front seat occupants.......	320 lb	85 in	272.0
R - Rear seat occupants..................	295 lb	121 in	357.0
F - Fuel (6 lb/gal)...........................	264 lb	75 in	198.0
B - Baggage.................................	56 lb	140 in	78.4
O - Oil (included in basic empty weight)..	.........lb	.........in	....
Totals	**2,950 lb**		**2,459.4 lb-in / 100**

Divide the total moments by the total weight

Arm or CG = $\frac{\text{total moments}}{\text{total weight}}$ $\frac{2,459.4\ (100)}{2,950\ \text{lb}}$ = $\frac{245,940\ \text{lb-in}}{2,950\ \text{lb}}$

Arm of CG = 83.4 inches aft of the datum line

Step 9: Compute the CG by dividing the total moments by the total weight.

Step 10: Determine if the CG and weight fall within acceptable limits by looking at Figure 19(G).

chart makes the computations easier since it allows you to determine proper loading without having to divide the total moments by the total weights. In other words, you compare total weight with the total moment to determine if the airplane is within proper CG limits. In this problem, the total moments was 2,459.4 (moment/100) and the total weights was 2,950 pounds. Compare the weight against the minimum and maximum moment limit (Figure 20, position A) and you'll see that we fall within acceptable limits for flight.

You may be wondering, "How do I know what items to include in the weight and balance calculations?" That's an excellent question. The following letter sequence provides you with an easy way to remember the items to include in a weight and balance calculation: EPRFBO. This stands for Every Pilot Regrets Flying Barely Overweight. (E) is for empty weight, (P) for pilot and front passenger, (R) for rear seat passengers, (F) for fuel, (B) for baggage and (O) for oil (if not included in the basic empty weight). When given a weight and balance problem to solve, simply list these letters

WEIGHT & BALANCE PROBLEM NO. 1
VISUAL EXAMPLE

Fig. 22

Fig. 23

WEIGHT AND BALANCE FORMAT

	Weight X	Arm =	Moment/100
E - Empty weight (basic).................	lb	in	
P - Pilot & front seat occupants.......	lb	in	
R - Rear seat occupants..................	lb	in	
F - Fuel (6 lb/gal)...........................	lb	in	
B - Baggage.................................	lb	in	
O - Oil (7.5 lb/gal).........................	lb	in	
Totals			**lb-in / 100**

A wise man says, "A pilot should always stay three mistakes above the ground.

vertically and write W × A=M (Weight × Arm=Moment) equation across the top of the page as shown in Figure 23. Then proceed to fill in the appropriate weights and moments.

Basic Weight and Balance: Problem No. 2 – OK, let's try a problem similar to the previous one. Take a piece of paper and draw the acronym EPRFBO on the left hand side and W × A=M across the top. Use the loading information below and Figures 19 and 20 to determine if the weight and balance is within safe limits:

Front seat occupants .... 415 pounds

Rear seat occupants 110

Fuel, main and aux tanks .... 63 gallons (both tanks full)

Baggage .... 32 pounds

Figure 24 shows the numbers you should have derived.

Consulting Block G in Figure 19 we see that the airplane's weight is within limits but the CG of 81.0 inches is 1.1 inches forward of the allowable limit. We can come to the same conclusion referring to Figure 20, position A. The moments don't fall within the allowable minimum and maximum shown on the chart. For the airplane to be legal for flight we'd need to increase the total moment. In other words, we'd need to move some weight rearward (we can't add more weight because we're already at the airplane's maximum weight limit of 2,950 pounds.) We might solve the problem by rearranging some of the passengers or moving some baggage.

There are formulas for figuring out how much weight to move and what distance to move it. They are, however, beyond the scope of this book. Personally, I would recommend just taking a guess at how much movement or reduction in weight is necessary to put the airplane within allowable CG limits, then working another problem to see if the results are successful. This doesn't take long at all when you are changing only one or two variables.

Hey, you're doing well. Once you understand the basics, the rest of these weight and balance problems should be fairly easy. There is, however, no better way to learn to do these problems than to jump in and give them a try. So, let's move onto something known as a weight change problem.

WEIGHT AND BALANCE PROBLEM NO. 2

Determine if the airplane's weight and balance are within safe limits. (Use Figures 19 and 20.)

Pilot & front seat occupants.......	415 lb
Rear seat occupants..................	110 lb
Fuel (main & aux tanks both full)	63 gallons
Baggage..................................	32 lb

These are the numbers you should have computed.

Fig. 23

	Weight X	Arm =	Moment/100
E - Empty weight (basic).................	2,015 lb	..........in	1,554.0
P - Pilot & front seat occupants.......	415 lb	85 in	352.8
R - Rear seat occupants..................	110 lb	121 in	133.1
F - Fuel (main) (44 gal. x 6 lb/gal)...	264 lb	75 in	198.0
(aux) (19 gal. x 6 lb/gal)...	114 lb	94 in	107.0
B - Baggage.................................	32 lb	140 in	44.8
O - Oil (included in basic empty weight)..	..........lb	..........in	....
Totals	**2,950 lb**		**2,389.7 lb-in / 100**

Divide the total moments by the total weights

Arm or CG = total moments 2,389.7 (100) = 238,970 lb-in / total weights = 2,950 lb

Arm of CG = 81.0 inches aft of the datum line **Fig. 24**

WEIGHT CHANGE PROBLEM NO. 3

Determine if the airplane's weight and balance are within safe limits. (Use Figure 19 & 20.)

Step 1. What is the weight change?	
Original weight of airplane	2,690 lb
Departing passenger	180 lb
New weight	2,510 lb

Step 2. How does the total moment change?	Weight	X Arm	= Moment/100
Original weight	2,690 lb		2,260.0
Passenger exiting front	-180 lb	85 in	-153.0
Passenger exiting rear	-204 lb	121 in	-246.8
Passenger into front	+204 lb	85 in	+173.4
New weight	2,510 lb		
New moment			2,033.6

Step 3. What is the new CG?
Divide the total moments by the total weights to find the new CG.
Total moments x 100 = 203,360 lb-in
Total weights   2,510 lb
New CG = 81" (position B on Figure 20)

Step 4. Answer the original question.
The original question asked what effect does this weight shift and change have on the original CG? To find out you need to know what the original CG was. Since you were given the total moments and weights before shifting, this is easy to compute:
Total original moments..2,260 x 100 = 226,000 lb-in
total original weight...........................= 2,690 lb
Original CG ....= 84"
You can see that the CG moved 3 inches (84-81=3) toward the datum line.

Weight Change: Problem No. 3 – Upon landing, the front seat passenger (180 pounds) departs the airplane (after it comes to a stop, fortunately). A rear passenger (204 pounds) moves to the front passenger position. What effect does this have on the CG if the airplane weighed 2,690 pounds and the moment/100 was 2,260 just prior the passenger transfer?

We'll use the same weight and balance information given in Figure 19 and 20 to solve this problem. Before you proceed, I want you to think about the problem in a step-by-step way as follows:

Step 1. To determine the final CG, you need to know the airplane's total weight and total moment. Ask yourself how much the total weight of the airplane changes.

Step 2. If any weight moves on the airplane (but doesn't exit or enter the airplane), its moment changes. In other words, the weight's moment before moving must be subtracted from the total moment. Then its new moment, based on its new location, must be added to the total moment once again.

Step 3. Divide the total moment by the total weight to obtain the new CG.

Step 4. Go back to the original problem and make sure you answer the question that was asked.

Fig. 25

Figure 25 shows how to proceed with the problem using the steps listed above. Go back and review the other problems to get a good feel for how this one was solved.

I do hope you believe me when I say that once you practice a few more problems, weight and balance is going to be a snap. Problem No. 3 dealt with weight change. Every time you fly you'll need to consider similar problems since the consumption of fuel changes and shifts the airplane's CG. Problem No. 4 deals with a changing CG based on the burning of fuel.

STEP RIGHT UP, GUESS Y'ER WEIGHT

I flew my airplane to an airshow. As in the past, I removed the operating handbook, which included the weight and balance data. I didn't want the book to be damaged by the maneuvers required in the aerobatic flight. Also, I took along a friend who weighed 240 lb. Upon arriving, an inspector immediately approached me wanting to know how much my passenger weighed. He thought I was over gross and out of CG. He asked me to do a weight and balance computation, to which I responded by telling him I didn't have the information in the airplane. Realizing my problem, I immediately grounded the airplane and didn't fly in the airshow. Later, I did a weight and balance computation and found the airplane had been 75 lb. over gross for operations in the normal category, but within CG limits. I believe it would be helpful to clarify the importance of having the proper paperwork in all airplanes.

ASRS Report

Fuel Burn Weight and Balance: Problem No. 4 – What effect does a 35 gallon fuel burn (main tanks) have on the weight and balance if the airplane weighed 2,890 pounds and the moment/100 was 2,452 at takeoff?

Refer to the weight and balance information in Figures 19 and 20 to solve this problem. Keep in mind that the same principles used in problem No. 3 are used in solving this problem. Fuel burn is nothing more than a weight and moment change problem. In this instance, weight (fuel) is leaving the airplane; therefore, the moment is also changing.

Figure 26 (below) shows how to proceed with the problem.

It's important to compute the CG change for fuel consumption. As is evident from this problem, the CG shifted aft as fuel was consumed. It may be necessary to shift weight in flight or prior to takeoff to compensate for this. Expect to have a problem like this when the CG, prior to takeoff, is near the aft or forward limit.

In the following problem, we have an airplane that's out of its safe CG limits and can't take off. The weight is within limits, but the CG is forward of the allowable limit. This doesn't mean you can't fly! All you usually need do is move some of the weight around to place the CG within its acceptable limits. Knowing how to calculate this is a valuable skill to have.

FUEL BURN PROBLEM NO. 4 **Fig. 26**

Determine if the airplane's weight and balance are within safe limits. (Use Figure 19 & 20.)

Step 1. What is the weight change?
35 gallons of fuel (6 lb/gal) 6 x 35 = 210 lb weight loss.

Step 2. How does the total moment change?
Using Figure 19, block B, 210 lb of fuel located at an arm of 75" equals a moment change of -158 lb-in/100. Remember, the weight is decreasing, therefore its moment is also decreasing.

Step 3. What is the new CG?

	Weight	Moment/100
Original weight	2,890 lb	2,452.0
Final weight loss	-210 lb	-158.0
New weight	2,680 lb	
New moment		2,294.0

New CG equals: Total moments 229,400 lb-in
Total weight 2,680 lb
New CG position = 85.6"

Step 4. Answer the original question.
The original question asked about the effect a 35 gallon fuel burn has on the CG. Using Figure 20, position C, we can see that at a weight of 2,680 lb, our new moment of 2,294.0 lb-in/100 is clearly beyond the limit for this weight. Even though our weight has been reduced by 210 lb, our CG is aft of limits (if the moment is greater than the maximum limit, the CG must also be aft of limits).

WEIGHT SHIFT PROBLEM NO. 5

With the airplane loaded as follows, what action must be taken to place the airplane within the proper CG limits (Use Figure 19 & 20.)

Fig. 27

Front seat occupants	411 lb
Rear seat occupants	100 lb
Main wing tanks	44 gallons

Step 1. Determine the present CG condition.

	Weight	X Arm	= Moment/100
E - Empty weight (basic)	2,015 lb	......in	1,554.0
P - Pilot & front seat occupants	411 lb	85 in	349.4
R - Rear seat occupants	100 lb	121 in	121.0
F - Fuel (main) (44 gal.x 6 lb-gal)	264 lb	75 in	198.0
B - Baggage	.........lb	.....in	....
O - Oil (included in basic empty weight)	.........lb	.....in	....
Totals	**2,790 lb**		**2,222.4** lb-in / 100

Step 2. Shift or add weight to get CG back in limits.
Using the moment limit vs. weight chart in Figure 20 (position D) we can see that the airplane is out of its CG limits. Let's add 100 lb of weight to the baggage compartment to obtain a normal CG condition.

Step 3. Compute the new CG with the added weight.

	Weight	X Arm	= Moment/100
Original weight	2,790 lb		2,222.4
Added weight	+100 lb	140 in	+140.0
New totals	2,890 lb		2,362.4

Step 4. Determine if new CG is within limits.
Using Figure 20 (position E), we see that the CG is within allowable limits.

Weight Shift: Problem No. 5 – With the airplane loaded as follows, what action must be taken to place the airplane within the proper weight and balance limits? Refer to the weight and balance information in Figures 19 and 20 to solve this problem.

Front seat occupants	411 pounds
Rear seat occupants	100 pounds
Main wing tanks	44 gallons

Figure 26 shows how to proceed with this problem.

Using the moment limits vs. weight chart in Figure 20 (see position D), the airplane is determined to be out of CG limits. In other words, our moment is smaller than the minimum moment required for flight. This means there isn't enough weight far enough aft of the datum to get the airplane within CG limits. How can we solve this type of problem?

You might think about transferring some fuel from the main tanks to the auxiliary fuel tanks but that won't help much. Looking closely at the difference in moments produced by the main and aux tanks for similar weights, there isn't much difference. Even if enough fuel was transferred to get the airplane within CG limits prior to takeoff, what's going to happen as fuel is used? Yes, the airplane will lose weight and the resulting moment will still be too small.

The best thing to do when you have a forward CG is to try and move weight aft, like a passenger (of course, only move them aft if there is a seat in back. Otherwise they might be reluctant to go). If that's not possible, and the airplane isn't near gross weight, add some weight to the baggage compartment. Let's try adding 100 pounds of weight to the baggage compartment and see if that brings us within CG limits. Step 3 in Figure 27 shows the results of adding this weight.

Looking at Figure 20, position E, we now see that the CG is within allowable limits. I'd still be cautious and determine what the CG will be as I burn off fuel. That's why I'd do another weight and balance problem based on the amount of fuel I expect to consume during my trip (see previous problem No. 4).

A Different Type Of Weight and Balance Chart

Here is a weight and balance chart similar to that we've already studied with a few significant difference. This chart shows two types of loaded moment envelopes for standard airworthy airplanes (no, not light sport airplanes)as shown in Figures 21 A and B. One

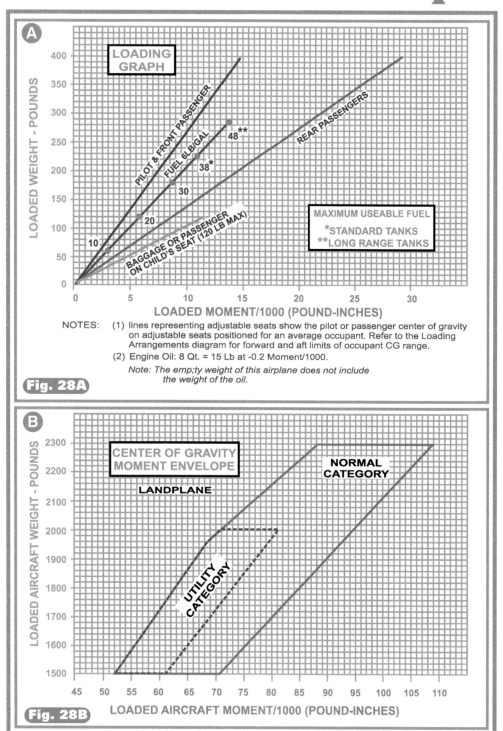

envelope is for operations in the *normal* category and one for the *utility* category. The utility category envelope's main purpose is to identify the CG limit in which spins are allowed in this airplane. The loading graph in Figure 28A has weights along the vertical axis and moments/1000 along the horizontal axis. A reduction factor of 1000 is used for the moments, but, as you'll see, you don't have to worry about using a reduction factor when using this format. To find the moments for specific weights, simply proceed horizontally along the weight lines. When reaching the desired diagonal line (for pilot, passenger, fuel or baggage) drop straight down to find the moments. That's easy!

When the total moments and weights are tallied, simply proceed to the center of gravity/moment envelope shown in Figure 28B. Compare weights and moments to see if they fall within the envelope. Notice that this airplane has both a normal and utility category envelope. Depending on the airplane, the CG must fall within the utility CG envelope for certain flight operations to be performed (such as spins).

Weight and Balance: Problem No. 6 – Using the airplane loading information shown in Figure 29A, determine if the airplane is within its proper CG limits. Figure 29B shows the solution for this problem. Figures 30A and 30B show the solution on the loading graph and CG/moment envelope.

This is a relatively straightforward weight and balance problem. Nothing tricky here. You should use caution, however, when calibrating moments from weights in Figure 28A. It's very easy to move up or down a line and end up with an incorrect moment. Watch the calibration for the individual chart lines. In Figure 28A, notice that each line along the weight (vertical) scale is calibrated in tens of pounds. Each line along the moment (horizontal) scale is calibrated in values of one-half.

WEIGHT AND BALANCE PROBLEM NO. 6

Using the loading graph in Figure 28A and the center of gravity envelope in Figure 28B, determine if the airplane is within the proper CG limits based on the information below.

Fig. 29A	Weight	X	Arm	=	Moment/1000
E - Empty weight	1,350 lb		.........in		51.5
P - Pilot & front seat occupants	310 lb		.........in		....
R - Rear seat occupants.................	96 lb		.........in		....
F - Fuel (38 gallons)	.........lb		.........in		....
B - Baggage	.........lb		.........in		....
O - Oil (8 quarts)	.........lb		.........in		-0.2

SOLUTION TO PROBLEM NO. 6

Step 1. Using the loading graph in Figure 28A, find the individual moments for the weights listed below. Remember that the oil weighs 7.5 lb/gal. Eight quarts of oil equals two gallons or 15 lb total. The oil moment is negative, indicating that it is ahead of the datum line.

Fig. 29B	Weight	X	Arm	=	Moment/1000
E - Empty weight	1,350 lb		.........in		51.5
P - Pilot & front seat occupants	310 lb		.........in		11.5
R - Rear seat occupants	96 lb		.........in		7.0
F - Fuel 38 gal. (6lb x 38 gal = 228 lb)	228 lb		.........in		11.0
B - Baggage	(no bags) lb		.........in		....
O - Oil (8 quarts)	15 lb		.........in		-0.2

Step 2. Add the totals   **Totals**   **1,999 lb**   <u>80.8</u> **lb-in**
                                                                  1000

Step 3. Using the center of gravity/moment envelope in Figure 28B, match the total weights on the left vertical axis against the total moments on the bottom horizontal axis. Since both values meet at a point within the envelope, the airplane is within the proper CG limits for safe flight. Figures 30A and 30B show how I calculated the moments and made the CG determination.

Fig. 30A

Fig. 30B

Weight and Balance: Problem No. 7 – The next problem, in Figure 31A, requires you to determine the maximum amount of baggage that can be carried in the airplane after all the other items have been loaded. Solving this problem simply requires you to find the current loaded weight of the airplane and subtract that from the maximum allowable weight. The difference is the amount of baggage (or any other item you're interested in) that can be carried onboard. After you determine the allowable weight of baggage, you must make sure that carrying this weight still keeps the airplane within its proper CG limits. Figures 31B, 32A and 32B show the solution to this problem.

WEIGHT AND BALANCE PROBLEM NO. 7

Using the loading graph in Figure 28A and the center of gravity/moment envelope shown in Figure 28B, determine the maximum amount of baggage that can be loaded aboard the airplane for the CG to remain within the center of gravity/moment envelope.

Fig. 31A

	Weight	X	Arm	=	Moment/1000
E - Empty weight	1,350 lb		.........in		51.5
P - Pilot & front seat occupants	250 lb		.........in		....
R - Rear seat occupants.................	400 lb		.........in		....
F - Fuel (30 gallons)	.........lb		.........in		....
B - Baggage	.........lb		.........in		....
O - Oil (8 quarts)	15 lb		.........in		-0.2

SOLUTION TO PROBLEM NO. 7

Step 1. Using the loading graph in Figure 28A, find the individual moments for the weights listed below. Figure 32A shows how I calculated the following moments.

Fig. 31B

	Weight	X	Arm	=	Moment/1000
E - Empty weight	1,350 lb		.........in		51.5
P - Pilot & front seat occupants	250 lb		.........in		9.3
R - Rear seat occupants	400 lb		.........in		29.3
F - Fuel 30 gal. (6lb x 30 gal = 180 lb)	180 lb		.........in		8.7
B - Baggage (this is unknown).......	? lb		.........in		?
O - Oil (8 quarts)	15 lb		.........in		-0.2

Step 2. Add the totals   **Totals   2,195 lb** $\dfrac{98.6 \text{ lb-in}}{1000}$

Step 3. The airplane's maximum allowable gross weight is 2,300 lb. I determined this by looking at the upper limit of the normal category CG/moment envelope in Figure 28B. Given this information, you can determine how much baggage can be carried by subtracting the present loaded weight from the maximum allowable gross weight to obtain (2,300 - 2,195 = 105 lb).

Step 4. Add the weight of the baggage and its moment to the totals you found in step 2. (The baggage produces a moment of 10.0 in-lb as determined from Figure 28A. This gives you a total weight of 2,300 lb and a total moment of 108.6 lb-in.)

Step 5. Using the center of gravity/moment envelope in Figure 28B, you determine that the airplane is just barely within its proper CG limits (at the edge of the envelope). Figures 32A and 32B show how I calculated the moments and made the CG determination.

Fig. 32A

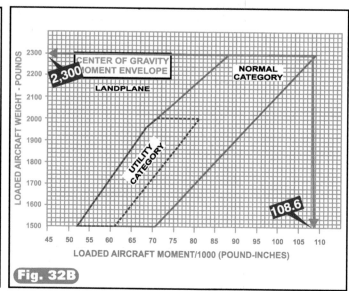

Fig. 32B

Weight and Balance: Problem No. 8 – Figure 33 is our final problem. This problem is similar to problem No. 7. Instead of finding the maximum amount of baggage that you can carry, this problem asks you to determine the maximum amount of fuel that can be carried aboard the aircraft for takeoff. It's solved in precisely the same way as problem No. 6. Solving this problem simply requires you to find the current loaded weight of the airplane without fuel and subtract that from the maximum weight allowable for that airplane. The difference is the amount of fuel that can be carried on board. After you determine the allowable weight of fuel, you must make sure that carrying this weight still keeps the airplane within its proper CG limits. Figures 34A, 34B and 34C show the solution to this problem.

SOLUTION TO PROBLEM NO. 8

Step 1. Using the loading graph in Figures 28A and B, you determine the individual moments for the weights listed to the right (except for the fuel which is our unknown). Figure 34A shows how these moments were derived.

Fig. 33	Weight	X	Arm	=	Moment/1000
E - Empty weight	1,350 lb		..........in		51.5
P - Pilot & front seat occupants	340 lb		..........in		12.6
R - Rear seat occupants	310 lb		..........in		22.6
F - Fuel 38 gal. (6lb x 38 gal = 228 lb)	? lb		..........in		?
B - Baggage	45 lb		..........in		4.2
O - Oil (8 quarts)	15 lb		..........in		-0.2

Step 2. Add the totals ⟶ **Totals**   **2,060 lb**   **90.7 lb-in / 1000**

Step 3. Using the upper limit of the center of gravity/moment envelope in Figure 28B, we determine that our maximum allowable gross weight is 2,300 lb. Subtracting 2,060 lb from 2,300 lb allows us to carry 240 lb of fuel. According to Figure 28A, this produces a moment of 11.5 lb-in.

Step 4. Adding the fuel weight and its moment to the totals in step 2 gives us a new total weight of 2,300 lb and a new total moment of 102.2 lb-in.

Step 5. Using the center of gravity/moment envelope shown in Figure 28B, we determine that the center of gravity is within proper limits for safe flight.

Step 6. Another method of determining if the airplane is within the proper CG limit is to use the *Center of Gravity Limits* chart found in some Airplane Flight Manuals. It's easy to use. First, calculate the airplane's center of gravity by dividing the total moments by the total weights. Multiply 102.2 lb-in x 1000 = 102200 lb-in and divide this by 2,300 lb, which gives a CG of 44.43 inches aft of datum (remember, moments in this example were divided by a reduction factor of 1000 and must be multiplied by that same value to get the actual moment). By matching the total weight to the CG location in Figure 34C, you see that the airplane falls within the allowable CG limits. I show the *Center of Gravity Limits* chart because it's another popular means of computing weight and balance and you're sure to see it in a manual someday.

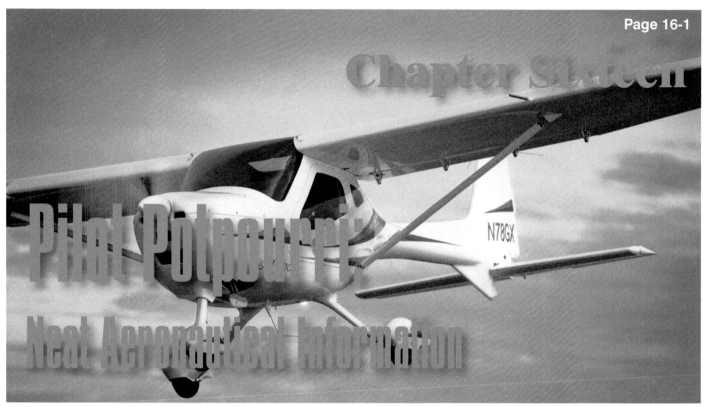

Chapter Sixteen

Pilot Potpourri:
Neat Aeronautical Information

"The time has come," the Walrus said,
"To talk of many things:
Of shoes—and ships—and sealing wax
Of cabbages—and kings—
And why the sea is boiling hot—
And whether pigs have wings"

Lewis Carroll
Alice in Wonderland

Pigs do not have wings; airplanes do.

We're almost done, so now the time has come to speak of many things. In this chapter I'll present some information morsels on a variety of topics, all of which I think you will find interesting, useful, and helpful to your flying.

As you read these munchies, keep in mind that part of the fun of aviation is that the learning never stops. New ways of doing old things always emerge, as do new ways of doing new things. We're continually learning new information about human performance and equipment capability. Flight instructors like to say that earning your sport pilot license is really getting a license to learn, and I think there's a lot of truth to that.

Taking AIM: The Aeronautical Information Manual

One night my wife awakened me from a sound sleep because she'd heard a noise. "Rod," she said, "I think there's someone outside."

Jostled out of REM sleep I replied, "Honey, that's where they're supposed to be—outside. If they come in here, then *we'll* go outside."

Without the full use of my faculties (brain not warmed up), the answer seemed perfectly reasonable to me. After all, everything has its place, correct? This is especially true with aviation information.

If you're ever looking for the source of aviation's wisdom, common sense and good operating principles, it has its place—in the Aeronautical Information Manual (AIM). Those who've been around aviation awhile knew the AIM under its maiden name, the *Airmen's* Information Manual. In 1995, as part of a government-wide effort to eliminate gender-specific terms wherever possible, the Airmen's Information Manual became the Aeronautical Information Manual. Fortunately, the AIM was the same.

Pilots have been known to behave strangely while under the influence of alcohol.

OK tower, (burp), I'm the man of the hour, (burp), so say it's OK to give it the power, (burp).

The AIM is the pilot's Bible. It is the official source of information on a variety of subjects, all of great importance to aviators, and of late has improved considerably in appearance. It's now replete with color illustrations. I encourage you to subscribe to this publication (now available on the internet at: *http://www.faa.gov/airports_airtraffic*).

Many of the topics and ideas in this chapter are drawn from the AIM, which also contains details about everything from the signal width of an instrument landing system to details on the right way to interact with controllers.

Fitness for Flight

All but sport pilots, and private pilots flying gliders and free balloons, are required to hold a valid medical certificate to act as pilot in command. You do not have to be Joe Weider (a one-time muscle man whose chest looked like an inverted pyramid) to pass the medical. Certain conditions, however, are disqualifying: personality disorders manifested by overt acts (I'm referring to the serious ones, not selfishness or rudeness), alcoholism, drug dependency, epilepsy, an unexplained disturbance of consciousness and heart attack to name a few.

Fortunately, pilots not meeting the medical standards can still be qualified under special issuance provisions of the certification process. This is why it's best for student pilots to visit an Aviation Medical Examiner as soon as possible after starting flight training. If there's going to be a problem getting a medical certificate, it's better to know about it early.

One thing you should be aware of is that the FARs prohibit you from acting as PIC if you have a known medical condition or worsening of a medical condition that would make you unable to meet the standards for a medical certificate. Just because you passed the medical in May does not mean you are legal in June if you had a heart attack in between.

I had a friend who flight instructed for two months with a partial cast on his right leg. I suppose he shouldn't

Reno, Nevada, September 17, 1983
RACE PILOT SURVIVES 200 MPH CRASH
By Danny Mortensen

Danny Mortensen

That was the headline on the AP wire. I had walked away from the race plane after scattering parts a thousand feet through the desert at the National Championship Air Races. My miraculous survival though is not as important as the lessons learned.

All pilots have heard of wake turbulence and associate it with large transports, but what many do not realize is that a small aircraft of the same size can put you over on your back and in the dirt. Do not follow another aircraft of any size at or below its altitude.

How would this apply to you? The traffic pattern! If you're following traffic that's close to you, make sure your ground track is offset to the right or left and slightly above its altitude. At the typical 1,000 foot pattern altitude, there is not enough room to recover from an unexpected inverted position for most student pilots.

Additionally, avoid flying while fatigued. I was up the night previous to the race frantically working to repair the airplane. This certainly didn't help my judgement. Fatigue and carelessness are dangerous combinations.

See you at the races.

Danny Mortensen is President of Airline Ground Schools, which specializes in written test preparation for the ATP and FE knowledge exams.

have been flying, but he did it anyway. He rationalized his decision by saying that he could still pass the medical. I suggested that if the doctor made him jump up and down on that leg for 20 seconds he might have jackhammered himself into the floor below. The only good thing about having a heavy cast on his right leg was that he didn't have any trouble using enough right rudder.

Illness

Be cautious if you're thinking about flying when ill. Many day-to-day illnesses will degrade your performance to unsafe levels. Judgment can be impaired, along with memory, the ability to calculate, and alertness. Beyond difficulty in filling out the Hobbs meter sheet, these problems are serious and could impair your ability to safely fly an airplane. You

owe it to yourself and your passenger to be as fit as possible when you park yourself in the pilot's seat of any airplane.

Medication

If you don't think your performance can be degraded by over-the-counter medication, then you've probably never taken any. Look on the back of a box on antihistamines. It usually says, "Don't operate heavy equipment after using this drug."

Does that mean you shouldn't take the family bulldozer to the market for some milk? Implied in this statement is a warning of performance degradation. Certainly this applies to airplanes as well as to cars (and bulldozers, too). For instance, some antihistamines can make a pilot more susceptible to hypoxia (oxygen deficiency). You're likely to feel the

Fig. 1 — TIME OF USEFUL CONSCIOUSNESS

Altitude	While Sitting Quietly	During Moderate Activity
40,000 Ft.	30 Sec.	18 Sec.
35,000 Ft.	45 Sec.	30 Sec.
30,000 Ft.	1 Min. & 15 Sec.	45 Sec.
25,000 Ft.	3 Min.	2 Min.
22,000 Ft.	10 Min.	5 Min.
20,000 Ft.	12 Min.	5 Min.

Physical exertion noticeably affects your time of useful consciousness when operating at higher altitudes. You may remain conscious beyond the time indicated for several minutes, but you simply won't function in a productive, useful manner.

effects of oxygen deficiency at lower altitudes. And most antihistamines cause some degree of drowsiness.

While antihistamines are an obvious no-no, many drugs have less-obvious effects that can cause a decrement in pilot performance. Quite frankly, if you're taking any medication, call your family physician to determine its side effects. A call to your Aviation Medical Examiner might be an even better idea, because AME's are often familiar with medications' effects that pose a risk to pilots, even though physicians might not think of them as side effects (or even be aware of them).

Alcohol:
Don't Fly High

Don't even think about mixing flying and alcohol. Your judgment, behavior and performance are all easily impaired by alcohol consumption. An older mariner who had spent many years on boats decided to take flying lessons. He showed up drunk for a flight, walked over to the airplane, untied all the ropes, threw them in the air and yelled, "Cast off!" A very embarrassing situation.

As little as one ounce of liquor, one bottle of beer or four ounces of wine can impair flying skills. Keep in mind that legally you may not operate an aircraft within 8 hours of having consumed *any* alcohol. Also be aware that the effects of alcohol can linger long after eight hours. Judgment,

coordination, and other items you really want to have available as a pilot can be impaired even when you don't have an obvious hangover. It's usually best to wait at least 12 to 24 hours between the bottle and the throttle, depending on the amount of alcohol consumed.

Hypoxia: Low O, Two

Hypoxia is a state of oxygen deficiency in the body sufficient to impair function of the brain and other organs. While the percentage of

Don't even think about mixing flying and alcohol.... As little as one ounce of liquor, one bottle of beer or four ounces of wine can impair flying skills.

oxygen in the atmosphere doesn't change with an increase in altitude (it stays about 21%), the amount of pressure that forces oxygen into our body decreases, causing hypoxia. Because of this lower pressure, pilots flying at higher altitudes (50,000 feet and above) often wear pressure suits. (That's pressure suit, not power suit—i.e., double breasted black suit with red tie—which would look pretty dumb at 50,000 feet anyway.)

The effects of hypoxia occur at altitudes as low as 5,000 feet, beginning with a deterioration of night vision. The eyes require a great deal of oxygen to function properly. They are one of the first organs to experience the effects of reduced oxygen within the body. Other significant effects of

hypoxia often don't occur in the normal, healthy pilot below 10,000 feet. If you smoke, however, then all bets are off. Smoking reduces the altitude at which the effects of hypoxia are experienced (it also increases the chance of your power suit catching on fire!).

Above 10,000 feet MSL, most individuals begin to experience some decrease in their judgment, memory, alertness and coordination. The ability to calculate also becomes impaired to some degree for most individuals with the increasing effects of hypoxia.

What makes hypoxia such a serious problem is that its effects are usually quite difficult to recognize, especially when they occur gradually. Headache, drowsiness, dizziness and either a sense of well being (otherwise known as euphoria) or belligerence can occur. (You sometimes get a similar feeling when studying the Federal Aviation Regulations—especially the headache and dizziness part.)

The higher the altitude, the less time it takes for hypoxia to start robbing you of your flying faculties. In fact, it's not unusual for pilot performance to seriously deteriorate within 15 minutes at 15,000 feet. Figure 1 identifies the time of useful consciousness at various altitudes without the use of supplemental oxygen.

Preventing hypoxia means using supplemental oxygen at higher altitudes. Since sport pilots are limited to altitudes of 10,000 feet MSL (or 2,000 feet AGL, whichever is higher), hypoxia is really a big concern for you. That doesn't, however, mean you can't get a mild form of hypoxia, especially if you have a cigarette habit so intense that your friends have to go on the nicotine patch after visiting with you.

Pilots using supplemental aviation breathing oxygen need to avoid using greasy or oily rags around oxygen systems. Petroleum-based products and oxygen don't mix. They are a very dangerous combination that could cause a fire, explosion, and definitely serious injury. In fact, the military recommends that their pilots not use lip balm (Chapstick) when they plan on using oxygen. Why? Because lip balm is petroleum based. Perhaps that's why it sounds like LIP-BOMB. You might have lips heavily coated with lip balm, go on oxygen, hear a boom, then spend the rest of the flight looking around the cockpit for your lips. Can you imagine how difficult it will be to call the tower on the radio without your lips?

Hyperventilation

I once asked a student in class what it means if a pilot starts panting or breathing quickly and shallow-like. This fellow replied, "It means he's been eating Milk Bone dog biscuits." This was the same guy from the airspace chapter who had a Coke machine fall on him.

Hyperventilation is abnormally quick, shallow breathing. It can happen when a person is scared, tense, or otherwise stressed. The rapid breathing has the effect of changing your blood chemistry by expelling a more-than-normal amount of carbon dioxide. The level of carbon dioxide is one of the signals the body uses to regulate breathing. The symptoms resulting from hyperventilation can include lightheadedness, suffocation, drowsiness, tingling in the extremi-

---

Hyperventilation is abnormally quick, shallow breathing. It can happen when a person is scared, tense, or otherwise stressed.

---

ties, and coolness. Incapacitation in the form of a lack of coordination, disorientation, and painful muscle spasms can eventually result, as can unconsciousness.

You can reduce and eliminate the symptoms of hyperventilation by bringing the rate and depth of your breathing under control. In other words, by purposely slowing your breathing rate, you allow the necessary carbon dioxide to rebuild within the body. The symptoms will disappear within a few minutes. Talking loud is one way to overcome the effects of hyperventilation. This forces you to wait longer between breaths and builds up the body's carbon dioxide level (it also causes other people to stare and point at you). Some people recommend breathing

into a paper bag to help build up the carbon dioxide. Simply hold it over your nose and mouth until the symptom subside. Don't put the entire bag over your head (even if you poke holes out for the eyes). This is no time to get a little instrument work in. Besides, it may scare your passenger!

The early symptoms of hyperventilation and hypoxia are similar. They can even occur at the same time (you'd definitely be having a bad flying day and M&Ms would probably melt in your hand). If you find yourself using an oxygen system because of hypoxia or hyperventilation, set the oxygen regulator to give you maximum oxygen flow. This may appear contradictory to you. After all, if we are hyperventilating, we need carbon dioxide, not oxygen. The problem is that you may not be sure which it is—hypoxia or hyperventilation. It's best to first attack the problem as hypoxia, by going on oxygen. After doing this you should check to see if the regulator has been functioning properly. Then you should give attention to consciously slowing your breathing rate.

CO Oh Oh

Carbon monoxide (CO) is a colorless, odorless, tasteless gas. It has a much stronger affinity than oxygen for *hemoglobin,* the substance in your blood that transports oxygen. If a hemoglobin molecule is occupied with a CO molecule, oxygen can't get aboard and be transported. Good night, Irene.

CO poisoning is cumulative and dangerous. It can incapacitate quickly, and is rapidly fatal. Because of the already-reduced oxygen supply at higher altitudes, you're even more vulnerable to the effects of CO poisoning as you head upward.

Carbon monoxide is a byproduct of combustion. Every winter, people across the country lose their lives when they burn charcoal or other substances indoors for heat without adequate ventilation. For pilots, the danger arises from exhaust gases

---

Smoking

Medical studies show us that cigarette smoking causes a relative deprivation of oxygen to the heart muscle and contributes to circulatory problems by constricting arteries. Thus, it affects the cardiovascular system and is significant in the development of coronary heart disease. Aside from nicotine and tar, carbon monoxide from cigarette smoke presents an immediate hazard for pilots.

Carbon Monoxide - A pilot who smokes will normally have 5% to 10% of his or her total hemoglobin taken up by carboxyhemoglobin (a mixture of carbon monoxide and oxygen). This results in hypemic hypoxia and lowers the pilot's altitude tolerance. Flying at a cabin altitude of 10,000 feet with 10% carboxyhemoglobin is physiologically equivalent to 15,000 feet cabin altitude. The chronic smoker who is breathing ambient air carries this additional hazard for several hours after the last cigarette. Lack of oxygen to the brain impairs judgment, so a smoker with hypemic hypoxia may suffer a diminished ability to make decisions about a flight even though he or she is not at the altitudes that require use of supplemental oxygen. Furthermore, this carbon monoxide hazard exists also for the non-smoker who is in the same area with the smoker. *Source: FAA Aviation News*

The Toynbee Maneuver: Open Eustachian

The *Toynbee maneuver* is a variation of the Valsalva maneuver. Both start by closing off the nostrils (pinch them closed). However, in the Toynbee maneuver, instead of blowing against the closed nostrils you simply swallow.

Swallowing with your nostrils closed off has the effect of decreasing the size of the oropharyngeal (mouth and throat) space, much as if you had stepped on one end of an inflated balloon. This increases the pressure of the air in that space on the eustachian tube, and with any luck at all the e-tube pops right open. If not, keep swallowing slowly, but *do not blow.* You can damage your inner ear, and even when it's successful, the Valsalva maneuver can force unwanted material into the middle ear.

Take a tip and Toynbee.

THE INSIDE OF THE HUMAN EAR

Ear Drum — Otolith Organs — Ear Canal — Middle Ear — Eustachian Tube — To Throat — **Fig. 2**

It's the eustachian tube that helps keep the pressure in the middle ear equalized with the atmospheric pressure. When the eustachian tube becomes blocked, the ear drum may extend in either direction to equalize the middle ear's pressure with atmospheric pressure.

---

leaking into the cockpit. This can occur because of a leak in the exhaust system, or because there is a leak in the heater, which uses exhaust gases to warm air that is sent to the cockpit. Heaters normally work by passing outside air over the heater's manifold, then directing the air into the cabin. If a leak occurs, raw exhaust can be imported directly into the cabin.

If you notice the odor of exhaust or experience symptoms of headache, drowsiness, dizziness or loss of muscular power when the aircraft heater is in use, immediately turn off the heater and open the air vents. Consider opening the windows if that can be done in flight in your aircraft (consult the Pilot's Operating Handbook). The smell of exhaust gas should be considered the prelude to an emergency. You must act immediately.

If your physical symptoms are severe or continue after landing, seek medical treatment.

Ear Ye, Ear Ye

The bane of many pilots is a tiny, flaccid tube connecting the middle ear to the back of the throat. It's normally closed. In an ascent, the eustachian (pronounced: U-STAY-SHUN) tube opens for a second or two, permitting higher pressure air from the middle ear to flow out, equalizing the pressure inside the ear with that of the cabin (see Figure 2).

This process, often accompanied by a slight crackling, is rarely a problem.

On the way down, however, things get tougher. Now there is high pressure on the outside, and low pressure trapped in the middle ear. The collapsed eustachian tube is like a hose with a crimp in it, and it doesn't open as readily as it did when you were upward bound. You're now in the position of trying to force water back into the hose. Any nasal congestion will make the problem a lot worse, since it puts additional pressure on the collapsed tube, making it even more difficult to get it open. If you can't get the tube open, you have what's known as an *ear block*. Contrary to the belief of some pilots, this is not a hit in the head from an NFL lineman, though if you ever get an ear block, you may well feel like you've got an entire football in your ear.

If you don't equalize the pressure, the results will be somewhere between excruciating and devastating. As the pressure differential builds, your eardrum bows inward, pressing on sensitive nerves. If the pressure differential is too great, the eardrum ruptures. This is not generally considered to be fun by any but the most bizarre of pilots.

The first line of defense against ear block is to stop descending, and even to climb back up to a higher altitude. The lower you go, the greater the pressure differential, and

the less likely you will be successful at springing that trapdoor open.

The second thing to do is to swallow, yawn, or tense the muscles in your throat. What you're trying to do is straighten the eustachian tube out a bit and give it the best chance of opening and equalizing the pressure. When this happens it's generally accompanied by a loud popping sound and an enormous sense of relief.

No go? OK, time for the heavy artillery. What virtually every pilot and flight instructor will tell you to do is perform the *Valsalva maneuver,* in which you close your mouth, pinch your nose, and breathe out in short puffs against the closed nostrils. *I don't recommend you do it.* The Valsalva maneuver is potentially damaging, and it's unfortunate that it has been so blithely handed down as the way to clear a closed eustachian tube. Even airline flight attendants will tell passengers to perform the Valsalva maneuver.

What's the right answer? Though almost nobody has heard of it, the Toynbee maneuver (see box) is a far preferable way of opening the eustachian tube. Tell a friend.

Don't fly with a cold.... The bad news is that I know you will eventually ignore this advice. The good news is that you'll only do it once.

Do NOT fly with a cold or other upper respiratory infection, even a little one. The bad news is that I know you will eventually ignore this advice. The good news is that I know you will probably only ignore it once, because the resulting ear block will be a very memorable experience.

An upper respiratory infection is like standing on the garden hose. The water just doesn't have much chance of getting through. When it comes to your ears, there is no such thing as a "minor" cold. The least bit of fluid and gunk in your head will compress the eustachian tube and make equalizing the pressure on descent almost impossible.

Now that you know better, share the information with your passenger. Don't subject them to the pain and possible injury of an ear block.

If you do land with an ear block, and it doesn't clear shortly after landing, give your doctor a call. On several occasions—one concerning me, another concerning a passenger—I had to climb back up to altitude to reduce the pain of ear block. A more gradual descent eventually helped relieve the pain.

Spatial Disorientation

During visual flight, our sense of sight determines the relationship between aircraft attitude and the earth's surface. When flying in the clouds, though, we control the airplane solely be reference to the instruments. Deprived of the normal visual cues, the body can send some very unusual messages to the brain, creating a profound conflict between what the "seat of your pants" is telling you and what the instruments say. Such a conflict is known as *spatial disorientation* or *vertigo*.

You're likely to experience vertigo during instrument training (as a sport pilot your instructor may provide you with some training on flight by reference to your instruments), or during day or night flights when the horizon isn't easily defined or identifiable. In such a condition you might find yourself convinced that you're turning, while

THE INNER EAR

3 Semicircular Canals
(each contains fluid)

Fig. 3

PITCH

ROLL

YAW

The three semicircular canals are positioned at right angles to each other to allow the brain to sense motion in three planes: yaw, pitch and roll. Fluid within these canals moves relative to the canal walls. This bends the small hair filaments lining the inside of the canal walls, activating nerves that alert the brain to movement.

the instruments are showing straight and level flight. Which do you believe? You must never forget the one most important rule about vertigo—trust your instruments. I can assure you that regardless of how much experience you have, vertigo can affect any pilot. Pilots experiencing vertigo should always believe their instruments instead of their bodily sensations.

Vertigo is caused by problems associated with three of our sensory systems: vestibular, kinesthetic, and visual.

The *visual system* is exactly what is sounds like—information sent to our brain from our eyes. The *kinesthetic system* is the sensory information sent to the brain by the seat of our pants. It's the information transmitted by sensors in our skin and from areas deeper within our body. You don't have to be a rocket scientist to understand how both of these systems work. The *vestibular system*, however, does require a little explanation.

The vestibular system consists of the semicircular canals located in the inner ear (Figure 3). These canals consists of three circular tubes each containing a fluid whose movement causes the bending of small hair filaments (known as *otolith organs*) located at the base of each canal (Figure 4). Movement of the fluid within the tubes, caused by acceleration (a change in direction or velocity), stimulates the otolith organs, alerting the brain that the body is in motion.

This is what students really see when they first look at the instruments while under the hood.

ACCELERATION AND THE INNER EAR

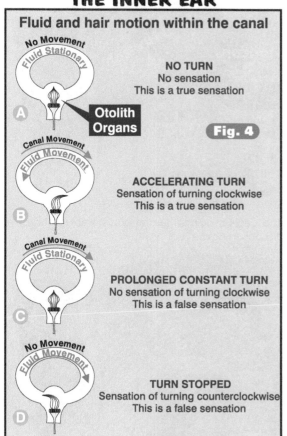

Fluid and hair motion within the canal

NO TURN
No sensation
This is a true sensation

Otolith Organs

Fig. 4

ACCELERATING TURN
Sensation of turning clockwise
This is a true sensation

PROLONGED CONSTANT TURN
No sensation of turning clockwise
This is a false sensation

TURN STOPPED
Sensation of turning counterclockwise
This is a false sensation

When the head is rotated (accelerated) in any direction, the fluid within one or more of the canals bends small hairs (known as otolith organs) at the base of the canals, as shown in position B. Because of inertia, the fluid lags behind the rotation of the canal, which bends the fine hairs. This stimulates nerve endings, alerting the brain that the body is turning. After acceleration, the fluid eventually catches up with the canal's movement and stimulation stops (position C). This signals the brain that you are no longer turning, even though you're still in a turn. When you stop the turn, the fluid moves in the opposite direction. This gives you a sensation of turning in the opposite direction (position D).

3 Semicircular Canals
(each contain fluid)

A wise man says, "A pilot shouldn't stop thinking before the airplane stops flying."

FORCES ACTING ON THE BODY

Fig. 5

Gravity

Centrifugal Force

Resultant Force

Gravity

While on the surface, gravity pulls the body straight downward. The ear's semicircular canal system provides perfect orientation to the earth's surface in this situation. In flight, however, both centrifugal force and gravity combine to form a resultant force that makes the seat-of-the-pants sense completely unreliable as a source of attitude information. This false sense is called *vertigo*.

Notice that all three tubes in Figure 3 seem to lie in three planes, corresponding somewhat to the three axes of the airplane. This alignment allows you to sense angular acceleration in any one of these planes. In other words, you can sense yaw, roll and pitch.

When you move your head or accelerate the airplane (change speed or direction), fluid within these canals move as shown in Figure 4, position B. Since the fluid within the canals has a small amount of inertia (a tendency to resist change of motion), it tends to remain stationary for a short period of time before moving. Thus, the canals can be said to rotate around the fluid within them. Eventually the fluid catches up to the movement of the canal and the feeling of turning stops (position C). Even though you're still turning, you don't feel it. When you stop turning, however, the fluid continues its motion for a short period of time because of its inertia (position D). This signals your mind that you've entered a turn in the opposite direction.

The semicircular canal system was designed as a ground based system where gravity always pulled the body in one direction—straight downward. In flight, however, gravity is not the only force pulling on the body. Centrifugal force as well as gravity tugs on the seat of the pilot's pants as shown in Figure 5.

This explains why your eyes may tell you one thing when looking at the instruments while your brain and your body tell you something entirely different. For instance, when the body is in a prolonged turn, the fluid in the canals eventually comes up to speed with the canal walls (hair no longer stimulated). If the head is then tipped or twisted, the fluid once again moves relative to the canal walls. Now a new sensation of rotation occurs (based on which way the head was turned) even though the airplane didn't change its attitude. Thus, abrupt head movements under instrument or instrument-like conditions can cause you to perceive maneuvers that aren't really happening. This vertigo-type illusion is called the *coriolis illusion*. If you try to correct or turn your airplane in compensation for the sensation, you could be in for a real surprise. Now you know why it's best to believe your instruments. When you start work on your instrument rating (which I hope you will do this some day), you'll learn all about detecting if and when your instruments are lying to you. Right now, it's best to believe them and avoid instrument or instrument-like conditions.

Visual Illusions

There are situations where, as a VFR pilot, you can encounter instrument-like conditions without being in a cloud. At night, a blending of the earth and sky is often responsible for creating an indiscernible horizon which is an instrument-like condition. This is most prevalent on moonless nights where stars take on the appearance of city lights and city lights appear to be stars (Figure 6A).

Another common visual illusion occurs when you are flying in the direction of a lit shoreline. With dark water underneath, it's easy for shoreline lights to be mistaken for stars as shown in Figure 6B.

Flying above a cloud deck can produce an illusion of a false horizon. If the clouds tops are sloped, you may find yourself attempting to align the aircraft with the horizon made by the clouds.

Flying towards the sun on a hazy day can eliminate the horizon, making it difficult to tell which way is up or down. Situations like these are best handled by climbing above the haze if possible, or getting closer to the surface to establish visual ground contact.

You should be cautious and avoid flying in inclement weather conditions. It's quite easy to lose reference when clouds or other obscuring phenomena are present. Problems with spatial disorientation occur when pilots no longer have sight of the horizon. Until you're instrument rated, avoid flight anywhere at any time where you might lose visual references.

Flight Vision

Make no mistake about it, vision is your most important sense. There is no such thing as a medical wavier for pilots without vision in both eyes. Your vision is important for many reasons. First, you obviously need it to fly the airplane. You also need it to read charts, look for traffic and scan instruments. Let's learn a little about how the eye functions.

FALSE HORIZONS

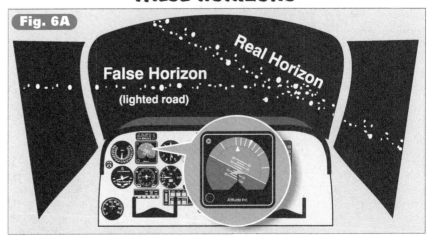

Fig. 6A

False Horizon (lighted road)

Real Horizon

In the example above, a lighted road can be misinterpreted as the actual horizon at night. Such an event is very disconcerting to a pilot.

Fig. 6B

(stars in sky)

Real Horizon

(unlit surface)

When the foreground is unlit and the background contains stars, it's relatively easy for a pilot to think he or she has gone inverted.

About Face

One of the most important maneuvers a new VFR pilot can learn to fly is a 180 degree turn, to be executed any time he or she inadvertently enters a cloud.

There should be no hesitancy or delay in executing this. Don't talk yourself into being convinced you can fly "just a little bit" in the clouds. That's like being a little bit pregnant. It's not a possible condition.

Of course, to make a 180 degree turn, you have to know what your heading is to start with. That sounds easy and obvious, but it can be downright terrifying to suddenly find yourself in a cloud, without an instrument rating.

Don't panic. Look at the bottom of the heading indicator and see what number the tail is pointing to. That's where you want to end up. Now begin a gentle turn in the direction of your choice. Be careful not to keep steepening the turn. Make it a nice, gentle, 15 to 20 degree bank, then hold steady until the number that was on the tail is on the nose. Then go straight and level. Faster than you can say *Rod Machado*, you'll be VFR again.

STRUCTURE OF THE HUMAN EYE

Fig. 7

Optic nerve to brain
Cone cell concentration
Fovea
Rod cell concentration
Lens
Iris
Pupil
Retina

RODS
Peripheral vision
Moving images
Non color images
Day and night use

CONES
Detailed imaging
Color imaging
Daylight use

RODS

The human eye has separate structures for aiding both night vision and day vision. Cone cells, located within the fovea, are very effective during the day for detailed imagery and color imagery. Rod cells, located outside the fovea, are best used for detection of moving images and noncolor images. They are effective during day and nighttime hours.

CONE CELLS OF THE HUMAN EYE

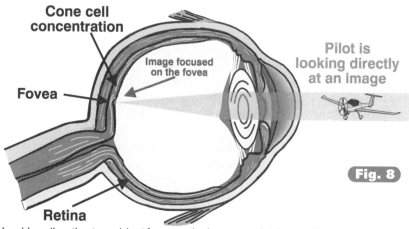

Cone cell concentration
Image focused on the fovea
Fovea
Retina

Pilot is looking directly at an image

Fig. 8

Looking directly at an object focuses the image on the fovea. The image falls on the cone cells that are effective at distinguishing color and image detail. Unfortunately, cone cells are less effective when it's dark. This is why it's difficult to distinguish color and detail at night.

Your Eye – Figure 7 shows a side view of the human eye. Light passes through the pupil and lens, then falls upon the retina at the very back of the eye. Light sensitive cells of the retina are made up of individual cells known as rods and cones.

Cone Cells – Cone cells are concentrated in a small section in the center of the retina known as the fovea. These cells decrease in number with distance from this center point.

While the eye can observe an approximate 200 degree arc at a glance, only the light falling on the fovea has the ability to send the brain a sharp, clearly-focused image. All light falling outside the fovea will be of less detail (Figure 8). For example, an airplane at a distance of 7 miles which appears in sharp focus within the foveal center of vision would have to be as close as 7/10 of a mile in order to be recognized if it were outside the foveal field of vision.

Cone cells are responsible for allowing you to perceive color. Looking directly at an object, most of the image is focused on the fovea. Unfortunately, the cones don't work well when it's dark. This explains why it's difficult to perceive color at night compared to the daylight hours.

Rod Cells – No, they didn't name them after me. Rod cells, concentrated on the outside of the fovea, are dim-light receptors. Since these rods are located outside the fovea, they are responsible for our peripheral vision, as shown in Figure 9. Moving images are more easily detected by rod cells than by cone cells. Catching an object out of the corner of your eye is an example of rod cells at work.

As I've already mentioned, cone cells don't work well in the dark, which explains why it's difficult to see an object at night even though you're looking directly at it. This is why we have a night blind spot in the center of our vision where the light from a dimly lit object falls directly onto the fovea (Figure 9).

If you want the best view of a dimly lit object you need to expose the rods to the light. You can do this by using your peripheral vision for off-center viewing. Simply look 5 to 10 degrees to the side from the center of the object you want to view. This allows some of the object's reflected light to fall on the rods. You can demonstrate this process at night by looking directly at an airplane's strobe light head on and offset a few degrees. A direct view dims the object while an indirect view increases its brightness. Think of looking at a dim object at night as you might think about looking at a carnival worker. In other words, try not to look directly at their tattoos for fear of finding misspelled words.

ROD CELLS OF THE HUMAN EYE

Rod cell concentration

Fig. 9

Fovea

Good night vision

Area of night blindness

Good night vision

Looking directly at an object at night makes it difficult to see. At night it's best to look 5 to 10 degrees offset from center for better vision. This allows the light from dimly lit objects to fall on the rod cells (surrounding the foveal region) which are better for night vision.

Night Vision

How well you see at night is determined by the amount of light passing through the pupil. Pupils close to prevent the eyes from receiving too much light and open when light intensity diminishes. The problem is that it may take at least 30 minutes for your eyes to completely adapt to the dark. This is one reason you want to avoid very bright lights for at least 30 minutes before the flight if you're planning on flying any time past sunset all the way until the end of evening civil twilight (when night officially begins and all sport pilots must be on the ground). The reason being that if you've spent the day sungazing and haven't adapted your eyes to darker conditions, it's possible that you may not be able to see the airport or the runway, much less other airplanes in flight. That's a fact!

Using sunglasses for protection from glare is most helpful in preventing night vision deterioration as well as preventing eye strain and eye damage. Find sunglasses that absorb at least 85% of the visible light (15% transmittance) and have minimal color distortion. Usually, a green or neutral gray is a satisfactory color. I'd recommend that you stay away from sunglass frames like Elton John wears (personally, flaming pink flamingo glasses don't do much for me at all and I can hardly see how they would help you during your sport pilot check ride). I make it a point to ensure all my sunglasses have a high degree of impact resistance. Why? They are excellent eye protectors in the event that something penetrates the windshield.

Bob, why can't you land softly at night?

Ahh, because dark air has less lift in it than white air?

Haze and Collision Avoidance

Keep in mind that all objects (traffic included) appear to be farther away in hazy conditions. The mind equates difficulty in seeing an object with increased distance. As a result, you might allow another airplane to get closer to you under hazy conditions before taking corrective action.

Wearing yellow lens sunglasses is often recommended for hazy, smoggy conditions. Yellow lenses allow for greater definition and contrast of objects. I keep a pair in my flight case for hazy days (I also have a pink-rimmed pair in case I meet Elton John at the airport). Yellow lens sunglasses put a little more strain on my eyes if I wear them for a long time, but the payoff is in easier identification of traffic in smoggy and hazy conditions.

Scanning for Traffic During the Day

Avoiding midairs is predicated upon one important premise: you must look outside the cockpit. Far too often, pilots spend their time with their head inside the cockpit staring at instruments instead of honoring the see and avoid concept. How much time should be spent looking outside and inside the cockpit? Many years ago a military

THE SECTOR SCANNING METHOD

One method of scanning is using the sector scanning method. You simply scan one area 10 degrees in width for one second before moving onto the next sector. By moving your head in a series of short movements, the eye is stationary long enough to focus on an object. This includes scanning the area behind you, too.

study indicated that on a 17 second cycle, approximately 3 seconds should be spent inside the cockpit with 14 seconds spent looking outside. That's approximately a 1 second inside to 5 second outside ratio. These are good numbers to follow.

Looking outside the cockpit is one thing; knowing how to look, another. Scanning for traffic requires that you understand another peculiarity about the eye: objects are difficult to detect when the eye is in motion. Effective scan-

SCANNING THROUGH 360 DEGREES

Effective scanning assumes that you'll scan 360 degrees for traffic. Starting at the rearmost window, scan in a clockwise direction until reaching the right rearmost window. Sometimes it may be physically difficult to turn your head in a rearward direction. If so, make right or left turns to effectively scan the rear of the airplane.

ning requires the eyes be held still for a very short time to detect objects. Perhaps the best way to scan is to move your eyes in a series of short, regularly spaced movements that bring successive areas of the sky into the central visual field. The FAA suggests that each movement should not exceed 10 degrees with each area being observed for at least 1 second to enable detection, as shown in Figure 10.

Since the brain is already trained to process sight information presented from left to right, you will probably find it easier to start your scan from over your left shoulder proceeding to the right across the windshield, as shown in Figure 11.

Whatever you do, don't forget to scan the area behind you. Many years ago an AOPA (Aircraft Owner's and Pilot's Association) study indicated that the majority of midairs occur with one aircraft overtaking another (one study indicated that 82% of the accidents occurred this way). Obviously this is a faster aircraft overtaking a slower one. This becomes a greater concern when you're operating in an area where fast and slow aircraft mix. Scanning the rear quadrants may take some neck bending or turning of the aircraft, depending on the aircraft configuration. Granted, unless you've seen the movie *The Exorcist,* you may not realize that such neck twisting is possible. Nevertheless, even if your head can't spin on its axis, make gentle turns in the airplane to take a peek at what's behind you (Figure 12). Making gentle turns is also a good idea when climbing or descending on an airway to check for traffic.

Another consideration when scanning is to prevent being a victim of *empty-field myopia.* This condition usually occurs when you're flying above a cloud or haze layer with nothing specific to focus on outside the airplane. This causes the eyes to relax and seek a comfortable focal distance ranging anywhere from 10 to 30 feet. This means you may be looking outside the airplane without actually being able to identify traffic. To overcome this problem you should try to momentarily fix your eyes on a ground object off in the distance (if possible) before commencing your scan.

If you spot a target and it has no apparent motion, then it means one of two things: it's either coming directly at you or moving away from you, or a big bug has smashed into your window. Targets moving directly toward you can close the distance in a very short time. Figure 13 demonstrates how quickly aircraft can converge. Little or no relative movement can also occur when aircraft are converging, as shown in Figure 14. If you detect a target with little or no relative motion in your windshield, it's best to take evasive action immediately. Don't just wait for the target to grow larger—make a turn. Make the target move.

Just remember to scan the *entire area* for collision avoidance prior to starting any maneuver. Also remember to raise the inside wing of a high wing airplane and look before beginning the turn. If you're flying a low wing airplane, don't forget to look in the direction opposite that which you'll turn. Why? The outside wing will often prevent you from seeing any converging traffic. In short, do what your mom told you to do: look both ways, then look up, down, behind and ahead. Keep your head outside the cockpit (no, that will mess up your hair. I mean keep your eyes outside the cockpit).

REARWARD CLEARING TURNS

In some airplanes, the only way to see what's behind you is to make clearing turns while looking rearward. Don't be reluctant to make turns as often as necessary to watch for faster traffic approaching from behind.

Fig. 12

AIRPLANES CONVERGING HEAD ON

Distance		Time to collision Slow**Fast ***		
*miles 10		100	60	seconds
6		60	36	
5		50	30	
4		40	24	
3		30	18	
2		20	12	
1		10	6	
1/2		5	3	

Fig. 13

*Miles between planes
**Converging at 360 mph or one airplane at 100 mph, the other at 260 mph (or any combo)
***Converging at 600 mph or one airplane at 400 mph and the other at 200 mph (any combo)

Airplanes converging head-on cover distances quickly. Additionally, there is little or no relative movement between targets making it more difficult to identify a collision threat. For instance, a slower airplane and a faster airplane converging at a rate of 360 mph (or any combination of speeds equaling 360 mph as shown by the "slow" speed column) have 20 seconds before impact when two miles apart. A 500 mph airliner and a 100 mph airplane (600 mph converging speed as shown by the "fast" speed column) have 12 seconds before colliding at a distance of 2 miles.

AIRPLANES ON A CONVERGING COURSE

As two airplanes approach on a converging course, there may be little or no apparent movement of the airplane in your windscreen. This is a sign to take evasive action.

Fig. 14

Night Scanning For Traffic

While it's easier to spot aircraft lights when it's dark (for a sport pilot, this is the time just after sunset up to evening civil twilight and just after morning civil twilight when it's still legal for you to fly) this doesn't necessarily mean it's easier to identify the aircraft's direction of movement, much less its size and shape. That's why airplanes are required to have their position lights on from sunset to sunrise (anticollision lights are to be on when the airplane is in operation). You can determine the direction of airplane travel by noting the position of the airplane's red navigation light (on the left wing), the green navigation light (on the right wing) and the steady white

DETERMINING THE DIRECTION OF AN AIRPLANE'S TRAVEL BY USE OF ITS POSITION LIGHTS

Fig. 15

Position lights are a visual clue as to the direction in which airplanes are moving at night. For instance, assume that you are in airplane A. Airplane B is moving from left to right, since you can see a green and (eventually) a white light. Airplane C is moving from right to left, since you see only a red and (eventually) a white light. Airplane D is moving toward you, since you see green and red lights but no white light. And airplane E is moving away from you, since you see a white light. Keep in mind that, at certain angles, the white tail light may not always be visible in combination with a red or green wingtip light. A flashing white or red anticollision light(s) is also required to be on when the airplane is in operation.

light (on the tail). The red or white anticollision light is often visible from many directions (see Figure 15).

One more thing before we leave the topic of night scanning. Something known as autokinesis (meaning self-moving) might occur at night if you don't keep up a regular scan pattern. Staring at a single light source for a few seconds at night can cause that light to appear to move, much like an airplane on a collision course. If you're using the light as an attitude reference, this apparent motion could cause you to lose your spatial orientation. You can prevent autokinesis by scanning in the manner I've previously discussed as well as by observing the flight instruments to affirm the correct attitude.

Airplane Blind Spots

All airplanes have blind spots where traffic is difficult to see. High wing aircraft make seeing above difficult, while low wing aircraft make

Professor Bob

Wisdom from Bob:
Professor Bob says that a pilot should treat aviation knowledge like food and make it a point never to fly on an empty head.

seeing below difficult (biplane pilots have both problems). Figure 16 shows how these blind spots look on different aircraft. This doesn't mean that it's impossible to see in the directions of blind spots. You may need to turn the airplane or lift a wing to compensate for those areas blocked by aircraft structure.

This is one reason I recommend that pilots of high wing airplanes lift their wing slightly and look before starting a turn (tell your passenger that you're looking for traffic if you're worried that he or she may think you don't know which way to turn). This prevents turning into an airplane that is descending from your direction of turn. Pilots of low wing airplanes need to be especially alert to clear the areas below them during descents. If you're flying a low wing airplane, be sure to make the necessary clearing turns during descents to check for traffic below you.

Whatever you do, don't be hesitant to turn that airplane and look when operating in areas of high traffic density. It's possible for a low wing and a high wing airplane to remain within each other's blind spot, as shown in Figure 17. This is good motivation to keep your eyes open and the airplane maneuvering to clear those blind spots.

BLIND AREAS COMMON IN HIGH AND LOW WING AIRPLANES

Fig. 16

It's not unusual to have a substantial portion of your view blocked by either the fuselage or the wings. Compensating for those areas of blocked view requires that you make turns and gentle pitch changes.

If there is ever a best time to remain vigilant for traffic, it's when you're within 5 miles of an airport below 3,000 feet AGL. One study of midair collisions found that 77% of all midairs occurred within these distances. That same study reported that 49% occurred within 5 miles and 500 feet AGL of the airport. This translates into a need to be careful when you're approaching an airport to land.

Don't let the presence of a tower controller relax your vigilance. Many a midair has occurred in the presence of a tower controlled field. Pilots are still responsible for their own see and avoid traffic separation even when the tower is in operation.

Filing a VFR Flight Plan

Although not required, it's simply good practice to file a VFR flight plan

OVERLAPPING BLIND AREAS

A low wing airplane above a high wing airplane presents a problem since both airplane blind areas overlap. There is a greater chance of a collision occurring when the low wing descends or the high wing climbs. **Fig. 17**

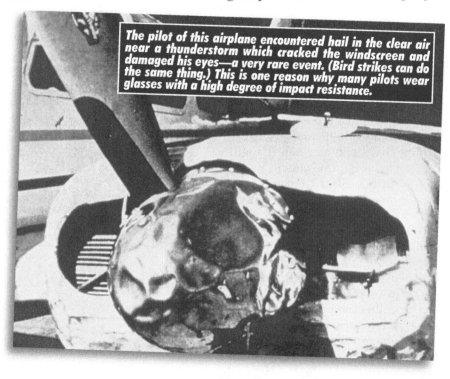

The pilot of this airplane encountered hail in the clear air near a thunderstorm which cracked the windscreen and damaged his eyes—a very rare event. (Bird strikes can do the same thing.) This is one reason why many pilots wear glasses with a high degree of impact resistance.

for all your cross country trips. A VFR flight plan, filed with the nearest Flight Service Station, is good insurance in case your airplane is forced down for any number of reasons, including bad weather or engine problems.

Since every flight plan has a departure time and an estimated time enroute (ETE), an FSS specialist will be expecting you to close that flight plan when the ETE has expired. After 30 minutes or so past the ETE time, search and rescue procedures are initiated. This usually starts with a ramp search of the destination airport and can end in a full scale search and rescue operation by local authorities.

Fortunately, most airplanes are found on the ramp at the destination airport, because the pilot forgot to close his or her flight plan (you can close it with the nearest FSS by phone or radio). Let's examine how to file one of these flight plans.

Figure 18 shows a typical flight plan form.

Block 1—Check the type of flight plan you're filing. In this instance, you'll be filing a VFR flight plan.

Block 2—Enter your compete aircraft identification including the N prefix if you're flying a U.S. registered aircraft.

Block 3—Enter the designator for the aircraft followed by a slant

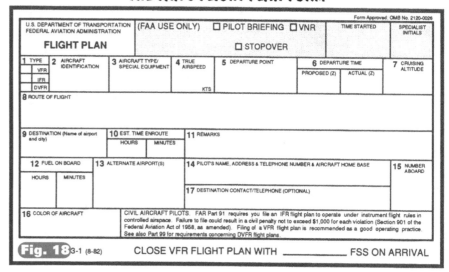

THE FAA'S FLIGHT PLAN FORM

(/) and the transponder or DME equipment code letter. This code tells ATC about some of the transponder and navigation equipment onboard your airplane. The following are the typical codes you might use:

/X - no transponder

/T - transponder with no altitude encoding capability

/U - transponder with altitude encoding capability

/D - DME, but no transponder

/B - DME with transponder, but no Mode C capability

/A - DME and transponder with altitude encoding capability

/G - Global Navigation Satellite System (GNSS), including GPS or Wide Area Augmentation System (WAAS), with enroute and terminal capability.

If you're flying a Cessna Skycatcher with DME and a transponder with altitude encoding capability, you would write "C-162/A" in block 3. In the unlikely event your airplane went down, ATC might be able to retrace your flight path based on their radar tapes if they know the equipment signature of your airplane. For instance, if your airplane has a transponder without an encoding altimeter, they could discount all airplanes appearing with an altitude readout.

Block 4—Enter the true airspeed you've computed based on your altitude and performance chart information.

Block 5—Enter the departure airport identifier or the name of the airport if the identifier is unknown. U.S. airports have three or four letter/number identifiers. Looking on the sectional chart next to the airport name, you may find the airport identifier in parentheses, as shown in Figure 19.

Block 6—Enter your proposed departure time in Coordinated Universal Time (UTC). If you are airborne and are filing the flight plan with the FSS, specify the actual or proposed time you'd like the flight

The airport identifier is found in the airport information block on the sectional chart.

Fig. 19

WHATEVER WORKS

I had not seen my son in a long time and [at the end of the flight, I] forgot to close flight plan. My Remedy? I purchased a 1/8 inch brazing rod and bent it to go over my head with yellow iridescent lettered tag attached. Causes laughs but accomplishes the correct results.

The following pilot dutifully closed flight plan, only to discover an ATC procedural breakdown didn't get the message through. Even though he wasn't at fault, he learned...*There is one thing I could have done that would have saved a lot of people a lot of unnecessary trouble: I could have provided FSS with a destination phone number. This item is optional on flight plan forms. From now on, I will provide a destination phone number if at all available because mistakes happen. The more information FSS has to work with the easier it is to correct a problem.* **ASRS Report**

plan activated. Keep in mind that the VFR flight plan is held by the FSS for one hour after the proposed departure time, then it's eliminated from the computer if it hasn't been activated. If you're running late and have filed a flight plan, call the FSS and give them a revised proposed departure time.

Block 7—Enter the VFR cruising altitude at which you intend to fly. If you're planning on using more than one cruising altitude, list the first one you intend to use.

Block 8—Define your route by navaid identifiers (such as three letter identifiers for VORs or NDBs, or names if you don't know the three letter identifiers), airways, or waypoints (if you're using RNAV). For instance, I could depict my route as:

SLI POM V197 EHF V165 PTV

This tells the FSS specialist that I'll fly from my departure airport (don't need to list the departure air-

port in the route since it's already listed in block 5) to the SLI VOR direct to the POM VOR then via Victor 197 (an airway) to the EHF VOR then via Victor 165 (airway) to the PTV VOR. I don't need to list my destination airport in the route section since it will be listed in block 9.

If you plan on stopping at different airports enroute, simply list them in the remarks section (block 11). For instance, with the routing listed above and with a final destination of Porterville, I might elect to stop at Brackett field to stock up on pilot supplies and Rosamond for lunch. In the remarks section I'd say, "Intermediate stops at Brackett and Rosamond." I could, of course, file three separate flight plans but this is more work.

Block 9: Enter the destination airport identifier code as you did with the departure airport. You can elect to file something unofficially known as a round robin flight plan. Suppose

you wanted your flight plan to reflect a flight to an airport with a return to the original airport of departure. In this instance, you'd simply list the departure airport in the destination airport block 9. The route listed in block 8 would be to the first airport and then reversed back to the departure airport. In the remarks section of the flight plan you can put the words round robin if you like. This signals the FSS specialist of your intention although it's not necessary to list this since the destination is self-explanatory.

If you plan on making one or more stops along the way, it's recommended that a separate flight plan be filed for each leg when the stop is expected to be longer than one hour.

Block 10—Enter your estimated time enroute based on the latest forecast winds. Give yourself a little time cushion (if necessary) so you don't need to rush to close a flight plan. While enroute, if you find that you're running late, simply call the nearest FSS and ask them to extend your flight plan. Remember, when the ETE is up, based on the actual time you opened your flight plan with the FSS, you're technically overdue. That doesn't mean that the FSS personnel are going to drop everything and start looking for you immediately. After a short grace period (usually 30 minutes), they'll make a call to the phone number listed in block 14. If they can't find you at home, they'll start a ramp search, then launch into a full scale search and rescue operation. That's why you want to close your flight plan as soon as possible after you land.

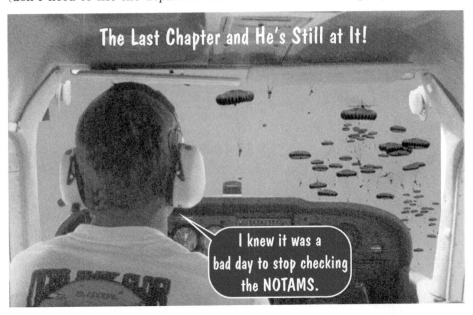

The Last Chapter and He's Still at It!

I knew it was a bad day to stop checking the NOTAMS.

Block 11—Enter the remarks you feel are important. Try to keep them as short as possible simply for clarity and ease of reading. You'll probably hear IFR pilots say that the remarks shouldn't be longer than 15 letters. While that's true for IFR pilots, it's not true for VFR pilots. If necessary, write whatever will fit into the block. Your flight plan is kept on file at the FSS at which it was filed. In the event search and rescue is necessary, the original flight plan is referred to—along with your original remarks. For instance, if your flight is over water, you might mention having flotation equipment, signaling devices and a portable ELT aboard. Write anything that might be useful to someone looking for you in the event of an emergency.

Block 12—Enter the amount of useable fuel on board, computed from the departure point and expressed in hours and minutes.

Block 13—Enter an alternate airport that you might land at in the event the destination airport becomes unavailable for whatever reasons (i.e., runway closed, bad weather, etc.). An alternate airport isn't required for a VFR flight plan. You can choose to leave this block blank.

Block 14—Enter the complete name, address and telephone number of the pilot in command.

Block 15—Enter the number of people on board the aircraft.

Block 16—Enter the predominant colors of the aircraft. This information is especially important for search and rescue.

You can file the flight plan by writing it out on paper and handing it to the FSS specialist or via DUATS (the computer flight plan and weather service) or via a service known as fast file. You can access fast file by calling 1-800-WX-BRIEF and listening for the appropriate keypad inputs. A recording starts and you simply read your flight plan into the phone. It will be put into the FSS computer a short time later by an FSS specialist.

When airborne, you open your flight plan by calling the nearest FSS

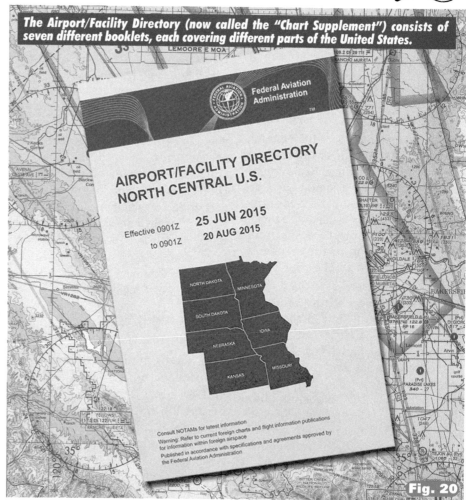

The Airport/Facility Directory (now called the "Chart Supplement") consists of seven different booklets, each covering different parts of the United States.

AIRPORT/FACILITY DIRECTORY
NORTH CENTRAL U.S.

25 JUN 2015

Effective 0901Z
to 0901Z
20 AUG 2015

Fig. 20

on the radio. If the departure airport has a tower, and they aren't too busy, you can ask them to open your VFR flight plan. They simply make the call to the FSS for you. The moment you open the flight plan, the time starts counting down from your ETE. This is why you always want to note this time and, as I've already mentioned, be prepared to extend the time with the nearest FSS if you're running late. Keep in mind that the tower doesn't automatically close your VFR flight plan upon landing (even assuming you land at a tower controlled field). If you ask them to and they agree, then you can assume the flight plan will be closed.

FAA and Industry Publications

Throughout this book I've mentioned several aviation documents, including the *Airport/Facility Directory* (*A/FD*), the *Aeronautical Information Manual* (AIM), NOTAMS and advisory circulars. These documents are all valuable sources of information that you need to help fly safely. Let's examine them again to ensure your familiarity with these valuable information sources. We'll also look at a few other sources of aviation information you might find useful.

Airport/Facility Directory

The *Airport/Facility Directory* consists of several booklets, each covering different parts of the United States (Figure 20). Each directory contains detailed information on all public-use airports including frequencies, runway information, services available and much, much more. Issued once every eight weeks, it's available on a subscription basis or free, via PDF download at http://www.faa.gov/.

Each public airport, heliport and seaplane base has an entry in the

A/FD (see Figure 21). Don't worry if you don't understand all this information. At the beginning of each A/FD a legend explains what each bit of data means. Believe me, there is ample information here to help with almost all questions you might have about the airport and its facilities.

In addition to airport information, the A/FD also provides information on updates and changes to aeronautical charts. Since sectional charts are revised only once every 6 months, while the A/FD is reissued every 8 weeks, any change to a sectional chart can be found in the aeronautical chart bulletin in the rear of the A/FD (Figure 22, box A).

Figure 22 shows all the additional information you'll find in the A/FD: FAA FSDO (Flight Standards District Office) and NWS telephone numbers (box B), and a section for special notices (box C), VOR receiver checkpoints (box D), parachute jump areas (box E), FSS frequencies (box F) and ARTCC frequencies (box G). The A/FD also contains information that's important for the IFR rated pilot.

You can't help but pay attention to the rocket firing area notice east of Reno, at the top of Figure 22 (box C). Of course this area extends vertically up to but not including 1,000 feet AGL, but you don't want to tempt anyone in charge of those rockets by flying a little lower than normal. If you don't think people become tempted, just think back to the time when you were at the driving range as a child. You saw that fellow in a steel caged tractor scooping up fallen golf balls. You probably thought, "Since he is protected, it probably won't hurt much if I do manage to hit the tractor..." It's best to avoid any area with the word rocket in it.

The Aeronautical Information Manual

At the beginning of the chapter I mentioned the Aeronautical Information Manual (AIM), shown in Figure 23, but it's hard to say too much about this encyclopedia of aviation information. It's your best guide to aviation information on the following topics:

High Priests Of Aviation Knowledge

As young flight instructors, we used to challenge each other about topics within the AIM. It was considered important to have knowledge of even the most esoteric data.

One day a fellow CFI and I decided to play a joke on a new instructor. We were going to ask each other questions and pretend we knew the answers by making them up. For instance, I would ask my friend what the candlelight power of an airport's rotating beacon was. He'd say, "11,200 foot-candles." Then he'd ask an even more esoteric question such as, "What is the minimum thickness of the white paint used to paint runway numbers?"

What really got our new CFI friend was when I asked this question. "If you're flying a Boeing 747 loaded with 15,000 live turkeys, and you're 8,516 pounds overweight, how many turkeys would you have to make jump into the air, with a stick, at one time, to get under gross weight?"

I think our friend gave up instructing and went back to being an automobile mechanic.

Rod

Air Navigation Radio Aids

Aeronautical Lighting and Other Airport Visual Aids

Airspace

Air Traffic Control

Air Traffic Procedures

Emergency Procedures

Safety of Flight

Medical Facts For Pilots

Aeronautical Charts and Related Publications

Pilot/Controller Glossary

Revised several times a year, this document is available on a subscription basis. It contains recommendations and procedures involving the safety of flight, and information that exists as regulations in other FAA publications.

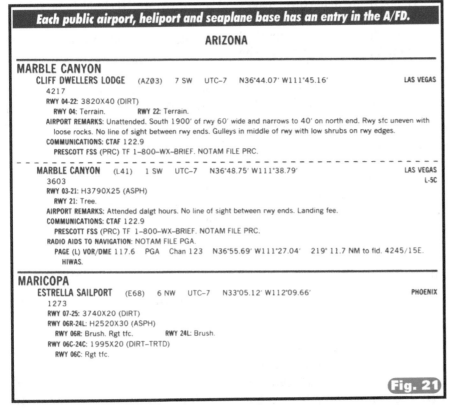

PUBLIC AIRPORTS AND THE AIRPORT/FACILITY DIRECTORY

Each public airport, heliport and seaplane base has an entry in the A/FD.

ARIZONA

MARBLE CANYON
  CLIFF DWELLERS LODGE (AZ03) 7 SW UTC-7 N36°44.07' W111°45.16'   LAS VEGAS
    4217
  RWY 04-22: 3820X40 (DIRT)
    RWY 04: Terrain.   RWY 22: Terrain.
  AIRPORT REMARKS: Unattended. South 1900' of rwy 60' wide and narrows to 40' on north end. Rwy sfc uneven with loose rocks. No line of sight between rwy ends. Gulleys in middle of rwy with low shrubs on rwy edges.
  COMMUNICATIONS: CTAF 122.9
    PRESCOTT FSS (PRC) TF 1-800-WX-BRIEF. NOTAM FILE PRC.

MARBLE CANYON (L41) 1 SW UTC-7 N36°48.75' W111°38.79'   LAS VEGAS
    3603   L-5C
  RWY 03-21: H3790X25 (ASPH)
    RWY 21: Tree.
  AIRPORT REMARKS: Attended dalgt hours. No line of sight between rwy ends. Landing fee.
  COMMUNICATIONS: CTAF 122.9
    PRESCOTT FSS (PRC) TF 1-800-WX-BRIEF. NOTAM FILE PRC.
  RADIO AIDS TO NAVIGATION: NOTAM FILE PGA.
    PAGE (L) VOR/DME 117.6 PGA Chan 123 N36°55.69' W111°27.04' 219° 11.7 NM to fld. 4245/15E.
    HIWAS.

MARICOPA
  ESTRELLA SAILPORT (E68) 6 NW UTC-7 N33°05.12' W112°09.66'   PHOENIX
    1273
  RWY 07-25: 3740X20 (DIRT)
  RWY 06R-24L: H2520X30 (ASPH)
    RWY 06R: Brush. Rgt tfc.   RWY 24L: Brush.
  RWY 06C-24C: 1995X20 (DIRT-TRTD)
    RWY 06C: Rgt tfc.

Fig. 21

LAS VEGAS SECTIONAL
85th Edition, 10 Mar 2011

OBSTRUCTIONS
10 Mar 2011 – 30 Jun 2011 No Major Changes.

AIRPORTS
10 Mar 2011 – 5 May 2011 No Major Changes.
30 Jun 2011 ST GEORGE arpt abandoned. 37°05'26"N. 113°35'35"W.

NAVAIDs
10 Mar 2011 – 5 May 2011 No Major Changes.
30 Jun 2011 Delete ST GEORGE VOR/DME. 37°05'17"N. 113°35'30"W.

AIRSPACE
10 Mar 2011 – 5 May 2011 No Major Changes.
30 Jun 2011 Revise BRYCE CANYON. UT. Class E: That airspace extending upward from 700 feet above

Fig. 22 Box A

FAA AND NWS   **Fig. 22 Box B**

FSS
TELEPHONE NUMBERS

Flight Service Station (FSS) facilities provide flight planning and weather briefing services to pilots. FSS services in the contiguous United States, Hawaii and Puerto Rico, are provided by a network of large FSS facilities and a few select remote facilities some of which operate part-time. Because of the interconnectivity between the facilities, all FSS services including radio frequencies are available continuously using published data.

Telephone Information Briefing Service (TIBS) is a FSS service that provides continuous recordings of meteorological and/or aeronautical information. A touch-tone telephone is required to fully utilize this service.

Further information can be found in the Aeronautical Information Manual (AIM).

NATIONAL FSS TELEPHONE NUMBER

Pilot Weather Briefings 1–800–WX–BRIEF (1–800–992–7433)

SPECIAL NOTICES   **Fig. 22 Box C**

DENVER TERMINAL RADAR APPROACH CONTROL
Denver, Colorado

The Denver Terminal Radar Approach Control has been issued a waiver which enables controllers to assign speed restrictions without obtaining pilot concurrences: e.g., speeds of less than 250 knots below FL280 and speeds of less than 210 knots when the aircraft is greater than 20 flying miles from the threshold of the airport of intended landing.

EXTENSIVE HELICOPTER FLIGHT TRAINING IN THE VICINITY OF ROCKY MOUNTAIN METROPOLITAN AIRPORT (BJC), BROOMFIELD, COLORADO

Frequent usage of Runway 11R-29L, Taxiway D, and the north end of Runway 20 by helicopter flight schools. Pilots are cautioned to listen carefully to ATC for turnoff instructions when landing on Runway 11R-29L. Helicopters flight schools use three primary local procedures: Charlie Two, Ball, and Erie. CHARLIE TWO: Expect departures to the south thence turning to the northwest. Expect arrivals from the northwest. BALL: Expect departures to the south thence turning east. Expect arrivals from the east. ERIE: Expect departures northbound. Expect arrivals from the north.

INTENSE HELICOPTER OPERATIONS
LOS ANGELES BASIN AREA, CALIFORNIA

VOR RECEIVER CHECK
VOR RECEIVER CHECKPOINTS
AND
VOR TEST FACILITIES (VOT)
ARIZONA
VOR RECEIVER CHECKPOINTS

Facility Name (Arpt Name)	Freq/Ident	Type Check Pt. Gnd. Fac. AB/ALT	Azimuth from Fac. Mag.	Dist. from Fac. N.M.	Checkpoint Description
Bard	116.8/BZA	A/2000	242	5.9	Over interstate 8 freeway crossing canal.
Drake (Ernest A. Love Fld)	114.1/DRK	A/7000	124	5.0	Over apch end Rwy 30.
Flagstaff (Pulliam)	113.85/FLG	A/8000	033	6.5	Over red and white square twr.
Fort Huachuca (Sierra Vista Muni/Libby AAF)	113.6/FHU	G	80		Runup area Twy G at 26 end.
Kingman (Kingman)	108.8/IGM	G	220		

Fig. 22 Box D

PARACHUTE JUMPING AREAS   **Fig. 22 Box E**

LOCATION	DISTANCE AND RADIAL FROM NEAREST VOR/VORTAC	MAXIMUM ALTITUDE	REMARKS
		ARIZONA	
(c) Buckeye Muni	8 NM; 089° Buckeye	14,000	Daily SR-2 hours after SS. 2 NM radius.
(c) Bullhead City, Eagle Airpark	10 NM; 300° Needles	15,000	3 NM Daily 0645-1835
(c) Casa Grande Muni	9 NM; 041° Stanfield	12,000	2 NM Daily 0600-1700.
(c) Coolidge Muni	25 NM; 070° Stanfield	17,999	15 NM radius, daily. High altitude, full canopy, free fall, and low level combat parachute jumping. Large military transports in vicinity of arpt.
(c) Cottonwood Arpt	22.1 NM; 072° Drake	14,000	Continuous during daylgt hrs. **Albuquerque Center 124.5**

NATIONAL FSS TELEPHONE NUMBER

Pilot Weather Briefings 1–800–WX–BRIEF (1–800–992–7433)

OTHER FSS TELEPHONE NUMBERS (except in Alaska)

TIBS (see description above) 1–877–4TIBS-WX (1–877–484–2799)

Clearance Delivery Only 1–888–766–8267

Lifeguard Flights Only 1–877–LIF-GRD3 (1–877–543–4733)

Flights within DC SFRA & FRZ * 1–866–225–7410

* District of Columbia Special Flight Rules Area & Flight Restricted Zone

Fig. 22 Box F

348	AIR ROUTE TRAFFIC CONTROL CENTERS	

Air Route Traffic Control Center frequencies and their remoted transmitter sites are listed below for the coverage of this volume. Bold face type indicates high altitude frequencies, light face type indicates low altitude frequencies. To insure unrestricted IFR operations within the high altitude enroute sectors, the use of 720 channel communications equipment (25 kHz channel spacing) is required.

®ALBUQUERQUE CENTER – 134.6 132.8	H-4-5-6-7, L-5-6-7-8-10-15-17-19
Alamogordo – 132.65 132.65	
Animas – 134.45 133.0	(KZAB)
Carlsbad – 135.875	
Childs Peak – 135.15 132.45 126.45 125.25	
Clines Corner – 133.65 132.8 125.075	
Globe Nr 1 – 135.725 132.9 132.9	
Globe Nr 2 – 135.15 133.85 132.35 132.35 125.4	
Mesa Rica – 128.675 125.075	
Mount Dora – 133.05 128.225 127.85	
Prescott – 135.325 134.325 128.45	

Fig. 22 Box G

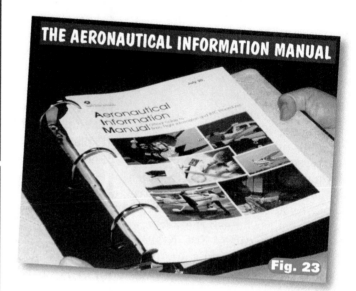

Fig. 23

Notices To Airmen (NOTAMS)

When there are significant and important changes in aeronautical information, you need to know about them. This becomes especially important when such information might affect the safety of your flight. NOTAMS contain information such as airport or primary runway closures, changes in the status of navigational aids, radar service availability and other information essential to planned enroute, terminal or landing operations. When such information is not known far enough in advance to be included in the *Airport/Facility Directory*, it's likely to be found in the listing of NOTAMS. Your job is to check these NOTAMS before every flight. You can ask the Flight Service Station specialist for all pertinent NOTAM information during your weather briefing or just download them when you obtain your weather briefing from an FAA approved service provider, such as DUATS.

There are two types of NOTAMS you should be familiar with: D NOTAMs and FDC NOTAMS. Let's examine both.

D NOTAMS – D (distant and local) NOTAMS contain information that directly affects your ability to fly an airplane safely. This includes information on airport or primary runway closures, changes in the status of navigational aids, radar service availability, and other information essential to planned enroute, terminal, or landing operations. In addition, these NOTAMS now contain less critical (but still very important) airport information such as taxiway closures, personnel and equipment near or crossing runways, and airport lighting aids such as VASIs.

FDC NOTAMS – Occasionally, it becomes necessary to issue information on changes that are regulatory in nature. A regulatory change might be an amendment to an instrument chart used by IFR pilots or the issuance of a temporary flight restriction (such as prohibition of flight over a natural disaster area, which is important to you as a VFR pilot). When such an action is necessary, the National Flight Data Center (NFDC) will issue an FDC NOTAM. FDC NOTAMS are issued once and kept on file at the FSS until published or canceled.

All this information is kept in a computer in Kansas City and is distributed automatically via several sources, such as the FSS when you call for your briefing or via DUATS, when you obtain your briefing by computer. (Note: If you call for a weather briefing, make sure you ask the FSS specialist for any pertinent FDC NOTAM information concerning your flight. They usually give these to you, but it's always best to ask, nevertheless.)

Just in case you're not getting enough mail at your house, NOTAMS are published once every 28 days (four weeks) in the Notices to Airmen Publication (NTAP), as shown in Figure 24. You can subscribe to these NOTAMS, but it's much more convenient to obtain them via the Flight Service Station or DUATS.

When reading D NOTAMS, they will have one of the following keywords as the first part of the text: RWY, TWY, RAMP, APRON, AD, OBST, NAV, COM, SVC, AIRSPACE, (U), or (O). Each keyword indicates the category of the NOTAM. For instance, RWY indicated this NOTAM

THE NOTICE TO AIRMEN PUBLICATION (NTAP)

Fig. 24

D NOTAM KEYWORDS, EXAMPLES AND EXPLANATIONS

RWY (Runway)
Example: !STL STL RWY 12L/30R CLSD EXC TXG
This NOTAM says that Runway Twelve Left and Runway Thirty Right are closed at St. Louis Lambert Airport, except for taxiing.

TWY (Taxiway)
Example: !LNS LNS TWY A LGTS OTS
NOTAM says that the lights on taxiway A are out of service at Lancaster Airport.

APRON (Apron)
Example: !ATL ATL APRON NORTH TWY L3 APRON CLSD
NOTAM indicates that the north taxiway L3 Apron is closed at Atlanta Hartsfield Airport.

AD (Aerodrome)
Example: !CEW CEW AD CLSD WEF 0802041400-0802041800
Explanation: Bob Sikes Airport is closed from 1400 till 1800 UTC on February 4, 2008.

OBST (Obstructions, including obstruction lighting outages)
Example: !PIE CLW OBST CRANE 195 (125 AGL) .25 NE (2755N08241W) TIL 0803032000
NOTAM indicates there is a crane, 195 feet MSL or 125 feet AGL, ¼ statute mile northeast of the Clearwater Air Park Airport until March 3, 2008 at 2000 UTC. The lat/longs of the crane are 27° 55″ North and 082° 41″ West.

NAV (Navigation Aids)
Example: !DCA DCA NAV GTN NDB OTS
NOTAM indicates that the Georgetown NDB, that services Washington National Airport, is out of service.

COM (Communications)
Example: !DCA PSK COM RCO OTS
NOTAM shows that the remote communications outlet is out of service at New River Valley Airport.

SVC (Services)
Example: !PBF PBF SVC TEMPO TWR 121.0 1400-2100 DLY
NOTAM indicates that at Grider Field, a temporary control tower is available between 1400 and 2100 UTC daily, and frequency 121.0 will be used to control aircraft on all movement areas and traffic patterns.

AIRSPACE (Airspace)
Example: !IPT RAV AIRSPACE R5802 ACT TIL 0802211230
NOTAM indicates that Restricted Area R5802A is active until February 21, 2008 at 1230 UTC

(U) – Unverified Aeronautical Information
Example: !ORT 6K8 (U) RWY ABANDONED VEHICLE
This is an unverified NOTAM indicating that there is an abandoned vehicle on the runway at Tok Junction Airport.

(O) – Other Aeronautical Information
Aeronautical information received from any authorized source that may be beneficial to aircraft operations and does not meet defined NOTAM criteria.
Example: !LOZ LOZ (O) CONTROLLED BURN OF HOUSE 8 NE APCH END RWY 23 WEF 0802271300-0802271700
NOTAM says that there is a controlled burn of a house 8 statute miles northeast of the approach end of Runway 23 at the London-Corbin Airport between 1300 and 1700 UTC on February 27, 2008.

Fig. 25

refs to the *runway*, and so on. Each NOTAM begins with an exclamation mark (they are important, right?), followed by the accountability location (the source generating the NOTAM), followed by the affected airport (or facility). Figure 25 shows all the major D NOTAM categories, along with examples and explanations. Take some time to familiarize yourself with these, since you'll most likely encounter similar type NOTAMS during the preflight briefing. If you have trouble interpreting the NOTAM codes, then see Postflight Briefing #16-1 at the end of this chapter.

FDC NOTAMS are shown in Figure 26. These are NOTAMS that pertain mostly to instrument rated pilots, although you should look them over for anything relevant to your flight.

Advisory Circulars

For years the FAA has been providing pilots with useful information in the form of advisory circulars (AC) (Figure 27). Advisory circulars are a means of disseminating nonregulatory information of interest. The subjects covered include procedures, techniques, aircraft, airmen, airspace, ATC, airports and general operating rules. Since these are advisory in nature only, their contents should not be considered legally binding unless they become regulations. You can order advisory circulars from the Superintendent of Documents, U.S. Government Printing Office or just download them for free at http://www.faa.gov/safety/.

FDC NOTAM EXAMPLE

```
FDC 4/0435 SJC FI/T NORMAN Y. MINETA SAN JOSE INTL,
    SAN JOSE, CA.
    NDB/DME RWY 30L, AMDT 6.                    Fig. 26
    S-30L MDA 780/HAT 723 ALL CATS.  VIS CAT C 1 1/2, CAT D 2.
    SIDESTEP RWY 29 MDA 780/HAT 728 ALL CATS.  VIS CAT C 2,
    CAT D 2 1/4.
    SIDESTEP RWY 30R MDA 780/HAT 725 ALL CATS.  VIS CAT C 2,
    CAT D 2 1/4.
```

This FDC NOTAM for San Jose airport contains information on instrument approach procedures. Nevertheless, it's always wise to ask the FSS specialist for FDC NOTAMS pertinent to your flight.

FAA ADVISORY CIRCULARS

U.S. Department of Transportation

Federal Aviation Administration

Advisory Circular

Fig. 27

Subject: HAZARDS ASSOCIATED WITH SPINS IN AIRPLANES PROHIBITED FROM INTENTIONAL SPINNING	Date: 10/8/82	AC No: 61-67.
	Initiated by: AFO-840	Change:

1. PURPOSE. This advisory circular has been published for the following p

    a. To inform pilots of the airworthiness standards for the type certif of small airplanes prescribed in Section 23.221 of the Federal Aviation Reg (FAR) concerning spin maneuvers;

    b. To emphasize the importance of observing restrictions which prohibi intentional spinning of certain airplanes;

    c. To recommend specific flight operations procedures to reduce the pr of entering an inadvertent spin during the performance of stall entries and recoveries; and

You'll find that advisory circulars are numbered according to the Federal Aviation Regulation numbering system. For instance, the advisory circulars in Figure 27 is numbered AC 61-67. AC's marked anywhere in the 60's represent information dealing with FAR Part 61— Certification: Pilots and Flight Instructors. AC's marked anywhere is the 90's represent information on Part 91—Air Traffic and General Operating Flight Rules. ACs marked anywhere is the 20's pertain to Certification and Testing of Aircraft (FAR Part 23) and deal with certification of small airplanes. AC's marked anywhere in the 70's represent information on airspace (FAR Part 71 deal with airspace construction).

Novel Student Pilot Solutions

A student of mine showed me that there are BETTER ways to deal with fast-talking controllers and an overabundance of communication on the frequency.

HUH?

We were doing touch and go landings at NAS Corpus Christi in a T-28B (This is important because it establishes the fact that I was BEHIND the student and couldn't really see what he was doing!) In any event, NAS Corpus has two parallel runways and on that day we had a full bag of left and right traffic, as well as occasional straight in instrument approaches to the instrument runway. On the downwind, I could barely hear my student doing his checklist items among all the chatter. Mercifully, there was a brief pause as we approached the 180 - and then I heard, "Delta 685, Corpus Christi Approach, cleared for the ILS 13, contact the Tower at the marker". I hollered up front, "What did you do?" The student replied, "Sir, there were too many people talking on that other frequency so I picked one that wasn't as busy".

A Fellow Instructor (name unknown)

Aviation Decision Making:
Thoughts for Life

The fact is, not everyone on this planet exercises good judgment. For instance, every so often you'll read that someone in a black wetsuit, floating on a surfboard and dangling four limbs over the side, was attacked by a great white shark. Isn't that amazing? What was this person thinking? Doesn't dressing up this way make you look like the shark's favorite food—the seal? Is it the shark's fault he was served breakfast on board? You could say the surfer sealed his own fate in opting to dress as he did. Clearly a bad decision.

Fortunately, exercising good judgment is something we can do on the ground or in the air. With a few simple tools, you can keep yourself from being eaten by some of aviation's well known predators.

It's true, the exercise of good judgment can be taught, despite a once-popular belief that good judgment only came with years of experience. We now know that you can learn to identify and control several of the variables leading to poor decisions. For instance, it's possible to identify attitudes that are hazardous to safe flight as well as learn how to modify our personal behavior. These are just a few of the useful techniques that help you make better decisions. Let's cover a few of the most important features of aviation decision making.

Two Types of Decisions

Decisions usually fall into two categories—those tied to time constraints and those that are not. A time-constrained decision often requires an immediate solution. For example, if you have an engine fire, this requires immediate action. If, on the other hand, your alternator just failed in VFR conditions, you need not rush to solve the problem. You can take your time and collect information before deciding on a course of action.

In fact, most of the aviation decisions you make will not require immediate action. Preflight is a good example. It's rare to hear of someone having an emergency when preflighting the airplane. You can take your time and carefully consider all the information available to you.

That's what makes the results of a NASA study all the more interesting. The research revealed that 80% of the poor decisions leading to an in-flight incident occurred during the preflight phase, when pilots had all the time in the world to get it right.

Fuel exhaustion is a good example of this type of error. If a pilot had taken more time to carefully think about fuel, he or she wouldn't have crashed short of the destination with bone-dry tanks. In case you're interested, one study found that 70% of fuel exhaustion accidents occurred within 10 miles of the destination airport and 50% occurred within one mile of the airport. Close, so close, and yet so far.

Of course, pilots could handle this problem by planning a flight, then switching the destination to an airport that's 10 miles closer. You're right, that seems ridiculous, doesn't it? I think it's much simpler to do some proper preflighting to begin with. Thoughtful preparation, having sufficient fuel reserves and careful planning are the ways to prevent accidents.

Factors That Influence Our Decisions

Knowledge

There are several factors that influence your ability to make good aviation decisions. First, in order to successfully cope with any aviation situation you need knowledge. This is typically acquired during flight training, where you'll learn things such as how to calculate airplane performance, evaluating weather, and selecting alternatives if the flight can't be completed as planned. These are a just a few of the many practical topics you'll be exposed to during the course of your training (I said practical topics, so don't expect to learn something like how to look good in scarf and goggles, etc.)

Skill

In addition to knowledge, you must develop skill in applying that knowledge. That's why the FAA requires a minimum of 20 hours of flight time for the sport pilot license. This also explains why you can't obtain a pilot's license via a home correspondence course (if you could, it would properly be called a crash course). In addition to this, you have to pass both a practical flight test and a knowledge exam to demonstrate your flight and knowledge skills.

Aids That Help With Decision Making

There are several aids available to help you make decisions properly. A checklist is a good example of one of these aids. Written-type checklists are normally used for repetitive tasks when it's not wise to rely on short- or long-term memory. Checklists are commonly used for the preflight inspection of the airplane, starting the engine,

THE AVIATION BRAIN   Professor Bob

Emotions Without Logic
+
Airplane
=
Bent Airplane

emergencies, and engine shutdown. Checklists can also be used during the preflight phase, and these don't necessarily need to be of the written variety, either. A simple acronym is often sufficient to cover the essentials.

For instance, before every flight you should take inventory of your psychological and physiological readiness to pilot an airplane. You can use the acronym "I'M SAFE" to do this. Here's what the acronym means.

1. *Illness.* Do I have any symptoms?

2. *Medication.* Have I been taking prescription or over-the-counter drugs?

3. *Stress.* Am I under psychological pressure from work or home situations? Do I have money, health, or family problems?

4. *Alcohol.* Have I been drinking within 8 hours? Within 24 hours?

5. *Fatigue.* Am I tired and not adequately rested?

6. *Eating.* Have I eaten enough of the proper foods to keep adequately nourished during the entire flight?

Pilots using this checklist are less likely to suffer some sort of impairment that can lead or at least contribute to an accident. Statistics show that impairment contributes to many more accidents than mechanical problems. Please commit this checklist to memory and use it before every flight.

Self Awareness and Hazardous Thinking

Common Behavioral Pilot Traps

If there is such a thing as an enemy to a pilot, then it's the pilot himself. It's a pilot's inability to deal with some very common behavioral traps that usually gets him or her into trouble. You don't want to fall into these traps. I'm specifically referring to traps like always trying to complete the flight the way you planned it, trying to please your passenger, trying to meet schedules, as well as trying to demonstrate that you have the right stuff. Well, at hundreds of miles per hour, the fabled right stuff can turn you and your airplane into bent stuff.

Here are 12 common traps of which you should be aware. Most experienced pilots have fallen into one or more of these somewhere along the way. If they were lucky, they escaped unscathed and learned from the experience. Here's your chance to learn before the experience. Avoiding these traps requires recognizing the behaviors or tendencies associated with them.

1. *Peer Pressure.* No, this doesn't have anything to do with flying near the beach. It's simply poor decision making based upon emotional response to peers rather than evaluating a situation objectively.

2. *Mindset.* This trap results from a pilot's inability to recognize and cope with situations that differ from those anticipated or planned. In other words, things change. When necessary, pilots should, too.

3. *Get-There-Itis.* This tendency, common among pilots, clouds the vision and impairs judgment. It's caused by a fixation on the original goal or destination combined with a total disregard for any alternative course of action. Get-There-Itis is suspected to be the root cause of another malady that I just made up called Break-and-Crumple-Your-Airplane-Itis.

4. *Duck-Under Syndrome.* This is a tendency instrument rated pilots have to sneak a peek by descending below minimum altitudes during an instrument approach. It's based on a belief that there is always a built-in fudge factor that can be used or on an unwillingness to admit defeat and shoot a missed approach. Pilots from China might call this the Peaking-Duck-Under-Glass-Syndrome.

5. *Scud Running.* Scud running involves pushing the capabilities of the pilot and the aircraft by flying in poor visibility and/or under low clouds while trying to maintain visual contact with the terrain (and trying to avoid physical contact with it as well. Very dangerous business).

6. *Continuing visual flight rules (VFR) into instrument conditions.* This often leads to spatial disorientation or collision with the ground and/or obstacles. It is even more dangerous if the pilot is not instrument qualified (and it's especially dangerous if the pilot isn't wrapped in a big, thick mattress, too).

7. *Getting Behind the Aircraft.* The only time it's good to get behind the aircraft is when you untie the tail before departure. Unfortunately, some pilots allow events or the situation to control their actions rather than the other way around. This condition is characterized by a

constant state of surprise at what happens next. Pilots in this condition often look like they drew their eyebrows in at too great an angle during makeup time.

8. *Loss of Positional or Situational Awareness.* Another case of getting behind the aircraft, which results in not knowing where you are, an inability to recognize deteriorating circumstances, and/or misjudging how fast your situation is worsening.

9. *Operating Without Adequate Fuel Reserves.* Ignoring minimum fuel reserve requirements, either VFR or Instrument Flight Rules (IFR), is generally the result of over-confidence, lack of flight planning, or ignoring the regulations. In other words, you can fuel some of the people some of the time but you can't fuel everyone all the time (especially when they need to be fueled).

10. *Descent Below the Minimum Enroute Altitude.* Here, the duck-under syndrome (discussed earlier) manifests itself during the enroute portion of an IFR flight.

11. *Flying Outside the Envelope.* This results from a pilot's unjustified reliance on the (usually mistaken) belief that the aircraft's high performance capability meets the demands imposed by his or her (usually overestimated) flying skills.

12. *Neglect of Flight Planning,* preflight inspections, checklists, etc. This is a problem associated with a pilot's unjustified reliance on his or her short and long term memory, regular flying skills, repetitive and familiar routes, etc.

Hazardous Thought Patterns And Their Antidotes

Another factor affecting the quality and safety of flight is a pilot's attitude. Unlike personality, most psychologists agree that you can change an attitude. Your attitude is a state of mind, a feeling, a disposition. Not all attitudes, unfortunately, are conducive to safe flying. The following are five attitudes that aviation psychologists believe to be particularly hazardous to safe flight:

Anti-authority—This attitude belongs to people who don't like being told what to do. Folks like these often rebel against the rules and regulations on which safe flying are built. This hazardous attitude causes some pilots to rebel against authority by deliberately breaking rules intended for safety. For

instance, I knew of a pilot who removed the right seat from his airplane so there would be no place for an instructor to sit and tell him what to do. It's a good bet that he had the North American distributorship on anti-authority attitudes.

Impulsivity—Some people often feel the need to do something and do it immediately even when it's not the right thing to do. Often these folks will do the first thing that comes to mind, without thinking about what the best alternative might be. This is why I always get a little nervous when a pilot I'm flying with suddenly says, "Hey, watch this." It's likely that he's about to engage in some strange behavior that he probably hasn't thought about very carefully. Having a front row seat at Aviation Impulsive Theater is not my idea of having a good time.

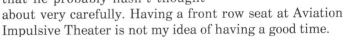

Invulnerability—It's not uncommon for people to feel that accidents only happen to others, not to them. These folks know that accidents can happen, and they know that anyone can be affected, but they never really feel or believe they will be personally involved. A pilot with this attitude is more likely to take chances and increase risk. Pilots like this often think they're Superman, but Superman doesn't really need an airplane, does he?

Macho—A macho pilot is someone with an exaggerated sense of masculinity, stressing attributes such as physical courage, virility, aggressiveness, overt manliness, etc. This can lead a pilot to rely on his "machismo" attributes rather than on rational information. Instead of checking the weather, a pilot with a macho attitude might say, "There's no weather problem I can't handle." Yikes!

Resignation—Pilots who thinks, "What's the use?" are people who don't feel in control of the events in their lives. They often blame bad luck for whatever happens. They tend to not seek information and to not make positive decisions. Instead, they drift along hoping that good things happen while doing little or nothing to ensure that they do. It's as if they fold their hands and sit back passively, doing nothing, like a little pilot-Gandhi. While that behavior may liberate a country from the clutches of foreign domination, it's not likely to make you any safer in the air.

Hazardous Attitude Antidotes	Fig. 28
Attitude	**Antidote**
Anti-authority—Don't tell me.	Follow the rules. They are usually right.
Impulsivity—Do something quickly.	Not so fast. Think first.
Invulnerability—It won't happen to me.	It could happen to me.
Macho—I can do it.	Taking chances is foolish.
Resignation—What's the use?	I'm not helpless. I can make a difference.

These attitudes can contribute to poor judgment. They can compel you to make decisions involving greater risk. Once you've recognized them, however, you've taken the first step in neutralizing their dangerous effects on your decision making process. Remember, most people have these attitudes to some degree. To be frank about it, all of us, at one time or another, have probably acted macho, impulsive or invulnerable. Avoiding problems with judgment means that you should be aware of how these attitudes can negatively influence flying safely.

Hazardous Attitude Antidotes

Recognition of hazardous thoughts is the first step toward neutralizing them. After recognizing a thought as hazardous, the pilot should label it as hazardous, and then state the corresponding antidote. Antidotes should be memorized for each of the hazardous attitudes so they automatically come to mind when needed (Figure 28).

At this point, however, any intelligent person is bound to ask, "If I am acting in a hazardous manner, how is it possible that I'd be self-reflective enough to identify it, much less apply an antidote to stop it?" Great question!

The fact is that hazardous attitudes are *temporary* dispositions, not *permanent* ones. Like the temporary feeling of fear or anxiety, hazardous attitudes stand out from the background of your personality sufficiently for you to recognize them, but only if you know they exist in the first place. That is why we're discussing them here. Now that you know they exist, you're in a better position to do something about them. Do what? How about talking to yourself.

Perhaps, at one time or another, you've found yourself anxious, rushed, or panicky and told yourself to, "Calm down, relax, take your time." The amazing thing is that self-talk actually works in modifying your behavior, especially in high anxiety conditions. That's why it also works well in controlling behavior associated with any of the five hazardous attitudes. The next time you recognize that you're demonstrating any of the five hazardous attitudes, apply the accompanying self-talk antidote.

Do antidotes actually work? You bet they do, and I'm not just saying that so that you'll keep reading this book, either. They work, and they can save your life for one very important reason. You can be the best stick and rudder pilot on the planet (or other planets, too), but this means nothing in terms of safety if you let a bad attitude influence your behavior. That's a fact. So be proactive, tune your personal antenna to recognize and identify these attitudes and, if you catch yourself exhibiting one or more, don't be surprised. It happens to the best of us. The difference is that good pilots use the antidote to prevent bad behavior

Professor Bob

Professor Bob has found proof, via X-ray pictures, that it's a pilot's bad attitude that can cause accidents. The X-ray shown is taken from a pilot who ran out of fuel because he didn't want to waste his valuable time stopping for gas. An X-ray from the other side of the pilot's head also proved he had a bad attitude, but you need a mirror to figure this out.

Being Pilot In Command

What would you think if I told you that even if you fly a Cessna Skycatcher, you have the same authority as the captain of a Boeing 777? It's true, though you have no say-so over his or her 777. There is only one regulation authorizing PIC authority, and that's FAR 91.3, which applies to anyone who flies anything (Area 51 UFO vehicles are an exception). This means that even if you're operating under FAR Part 121 or 135, this regulation is the one that applies to the PIC. The problem here is that most pilots aren't taught how to be pilot in command. They sort of accept the authority without acknowledging or really understanding the responsibility.

TWA Captain Dave Gwinn

The way the FAA looks at it, as PIC you have the final authority and the final say as to the operation of your aircraft. FAR 91.3 is one of the clearest, most succinct and least ambiguous regulations ever written, and for good reason, too. The FAA wants to make sure you know, unambiguously, that you're the one in command and you're the one responsible for making the proper decisions on an airplane. And finally, that you're the one on whom they'll pin the tail if anything goes wrong.

Years ago I met a fellow who ran a medevac helicopter operation. He said that when he hired someone to fly his medical helicopters, he hired them on the basis that these people would tell him "no" when it was appropriate to do so. In other words, he wanted his pilots to have the leadership and strength of character to say that they shouldn't go flying when the risks were too great.

The reality is that many people are just plain scared to say "no" when it's not safe to fly. That's not the type of person this man wanted piloting his machines. Just imagine how difficult a decision it must be to say "no" to a medevac flight to retrieve someone injured on a freeway somewhere when the weather makes it unsafe to fly. Do you have the mental sinew to make this call, based on your level of experience? If not, then you need to reconsider your priorities, because this is precisely what the pilot in command is expected to do.

Sure, you say that telling the boss "no" might mean you get fired. OK, that's possible. You might also say that this is just unfair, even though it's the right thing to do. Yes, that's true. My reply would be that life doesn't have to be fair (check your contract), but it's not as if death gives you some sort of advantage. Being PIC means that you have to be willing to take charge, be in charge and make the necessary decisions willingly, without concern for your personal needs, especially when the needs of others are more important. That's hard language, but it's the way the world works.

A friend who once did the hiring for Flying Tiger airlines told me that they never hired pilots. Instead, they hired captains, even though this person would sit in the flight engineer's seat for many years. Flying Tigers wanted pilots who were captain material, not just pilot material. There *is* a difference.

Sometimes you'll have to make decisions that are unpopular and might upset or disappoint your passenger. The weather might require delaying or even canceling a flight. Sure, your passenger won't like it, but if that's the appropriate thing to do, then it must be done. Do you have the character to behave in the right way? Hopefully you do, since this is part of what being PIC is all about. Of course, there's much more to being PIC of an airplane, too. So let's see what else is involved.

Crew/Cockpit Resource Management

Crew/cockpit resource management (CRM) is all about using the resources that are available to you during your duty as PIC. These resources might be the human resources you have in a copilot, the hardware you have in the cockpit, or the information available to you via that hardware or from ATC. It's a major misconception that only pilots of multi-pilot crews can use CRM or CRM philosophy. Single-pilot operators also need to know how to make better use of all the resources available to them, perhaps even more so than those who've got triple redundancy and a six-planet GPS.

Human Resources

Those resources include all the people with whom you routinely work in preparing and executing a flight—weather briefers, line personnel, mechanics, crewmembers, pilots and air traffic controllers. The real issue here is whether or not you're making good use of these resources. Let's examine how you'd use a copilot (or a capable, non-pilot passenger) if you had one on your flight.

Let's say you're flying for a Part 135 charter operation and the flight requires a copilot. Obviously this flight won't be in a Piper Cub or there wouldn't be much room for the passenger, would there? What does a copilot do for you? The answer is, anything you want. Within reason, of course. They don't do windows or ironing.

Copilots are wonderful resources if you know how to use them properly. Tuning radios, finding charts, making calls to ATC or the automated flight service station, monitoring your performance and gaining experience are all

Thanks for the Memories

Most folks want a better memory, at least when they can remember that they want it. Memory is an important part of the flying process. A pilot has to remember a lot of small things as well a lot of big things, not to mention many in-between things. Here are a few concepts to consider about how your memory works and how to make it work better for you.

Memory works in a multistage process involving three systems: *the sensory register*, *working* or *short term memory* and *long term memory*. Each functions in a slightly different way.

The sensory register receives input from the environment through your senses based on what you think is important, and discards what's perceived as extraneous. This is why a mother responds immediately to the sound of her crying baby at night, while other family members might not notice it (or pretend not to notice if getting out of bed is involved).

That is also why you will usually respond to certain environmental stimuli such as a panel warning light, regardless of the flying chores you may be involved at the time. The moment you notice the warning light, important information passes into working or short term memory. Here, the information may stay or fade rapidly, depending on your priorities. For instance, when ATC calls your "N" number, this activates the sensory register and places the controller's call in your short term memory queue. Trained pilot that you are (or will be), you know that you'll soon have to respond or the controller will call again (requiring you to dredge up some good excuses from long term memory). If ATC calls and gives you a new transponder code, and this information makes it to your short-term memory (you register it), it won't remain there for long. That's why it's called *short term* memory!

Normally, information only has about a 20 second lifespan in short term memory, varying slightly depending on the nature of your priorities. You can help information stay longer by repeating it out loud. This is one good reason to always read back your clearances. Rehearsing, repetition, sorting, rhyming, associations, mnemonics or categorizing the material into systematic chunks is called *coding,* and it's another way to help information stay in short term memory and move it into long-term memory if you want. Most commercial memory courses just teach various coding techniques.

For instance, if ATC instructs you to fly via Victor 11 and climb to 11,500 feet, you may notice the similarities between the first two numerical values to help remember the information until you can write it down. Saying to yourself, "Fly eleven-five to eleven," should keep the information present until you grab your pencil

(or spray can, chunk of charcoal or whatever you copy clearances with). If you want to remember to place your GPS in OBS mode versus Leg mode before crossing FISHY intersection, you could visualize a big FISH (for FISHY intersection), swallowing a BUS (for OBS) out of which runs a lone LEG (for Leg mode). Depending on the amount of information given and your skill, it can take several seconds to properly code information (to make the chunks, rhymes, verbal repetitions, etc.). Interrupt the process and all the short-term information is likely to be lost from short-term memory within 20 seconds.

Short term memory has a capacity limit, in addition to its time limit. It's usually capable of handling about seven bits or chunks of information at a time. A seven digit telephone number is a good example. If your friend has too many digits for a phone number, you might want to get some friends in your area code (or get used to playing with the cat on Saturday night). This is why you shouldn't count on keeping a long clearance in short term memory. Of course, if you're good at coding you can overcome this problem, keeping the material in short-term memory for a much longer period of time.

Actual learning doesn't take place until the information moves into long term memory, where it's stored for future use. By use of the coding concepts listed above as well as by rote memorization, it's possible for information to move from short term to long term memory, where it can remain stored for a lifetime. I'm not speaking of remembering all the transponder codes and clearances you've ever received, either. You're not Rainman. I'm speaking of the information that will have value to you in the long term, like flying skills, foreign languages or, heaven forbid, foreign flying skills. The more extensive the coding process, the easier it is to recall information in the long term.

Keep in mind, however, that it takes effort to move information beyond short term memory. Good students are hip to this point and go out of their way to acquire some basic skill at mnemonics to help them learn more efficiently. A mnemonic is a word whose letters (or the word itself) help trigger your memory. I'M SAFE, for *illness, medication, stress, alcohol, fatigue,* and *eating,* is an example of a mnemonic.

Make a quick trip to the bookstore and ask the book specialist where the self-help section is. If this person says, "If I do that, then you won't be helping yourself," suggest that you're also looking for a book on how to do karate chops. I'm sure the specialist will immediately offer to help you find a book on memory techniques.

Environmental Input	Sensory Register	Working or Short Term Memory	Long Term Memory
Stimuli	• Quick Scan for Importance • Precoding	• Coding • Rehearsal • Recoding	• Process • Store • Recall

part of what copilots do. My friend, retired TWA Captain Dave Gwinn, once told me that when he was a copilot he looked at his job as one where he always tried to make the captain look good. In other words, he'd remind the captain of the assigned altitude as they approached it, he'd call out localizer or airway intercepts, he'd tune radios and make ATC calls and so on.

The real problem with copilots is pilots. Most pilots are independent people and like to do things themselves. That may be OK as long as the situation isn't demanding. But in some situations it's easy to be overwhelmed by the workload. Even then, some pilots will try doing it all themselves while their copilots sit nearby, actively idle. Improper (or no) use of a copilot is one of the main reasons pilots fail checkrides on airplanes where there's a two pilot crew.

I'll take this a step further and say that even on airplanes where only one pilot is necessary, but a passenger occupies the right seat, this person should be informed that he or she might be asked to do a bit of work. I don't mean fly, but perhaps hold or fold a chart. Of course, the more aviation experience a person has, the more they can do for you.

Bob, that's not how I asked you to help me with the sectional chart!

With an experienced copilot sitting in the right seat, you have a wonderful resource to tap. You can bounce ideas and questions off this person. But don't bounce paper balls off his forehead (copilots hate that). Remember, two heads are better than one, unless you don't know where you're heading or you're paying for everyone's haircuts.

Using your copilot (and other human resources) properly means that you know something about communications, teamwork, task allocation, and decision making. You must be able to communicate your thoughts, needs, and wishes properly to these resources. So how do you know if you're communicating properly? The best way to tell is to ask yourself if you're getting the help you requested. It's simply a matter of feedback. If you ask your copilot for assistance in finding a chart and he's busy wadding up a paper ball to throw at the flight attendant, then you're not communicating properly, are you?

Looked at in a more academic way, the communications aspect of CRM becomes a matter of inquiry, advocacy, and assertion. As PIC, you may have to ask a lot of questions to get the information you need. Once you have these information tidbits, you may need to press ATC, your copilot, and your company to do what you think is safe at the time. For instance, if your copilot is suggesting that you fly to the destination despite one of your two engines running rough, you might need to explain and justify your position to the copilot. This assumes, of course, that you have the time to do this.

Which brings us back to the fact that when all is said and done and communicated, *you* are the pilot in command and the final decision is entirely yours. That's true whether the flight vessel is a Remos G3 or a 757. Your job is to make the best possible use of all resources to gather the information needed to make a wise decision, but making that decision is your job. That's why you are called the *pilot in command*. When it comes to the cockpit, it's one man or woman, one vote.

One of the initial problems with CRM was the failure of crew members to recognize the difference between experience and inexperience. If a copilot said, "Captain, I'm not comfortable with what you're going to do," and the captain replied, "Well, I'm going to do it," then this certainly wasn't what the spirit of CRM intended.

Instead, the captain should reply with something like, "Well, here's why we need to do it this way," followed by an explanation. The intent here is for the captain to educate the copilot based on his or her years of experience. After all, the first officer will eventually replace the captain and he or she would certainly benefit from the captain's experience. In this sense, CRM implies that captains should be educators as well as professional pilots. This shouldn't be too demanding, since most folks fill an educational role in one way or another, especially if they have children. Of course, I'm not suggesting that a captain treat a copilot like a child. After all, he can't restrict a copilot's allowance, since the airline the copilot's working for has probably already done this based on the typical new-hire pay rate.

Hardware

When I say "hardware," I don't mean things like wrenches and screwdrivers. I mean things like the advanced, automated equipment found on many of today's modern airplanes. CRM means knowing how to use this equipment and when to use it (or stop using it, as the case might be).

Take, for instance, the newest primary and multi-function flight displays (see Figure 30, page 1-10, Chapter 1). This is amazing equipment that can provide you with flight instrumentation when used as the primary flight display (PFD), or location when used as a multi-function display (MFD). It can provide you with checklist information and engine instrumentation readings and help you with situational awareness, among many other things. There are rumors it will provide dinner recipes and advice for the lovelorn if you know certain secret codes.

THE WORKLOAD-PERFORMANCE GRAPH

The amount of effort exerted by a pilot for a given period of time varies based on the demands of the task. As this accompanying graph clearly shows, preflight requires very little extended effort compared to approaching and landing an airplane.

The versatility comes at the cost of complexity. Some instructors say that it can take as much as 20 hours of flight and ground training to become sufficiently familiar with some primary flight displays. Twenty hours? Yep. What about those who use this equipment but don't use it often enough to remain proficient in its use? You can bet that more than one pilot has scared himself by hopping into an airplane with advanced avionics equipment for a simple VFR flight only to find out that he can't remember how to set the GPS unit up for basic navigation. If the display flashes "Dear Abby," or has a recipe for Salisbury Steak, you are in over your head, especially if you're a vegetarian. You don't want to go there.

That's why the use of an autopilot is so valuable on airplanes with advanced equipment. The autopilot is the ultimate CRM tool. It's like a copilot except that it doesn't wad up paper balls and throw them back at you (at least the older versions don't).

Many years ago, a NASA study of single-pilot operations suggested that pilots were often best served by autopilots having only a single axis control (i.e., heading hold). Two axis autopilots (those with altitude and heading control) tended to take the pilot out of the performance loop. In other words, the pilot ended up fly-

ing the autopilot and not the airplane. That led to the pilot often getting so far behind the airplane that if there were a crash, he wouldn't arrive at the scene for an additional 30 minutes.

Things have changed. Now, if you're using a primary and multifunction flight display, it's just too easy to be overwhelmed by the need to push buttons, checking menus, etc. So, you'll definitely want to put that autopilot to use when operating in airplanes having this equipment. It means you're less likely to drift from your heading, altitude or clearance.

Information Workload

VFR pilots, especially those operating in high density traffic areas, can only do so many things at one time. That's usually one less than the number of things that need doing. Sure, there are some among us who can multitask in the sense that we can fly and talk on the radio at the same time. Copying a clearance while flying, navigating, and working advanced avionics often overloads even the most capable pilot, especially if he's fiddling with the CD changer at the same time. That's why the very best pilots know two secret words that helps reduce cockpit workload to a workable minimum. Would you like to know what they are? *Stand by.* Those are the words to say.

When you're busy and ATC calls, you don't have to immediately honor the controller's request. You can simply say, "Stand by." ATC understands that, don't they? After all, this is exactly what they tell you when you call and *they're* busy? And guess what? They'll respect you in the morning (or afternoon, or whenever you get back to them). Some pilots, in an attempt to maintain their burnished on-the-air image, never turn down an ATC call, even when they've got a one-track mind and four channels of input happening. The result is mistakes, repeats, and other things that compromise the safety of flight. As soon as you're really ready, call ATC and communicate. That's how smart pilots fly.

Sometimes things get busy in the cockpit. That's why the two most important things in aviation are the next two things. By that I mean you should always be asking yourself what the next two things are that you need to accomplish to get the flying job done. Doing your chores ahead of time (like obtaining the ATIS, completing a checklist, etc.) is essential to minimizing your cockpit workload.

In fact, you could become so overwhelmed when preparing to fly into a high density traffic area like the Los Angeles basin or the New York area, that you might accidentally drift into Class D, C or B airspace. That is why it's important to do as much as possible as early as possible in the flight. You never know what will happen later. You can be sitting there eating your tuna sandwich and thinking, "I'll get the ATIS in a few minutes," when suddenly the controller who's providing flight following gives you a heading change that takes you directly toward a cloud (which you should not fly into under any circumstance as a non-instrument rated pilot). Now who's got time to get the ATIS? The graph shown in Figure 29 gives you a good idea of just where the workload increases and pushes the limits of our performance during flight.

Aeronautical Decision Making (ADM)

As a general rule, very few pilots receive formal training in aeronautical decision making (ADM), yet many are effective decision makers. Why? They developed some strategy that lets them to make the right decision at the right time. Perhaps they learned it by watching their instructor, or they acquired the common base of knowledge possessed by most people. Maybe the tooth fairy gave it to them as a bonus. It doesn't matter. They've got it. But even if they and you do have it, there's nothing that says you can't become a better aviation decision maker by using some of the ADM tools presented in this chapter.

ADM is a systematic approach to understanding and modifying the mental process used by pilots to determine the best course of action in any given circumstance. This is a process that builds on the traditional concepts of decision making, as shown in Figure 30, but is modified slightly in consideration of the fact that the person making the decision is probably moving in a metal tube at a hundred miles per hour or more. Thus, ADM helps minimize the probability of pilot error by providing the means to analyze changes that occur in flight and evaluate how these changes could affect the outcome of that flight.

For instance, in the traditional decision making model (Figure 30), the need to make a decision occurs when the pilot notices that something has changed or hasn't changed when it was expected to (Figure 30, position 1). The engine begins to run rough (change) or the throttle is moved forward in cruise flight and the power doesn't increase (no change). The pilot must recognize this change or the lack of it for good decision making to occur (Figure 30, position 2). Failure to notice the change can lead to a mishap. Change indicates an appropriate response is necessary to favorably modify the situation (Figure 30, position 3). Now the pilot must evaluate all the possible responses using skills, procedures, techniques or book knowhow to solve the problem (Figure 30,

position 4). Lack of ability in any of these areas can lead to a mishap (Figure 30, position 5).

Traditionally, ADM addresses all aspects of decision making in the cockpit and identifies the steps involved in good decision making. Here they are for your consideration:

1. Identifying any personal hazardous attitudes.
2. Learning behavior modification techniques.
3. Learning how to recognize and cope with stress.
4. Developing risk assessment skills.
5. Using all resources.
6. Evaluating the effectiveness of one's ADM skills.

Let's look at what we've already learned, and examine in some detail the factors we haven't discussed so far.

We've already learned to identify personal attitudes hazardous to safe flight along with the behavior modification techniques that work as antidotes to counter these attitudes. We've learned a bit about stress and how to use CRM. Now it's time to develop some useful risk assessment skills. One of the most useful tools from ADM is the risk assessment checklist in the form of the acronym DECIDE—detect, estimate, choose, identify, do, evaluate.

This is a six-step checklist that provides you with a logical way to approach decision making. The model represents a continuous loop process of decision making that is useful when a pilot is faced with a change in a situation where somebody had better decide something pretty soon. This model focuses on the intellectual component of the decision process, but it can also influence the motivational component of judgment as well.

The secret here is to practice using the DECIDE checklist in all your decision making. Then, when it's needed aloft, the process will be more natural and more likely to positively affect the outcome of important decisions in the air.

I don't want you to think that in the event of an inflight problem, you'll simply pull out a piece of paper,

A Good or Bad Decision?

Handpropping
(done improperly)

First Aid

Yes, people still handprop airplanes. It is, however, risky business. In spite of the risks, I believe you should be taught the basics of handpropping. Why? I know from experience that one day you might find yourself in a situation where you'll be tempted to try this on your own. Doing so without prior training is not very wise. Besides, even if you elect not to handprop your airplane, basic instruction in the correct techniques will enhance your respect for the propeller.

Find a qualified instructor who's experienced in handpropping airplanes (he shouldn't look like the guy to the left). Have that person show you the correct procedures, which include how to grip the propeller, the stance for best leverage and maximum safety, body movement and communication with the person inside the cockpit.

Perhaps the most important rule for handpropping is to have a *competent pilot, who's familiar with the airplane, at the controls.* Why? Once that engine starts, an airplane can move on its own and do a lot of damage. You don't want this to happen to you. There are several recorded cases of airplanes taking off without a pilot on board after being incorrectly handpropped (try explaining that to the owner of the flight school).

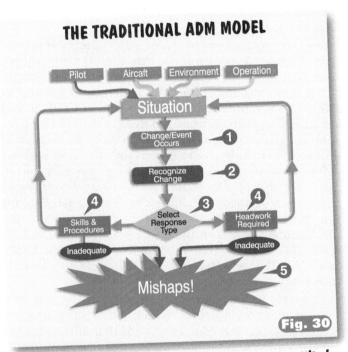

THE TRADITIONAL ADM MODEL

Fig. 30

The traditional decision model doesn't incorporate attitude awareness, stress management and CRM as does the non-traditional ADM model (Figure 31).

review the DECIDE checklist, and excellent answers will appear (brought by that same tooth fairy, no doubt). It doesn't work that way. This checklist works best when it is internalized to the point of being intuitive. When you need it most is when you'll have the least time to think about each step.

Detect. The decision maker detects the fact that change has occurred.

Estimate. The decision maker estimates the need to counter or react to the change.

Choose. The decision maker chooses a desirable outcome (in terms of success) for the flight.

Identify. The decision maker identifies actions that could successfully control the change.

Do. The decision maker takes the necessary action.

Evaluate. The decision maker evaluates the effect(s) of his action countering the change.

Let's see how this is applied to a critical in-flight situation by assuming you're climbing to cruise altitude and notice an increase in oil temperature. We'll follow the DECIDE checklist here and refer it to a more comprehensive and effective non-traditional ADM model. This model allows us to incorporate several additional tools of psychology, such as attitude awareness, stress management and CRM.

The first step is to *detect* the problem (Figure 31, position 1). Let's say that our oil temperature is increasing and approaching red line on the gauge. This is easy to detect if you make it a habit to scan your engine instruments during flight. It's a bit more difficult if you never look at the panel or you don't know where the oil temperature gauge is on the panel.

Step two requires you to *estimate* the need to counter or react to this change (Figure 31, position 2). Without experience in this type of problem, you may not be sure of the severity of the problem. It is, after all, normal for the oil temperature to increase somewhat during a climb (along with cylinder head temperatures, too). Nevertheless, because you've read Chapter Three of this book, you know that the oil temperature should never reach or exceed redline without your taking immediate action to reduce the temperature. Fortunately, you also learned in Chapter Three that a decrease in oil pressure is followed by an increase in oil temperature. After checking your oil pressure, you notice that it is reading within normal limits.

You estimate that there is a need to act, but it's not an urgent need to act. In other words, you don't have an emergency—not yet, anyway!

Step three requires you to *choose* a desirable outcome for this situation (Figure 31, position 3). Lowering your oil temperature to a normal level is your objective here.

Step four wants you to *identify* the actions needed to accomplish step three (Figure 31, positions 3 and 4). This is often a decision about which of your skills and procedures to use, plus attitude management, stress management, and CRM necessary to solve the problem. These include, decreasing the airplane's attitude (if you're in a climb), opening the cowl flaps, reducing power (if you're operating at high power settings), and so on.

Since it's a hot day and you are climbing, you decide that it's best to try increasing the airflow through the engine as a solution to the problem. If, at any time, you

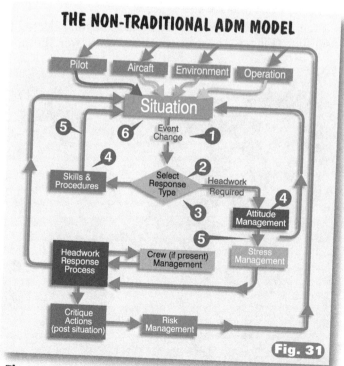

THE NON-TRADITIONAL ADM MODEL

Fig. 31

The non-traditional aviation decision making (ADM) model incorporates attitude awareness, stress management and CRM. This provides a pilot with a better chance of making a good decision.

THE NON-TRADITIONAL ADM MODEL

Pilot   Aircraft   Environment   Operation

Situation

5   6   Event Change   1

4

Skills & Procedures   Select Response Type   2   Headwork Required

3   4

Attitude Management

5

Headwork Response Process   Crew (if present) Management   Stress Management

Critique Actions (post situation)   Risk Management

Fig. 31-Repeat

The non-traditional aviation decision making (ADM) model incorporate attitude awareness, stress management and CRM. This provides a pilot with a better chance of making a good decision.

identify that you're feeling nervous, like you have no control over the situation, you might engage in a little attitude management and invoke the resignation hazardous thought antidote and say to yourself, "I'm not helpless. I can make a difference."

Step five requires you to *do* the action you selected in step four (Figure 31, position 5). So you lower the nose

and increase the airspeed. You also make sure the cowl flaps are opened fully.

Step six requires you to *evaluate* the effect of this decision (Figure 31, position 6). Has the oil temperature decreased to within normal limits? It has. It's still high, but it is decreasing. Fine. You're flying and doing so safely. Now you can run through the DECIDE model again, asking yourself what you need to do if the oil temperature remains high and never returns to its normal limits. It's entirely possible that you departed without sufficient oil to provide reasonable engine cooling. Given that it's a hot day, this could lead to engine detonation at high power settings in a climb. That's not good. Perhaps you may need to land and check the oil. That's a potential problem that requires full use of the DECIDE model. It's possible that in running through the model again, you'll decide that it's best to land at an alternate with fuel services and oil up if necessary.

There's a bit more to good decision making, however, than just having a useful model in the ADM process. Sometimes you need additional skills that fall outside the normal parameters of academic psychology. And these are the skills you'll learn as you gain flying experience. So start slowly, then try new things, visit new places and fly new airplanes. Each action will contribute to your continuing education.

Final Thoughts on Thoughts

Here's something else I want you to consider. It's possible that the very qualities that make pilots good are the same ones that can injure them. There seems to be a thin line between positive personality traits for aviators and an extension of those same traits that lead to hazardous thinking. For example, wimpy pilots aren't safe pilots; neither are macho pilots. A certain degree of self-confi-

---

When Decisions Go Right

The outstanding performance of this student pilot during a solo cross-country emergency was enhanced by helicopter training, and a thorough understanding of flight dynamics.

...During solo cross-country...the engine began to run rough. I put the mixture in full rich with the problem getting worse. I put the carb heat on and trimmed the C-150 to its best glide speed. Within 30 seconds, the engine at full power would only develop 1700-1800 rpm. At that time I turned 180 degrees into the wind while putting a direct to ZZZ1 airport. I was tuned on the ZZZ1 VOR and centered the needle so as to not drift my course. I then checked both magnetos and engine oil pressure/temperature, all of which were normal. I was over rolling hills and knew I wasn't going to make the airport.

The pilot made several Mayday calls on local frequencies, but no one responded.

As I passed through 1,700 feet MSL, I saw a small set of telephone lines in my original landing area. With partial power applied, I was unable to maintain my altitude, but could reduce my rate of descent. I dropped 10 degrees of flaps to gain lift and banked hard at about 300 feet. I crossed a hedgerow of 80-foot trees, knowing I would make my landing area. [I] dropped full flaps to get down, because slipping the aircraft into the field would not have allowed me to line up with the rows in the field made by the owner's tractor. At about 15 feet AGL, I cut the fuel off to the motor, and pulled the engine off. At 5 feet I flared, holding the nose up until I heard the stall horn. I continued to hold the nose off as the mains touched. I applied full brake pressure after the nose settled. The aircraft was landed with about 75 feet of ground run and no damage.

The cause of the failure is believed to be a dropped cylinder or valve. As a student fixed wing pilot, I was able to use my experience as a commercial instrument sport helicopter pilot to safely land the aircraft without damage. I attribute this to proper emergency procedures, and a thorough understanding of aerodynamics.

Courtesy NASA Callback Report

dence and assertiveness is necessary to fly an airplane, so these personality traits are over represented in the pilot population. They are useful, up to a point. There is, however, a very thin line between these traits being productive and counter-productive. Confidence is good, cockiness isn't, and it's not a long distance between the two.

You may be sitting there thinking to yourself silently, "I'm not afraid of anything. You can't scare me off with some clouds or the threat of fuel exhaustion. Heck, if I run out of fuel, I just land that bad boy in a field, light a cigarette, and have a soda from the cooler." That is certainly a macho attitude, but you may not realize it despite having it. You may just think that you're naturally braver that everyone else.

Canine Conniptions (When Decisions Go Bad)

A PA-28 pilot took off with two dogs as passengers. The pilot, who had not filed a flight plan, was talking to Approach, when...

My two large dogs went crazy. [They] jumped on me and with no one in the co-pilot seat, one of my dogs pushed the control yoke and caught his front leg on the yoke, causing an uncontrolled turn to the right. This turn put me in the clouds (IMC). Once I regained control of the plane and the dogs, I realized I had turned toward Class B airspace... ATC did advise me that I was not cleared [into this airspace]. My dog, with headphones hanging from mouth, caused me to enter Class B and descend below 5,000 feet AGL. Shortly thereafter ATC asked me if I was in VFR conditions and if I could I see the ground. I was then in VFR and could see the ground....

The moral of this flight is that I should have secured my dogs with seat belts. This is the main error I committed. My second error was flying VFR into IMC without an IFR clearance. **ASRS Report**

The fact is that we (every one of us) may harbor a hazardous thought attitude and not even recognize it as being hazardous. It is, after all, normal for most people to think that they are pilots capable of handling even the most unusual circumstances. So there is a dividing line between normal confidence and hazardous thinking, but only you can know where that is. That means you have a chance of figuring out where that line is, but only if you monitor the internal dialogue that is constantly going on in your head. Given that pilots may have personality characteristics that can evolve into some forms of hazardous thinking, it makes sense that they should monitor their attitudes for signs of this behavior. The moment an attitude is detected that's a counterproductive extension of a normal, safe mode of thinking, they should apply one or more of the appropriate hazardous-thought antidotes. Said another way, if pilots don't modify their behavior when necessary, Mother Nature will. Finally, be aware that almost all aviation accidents are caused by human error. Pilots can do something to prevent accidents. They are not subject to the vicissitudes of luck or poor maintenance. Safe flying is within the control of every pilot. Fate is not the hunter!

The Aviation Super High Way

Books, books and more books, not to mention pamphlets, magazines, videotapes, audio tapes, computer programs, aviation forums, the Internet—it sometimes seems that airplanes are supported by an information jetstream. There is so much to learn and so little time to fly.

Every source of information makes its own unique contribution. You will eventually evolve your own combination of resources that works in terms of keeping up and having fun. On days when the weather doesn't cooperate, or there isn't time to go flying, it can be entertaining to crank up a video or read a pilot publication and share the experiences and knowledge of others.

I'm glad you were able to join me for this tour of the aviation wonderland. May all your skies be blue, and all your flying hours as interesting and exciting as mine have been.

BORN TO FLY
We see the emergence of a new breed of man:
Homoflighticus

Postflight Briefing #16-1

NOTAM Abbreviations

AADC - Approach and Departure Control
ABV - Above
A/C - Approach Control
ACCUM - Accumulate
ACFT - Aircraft
ACR - Air Carrier
ACTV/ACTVT - Active/Activate
ADJ - Adjacent
ADZ/ADZD - Advise/Advised
AFD - Airport/Facility Directory
AFSS - Automated Flight Service Station
ALSA - Approach Light System
ALTM - Altimeter
ALTN - Alternate
ALTNLY - Alternately
ALSTG - Altimeter Setting
AMDT - Amendment
APCH - Approach
APL - Airport Lights
ARPT - Airport
ARSR - Air Route Surveillance Radar
ASDE - Airport Surface Detection Equipment
ASOS - Automated Surface Observing System
ASPH - Asphalt
ASR - Airport Surveillance Radar
ATC - Air Traffic Control
ATCT - Airport Traffic Control Tower
ATIS - Automated Terminal Information Service
AVBL - Available
AZM - Azimuth
BC - Back Course
BCN - Beacon
BERM - Snowbank/s of Earth/Gravel
BLO - Below
BND - Bound
BRAF - Braking Action Fair
BRAG - Braking Action Good
BRAN - Braking Action Nil
BRAP - Braking Action Poor
BYD -Beyond
CAAS - Class A Airspace
CAT - Category
CBAS - Class B Airspace
CBSA - Class B Surface Area
CCAS - Class C Airspace
CCLKWS - Counterclockwise
CCSA - Class C Surface Area
CD - Clearance Delivery
CDAS - Class D Airspace
CDSA - Class D Surface Area
CEAS - Class E Airspace
CESA - Class E Surface Area
CFA - Controlled Firing Area
CGAS - Class G Airspace
CHG - Change
CLKWS - Clockwise
CLNC - Clearance
CLSD - Closed
CMSN - Commission
CMSND - Commissioned
CNCL/CNCLD/CNL - Cancel/Canceled/Cancel

CNTRLN - Centerline
CONC - Concrete
CONT - Continuously
CRS - Course
DALGT - Daylight
DCMS - Decommission
DCMSND - Decommissioned
DCT - Direct
DEP - Depart/Departure
DEPT - Department
DH - Decision Height
DISABLD - Disabled
DLA/DLAD - Delay/Delayed
DLT/DLTD - Delete/Deleted
DLY - Daily
DMSTN - Demonstration
DPCR - Departure Procedure
DRCT - Direct
DRFT - Drift Snowbank/s
DRFTD - Drifted Snowbank/s
DSPLCD - Displaced
DSTC - Distance
DWPNT - Dewpoint
E- East
EBND - Eastbound
EFF - Effective
ELEV - Elevate/Elevation
ENG - Engine
ENTR - Entire
EXCP - Except
FAC - Facility
FAF - Final Approach Fix
FDC - Flight Data Center
FM - Fan Marker
FREQ - Frequency
FRH - Fly Runway Heading
FRZN - Frozen
FRNZ SLR - Frozen Slush on Runway/s
FSS - Flight Service Station
GC - Ground Control
GP - Glide Path
GRVL - Gravel
GS - Glide Slope
HAA - Height Above Airport
HAT - Height Above Touchdown
HAZ - Hazard
HEL - Helicopter
HELI - Heliport
HF - High Frequency
HIRL - High Intensity Rwy Lights
HOL - Holiday
HP - Holding Pattern
IBND - Inbound
ID - Identification
IDENT - Identifier/Identification
IFR - Instrument Flight Rules
ILS - Instrument Landing System
IM - Inner Marker
IN - Inch/Inches
INDEFLY - Indefinitely
INOP - Inoperative
INST - Instrument
INT - Intersection
INTST - Intensity
IR - Ice On Runway/s
L - Left
LAA - Local Airport Advisory
LAT - Latitude

LB - Pound/Pounds
LC - Local Control
LCL - Local
LCTD - Located
LDA - Localizer Type Directional Aid
LDIN - Lead In Lighting System
LGT/LGTD/LGTS- Light/Lighted/Lights
LIRL - Low Intensity Runway Edge Lights
LLWAS - Low Level Wind Shear Alert System
LMM - Compass Locator at ILS Middle Marker
LNDG - Landing
LOC - Localizer
LOM - Compass Locator at ILS Outer Marker
LONG - Longitude
LRN - LORAN
LSR - Loose Snow on Runway/s
LT - Left Turn After Take-off
MAP - Missed Approach Point
MED - Medium
MIN - Minute
MIRL - Medium Intensity Runway Edge Lights
MM - Middle Marker
MNM - Minimum
MOCA - Minimum Obstruction Clearance Altitude
MONTR - Monitor
MSA - Minimum Safe Altitude
MSAW - Minimum Safe altitude Warning
MSL - Mean Sea Level
MU - Designate a Friction Value Representing Runway Surface Conditions
MUD - Mud
MUNI - Municipal
N - North
NA - Not Authorized
NBND - Northbound
NE - Northeast
NGT - Night
NM - Nautical Mile/s
NMR - Nautical Mile Radius
NW - Northwest
OBSC - Obscured
OBSTN - Obstruction
OM - Outer Marker
OPER - Operate
OPN - Operation
ORIG - Original
OTS - Out of Service
OVR - Over
PAEW - Personnel and Equipment Working
PAJA - Parachute Jumping Activities
PAPI - Precision Approach Path Indicator
PAR - Precision Approach Radar
PARL - Parallel

PAT - Pattern
PCL - Pilot Controlled Lighting
PERM - Permanent
PERMLY - Permanently
PLA - Practice Low Approach
PLW - Plow/Plowed
PN - Prior Notice Required
PPR - Prior Permission Required
PREV - Previous
PRIRA - Primary Radar
PROC - Procedure
PROP - Propeller
PSGR - Passenger/s
PSR - Packed Snow on Runway/s
PT/PTN - Procedure Turn
PVT - Private
RAIL - Runway Alignment Indicator Lights
RCAG - Remote Communication Air/Ground Facility
RCL - Runway Centerline
RCLS - Runway Centerline Light System
RCO - Remote Communication Outlet
RCV/RCVR - Receive/Receiver
REF - Reference
REIL - Runway End Identifier Lights
RELCTD - Relocated
RMDR - Remainder
RNAV - Area Navigation
RPRT - Report
RQRD - Required
RRL - Runway Remaining Lights
RSVN - Reservation
RT - Right Turn after Take-off
RTE - Route
RTR - Remote Transmitter Receiver
RTS - Return to Service
RUF - Rough
RVR - Runway Visual Range
RVRM RVR Midpoint
RVRR - RVR Rollout
RVRT - RVR Touchdown
RVV - Runway Visibility Value
RY/RWY - Runway
S - South
SBND - Southbound
SDF - Simplified Directional Facility
SE - Southeast
SECRA - Secondary Radar
SFL - Sequenced Flashing Lights
SI - Straight-In Approach
SIR - Packed or Compacted Snow and Ice on Runway/s
SKED - Scheduled
SLR - Slush on Runway/s
SNBNK- Snowbank/s Caused by Plowing
SND - Sand/Sanded
SNGL - Single

SNW - Snow
SPD - Speed
SR - Sunrise
SS - Sunset
SVC - Service
SW - Southwest
SWEPT - Swept or Broom/Broomed
TACAN - Tactical Air Navigational Aid
TFC - Traffic
TFR - Temporary Flight Restriction
TGL - Touch and Go Landings
THN - Thin
THR - Threshold
THRU - Through
TIL - Until
TKOF - Takeoff
TMPRY - Temporary
TRML - Terminal
TRNG - Training
TRSN - Transition
TSNT - Transient
TWR - Tower
TWY - Taxiway
UNAVBL - Unavailable
UNLGTD - Unlighted
UNMKD - Unmarked
UNMON - Unmonitored
UNRELBL - Unreliable
UNUSBL - Unusable
VASI - Visual Approach Slope Indicator
VDP - Visual Descent Point
VFR - Visual Flight Rules
VIA - By Way Of
VICE - Instead/Versus
VIS/VSBY - Visibility
VMC - Visual Meteorological Conditions
VOL - Volume
VOLMET - Meteorlogical Information for Aircraft in Flight
VOR - VHF Omni-Directional Radio Range
VORTAC - VOR and TACAN
VOT - VOR Test Signal
W - West
WBND - Westbound
WEA/WX - Weather
WI - Within
WKDAYS - Monday through Friday
WKEND - Saturday and Sunday
WND - Wind
WP - Waypoint
WSR - Wet Snow on Runway/s
WTR - Water on Runway/s
- WX Weather
/ - And
+ - In Addition/Also

Brian Weiss is the owner of WORD'SWORTH, a marketing communications and design company. WORD'SWORTH provides services for all forms and formats of communications materials. Capabilities include the creation of brochures, books, newsletters, direct response letters, advertising, catalog sheets, slide shows and videos.

WORD'SWORTH clients have included Bank of America, Xerox Corporation, the National Childhood Cancer Foundation, Childrens Hospital (Los Angeles), the University of California (Irvine and Los Angeles campuses), Health Valley Foods, McGraw-Hill/CRM Films, Saint Joseph Hospital, *American Health* magazine, *Psychology Today* magazine, *Equity Quarterly*, Saint John's Hospital, *Aviation Safety* magazine, Long Beach and Santa Monica airports, and many others in a wide variety of fields.

In addition to general business expertise, WORD'SWORTH provides specialized background and knowledge in the areas of medicine and health care, science and technology, aviation and fundraising.

WORD'SWORTH also offers consulting on marketing strategies, direct mail campaigns, and fundraising proposals.

The Senior Editor: Mr. Brian Weiss

A little about Brian Weiss:

Founder (1977) and owner, WORD'SWORTH
Former editor, *Baja Explorer* magazine
Former associate editor, *Psychology Today* magazine
Served on the faculties of UCLA and the University of Michigan teaching introductory courses and advanced seminars in departments of human behavior, geography, and journalism.
Author for six years of a nationally syndicated consumer newspaper column (*FREEBIES*), and creator of a national magazine of the same name
Former medical/science editor, *Aviation Safety* magazine
Member (and former Board of Directors member), of Angel Flight, a not-for-profit community service organization.
Brian has been a pilot since 1980. He packs a private pilot certificate with an instrument rating and is the proud owner of a Cessna 172. He's one of the organizers of Flight Log, a group which provides information for pilots flying in Baja and throughout Mexico.

Brian Weiss

WORD'SWORTH
626-510-9180
bweiss@aol.com

"Brian is one of the most talented, energetic and intelligent people with whom I've had the pleasure of working. His advice and dedication to this project were simply invaluable!"

Rod Machado

The Aviation Speakers Bureau
Providing Quality Aviation Speakers Since 1986

The Aviation Speakers Bureau features speakers for your banquet, educational seminar, safety standdown, convention, conference, forum, trade show, keynote, corporate training, airshow, safety program or association meeting. We guarantee a perfect match for your needs and objectives, and recommend only the very best in speakers. Our professionals shine and make YOU look good every time!

"We will help you find the perfect speaker for your budget and there is <u>never</u> a charge for our service."

Presentation and Topics

Safety, Weather, Instrument Flying, Inspirational, Cockpit Resource Management, Aviation Humor, Understanding Airspace, Test Pilots, Teamwork, Stress, Fighter Pilots and Aces, Weather Radar, In-flight Emergencies, Multi-engine Procedures, Celebrities and Heroes, Vietnam Pilots, Aviation Management, Interpreting Instrument Charts, Comedy, Air Racers, Policies and Politics of Aviation, Motivational, Industry Specific Training, Maneuvers, Success, Patriotic, Aviation Firsts, Stunt Flying, Air Combat, Aviation Psychology, Survival, Aviation Careers, Jeppesen Charts, Aerobatic Pilots, Wright Brothers, Accident Investigations, Survival and much more.

For information on our speakers call
800-247-1215
For all other calls 949-498-2498

P.O. Box 6030
San Clemente, CA 92674-6030

Read speaker biographies and view video clips:
www.aviationspeakers.com

Charter Member

IASB
INTERNATIONAL ASSOCIATION OF
SPEAKERS BUREAUS

Diane Titterington

The Ongoing Editor: Diane Titterington

Learning to fly in 1973, Diane holds a commercial certificate with an instrument rating. Her logbook is a Heinz 57 mixture of different makes and models. Flights include ferrying aircraft from the factory, flying fire patrol and a number of air races. Until 1981, she worked as a radar qualified air traffic controller on the high/low sectors at Houston Center. Diane has been a passenger on a carrier landing and takeoff, flown a T-38, rode dozens of airline jumpseats and logged a few blimp flights.

Her father, who worked at WPAFB, told tales of test pilots Bob Hoover, Scott Crossfield and Chuck Yeager when she was young. Diane never dreamed that she would later work with such aviation greats. As the President of The Aviation Speakers Bureau, Diane supplies speakers for hundreds of safety seminars, banquets and conventions. She places aviation speakers, celebrities and specialists at events across the United States, Canada and other countries.

"It is a pure pleasure to work with dozens of brilliant and gifted individuals such as Jim Tucker, Bob Hoover, Col. Joe Kittinger, Brian Udell, Al Haynes, Dave Gwinn, Dr. Jerry Cockrell and Ralph Hood. With their unusual experiences, unique delivery styles, and vast knowledge of aviation, our speakers are the most sought after in the business. By providing inspiring speakers for aviation events, we help motivate and educate. And we help to keep the skies safe too." Visit our web site: www.aviationspeakers.com

Diane has been the ongoing editor of *Rod Machado's Private Pilot Handbook* and *Rod Machado's Instrument Pilot's Survival Manual*. She is the designer, compiler, managing editor and producer of *Speaking of Flying*, a book of stories from 44 aviation speakers.

See website for eBook version!

"As if your instructor is explaining everything in *PLANE* English."

Rod Machado's Private Pilot Handbook is a serious text written in a fun and witty style. With more than 1,100 illustrations and photos and 624 pages in full color, this hardbound manual makes preparation for the FAA private pilot oral and knowledge exams (flight reviews too) a pleasant and enjoyable experience. Here's some of what's inside:

- Easy to understand analogies and examples for technical subjects such as engines, aerodynamics, flight instruments and the airplane's electrical system.
- New weather codes: METAR 8 TAF
- Alphabet airspace made E-Z with 3-D color illustrations
- Step-by-step procedures for planning a cross country
- Clear, down-to-earth explanations of pertinent FARs –Part 61 and 91
- Easy to apply navigation methods for VOR, GPS and ADF
- Practical tips and techniques for ensuring safe and enjoyable flight

$64.95

Rod Machado's Private Pilot Handbook 624 pages
8-9/18 x 11-1/8, hardbound, color
ISBN 978-0-9631229-9-5

Visit our web site at: *www.rodmachado.com*

Rod Machado's Private Pilot Audiobook - MP3 Files (30 Hours+)
Retention can increase by 70% with auditory learning!
SHOULDN'T YOU BE REVIEWING?

Welcome to your instructor in an audiobook. Rod's entire Handbook is presented in a warm, conversational manner. His tried-and-true method of instruction can be enjoyed during your commute, relaxing at home, or almost anywhere. It allows you to learn in a new, novel and often more efficient manner. Turn wasted freeway time into learning time. As one pilot said, "I felt like I had a flight instructor right there in the car with me."

Perfect if you don't have the time or inclination to read, or for "tired" eyes at the end of the day. It's a pleasure to be read to, especially from a lively text spiced with humor. You can listen to the first eight chapters without referring to the book's graphics. For some chapters, you'll want to review pictures, picture text, graphs and charts in the Handbook.

This valuable one-stop audiobook will help you:

Fly as a knowledgeable and competent pilot
Prepare for the Private Pilot FAA Knowledge Exam
Prepare for the Private Pilot practical oral exam
Refresh for required currency training
Remain an up-to-date confident pilot

Download MP3 Version $99.95

See website for download version!

Narrator: Capt. Philip E. Hewitt Ph.D., CFII, ATP, Pilot Examiner, pro narrator
Guest Narrator: Alec Cody, CFII, comedic impressionist

LISTEN and LEARN while:
- DRIVING
- RELAXING
- GARDENING
- EXERCISING
- EATING LUNCH
- BUILDING A KITPLANE

**Rod Machado's
Private Pilot Handbook
on 30 Audio CDs**

ISBN 978-0-9712015-7-6

Price: $119.95

Rod Machado's Private Pilot Workbook

The new *Rod Machado's Private Pilot Workbook* is now available. As a programmed learning guide, this book will help prepare you for the FAA Private Pilot Knowledge Exam. The questions are organized to follow the presentation of material, section for section, as found in the *Handbook*. Not only will this book prepare you for the Private Pilot Knowledge Exam, it will help you understand and absorb the knowledge necessary for you to fly safely. You can test your knowledge and comprehension in each subject area with numerous weight and balance, performance, and flight planning problems.

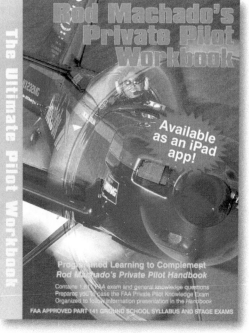

This valuable one-stop workbook contains:

- An excellent, thorough and complete self-study system when used with *Rod Machado's Private Pilot Handbook*.
- 1,811 FAA Private Pilot Knowledge Exam and general aviation knowledge questions.
- Questions organized to follow the layout of *Rod Machado's Private Pilot Handbook* so you can test your knowledge and comprehension in each subject area.
- Color navigation charts & numerous weight-and-balance, performance, and flight planning problems.
- An FAA approved, Part 141 ground training syllabus for use in an FAA approved Part 141 ground school.

$24.95

Speaking of Flying

This wonderful 438 page hardbound book was written by 44 pilots who are speakers with The Aviation Speakers Bureau. These funny, dramatic, and inspiring stories are some of aviation's finest tales. You would expect nothing less from aviation's celebrities, experts and specialists.

Our flight plan sees us barnstorming in the U.S., flying aerial combat missions in World War II and Vietnam, test piloting new aircraft, performing air rescue, winging to exotic places, and flying to historically important aviation places from Kitty Hawk to the moon. You will go along as history is being made and hear the pilot's perspective on some of these aviation firsts. You will find ACES and true heroes within these pages. *Speaking of Flying* is your ticket to adventure. Step aboard, and be prepared to laugh, cry, and feel the excitement.

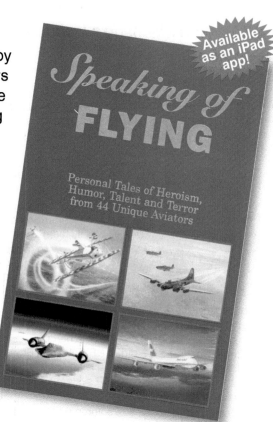

$29.95

Rod Machado's eLearning Courses

Would you like to try a fun, new and exciting way to learn? Then purchase one of Rod Machado's *Interactive eLearning Courses*.

Each course is narrated and accompanied by interesting graphics, animations, videos and educational interactions. In addition, each section within a course is accompanied by questions to help test your knowledge and reinforce important concepts. Of course, if questions aren't your thing, then simply skip them and continue with the course. While this course can be viewed on an iPhone or Android phone, the graphics would be difficult to see (unless you are an ant). These courses were designed to be used on an iPad, Android tablet device, laptop or desktop computer. Check them out at: rodmachdo.com.

Aviation Humor Video/DVD

Laugh along with over 2,000 pilots as Rod delights and entertains his audience with some of the best of his aviation stories. As a professional humorist, Rod has always been known for his ability to move people off the edge of their seats and onto the floor with his fast paced, humorous presentations. As Scott Spangler, Editor of *Flight Training* magazine says, ".. Get a copy of Aviation Humor. It's Rod Machado at his best. His humor is effective and funny because it strikes at the truth pilots seldom admit, such as the pride a new pilot feels when he uses his certificate as identification when cashing a check and the clerk asks, 'What is that?' If you're in need of a good laugh, get this video. You won't regret it. "After so many requests for a video version of his very popular audio tapes, this video of Rod's is sure to be a popular addition to your library. Funny, Funny stuff!

Aviation Humor - $29.95   Approximate Length 1:00

Rod Machado's Instrument Pilot's Survival Manual
Third Edition-eBook Only

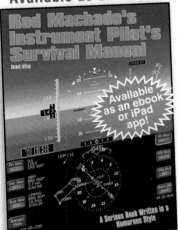

Rod Machado's *Instrument Pilot's Survival Manual* is written to answer the instrument pilot's most important and frequently unanswered questions. For the price of one hour's worth of dual you will learn the following:

1. How GPS approaches are constructed and how to fly them
2. How to differentiate between benign cumulus clouds and those that can damage an airplane
3. How to measure flight visibility at DA & MDA
4. A unique three-step method of scanning your instruments
5. Secrets of using Jeppesen and NACO charts
6. Using Center radar, ASR-9 radar, NEXRAD and Stormscope (sferics) to avoid thunderstorm and icing conditions
7. New ways of thinking about the IFR system and managing cockpit resources and much more!

(Available as an ebook only, 509 colored pages) $29.95

IFR Flying *Tips & Techniques* Video/DVD

If you've enjoyed Rod's presentation in the *ABC's Wide World of Flying* and *Wonderful World of Flying* video magazine, you're sure to enjoy this tape. Rod has incorporated six of his most popular IFR segments into this educational video and interspersed live, humorous clips from one of his popular seminars between each story segment.

Rod shows you:
1. *A unique, multi-step instrument scan*
2. *Single pilot IFR cockpit management*
3. *How to properly use the approach lighting system*
4. *Techniques to make safe IFR departures*
5. *What maneuvering speed means and how to use it*

IFR Flying Tips & Techniques - $29.95   Appx. Length 1:30

Rod Machado's Plane Talk
The Mental Art of Flying an Airplane
You'll Learn, You'll Laugh, You'll Remember!

Welcome to a collection of Rod Machado's most popular aviation articles and stories from the last 15 years. *Rod Machado's Plane Talk* contains nearly 100 flights of fun and knowledge that will stimulate your aviation brain and tickle your funny bone. In addition to the educational topics listed below, you'll read about higher learning, the value of aviation history, aviation literature, aviation art and how an artist's perspective can help you better understand weather. You'll also find more than a few articles written just to make you laugh.

In this book you'll discover...

How to Assess and Manage Aviation Risks
Learn how safe pilots think, how to apply the safety strategy used by General Jimmy Doolittle (known as the master of the calculated risk), how famed gunfighter Wyatt Earp can help you cope with aviation's risks, how misleading aviation statistics can be and why flying isn't as dangerous as some folks say it is.

Several Techniques for Making Better Cockpit Decisions
Discover how to use your inner copilot in the cockpit and the value of one good question asked upside down.

New Ways to Help You Cope With Temptation
Fly safer by developing an aviation code of ethics, understand how human nature can trick you into flying beyond your limits, why good pilots are prejudiced and how a concept like honor will protect you while aloft.

How to Use Your Brain for a Change
You can learn faster by understanding how the learning curve—the brain's performance chart—is affected by the little lies we tell ourselves, the mistakes we need to make, our need to please our instructors, and simulator and memory training.

The Truth About Flying, Anxiety and Fear
Learn why it's often the safest of pilots that make excuses instead of flights, why anxiety should be treated as a normal part of flying, and a three-step process to avoiding panic in the cockpit.

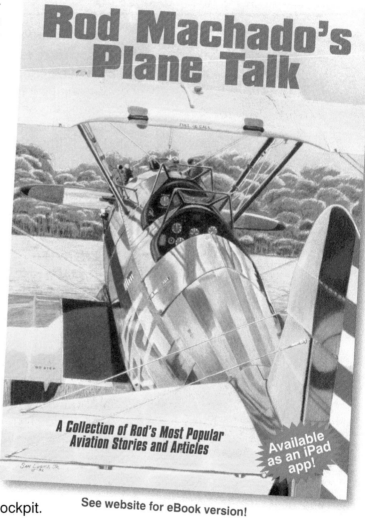

See website for eBook version!

How to Handle First Time Flyers and Anxious Passengers
Discover how to behave around new passengers, how to avoid most common mistakes that scare passengers in airplanes and how to reduce the cockpit stress between pilot and spouse.

Favorite Skills Used By Good Pilots
Learn why good pilots scan behind an airplane as well as ahead of it, are sometimes rough and bully-like on the flight controls, occasionally fly without using any of the airplane's electronic navigation equipment, don't worry about turbulence breaking their airplanes, master airspeed control as a means of making better landings and much more.

$29.95

DVD containing MP3 files - Price: $119.95

Rod Machado's Instrument Pilot Audiobook in MP3 Format

Now you can enjoy Rod's popular *Instrument Pilot's Handbook* during your daily commute or at home in the comfort of your own chair. This audiobook is a 30 hour narration of the *Instrument Pilot Handbook* by Rod Machado.

While you can listen to the first ten chapters of the book without referring to the text, you'll still want to use the actual *Instrument Pilot's Handbook* as a reference for reviewing pictures, graphs and many of the incidental ASRS stories scattered throughout the text. This exciting audiobook is the key to learning quickly and efficiently while maximizing use of your scarce time.

Download MP3 Version $99.95

See www.rodmachado.com for download version!

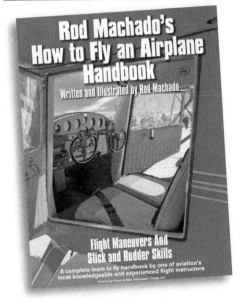

Book-$59.95/eBook-$44.95

Rod Machado's How to Fly an Airplane Handbook & Audiobook

Rod Machado's *How to Fly an Airplane Handbook* (or audiobook recorded by Rod Machado) is a full color, 597 page softbound handbook. It contains all the information you need to learn the physical skills associated with flying an airplane. The book was written to help all pilots learn the basic maneuvers for flying an airplane as well as helping already rated pilots improve their stick and rudder skills.

This handbook contains the information necessary to:
- Learn the basic fundamentals of flying any airplane.
- Make flight training easier, less expensive and more enjoyable.
- Master all the private and commercial checkride maneuvers.
- Learn the "stick and rudder" philosophy of flying an airplane.
- Prevent an airplane from accidentally stalling and spinning.
- Allow you to learn to land an airplane quickly and enjoyably.
- Make you a better instructor by providing unique teaching strategies and explanations for student training.

These pages include:
- Practical flying skills that rely on sights, sounds and touch.
- The theory and practice of attitude flying for pilots of all levels.
- Multiple strategies for evaluating the roundout and flare.
- Multiple methods for controlling the airplane's glidepath.
- Strategies for evaluating the desired landing spot.
- Techniques for flying ground reference maneuvers.
- Handling bounces, floating, porpoising and ballooning.
- Wisdom and insights based on practical flying experience.
- Complex airplane operations, night flying, traffic pattern operations, slow flight, stall and spin recognition and recovery, and much more.

With this book you are ensured an enjoyable learning experience and quality instruction.

Audiobook DVD w/MP3 files - $89.95
Download Version - $69.95

See www.rodmachado.com for download version!

The Best of Rod Machado Live in MP3 Format

Rod combined 10 of his best "live audience" recordings from the original "Laugh and Learn" tape series and added four additional live recordings to produce this exciting 14 program set (12.5 hours of recorded material). Included are Rod's popular *Handling In-flight Emergencies* seminar and his latest programs on defensive flying, the art of flying, the nonpilot's guide to landing an airplane, and three additional live programs containing some of Rod's funniest standup aviation humor. You can laugh and learn while driving, gardening, or building your own plane. DVD contains files in MP3 format that are transferred to your MP3 player via computer for use.

Download MP3 Version $59.95

See website for download version!

DVD containing MP3 files - Price: $99.95/Download Version $59.95 (see www.rodmachado.com)

CONTENTS

Auido-1 Laugh Your Empennage Off (95/5)*
Auido-2 Samurai Airmanship (30/70)*
Auido-3 Reducing Cockpit Stress Between the Sexes (60/40)*
Auido-4 Cockpit Management (40/60)*
Auido-5 An Aviation Sense of Humor (95/5)*
Auido-6 Creative Solutions to Common Problems (40/60)*
Auido-7 Handling In-flight Emergencies 1 (10/90)*

Auido-8 Handling In-flight Emergencies 2 (10/90)*
Auido-9 Handling In-flight Emergencies 3 (10/90)*
Auido-10 Handling In-flight Emergencies 4 (10/90)*
Auido-11 The Nonpilot's Guide to Landing an Airplane (30/70)*
Auido-12 Aviation Humor: The Light Stuff (95/5)*
Auido-13 Yoke and Pedal: The Art of Flying (10/90)*
Auido-14 More Defensive Flying (10/90)*

*(% Humor content / % Information content)

"Rod has a wonderful sense of humor that will keep you in stitches and when you're done laughing, you'll be amazed at how much you've learned." **John & Martha King,** King Video

"Mary Poppins once sang, 'A spoon full of sugar helps the medicine go down.' Rod Machado goes one step further by sugar coating invaluable aeronautical wisdom with entertaining wit and humor." **Barry Schiff,** TWA Captain/Noted Author

How to Order

Free Samples! Go to: www.rodmachado.com for page and CD samples

COPY & MAIL COMPLETED FORM TO: THE AVIATION SPEAKERS BUREAU, P.O. BOX 6030 SAN CLEMENTE, CA 92674-6030

Order Form

Credit card ordering 24 hours - 7 days a week
Call: **(800) 437-7080** for ordering only

Title	Quantity	X	=	Total
Defensive Flying Video - DVD		$29.95		
Aviation Humor Video - DVD		$29.95		
Instrument Flying Tips - DVD		$29.95		
Rod Machado Live on 14 Audio CDs		$99.95		
Instrument Pilot's Survival Manual		$34.95		
Rod Machado's Instrument Pilot's Handbook		$64.95		
Rod Machado's Private Pilot Handbook		$64.95		
Rod Machado's Private Pilot Workbook		$24.95		
Rod Machado's Sport Pilot Handbook		$59.95		
Rod Machado's Private Pilot Audiobook-Mp3 DVD		$119.95		
Rod Machado's IFR Handbook Audiobook-Mp3 DVD		$119.95		
Rod Machado's How to Fly an Airplane Book		$59.95		
Rod Machado's How to Fly an Airplane Audiobook		$79.95		
Rod Machado's Plane Talk		$29.95		
Speaking of Flying		$29.95		
		Product Subtotal		
Sales Tax - CA Residents only	Product Subtotal x .0775			
Product shipping & handling				
		Total		

For more information and secure internet ordering visit *www.rodmachado.com*
Questions: Email us from web site.
FAX: (888) MACHADO (622-4236)

Name _____

Address _____

City _____ State _____

Zip _____

Phone (____) _____

Check # _____ or:

We accept checks, money orders, MasterCard, VISA, American Express and Discover.

Credit Card # _____

Expiration Date: _____

Authorized Signature _____

Index

GLOSSARY

A

ABEAM-An aircraft is "abeam" a fix, point, or object when that fix, point, or object is approximately 90 degrees to the right or left of the aircraft track. Abeam indicates a general position rather than a precise point.

ABORT-To terminate a preplanned aircraft maneuver; e.g., an aborted takeoff.

ACKNOWLEDGE-Let me know that you have received my message.

ACROBATIC FLIGHT- An intentional maneuver involving an abrupt change in an aircraft's attitude, an abnormal attitude, or abnormal acceleration not necessary for normal flight.

ADMINISTRATOR- The Federal Aviation Administrator or any person to whom he/she has delegated his/her authority in the matter concerned.

ADVISE INTENTIONS-Tell me what you plan to do.

ADVISORY- Advice and information provided to assist pilots in the safe conduct of flight and aircraft movement.

ADVISORY FREQUENCY- The appropriate frequency to be used for Airport Advisory Service.

ADVISORY SERVICE- Advice and information provided by a facility to assist pilots in the safe conduct of

AERODROME- A defined area on land or water (including any buildings, installations and equipment) intended to be used either wholly or in part for the arrival, departure, and movement of aircraft.

AERONAUTICAL BEACON- A visual NAVAID displaying flashes of white and/or colored light to indicate the location of an airport, a heliport, a landmark, a certain point of a Federal airway in mountainous terrain, or an obstruction.

AERONAUTICAL INFORMATION MANUAL (AIM)- A primary FAA publication whose purpose is to instruct airmen about operating in the National Airspace System of the U.S. It provides basic flight information, ATC Procedures and general instructional information concerning health, medical facts, factors affecting flight safety, accident and hazard reporting, and types of aeronautical charts and their use.

AIR DEFENSE IDENTIFICATION ZONE (ADIZ)- The area of airspace over land or water, extending upward from the surface, within which the ready identification, the location, and the control of aircraft are required in the interest of national security.

a. Domestic Air Defense Identification Zone. An ADIZ within the United States along an international boundary of the United States.

b. Coastal Air Defense Identification Zone. An ADIZ over the coastal waters of the United States.

c. Distant Early Warning Identification Zone (DEWIZ). An ADIZ over the coastal waters of the State of Alaska.

d. Land-Based Air Defense Identification Zone. An ADIZ over U.S. metropolitan areas, which is activated and deactivated as needed, with dimensions, activation dates and other relevant information disseminated via NOTAM.

AIR ROUTE SURVEILLANCE RADAR- Air route traffic control center (ARTCC) radar used primarily to detect and display an aircraft's position while en route between terminal areas. The ARSR enables controllers to provide radar air traffic control service when aircraft are within the ARSR coverage. In some instances, ARSR may enable an ARTCC to provide terminal radar services similar to but usually more limited than those provided by a radar approach control.

AIR ROUTE TRAFFIC CONTROL CENTER- A facility established to provide air traffic control service to aircraft operating on IFR flight plans within controlled airspace and principally during the en route phase of flight. When equipment capabilities and controller workload permit, certain advisory/assistance services may be provided to VFR aircraft.

AIR TAXI- Used to describe a helicopter/VTOL aircraft movement conducted above the surface but normally not above 100 feet AGL. The aircraft may proceed either via hover taxi or flight at speeds more than 20 knots. The pilot is solely responsible for selecting a safe airspeed/altitude for the operation being conducted.

AIR TRAFFIC- Aircraft operating in the air or on an airport surface, exclusive of loading ramps and parking areas.

AIR TRAFFIC CLEARANCE- An authorization by air traffic control for the purpose of preventing collision between known aircraft, for an aircraft to proceed under specified traffic conditions within controlled airspace. The pilot-in-command of an aircraft may not deviate from the provisions of a visual flight rules (VFR) or instrument flight rules (IFR) air traffic clearance except in an emergency or unless an amended clearance has been obtained. Additionally, the pilot may request a different clearance from that which has been issued by air traffic control (ATC) if information available to the pilot makes another course of action more practicable or if aircraft equipment limitations or company procedures forbid compliance with the clearance issued. Pilots may also request clarification or amendment, as appropriate, any time a clearance is not fully understood, or considered unacceptable because of safety of flight. Controllers should, in such instances and to the extent of operational practicality and safety, honor the pilot's request. 14 CFR Part 91.3(a) states: "The pilot in command of an aircraft is directly responsible for, and is the final authority as to, the operation of that aircraft." THE PILOT IS RESPONSIBLE TO REQUEST AN AMENDED CLEARANCE if ATC issues a clearance that would cause a pilot to deviate from a rule or regulation, or in the pilot's opinion, would place the aircraft in jeopardy.

AIR TRAFFIC CONTROL- A service operated by appropriate authority to promote the safe, orderly and expeditious flow of air traffic.

AIRCRAFT- Device(s) that are used or intended to be used for flight in the air, and when used in air traffic control terminology, may include the flight crew.

AIRCRAFT CLASSES- For the purposes of Wake Turbulence Separation Minima, ATC classifies aircraft as Heavy, Large, and Small as follows:

a. Heavy- Aircraft capable of takeoff weights of 300,000 pounds or more whether or not they are operating at this weight during a particular phase of flight.

b. Large- Aircraft of more than 41,000 pounds, maximum certificated takeoff weight, up to but not including 300,000 pounds.

c. Small- Aircraft of 41,000 pounds or less maximum certificated takeoff weight.

AIRMET-In-flight weather advisories issued only to amend the area forecast concerning weather phenomena which are of operational interest to all aircraft and potentially hazardous to aircraft having limited capability because of lack of equipment, instrumentation, or pilot qualifications. AIRMETs concern weather of less severity than that covered by SIGMETs or Convective SIGMETs. AIRMETs cover moderate icing, moderate turbulence, sustained winds of 30 knots or more at the surface, widespread areas of ceilings less than 1,000 feet and/or visibility less than 3 miles, and extensive mountain obscurement.

AIRPORT- An area on land or water that is used or intended to be used for the landing and takeoff of aircraft and includes its buildings and facilities, if any.

AIRPORT ADVISORY AREA- The area within ten miles of an airport without a control tower or where the tower is not in operation, and on which a Flight Service Station is located.

AIRPORT ELEVATION- The highest point of an airport's usable runways measured in feet from mean sea level.

AIRPORT/FACILITY DIRECTORY- A publication designed primarily as a pilot's operational manual containing all airports, seaplane bases, and heliports open to the public including communications data, navigational facilities, and certain special notices and procedures. This publication is issued in seven volumes according to geographical area.

AIRPORT LIGHTING- Various lighting aids that may be installed on an airport. Types of airport lighting include:...

b. Runway Lights/Runway Edge Lights- Lights having a prescribed angle of emission used to define the lateral limits of a runway. Runway lights are uniformly spaced at intervals of approximately 200 feet, and the intensity may be controlled or preset.

c. Touchdown Zone Lighting-Two rows of transverse light bars located symmetrically about the runway centerline normally at 100 foot intervals. The basic system extends 3,000 feet along the runway.

d. Runway Centerline Lighting- Flush centerline lights spaced at 50-foot intervals beginning 75 feet from the landing threshold and extending to within 75 feet of the opposite end of the runway.

e. Threshold Lights- Fixed green lights arranged symmetrically left and right of the runway centerline, identifying the runway threshold.

f. Runway End Identifier Lights (REIL)- Two synchronized flashing lights, one on each side of the runway threshold, which provide rapid and positive identification of the approach end of a particular runway.

g. Visual Approach Slope Indicator (VASI)- An airport lighting facility providing vertical visual approach slope guidance to aircraft during approach to landing by radiating a directional pattern of high intensity red and white focused light beams which indicate to the pilot that he/she is "on path" if he/she sees red/white, "above path" if white/white, and "below path" if red/red. Some airports serving large aircraft have three-bar VASIs which provide two visual glide paths to the same runway.

h. Precision Approach Path Indicator (PAPI)- An airport lighting facility, similar to VASI, providing vertical approach slope guidance to aircraft during approach to landing. PAPIs consist of a single row of either two or four lights, normally installed on the left side of the runway, and have an effective visual range of about 5 miles during the day and up to 20 miles at night. PAPIs radiate a directional pattern of high intensity red and white focused light beams which indicate that the pilot is "on path" if the pilot sees an equal number of white lights and red lights, with white to the left of the red; "above path" if the pilot sees more white than red lights; and "below path" if the pilot sees more red than white lights.

i. Boundary Lights- Lights defining the perimeter of an airport or landing area. (Refer to AIM.)

AIRPORT MARKING AIDS- Markings used on runway and taxiway surfaces to identify a specific runway, a runway threshold, a centerline, a hold line, etc. A runway should be marked in accordance with its present usage such as:

a. Visual.

b. Nonprecision instrument.

c. Precision instrument.

AIRPORT REFERENCE POINT (ARP)-The approximate geometric center of all usable runway surfaces.

AIRPORT ROTATING BEACON- A visual NAVAID operated at many airports. At civil airports, alternating white and green flashes indicate the location of the airport. At military airports, the beacons flash alternately white and green, but are differentiated from civil beacons by dualpeaked (two quick) white flashes between the green flashes.

AIRPORT SURFACE DETECTION EQUIPMENT (ASDE)-Surveillance equipment specifically designed to detect aircraft, vehicular traffic, and other objects, on the surface of an airport, and to present the image on a tower display. Used to augment visual observation by tower personnel of aircraft and/or vehicular movements on runways and taxiways. There are three ASDE systems deployed in the NAS:

a. ASDE-3- a Surface Movement Radar.

b. ASDE-X- a system that uses a X-band Surface Movement Radar and multilateration.

Data from these two sources are fused and presented on a digital display.

c. ASDE-3X- an ASDE-X system that uses the ASDE-3 Surface Movement Radar.

AIRPORT SURVEILLANCE RADAR- Approach control radar used to detect and display an aircraft's position in the terminal area. ASR provides range and azimuth information but does not provide elevation data. Coverage of the ASR can extend up to 60 miles.

AIRWAY BEACON- Used to mark airway segments in remote mountain areas. The light flashes Morse Code to identify the beacon site.

ALONG-TRACK DISTANCE (ATD)- The distance measured from a point-in-space by systems using area navigation reference capabilities that are not subject to slant range errors.

ALPHANUMERIC DISPLAY- Letters and numerals used to show identification, altitude, beacon code, and other information concerning a target on a radar display.

ALTERNATE AIRPORT- An airport at which an aircraft may land if a landing at the intended airport becomes inadvisable.

ALTIMETER SETTING- The barometric pressure reading used to adjust a pressure altimeter for variations in existing atmospheric pressure or to the standard altimeter setting (29.92).

ALTITUDE- The height of a level, point, or object measured in feet Above Ground Level (AGL) or from Mean Sea Level (MSL).

a. MSL Altitude-Altitude expressed in feet measured from mean sea level.

b. AGL Altitude-Altitude expressed in feet measured above ground level.

c. Indicated Altitude- The altitude as shown by an altimeter. On a pressure or barometric altimeter it is altitude as shown uncorrected for instrument error and uncompensated for variation from standard atmospheric conditions.

ALTITUDE READOUT-An aircraft's altitude, transmitted via the Mode C transponder feature, that is visually displayed in 100-foot increments on a radar scope having readout capability.

ALTITUDE RESTRICTION- An altitude or altitudes, stated in the order flown, which are to be maintained until reaching a specific point or time. Altitude restrictions may be issued by ATC due to traffic, terrain, or other airspace considerations.

APPROACH CLEARANCE- Authorization by ATC for a pilot to conduct an instrument approach. The type of instrument approach for which a clearance and other pertinent information is provided in the approach clearance when required.

APPROACH CONTROL FACILITY- A terminal ATC facility that provides approach control service in a terminal area.

APRON- A defined area on an airport or heliport intended to accommodate aircraft for purposes of loading or unloading passengers or cargo, refueling, parking, or maintenance. With regard to seaplanes, a ramp is used for access to the apron from the water.

ARC- The track over the ground of an aircraft flying at a constant distance from a navigational aid by reference to distance measuring equipment (DME).

AREA NAVIGATION (RNAV)- A method of navigation which permits aircraft operation on any desired flight path within the coverage of ground- or space-based navigation aids or within the limits of the capability of self-contained aids, or a combination of these.

Note: Area navigation includes performance-based navigation as well as other operations that do not meet the definition of performance-based navigation.

ARRIVAL DELAY- A parameter which specifies a period of time in which no aircraft will be metered for arrival at the specified airport.

ARRIVAL SECTOR- An operational control sector containing one or more meter fixes.

ARRIVAL TIME- The time an aircraft touches down on arrival.

ATC ADVISES- Used to prefix a message of noncontrol information when it is relayed to an aircraft by other than an air traffic controller.

ATC ASSIGNED AIRSPACE- Airspace of defined vertical/lateral limits, assigned by ATC, for the purpose of providing air traffic segregation between the specified activities being conducted within the assigned airspace and other IFR air traffic.

ATC CLEARS- Used to prefix an ATC clearance when it is relayed to an aircraft by other than an air traffic controller.

ATC INSTRUCTIONS- Directives issued by air traffic control for the purpose of requiring a pilot to take specific actions; e.g., "Turn left heading two five zero," "Go around," "Clear the runway."

ATC PREFERRED ROUTE NOTIFICATION-URET notification to the appropriate controller of the need to determine if an ATC preferred route needs to be applied, based on destination airport.

ATC REQUESTS- Used to prefix an ATC request when it is relayed to an aircraft by other than an air traffic controller.

AUTOMATED WEATHER SYSTEM- Any of the automated weather sensor platforms that collect weather data at airports and disseminate the weather information via radio and/or landline. The systems currently consist of the Automated Surface Observing System (ASOS), Automated Weather Sensor System (AWSS) and Automated Weather Observation System (AWOS).

AUTOMATED UNICOM- Provides completely automated weather, radio check capability and airport advisory information on an Automated UNICOM system. These systems offer a variety of features, typically selectable by microphone clicks, on the UNICOM frequency. Availability will be published in the Airport/Facility Directory and approach charts.

AUTOMATIC ALTITUDE REPORTING- That function of a transponder which responds to Mode C interrogations by transmitting the aircraft's altitude in 100-foot increments.

AUTOMATIC DEPENDENT SURVEILLANCE-BROADCAST (ADS-B)- A surveillance system in which an aircraft or vehicle to be detected is fit-

GLOSSARY

ted with cooperative equipment in the form of a data link transmitter. The aircraft or vehicle periodically broadcasts its GPS-derived position and other information such as velocity over the data link, which is received by a ground-based transmitter/receiver (transceiver) for processing and display at an air traffic control facility.

AUTOMATIC DIRECTION FINDER- An aircraft radio navigation system which senses and indicates the direction to a L/MF nondirectional radio beacon (NDB) ground transmitter. Direction is indicated to the pilot as a magnetic bearing or as a relative bearing to the longitudinal axis of the aircraft depending on the type of indicator installed in the aircraft. In certain applications, such as military, ADF operations may be based on airborne and ground transmitters in the VHF/UHF frequency spectrum.

AUTOMATIC TERMINAL INFORMATION SERVICE- The continuous broadcast of recorded noncontrol information in selected terminal areas. Its purpose is to improve controller effectiveness and to relieve frequency congestion by automating the repetitive transmission of essential but routine information; e.g., "Los Angeles information Alfa. One three zero zero Coordinated Universal Time. Weather, measured ceiling two thousand overcast, visibility three, haze, smoke, temperature seven one, dew point five seven, wind two five zero at five, altimeter two niner niner six. I-L-S Runway Two Five Left approach in use, Runway Two Five Right closed, advise you have Alfa."

AVAILABLE LANDING DISTANCE (ALD)- The portion of a runway available for landing and roll-out for aircraft cleared for LAHSO. This distance is measured from the landing threshold to the hold-short point.

AVIATION WEATHER SERVICE- A service provided by the National Weather Service (NWS) and FAA which collects and disseminates pertinent weather information for pilots, aircraft operators, and ATC. Available aviation weather reports and forecasts are displayed at each NWS office and FAA FSS.

AZIMUTH (MLS)- A magnetic bearing extending from an MLS navigation facility.

B

BACK-TAXI- A term used by air traffic controllers to taxi an aircraft on the runway opposite to the traffic flow. The aircraft may be instructed to back-taxi to the beginning of the runway or at some point before reaching the runway end for the purpose of departure or to exit the runway.

BEARING- The horizontal direction to or from any point, usually measured clockwise from true north, magnetic north, or some other reference point through 360 degrees.

BELOW MINIMUMS- Weather conditions below the minimums prescribed by regulation for the particular action involved; e.g., landing minimums, takeoff minimums.

BLOCKED-Phraseology used to indicate that a radio transmission has been distorted or interrupted due to multiple simultaneous radio transmissions.

BRAKING ACTION (GOOD, FAIR, POOR, OR NIL)-A report of conditions on the airport movement area providing a pilot with a degree/quality of braking that he/she might expect. Braking action is reported in terms of good, fair, poor, or nil.

BRAKING ACTION ADVISORIES- When tower controllers have received runway braking action reports which include the terms "fair," "poor," or "nil," or whenever weather conditions are conducive to deteriorating or rapidly changing runway braking conditions, the tower will include on the ATIS broadcast the statement, "Braking action advisories are in effect" on the ATIS broadcast. During the time braking action advisories are in effect, ATC will issue the latest braking action report for the runway in use to each arriving and departing aircraft. Pilots should be prepared for deteriorating braking conditions and should request current runway condition information if not volunteered by controllers. Pilots should also be prepared to provide a descriptive runway condition report to controllers after landing.

C

CALCULATED LANDING TIME- A term that may be used in place of tentative or actual calculated landing time, whichever applies.

CARDINAL ALTITUDES-"Odd" or "Even" thousand-foot altitudes or flight levels; e.g., 5,000, 6,000, 7,000, FL 250, FL 260, FL 270.

CEILING- The heights above the earth's surface of the lowest layer of clouds or obscuring phenomena that is reported as "broken," "overcast," or "obscuration," and not classified as "thin" or "partial."

CHARTED VFR FLYWAYS- Charted VFR Flyways are flight paths recommended for use to bypass areas heavily traversed by large turbine-powered aircraft. Pilot compliance with recommended flyways and associated altitudes is strictly voluntary. VFR Flyway Planning charts are published on the back of existing VFR Terminal Area charts.

CIRCLE-TO-LAND MANEUVER- A maneuver initiated by the pilot to align the aircraft with a runway for landing when a straight-in landing from an instrument approach is not possible or is not desirable. At tower controlled airports, this maneuver is made only after ATC authorization has been obtained and the pilot has established required visual reference to the airport.

CIRCLE TO RUNWAY (RUNWAY NUMBER)- Used by ATC to inform the pilot that he/she must circle to land because the runway in use is other than the runway aligned with the instrument approach procedure. When the direction of the circling maneuver in relation to the airport/runway is required, the controller will state the direction (eight cardinal compass points) and specify a left or right downwind or base leg as appropriate; e.g., "Cleared VOR Runway Three Six Approach circle to Runway Two Two," or "Circle northwest of the airport for a right downwind to Runway Two Two."

CLASS G AIRSPACE- That airspace not designated as Class A, B, C, D or E.

CLEAR AIR TURBULENCE (CAT)-Turbulence encountered in air where no clouds are present. This term is commonly applied to high-level turbulence associated with wind shear. CAT is often encountered in the vicinity of the jet stream.

CLEAR OF THE RUNWAY-

a. Taxiing aircraft, which is approaching a runway, is clear of the runway when all parts of the aircraft are held short of the applicable runway holding position marking.

b. A pilot or controller may consider an aircraft, which is exiting or crossing a runway, to be clear of the runway when all parts of the aircraft are beyond the runway edge and there are no restrictions to its continued movement beyond the applicable runway holding position marking.

c. Pilots and controllers shall exercise good judgement to ensure that adequate separation exists between all aircraft on runways and taxiways at airports with inadequate runway edge lines or holding position markings.

CLEARANCE LIMIT- The fix, point, or location to which an aircraft is cleared when issued an air traffic clearance.

CLEARANCE VOID IF NOT OFF BY (TIME)- Used by ATC to advise an aircraft that the departure clearance is automatically canceled if takeoff is not made prior to a specified time. The pilot must obtain a new clearance or cancel his/her IFR flight plan if not off by the specified time.

CLEARED APPROACH- ATC authorization for an aircraft to execute any standard or special instrument approach procedure for that airport. Normally, an aircraft will be cleared for a specific instrument approach procedure.

CLEARED (Type of) APPROACH- ATC authorization for an aircraft to execute a specific instrument approach procedure to an airport; e.g., "Cleared ILS Runway Three Six Approach."

CLEARED AS FILED- Means the aircraft is cleared to proceed in accordance with the route of flight filed in the flight plan. This clearance does not include the altitude, DP, or DP Transition.

CLEARED FOR TAKEOFF- ATC authorization for an aircraft to depart. It is predicated on known traffic and known physical airport conditions.

CLEARED FOR THE OPTION- ATC authorization for an aircraft to make a touch-and-go, low approach, missed approach, stop and go, or full stop landing at the discretion of the pilot. It is normally used in training so that an instructor can evaluate a student's performance under changing situations.

CLEARED THROUGH-ATC authorization for an aircraft to make intermediate stops at specified airports without refiling a flight plan while en route to the clearance limit.

CLEARED TO LAND- ATC authorization for an aircraft to land. It is predicated on known traffic and known physical airport conditions.

CLIMB TO VFR- ATC authorization for an aircraft to climb to VFR conditions within Class B, C, D, and E surface areas when the only weather limitation is restricted visibility. The aircraft must remain clear of clouds while climbing to VFR.

CLIMBOUT- That portion of flight operation between takeoff and the initial cruising altitude.

CLOSED RUNWAY- A runway that is unusable for aircraft operations. Only the airport management/military operations office can close a runway.

CLOSED TRAFFIC- Successive operations involving takeoffs and landings or low approaches where the aircraft does not exit the traffic pattern.

CLOUD- A cloud is a visible accumulation of minute water droplets and/or ice particles in the atmosphere above the Earth's surface. Cloud differs from ground fog, fog, or ice fog only in that the latter are, by definition, in contact with the Earth's surface.

COMBINED CENTER-RAPCON- An air traffic facility which combines the functions of an ARTCC and a radar approach control facility.

COMMON TRAFFIC ADVISORY FREQUENCY (CTAF)- A frequency designed for the purpose of carrying out airport advisory practices while operating to or from an airport without an operating control tower. The CTAF may be a UNICOM, Multicom, FSS, or tower frequency and is identified in appropriate aeronautical publications.

COMPASS LOCATOR- A low power, low or medium frequency (L/MF) radio beacon installed at the site of the outer or middle marker of an instrument landing system (ILS). It can be used for navigation at distances of approximately 15 miles or as authorized in the approach procedure.

a. Outer Compass Locator (LOM)- A compass locator installed at the site of the outer marker of an instrument landing system.

b. Middle Compass Locator (LMM)- A compass locator installed at the site of the middle marker of an instrument landing system.

COMPASS ROSE- A circle, graduated in degrees, printed on some charts or marked on the ground at an airport. It is used as a reference to either true or magnetic direction.

CONFIDENCE MANEUVER- A confidence maneuver consists of one or more turns, a climb or descent, or other maneuver to determine if the pilot in command (PIC) is able to receive and comply with ATC instructions.

CONFLICT ALERT- A function of certain air traffic control automated systems designed to alert radar controllers to existing or pending situations between tracked targets (known IFR or VFR aircraft) that require his/her immediate attention/action.

CONFLICT RESOLUTION- The resolution of potential conflictions between aircraft that are radar identified and in communication with ATC by ensuring that radar targets do not touch. Pertinent traffic advisories shall be issued when this procedure is applied.

Note: This procedure shall not be provided utilizing mosaic radar systems.

CONTACT-

a. Establish communication with (followed by the name of the facility and, if appropriate, the frequency to be used).

b. A flight condition wherein the pilot ascer-

tains the attitude of his/her aircraft and navigates by visual reference to the surface.

CONTERMINOUS U.S.- The 48 adjoining States and the District of Columbia.

CONTINENTAL UNITED STATES- The 49 States located on the continent of North America and the District of Columbia.

CONTINUE- When used as a control instruction should be followed by another word or words clarifying what is expected of the pilot. Example: "continue taxi," "continue descent," "continue inbound," etc.

CONVECTIVE SIGMET- A weather advisory concerning convective weather significant to the safety of all aircraft. Convective SIGMETs are issued for tornadoes, lines of thunderstorms, embedded thunderstorms of any intensity level, areas of thunderstorms greater than or equal to VIP level 4 with an area coverage of 4/10 (40%) or more, and hail 3/4 inch or greater.

COORDINATES- The intersection of lines of reference, usually expressed in degrees/minutes/seconds of latitude and longitude, used to determine position or location.

CORRECTION- An error has been made in the transmission and the correct version follows.

COURSE-

a. The intended direction of flight in the horizontal plane measured in degrees from north.

b. The ILS localizer signal pattern usually specified as the front course or the back course.

c. The intended track along a straight, curved, or segmented MLS path.

CROSS (FIX) AT (ALTITUDE)- Used by ATC when a specific altitude restriction at a specified fix is required.

CROSS (FIX) AT OR ABOVE (ALTITUDE)- Used by ATC when an altitude restriction at a specified fix is required. It does not prohibit the aircraft from crossing the fix at a higher altitude than specified; however, the higher altitude may not be one that will violate a succeeding altitude restriction or altitude assignment.

CROSS (FIX) AT OR BELOW (ALTITUDE)- Used by ATC when a maximum crossing altitude at a specific fix is required. It does not prohibit the aircraft from crossing the fix at a lower altitude; however, it must be at or above the minimum IFR altitude.

CROSSWIND-

a. When used concerning the traffic pattern, the word means "crosswind leg."

b. When used concerning wind conditions, the word means a wind not parallel to the runway or the path of an aircraft.

CROSSWIND COMPONENT- The wind component measured in knots at 90 degrees to the longitudinal axis of the runway.

CRUISE CLIMB- A climb technique employed by aircraft, usually at a constant power setting, resulting in an increase of altitude as the aircraft weight decreases.

CRUISING ALTITUDE- An altitude or flight level maintained during en route level flight. This is a constant altitude and should not be confused with a cruise clearance.

D

DEAD RECKONING- Dead reckoning, as applied to flying, is the navigation of an airplane solely by means of computations based on airspeed, course, heading, wind direction, and speed, groundspeed, and elapsed time.

DECISION ALTITUDE/DECISION HEIGHT-A specified altitude or height (A/H) in the precision approach at which a missed approach must be initiated if the required visual reference to continue the approach has not been established.

DECISION HEIGHT- With respect to the operation of aircraft, means the height at which a decision must be made during an ILS, MLS, or PAR instrument approach to either continue the approach or to execute a missed approach.

DEFENSE VISUAL FLIGHT RULES-Rules applicable to flights within an ADIZ conducted under the visual flight rules in 14 CFR Part 91.

DELAY INDEFINITE (REASON IF KNOWN) EXPECT FURTHER CLEARANCE (TIME)- Used by ATC to inform a pilot when an accurate estimate of the delay time and the reason for the delay cannot immediately be determined; e.g., a disabled aircraft on the runway, terminal or center area saturation, weather below landing minimums, etc.

DEPARTURE CONTROL- A function of an approach control facility providing air traffic control service for departing IFR and, under certain conditions, VFR aircraft.

DEPARTURE TIME- The time an aircraft becomes airborne.

DESIRED COURSE-

a. True- A predetermined desired course direction to be followed (measured in degrees from true north).

b. Magnetic- A predetermined desired course direction to be followed (measured in degrees from local magnetic north).

DESIRED TRACK- The planned or intended track between two waypoints. It is measured in degrees from either magnetic or true north. The instantaneous angle may change from point to point along the great circle track between waypoints.

DEVIATIONS-

a. A departure from a current clearance, such as an off course maneuver to avoid weather or turbulence.

b. Where specifically authorized in the CFRs and requested by the pilot, ATC may permit pilots to

DIGITAL-AUTOMATIC TERMINAL INFORMATION SERVICE (D-ATIS)- The service provides text messages to aircraft, airlines, and other users outside the standard reception range of conventional ATIS via landline and data link communications to the cockpit. Also, the service provides a computer-synthesized voice message that can be transmitted to all aircraft within range of existing transmitters. The Terminal Data Link System (TDLS) D-ATIS application uses weather inputs from local automated weather sources or manually entered meteorological data together with preprogrammed menus to provide standard information to users. Airports with D-ATIS capability are listed in the Airport/Facility Directory.

DIRECT-Straight line flight between two navigational aids, fixes, points, or any combination thereof. When used by pilots in describing off-airway routes, points defining direct route segments become compulsory reporting points unless the aircraft is under radar contact.

DISCRETE CODE-As used in the Air Traffic Control Radar Beacon System (ATCRBS), any one of the 4096 selectable Mode 3/A aircraft transponder codes except those ending in zero zero; e.g., discrete codes: 0010, 1201, 2317, 7777; nondiscrete codes: 0100, 1200, 7700. Nondiscrete codes are normally reserved for radar facilities that are not equipped with discrete decoding capability and for other purposes such as emergencies (7700), VFR aircraft (1200), etc.

DISCRETE FREQUENCY- A separate radio frequency for use in direct pilot-controller communications in air traffic control which reduces frequency congestion by controlling the number of aircraft operating on a particular frequency at one time. Discrete frequencies are normally designated for each control sector in en route/terminal ATC facilities. Discrete frequencies are listed in the Airport/Facility Directory and the DOD FLIP IFR En Route Supplement.

DISPLACED THRESHOLD- A threshold that is located at a point on the runway other than the designated beginning of the runway.

DISTANCE MEASURING EQUIPMENT- Equipment (airborne and ground) used to measure, in nautical miles, the slant range distance of an aircraft from the DME navigational aid.

DISTRESS- A condition of being threatened by serious and/or imminent danger and of requiring immediate assistance.

DME FIX- A geographical position determined by reference to a navigational aid which provides distance and azimuth information. It is defined by a specific distance in nautical miles and a radial, azimuth, or course (i.e., localizer) in degrees magnetic from that aid.

DOMESTIC AIRSPACE- Airspace which overlies the continental land mass of the United States plus Hawaii and U.S. possessions. Domestic airspace extends to 12 miles offshore.

DOWNBURST- A strong downdraft which induces an outburst of damaging winds on or near the ground. Damaging winds, either straight or curved, are highly divergent. The sizes of downbursts vary from 1/2 mile or less to more than 10 miles. An intense downburst often causes widespread damage. Damaging winds, lasting 5 to 30 minutes, could reach speeds as high as 120 knots.

DVFR FLIGHT PLAN- A flight plan filed for a VFR aircraft which intends to operate in airspace within which the ready identification, location, and control of aircraft are required in the interest of national security.

E

EMERGENCY-A distress or an urgency condition.

EMERGENCY LOCATOR TRANSMITTER-A radio transmitter attached to the aircraft structure which operates from its own power source on 121.5 MHz and 243.0 MHz. It aids in locating downed aircraft by radiating a downward sweeping audio tone, 2-4 times per second. It is designed to function without human action after an accident.

EN ROUTE AIR TRAFFIC CONTROL SERVICES-Air traffic control service provided aircraft on IFR flight plans, generally by centers, when these aircraft are operating between departure and destination terminal areas. When equipment, capabilities, and controller workload permit, certain advisory/assistance services may be provided to VFR aircraft.

EN ROUTE FLIGHT ADVISORY SERVICE- A service specifically designed to provide, upon pilot request, timely weather information pertinent to his/her type of flight, intended route of flight, and altitude. The FSSs providing this service are listed in the Airport/Facility Directory.

EN ROUTE MINIMUM SAFE ALTITUDE WARNING- A function of the EAS that aids the controller by providing an alert when a tracked aircraft is below or predicted by the computer to go below a predetermined minimum IFR altitude (MIA).

ESTABLISHED-To be stable or fixed on a route, route segment, altitude, heading, etc.

ESTIMATED ELAPSED TIME [ICAO]-The estimated time required to proceed from one significant point to another.

ESTIMATED TIME OF ARRIVAL- The time the flight is estimated to arrive at the gate (scheduled operators) or the actual runway on times for nonscheduled operators.

ESTIMATED TIME EN ROUTE- The estimated flying time from departure point to destination (lift-off to touchdown).

EXPECT DEPARTURE CLEARANCE TIME (EDCT)- The runway release time assigned to an aircraft in a traffic management program and shown on the flight progress strip as an EDCT.

EXPEDITE-Used by ATC when prompt compliance is required to avoid the development of an imminent situation. Expedite climb/descent normally indicates to a pilot that the approximate best rate of climb/descent should be used without requiring an exceptional change in aircraft handling characteristics.

F

FAST FILE- A system whereby a pilot files a flight plan via telephone that is tape recorded and then transcribed for transmission to the appropriate air traffic facility. Locations having a fast file capability are contained in the Airport/Facility Directory.

FINAL-Commonly used to mean that an aircraft is on the final approach course or is aligned with a landing area.

FINAL APPROACH COURSE- A bearing /radial/track of an instrument approach leading to a runway or an extended runway centerline all without regard to distance.

FIX- A geographical position determined by visual reference to the surface, by reference to one or more radio NAVAIDs, by celestial plotting, or by another navigational device.

FLIGHT INFORMATION REGION- An airspace of defined dimensions within which Flight Information

FLIGHT LEVEL-A level of constant atmospheric pressure related to a reference datum of 29.92 inches of mercury. Each is stated in three digits that represent hundreds of feet. For example, flight level (FL) 250 represents a barometric altimeter indication of 25,000 feet; FL 255, an indication of 25,500 feet.

FLIGHT MANAGEMENT SYSTEMS- A computer system that uses a large data base to allow routes to be preprogrammed and fed into the system by means of a data loader. The system is constantly updated with respect to position accuracy by reference to conventional navigation aids. The sophisticated program and its associated data base insures that the most appropriate aids are automatically selected during the information update cycle.

FLIGHT PLAN- Specified information relating to the intended flight of an aircraft that is filed orally or in writing with an FSS or an ATC facility.

FLIGHT SERVICE STATION (FSS) - An air traffic facility which provides pilot briefings, flight plan processing, en route radio communications, search and rescue services, and assistance to lost aircraft and aircraft in emergency situations. FSSs also relay ATC clearances, process Notices to Airmen, broadcast aviation weather and aeronautical information, and notify Customs and Border Protection of transborder flights. In addition, at selected locations, FSSs provide En Route Flight Advisory Service (Flight Watch) and Airport Advisory Service (AAS). In Alaska, designated FSSs also provide TWEB recordings and take weather observations.

FLIGHT STANDARDS DISTRICT OFFICE- An FAA field office serving an assigned geographical area and staffed with Flight Standards personnel who serve the aviation industry and the general public on matters relating to the certification and operation of air carrier and general aviation aircraft. Activities include general surveillance of operational safety, certification of airmen and aircraft, accident prevention, investigation, enforcement, etc.

FLIGHT WATCH- A shortened term for use in air-ground contacts to identify the flight service station providing En Route Flight Advisory Service; e.g., "Oakland Flight Watch."

FLY HEADING (DEGREES)- Informs the pilot of the heading he/she should fly. The pilot may have to turn to, or continue on, a specific compass direction in order to comply with the instructions. The pilot is expected to turn in the shorter direction to the heading unless otherwise instructed by ATC.

FLY-BY WAYPOINT- A fly-by waypoint requires the use of turn anticipation to avoid overshoot of the next flight segment.

FLY-OVER WAYPOINT- A fly-over waypoint precludes any turn until the waypoint is overflown and is followed by an intercept maneuver of the next flight segment.

FORMATION FLIGHT-More than one aircraft which, by prior arrangement between the pilots, operate as a single aircraft with regard to navigation and position reporting. Separation between aircraft within the formation is the responsibility of the flight leader and the pilots of the other aircraft in the flight. This includes transition periods when aircraft within the formation are maneuvering to attain separation from each other to effect individual control and during join-up and breakaway.

FUEL REMAINING- A phrase used by either pilots or controllers when relating to the fuel remaining on board until actual fuel exhaustion. When transmitting such information in response to either a controller question or pilot initiated cautionary advisory to air traffic control, pilots will state the APPROXIMATE NUMBER OF MINUTES the flight can continue with the fuel remaining. All reserve fuel SHOULD BE INCLUDED in the time stated, as should an allowance for established fuel gauge system error.

G

GATE HOLD PROCEDURES-Procedures at selected airports to hold aircraft at the gate or other ground location whenever departure delays exceed or are anticipated to exceed 15 minutes. The sequence for departure will be maintained in accordance with initial call-up unless modified by flow control restrictions. Pilots should monitor the ground control/clearance delivery frequency for engine start/taxi advisories or new proposed start/taxi time if the delay changes.

GENERAL AVIATION- That portion of civil aviation which encompasses all facets of aviation except air carriers holding a certificate of public convenience and necessity from the Civil Aeronautics Board and large aircraft commercial operators.

GLIDESLOPE- Provides vertical guidance for aircraft during approach and landing. The glideslope/glidepath is based on the following:

a. Electronic components emitting signals which provide vertical guidance by reference to airborne instruments during instrument approaches such as ILS/MLS, or

b. Visual ground aids, such as VASI, which provide vertical guidance for a VFR approach or for the visual portion of an instrument approach and landing.

c. PAR. Used by ATC to inform an aircraft making a PAR approach of its vertical position (elevation) relative to the descent profile.

GLOBAL POSITIONING SYSTEM (GPS)-A space-base radio positioning, navigation, and time-transfer system. The system provides highly accurate position and velocity information, and precise time, on a continuous global basis, to an unlimited number of properly equipped users. The system is unaffected by weather, and provides a worldwide common grid reference system. The GPS concept is predicated upon accurate and continuous knowledge of the spatial position of each satellite in the system with respect to time and distance from a transmitting satellite to the user. The GPS receiver automatically selects appropriate sig-

nals from the satellites in view and translates these into three-dimensional position, velocity, and time. System accuracy for civil users is normally 100 meters horizontally.

GO AHEAD-Proceed with your message. Not to be used for any other purpose.

GO AROUND-Instructions for a pilot to abandon his/her approach to landing. Additional instructions may follow. Unless otherwise advised by ATC, a VFR aircraft or an aircraft conducting visual approach should overfly the runway while climbing to traffic pattern altitude and enter the traffic pattern via the crosswind leg. A pilot on an IFR flight plan making an instrument approach should execute the published missed approach procedure or proceed as instructed by ATC; e.g., "Go around" (additional instructions if required).

GROUND SPEED- The speed of an aircraft relative to the surface of the earth.

H

HAVE NUMBERS- Used by pilots to inform ATC that they have received runway, wind, and altimeter information only.

HAZARDOUS INFLIGHT WEATHER ADVISORY SERVICE-Continuous recorded hazardous inflight weather forecasts broadcasted to airborne pilots over selected VOR outlets defined as an HIWAS BROADCAST AREA.

HAZARDOUS WEATHER INFORMATION-Summary of significant meteorological information (SIGMET/WS), convective significant meteorological information (convective SIGMET/ WST), urgent pilot weather reports (urgent PIREP/UUA), center weather advisories (CWA), airmen's meteorological information (AIRMET/WA) and any other weather such as isolated thunderstorms that are rapidly developing and increasing in intensity, or low ceilings and visibilities that are becoming widespread which is considered significant and are not included in a current hazardous weather advisory.

HELIPAD- A small, designated area, usually with a prepared surface, on a heliport, airport, landing/takeoff area, apron/ramp, or movement area used for takeoff, landing, or parking of helicopters.

HELIPORT- An area of land, water, or structure used or intended to be used for the landing and takeoff of helicopters and includes its buildings and facilities if any.

HERTZ- The standard radio equivalent of frequency in cycles per second of an electromagnetic wave. Kilohertz (kHz) is a frequency of one thousand cycles per second. Megahertz (MHz) is a frequency of one million cycles per second.

HIGH SPEED TAXIWAY- A long radius taxiway designed and provided with lighting or marking to define the path of aircraft, traveling at high speed (up to 60 knots), from the runway center to a point on the center of a taxiway. Also referred to as long radius exit or turn-off taxiway. The high speed taxiway is designed to expedite aircraft turning off the runway after landing, thus reducing runway occupancy time.

HIWAS BROADCAST AREA- A geographical area of responsibility including one or more HIWAS outlet areas assigned to an AFSS/FSS for hazardous weather advisory broadcasting.

HOLD FOR RELEASE- Used by ATC to delay an aircraft for traffic management reasons; i.e., weather, traffic volume, etc. Hold for release instructions (including departure delay information) are used to inform a pilot or a controller (either directly or through an authorized relay) that an IFR departure clearance is not valid until a release time or additional instructions have been received.

HOLD IN LIEU OF PROCEDURE TURN- A hold in lieu of procedure turn shall be established over a final or intermediate fix when an approach can be made from a properly aligned holding pattern. The hold in lieu of procedure turn permits the pilot to align with the final or intermediate segment of the approach and/or descend in the holding pattern to an altitude that will permit a normal descent to the final approach fix altitude. The hold in lieu of procedure turn is a required maneuver (the same as a procedure turn) unless the aircraft is being radar vectored to the final approach course, when "NoPT" is shown on the approach chart, or when the pilot requests or the controller advises the pilot to make a "straight-in" approach.

HOLD-SHORT POSITION MARKING-The painted runway marking located at the hold-short point on all LAHSO runways.

HOLD-SHORT POSITION SIGNS- Red and white holding position signs located alongside the hold-short point.

HOMING-Flight toward a NAVAID, without correcting for wind, by adjusting the aircraft heading to maintain a relative bearing of zero degrees.

HOW DO YOU HEAR ME?- A question relating to the quality of the transmission or to determine how well the transmission is being received.**I**

I SAY AGAIN- The message will be repeated.

ICING- The accumulation of airframe ice.

IDENT-A request for a pilot to activate the aircraft transponder identification feature. This will help the controller to confirm an aircraft identity or to identify an aircraft.

IFR AIRCRAFT- An aircraft conducting flight in accordance with instrument flight rules.

IFR MILITARY TRAINING ROUTES (IR)- Routes used by the Department of Defense and associated Reserve and Air Guard units for the purpose of conducting low-altitude navigation and tactical training in both IFR and VFR weather conditions below 10,000 feet MSL at airspeeds in excess of 250 knots IAS.

IMMEDIATELY- Used by ATC or pilots when such action compliance is required to avoid an imminent situation.

INERTIAL NAVIGATION SYSTEM- An RNAV system which is a form of self-contained navigation.

INSTRUMENT APPROACH PROCEDURE-A series of predetermined maneuvers for the orderly transfer of an aircraft under instrument flight conditions from the beginning of the initial approach to a landing or to a point from which a landing may be made visually. It is prescribed and approved for a specific airport by competent authority.

INSTRUMENT FLIGHT RULES- Rules governing the procedures for conducting instrument flight. Also a term used by pilots and controllers to indicate type of flight plan.

INSTRUMENT METEOROLOGICAL CONDITIONS- Meteorological conditions expressed in terms of visibility, distance from cloud, and ceiling less than the minima specified for visual meteorological conditions.

INSTRUMENT RUNWAY- A runway equipped with electronic and visual navigation aids for which a precision or nonprecision approach procedure having straight-in landing minimums has been approved.

INTERNATIONAL CIVIL AVIATION ORGANIZATION [ICAO]- A specialized agency of the United Nations whose objective is to develop the principles and techniques of international air navigation and to foster planning and development of international civil air transport.

INTERSECTION-

a. A point defined by any combination of courses, radials, or bearings of two or more navigational aids.

b. Used to describe the point where two runways, a runway and a taxiway, or two taxiways cross or meet.

INTERSECTION DEPARTURE- A departure from any runway intersection except the end of the runway.

J

JET STREAM- A migrating stream of high-speed winds present at high altitudes.

JET BLAST-Jet engine exhaust (thrust stream turbulence).

JET ROUTE- A route designed to serve aircraft operations from 18,000 feet MSL up to and including flight level 450. The routes are referred to as "J" routes with numbering to identify the designated route; e.g., J105.

K

KNOWN TRAFFIC- With respect to ATC clearances, means aircraft whose altitude, position, and intentions are known to ATC.

L

LAHSO- An acronym for "Land and Hold Short Operation." These operations include landing and holding short of an intersecting runway, a taxiway, a predetermined point, or an approach/departure flightpath.

LAND AND HOLD SHORT OPERATIONS-Operations which include simultaneous takeoffs and landings and/or simultaneous landings when a landing aircraft is able and is instructed by the controller to hold-short of the intersecting runway/ taxiway or designated hold-short point. Pilots are expected to promptly inform the controller if the hold short clearance cannot be accepted.

LANDING DIRECTION INDICATOR- A device which visually indicates the direction in which landings and takeoffs should be made.

LANDING ROLL- The distance from the point of touchdown to the point where the aircraft can be brought to a stop or exit the runway.

LANDING SEQUENCE- The order in which aircraft are positioned for landing.

LAST ASSIGNED ALTITUDE- The last altitude/flight level assigned by ATC and acknowledged by the pilot.

LATERAL NAVIGATION (LNAV)– A function of area navigation (RNAV) equipment which calculates, displays, and provides lateral guidance to a profile or path.

LATERAL SEPARATION- The lateral spacing of aircraft at the same altitude by requiring operation on different routes or in different geographical locations.

LIGHTED AIRPORT- An airport where runway and obstruction lighting is available.

LIGHT GUN- A handheld directional light signaling device which emits a brilliant narrow beam of white, green, or red light as selected by the tower controller. The color and type of light transmitted can be used to approve or disapprove anticipated pilot actions where radio communication is not available. The light gun is used for controlling traffic operating in the vicinity of the airport and on the airport movement area.

LINE UP AND WAIT (LUAW)- Used by ATC to inform a pilot to taxi onto the departure runway to line up and wait. It is not authorization for takeoff. It is used when takeoff clearance cannot immediately be issued because of traffic or other reasons.

LOCAL AIRPORT ADVISORY (LAA)- A service provided by facilities, which are located on the landing airport, have a discrete ground-to-air communication frequency or the tower frequency when the tower is closed, automated weather reporting with voice broadcasting, and a continuous ASOS/AWSS/AWOS data display, other continuous direct reading instruments, or manual observations available to the specialist.

LOCALIZER- The component of an ILS which provides course guidance to the runway.

LONGITUDINAL SEPARATION- The longitudinal spacing of aircraft at the same altitude by a minimum distance expressed in units of time or miles.

LOST COMMUNICATIONS- Loss of the ability to communicate by radio. Aircraft are sometimes referred to as NORDO (No Radio). Standard pilot procedures are specified in 14 CFR Part 91. Radar controllers issue procedures for pilots to follow in the event of lost communications during a radar approach when weather reports indicate that an aircraft will likely encounter IFR weather conditions during the approach.

LOW ALTITUDE AIRWAY STRUCTURE- The network of airways serving aircraft operations up to but not including 18,000 feet MSL.

LOW ALTITUDE ALERT SYSTEM- An automated function of the TPX-42 that alerts the controller when a Mode C transponder equipped aircraft on an IFR flight plan is below a predetermined minimum safe altitude. If requested by the pilot, Low Altitude Alert System monitoring

is also available to VFR Mode C transponder equipped aircraft.

LOW APPROACH- An approach over an airport or runway following an instrument approach or a VFR approach including the go-around maneuver where the pilot intentionally does not make contact with the runway.

LPV- A type of approach with vertical guidance (APV) based on WAAS, published on RNAV (GPS) approach charts. This procedure takes advantage of the precise lateral guidance available from WAAS. The minima is published as a decision altitude (DA).

M

MAINTAIN-

a. Concerning altitude/flight level, the term means to remain at the altitude/flight level specified. The phrase "climb and" or "descend and" normally precedes "maintain" and the altitude assignment; e.g., "descend and maintain 5,000."

b. Concerning other ATC instructions, the term is used in its literal sense; e.g., maintain VFR.

MAKE SHORT APPROACH-Used by ATC to inform a pilot to alter his/her traffic pattern so as to make a short final approach.

MANDATORY ALTITUDE- An altitude depicted on an instrument Approach Procedure Chart requiring the aircraft to maintain altitude at the depicted value.

MARKER BEACON-An electronic navigation facility transmitting a 75 MHz vertical fan or boneshaped radiation pattern. Marker beacons are identified by their modulation frequency and keying code, and when received by compatible airborne equipment, indicate to the pilot, both aurally and visually, that he/she is passing over the facility.

MAYDAY- The international radiotelephony distress signal. When repeated three times, it indicates imminent and grave danger and that immediate assistance is requested.

METEOROLOGICAL IMPACT STATEMENT- An unscheduled planning forecast describing conditions expected to begin within 4 to 12 hours which may impact the flow of air traffic in a specific center's (ARTCC) area.

MICROBURST- A small downburst with outbursts of damaging winds extending 2.5 miles or less. In spite of its small horizontal scale, an intense microburst could induce wind speeds as high as 150 knots

MILES-IN-TRAIL- A specified distance between aircraft, normally, in the same stratum associated with the same destination or route of flight.

MILITARY TRAINING ROUTES-Airspace of defined vertical and lateral dimensions established for the conduct of military flight training at airspeeds in excess of 250 knots IAS.

MINIMUM VECTORING ALTITUDE (MVA) - The lowest MSL altitude at which an IFR aircraft will be vectored by a radar controller, except as otherwise authorized for radar approaches, departures, and missed approaches. The altitude meets IFR obstacle clearance criteria. It may be lower than the published MEA along an airway or J-route segment. It may be utilized for radar vectoring only upon the controller's determination that an adequate radar return is being received from the aircraft being controlled. Charts depicting minimum vectoring altitudes are normally available only to the controllers and not to pilots.

MINUTES-IN-TRAIL- A specified interval between aircraft expressed in time. This method would more likely be utilized regardless of altitude.

MONITOR- (When used with communication transfer) listen on a specific frequency and stand by for instructions. Under normal circumstances do not establish communications.

MOVING TARGET INDICATOR- An electronic device which will permit radar scope presentation only from targets which are in motion. A partial remedy for ground clutter.

MULTICOM- A mobile service not open to public correspondence used to provide communications essential to conduct the activities being performed by or directed from private aircraft.

N

NATIONAL AIRSPACE SYSTEM- The common network of U.S. airspace; air navigation facilities, equipment and services, airports or landing areas; aeronautical charts, information and services; rules, regulations and procedures, technical information, and manpower and material. Included are system components shared jointly with the military.

NAVAID CLASSES- VOR, VORTAC, and TACAN aids are classed according to their operational use.

The three classes of NAVAIDs are:

a. T- Terminal.

b. L- Low altitude.

c. H- High altitude.

NEGATIVE-"No," or "permission not granted," or "that is not correct."

NEGATIVE CONTACT- Used by pilots to inform ATC that:

a. Previously issued traffic is not in sight. It may be followed by the pilot's request for the controller to provide assistance in avoiding the traffic.

b. They were unable to contact ATC on a particular frequency.

NIGHT- The time between the end of evening civil twilight and the beginning of morning civil twilight, as published in the American Air Almanac, converted to local time.

NONDIRECTIONAL BEACON- An L/MF or UHF radio beacon transmitting nondirectional signals whereby the pilot of an aircraft equipped with direction finding equipment can determine his/her bearing to or from the radio beacon and "home" on or track to or from the station. When the radio beacon is installed in conjunction with the Instrument Landing System marker, it is normally called a Compass Locator.

NONMOVEMENT AREAS- Taxiways and apron (ramp) areas not under the control of air traffic.

NONPRECISION APPROACH PROCEDURE- A standard instrument approach procedure in which no electronic glideslope is provided; e.g., VOR, TACAN, NDB, LOC, ASR, LDA, or SDF approaches.

NORDO (No Radio)- Aircraft that cannot or do not communicate by radio when radio communication is required are referred to as "NORDO."

NOTICE TO AIRMEN- A notice containing information (not known sufficiently in advance to publicize by other means) concerning the establishment, condition, or change in any component (facility, service, or procedure of, or hazard in the National Airspace System) the timely knowledge of which is essential to personnel concerned with flight operations.

a. NOTAM(D)- A NOTAM given (in addition to local dissemination) distant dissemination beyond the area of responsibility of the Flight Service Station. These NOTAMs will be stored and available until canceled.

b. FDC NOTAM- A NOTAM regulatory in nature, transmitted by USNOF and given system wide dissemination.

NOTICES TO AIRMEN PUBLICATION- A publication issued every 28 days, designed primarily for the pilot, which contains current NOTAM information considered essential to the safety of flight as well as supplemental data to other aeronautical publications. The contraction NTAP is used in NOTAM text.

NUMEROUS TARGETS VICINITY (LOCATION)- A traffic advisory issued by ATC to advise pilots that targets on the radar scope are too numerous to issue individually.

O

OBSTACLE- An existing object, object of natural growth, or terrain at a fixed geographical location or which may be expected at a fixed location within a prescribed area with reference to which vertical clearance is or must be provided during flight operation.

OBSTRUCTION- Any object/obstacle exceeding the obstruction standards specified by 14 CFR Part 77, Subpart C.

OBSTRUCTION LIGHT- A light or one of a group of lights, usually red or white, frequently mounted on a surface structure or natural terrain to warn pilots of the presence of an obstruction.

ONE-MINUTE WEATHER- The most recent one minute updated weather broadcast received by a pilot from an uncontrolled airport ASOS/AWSS/AWOS.

OPTION APPROACH- An approach requested and conducted by a pilot which will result in either a touch-and-go, missed approach, low approach, stop-and-go, or full stop landing.

OUT-The conversation is ended and no response is expected.

OUTER AREA (associated with Class C airspace)- Nonregulatory airspace surrounding designated Class C airspace airports wherein ATC provides radar vectoring and sequencing on a full-time basis for all IFR and participating VFR aircraft. The service provided in the outer area is called Class C service which includes:

IFR/IFR-standard IFR separation; IFR/VFR-traffic advisories and conflict resolution; and VFR/VFR-traffic advisories and, as appropriate, safety alerts. The normal radius will be 20 nautical miles with some variations based on site-specific requirements. The outer area extends outward from the primary Class C airspace airport and extends from the lower limits of radar/radio coverage up to the ceiling of the approach control's delegated airspace excluding the Class C charted area and other airspace as appropriate.

OVER-My transmission is ended; I expect a response.

P

PAN-PAN- The international radio-telephony urgency signal. When repeated three times, indicates uncertainty or alert followed by the nature of the urgency.

PARALLEL RUNWAYS- Two or more runways at the same airport whose centerlines are parallel. In addition to runway number, parallel runways are designated as L (left) and R (right) or, if three parallel runways exist, L (left), C (center), and R (right).

PILOT'S DISCRETION- When used in conjunction with altitude assignments, means that ATC has offered the pilot the option of starting climb or descent whenever he/she wishes and conducting the climb or descent at any rate he/she wishes. He/she may temporarily level off at any intermediate altitude. However, once he/she has vacated an altitude, he/she may not return to that altitude.

POSITION REPORT- A report over a known location as transmitted by an aircraft to ATC.

POSITIVE CONTROL- The separation of all air traffic within designated airspace by air traffic control.

PRECIPITATION- Any or all forms of water particles (rain, sleet, hail, or snow) that fall from the atmosphere and reach the surface.

PRECIPITATION RADAR WEATHER DESCRIPTIONS - Existing radar systems cannot detect turbulence. However, there is a direct correlation between the degree of turbulence and other weather features associated with thunderstorms and the weather radar precipitation intensity. Controllers will issue (where capable) precipitation intensity as observed by radar when using weather and radar processor (WARP) or NAS ground based digital radars with weather capabilities. When precipitation intensity information is not available, the intensity will be described as UNKNOWN. When intensity levels can be determined, they shall be described as:

a. LIGHT (< 30 dBZ)

b. MODERATE (30 to 40 dBZ)

c. HEAVY (> 40 to 50 dBZ)

d. EXTREME (> 50 dBZ)

PRECISION APPROACH RADAR- Radar equipment in some ATC facilities operated by the FAA and/or the military services at joint-use civil/military locations and separate military installations to detect and display azimuth, elevation, and range of aircraft on the final approach course to a runway. This equipment may be used to monitor certain nonradar approaches, but is primarily used to conduct a precision instrument approach (PAR) wherein the controller issues guidance instructions to the pilot based on the aircraft's position in relation to the final approach course (azimuth), the glidepath (elevation), and the distance (range) from the touchdown point on the runway as displayed on the radar scope.

PRIMARY RADAR TARGET- An analog or digital target, exclusive of a secondary radar target, presented on a radar display.

PROGRESSIVE TAXI- Precise taxi instructions given to a pilot unfamiliar with the airport or issued in stages as the aircraft proceeds along the taxi route.

PROPOSED DEPARTURE TIME- The time that the aircraft expects to become airborne.

PROTECTED AIRSPACE- The airspace on either side of an oceanic route/track that is equal to one-half the lateral separation minimum except where reduction of protected airspace has been authorized.

Q

QNE- The barometric pressure used for the standard altimeter setting (29.92 inches Hg.).

QNH- The barometric pressure as reported by a particular station.

R

RADAR ADVISORY- The provision of advice and information based on radar observations.

RADAR APPROACH-An instrument approach procedure which utilizes Precision Approach Radar (PAR) or Airport Surveillance Radar (ASR).

RADAR APPROACH CONTROL FACILITY- A terminal ATC facility that uses radar and nonradar capabilities to provide approach control services to aircraft arriving, departing, or transiting airspace controlled by the facility.

RADAR CONTACT-

a. Used by ATC to inform an aircraft that it is identified on the radar display and radar flight following will be provided until radar identification is terminated. Radar service may also be provided within the limits of necessity and capability. When a pilot is informed of "radar contact," he/she automatically discontinues reporting over compulsory reporting points.

b. The term used to inform the controller that the aircraft is identified and approval is granted for the aircraft to enter the receiving controllers airspace.

RADAR CONTACT LOST- Used by ATC to inform a pilot that radar data used to determine the aircraft's position is no longer being received, or is no longer reliable and radar service is no longer being provided. The loss may be attributed to several factors including the aircraft merging with weather or ground clutter, the aircraft operating below radar line of sight coverage, the aircraft entering an area of poor radar return, failure of the aircraft transponder, or failure of the ground radar equipment.

RADAR FLIGHT FOLLOWING- The observation of the progress of radar identified aircraft,

whose primary navigation is being provided by the pilot, wherein the controller retains and correlates the aircraft identity with the appropriate target or target symbol displayed on the radar scope.

RADAR IDENTIFIED AIRCRAFT- An aircraft, the position of which has been correlated with an observed target or symbol on the radar display.

RADAR SERVICE TERMINATED-Used by ATC to inform a pilot that he/she will no longer be provided any of the services that could be received while in radar contact. Radar service is automatically terminated, and the pilot is not advised in the following cases:

a. An aircraft cancels its IFR flight plan, except within Class B airspace, Class C airspace, a TRSA, or where Basic Radar service is provided.

b. An aircraft conducting an instrument, visual, or contact approach has landed or has been instructed to change to advisory frequency.

c. An arriving VFR aircraft, receiving radar service to a tower-controlled airport within Class B airspace, Class C airspace, a TRSA, or where sequencing service is provided, has landed; or to all other airports, is instructed to change to tower or advisory frequency.

d. An aircraft completes a radar approach.

RADIAL- A magnetic bearing extending from a VOR/VORTAC/TACAN navigation facility.

RADIO ALTIMETER- Aircraft equipment which makes use of the reflection of radio waves from the ground to determine the height of the aircraft above the surface.

RADIO MAGNETIC INDICATOR-An aircraft navigational instrument coupled with a gyro compass or similar compass that indicates the direction of a selected NAVAID and indicates bearing with respect to the heading of the aircraft.

RECEIVER AUTONOMOUS INTEGRITY MONITORING (RAIM)- A technique whereby a civil GNSS receiver/processor determines the integrity of the GNSS navigation signals without reference to sensors or non-DoD integrity systems other than the receiver itself. This determination is achieved by a consistency check among redundant pseudorange measurements.

RELEASE TIME- A departure time restriction issued to a pilot by ATC (either directly or through an authorized relay) when necessary to separate a departing aircraft from other traffic.

REMOTE AIRPORT ADVISORY (RAA)- A remote service which may be provided by facilities, which are not located on the landing airport, but have a discrete ground-to-air communication frequency or tower frequency when the tower is closed, automated weather reporting with voice available to the pilot at the landing airport, and a continuous ASOS/AWSS/AWOS data display, other direct reading instruments, or manual observation is available to the AFSS specialist.

REMOTE AIRPORT INFORMATION SERVICE (RAIS)- A temporary service provided by facilities, which are not located on the landing airport, but have communication capability and automated weather reporting available to the pilot at the landing airport.

REMOTE COMMUNICATIONS OUTLET-An unmanned communications facility remotely controlled by air traffic personnel. RCOs serve FSSs. RTRs serve terminal ATC facilities. An RCO or RTR may be UHF or VHF and will extend the communication range of the air traffic facility. There are several classes of RCOs and RTRs. The class is determined by the number of transmitters or receivers. Classes A through G are used primarily for air/ground purposes. RCO and RTR class O facilities are non-protected outlets subject to undetected and prolonged outages. RCO (O's) and RTR (O's) were established for the express purpose of providing ground-to-ground communications between air traffic control specialists and pilots located at a satellite airport for delivering en route clearances, issuing departure authorizations, and acknowledging instrument flight rules cancellations or departure/landing times. As a secondary function, they may be used for advisory purposes whenever the aircraft is below the coverage of the primary air/ground frequency.

REPORTING POINT- A geographical location in relation to which the position of an aircraft is reported.

RESUME OWN NAVIGATION- Used by ATC to advise a pilot to resume his/her own navigational responsibility. It is issued after completion of a radar vector or when radar contact is lost while the aircraft is being radar vectored.

ROGER- I have received all of your last transmission. It should not be used to answer a question requiring a yes or a no answer.

RUNWAY- A defined rectangular area on a land airport prepared for the landing and takeoff run of aircraft along its length. Runways are normally numbered in relation to their magnetic direction rounded off to the nearest 10 degrees; e.g., Runway 1, Runway 25.

RUNWAY GRADIENT- The average slope, measured in percent, between two ends or points on a runway. Runway gradient is depicted on Government aerodrome sketches when total runway gradient exceeds 0.3%.

RUNWAY HEADING- The magnetic direction that corresponds with the runway centerline extended, not the painted runway number. When cleared to "fly or maintain runway heading," pilots are expected to fly or maintain the heading that corresponds with the extended centerline of the departure runway. Drift correction shall not be applied; e.g., Runway 4, actual magnetic heading of the runway centerline 044, fly 044.

RUNWAY IN USE/ACTIVE RUNWAY/DUTY RUNWAY- Any runway or runways currently being used for takeoff or landing. When multiple runways are used, they are all considered active runways. In the metering sense, a selectable adapted item which specifies the landing runway configuration or direction of traffic flow. The adapted optimum flight plan from each transition fix to the vertex is determined by the runway configuration for arrival metering processing purposes.

RUNWAY OVERRUN- In military aviation exclusively, a stabilized or paved area beyond the end of a runway, of the same width as the runway plus shoulders, centered on the extended runway centerline.

S

SAY AGAIN- Used to request a repeat of the last transmission. Usually specifies transmission or portion thereof not understood or received; e.g., "Say again all after ABRAM VOR."

SAY ALTITUDE-Used by ATC to ascertain an aircraft's specific altitude/flight level. When the aircraft is climbing or descending, the pilot should state the indicated altitude rounded to the nearest 100 feet.

SAY HEADING- Used by ATC to request an aircraft heading. The pilot should state the actual heading of the aircraft.

SEARCH AND RESCUE- A service which seeks missing aircraft and assists those found to be in need of assistance. It is a cooperative effort using the facilities and services of available Federal, state and local agencies. The U.S. Coast Guard is responsible for coordination of search and rescue for the Maritime Region, and the U.S. Air Force is responsible for search and rescue for the Inland Region. Information pertinent to search and rescue should be passed through any air traffic facility or be transmitted directly to the Rescue Coordination Center by telephone.

SECONDARY RADAR TARGET- A target derived from a transponder return presented on a radar display.

SEE AND AVOID-When weather conditions permit, pilots operating IFR or VFR are required to observe and maneuver to avoid other aircraft. Right-of-way rules are contained in 14 CFR Part 91.

SEGMENTED CIRCLE- A system of visual indicators designed to provide traffic pattern information at airports without operating control towers.

SEPARATION MINIMA- The minimum longitudinal, lateral, or vertical distances by which aircraft are spaced through the application of air traffic control procedures.

SIGMET-A weather advisory issued concerning weather significant to the safety of all aircraft. SIGMET advisories cover severe and extreme turbulence, severe icing, and widespread dust or sandstorms that reduce visibility to less than 3 miles.

SPEAK SLOWER- Used in verbal communications as a request to reduce speech rate.

SPECIAL USE AIRSPACE- Airspace of defined dimensions identified by an area on the surface of the earth wherein activities must be confined because of their nature and/or wherein limitations may be imposed upon aircraft operations that are not a part of those activities. Types of special use airspace are:

a. Alert Area- Airspace which may contain a high volume of pilot training activities or an unusual type of aerial activity, neither of which is hazardous to aircraft. Alert Areas are depicted on aeronautical charts for the information of nonparticipating pilots. All activities within an Alert Area are conducted in accordance with Federal Aviation Regulations, and pilots of participating aircraft as well as pilots transiting the area are equally responsible for collision avoidance.

b. Controlled Firing Area- Airspace wherein activities are conducted under conditions so controlled as to eliminate hazards to nonparticipating aircraft and to ensure the safety of persons and property on the ground.

c. Military Operations Area (MOA)- A MOA is airspace established outside of Class A airspace area to separate or segregate certain nonhazardous military activities from IFR traffic and to identify for VFR traffic where these activities are conducted.

d. Prohibited Area- Airspace designated under 14 CFR Part 73 within which no person may operate an aircraft without the permission of the using agency.

e. Restricted Area- Airspace designated under 14 CFR Part 73, within which the flight of aircraft, while not wholly prohibited, is subject to restriction. Most restricted areas are designated joint use and IFR/VFR operations in the area may be authorized by the controlling ATC facility when it is not being utilized by the using agency. Restricted areas are depicted on en route charts. Where joint use is authorized, the name of the ATC controlling facility is also shown.

f. Warning Area- A warning area is airspace of defined dimensions extending from 3 nautical miles outward from the coast of the United States, that contains activity that may be hazardous to nonparticipating aircraft. The purpose of such warning area is to warn nonparticipating pilots of the potential danger. A warning area may be located over domestic or international waters or both.

SPECIAL VFR CONDITIONS- Meteorological conditions that are less than those required for basic VFR flight in Class B, C, D, or E surface areas and in which some aircraft are permitted flight under visual flight rules.

SPECIAL VFR OPERATIONS- Aircraft operating in accordance with clearances within Class B, C, D, and E surface areas in weather conditions less than the basic VFR weather minima. Such operations must be requested by the pilot and approved by ATC.

SPEED BRAKES- Moveable aerodynamic devices on aircraft that reduce airspeed during descent and landing.

SQUAWK (Mode, Code, Function)-Activate specific modes/codes/functions on the aircraft transponder; e.g., "Squawk three/alpha, two one zero five, low."

STAND BY-Means the controller or pilot must pause for a few seconds, usually to attend to other duties of a higher priority. Also means to wait as in "stand by for clearance." The caller should reestablish contact if a delay is lengthy. "Stand by" is not an approval or denial.

STANDARD RATE TURN- A turn of three degrees per second.

STEP TURN- A maneuver used to put a float plane in a planing configuration prior to entering an active sea lane for takeoff. The STEP TURN maneuver should only be used upon pilot request.

STOP ALTITUDE SQUAWK-Used by ATC to inform an aircraft to turn-off the automatic altitude reporting feature of its transponder. It is issued when the verbally reported altitude varies 300 feet or more from the automatic altitude report.

STOP AND GO- A procedure wherein an aircraft will land, make a complete stop on the runway, and then commence a takeoff from that point.

STOP SQUAWK (Mode or Code)- Used by ATC to tell the pilot to turn specified functions of the aircraft transponder off.

STOPOVER FLIGHT PLAN- A flight plan format which permits in a single submission the filing of a sequence of flight plans through interim full-stop destinations to a final destination.

STOPWAY- An area beyond the takeoff runway no less wide than the runway and centered upon the extended centerline of the runway, able to support the airplane during an aborted takeoff, without causing structural damage to the airplane, and designated by the airport authorities for use in decelerating the airplane during an aborted takeoff.

STRAIGHT-IN APPROACH VFR- Entry into the traffic pattern by interception of the extended runway centerline (final approach course) without executing any other portion of the traffic pattern.

SUNSET AND SUNRISE- The mean solar times of sunset and sunrise as published in the Nautical Almanac, converted to local standard time for the locality concerned. Within Alaska, the end of evening civil twilight and the beginning of morning civil twilight, as defined for each locality.

SURFACE AREA- The airspace contained by the lateral boundary of the Class B, C, D, or E airspace designated for an airport that begins at the surface and extends upward.

T

TACTICAL AIR NAVIGATION- An ultra-high frequency electronic rho-theta air navigation aid which provides suitably equipped aircraft a continuous indication of bearing and distance to the TACAN station.

TAILWIND- Any wind more than 90 degrees to the longitudinal axis of the runway. The magnetic direction of the runway shall be used as the basis for determining the longitudinal axis.

TARMAC DELAY- The holding of an aircraft on the ground either before departure or after landing with no opportunity for its passengers to deplane.

TAXI- The movement of an airplane under its own power on the surface of an airport (14 CFR Section 135.100 [Note]). Also, it describes the surface movement of helicopters equipped with wheels.

TAXI PATTERNS- Patterns established to illustrate the desired flow of ground traffic for the different runways or airport areas available for use.

TELEPHONE INFORMATION BRIEFING SERVICE- A continuous telephone recording of meteorological and/or aeronautical information.

TERMINAL RADAR SERVICE AREA- Airspace surrounding designated airports wherein ATC provides radar vectoring, sequencing, and separation on a full-time basis for all IFR and participating VFR aircraft. The AIM contains an explanation of TRSA. TRSAs are depicted on VFR aeronautical charts. Pilot participation is urged but is not mandatory.

TERRAIN AWARENESS WARNING SYSTEM (TAWS)- An on-board, terrain proximity alerting system providing the aircrew 'Low Altitude warnings' to allow immediate pilot action.

TETRAHEDRON- A device normally located on uncontrolled airports and used as a landing direction indicator. The small end of a tetrahedron points in the direction of landing. At controlled airports, the tetrahedron, if installed, should be disregarded because tower instructions supersede the indicator.

THAT IS CORRECT- The understanding you have is right.

THRESHOLD- The beginning of that portion of the runway usable for landing.

TOUCH-AND-GO- An operation by an aircraft that lands and departs on a runway without stopping or exiting the runway.

TOWER- A terminal facility that uses air/ground communications, visual signaling, and other devices to provide ATC services to aircraft operating in the vicinity of an airport or on the movement area. Authorizes aircraft to land or takeoff at the airport controlled by the tower or to transit the Class D airspace area regardless of flight plan or weather conditions (IFR or VFR). A tower may also provide approach control services (radar or nonradar).

TRAFFIC ADVISORIES- Advisories issued to alert pilots to other known or observed air traffic which may be in such proximity to the position or intended route of flight of their aircraft to warrant their attention. Such advisories may be based on:

a. Visual observation.

b. Observation of radar identified and non-identified aircraft targets on an ATC radar display, or

c. Verbal reports from pilots or other facilities.

Note 1: The word "traffic" followed by additional information, if known, is used to provide such advisories; e.g., "Traffic, 2 o'clock, one zero miles, southbound, eight thousand."

Note 2: Traffic advisory service will be provided to the extent possible depending on higher priority duties of the controller or other limitations; e.g., radar limitations, volume of traffic, frequency congestion, or controller workload. Radar/nonradar traffic advisories do not relieve the pilot of his/her responsibility to see and avoid other aircraft. Pilots are cautioned that there are many times when the controller is not able to give traffic advisories concerning all traffic in the aircraft's proximity; in other words, when a pilot requests or is receiving traffic advisories, he/she should not assume that all traffic will be issued.

TRAFFIC ALERT (aircraft call sign), TURN (left/right) IMMEDIATELY, (climb/descend) AND MAINTAIN (altitude).

TRAFFIC ALERT AND COLLISION AVOIDANCE SYSTEM- An airborne collision avoidance system based on radar beacon signals which operates independent of ground-based equipment. TCAS-I generates traffic advisories only. TCAS-II generates traffic advisories, and resolution (collision avoidance) advisories in the vertical plane.

TRAFFIC INFORMATION SERVICE- BROADCAST (TIS-B)- The broadcast of ATC derived traffic information to ADS-B equipped (1090ES or UAT) aircraft. The source of this traffic information is derived from ground-based air traffic surveillance sensors, typically from radar targets. TIS-B service will be available throughout the NAS where there are both adequate surveillance coverage (radar) and adequate broadcast coverage from ADS-B ground stations. Loss of TIS-B will occur when an aircraft enters an area not covered by the GBT network. If this occurs in an area with adequate surveillance coverage (radar), nearby aircraft that remain within the adequate broadcast coverage (ADS-B) area will view the first aircraft. TIS-B may continue when an aircraft enters an area with inadequate surveillance coverage (radar); nearby aircraft that remain within the adequate broadcast coverage (ADS-B) area will not view the first aircraft.

TRAFFIC IN SIGHT- Used by pilots to inform a controller that previously issued traffic is in sight.

TRAFFIC NO FACTOR- Indicates that the traffic described in a previously issued traffic advisory is no factor.

TRAFFIC NO LONGER OBSERVED- Indicates that the traffic described in a previously issued traffic advisory is no longer depicted on radar, but may still be a factor.

TRAFFIC PATTERN- The traffic flow that is prescribed for aircraft landing at, taxiing on, or taking off from an airport. The components of a typical traffic pattern are upwind leg, crosswind leg, downwind leg, base leg, and final approach.

a. Upwind Leg- A flight path parallel to the landing runway in the direction of landing.

b. Crosswind Leg- A flight path at right angles to the landing runway off its upwind end.

c. Downwind Leg- A flight path parallel to the landing runway in the direction opposite to landing. The downwind leg normally extends between the crosswind leg and the base leg.

d. Base Leg- A flight path at right angles to the landing runway off its approach end. The base leg normally extends from the downwind leg to the intersection of the extended runway centerline.

e. Final Approach. A flight path in the direction of landing along the extended runway centerline. The final approach normally extends from the base leg to the runway. An aircraft making a straight-in approach VFR is also considered to be on final approach.

TRAFFIC SITUATION DISPLAY (TSD)- TSD is a computer system that receives radar track data from all 20 CONUS ARTCCs, organizes this data into a mosaic display, and presents it on a computer screen. The display allows the traffic management coordinator multiple methods of selection and highlighting of individual aircraft or groups of aircraft. The user has the option of superimposing these aircraft positions over any number of background displays. These background options include ARTCC boundaries, any stratum of en route sector boundaries, fixes, airways, military and other special use airspace, airports, and geopolitical boundaries. By using the TSD, a coordinator can monitor any number of traffic situations or the entire systemwide traffic flows.

TRANSMISSOMETER- An apparatus used to determine visibility by measuring the transmission of light through the atmosphere. It is the measurement source for determining runway visual range (RVR) and runway visibility value (RVV).

TRANSPONDER- The airborne radar beacon receiver/transmitter portion of the Air Traffic Control Radar Beacon System (ATCRBS) which automatically receives radio signals from interrogators on the ground, and selectively replies with a specific reply pulse or pulse group only to those interrogations being received on the mode to which it is set to respond.

TURBOJET AIRCRAFT- An aircraft having a jet engine in which the energy of the jet operates a turbine which in turn operates the air compressor.

TURBOPROP AIRCRAFT- An aircraft having a jet engine in which the energy of the jet operates a turbine which drives the propeller.

TURN ANTICIPATION- (maneuver anticipation).

U

ULTRAHIGH FREQUENCY- The frequency band between 300 and 3,000 MHz. The bank of radio frequencies used for military air/ground voice communications. In some instances this may go as low as 225 MHz and still be referred to as UHF.

ULTRALIGHT VEHICLE- An aeronautical vehicle operated for sport or recreational purposes which does not require FAA registration, an airworthiness certificate, nor pilot certification. They are primarily single occupant vehicles, although some two-place vehicles are authorized for training purposes. Operation of an ultralight vehicle in certain airspace requires authorization from ATC.

UNABLE-Indicates inability to comply with a specific instruction, request, or clearance.

UNDER THE HOOD- Indicates that the pilot is using a hood to restrict visibility outside the cockpit while simulating instrument flight. An appropriately rated pilot is required in the other control seat while this operation is being conducted.

UNICOM- A nongovernment communication facility which may provide airport information at certain airports. Locations and frequencies of UNICOMs are shown on aeronautical charts and publications.

UNPUBLISHED ROUTE- A route for which no minimum altitude is published or charted for pilot use. It may include a direct route between NAVAIDs, a radial, a radar vector, or a final approach course beyond the segments of an instrument approach procedure.

UNRELIABLE (GPS/WAAS)- An advisory to pilots indicating the expected level of service of the GPS and/or WAAS may not be available. Pilots must then determine the adequacy of the signal for desired use.

V

VECTOR- A heading issued to an aircraft to provide navigational guidance by radar.

VERIFY- Request confirmation of information; e.g., "verify assigned altitude."

VERTICAL TAKEOFF AND LANDING AIRCRAFT- Aircraft capable of vertical climbs and/or descents and of using very short runways or small areas for takeoff and landings. These aircraft include, but are not limited to, helicopters.

VERY HIGH FREQUENCY- The frequency band between 30 and 300 MHz. Portions of this band, 108 to 118 MHz, are used for certain NAVAIDs; 118 to 136 MHz are used for civil air/ground voice communications. Other frequencies in this band are used for purposes not related to air traffic control.

VFR AIRCRAFT- An aircraft conducting flight in accordance with visual flight rules.

VFR CONDITIONS- Weather conditions equal to or better than the minimum for flight under visual flight rules. The term may be used as an ATC clearance/instruction only when:

a. An IFR aircraft requests a climb/descent in VFR conditions.

b. The clearance will result in noise abatement benefits where part of the IFR departure route does not conform to an FAA approved noise abatement route or altitude.

c. A pilot has requested a practice instrument approach and is not on an IFR flight plan.

VFR MILITARY TRAINING ROUTES- Routes used by the Department of Defense and associated Reserve and Air Guard units for the purpose of conducting low-altitude navigation and tactical training under VFR below 10,000 feet MSL at airspeeds in excess of 250 knots IAS.

VFR NOT RECOMMENDED- An advisory provided by a flight service station to a pilot during a preflight or inflight weather briefing that flight under visual flight rules is not recommended. To be given when the current and/or forecast weather conditions are at or below VFR minimums. It does not abrogate the pilot's authority to make his/her own decision.

VFR-ON-TOP- ATC authorization for an IFR aircraft to operate in VFR conditions at any appropriate VFR altitude (as specified in 14 CFR and as restricted by ATC). A pilot receiving this authorization must comply with the VFR visibility, distance from cloud criteria, and the minimum IFR altitudes specified in 14 CFR Part 91. The use of this term does not relieve controllers of their responsibility to separate aircraft in Class B and Class C airspace or TRSAs as required by FAAO JO 7110.65.

VISIBILITY- The ability, as determined by atmospheric conditions and expressed in units of distance, to see and identify prominent unlighted objects by day and prominent lighted objects by night. Visibility is reported as statute miles, hundreds of feet or meters.

VISUAL APPROACH- An approach conducted on an instrument flight rules (IFR) flight plan which authorizes the pilot to proceed visually and clear of clouds to the airport. The pilot must, at all times, have either the airport or the preceding aircraft in sight. This approach must be authorized and under the control of the appropriate air traffic control facility. Reported weather at the airport must be ceiling at or above 1,000 feet and visibility of 3 miles or greater.

VISUAL DESCENT POINT- A defined point on the final approach course of a nonprecision straight-in approach procedure from which normal descent from the MDA to the runway touchdown point may be commenced, provided the approach threshold of that runway, or approach lights, or other markings identifiable with the approach end of that runway are clearly visible to the pilot.

VISUAL FLIGHT RULES- Rules that govern the procedures for conducting flight under visual conditions. The term "VFR" is also used in the United States to indicate weather conditions that are equal to or greater than minimum VFR requirements. In addition, it is used by pilots and controllers to indicate type of flight plan.

VISUAL METEOROLOGICAL CONDITIONS- Meteorological conditions expressed in terms of visibility, distance from cloud, and ceiling equal to or better than specified minima.

VISUAL SEPARATION- A means employed by ATC to separate aircraft in terminal areas and en route airspace in the NAS. There are two ways to effect this separation:

a. The tower controller sees the aircraft involved and issues instructions, as necessary, to ensure that the aircraft avoid each other.

b. A pilot sees the other aircraft involved and upon instructions from the controller provides his/her own separation by maneuvering his/her aircraft as necessary to avoid it. This may involve following another aircraft or keeping it in sight until it is no longer a factor.

VOR- A ground-based electronic navigation aid transmitting very high frequency navigation signals, 360 degrees in azimuth, oriented from magnetic north. Used as the basis for navigation in the National Airspace System. The VOR periodically identifies itself by Morse Code and may have an additional voice identification feature. Voice features may be used by ATC or FSS for transmitting instructions/information to pilots.

VORTAC- A navigation aid providing VOR azimuth, TACAN azimuth, and TACAN distance measuring equipment (DME) at one site.

VORTICES- Circular patterns of air created by the movement of an airfoil through the air when generating lift. As an airfoil moves through the atmosphere in sustained flight, an area of area of low pressure is created above it. The air flowing from the high pressure area to the low pressure area around and about the tips of the airfoil tends to roll up into two rapidly rotating vortices, cylindrical in shape. These vortices are the most predominant parts of aircraft wake turbulence and their rotational force is dependent upon the wing loading, gross weight, and

speed of the generating aircraft. The vortices from medium to heavy aircraft can be of extremely high velocity and hazardous to smaller aircraft.

VOT- A ground facility which emits a test signal to check VOR receiver accuracy. Some VOTs are available to the user while airborne, and others are limited to ground use only.

W

WAKE TURBULENCE- Phenomena resulting from the passage of an aircraft through the atmosphere. The term includes vortices, thrust stream turbulence, jet blast, jet wash, propeller wash, and rotor wash both on the ground and in the air.

WAYPOINT- A predetermined geographical position used for route/instrument approach definition, progress reports, published VFR routes, visual reporting points or points for transitioning and/or circumnavigating controlled and/or special use airspace, that is defined relative to a VORTAC station or in terms of latitude/longitude coordinates.

WHEN ABLE- When used in conjunction with ATC instructions, gives the pilot the latitude to delay compliance until a condition or event has been reconciled. Unlike "pilot discretion," when instructions are prefaced "when able," the pilot is expected to seek the first opportunity to comply. Once a maneuver has been initiated, the pilot is expected to continue until the specifications of the instructions have been met. "When able," should not be used when expeditious compliance is required.

WIDE-AREA AUGMENTATION SYSTEM (WAAS)- The WAAS is a satellite navigation system consisting of the equipment and software which augments the GPS Standard Positioning Service (SPS). The WAAS provides enhanced integrity, accuracy, availability, and continuity over and above GPS SPS. The differential correction function provides improved accuracy required for precision approach.

WILCO- I have received your message, understand it, and will comply with it.

WIND SHEAR- A change in wind speed and/or wind direction in a short distance resulting in a tearing or shearing effect. It can exist in a horizontal or vertical direction and occasionally in both.

WORD TWICE -

a. As a request: "Communication is difficult. Please say every phrase twice."

b. As information: "Since communications are difficult, every phrase in this message will be spoken twice."

Z

ZULU TIME - Greenwich Mean Time, or the time in Greenwich, England.